Biotechnology

Fundamental and Applications

Fourth Enlarged Edition

S. S. Purohit
Ex-Head, Post Graduate Department of Botany
Dungar College, Bikaner

STUDENT
EDITION

Published by:

Student Edition
Behind Nasrani Cinema
Chopasani Road, Jodhpur 342 002
Phone: 91-0291-2642319, Fax: 2643993

First Published (2003)
Impression (2004, 2005, 2006, 2007, 2008, 2014)
Fourth Edition 2014

ISBN (10): 81-88826-00-6
ISBN: 978-81-8882651-2
Rs. 750.00 / US$ 38.00

Published by: Mrs. Saraswati Purohit for Student Edition, India
Laser Typeset at: Yashee Computers and Printers, Jodhpur
Cover Design by: Reena
Printed at: Agrobios Digitals, Jodhpur

Preface

Biotechnology is technology based on biology, especially when used in agriculture, food science, and medicine. It is defined as *any technological application that uses biological systems, dead organisms, or derivatives thereof, to make or modify products or processes for specific use.*

Biotechnology is the manipulation of biological organisms to make products that benefit human beings. Biotechnology contributes to such diverse areas as food production, waste disposal, mining, and medicine. Although biotechnology has existed since ancient times, some of its most dramatic advances have come in more recent years. Modern achievements include the transferal of a specific gene from one organism to another (by means of a set of genetic engineering techniques known as transgenics); the maintenance and growth of genetically uniform plant- and animal-cell cultures, called clones; and the fusing of different types of cells to produce beneficial medical products such as monoclonal antibodies, which are designed to attack a specific type of foreign substance.

The present book has been designed for under and post graduate students of all universities. The book includes basic and applied aspects of Biotechnology. The important chapters are: Biotechnology: An Overview, DNA, Gene, Genome, Protein Synthesis and DNA Chip Technology, Applications of Genetic Engineering, Enzymes in Genetic Engineering (Nucleic Acid Enzymology), Gene Cloning Vectors, Recombinant DNA Technology, Genetic Engineering Techniques, Expression of Induced Genes, Gene Silincing and Antisense Technology, Scope, Achievements and Hazards of Genetically Modified Crops, Plant Tissue Culture: Principles and Methodology, Protoplast Technology, Micropropagation in Plants, Somatic Embryogenesis, Somaclonal and Gametoclonal Variant Selection, Gynogenesis and Crop Improvement, Synseeds or Synthetic Seeds, Animal Cell and Tissue Culture, Immunology, Serology and Vaccines, Animal Health Biotechnology, Antimicrobial Drugs and Biotechnology, Transgenic Animal Technology, Biotechnology and Transgenic Plant, Biotechnology and Forestry, Biotechnology of Biofertilizers Production, Enzymes and Biotechnology, Production of Enzymes and Fermentation technology, Enzyme Immobilization, Industrial Fermentation Technology, Enzyme-based Industrial Fermentation Technology, Applications of Enzymes in Industries, Biotechnology Biomass Energy, Biotechnology Environmental Protection, Biosensors, Biochips, Biofilms and Biosurfactents, Biotechnology and Biodiversity Conservation, Bioinformatics, and Nanotechnology.

I am deeply indebted to Dr. Updesh Purohit, Managing Director. Agrobios (India) for the valuable support. In preparing this book, we have received helps, suggestions and encouragements from various sources, we are grateful to all of them.

Author

Contents

CHAPTER 1

Biotechnology: An Overview

Biotechnology is the manipulation of biological organisms to make products that benefit human beings. Biotechnology contributes to such diverse areas as food production, waste disposal, mining, and medicine. Although biotechnology has existed since ancient times, some of its most dramatic advances have come in more recent years. Modern achievements include the transferal of a specific gene from one organism to another (by means of a set of genetic engineering techniques known as transgenics); the maintenance and growth of genetically uniform plant- and animal-cell cultures, called clones; and the fusing of different types of cells to produce beneficial medical products such as monoclonal antibodies, which are designed to attack a specific type of foreign substance.

ORIGIN AND DEFINITIONS

The oldest examples of what we now call biotechnology are the manufacture of beer, wine, and other alcoholic beverages. Many societies in the distant past discovered that sugary and starchy materials sometimes changed spontaneously, generating alcohol. The phenomenon was gradually brought under conscious control and in the 19th century the French chemist Louis Pasteur showed that fermentation was promoted by microbes. He also found that other microorganisms, different in appearance, were responsible for processes such as vinegar production.

Pasteur's work not only revolutionized the technology of beer and wine making by, for example, excluding microbes that could contaminate the fermentation and cause deleterious changes - it also indicated that other chemicals could be manufactured in bulk by microbes. One of these was Propanone (acetone), a solvent used to make the explosive cordite. During World War I the chemist (and later first President of Israel) Chaim Weizmann showed that propanone could be produced by the bacterium *Clostridium acetobutylicum*.

Biotechnology (*bio* = the use of biological processes, and *technology* = to solve problems or make useful products), in the recent years, has created unprecedented opportunities, not only for the manipulation of biological systems for the benefit of logical systems for the benefit of mankind but also for undertaking studies to understand the fundamental life processes. Consequently, it has become the world's fastest growing and most rapidly changing technology.

The story of the use of biological systems for the fulfillment of human needs perhaps started in 6000 BC when Sumerians and Babylonians fermented a kind of beer. Beginning with fermentation, use of biological processes then experienced many changes over the centuries. However, greatest revolution until now commenced with 1970's and 1980's, when a product of interaction between the science of biology and technology came into wider existence. This relationship got the name *Biotechnology*. Fermentation, antibiotic production, baking and brewing are included in old biotechnology, whereas, techniques related with cell culture, fusion, bioprocessing, genetic engineering etc. were named as *new biotechnology*. Besides the several educational institutions, many commercial companies also engaged themselves in biotechnology research for potential gains.

Definitions

There are many definitions of biotechnology and yet there is *more confusion* as to what it is, and what is involved in the practice activity; is practiced in University and Polytechnic Laboratories, Government and private research institutes and large and small industries, who are each involved to some extent in research, development, testing, evaluation and production exercises. Clearly, what goes on in industries is better defined as **Process Biotechnology.** This is simply described as a discipline which enables its exponents to convert raw materials to final products when either the raw material and/or a stage in the production process involve biological entities. Biotechnology in the broad sense, however, involves the cloners, the hybridisers, and the molecular and cell biologists. It involves the conjoint interaction of two identifiable sub-components; *bio***Science** and *bio***Technology**.

- Biotechnology is also defined as the applications of scientific and engineering principles to the processing of material by biological agents to provide goods and services.
- **The Spinks Report** (1980) defined biotechnology as the application of biological organisms, systems or processes to the manufacturing and service industries.
- **United States Congress's Office of Technology Assessment** defined biotechnology as any technique that used living organisms to make or modify a product, to improve plants or animals or to develop microorganisms for specific uses. The document focuses on the development and application of modern biotechnology based on new enabling techniques of recombinant-DNA technology, often referred to as genetic engineering.
- **British Biotechnologist:** Application of biological organisms, system or processes to manufacturing and service industries.
- **European Federation of Biotechnology:** The integrated use of biochemistry, microbiology and engineering sciences in order to achieve technological (industrial) application of the capabilities of microorganisms, cultured tissue cells, and parts thereof.
- **Japanese Biotechnologists:** A technology using biological phenomena for copying and manufacturing various kinds of useful substances.
- **US National Science Foundation:** The controlled use of biological agents, such as microorganisms or cellular components for beneficial use.

Unfortunately, biotechnologies, are still in the process of early development, do not possess a sharp and easily defined form. Only in last fifteen years progress have been made by microbiologists and genetic engineers, and we are hopeful to solve many fold problems of the present day, specially energy and food crisis to cater the need of growing population of the world. Mineral ore deposits are also becoming more scarce and expensive to recover from earth's crust. Microorganisms can be used to enhance the recovery of metals from low-grade ores and from effluents containing undesirable quantities of heavy metals or other toxins.

When these technologies are applied at industrial level, they constitute bio-industry which include, on the one hand, industrial activities where biotechnologies can replace technologies normally or currently in use and, on the other hand, industrial activities where biotechnologies play an important driving role. There are several areas in which these technologies are being used, the important are chemical industry, food industry (mass production of yeast, algae and bacteria with a view of providing proteins, amino acids, vitamins, and use of enzymes), agricultural productivity, pharmaceutical industry, environmental protection and abatement of pollution, etc.

TABLE 1.1: Biotechnology through ages

Time Period	Work
8000 B.C.	• Humans domesticate crops and livestock. • Potatoes first cultivated for food.
4000-2000 B.C.	• Biotechnology first used to leaven bread and ferment beer, using yeast (Egypt). • Production of cheese and fermentation of wine (Susmeria, China and Egypt). • Babylonians control date palm breeding by selectively pollinating female trees with pollen from certain male trees.
500 B.C.	• First antibiotic-Moldy soybean curds used to treat boils (China).
A.D. 100	• First insecticide-Powdered chrysanthemums (China).
1322	• An Arab chieftain first uses artificial insemination to produce superior horses.
1590-1875	• It took more than 300 years to discover and understand cells: • 1590-Janssen invents the microscope. • 1663-Hooke discovers existence of the cell. • 1675-Leeuwenhoek discovers bacteria.
1761	• Koelreuter reports successful crossbreeding of crop plants in different species.
1797	• Jenner inoculates a child with a viral vaccine to protect him from smallpox.
1830-1833	• 1830-Proteins discovered. • 1833-First enzyme discovered and isolated.
1835-1855	• Scheiden and Schwann propose that all organisms are composed of cells, and Viichow declares, "Every cell arises from a cell."
1857	• Pasteur proposes microbes cause fermentation.
1859	• Charles Darwin publishes the theory of evolution by natural selection. The concept of carefully selecting parents and culling the variable progeny greatly influences plant and animal breeders in the late 1800s despite their ignorance of genetics.
1865	• Science of genetics begins: Austrian monk Gregor Mendel studies garden peas and discovers that genetic traits are passed from parents to offspring in a predictable way-the laws of heredity.
1870-1890	• Using Darwin's theory, plant breeders cross-breed cotton, developing hundreds of varieties with superior qualities. • Farmers first inoculate fields with nitrogen-fixation bacteria to improve yields. • William James Beal produces first experimental corn hybrid in the laboratory. • 1877-A technique for staining and identifying bacteria is developed by Koch. • 1878-The first centrifuge is developed by Laval. • 1879-Flemign discovers chromatin, the rod-like structures inside the cell nucleus that later came to be called chromosomes.
1900	• *Drosophila* (fruit flies) used in early studies of genes.
1902	• The term "immunology" first appears.
1906	• The term "genetics" in introduced.
1911	• The first cancer-causing virus is discovered by Rous.
1914	• Bacteria are used to treat sewage for the first time in Manchester, England.

Time Period	Work
1915	• Phages, or bacterial viruses, are discovered.
1919	• First use of the word "biotechnology" in print.
1920	• The human growth hormone is discovered by Evans and Long.
1928	• Penicillin discovered as an antibiotic Alexander Fleming. • A small-scale test of formulated *Bacillus thuringiensis* (Bt) for corn borer control begins in Europe. Commercial production of this biopesticide begins in France in 1938. • Karpechenko crosses radishes and cabbages, creating fertile offspring between plans in different genera. • Laibach first uses embryo rescue to obtain hybrids from wide crosses in crop plants-known today as hybridization.
1930	• U.S. Congress passes the Plant Patent Act, enabling the products of plant breeding to be patented.
1933	• Hybrid corn, developed by Henry Wallace in the 1920s, is commercialized. Growing hybrid corn eliminates the option of saving seeds. The remarkable yields outweigh the increased costs of annual seed purchases, and by 1945, hybrid corn accounts for 78 percent of U.S.-grown corn.
1938	• The term "molecular biology" is confined.
1941	• The term "genetic engineering" is first used by Danish microbiologist A. Jost in a lecture on reproduction in yeast at the technical institute in Lwow, Poland.
1942	• The electron microscope is used to identify and characterize a bacteriophage-a virus that infects bacteria. • Penicillin mass-produced in microbes.
1944	• DNA is proven to carry genetic information-Avery et al. • Waksman isolates streptomycin, an effective antibiotic for tuberculosis.
1946	• Discovery that genetic material from different viruses can be combined to form a new type of virus, an example of genetic recombination. • Recognizing the threat posed by loss of genetic diversity, the U.S. Congress provides funds for systematic and extensive plant collection, preservation and introduction that U.S. agriculturalists had pursued on a limited and random basis for 200 years.
1947	• McClintock discovers transposable elements, or "jumping genes," in corn.
1949	• Pauling shows that sickle cell anemia is a "molecular disease" resulting from a mutation in the protein molecule hemoglobin.
1951	• Artificial insemination of livestock using frozen semen (a longtime dream of farmers) is successfully accomplished.
1953	• The scientific journal *Nature* publishes James Watson and Francis Crick's manuscript describing the double helical structure of DNA, which marks the beginning of the modern era of genetics.
1954	• Cell-culturing techniques are developed.
1955	• An enzyme involved in the synthesis of a nucleic acid is isolated for the first time.
1956	• The fermentation process is perfected in Japan. • Kornberg discovers the enzymes DNA polymerase, I leading to an understanding of how DNA is replicated.
1958	• Sickle cell anemia is shown to occur due to a change of single amino acid. • DNA is made in a test tube for the first time.
1959	• Systemic fungicides are developed. The steps in protein biosynthesis are delineated.
Also in the 1950s	• Discovery of interferons. • First synthetic antibiotic.

Time Period	Work
1960	• Exploiting base pairing, hybrid DNA-RNA molecules are created. • Messenger RNA is discovered.
1961	• USDA registers first biopesticide; *Bacillus thuringiensis*, or Bt.
1963	• New wheat varieties increase yields by 70 percent by Norman Borlaug.
1964	• The international Rice Research Institute in the Philippines starts the Green Revolution with new strains rice that double the yield of previous strains if given sufficient fertilizers.
1965	• Harris and Watkins successfully fuse mouse and human cells.
1966	• The genetic code is cracked, demonstrating that a sequence of three nucleotide bases (a codon) determines each of 20 amino acids.
1967	• The first automatic protein sequencer is perfected.
1969	• An enzyme is synthesized *in vitro* for the first time.
1970	• Specific restriction nucleases are identified, opening the way for gene cloning. • Norman Borlaug receives the Nobel Peace Prize. • Discovery of restriction enzymes that cut and splice genetic material.
1971	• First complete synthesis of a gene.
1972	• The DNA composition of humans is discovered to be 99 percent similar to that of chimpanzees and gorillas. • Initial work with embryo transfer.
1973	• Stanley Cohen and Herbert Boyer perfect genetic engineering techniques to cut and paste DNA (using restriction enzymes and ligases) and reproduce the new DNA in bacteria.
1974	• The National Institutes of Health forms a Recombinant DNA Advisory Committee to oversee recombinant genetic research.
1975	• Government first urged to develop guidelines for regulating experiments in recombinant DNA: Asilomar Conference, California. • The first monoclonal antibiotics are produced.
1976	• The tools of recombinant DNA are first applied to a human inherited disorder. • Molecular hybridization is used for the prenatal diagnosis of alpha thalassemia. • Yeast genes are expressed in *E. coli* bacteria. • First time the sequence of base pairs for a specific gene is determined (A, C, T, G). • First guidelines for recombinant DNA experiments released: National Institutes of Health.
1977	• First expression of human gene in bacteria. • Procedures developed for rapidly sequencing long sections of DNA using electorphoresis.
1978	• High-level structure of virus first identified. • Recombinant human insulin first produced. • North Carolina scientists show it is possible to introduce specific mutations at specific sits in a DNA molecule.
1979	• Human growth hormone first synthesized.
Also in the 1970s	• First commercial company founded to develop genetically engineered products. • Discovery of polymerases. • Techniques for rapid sequencing of nucleotides perfected. • Gene targeting. • RNA splicing.
1980	• The U.S. Supreme Court, in the landmark case *Diamond v. Chakrabarty,* approves the principle of patenting genetically engineered life forms, which allows the Exxon oil company to patent an oil-eating microorganism.

Time Period	Work
	• The U.S. patent for gene cloning is awarded to Cohen and Boyer. • The first gene-synthesizing machines are developed. • Researcher successfully introduces a human gene-one that codes for the protein interferon-into a bacterium. • Nobel Prize in Chemistry awarded fro creation of the first recombinant molecule: Berg, Gilbert, and Sanger.
1981	• Scientists at Ohio University produce the first transgenic animals by transferring genes from other animals into mice. • Chinese scientist becomes the first to clone a fish-a golden carp.
1982	• Applied Biosystems, Inc., introduces the first commercial gas phase protein sequencer, dramatically reducing the amount of protein sample needed for sequencing. • First recombinant DNA vaccine for livestock developed. • First biotech drug approved by FDA: human insulin produced in genetically modified bacteria. • Fist genetic transformation of a plant cell: petunia.
1983	• The polymerae chain reaction (PCR) technique is conceived. PCR, which uses heat and enzymes to make unlimited copies of genes and gene fragments, later becomes a major tool in biotech research and product development worldwide. • The first genetic transformation of plant cells by TI plasmids is performed. • The first artificial chromosome is synthesized. • The first genetic markers for specific inherited diseases are found. • First whole plant grown from biotechnology: petunia. • First proof that modified plants pass their new traits of offspring: petunia.
1984	• The DNA fingerprinting technique is developed. • The entire genome of the human immunodeficiency virus is cloned and sequenced.
1985	• Genetic markers found for kidney disease and cystic fibrosis. • Genetic fingerprinting entered as evidence in a courtroom. • Genetically engineered plants resistant to insects, viruses and bacteria are field-tested for the first time. • The NIH approves guidelines for performing experiments in gene therapy on humans.
1986	• First genetically engineered vaccine for humans: hepatitis B. • First anti-cancer drug produced through biotech: interferon. • The U.S. government publishes the Coordinated Framework for Regulation of Biotechnology, establishing more stringent regulations for DNA organisms than for those produced with traditional genetic modification techniques. • A University of California-Berkeley chemist describes how to combine antibodies and enzymes (abzymes) to create pharmaceuticals. • The first field tests of genetically engineered plants (tobacco) are conducted. • The Environmental Protection Agency approves the release of the first genetically engineered crop-gene-altered tobacco plants. • The OECD Group of National Experts on Safety in Biotechnology states: "Genetic changes from rDNA techniques will often have inherently greater predictability compared to traditional techniques" and "risks associated with rDNA organisms may be assessed in generally the same way as those associated with non-rDNA organisms."
1987	• First approval for field test of modified food plants: virus-resistant tomatoes. • Frostban, a genetically altered bacterium that inhibits frost formation on crop plants; is field-tested on strawberry and potato plants in California, the first authorized outdoor tests of an engineered bacterium.

Time Period	Work
1988	• Harvard molecular geneticists are awarded the first U.S. patent for a genetically altered animal-a transgenic mouse. • A patent for a process to make bleach-resistant protease enzymes to use in detergents is awarded. • Congress funds the Human Genome Project, a massive effort to map and sequence the human genetic code as well as the genomes of other species.
1989	• First approval for field test of modified cotton: insect-protected (Bt) cotton. • Plant Genome Project begins.
Also in the 1980s	• Studies of DNA used to determine evolutionary history. • Recombinant DNA animal vaccine approved for use in Europe. • Use of microbes in oil spill cleanup: bioremediation technology. • Ribozymes and retinoblastomas identified.
1990	• Chy-Max™, an artificially produced form of the chymosin enzyme for cheese-making, is introduced. It is the first product of recombinant DNA technology in the U.S. food supply. • The Human Genome Project-an international effort to map all the genes in the human body-is launched. • The first federally approved gene therapy treatment is performed successfully on a 4-year-old girl suffering from an immune disorder. • The first transgenic dairy cow-used to produce human milk proteins for infant formula-is created. • First insect-protected corn: Bt corn. • First food product of biotechnology approved in U.K. modified yeast. • First field test of a genetically modified vertebrate; trout.
1992	• American and British scientists unveil a technique for testing embryos *in vitro* for genetic abnormalities such as cystic fibrosis and hemophilia.
1993	• The FDA declares that genetically engineered foods are "not inherently dangerous" and do not require special regulation. • Merging two smaller trade associations creates the Biotechnology Industry Organization (BIO). • FDA approves bovine somatotropin (BST) for increased milk production in dairy cows.
1994	• First FDA approval for a whole food produced through biotechnology: FLAVRSAVR™ tomato. • The first breast cancer gene is discovered. • Approval of genetically engineered version of human DNAase, which breaks down protein accumulation in the lungs of CF patients. • BST commercialized as POSILAC bovine somatotropin.
1995	• The fist baboon-to-human bone marrow transplant is performed on an AIDS patient. • The first full gene sequence of living organism other than a virus is completed for the bacterium *Hemophilus influenzae*. • Gene therapy, immune system modulation and genetically engineered antibodies enter the clinics in the war against cancer.
1996	• The discovery of a gene associated with Parkinson's disease provides an important new avenue of research into the cause and potential treatment of the debilitating neurological ailment.
1997	• First animal cloned from an adult cell: a sheep named Dolly in Scotland. • First weed-and insect-resistant biotech crops commercialized; Roundup Ready® soybeans and Bollgard® insect-protected cotton. • Biotech crops grown commercially on nearly 5 million acres worldwide: Argentina,

Time Period	Work
	Australia, Canada, China, Mexico and the United States. • A group of Oregon researchers claims to have cloned two Rhesus monkeys. • A new DNA technique combines PCR, DNA chips and a computer program to create a new tool in the search for disease-causing genes.
1998	• University of Hawaii scientists clone three generations of mice from nuclei of adult ovarian cumulus cells. • Embryonic stem cells can be used to regenerate tissue and create disorders mimicking diseases. • Scientists at Japhan's Kinki University clone eight identical calves using cells taken from a single adult cow. • The first complete animal genome, for the C. elegans worm, is sequenced. • A rough draft of the human genome map is produced. Showing the locations of more than 30,000 genes. • Five Southeast Asian countries form a consortium to develop disease-resistant papayas.
Also in the 1990s	• First conviction using genetic fingerprinting in the U.K. • Isolation of gene that clearly participates in the normal process of regulating weight. • Discovery that hereditary colon cancer is caused by defective DNA repair gene. • Genetically engineered rabies vaccine tested in raccoons. • Genetically engineered biopesticide approved for sale in the United State. • Patients issued for mice with specific transplanted genes. • First European patent issued for genetically engineered mouse sensitive to carcinogens. • Breast cancer susceptibility genes cloned.
2000	• First complete map of a plant genome developed: *Arabidopsis thaliana*. • 108.9 million acres to biotech crops grown in 13 countries. • "Golden Rice" announcement allows the technology to be available to developing countries in hopes of improving the health of undernourished people and preventing some forms of blindness. • First biotech crop field-tested in Kenya: virus-resistant sweet potato. • Rough draft of the human genome sequence is announced; it paves the way for advances in developing cures for disease.
2001	• First complete map of the genome of a food plant completed: rice. • Scientific journals publish complete human genome sequence.

MULTIPLE FACES OF BIOTECHNOLOGY

The expansion of biotechnology in the medical arena often overshadows the emerging role of agricultural biotechnology. However, many more people around the world die from famine and malnutrition than from Western diseases. With the human population expected to reach 10 billion by the year 2050, the challenges facing agriculture and food research are enormous. Therefore, there is an urgent need to intensify our development of agricultural biotechnologies.

While established agricultural techniques, such as breeding and growth control have resulted in remarkable achievements since the dawn of plant and animal domestication, new methodologies are clearly required. Emerging biotechnologies have seen dramatic developments during the last decade and should be able to overcome and complement the limits of former standard procedures.

1. Biotechnology of plants and specific crops, including genetic engineering for yield and quality traits, metabolite production, rapid clonal propagation, and

germplasm conservation.

2. **Microbial agro-biotechnology**, including new approaches to plant pest control, biofertilization, bioremediation, and fermentation of agricultural products.
3. **Livestock biotechnology**, including genetic manipulations for improving fertility and reproduction, growth, milk quality, egg production and disease control.
4. **Marine biotechnology**, including the use and improvement of fish, macro- and micro-algae for food and biochemical production and environmental uses.

Mendel, Gregor Johann

James Watson and Francis Crick

Deadle, George Wells

Marshall Nirengerg

Arthur Korenberg

Har Govind Khorana

Monod, Jacques Lucien

Sanger, Frederick

All these domains are concerned with food production and the conservation of our environment. They share a search into the regulation of genes that are responsible for specific qualitative or quantitative traits. Agricultural biotechnology should be continuously monitored and regulated as to its effect on humanity and the environment.

Biotechnology is a most powerful tool to further advance the various fields of agriculture. However, it can work practically only if it can be combined with established breeding strategies and with common agricultural practices. In fact, all agricultural biotechnologies should be looked upon as an extension and integral part of traditional breeding and agriculture, contributing successfully to shortening the breeding cycle, and to production of quality agricultural commodities. The basic biotechnological methodologies are available. They need to be adapted and oriented to the specific needs of agriculture. They should be integrated with a better comprehension of the physiology and metabolism of the organism in question, and standard agricultural practices.

Biotechnology is a applied science and has made advances in two major areas, *viz.*, molecular biology and production of industrially important biochemicals (including enzymes). The science has following multiple applications in agriculture:

1. Automated bio-screening.
2. Bio-processing alkenes to valuable oxides and glycoles.
3. Developing immobilized cell and enzyme systems for chemical process industries.
4. Engineering of a series of organisms for specific industrial use.
5. Genetical improvement of microorganisms for production of pharmaceutical products.
6. Human gene therapy.
7. Improved production of Vitamin B_{12}.
8. Large scale production of fructose from inexpensive forms of glucose.
9. Manufacturing ethanol by continuous fermentation.
10. Microbiological based production of human insulin and interferons.
11. Microbiologically upgradation of hydrocarbons.
12. Production and development of vaccine to prevent calibacillosis (a disease develops in newborn calves and piglets).
13. Production of biopesticide and biofertilizers.
14. Production of diagnostic kits for toxoplasmosis identification.
15. Production of monoclonal antibodies for organ transplant tissue typing.
16. Production of photosynthetically efficient plants.
17. Production of transgenic plants and animals.
18. Production of xanthan gum in oil fields for recovery of crude mineral oils.

THE POWER OF BIOTECHNOLOGY

The power of biotechnology is no longer fantasy. Biotechnology is the use of technologies based on living systems to develop commercial processes and products, now includes the techniques of recombinant DNA, gene transfer, embryo manipulation and transfer, plant regeneration, cell culture, monoclonal antibodies, and bioprocess engineering. Using these techniques, we have begun to transform ideas into practical applications. For instance, scientists have learned to genetically alter certain crops to increase their tolerance to certain herbicides. Biotechnology has also been used to develop safer vaccines against viral and bacterial diseases such as pseudorabies, enteric colibacillosis (scours), and foot-and-mouth disease. Yet we have barely scratched the surface of the many potential benefits. Biotechnology offers new ideas and techniques applicable to agriculture. It offers tools to develop a better understanding of living systems, of our environment, and of ourselves. Yet, continued advances will take a serious commitment of talent and funds. Biotechnology offers tremendous potential for improving crop production, animal agriculture, and bioprocessing. It can provide scientists with new approaches to develop higher yielding and more nutritious crop varieties, improve resistance to diseases and adverse conditions, or reduce the need for fertilizers and other expensive agricultural chemicals. In animal agriculture, its greatest immediate potential lies in therapeutics and vaccines for disease control. Bioprocessing, the use of living systems or their components to create useful products offers opportunities to manufacture new products and foods, treat and use wastes, and use renewable resources for fuel. Biotechnology could also improve forestry and its products, fiber crops, and chemical feed stocks.

Biotechnology: Strategies for Agricultural Development

India needs to frame important strategies for agricultural development through biotechnology, which will offer new opportunities for increased sustainability, profitability, and international competitiveness in agriculture. Such a strategy should address improving the full spectrum of activities, from the quality and direction of research to the realization of the benefits of this research in agricultural production. The potential benefits of biotechnology will not be realized without a continued commitment to basic research. Six research areas merit emphasis are:

Gene Transfer to Enhance Agriculture	
• Gene identification	Locating and identifying agriculturally important genes and creating chromosome maps.
• Gene regulation	Understanding the mechanisms of regulation and expression of these genes and refining the methods by which they may be genetically engineered.
• Structure and function of gene products	Understanding the structure and function of gene products in metabolisms and the development of agriculturally important traits, specially, genetically modified organisms (GMO).
Tissue Culture Techniques	
• Cellular techniques	Developing and refining techniques for cell culture, cell fusion, regeneration of plants, and other manipulations of plant and animal cells and embryos.
Environmental Biotechnology	
• Development in organisms and communities	Understanding the complex physiological and genetic interactions and associations that occur within an organism and between organisms.
• Environmental considerations	Understanding the behavior and effect of genetically engineered organisms in the environment.

GENETIC ENGINEERING TECHNIQUES

Cloning Technology

Cloning technology allows us to generate a population of genetically identical molecules, cells, plants or animals. In molecular cloning, the word "clone" refers to a gene or DNA fragment and also to the collection of cells or organisms, such as bacteria, containing the cloned piece of DNA. Cellular cloning, a type of cell culture, produces "cell lines" of identical cells. In Monoclonal antibody technology, scientists isolate one cell from an array of antibody-producing cells, then generate a clonal cell line from that cell. We can produce plant clones by rooting small pieces of fully developed plants, but animal cloning requires cells specialized for reproduction:

either eggs or embryonic cells at the very earliest stages of development.

Although the debut of the cloned sheep Dolly in 1997 brought animal cloning technology into the spotlight, biologists first cloned animals in 1952 by transferring genetic material from the nucleus of frog embryonic cells to frog eggs, which then developed into genetically identical tadpoles. Using similar nuclear transfer techniques, scientists first cloned cattle in the mid-1980s and have now produced hundreds of cattle, sheep and swine embryos that have been carried to term by surrogate females. For two decades, animal breeders have also used another cloning technology, embryo twinning, to improve livestock herds. They artificially inseminate a genetically superior cow, then divide a 3 to 4-day-old embryo into two and implant the twin embryos into surrogate females.

- ***Molecular cloning*** refers to the procedure of isolating a defined DNA sequence and obtaining multiple copies of it *in vivo*. Cloning is frequently employed to amplify DNA fragments containing genes, but it can be used to amplify any DNA sequence such as promoters, non-coding sequences, chemically synthesised oligonucleotides and randomly fragmented DNA. Cloning is used in a wide array of biological experiments and technological applications such as large scale protein production.
- ***Cellular cloning*** means to derive a population of cells from a single cell. In the case of unicellular organisms such as bacteria and yeast, this process is remarkably simple and essentially only requires the inoculation of the appropriate medium. However, in the case of cell cultures from multi-cellular organisms, cell cloning is an arduous task as these cells will not readily grow in standard media is also a fundamental and essential tool of biotechnology research, development and commercialization. All applications of monoclonal antibody technology; the regeneration of transgenic plants from single cells; pharmaceutical manufacturing based on mammalian cell culture; and generation of therapeutic cells and tissues depend on cellular cloning. These and other potential applications must also be taken into account in any legislative actions directed at cloning.
- ***Animal cloning*** is the process by which an entire organism is reproduced from a single cell taken from the parent organism and in a genetically identical manner. This means the cloned animal is an exact duplicate in every way of its parent; it has the same exact DNA. Cloning happens quite frequently in nature. Asexual reproduction in certain organisms and the development of twins from a single fertilized egg are both instances of Cloning. With the advancement of biological technology, it is now possible to artificially recreate the process of animal cloning.

Genetic Modification Technology

Genetic modification technology is often referred to as recombinant DNA technology. Recombinant DNA is made, both in nature and by humans, by combining genetic material from two different sources. Humans began to preferentially combine the genetic material of domesticated plants and animals thousands of years ago by selecting which individuals would reproduce. By selectively breeding, individuals with valuable genetic traits while excluding others from reproduction, we intentionally changed the genetic makeup of the plants and animals we domesticated. Techniques for making selective breeding more predictable and precise have been continually evolving, especially since we discovered the genetic basis of heredity in the early 1900s.

In genetic modification, we move single genes whose functions we know from one organism to another; in selective breeding, large sets of genes of unknown function are transferred. By making our manipulations more precise and our out comes more certain, we decrease the risk of producing organisms with unexpected traits and avoid the time-consuming trial-and-error approach of selective breeding.

Currently, we are using genetic modification techniques to:

- Produce new medicines and safer vaccines,
- Treat some genetic diseases,
- Enhance bio-control agents in agriculture,
- Increase agricultural yields and decrease production costs,
- Decrease allergy-producing characteristics of some foods,
- Improve food's nutritional value,
- Develop biodegradable plastics and
- Decrease water and air pollution.

A special type of genetic modification technology, antisense technology, uses small nucleic acids to block the protein production of specific genes. Currently, researchers use antisense to:

- Slow food spoilage
- Control viral diseases
- Inhibit inflammation

Hybrid Technologies

The biotechnologies described above, which rely almost exclusively on knowledge of cells and biological molecules, have provided us with an extraordinary array of new options. We are also combining our understanding of biological processes with scientific advances and technological innovations in other disciplines, which gives birth to a synergistic set of new technologies.

Genetic engineering is the most fundamental mechanics of biotechnologies and is a recent offshoot of biotechnological research. It involves gene splicing, recombinant DNA cloning and tissue culture technology. The technique overall involves into two steps:

1. The in vitro incorporation of the gene or segment of DNA of interest into a small, self-replicating chromosomes and,
2. The introduction of the recombinant minichromosome into a host cell where it will replicate. Step one involves synthesis of **recombinant DNA** and step two is the **Gene cloning**.

These two, **recombinant DNA** and **gene cloning** technologies are the most powerful tools developed in field of biology. Genetic Engineering involves manipulation of the genetic material of an organism to give an altered expression of our choice. It deals with identification and isolation of desired gene and then joining this gene of interest into another organism. The desired gene expresses itself in that organism by the gene product. Various steps of genetic engineering are:

Gene isolation: Desired gene is identified, isolated and purified. This DNA of interest is also called donor DNA or target DNA.

Selection of vector	A vector is a self-replicating molecule of DNA or replicon to which desired gene is linked. Vector molecule with foreign DNA inserted is known as chimeric DNA. Vector acts as carrier and transports the gene into the host cell. Thus, it is also known as a cloning vehicle or a carrier molecule. Suitable vector is identified for a system; commonly used vectors are plasmids and viral DNA molecule. However, recent techniques involve physical delivery of DNA by various methods.
Cloning of desired gene	Multiple copies of desired gene can be obtained by placing them in host cell with the help of vectors. Here, the desired gene along with the vector is amplified. Large numbers of identical copies of gene of interest are produced for subsequent gene transfer into target cell. Now, gene cloning is a fast and mechanized process, using polymerase chain reaction (PCR) machines.
Specific gene transfer	The gene of interest is finally transferred to host cells. Transformed cells are selected, multiplied and produce transgenic plants by tissue culture technique.
Expression of desired gene	The desired gene produce, the product in new environment of host, thus the desired traits.

Gene Transfer

Throughout the history of agriculture, humans have taken advantage of the natural process of genetic exchange through breeding that creates variation in biological traits. This fact underlies all attempts to improve agricultural species, whether through traditional breeding or through techniques of molecular biology. In both cases, people manipulate and natural process to produce varieties of organisms that display desired characteristics or traits, such as disease-resistant crops or food animals with a higher proportion of muscle to fat.

The major differences between traditional breeding and molecular biological methods of gene transfer lie neither in goals nor processes, but rather in speed, precision, reliability, and scope. When traditional breeders cross two sexually reproducing plants or animals, tens of thousands of genes are mixed.

Gene transfer techniques are keys to many applications of biotechnology. The essence of genetic engineering is the ability to identify a particular gene, one that encodes a desired trait in an organism, isolate the gene, study its function and regulation, modify the gene, and reintroduce it into its natural host or another organism. These techniques are tools, not ends in themselves. They can be used to understand the nature and function of genes, unlock secrets of disease resistance, regulate growth and development, or manipulate communication among cells and among organisms.

Isolation of Important Genes

The first step in an effort to genetically engineer an organism is to locate the relevant gene(s) among the tens of thousand that make up the genome. This task is made easier with restriction enzymes that can cut complex, double-stranded macromolecules of DNA into manageable pieces. A restriction enzyme recognizes a unique sequence in the DNA, where it snips the strands. By using a series of different restriction enzymes, an organism's genomic DNA can be reduced to lengths equivalent to one or several genes. These smaller segments can be sorted and then cloned to produce a quantity of genetic material for further analysis. The collection of DNA segments from one genotype – a gene library – can be searched to locate a desired gene. Patterns can also be analyzed to link a particular a desired gene. Patterns can also be analyzed to link a particular sequence – a marker – to a particular traitor disease, even though the specific gene responsible is still unknown.

Restriction enzymes are also used in cloning genes. The ability to isolate and clone individual genes has played a critical role in the development of biotechnology. Cloned genes are necessary research tools for studies of the structure, function, and expression of genes. Further, specific gene traits could not be transferred into new organisms unless numerous gene copies were available. Cloned genes also are used as diagnostic test probes in medicine and agriculture to detect specific diseases.

Gene Transfer Technology

Genes transfer from one organism to another, molecular biologists use vectors. Vectors are the carriers used to pass genes to a new host, and they can mediate the entry, maintenance, and expression of foreign genes in cells. Vectors used to transfer genes include viruses, plasmids, and mobile segments of DNA called transposable elements. Genes can also be introduced by laboratory means, such as chemical treatments including injection with microneedles. The basic principles behind these technologies are the same for animals, plants, and microbes, although specific modifications may be necessary.

Vectors based on viruses, plasmids, and transposable elements have been adapted from naturally occurring systems and engineered to transfer desired genes into animals, plants, and microbes. For plants, the classic example is the Ti plasmid from the soil bacterium *Agrobacterium tumefaciens*, which in nature transfers a segment of DNA into plant cells, causing the recipient cells to grow into a tumor. Scientists have adapted this plasmid by eliminating its tumor-causing properties to create a versatile vector than can transfer foreign genes into many types of plants.

Molecular Markers

Molecular markers are specific fragments of DNA that can be identified within the whole genome. They are found at specific locations of the genome. They are used to 'flag' the position of a particular gene or the inheritance of a particular characteristic. In a genetic cross, the characteristics of interest will usually stay linked with the molecular markers. Thus, individuals can be selected in which the molecular marker is present, since the marker indicates the presence of the desired characteristic.

It is an identifiable physical location on a chromosome whose inheritance can be monitored (e.g. gene, restriction enzyme site or RFLP marker).

In terms of **Cancer Research**, molecukar marker is a biological molecule found in blood, other body fluids, or tissues that is a sign of a normal or abnormal process, or of a condition or disease. A molecular marker may be used to see how well the body responds to a treatment for a disease or condition. Also called biomarker and signature molecule.

Molecular marker is a term with a number of uses. It is any kind of molecule indicating the existence of a chemical or physical process. In particular, in the fields of geology and astrobiology, biomarkers (also known as biosignatures) are sometimes understood as molecules indicating the presence (past or present) of living organisms. It can also be a molecule used as **fiscal marker** to distinguish lower-taxed items from higher-taxed ones when they otherwise can be substituted.

In medicine, a molecular marker can be a substance that is introduced in an organism as a means to examine something. For example, rubidium chloride is used as a radioactive isotope to evaluate perfusion of heart muscle. In biology and medicine, a molecular marker (biomarker means an indicator of a particular disease state or a particular state of an organism) can be a substance native to the organism whose detection indicates a particular disease state (for example, the presence of an antibody may indicate an infection). In genetics, a molecular marker (identified as genetic marker) is a fragment of DNA sequence that is associated to a part of the genome. A genetic marker is can be described as a variation, which may arise due to mutation or alteration in the genomic loci, that can be observed. A genetic marker may be a short DNA sequence, such as a sequence surrounding a single base-pair change (single nucleotide polymorphism, SNP), or a long one, like minisatellites.

A **single nucleotide polymorphism** (**SNP**, pronounced *snip*), is a DNA sequence variation occurring when a single nucleotide - A, T, C, or G - in the genome (or other shared sequence) differs between members of a species (or between paired chromosomes in an individual). For example, two sequenced DNA fragments from different individuals, AAGC**C**TA to AAGC**T**TA, contain a difference in a single nucleotide. In this case we say that there are two alleles: C and T. Almost all common SNPs have only two alleles. For a variation to be considered a SNP, it must occur in at least 1% of the population.

Molecular markers are used in molecular biology and biotechnology experiments where they use to identify a particular sequence of DNA. As the DNA sequences are very highly specific, they can be identified with the help of the known molecular markers which can find out a particular sequence of DNA from a group of unknown.

DNA-based markers are used in cultivar identification, germplasm management, characterization of genetic diversity, population structure of wild relatives, phylogenetic analyses, and marker assisted selection.

Molecular markers and genome mapping are used in detecting new desirable genes in plant improvement specially for tomato, potato, pea, melon, cabbage, etc. The markers help in identifying important quantitative trait loci (QTL). The QTLs affecting salt tolerance in tomato during germination have been identified. As many as 700 tomato markers were known in 1990 (De Verna and Paterson, 1990). DNA fingerprinting helps in identification, characterization and evaluation of genetic uniformity of regenerated new plants of vegetatively propagated fruit crops at cultivar level.

Marker-Assisted Selection: Fast Track to New Crop Varieties

Back in 1930, when a Manitoba farmer came across a few stems of rust-free wheat in a rust-infested field, it took plant scientists several years of work before they could develop those rust-resistant kernels into a new wheat variety. Almost 25 years later, the new variety called Selkirk was released. It happened at a good time, though. Selkirk arrived just as another rust outbreak was occurring on the Prairies in 1954.

The process of developing new crop varieties still requires many steps. But now, applications of biotechnology have considerably shortened the time it takes to bring them to market. Where it once took almost 25 years, it currently takes about seven to 10 years.

One of the tools, which is making it easier for scientists to select plant traits, further reducing the time needed to develop a new variety, is called marker-assisted selection **(MAS)**.

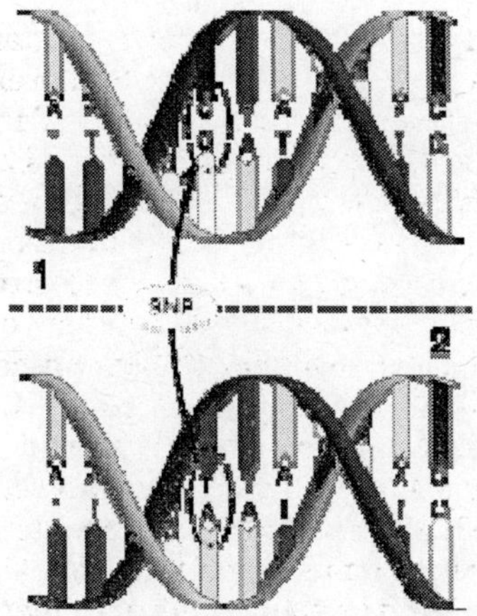

FIGURE 1.1: DNA strand 1 differs from DNA strand 2 at a single base-pair location (a C/T polymorphism).

Molecular Shortcut

The differences, which distinguish one plant from another are encoded in the plant's genetic material, the DNA. The DNA occurs in pairs of chromosomes (strands of genetic material), one coming from each parent. The genes, which control the plant's characteristics, are specific segments of each chromosome. All of the plant's genes together make up its genome. Some traits, like flower color, may be controlled by only one gene, however, other more complex characteristics, like crop yield or starch content, may be influenced by many genes.

Traditionally, plant breeders have selected plants based on their visible or measurable traits, called the phenotype. But, as indicated by the development of the Selkirk wheat variety, this process can be difficult, slow and costly, not only in the development itself, but also for the economy, as farmers suffer crop losses.

As a shortcut, plant breeders now use marker-assisted selection. To help identify specific genes, scientists use what are called molecular markers. The markers are a string or sequence of nucleic acid which makes up a segment of DNA. The markers are near the DNA sequence of the desired gene. Since the markers and the genes are close together on the same chromosome, they tend to stay together as each generation of plants is produced. This is called genetic linkage. This linkage helps scientists to predict whether a plant will have a desired gene. If researchers can find the marker for the gene, it means the gene itself is present.

As scientists learn where each of the markers occurs on a chromosome, and how close it is to a specific gene, they can create a map of the markers and genes on specific chromosomes. These genetic linkage maps show the location of markers and genes, and show their distance from other known genes. Scientists can produce detailed maps in only one generation of plant breeding.

Previously, scientists produced very simple genetic maps using conventional techniques. It was long ago observed that as generations of plants were crossed, some traits consistently appeared together in the new generations (genetic linkage). However, since researchers could concentrate on only a few traits in each attempt at crossbreeding, it took many crosses to obtain even a very simple genetic map. Using very detailed genetic maps and better knowledge of the molecular structure of a plant's DNA, researchers can analyze a tiny bit of tissue from a newly germinated seedling. They do not have to wait for the seedling to grow into a mature plant so that they can test for a specific characteristic. Once the tissue is analyzed, scientists know whether that seedling contains the appropriate gene. If it does not, they can quickly move on and concentrate analysis on another seedling, eventually working only with the plants which contain a specific trait.

Molecular Shortcut

The differences, which distinguish one plant from another are encoded in the plant's genetic material, the DNA. The DNA occurs in pairs of chromosomes (strands of genetic material), one coming from each parent. The genes, which control the plant's characteristics, are specific segments of each chromosome. All of the plant's genes together make up its genome. Some traits, like flower color, may be controlled by only one gene, however, other more complex characteristics, like crop yield or starch content, may be influenced by many genes.

As a shortcut, plant breeders now use marker-assisted selection. To help identify specific genes, scientists use what are called molecular markers. The markers are a string or sequence of nucleic acid which makes up a segment of DNA. The markers are near the DNA sequence of the desired gene. Since the markers and the genes are close together on the same chromosome, they tend to stay together as each generation of plants is produced. This is called genetic linkage. This linkage helps scientists to predict whether a plant will have a desired gene. If researchers can find the marker for the gene, it means the gene itself is present.

Marked Benefits

Some crops, like canola, have relatively simple genomes. This means it is easier for scientists to develop markers for specific traits and produce genetic maps. Some crops, like wheat, have complicated genomes. Each wheat cell contains approximately 10 times more DNA than a human cell. As well, there are very few differences in the DNA sequences that distinguish varieties. In these cases, it may be much more difficult to develop markers.

Marker-assisted selection can also be used to pyramid genes in a new plant variety. Pyramiding genes means putting two or more desirable genetic traits into one crop variety. The goal is to produce varieties with not just one, but several, desirable characteristics.

More and more pathologists are using molecular probes for early detection of diseases. However, the main contributions of modern biotechnology remain probably in the hands of the plant breeders. Indeed, molecular markers are of great use in detecting desirable new genes, or to identify important QTL. This marker-assisted selection is very useful for many vegetable plants. Other applications are DNA - fingerprinting and genetic engineering. This recent technology aims to insert and to express new specific genes into a selected plant.

Marker-Assisted Selection

Molecular markers and genome mapping will reach a large extension in the next breeding programmes of tomatoes, peas, cabbages, melons, potatoes. It will be possible to improve the speed and the incorporation efficiency of desirable new genes by utilizing of closely linked selectable molecular markers. The number of backcross will be reduced. The utilization of molecular markers could also identify important quantitative trait loci (QTL).

DNA Fingerprinting

The chemical structure of everyone's DNA is the same. The only difference between people (or any animal) is the order of the base pairs. There are so many millions of base pairs in each person's DNA that every person has a different sequence. Using these sequences, every person could be identified solely by the sequence of their base pairs. However, because there are so many millions of base pairs, the task would be very time-consuming. Instead, scientists are able to use a shorter method, because of repeating patterns in DNA. These patterns do not, however, give an individual "fingerprint," but they are able to determine whether two DNA samples are from the same person, related people, or non-related people. Scientists use a small number of sequences of DNA that are known to vary among individuals a great deal, and analyze those to get a certain probability of a match.

Genetic Engineering of Microorganisms Associated with Plants

Microorganisms in the environment affect the growth of plants in a variety of ways, many of which are still poorly understood. Their effects can be either beneficial or harmful. For instance, some microorganisms protect plants from bacterial or fungal infections. Others protect plants from environmental stresses such as acidity, salinity, or high concentrations of toxic metals. Still others attack weeds that compete with crops. The best-known association between microorganisms and plants is the symbiotic relationship between nitrogen-fixing bacteria of the genus *Rhizobium* and members of the legume family, such as soybeans.

As our understanding of the relationships between microorganisms and crops improves, the genes controlling these relationships – whether in the microorganism or in the plant – can be engineered to enhance the abilities of beneficial microorganisms or inhibit the effects of harmful microorganisms.

Genetically Modified (GM) Crops

Genetically modified (GM) foods are foods derived from genetically modified organisms. The DNA of genetically modified organisms has been modified through genetic engineering, unlike similar food organisms developed through the conventional genetic modification of selective breeding (plant breeding and animal breeding) or mutation breeding. GM foods were first put on the market in the early 1990s. Typically, genetically modified foods are transgenic plant products: soybean, corn, canola, and cotton seed oil, but animal products have been developed.

The establishment and commercialization of GM crops has been very rapid in past years. In 1995, however, there were no commercial plantings of GM crops. About 99 per cent of the two important transgenic traits - herbicide and insect resistance (Bt) are of common use. Less than 1% of GM acreage was devoted to "quality" traits, such as controlled ripening and enhanced oil profiles. Globally, herbicide-resistant soybean dominates GM crop acreage (52%), followed by Bt corn (24%).

Genetically modified crops have also been developed for food industries, such as enzymes from microorganisms in processed products like soft drinks, cakes, cheese, bread, fish, and meats, etc. About 90 per cent of common foodstuffs contain GM-components.

PROTEIN (OR ENZYME) ENGINEERING

Protein engineering is an important area of biotechnology, through which it is possible to produce superior enzymes and storage proteins. In this area, a protein engineer first a computer aided protein model for a specific function and then prepares a synthetic gene which produces the desired protein in a predictable manner. Use of immobilized enzyme has made possible the production of a variety of substances *e.g.*, high-fructose corn syrup (as sweetening agent for soft drink industry), glucose isomerase, etc.

Enzyme technology is an area of considerable current interest and development. Enzymes are biological catalysts and have been used for many years as isolated agents particularly in food industry, *e.g.*, rennin, papain, and invertase. Microorganisms are very convenient enzyme sources, because the enzymes concentration may be markedly increased by acting on environmental conditions and by genetic manipulation. These enzymes have increasingly replaced plant and animal enzymes: thus, amylases from *Bacillus* and *Aspergillus* have substituted those of malted wheat and barley in brewing, backing and biscuit making, and in the textile industry, etc.

CELL CULTURE TECHNOLOGY

Cell culture technology is the growing of cells outside of living organisms. With mammalian cell culture, we can replace animal testing with cell testing when evaluating the safety and efficacy of medicines. Cellular therapeutics are one the horizon as well. New, healthy cells, produced with embryonic stem cell culture, could replace the malfunctioning cells in people with Parkinson's disease and restore function in stroke and heart attack victims.

Plant cell culture provides us with an environmentally sound an economically feasible option for obtaining naturally occurring products with therapeutic value, such as the chemotherapeutic agent paclitaxel, a compound found in yew trees and marketed under the name Taxol.

By using cell culture to grow microorganisms that infect insects, we will be able to kill insect pests, such as mosquitoes and caterpillars. Biocontrol agents infect only certain insects without harming beneficial insects, such as honeybees.

TISSUE CULTURE TECHNIQUES

The ability to regenerate plants from single cells is important for progress with gene transfer into plans. Animals cannot be regenerated asexually, so the only way to introduce a foreign gene into all cells of an animal is to insert it into the sperm, egg, or zygote. Cell culture techniques are important for the regeneration of plants. They are also critical for fundamental studies on both plant and animal cells, and for the manipulation of microorganisms.

The vegetative propagation of stem cuttings or other growing plant parts to produce genetic clones is common for some agricultural crops. Potatoes, sugarcane, bananas, and some horticultural species, for example, are cultivated by vegetative propagation. Techniques exist to propagate and regenerate whole plants from tissues, isolated plant cells, or even protoplast (plant cells from which the cell all has been enzymatically removed) in culture. This set of techniques is complete for some agricultural species, such as alfalfa, carrots, oilseed rape, soybeans, tobacco, tomatoes, and turnips. Progress on other crops, including major food species such as many cereals and legumes, has been slower.

Cell culture techniques have taken on added importance as biotechnology has progressed. Genetic engineering requires an ability to manipulate individual cells as recipients of isolated genes. Cell culture techniques allow scientists to maintain and grow cells outside the organism and thus expand their ability to perform gene transfer and study the results. In addition, cell culture allows scientists to regenerate numerous copies (clones) of the manipulated varieties, which is easier, more efficient, and more convenient, especially for producing significant quantities of stock plants. A third use of cell culture is to regenerate *somaclonal variants*, plants with altered genetic traits that can prove useful as new or improved crops. Thus, cell culture techniques are important to increasing the productivity and versatility of agriculture.

However, there are some important limitations. Chromosomal abnormalities appear as cultures age. These changes are related to the phenomenon of somaclonal variation, which may prove useful to agriculture, but in many instances the changes are undesirable. Therefore, scientists must learn how to prevent chromosomal changes in cell cultures. Second, long-term cultures lose regenerative potential.

Tissue culture can serve a number of following purposes:

1. Seed-grown products lack uniformity.
2. Seed-grown products are not true to type.
3. Seeds take too long to grow to mature plants.
4. Seeds are difficult to handle.
5. Seeds are not available.
6. Cuttings grow too slowly.
7. Cuttings have poor survival rate.
8. Cuttings require too much care.
9. Cuttings are too vulnerable to disease.
10. Tissue culture is often the only practical way to produce the large numbers required.
11. There is a shortage of stock plants from which to take cuttings because there is:
    a) only one hybrid,
    b) only one virus-free plant,
    c) only one desirable mutant.
12. There is insufficient room for stock plants and it is not cost effective to maintain the stock plants.

Tissue Culture: Production of True to Type Plant

Plant tissue culture is a field of many facets. The term *tissue culture* is actually a misnomer borrowed from the field of animal tissue culture. It is a misnomer because plant micropropagation is concerned with the whole plantlet and not just isolated tissues, though the explant may be a particular tissue. The terms *plantlet culture* or *micropropagation*, therefore, are more accurate. Plant tissue culture is the technique of growing plant cells, tissues and organs in an artificial prepared nutrient medium static or liquid, under aseptic conditions. Better control of environmental conditions like light, temperature, gas mixtures and nutrients can be achieved for plant tissues growing *in vitro*. Whether we call it cloning, tissue culture, micropropagation, or growing *in vitro*, the process remains the same; it is a vegetative method for multiplying plants. Tissue culture is the ever-ready tool for specialists who hybridize plants by either sexual or asexual means. It is a clean and rapid way for genetic engineers to grow material for identifying and manipulating genes or to transfer individual characteristics from one plant to another. It plays a role in a wide array of fields, such as botany, chemistry, physics, genetic engineering, molecular biology, hybrid development, pesticide testing, and food science.

Regeneration protocols for haploids and homozygous diploids, and woody perennials -mango, litchi, apple, walnut, cashew, coconut and oilpalm –are required to be developed. Meristem culture, callus culture, anther culture and organ cultures are usually employed. The use of meristem culture technique successfully been used in banana, citrus, cardamom, papaya, carnation, chrysanthemum, etc. to produce virus-free plants in a large number. Cloning technique is being used in a number of horticultural crops and shoot-tip grafting for virus cleaning in citrus.

Tissue Culture Techniques to Increase Genetic Variability

The haploid plantlets (n chromosomes) are treated with colchicine to produce fertile homozygous lines, called *double haploid lines*. This haplodiploïdisation technique could give immediately new elite genotypes, hybrid parents after *in vitro* propagation, as asparagus supermales (MM), or useful genetic material to establish gene mapping.

Protoplast Culture and Micropropagation

Protoplasts are the smallest units able to regenerate a whole plant. Therefore protoplasts cultures can serve to enlarge genetic variability by introducing somaclonal variation. However, the main interest of protoplasts is their capacity to fuse and to produce hybrids or cybrids, new organisms most often unknown in nature. Indeed, protoplasts allow to transgress the barrier of the botanical species or genus. Naked protoplasts can accept without rejection external elements: nuclei, cytoplasmic organelles, liposomes, containing genetic information.

The protoplast culture technique can be suitably used for microinjection and other genetic engineering experiments. The techniques are important, specially, because of their far-reaching effects on crop improvement by somatic hybridization and cell modification. The protoplast culture can be regenerated into an entire plant. It is imperative that the technique in future will be one of the most frequently used research tools for tissue culturists, physiologists, pathologists, molecular biologists, cytogeneticists, and biotechnologists. The discovery of enzymes which could separate the cells and remove the cell wall revolutionized the concept of plant tissue culture. It has provided a tool for isolating protoplasts and exploring the possibilities of genetic engineering.

Somatic Hybrids and Cybrids

The first protoplast fusion application was a cytoplasmic transfer from one genotype to another to induce male sterility (CMS) from mitochondrial origin. These male sterile hybrids are interesting to produce F1 hybrids (*Brassica*, *Cichorium*).

Since long protoplast fusion was proposed as a novel and important method for producing hybrid plants that can be obtained by sexual means. Mechanical or enzymatic removal of cell wall from a plant cell yields, a protoplast, which is bound by plasma membrane. An isolated protoplast, under suitable culture condition can regenerate entire plant.

Production of Virus-Free Plants

In 1952, Morel and Martin were successful in regenerating a virus-free dahlia plant by the excision of some meristematic domes from virus infected shoots. Three years later, the same authors were able to eliminate virus A and Y from virus infected potato. Semal and Lepoivre (1992) reported that a virus-free sweet potato was producing 40T/ha in China by comparison of the 20 T/ha produced before meristem culture.

Virus eradication is dependent on several parameters, but to take advantage of the non uniform and imperfect virus distribution in the host plant body, the size of the excised meristem should be as small as possible. Today, no definitive explanation can be given to understand this virus eradication (Wang and Charles, 1991).

Shoot Tip Micrografting

When meristem tip culture fails, it is possible to graft small meristematic domes on young seedlings growing *in vitro*. In this way, Navarro et al. (1975) eradicated all the virus diseases from Spanish Citrus orchards. This technique was also very successful in eliminating virus diseases from peach trees (Mosella et al 1980).

Micropropagation Techniques

During the micropropagation process, the genetic stability of the new shoots is dependent upon their origin. Axillary shoots issue from pre-existing buds and are normally true to type, indeed the meristematic cells are genetically very stable. Adventitious shoots, such as somatic embryos, are neoformed buds developed directly on some organs, or indirectly through a callus phase formed on this organ. So, if the mother plant presents a cell mosaic or chimaeric tissues, risks of genetic variation exists. It is similar in the case of an indirect regeneration, when the callus phase is too long.

Propagation by Axillary Shooting

This technique has proved to be the most applicable and reliable method of *in vitro* propagation. Axillary shoot growth is stimulated by overcoming apical meristem dominance. Commercial tissue culture laboratories are now able to propagate a large number of herbaceous ornamental species and several woody plants in this way. However, the propagation of *Pelargonium*, Howea, and a few other horticultural plants are always difficult to propagate by axillary branching.

Propagation by Direct or Indirect Organogenesis

Adventitious shoots could arise directly from the tissue of explants without callus formation. Several plants of the family gesneriaceae (*Saintpaulia*, *Streptocarpus*) regenerate directly buds on leaf explants, likewise *Lilium* regenerates on scales. However more often, like for *Ficus lyrata*, adventitious buds appear on callus. While coffee, cocoa trees, and many conifers are produced by somatic embryogenesis developed on callus or cell suspensions.

Improvement of Axillary Branching

The more simple method was *in vitro* layering developed by Wang (1977) to clone PVX-free potato plants. The first plantlets placed on the medium in a horizontal position developed axillary shoots. They are harvested by cutting one centimeter above the medium surface, at 3 weeks intervals. A similar technique called **hedging system** by Aitken Christie and Jones (1987) was later used to produce *Pinus radiata*.

Somatic Embryogenesis Propagation

For genetically stable species, somatic embryogenesis offers a very fast scaling-up system, especially when it's possible to produce embryos in bioreactors. Several bottlenecks limit the use of this interesting technology. One of the main problems is genetic stability.

Synseeds

Another very interesting possibility of the somatic embryogenesis technology has been developed during the past fifteen years by Redenbaugh and his team (1991, 1993). They were able to encapsulate somatic embryos by hydrogel coatings (sodium alginate), producing single embryo artificial seeds. To date, some improvements offer the possibility to directly plant the artificial seeds in the greenhouse on special substrates (vermiculite, sans.). This methodology will provide in the future a good technique to reduce the cost of transplants.

Somaclonal Variations

The production of plantlets by callus regeneration, cell suspensions, protoplast cultures, could present some deviations with regard to the mother plant. This is a way to increase the genetic variability. Associated with a selective pressure (stress to toxins, pH, salinity, cold) it's used to obtain resistant lines. Indeed, after regeneration, plants can express new potentialities rarely obtained another way.

Haplodiploidisation

Many species are able to produce haploids through different *in vitro* techniques. Solanae (datura, tobacco, red pepper, eggplant, petunia), cereals (wheat, barley, rice, triticale, maize) or crucifers (soybean, cabbage) are species easy to regenerate by anther culture.

Germplasm Conservation (Gene Bank)

Tissue culture methods offer the opportunity for *in vitro* collecting, rapid multiplication and distribution of important, elite, or rare plants that are threatened with extinction. The two major *in vitro* storage strategies are slow growth and cryopreservation. Dereuddre et al. (1991) have provided a very simple technology to freeze encapsulated meristems in dried alginate beads. It works for pear, strawberry, eucalyptus, and potato.

TISSUE ENGINEERING TECHNOLOGY

Tissue engineering technology combines advances in cell biology and materials science, allowing us to create semi-synthetic tissues and organs in the laboratory. These tissues consist of biodegradable scaffolding material plus living cells produced through cell culture.

Simple tissues, such as skin and cartilage, were the first to be engineered successfully. Ultimately the goal is to create complex organs, consisting of a number of tissue types that can replace diseased or injured organs.

DNA CHIP TECHNOLOGY

DNA chip technology, a marriage of the semi-conductor manufacturing industry and molecular genetics, will transform genetic analysis because it allows us to analyze tens of thousands of genes simultaneously on a single chip. The manufacturing process of microchips and DNA chips is similar, in principle; but instead of shining light through a series of masks to etch circuits into silicon, automated DNA chipmakers use a series of masks to lay down an array of DNA fragments on a glass slide. DNA chip technology is being used for:

1. Detect mutations in disease-causing genes.
2. Monitor gene activity.
3. Diagnose infectious diseases and identify the best antibiotic treatment.
4. Identify genes important to crop productivity.
5. Improve screening for microbes used in bioremediation.

DNA chips will be essential for converting the raw genetic data provided by the Human Genome Project into useful products. Sequencing the human genome, while a remarkable achievement, provides only the first milestone in the upcoming medical revolution. The gene sequence and mapping data mean little until we determine what those genes do. This field of study, known as functional genomics, helps us translate gene identification and DNA sequence data into biological functions.

Neither functional genomics nor proteomics is an end in itself. Their medical value will be in identifying specific therapeutic targets and helping us understand the complex biochemistry of disease processes. For more information on the exciting advances spawned by genomics and proteomics, see the "Health Care" section.

BIOINFORMATICS TECHNOLOGY

Bioinformatics technology uses computational tools provided by the information technology revolution, such as statistical software, graphics simulation and database management, to organize and analyze information about biological systems, which, for biotechnology, information about cells and biological molecules. Using another product of the information revolution, the Internet, scientists broadcast this information around the world.

Bioinformatics technology provides us with tools and methods for consistently organizing, accessing, processing and integrating data from different sources. Bioinformatics technology helps us to:

- Map genomes and identify genes
- Determine protein structure and simulate protein interactions
- Discover new therapeutic targets and design medicines aimed at the targets and
- Assess the effects of virtual mutations on gene function.

MICROBIAL BIOPESTICIDES, BIOFUNGICIED, HERBICIDES AND AGRICULTURAL ANTIBIOTICS

Using biotechnology, it is possible to make crop plants tolerant of specific herbicides. Several blopesticides are in use today. Biopesticide products are based on natural agents such as microorganisms and fatty acid compounds. They are toxic to targeted pests (such as the European corn borer) and do not harm humans, animals, fish, birds or beneficial insects. In addition, because biopesticides act in unique ways, they can control pest populations that have developed resistance to conventional pesticides.

When the herbicide is sprayed, it will kill the weeds but have no effect on the crop plants. This lets farmers reduce the number of times herbicides have to be applied and reduces the cost of producing crops and damage to the environment.

The contributions of biotechnology to the practice of medicine through the discovery and development of a number of potent antibacterial antibiotics is widely recognized. A major effort concerned with the discovery of new structures with antibacterial activities and the chemical modification of existing natural products is still ongoing. The development of low cost production methods and successful formulation of products such as microbial insecticides represents the commercial cutting edge of biotechnology.

The term insecticide usually bring thoughts of poisonous, non-selective, energy-consuming chemicals that are used to kill pest insects. However, not all insecticides fit this generally accepted stereotype. Those microorganisms which often suppress and naturally control populations of pests which injure man and causes extensive damage to food and fibre crops. Formulation of living viruses, bacteria, fungi and protozoa are called **microbial insecticides**.

Introduction is not theoretically limited to insects and vertebrate predators; the use of the myxomatosis virus to control rabbits in Australia suggests that microbes may be able to play similar roles. However, introductions have two fundamental limitations:

1. They have an extra dimension of unpredictability because an organisms, hitherto unknown, is being brought to a new area which it might find futile in unanticipated ways and/or may not acclimatized in changed conditions and
2. There is no clear way to make a profit from one-of introductions.

Natural Protections for Plants

Biotechnology helps us to transplant the genetic information that makes a given bacterium – such as the Bt bacterium – lethal only to a specific insect (but not to humans or animals) into plants on which that insect feeds. The plant that once was a food source for the insect now kills it. This process, which less no effect whatsoever on humans, means that it becomes less necessary to spray crops with chemical pesticides to control infestations. Several products have been developed which control insects as well as conventional insecticides, thereby reducing the use of chemical products. Bt technology is used to develop and specially formulate a lien of biotoxin and fatty acid-based products for field-testing in the poultry and livestock industries.

Biosensor Technology

The natural biosensors are the *sense organs* primarily the chemical sensors of smell and taste. Biosensors technically in their various forms share a reliance of biological materials as sensing elements. Technical biosensors have been under intense development since the middle of 1960 with the prospects of commercial potential offered by biotechnology. Biosensors are the combinations of biologically active material displaying characteristic specifically with chemical or electronic sensor to convert the response into electrical signals. Biosensors have their roots in military research, as means of detecting nerve gases and other chemical warfare toxins. Their applications have branched out to include simple-t-use *alternate site* diagnostic devices for home, doctor's office, or drug use screening; medical and surgical monitors (small enough to fit inside a blood vessel) and environmental quality monitors.

Biochips Technology

Biochips are made from different biological materials and can control the computer by replacing silicon chips. Biomolecular computers thus made, promise to be ten to thousand times smaller than the best super computers with much faster switching times and extremely low power dissipation. They are made up of **semi-conducing molecules** inserted into the protein framework and fix the whole on to a protein support. They can be used in implanting of several sorts in human body, like regulation of heartbeats, responses to nerve impulses by artificial limbs (bearing such computer device), overcoming of blindness and deafness, etc. Biochips may be infected by microbes since they are made up of proteins.

Biofilm Technology

A biofilm is an accumulation of microbial cells and inorganic components held together in a polymeric matrix and firmly attached to a substratum. Accumulation of biofilms is encountered in many natural and modulated environments. It may be fundamental to process performance *i.e.*, for fixed-film biological wastewater treatment, sudden deterioration of water quality and deterioration of substrata.

Biosurfactents Technology

Biosurfactents are surface-active compounds produced by microorganisms. Biological surfactants possess a number of potential advantages over their chemically manufactured counterparts, including lower toxicity, biodegradability, a wide variety of possible structures, and ease of synthesis from inexpensive, renewable feed stocks. Consequently, biosurfactents may have applications in numerous areas, particularly for enhance oil recovery and in foods, beverages, cosmetics, pharmaceutical preparations, etc.

MONOCLONAL ANTIBODY TECHNOLOGIES

Monoclonal antibodies (mAb or moAb) are monospecific antibodies that are identical because they are produced by one type of immune cell that are all clones of a single parent cell. Given almost any substance, it is possible to create monoclonal antibodies that specifically bind to that substance; they can then serve to detect or purify that substance. This has become an important tool in biochemistry, molecular biology and medicine. When used as medications, the generic drug name ends in –*mab*.

Monoclonal antibody technology uses immune system cells that make proteins called antibodies which attack a flu virus one winter do nothing to protect us from a slightly different flu virus the next year. The specificity of antibodies makes them powerful tools for locating substances that occur in minuscule amounts and measuring them with great accuracy. Monoclonal antibodies are used in following aspects:

1. Distinguish cancer cells from normal cells.
2. Locate environmental pollutants.
3. Detect harmful microorganisms in food.
4. Diagnose infectious diseases in humans, animals and plants more quickly and

more accurately than every before.

The development of monoclonal antibody technology is based on advances in our ability to culture cells. Antibodies are the protein components of the immune system found in the blood of mammals. They have a unique ability to identify particular molecules and select them out. When a foreign substance (an antigen) enters the body, specialized cells called B-lymphocytes produce a protein (an antibody) to combat it. To envision how antibodies work, think of a lock and key: The antibody key *fits* only the specific antigen lock. This marks the antigen for destruction. Each of the specialized B lymphocyte cells produces only a single type of antibody and thus recognizes only one antigen.

To conclude, biotechnology is at present used as a techniques for:

1. Use of biotechnology for the new approaches in crop production.
2. To develop genetic engineered microorganisms associated with plants.
3. Genetic engineering for crop improvement and protection.
4. In improveing animal breed through animal breeding.
5. Use in pregnancy tests.
6. Low-cost production of large quantities of animal growth hormone.
7. Gene mapping is essential as the foundation for genetic manipulation e.g., Booroola Gene.
8. To develop better quality products, such as animals with less fat and leaner meat.
9. To improve fisheries and aquaculture technology.
10. Development of vaccines against animal diseases
11. Development of vaccines from vaccinia virus.
12. Use of bioprocessing for production of industrial chemicals.
13. To develop sources of alternative fuels.
14. To develop alternative feed and food sources.

CHAPTER 2

DNA, Gene, Genome, Protein Synthesis and DNA Chip Technology

Meischer (1868) isolated a substance from the nucleus of pus cells. He separated this substance from pus cells by digesting them for a week with dilute hydrochloric acid and then shaking the mixture with ether in a separatory funnel. A heavy solid layer separated at the bottom of the funnel and consisted of pure nuclear material. Meischer then obtained this material by digesting pus cells with artificial gastric juice. He considered the product the characteristic constituent of the cell nucleus and called it *nuclein*. The nuclein possessed much stronger acidic properties than proteins. It was soluble in dilute alkalies, but insoluble in dilute acids, water, and organic solvents. It contained a relatively large amount of phosphorus.

Meischer also studied the nuclear material of ripe salmon sperm. He found this material to consist of a salt of the acidic nuclein and a basic substance, called protamin. Nuclein was shown to be a mixture of a basic protein and a phosphorus-containing organic acid of high molecular weight.

Altmann (1889), introduced the term nucleic acid, developed general methods for the isolation of nucleic acids from many sources. He established the existence of two main types of nucleic acids, namely ribonucleic acid (RNA) and deoxyribonucleic acid (DNA).

The discovery of the building block units of the nucleic acids was followed by some generalizations about structure, such as the trinucleotide hypothesis of Stendel and of Jones and the tetranucleotide hypothesis of Levene. The modern era of structural determination was initiated by analytical research of Chargaff and his co-workers by the development of methods of synthesis of nucleosides, nucleotides, and polynucleotides, first by Todd and later by G. Khorana, and finally by X- ray and physicochemical studies of the tertiary and quaternary structure of nucleic acids and their successful interpretation by Wilkins, Watson, Crick, and others.

Nucleic acids are macromolecules of the atmost biological importance. All living organism contain nucleic acids in the form of deoxyribonucleic acid (DNA) and ribonucleic acid (RNA). Some viruses may contain only RNA, while others have only DNA.

In higher cells DNA is localized mainly in the nucleus as part of the chromosomes. A small amount of DNA is present in the cytoplasm and found within mitochondria and chloroplasts. RNA is found both in the nucleus and in the cytoplasm.

According the Watson and Crick, a DNA molecule has double helix, *i.e.*, it is composed of two long and parallel polynucleotide chains or strands helically coiled around the same axis like spiral staircase or ladder.

The Physical Structure of DNA: The Double Helix

In 1953, James D. Watson and Francis H. C. Crick, published a paper in which they proposed a model for the physical and chemical structure of the DNA molecule. According to their model, most DNA consists of two polynucleotide chains wound around each other in a right-handed (clockwise) helix. In generating their model, Watson and Crick used three main pieces of evidence.

1. The DNA molecule was known to be composed of bases, sugars, and phosphate groups linked together as a polynucleotide (deoxyribonucleotide) chain.
2. Erwin Chargaff hydrolyzed the DNA of a number of organisms by chemical treatment. He had quantified the purines and pyrimidines released. His studies showed that in all the DNAs the amount of the purines was equal to the amount of the pyrimidines. The amount of adenine (A) was equal to that of thymine (T), and the amount of guanine (G) was equal to that of cytosine (C). These equivalencies are known as Chargaff's rules. In comparisons of DNA's from different organisms, the A/T and G/C ratios are always the same, although the (A + T) (G + C) ratio (presented as % GC) varies.

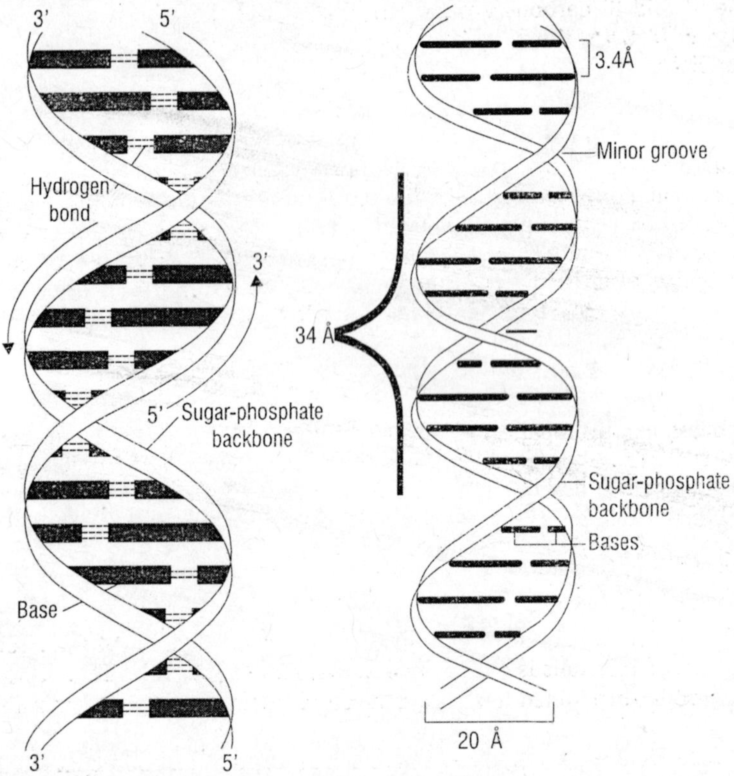

FIGURE 2.1: DNA molecule -the basic tool for genetic engineering.

Rosalind Franklin, working with Maurice H.F. Wilkins, studied isolated fibers of DNA by using the X- ray diffraction technique.

The simplest way of looking at the structure of DNA is as two strings of molecular units, almost like beads on a string. These winds around each other and what has been called the double helix. The structure of an individual string of beads or DNA strand is made of repeating units, the **beads**. However, each of these is one of only four types, and each of these types is related and is, in fact, very similar. Each of the simplified units shown is referred to as a **monomer**, and many of these will join together, or polymerize, to make the **polymer. This is called DNA.**

Native DNA

Double-stranded, non denatured DNA in a preparation that has been extracted from a particular known biological source-viral, bacterial, or eukaryotic tissue as distinct from any additional material added as a probe or marker is called **native DNA**. The technique used to determine the precise sequence of basses in a length of DNA is called **DNA sequencing**.

The **sugar** (five-carbon sugar or pentose sugar) is also involved in making DNA structure. Sugar is of two forms, either as a **ring** structure or as a **long**, five-carbon chain. In DNA ring form of sugar is found. One of the important points to see here is that the 2' carbon (pronounced **two prime carbon**) has no OH group attached to it, unlike the 1' and 3' carbons around the ring, and hence this sugar is called **2'-deoxyribose**. In RNA, the 2' carbon does attach to an OH group. In this way DNA differ from RNA.

Sugar

A sugar unit is attached to a second unit known as a **base** (a nitrogenous base due to its nitrogen atom content). Together, the sugar and the base are collectively called a **nucleoside**. In DNA four types of base, and so four types of monomer units are found. The information, which is stored in the DNA molecule is found according to base arrangement that is the order of these bases in the polymer, which ultimately determines the protein, which is being encoded by a particular stretch of DNA polymer.

Bases

The four bases can be separated into two groups, each group having two members. The simplest bases are the **pyrimidines**, which have a single ring structure. The two forms found in DNA are *thymine* (T) and *cytosine* (C). The other bases are the **purines**, where there are two rings found in the structure. The forms found in DNA are *adenine* (A) and *guanine* (G).

The Phosphates

To complete the monomer structure addition of a phosphate unit to the nucleoside. This whole monomer unit is called a **nucleotide** is required. In a nucleotide, three phosphate groups are joined in a long chain. The phosphate groups are labelled α, β and γ.

Therefore DNA is a polymer of nucleotide units. The four bases, which are incorporated into the nucleotide are:

- 2'-deoxythymidine 5'-triphosphate, using thymine as the base (dTTP).
- 2'-deoxyguanosine 5'-triphosphate, using guanine as the base (dGTP).
- 2'-deoxyadenosine 5'-triphosphate, using adenine as the base (dATP).
- 2'-deoxycytidine 5'-triphosphate, using cytosine as the base (dCTP).

where *d* denotes deoxy sugar while the first letter refer to the base incorporated.

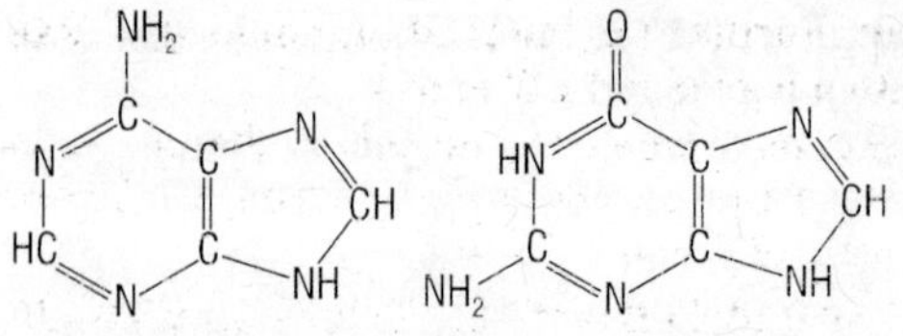

Adenine ***Guanine***

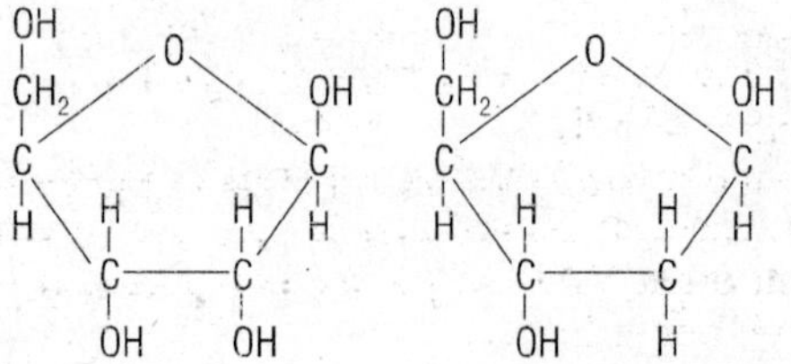

Ribose sugars ***Deoxy ribose sugars***

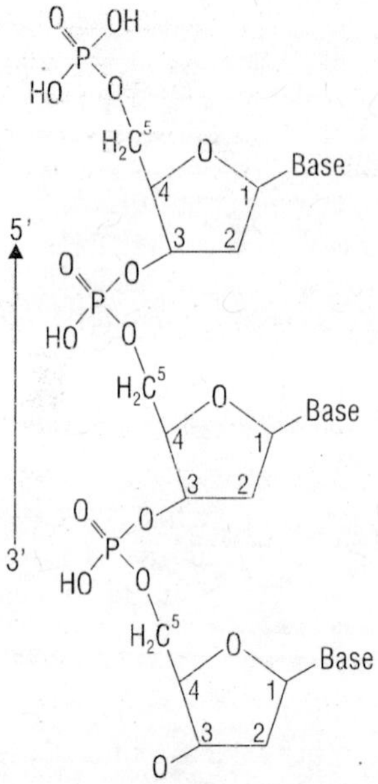

A polynucleotide chain showing phosphodiester bonds.

The above building blocks when polymerize they form a long chain, or **polynucleotide**. Here, the nucleotides are held together by the bonding of the **3' carbon** of the deoxyribose sugar to the first or α phosphate group of the next nucleotide. This bond is called **phosphodiester** bond, and results in β and γ phosphate groups of the bonding phosphate chain.

The polynucleotide has a direction to it, that is, the ends are not the same. At one end there is still a triphosphate unit attached to the **5' carbon** of the sugar, and therefore this end of the chain is called the 5' end (or **five prime**). At the other end is an unused 3' (**three prime**) carbon still attached to an untouched OH group. This is the 3' end of the chain. Further polymerization could still take place but, even if it did, we still end up with a 5' end and a 3' end.

The phosphate groups contain a negative charge. It develops due to the dissociation of a proton from on OH group, leaving O^-. Therefore the molecule is both acidic and negatively charged.

DNA consisted of two polynucleotide strands. They run in opposite directions. These DNA strands wound around each other to form a double helix. The sugars and phosphate groups effectively form the staging of the helix and make two continuous strands from one end to the other. These bases are like the steps on a spiral staircase. Each step of the staircase is actually two bases, holding each other's 'hands' by way of **hydrogen bonding.**

Thymine on one strand always hydrogen bonds to adenine on the other strand while cytosine always hydrogen bonds to guanine. These two strands are called **complementary** to each other, and the phrase **complement strand** is often used. There are **three** hydrogen bonds between guanine and cytosine, while there are only **two** hydrogen bonds between adenine and thymine. **DNA topology** is the configuration of DNA which might be circular of linear.

Model of DNA molecule shows that DNA is in helix and has a regular pattern. The helix is approximately 20 Å across, and has two grooves running around and along it. One groove is referred to as the **wide groove**, while the other is the **narrow groove**. One total rotation of the molecule takes place every 34 Å along, while the distance between the bases, the step height so to speak, is 3.4 Å.

TYPES OF DNA

A more thorough analysis of the X- ray diffraction patterns of DNA fibers revealed that DNA can exist in different forms depending on the conditions. The important types of DNA are:

- **Z DNA:** The helix of this kind of DNA is left-handed. The nucleotide sequence of the DNA appears to be influential in the structure adopted and areas of naturally occurring DNA have been identified, which take up the Z form structure. The significance of this is as yet unknown.
- **Noncoding DNA:** A large proportion of the DNA in eukaryotic cells does not code for protein; most genes have large intron sequences, and genes or gene clusters are separated by large stretches of sequence of unknown function. Much of this DNA consists of multiple repeats, sometimes thousands or hundreds of thousands of copies, of a few relatively short sequence elements.
- **Genomic DNA:** DNA of the genome, which in bacteria, is a single, circular loop, and in eukaryotic cells is the entire haploid nuclear complement of DNA. Non-genomic DNA includes, in bacteria, the DNA of plasmids, and in eukaryotes the DNA of viruses or other contaminants. Note that in eukaryotes the mitochondrial genome and chloroplast genome are often considered separately from the nuclear genome.
- **Unique sequence DNA:** The fraction of DNA which reassociates most slowly is unique sequence, essentially comprising single – copy genes, or those repeated a few times, *Escherichia coli* DNA is essentially all unique sequence.
- **Dispersed repetitive DNA:** Much of the moderately repetitive DNA comprises a number of DNA sequences of a few hundred base pairs (SINES or short interspersed elements) or between one and five thousand base pairs (LINES, or long interspersed elements), each repeated more than 100000 times and

scattered throughout the genome. The most prominent examples in humans are the *Alu* and the *L1* elements, which may be parasitic DNA sequences, replicating themselves by transposition.

- **Satellite DNA:** Satellite DNA, which occurs mostly near the centromeres of chromosomes, and may be involved in attachment of the mitotic spindle, consists of huge numbers of tandem repeats of short (up to 30 bp) sequences. Hypervariability in satellite DNA is the basis of the DNA fingerprinting techniques.

When humidity is high, DNA is in the B form (the double-helical form deduced by Watson and Crick). When the humidity is relatively low, DNA is found in the A form. Both of these DNA forms involve right handed helices. In A-DNA the base pairs are tilted and pulled away from the axis of the double helix. In B-DNA the helix axis passes through the base pairs, which are oriented perpendicular to that axis.

An inherent problem in analyzing DNA fibers by X- ray diffraction is that the DNA strands are generally not regularly ordered around and along the fiber axis. Thus the DNA models generated from the resulting data show averaged helical structures. These can not show local structural variations that might occur because of the presence of particular base sequences. This limitation has been overcome by methods to synthesize short DNA molecules (called oligomers) of defined sequences. The pure DNA oligomers can be crystallized and analyzed by single-crystal X- ray diffraction. Some sequences produced the B helix while others produced the A helix. Unexpectedly certain sequences produced a third DNA form called Z- DNA, which has a left-handed helix and a zigzag sugar-phosphate backbone. The latter property gave this DNA form its **Z** designation.

Features of A-DNA and B-DNA

A-DNA and B-DNA are right-handed double helices. They have 10.9 and 10.0 base pairs per 360- degree turn of the helix, respectively. These values correspond closely with the data derived from DNA fiber studies. The bases are inclined away from the perpendicular from the helix axis by 13 degrees in A-DNA and 2- degrees in B-DNA.

The single crystal studies showed a significant deviation from the fiber studies predictions in a property of individual base pairs called propeller twist. Propeller twist is a rotation of the two bases of a base pair in opposite directions about their long axis. Fiber studies did not predict any propeller twist. The resulting models showed the flat purine and pyrimidine rings aligned relative to each other in the same plane. It is now known that propeller twist exists. It serves to stabilize the helix. The mean values for propeler twist are 15 degrees for A-DNA and 12 degrees for B-DNA. Individual propeller twist values for specific base pairs in the helix vary considerably to produce the most stable double helix structure. The range is 3 to 25 degrees.

The single crystal studies confirmed the fiber studies conclusion that the A-DNA double helix is short and broad with a deep major groove and a broad and shallow minor groove. The B-DNA double helix is thinner and taller for the same number of base pairs than A-DNA, with a wide major groove and a narrow minor groove, both grooves are of similar depths.

Features of Z-DNA

Z-DNA was discovered when single crystals of an alternating cytosine-guanine DNA oligomer were subjected to X-ray diffraction analysis. DNA oligomers containing A-T base pairs do not form Z-DNA. Z-DNA is a left-handed helix generated because of a different bond conformation between one of its bases and the deoxyribose sugar. This bond is called a glycosidic bond. The syn conformation is found at the guanines in Z-DNA. The alternation of a purine (G) and a pyrimidine (c) along a Z-DNA double strand produces the anti-syn alternation that gives the backbone of Z-DNA a zigzag appearance.

In Z-DNA there are 12.0 base pairs per complete helical turn. The bases are inclined away from the perpendicular from the helix axis by 8.8 degrees. The base pairs have smaller mean propeler twist values than A- or B-DNA that is 4.4 degrees. The Z-DNA helix is thin and elongated with a deep, minor groove. The major groove is pushed to the surface of the helix so that it is not really evident as a distinct groove. The helix axis passes through the minor groove in Z-DNA, through the major groove in A-DNA, and through the base pairs in B-DNA.

DNA in the Cell

In solution, DNA usually is found in the B form. Hence B-DNA is the form typically found in cells. Since A-DNA is found only under relatively low humidity conditions. It is unlikely that any lengthy sections of A-DNA exist within cells. There is evidence, however, that Z-DNA exists in at least some cells. This evidence has come from the use of antibodies made against Z-DNA molecules. That is, Z-DNA is much more immunogenic (capable of inducing antibodies against it) than B-DNA. Experiments have been done in which anti-Z-DNA antibodies have been added to fixed cells and chromosomes. These antibodies will bind to any region of the chromosomes that contain stretches of Z-DNA. The locations where these antibodies bound could not be seen directly. To do that, antibodies were prepared against the anti-Z-DNA antibodies and fluorescent molecules were attached to these new antibodies. When the new antibodies were added to the fixed cells they bound specifically to the anti-Z-DNA antibodies and the fluorescent tags they carried served to pinpoint the Z-DNA regions. The fluorescence is evidence for the presence of Z-DNA in the chromosomes.

It is possible that the Z-DNA has an important biological role, although at present this is uncertain. It has been postulated that Z-DNA may be involved in gene regulation. Although it has not been proved that any proteins bind specifically to Z-DNA, which presumably would be a facet of gene regulatory events.

Bends in DNA

Even though the DNA molecule is drawn in text books as a very straight, helical molecule, implying that it is a rigid rod like molecule, this is actually not so. In solution, B-DNA is a flexible molecule, undergoing shape changes as it responds to the local environmental ionic and temperature conditions. It is possible that particular bends in DNA might favour the binding of specific protein molecules. This could be part of the gene regulation process. The ability of B-DNA to bend slightly is enhanced by the presence of specific base-pair sequences. The sequence CAAAAAT, for example, particularly if it is repeated three or four times separated by 10 base pairs, has been shown to cause DNA to bend.

Size, Organization, and Topology of DNA

DNA molecules are very long. For example the DNA in a bacterial cell is contained within a single double-helical molecule. When spread out, it is about 1,000 times as long as the diameter of the rod-shaped cell. This molecule carries all the genetic information of the cell and thus describes the genome (a single complement of the genetic material).

The term chromosome refers to a physical or organizational unit. Within which part of or all the genome is contained. Thus, the *Escherichia coli* genome is contained within just one chromosome, comprising a single DNA molecule. It has a size of 2.5×10^9 daltons. It contains approximately 4×10^6 base pairs. The size of DNA molecules is more commonly expressed in kilo base pairs (Kb, 1000 base pairs). The *E. coli* chromosome is 4,000 Kb in size. Another feature of this particular molecule is that it is a closed, or circular structure.

The DNA of bacteriophage ϕX 174 is single stranded. In this case the genome size given in Kb. It refers to the number of base pairs in an equivalent duplex form. In progressing from the simple viruses to eukaryotes, the amount of information in the genome increases through many orders of magnitude. Approximately the number of kilobases in the genome of viruses and bacteria can be considered equivalent to the number of genes. This equivalency of base number to genes does not exist in eukaryotes because of the presence of unexpressed sequences of bases. In viruses and bacteria, circular DNAs are common. In eukaryotes, each chromosome contains a single linear molecule of double helical DNA. In eukaryotes, DNA does not exist free. It is complexed with an approximately equal mass of basic proteins called histones. For a long time it was thought that bacterial DNA did not form such complexes. While histones are absent from bacteria. There is evidence for the presence of histone like proteins in them that enable condensation of their DNA into its compact nucleoid form.

There are five types of histones, designated H1, H2A, H2B, H3, and H4. They are of low molecular weight (11,000 - 23,000). They contain a large portion of the basic amino acids arginine and lysine. In each case there is an unusual distribution of amino acids along the single polypeptide chain. The basic amino acids are being clusteredin one half, with the other half being relatively hydrophobic. In addition, the histones contain many modified amino acid side chains, *e.g.*, methylated arginines and acetylated lysines.

The nucleoprotein complex that is formed is called chromatin. Chromatin can be isolated as fibres from nuclei. When the fibers are spread and examined under the electron microscope, they appear as beads on a string. Most of the histone is contained in the beads, called nucleosomes. The nucleosome bead consists of a set of eight histones, two each of H2A, H2B, H3 and H4 around which approximately 200 base pairs of DNA are wrapped. Digestion of chromatin with nucleases yields a core particle still containing the eight histones but only 140 base pairs of DNA. The rest of the DNA, which is digested, functions as a linker between the cores, and histone H1 is associated with this linker. The structure of the core particles has been examined by X- ray diffraction. To compact the DNA further within the nucleus. The nucleosoms are organized into condensed higher-order structures.

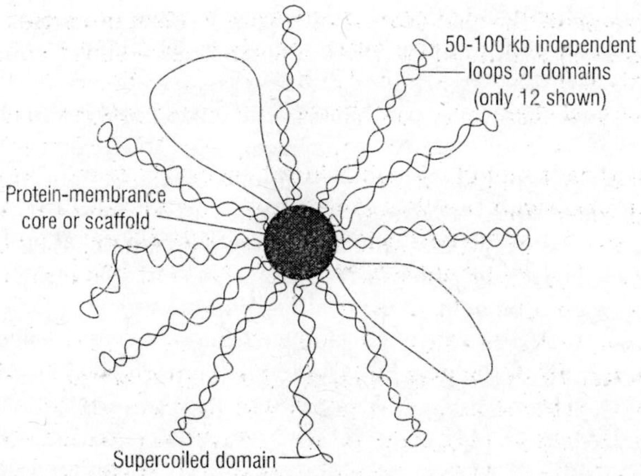

FIGURE 2.2: Presentation of *E. coli* chromosome (4600 kb). The thin line present double halix.

Supercoiled DNA

When DNA is twisted it into a structure known as a **supercoil**. This can only be achieved if the ends of the DNA are prevented from rotating, for example if the DNA is circular in a plasmid. Enzymes known as **topoisomerases** can introduce or remove turns in the DNA double helix and, if this is done, the DNA twists up into a helical structure, that is the double helix as described is then further twisted into a helix. This super-coiling may be **positive super-coiling**, resulting from the addition of turns to the double helix, or alternatively **negative super-coiling** as a result of the removal of turns from the helix.

Genetic Polymorphism

Base changes (mutations) in a gene or a chromosomal locus can create multiple forms (polymorphs) of that locus which is then said to show genetic polymorphism. The term can describe different alleles of a single copy gene in a single individual as well as the different sequences present in different individual in a population. Common types are single nucleotide polymorphisms (SNPs) and simple sequences length polymorphisms (SSLPs). Where SNPs create or destroy the sequence recognized by a restriction enzyme, restriction fragment length polymorphism (RFLP) will result.

The structure of many biological molecules, including that of DNA and many proteins, can be elucidated by an experimental method known as **X-ray diffraction**. Erwin Chargaff determined the exact composition of the bases within a DNA molecule. The method he used was **paper chromatography**.

DNA REPLICATION

Every cell in a body synthesizes proteins and contains the appropriate DNA encoding for that information. All the cells are derived from a single cell in the very early stages of development, then DNA has to be replicated many millions of times in order for all the cells to receive their complement.

DNA replication is the process whereby a copy of a DNA molecule is made and thus the genetic information it contains is duplicated. The parental double-stranded

DNA molecule is replicated semi-conservatively, i. e. each copy contains one of the original strands paired with a newly synthesised strand which is complementary in terms of AT and GC base pairing and of opposite chemical polarity. Though conceptually it is simple, however mechanistically it is a complex process involving a number of enzymes.

The whole molecule may be replicated into a new molecule in which the **old** DNA remains the same and the **new** DNA is made of all new components. This is called **conservative replication**. The DNA may be broken up and new bits are added in a random pattern in which both strands of both resulting DNA molecules contain old and new components. This is called **dispersive replication**.

DNA could be unzipped into two single strands and use each one of these strands to form the basis of the new DNA molecules. This type of replication is called **semiconservative replication.** The direction of replication is always in 5'-3' direction.

D Loop (Displacement Loop)

Structure produced in replicating DNA when a *bubble* or *eye* of DNA is formed and can be visualized in the electron microscope. The production of the loop results from the DNA being double stranded on one side of the bubble and single-stranded on the other and it is exploited as a technique to demonstrate hybridization of an exogenous sequence to one of the complementary strands, leaving the other displaced strand looping out from the helix.

How Replication is Achieved?

Firstly the DNA is in a double helical structure and therefore, for each of the new DNA molecules to receive an old strand, this helical structure has to be **unzipped** (unwinding) and then the new DNA is synthesized. The unwinding of the DNA helix is carried out by a group of enzymes called **topoisomerases**. These enzymes fall into two groups, Type I and Type II. Type I enzymes. These enzymes (Type I) break one of the DNA strands, while Type II enzymes break both DNA strands. **DNA gyrase** is common examples is an enzyme.

Once the DNA has been unwound the two strands have to be separated. This starts at a point known as the **replication origin**. The DNA strands are separated by breakage of the **hydrogen bonding** between the bases. This process should remain continue to enable the replication. This process is catalyzed by an enzyme called a **helicase** and the break points are refereed to as the **replication forks**. However, DNA would naturally reanneal back to the double helix with the reformation of the double bonds is allowed to do so. Therefore, proteins known as **single-strand binding proteins** (SSBs) bind to the single-stranded DNA formed by the helicase and stop the rennealing process from taking place.

Once the DNA is opened up into a single-stranded structure, then the synthesis of new strand starts. However, how does this process start, as the first bases have to be there for strand extension to take place? The process starts by using a **primer**. This is a short length of RNA synthesized by an enzyme called **RNA polymerase,** or **primase**. The RNA primer may be of 6 to 30 bases length. **DNA polymerase** catalyzes synthesis of the DNA strand. In *E. coli* there are three DNA polymerases, but types I and III seem to be most essential for DNA replication, the function of type II remaining more obscure. Most of the DNA synthesis is carried out by polymerase III, with polymerase I removing the RNA primers and basically tidying up the missing bits.

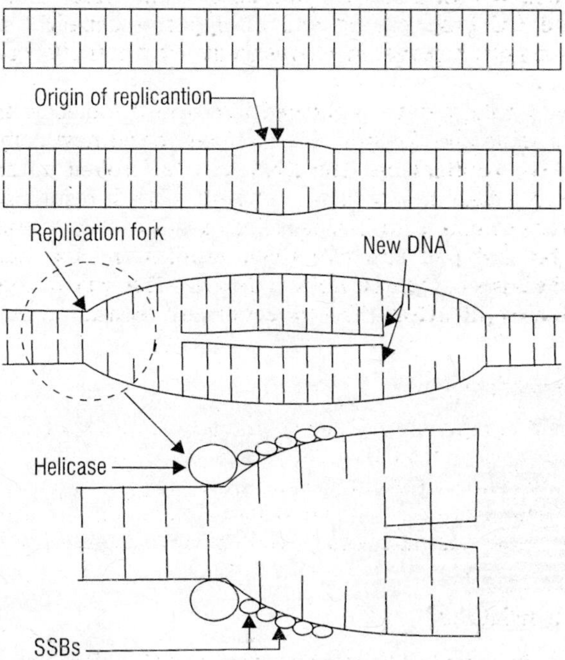

FIGURE 2.3: The initiation of DNA replication. The DNA strands are parted at an origin of replication. It results in two replication forks. One of the instrumental enzymes is helicase, which is added by SSBs (single strand binding proteins).

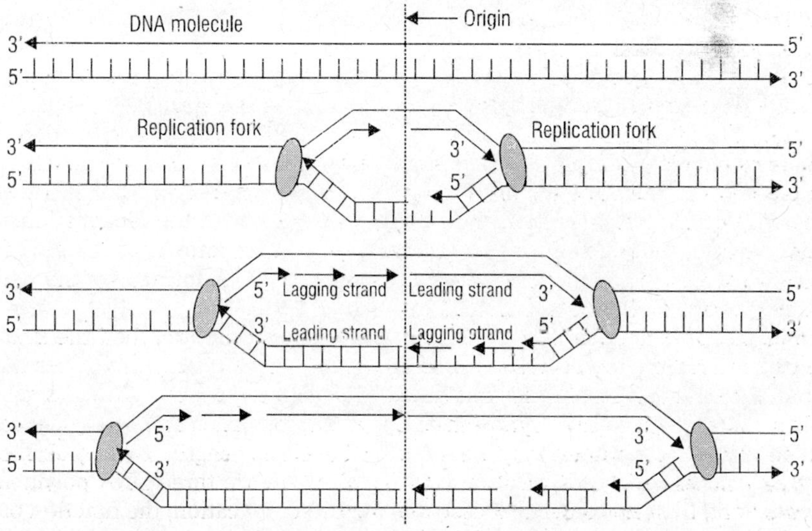

FIGURE 2.4: A diagram showing bidirectional replication of DNA.

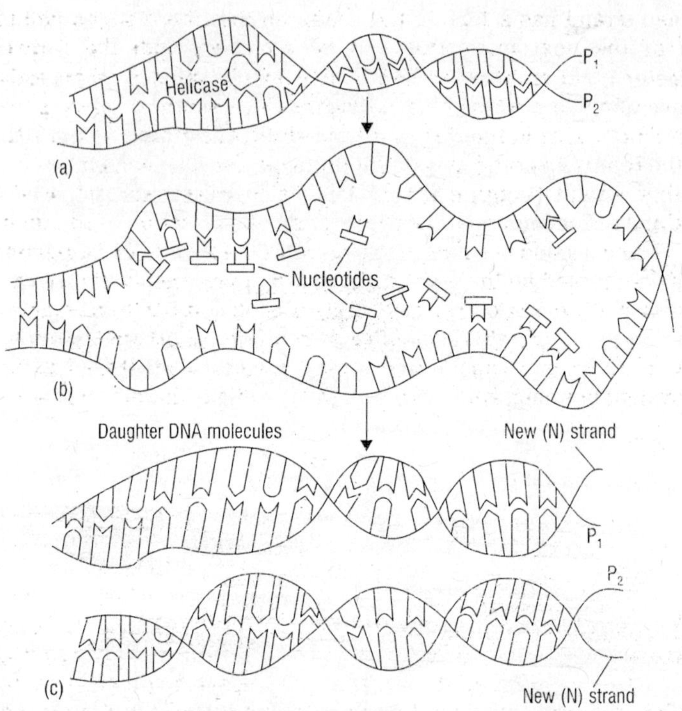

FIGURE 2.5: Simplified steps in semiconservative replication of DNA. (*a*) A helicase unwinds the double helix into two parent strands (P_1 and P_2). (*b*) The replication of new complementary strands proceeds through the action of an enzyme that attaches nucleotides, using the exposed strands as templates. (*c*) Completed daughter molecules each contain one strand that is newly synthesized and one of the original parent strands.

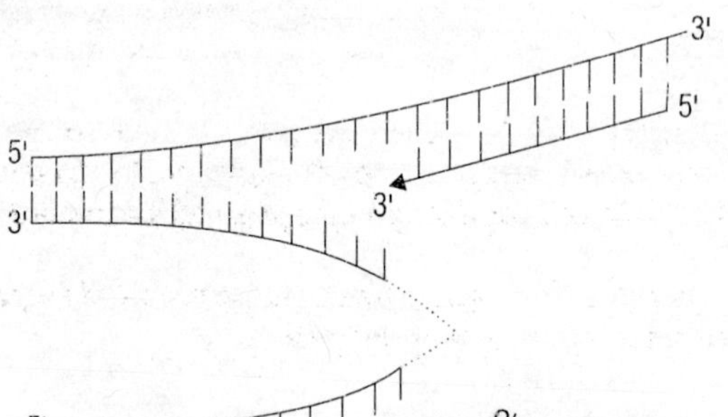

FIGURE 2.6: Synthesis of DNA in the 5' to 3' direction. This results in continuous 5'-3' synthesis on one strand but discontinous 5'-3' synthesis on the other strand with the formation of Okazaki fragments.

The polymerases catalyse the formation of new **phosphodiester bonds**. The newly formed strand has a **free 3'** OH group on the ribose sugar, and to this the α phosphate of the next nucleotide can be attached, with the formation of the phosphodiester bond and the release of the β-γ phosphates as an orthophosphate unit. However, such a process means that the DNA synthesis always takes place in the 5'-3' direction. This is fine for synthesis along one strand of the DNA molecule, known as the **leading strand**, as continuous synthesis is obtained.

The other strand **(lagging strand)** is being effectively unteased backwards, synthesis along the second strand cannot follow the direction of the replication fork. Therefore, on the second strand the synthesis of the new DNA is **discontinuous** - a process was confirmed by the work of **Okazaki** (1968). Hence the short stretches of DNA are known as **Okazaki fragments**. Each fragment has to be started by its own RNA primer and so, along this strand, you would find short DNA stretches following short RNA stretches and gaps between. An enzyme called **DNA ligase** carries out the final covalent bonding, which joins all the resulting Okazaki fragments together.

Enzymes Involved in Replication

The initiation of the replication process requires a **primer**. It is a short RNA molecule, which is complementary to one of the DNA strands. Once the RNA molecule is formed by the enzyme RNA polymerase, DNA synthesis begins. Next, the RNA primer is removed and replaced by newly formed DNA. The replication process continues with the enzyme DNA polymerase adding nucleotides only to the 3' hydroxyl (OH) end of the replicating DNA strand or strands in a 5 to 3' direction. The fact that this polymerase can only add nucleotides to the 3' hydroxyl group of the strand raises the question of how DNA synthesis can proceed in proper order (sequentially) from the single starting point along *both* DNA strands. As mentioned earlier, the two strands of DNA are antiparallel, since on strand runs from the 5' OH to the 3' OH free end and the complementary strand runs from the 3' OH to the 5' OH free end. Therefore, the formation of the complementary strands must proceed in opposite directions. One of the new strands is formed *continuously* as the replication fork moves, since it runs in the appropriate direction for the addition of nucleotides to the free 3' OH of the primer. The other new DNA strand can start only after unwinding of the DNA molecule has begun, it will leg behind the continuous strand.

The enzyme **DNA helicase** uses the hydrolysis of ATP to unwind the DNA helix, usually at the replication fork, to allow the resulting single strands to be copied. Two molecules of ATP are required for each nucleotide pair of the duplex. It is also called **unwindase**.

The enzyme **DNA ligase** catalyses the covalent union of segments of interrupted sugar-phosphate strand in double- stranded DNA.

DNA Polymerase

Any one of the systems of enzymes that catalyze the formation of DNA from deoxyribonucleotides, using one strand of DNA as a tempelate. **DNA Polymerase I, Holoenzyme.** It has 5' exonuclease activity in addition to DNA synthesis. This bifunctional activity enables the enzyme to use nicks or gaps in double stranded DNA as a starting point for DNA synthesis. The 5'-exonuclease activity degrades that DNA strand which is complementary to the template strand and thus forming nick. DNA synthesis begins at 3'-end of nick and produces a new strand of DNA complementary to the template. The net result is the movement of nick along the template strand (nick translation) until all the DNA complementary to the template strand (starting from the site of the origin of nick to the 5'-end of the template strand) is replaced.

Enzyme is used with radioactive or biotinylated nucleotides to prepare labelled DNA of high specific activity. It can also catalyze *de novo* DNA synthesis. **DNA Polymerase I, Klenow Fragment.** Treatment of DNA polymerase I holoenzyme with protease results in production of two protein fragments. The larger fragment, also known as Klenow fragment does not exhibits 5'-exonuclease activity (5'-exonuclease activity is exhibited by intact enzyme). This Klenow fragment is used to synthesize DNA when there is no need of removing the DNA strand which is complementary to the template strand.

Applications of Klenow Fragment: (1) In DNA sequencing by dideoxy-method. (2) For production of second strand of cDNA. (3) Radiolabelling by filling in 5'-single stranded extension on double stranded DNA. (4) Mutagenesis of DNA with synthetic oligonucleotides. (5) In labelling the DNA by random primer method.

T4 DNA Polymerase: T4 DNA polymerase lacks 5' exonuclease activity but has a very active 3'-exonuclease action. This allows radiolabelling of DNA fragment by replacement synthesis. In this method it acts on both the 3'-end of double stranded DNA resulting in long 5'-single stranded extensions. DNA complementary to these single strands are synthesized with deoxynucleoside triphosphase enzyme in the presence of radiolabelled compounds. It is useful in generating 5'-single stranded ends. The enzyme can also be used in radiolabelling of DNA.

Taq DNA Polymerase: Taq DNA polymerase is isolated from the thermophilic bacterium *Thermus aquaticus*. This enzyme has the highest DNA polymerase activity at a pH of 9 and temperature around 75 °C. DNA polymerase activity is resistant to incubation at high temperatures like 95 °C. This enzyme consists of a single polypeptide chain with a molecular weight of 95,000. It lacks 5'to 3' and 3'to 5' exonuclease activities. The highly thermostable DNA polymerase from *Thermus aquaticus* (Taq) is ideal for both manual and automated DNA sequencing because it is fast, highly progressive, has little or no 3'- exonuclease activity and is active over a broad range of temperatures. It can be used in DNA sequencing studies. (2) It is used in 'Polymerase chain reaction (PCR)' as it can withstand high temperatures.

Replication of Bacterial DNA

The genetic material of a bacterium is contained within a single double-stranded molecule that is generally organized into one circular chromosome. Unlike eukaryotic chromosomes, the bacterial chromosome is not enclosed by a nuclear envelope and may be attached to one or several points along a bacterium cell membrane. While the replication process in bacteria is complex, and involves the enzymes described earlier, it is not difficult to visualize overall process.

The DNA replication process begins at single points of origin, or nick site, and moves in two opposite directions (*bi-directional*) around the chromosome, resulting in the formation of two replicating forks. The newly created replication forks move away from the original starting site and around the circular chromosome to form a newly replicated DNA molecule. Since the chromosome is a circular structure, the forks eventually meet when the process is completed. DNA replication is relatively rapid process in bacteria at their respective optimal temperatures. Bacterial cells regulate the initiation of the process to conserve energy and limit the formation of unwanted products.

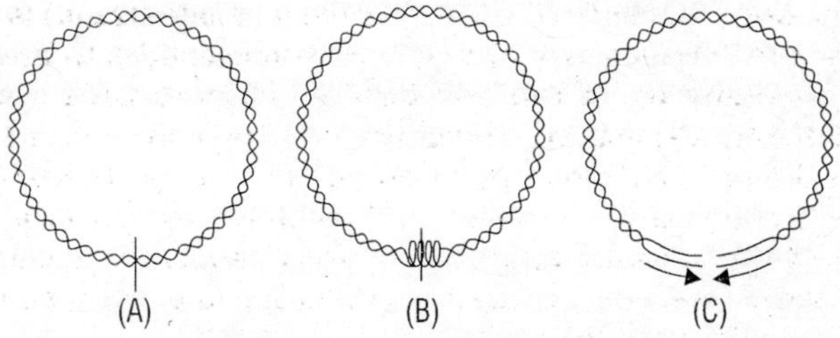

FIGURE 2.7: Generation of supercoiled DNA. If a closed circle (a) of DNA is cut, rotated in the opposite direction to the twist of the helix (b), and then cut ends rejoined, (c), the DNA becomes negatively supercoiled.

DNA gyrase (swivelase) is an enzyme that increases or introduces positive Supercoiling in covalently closed circular DNA molecules generated by DNA replication. This is achieved by breakage of at least one DNA strand followed by untwisting and subsequent resealing of the duplex. DNA gyrase is an alternative term for a 2Topoisomerase.

Although the functions of the three major kinds of RNA are different, the mechanism for their formation is identical. The enzyme *DNA-dependent RNA polymerase* (also called *RNA polymerase*) catalyzes their polymerization from the ribonucleotides: adenosine triphosphate (ATP), cytodine triphosphate (CTP), guanosine triphosphate (GTP) or uridine triphosphate (UTP). One strand of DNA serves as a template or pattern.

RNA molecule is lengthened by the addition of one ribonucleotide. The specific nucleotide added does the DNA template specify difected by the hydrogen bonding. The same hydrogen bondings occur in RNA formation as in the case of DNA replication with *exception that thymine is replaced by uracil.* A pyrophosphate (P-P) molecule that is formed with each step subsequently is split into two inorganic phosphate molecules.

RIBONUCLEIC ACID (RNA)

Like DNA, RNA also consists of a sequence of nucleotides, but unlike DNA, it usually exists as a single-stranded molecule. There are two other basic differences: in RNA the pentose ribose is substituted for deoxyribose, and the pyrimidines base, uracil, is substituted for thymine. RNA participates in several different ways to bring about the expression of the genetic information enclosed within DNA molecules. The genetic or hereditary information specifies the particular type and position of amino acids in a protein molecule (amino acid sequence). Based on their respective functions and roles, three different forms of RNA are recognized: *messenger RNA (mRNA), transfer RNA (tRNA), and ribosomal RNA (rRNA).* All RNA is synthesized as a complementary copy of a DNA sequence.

- **Messenger RNA (mRNA):** This form of RNA is synthesized as a complementary copy of a DNA nucleotide sequence. The function of mRNA is to obtain and carry the genetic information encoded in the RNA to the location where proteins are to be synthesized. Messenger RNA molecules are very unstable and survive for only a short time in microbial cells.
- **Transfer RNA (tRNA):** Transfer RNA is the shortest of the ribonucleic acid molecules. It assumes a three dimensional structure, which is usually shown in

the shape of a cloverleaf. Each tRNA molecule, of which there are at least 20, is equipped to transport a single amino acid to the site of protein synthesis. Transfer RNA makes up approximately 15 per cent of a cell's total RNA.

- **Ribosomal RNA (rRNA):** Ribosomal RNA is combined with specific ribosomal proteins to form the structural units known as *ribosomes*. Ribosomes serve as the sites or workbenches where the information in mRNA is read and proteins are formed. Ribosomal RNA comprises the bulk of the RNA in cells.

The expression of the information encoded in the base sequence of DNA begins with the synthesis of an RNA copy of DNA sequence making up a gene. This is called **transcription** because the DNA base sequence is being copied into an RNA base sequence. The RNA that carries information from DNA and directs protein synthesis is mRNA. The last phase of gene expression is **translation** or protein synthesis.

RNA can also Function as a Genetic Molecule

In addition to its role as the template for protein synthesis, RNA has the capacity to act, like DNA, as a genetic molecule. That RNA can store genetic information was first hinted in the late 1930s, when several plant viruses were found to contain RNA but no DNA. Other viruses (influenza and polio) also have RNA as their genetic molecule.

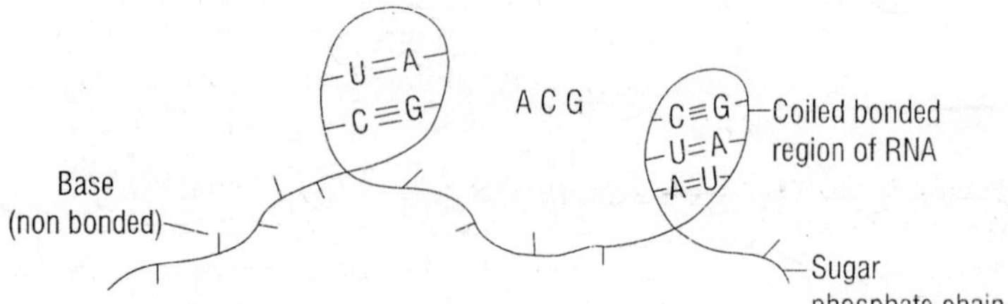

FIGURE 2.8: Structure of single stranded RNA.

FIGURE 2.9: A diagram showing different regions of mRNA.

Because the structure of RNA is very similar to that of DNA, it seemed logical to assume that RNA replication followed the same principles established for DNA. Proof that RNA can be so replicated came first from experiments with a class of small viruses that multiply in bacteria and which contain single-stranded RNA molecules as their genetic component. A key breakthrough came from the 1965 isolation at the University of Illinois by I. Haruna and S. Spiegelman of a virally coded *replicase*, an enzyme that catalyzes the formation of new infectious viral RNA molecules in the presence of the appropriate precursors. How these new molecules are made was at first debatable, but by 1968, C. Weissmann and J. August, independently working in different New York laboratories, conclusively demonstrated the involvement of a double-stranded RNA intermediate. The self-replication of RNA as well as DNA thus involves base pairing between chains of complementary sequences.

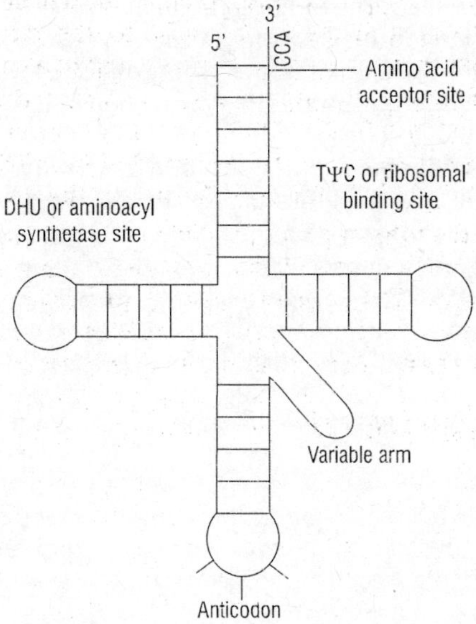

FIGURE 2.10: A clover leaf model proposed for structure of tRNA.

GENE

The genetic information is stored in packages, on **genes**, where one gene holds the information for the production of one polypeptide sequence. This idea was first hypothesized by Beadle the Tatum in 1941. *Gene is a presumed unit of heredity.* They are defined *as discrete sequences of DNA which code for given biological molecules such as structural proteins and enzymes. Thus a gene might be defined as a polynucleotide, tRNA, or rRNA.*

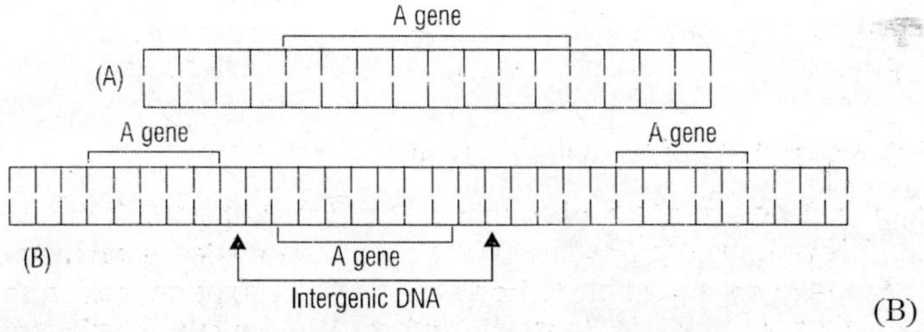

FIGURE 2.11: Gene. (A) A gene is simply stretch of DNA segment. (B) Genes may be on either strand of the DNA molcculc.

As the information is in the form of a series of bases along the DNA molecule, a gene is simply a **stretch of DNA**, with a defined start site and a defined end. It can then be processed as a unit and the information passed on to the machinery, which will make the protein.

Not all the DNAs of cell are used for the storage of information therefore not all the DNA is used as part of a gene. The stretches of DNA that lie between genes are known as **intergenic DNA**.

Any stretch of DNA has two strands and therefore the capacity for holding two different sequences of bases, depending on which strand is read. However, a gene will only use the information held by one of the strands. That is not to say though that both strands are not used. Some genes will be on one strand while others will be of the other strand. Therefore, varied terms have been coined to refer to the strands, which hold the important sequence information and those which do not, such as **sense** and **antisense**, **coding** and **non-coding.** A gene sequence is always read from the 3' end to the 5' end, and therefore genes, which reside on different strands are read in opposite directions; again a fact that needs considering when a researcher is trying to decipher the gene sequence.

3' end → to the 5' end

The arrangement of genes: In most of the eukaryotic organisms, each cell may contain more than one DNA molecule and these together are known as chromosomes. The DNA is packaged and each DNA molecule may carry thousands of genes. Therefore, on each DNA molecule thousands of genes are found in apparently random manner. The genes may be grouped into clusters of related genes. While in prokaryotes (bacteria), it is not unusual to have the need to express several genes, which are not the same but are related, in that the proteins, which are encoded by the genes are required along a common metabolic pathway. These clusters of genes are known as **operons.**

Operons: Operons do not occur in higher organisms. The most studied operon is known as the lactose operon in *E. coli*. This operon contains three genes, which are required for the utilization of lactose as a metabolic fuel in the cell. The operon encodes for a **permease** to allow entry of the lactose into the cell along with a transacetylase and β-galactosidase used in the metabolic pathway using lactose. The operon also contains all the control sequences needed to ensure efficient expression of the genes together.

The clusters of genes, which either encodes for the same protein or very similar proteins are called **homologous.** Their nucleotide sequences are very similar. Clusters of similar genes are called **multigene families.** These are of two kinds:

1. Simple multigene families: These are clusters of identical or extremely homologous genes, e.g., the genes for 5S rRNA.
2. Globin genes: These are made up of related but different genes. The two clusters are found one for the β-like subunits. The β clusters are located on chromosomes 11 in humans. They contains six globin genes, referred to as ε. $^{G}\gamma$ $^{\psi}\beta_1$, $^{A}\gamma$ δ and β. Different genes from the cluster are expressed at different times during the development of the animal.

The genes clusters come about because of **gene duplication** events in the DNA. DNA contains a single copy of the gene, which is duplicated. Therefore the DNA will have two copies of the gene. The areas within the base sequence of any one gene may not be very important. The regions within the protein encoded by that gene may be fairly redundant, and these can be changed without major changes to the protein's function. Therefore, nucleotide changes may take place, which can alter the protein sequence quite markedly, but the areas of importance within the protein remain the same, as alterations here would be catastrophic.

- **Pseudogenes:** Not all genes that can be identified on a chromosome are functional. Such genes are called pseudogenes.
- **Tandem gene clusters** – Regions of the genome where certain gene or gene

clusters are tandemly repeated up to a few hundred times comprise part of the moderately repetitive DNA. Examples include r RNA genes and histone gene clusters.

- **Genes may not be continuous:** Although a gene is sequences of bases along a length of DNA, this sequence is not necessarily continuous and may be interrupted by non-coding regions.
- **Exons:** The stretches of coding DNA are known as exons.
- **Intervening sequences (introns)**: The stretches interrupting the coding area are known as **intervening sequences** (IVSs). A gene may have no introns or several. When the DNA sequence is uncoded, the intron areas have to be ignored.

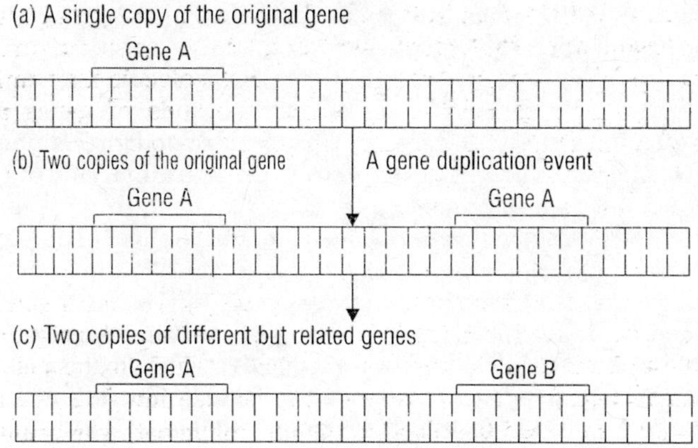

FIGURE 2.12: Duplication of gene. Gene duplication can account for the presence of gene clusters.

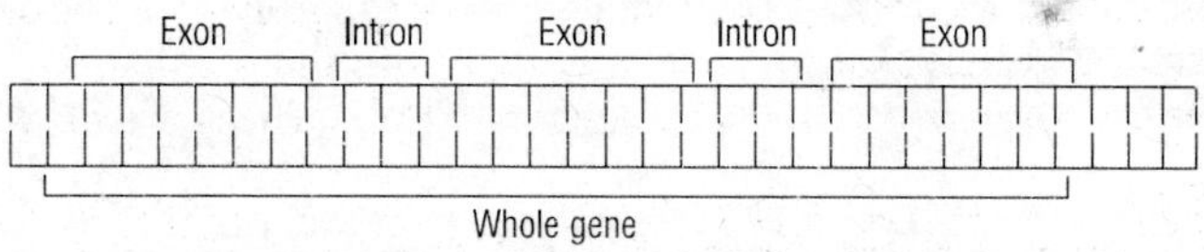

FIGURE 2.13: Genes may contain intron, which do not encode protein sequence.

A simplicified rule is that the sequence GT is found at the start of the intron with AG at the end of the intron, giving the gene sequence.

exon/GT-intron-AG/exon

However, four nucleotides seem hardly sufficient to ensure that such an important event takes place properly, and by the use of the technique known as **site-directed mutagenesis**, that is, where individual bases are changed in a sequence and the effects are studied, **consensus sequences** for the splice sites in genes have been identified. These bases in the consensus sequence have been studied in natural mutations, where the splicing of a gene's introns is defective and therefore a non-functioning product is formed. The process of splicing involves other RNA molecular. It is called **U-RNA,** or **small nuclear RNA**s (snRNAs).

Procaryotic and viral gene structure differs greatly from that of eukaryotes. In bacterial and viral systems, the coding information within a cistron normally is continuous (some bacterial genes do contain introns); however, in eukaryotic organisms, many if not most genes contain coding information (**exons**) interrupted periodically by noncoding sequences (**introns**). An interesting exception to this rule in eukaryotic histone genes lack introns.

Functional Genes

- **Genes encoding RNA molecule:** The genes encoding 80S rRNA are located in nucleolus. Both subunits as well as 5s rRNA (genes not in nucleolus) are transcribed from tandemly arranged repeat sequence. Coding sequences are separated by spaces sequences of differing sizes.
- **Genes encoding proteins:** Protein-encoding genes are distributed in the euchromatic regions of chromosomes.
- **Multigene families:** These are structurally related and their products may have similar physical and biochemical properties, and include storage proteins of cereals, isoenzymes etc.

Genes of Structure and Genes of Regulation

A gene that determines the structure of a particular protein (*e.g.*, an enzyme) is called a **structural gene**. The activity of a structural gene, in terms of production of messenger RNA for enzyme synthesis, is strictly regulated in the cell. It has been shown that many structural genes lie adjacent to specific sites concerned with the regulation of structural gene activity. Such a site is called an **operator**. Under certain conditions, the cell produces cytoplasmic proteins called **repressors**; when an operator gene binds its specific repressor, the structural gene adjacent to it is prevented from producing mRNA and is thus inactivated. In many cases, a series of structural genes determining a series of coordinated enzymes (*e.g.*, the enzymes of a particular metabolic pathway) form a continuous segment of DNA under the control of a single adjacent operator gene. A gene sequence under the coordinated control of a single operator is called an **operon**.

Each specific type of repressor molecule of the cell must, of course, be formed by its own structural gene. A gene concerned with the production of a repressor is called a **regulator gene**. Both operator genes and regulator genes can be detected when they occur in mutant form. For example, the operator can mutate to a state in which it is unable to bind repressor. The operon now functions under all conditions and is said to be **derepressed**.

Mutations of the regulator gene produce phenotypes similar to those produced by mutations of the corresponding operator gene. For example, a mutated regulator gene may fail to make repressor, giving rise to the derepressed phenotype. Regulator genes can be distinguished from operator genes, however, by the behaviour of diploid cells carrying one normal gene and one mutated gene. In such diploids the derepressed state is dominant if the mutation has altered the operator gene but recessive if the mutation has inactivated the regulator gene.

Note that the set of structural genes, which makes up an operon is transcribed as a unit, forming a polygenic mRNA molecule. Transcription begins at the operator end of the operon; a nonsense mutation in one of the genes proximal to the operator may stop translation not only of that gene but also of all genes in the operon distal to it. Such mutations are called **polar mutations**; the polarity of nonsense mutations reflects the inability of a ribosome, once discharged from the mRNA, to reinitiate translation further downstream.

Prokaryotic Genes

The genes of prokaryotic organisms and their regulation were the first to be studied. In bacteria, genes for proteins catalyzing related activities are often arranged tandem so that they are transcribed on a single polycistronic mRNA in which each cistronic component is the messenger template for a single protein. Such a collection of genes is referred to as an operon. Bacteria must be able to adapt to rapid environmental changes in a similar manner as plants hence their genes are constructed to enable them to function at highly variable rates. When required mRNA molecules can be produced at high levels, but only when their genes receive appropriate signals. The compounds responsible for these signals are called **inducers**.

The classical study of Jacob and Monod in 1961 on the lactose (lac) operon in *Escherichia coli* paved the way to an understanding of the regulatory components of prokaryotic genes. The lac operon contains the structural genes for three proteins β-galactosidase, which hydrolyzes lactose into glucose and galactose, lactose permease that is the transporter for the uptake of lactose into the cell and thiogalactosidase transacetylase, an enzyme that transfers an acetyl group from acetyl-CoA to β-galactosides. The last enzyme appears to be involved in the detoxification of non-metabolizable β- galactosides, which can then be secreted from the cell.

Structure of Cyanobacterial Genes

The available knowledge of cyanobacterial gene organization is not as extensive as that for bacterial genes. There is reason to believe that they are very similar and probably regulated identically. The genes of the nitrogenase complex of the bacterium *Klebsiella* are sufficiently homologous to those from the cyanobacterium-*Anabaena*, that they can be used as high stringency probes to detect these genes in the blue-green alga (Haselkorn, 1986). In the bacterium the genes are arranged in the *nif*HDK operon which contains three open reading frames, each for a polypeptide component of the complex. This is also the case in heterocysts in *Anabaena*. During the differentiation of heterocysts from normal vegetative cells an interesting gene rearrangement occur which results in a novel means of gene regulation.

Anabaena genes sometimes possess more than one promoter. This is the case with *gln*A, a gene involved in ammonium assimilation. When ammonia is plentiful, promoter sequences similar to those of *E. coli* are regulatory. However, under conditions where anaerobic nitrogen fixation occurs and involves the *nif* gene products, a promoter region similar to those of the *nif* genes controls transcription.

Gene Arrangement in the Cauliflower Mosaic Virus

The cauliflower mosaic virus (CaMV) genome is a circular double stranded DNA molecule approximately 8 kbp in length. In the host two transcripts are produced. One is from the entire viral genome (35S) and the other (19S) is the messenger for the portion of the genome responsible for the inclusion body protein involved in viral assembly.

Eukaryotic Genes

Eukaryotic genes differ in a number of ways from those of lower organisms. For example, *they are not arranged in operons* and, therefore, each coding region is associated with its own regulatory sequence. Transcription of mRNA is performed by RNA polymerase II, one of three eukaryotic RNA polymerases. RNA polymerase I and III are responsible for the synthesis of ribosomal and transfer RNA, respectively. In prokaryotes all these functions are performed by a single RNA polymerase.

Organelle Genes

Mitochondrial and plastid genomes code for some, but not all, proteins found in these organelles. They produce their own ribosomal and transfer RNAs, and a small number of mRNAs (*i.e.*, around 90 in chloroplasts and 8 or more in mitochondria). The nuclear genome codes for most of the organellar proteins, which are imported from the cytoplast. In some cases separate protein subunits are encoded in the different genomes (*e.g.*, nuclear *rbcS* and chloroplast *rbcL* genes of ribulose biphosphate carboxylase), which poses interesting questions regarding regulatory interactions.

Organelle genes are essentially prokaryotic in nature. They possess Shine-Dalgarno promoter sequences, which have been recognized by *E. coli* RNA polymerase. They are usually polycistronic, but they do occasionally contain introns, characteristics very rarely seen in prokaryotic genes.

Gene that Code for Proteins

During transcription DNA is double stranded, only strand contains coded information and directs RNA synthesis. This strand is called the **sense strand**, and the complementing strand is known as the **natisense strand**. Since the mRNA is made from the 5' to the 3' end, the polarity of the DNA sense strand is therefore 3' to 5'. Therefore, the beginning of the gene is at the 3' end of the sense strand (also the 5' end of the netisense strand). An RNA polymerase recognition/binding the regulatory site known as the **promoter** is located at the start of the gene.

Promoters are sequences of DNA on the sense strand that are usually upstream from the actual coding or transcribed region - that is, the promoter is located before or upstream from the coding region in relationship to the direction of transcription (*the direction of transcription is referred to as downstream*). In *E. coli* the promoter has two important functions, and these relate to two specific segments within the promoter. Although these two segments do vary slightly in sequence between bacterial strains, they are fairly constant and may be represented by consensus sequences. These are idealized sequences composed of the bases most often found at each position when the sequences from different bacteria are compared. The RNA polymerase recognition site, with a consensus sequence of 5'TTGACA3' on the antisense strand, is located about 35 base pairs before (the- 35 region) the transcriptional start point (labeled as +1) of RNA synthesis. This sequence seems to be the site of the initial association of the RNA polymerase with the DNA.

The **RNA polymerase binding site**, also known as the **Pribnow box**, is located at the -10 region and has a consensus sequence 5'TATAAT3' (*a sequence that favors the localized unwinding of DNA*). This is where the RNA polymerase begins to unwind the DNA for eventual transcription. The initially transcribed portion of the gene is not necessarily sense or coding material. Rather, a **leader sequence** may be synthesized first. The leader is usually a nontranslated sequence that is important in the initiation of translation and sometimes is involved regulation of transcription.

Shine-Dalgarno sequence: The leader in prokaryotes generally contains a consensus sequence known as the Shine-Dalgarno sequence, 5'AGGA3', the transcript of which complements a sequence on the 16S rRNA in the small subunit of the ribosome. The binding of mRNA leader with 16S rRNA properly orients the mRNA on the ribosome. The leader also sometimes regulates transcription by attenuation. Downstream and next to the leader is the most important part of the structural gene, the coding region.

The **coding region** of genes that direct the synthesis of proteins typically begins with the sense DNA sequence 3'TAC5'. This produces the RNA translation initiation codon 5'AUG3', which codes for N-formylmethionine. This modified form of methionine. is the first amino acid incorporated in most procaryotic proteins. The reminder of the coding region of the gene consists of a sequence of codons that specifies the sequence of amino acids for the particular protein. Transcription does not stop the translation stop codon but rather at a **terminator sequence**. The terminator often lies after a nontranslated **trailer sequence** located downstream from the coding region. The trailer sequence, like the leader, is needed for the proper expression of the sense portion of the gene.

Gene that Code for Trna and tRNA

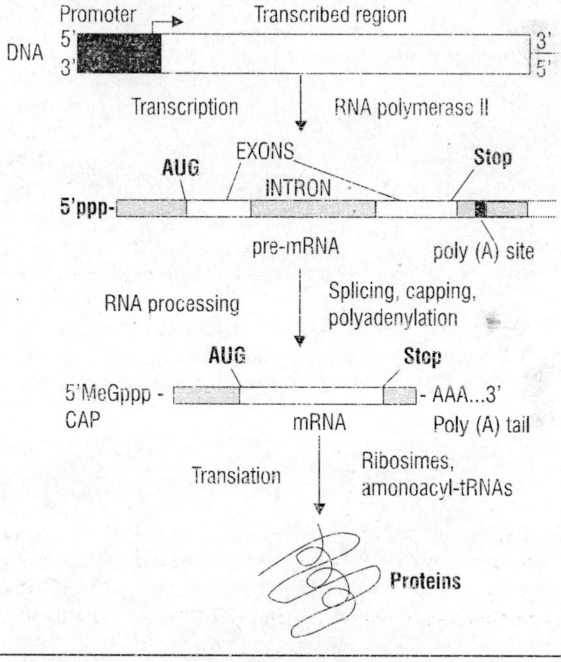

FIGURE 2.14: Presentation of eukaryotic gene expression.

The DNA segments that code for tRNA and rRNA also are considered genes, although they give rise to structurally important RNA rather than protein. Genes coding for tRNA may code for more than a single tRNA molecule or type of tRNA. The segments coding for tRNAs are separated by short spacer sequences that are removed after transcription by special ribonucleases, at least one of which contains catalytic RNA. Thus the synthesis of tRNA and rRNA involve post-transcriptional modification, a relatively rate process in prokaryotes.

Eukaryotic Gene Organization and Expression

The major difference between prokaryotic and eukaryotic gene expression is that, in a eukaryotic cell, mRNA must pass from the nucleus to the cytoplasm for translation. There is a complex processing pathway for mRNA precursors in the nucleus, and the cytoplasmic mRNA differs in structure from prokaryotic mRNA.

In eukaryotes, there are three different RNA polymerases, I, II, and III. RNA polymerase I is located in the nucleolus and catalyzes the synthesis of rRNA. RNA polymerases II and III are present in the nucleoplasm (outside the nucleolus). RNA polymerase III transcribes the genes for small nuclear RNAs and tRNAs. Its binding sites are located within these genes, rather than on the 5' or "upstream" sides of the genes.

RNA polymerase II transcribes the majority of the nuclear structural genes; it is responsible for pre- mRNA synthesis. Comparisons of the sequences of the promoters or RNA polymerase II-binding sites of over 200 different eukaryotic genes reveal consensus sequences located at about 25 and 75 nucleotide-pairs, respectively, before the transcription-start site. The consensus sequences for the **-25 sequence** (also called the **Hogness box** and the **TATA box**) and the **-75 sequence** (also called the **CAAT box**) are **TATAAAA** and **GGCCAATCT** respectively.

While in prokaryotes, all well-characterized genes consist of continuous sequences of nucleotide pairs, in case of eukaryotes, coding sequences (called **exons** for **expressed** sequences) of these genes (sequences specifying the functional gene-products RNA or protein) are often, but not always interrupted by noncoding **intervening sequences** or **introns**. This mRNA transcript with both introns & exon sequences of gene is called heterogeneous nuclear RNA (hn RNA). The mRNAs of eukaryotes, derived from primary gene transcript then undergoes processing, which includes:

1. addition of 7-methyl guanosine caps to 5'end of mRNA.
2. addition of poly adenylated nucleotide laid to the 3'end of mRNA
3. mRNA splicing for removal of introns. Spliced mRNA is then translated to form proteins.

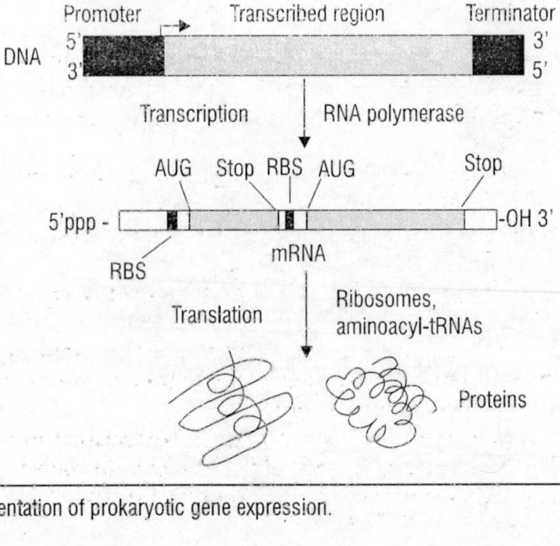

FIGURE 2.15: Presentation of prokaryotic gene expression.

Eukaryotic genes are regulated by the **promoter elements** located just upstream (5' terminus) from the transcription initiation sites in a manner similar to prokaryotic gene regulation. However, these eukaryotic promoters may be very complex with binding sites for many different regulatory proteins. In addition to the nearby promoters, many eukaryotic genes are also regulated by more distant cis-acting elements called enhancers and silencers.

Prokaryotic Gene Organization and Expression

The primary difference between cells of a eukaryote and a prokaryote is the presence or absence of nuclear membrane, which acts as barrier, separating the genetic information contained within the chromosomes from the cytoplasm. Genetic Engineering makes use of eukaryotic as well as prokaryotic cell and its application concern gene organization and their expression.

The mechanism of gene expression was first understood in *E. coli.* The genetic information of this bacterium is contained within a circular chromosome of approximately three million base pairs. Most genes are tightly packed together, with very little superfluous DNA between them. As there is no nuclear membrane, the transcription and translation of prokaryotic gene is co-temporaneous.

In each gene in the **operon** of prokaryotes, there is a short sequence just upstream from the start codon (AUG), known as **Shine-Dalgarno sequence** (after its discoverer). It is the binding site for ribosome and is essential for efficient translation.

RNA polymerase enzyme transcribes the gene. This enzyme contains five distinct polypeptides (2α, ß,ß' and ω together make core enzyme) and one subunit (sigma=σ factor) which is involved in initiation of transcription. Holoenzyme (core enzyme with sigma factor) initiates synthesis of RNA chain followed by release of σ factor and chain elongation by core enzyme. The function of sigma factor is to recognize and bind RNA polymerase to the correct initiation sites, the *promoter* sites, on DNA. Hundreds of promoters have now been sequenced in *E. coli*, and these sequences have surprisingly little in common. Two short sequences within these promoters are sufficiently conserved to be recognized, but even these are seldom identical in two different promoters. The midpoints of the two conserved sequences occur at about 10 and 35 nucleotide-pairs, respectively, before the transcription-initiation site. Thus, they are often called the **-10 sequence** and the **-35 sequence**, respectively. The most common or consensus -10 sequence (also called the **Pribnow box**) is **TATAAT.** The consensus -35 sequence (also called the **recognition sequence**) is **TTAGACA.**

If RNA polymerase is arrested during elongation (typically by omission of precursor nucleotides during *in vitro* reaction) then two proteins (Gre A and Gre B proteins) of *E. coli* release the RNA polymerase from elongation arrest. Gre A can act only if it is present before the polymerase arrest.

The termination of transcription occurs at specific **terminator sequences** in DNA. Most prokaryotic mRNAs terminate with the sequence 5'UUUUUUA-3' suggesting that the sequence 3'-AAAAAAT-5' in the sense strand of DNA is at least part of the transcription terminator sequence. Some transcription-termination signals require the presence of a protein called **rho.**

Although only one of the two DNA strands is transcribed in any given region, both strands of DNA in a chromosome usually participate in transcription, with some mRNAs being transcribed from one strand and other mRNAs (from different genes) being transcribed from the other strand. Because the two strands of a DNA double helix have opposite polarity, transcription events using opposite strands, as templates will proceed in opposite direction along the DNA molecule. In T4 viruses, transcription occurs off both DNA strands (but only rarely in the same region). It is important to study the basic features of gene organization and expression in *E. coli* and other prokaryotes as they are of central importance in genetic engineering. *E. coli* has been mapped and the information is useful for cloning techniques.

In eukaryotic cells comprise three interacting genetic systems *viz.* nuclear genome and chloroplast and mitochondria are semiautonomous bodies with their own organizational and functional properties but they do not synthesize all their proteins. The nuclear genome plays an important role in organelle biogenesis.

A genome is the complete set of chromosomes found in each nucleus of a given species, which contain entire genetic material (measured in picograms).

Gene Isolation

The removal of the genetic information in the form of a DNA sequence froms a selected organism in order to study its structure or insert it into a vector during gene manipulation. For isolation of important genes, the first step in an effort to genetically engineer an organism is to locate the relevant gene(s) among the tens of thousand that make up the genome. Perhaps the researcher is searching for genes to improve tolerance to some environmental stress or to increase disease resistant. This can be a difficult task – similar to trying to find a citation in a book without an index.

This task is made easier with restriction enzymes that can cut complex, double-stranded macromolecules of DNA into manageable pieces. A restriction enzyme recognizes a unique sequence in the DNA, where it snips the strands. By using a series of different restriction enzymes, an organism's genomic DNA can be reduced to lengths equivalent to one or several genes. These smaller segments can be sorted and then cloned to produce a quantity of genetic material for further analysis. The collection of DNA segments from one genotype – a gene library – can be searched to locate a desired gene. Patterns can also be analyzed to link a particular a desired gene. Patterns can also be analyzed to link a particular sequence – a marker – to a particular traitor disease, even though the specific gene responsible is still unknown.

Restriction enzymes are also used in cloning genes. To clone a gene, a small circle of DNA that exists separate from an organism's main chromosomal complement – a plasmid is cut open using the same restriction enzyme that was used to isolate a desired gene. When the cut plasmid and the isolated gene are mixed together with an enzyme that rejoins the cut ends of DNA molecules, the isolated gene fragment is incorporated into the plasmid ring. As the repaired plasmid replicates, the clones gene is also replicated. In this way, numerous reproductions of the clones gene are produced within the host cell, usually a bacterium. After replication, the same restriction enzyme is used to snip out the cloned gene, allowing numerous copies of that gene to be isolated.

The ability to isolate and clone individual genes has played a critical role in the development of biotechnology. Cloned genes are necessary research tools for studies of the structure, function, and expression of genes. Further, specific gene traits could not be transferred into new organisms unless numerous gene copies were available. Cloned genes also are used as diagnostic test probes in medicine and agriculture to detect specific diseases.

Important Terms Related to Gene

- **Gene library**. A random collection of DNA fragments that includes all the genetic information of a given species; sometimes called a Shotgun Collection.
- **Gene locus** (genetic locus). Position on a particular chromosomes on which a specific gene is located, either relative to other genes which are adjacent on the same chromosome or in terms of a particular mapping distance from the centromere of the particular chromosomes.
- **Gene machine**. An idomatic description of an automated olignucleotide synthesizes.
- **Gene magnification**. Phenomenon in which the number of copies of the ribosomal genes is increased in mutants of Drosophila. Such mutants are termed Bobbed, since they also have reduced number of bristels.
- **Gene map** (genetic map). Order of nucleotides and genes that is deduced from genetic recombination experiments. Individual genes can be assigned to specific loci within a genome or a chromosome as a result of gene mapping.
- **Gene pool**. The total of all genes in an interbreeding population at a given time.
- **Gene redundancy**. Presence in a cell of many copies of a single gene.
- **Gene reduplication**. The duplication of genes in the chromosomes at cell division so that each daughter gene and chromosome is an exact replica of its original.
- **Gene regulatory protein.** Protein that functions by altering the transcriptional state of a specific gene. The repressor protein that regulates the activity of the lac operon in *E. coli* is one such protein, and they are widely believed to be an important aspect of eukaryotic gene regulation also.
- **Genetic Linkage Mapping.** This form of mapping is used to construct genetic linkage maps of individual chromosomes and also to localize genes involved in genetic disease. Genetic linkage analysis relies on an ability to estimate the frequency of crossing over (recombination) that occurs between homologous chromosomes during meiosis. The closer two genetic markers are to each other then the lower is the chance that they will be separated during meiosis. The statistical probability that two markers are linked is measured as the logarithm of the odds (Lod). A Lod score of 3 is usually taken as the threshold of significance, while a Lod score below -2 suggests that the two loci are not linked. Lods between -2 and +3 are not significant.
- **Gene sequencing**. A technique used to determine the sequence of bases in the length of DNA coding for particular polypeptide.
- **Gene splicing**. The enzymatic attachment of one gene or part of a gene to another; also removal of introns and splicing of exons during mRNA synthesis.
- **Gene starvation theory**. A theory put forward by Thompson (1938) suggesting that to reproduce itself normally a gene must have available in its vicinity all the necessary 'parts'. Lack of any 'part' during the stage between successive nuclear division is suggested as the cause of mutation, or alternatively of gene deficiency, at the 'starved' locus. On this theory, differential nutrition in the early stages of segmentation of the fertilized ovum gives rise of cells from which are produced the primordial of the differentiated adult tissues.
- **Gene string**. The central chromosome thread on which the genes are assumedly, arranged in sequence.
- **Gene substitution**. The replacement of one gene by its allele all the other genes

remaining unchanged.

- **Gene switch**. Change in a cell or organism from the expression of one type of gene, or set of genes, to another related one, or set. Classic examples of gene switching occur during the developmental processes of higher organism.
- **Gene synthesis**. The production of base sequences in lengths of DNA which can subsequently be expressed as peptides after insertion into a suitable host.
- **Gene therapy**. Procedures that could theoretically be used to treat or cure an inherited disorder; to date the procedure has not been used successfully. It consists of providing copies of a specific gene sequence to replace a defective allele present in the patient. Such therapy could involve injecting multiple copies of the novel gene sequence in the hope that some would be integrated into cellular DNA in tissues expressing the gene, or could involve simple replacement of cells carrying and expressing the deleterious gene with donor cells expressing the wild-type allele. Sickle cell anaemioa and certain forms of thalassaemia have been suggested as disease in which gene therapy could prove useful.

GENOME

Understanding the information contained in genome sequence will be the major challenge of the early 21st century. The genome is the entire DNA content of a cell, including all of the genes and all of the intergenic regions. Prokaryotic genomes are small with very little space between genes. The yeast genome contains 6000 genes and has a more compact organization.

Every organism is specified by genomes, which contain the biological information needed to construct and maintain a living example of that organism. Most genomes, including those for all cellular life forms, are made of DNA (deoxyribonucleic acid) but a few viruses have RNA (ribonucleic acid) genomes. DNA and RNA are polymeric molecules made up of linear, unbranched chains of monomeric subunits called nucleotides (see structure of DNA and RNA).

The biological information contained in a genome is encoded in the nucleotide sequence of its DNA or RNA molecules and is divided into discrete units called **genes**. The information in a gene is read by proteins that attach to the genome at the appropriate positions and initiate a series of biochemical reactions referred to as gene expression.

For organisms with DNA genomes, this process was originally looked on as comprising following two stages:

1. ***Transcription:*** First producing an RNA copy of the gene.
2. ***Translation:*** Resulting in synthesis of protein whose amino acid sequence is determined, via the genetic code, by the nucleotide sequence of the RNA transcript.

This is still an accurate description of gene expression in simple organisms such as bacteria, but it gives an incomplete picture of the events involved in conversion of genomic.

Complete copy of the genome: A complete copy of the genome must be made every time a cell divides. DNA replication has to be extremely accurate in order to avoid the introduction of mutations into the genome copies. Some mutations do, however, occur, either as errors in replication. It may be due to the effects of chemical and physical mutagens that directly alter the chemical structure of DNA. DNA repair enzymes. These enzymes correct many of these errors. Those that escape the repair processes become permanent features of the lineage descending from the original mutated genome. These events, along with genome rearrangements resulting from recombination, underlie molecular evolution, the driving force behind the evolution of living organism.

Genome of Bacteriophages

Bacteriophages or commonly just **phages**, are viruses, which attack and use bacteria as host cells. They are composed of two components: a protein coat or **capsid** and a nucleic acid, either DNA and RNA. The protein coats of phages are arranged in one of three basic forms:

1. **Icosahedral form:** It has the nucleic acid surrounded by a three-dimensional pattern of protein subunits, or **protomers**. Example, MS2 phage (it uses E. coli as a host).

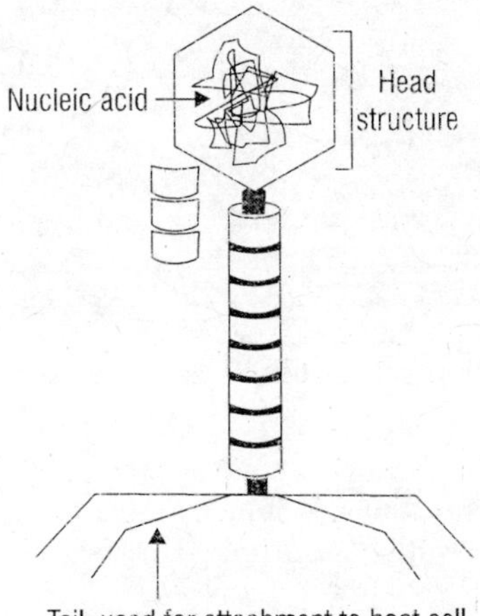

FIGURE 2.16: Schematic representation of a typical heat-and-tail bacteirophage.

2. **Filamentous phage:** The protein subunits are arranged in a rod formation with the nucleic acid running helical. Example, M13 phage (it uses E. coli as a host).
3. **Head-and-tail type:** It has complex structure. It has a head structure, which resembles an icosahedral virus, on top of a filamentous tail structure, to which is attached a base structure. It is used in host recognition and for entry of the nucleic acid into the host cell. Examples, T2, T4, T7 and λ (they attack E. coli and SPO1, and uses Bacillus subtilis as a host).
4. **Variation in Phage Genome:** The genomes of the phages are varied. It may be a single stranded RNA or double-stranded circular DNA and double-stranded linear DNA. Genomes are varied in size. The genomes size of MS2 virus has 3.6 thousand bases (3.6 kb) and contains only three genes, while genomes of T2 and T4 virus are approximately 166 thousand bases (166 kb) and contain over 150 genes.

Bacteriophages are used as vehicles (**vectors**) for the entry of genes into cells. The life cycle of bacteriophages falls into two categories: **lytic** and **lysogenic**.

- **Lytic cycle:** The bacteriophage recognizes and attaches itself to the host surface. It is followed by injection of the nucleic acid material into the host cell. After a short period of 20 minutes (for manufacture of new bacteriophage components) the host cell bursts and new phages are released which can then go on to infect new cells with the synthesis of yet more phages. Phages, which commonly follow the lytic pathway include the T2 and T4 *E. coli* phages.
- **Lysogenic cycle:** In this cycle, the phage genome becomes integrated into the genome of the host cell. This stage is called **prophage**, while the infected cell is called **lysogen**. Integration of the phage genes into the host genome takes place through a **recombination event**. The transcription and expression of the phage genome can be prevented by the production from the phage genome of a **repressor protein**, such as *c*I. The lysogenic state can be maintained for many generation of the host, the genome of the phage being replicated along with that of the host.

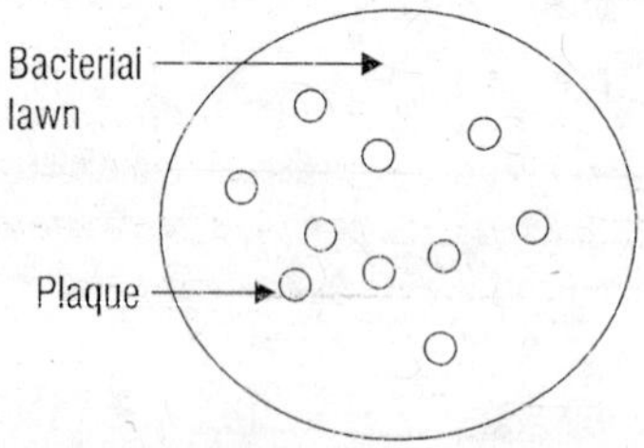

FIGURE 2.17: Phage on an agar plate. Each 'hole' in the bacterial lawn represents the original presence of one phage.

The phages may be observed in laboratory by making a mixture of bacteria and phages are grown on a solid agar medium. The plate is incubated until the bacteria have formed a **lawn** over the agar surface. However, the presence of phages will mean that bacteria have been lysed and new phages released, which will infect surrounding bacteria and again bacterial lysis will result. After incubation, therefore, one would see a lawn of bacteria, which have gaps or **plaques**, with each plaque representing the original presence of a phage.

Genomes of Viruses of Eukaryotic Hosts

Viruses that attack and use eukaryotic cells as hosts are similar in many ways to the phages. These phages have **icosahedral** or **filamentous** structures. These viruses have varied genomes from single-stranded linear RNA or DNA to double-stranded linear or circular DNA. The small viruses may have a small genome size (less than 2 kb and contain four or five genes) or large genome size (contain over 200 genes; example the vaccinia virus). These viruses use mammalian host has a genome size of 240 kb and has 240 genes. The eukaryotic-specific viruses follow a lytic or lysogenic cycle. Lysogenic cycles leads to transformation of the host cells, where loss of control of proliferation takes place.

Retroviruses

They are single-stranded RNA (between 6 kb and 9 kb long) containing viruses and encode an enzyme called **reverse transcriptase**. The genome contains three genes needed for integration of the viral genome into the host genome. These genomes are:

gag (encodes capsid proteins), *pol* (encodes proteins needed for viral replication) and *env* (encodes membrane envelope proteins). After entry into the cell the RNA has is copied into DNA, which is carried out by the enzyme reverse transcriptase, encoded by *pol*. Once in the form of double-stranded DNA, incorporation into the host genome is possible.

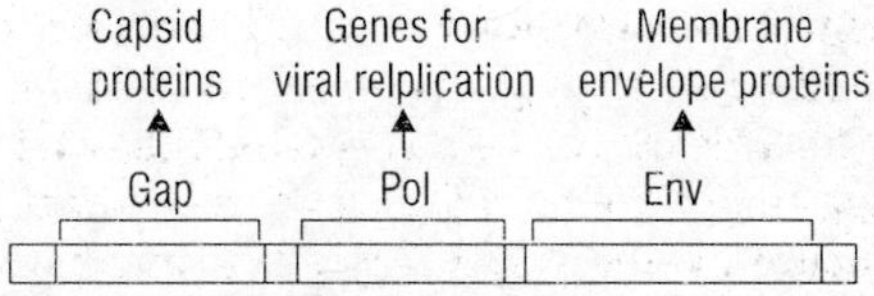

FIGURE 2.18: The genes encoded by a typical retrovirus.

This incorporation is random, which may cause problems if such a virus is being used as a gene vector. However, once incorporated, the genes from the virus genome can be expressed and new viruses synthesized. **Reverse transcriptase** is extensively used in molecular genetics. Many researchers study the presence of mRNA in cells as a measure of gene expression. However, RNA is inherently very unstable, and therefore a DNA copy can be made which is much more stable using reverse transcriptase. Such methodology is commonly combined with **polymerase chain reaction** (PCR) in a technique referred to as RT-PCR (reverse transcriptase-PCR).

HIV viruses which cause the immunodeficiency disease AIDS are retro, viruses and because some retroviruses encode **oncogenes**, and therefore may lead to cancer.

Genomes of Microorganisms

Those cells, which contain membrane-bound compartments, including a nucleus and organelles such as mitochondria and, in the case of plant cells, chloroplasts, called **eukaryotes**. They include animals, plants, fungi and protozoa. Those cells, which lack extensive internal compartments, called **prokaryotes**. Eukaryotes and prokaryotes have quite different types of genome and we must therefore consider them separately. There are two very different groups of prokaryotes, distinguished from one another by characteristic genetic and biochemical features:

Bacteria	Archaea
The bacteria, which include most of the commonly encountered prokaryotes such as the gram-negatives (e.g. Escherichia coli), the gram-positives (e.g. Bacillus subtilis), the cyanobacteria (e.g. Anabaena) and many more.	The archaea, which are less well studied, and have mostly been found in extreme environments such as hot springs, brine pools and anaerobic lake bottoms.

The variability in size coincides to a certain extent with the complexity of the organism, the simplest eukaryotes such as fungi having the smallest genomes, and higher eukaryotes such as vertebrates and flowering plants having the largest ones.

This makes sense as one would expect the complexity of an organism to be related to the number of an organism to be related to the number of genes in its genome – higher eukaryotes need larger genomes to accommodate the extra genes. However, the correlation is not precise: if it was, then the nuclear genome of the yeast *Saccharomyces cerevisiae*, which at 12Mb is 0.004 times the size of the human nuclear genome, would be expected to contain $0.004 \times 80\ 000$ genes, which is just

320. The *S. cerevisiae* genome contains about 6000 genes.

TABLE 2.1: Sizes of genomes in microorganisms

Organism	Genome size (Mb)
Prokaryotes	
Mycoplasma genitolium	0.58
Escherichia coli	4.64
Bacillus megaterium	30
Eukaryotes	
Fungi	
Saccharomyces cerevisiae (yeast)	12.1
Aspergillus nidulans	25.4
Protozoa	
Tetrahymena pyriformis	190

A correlation between the complexity of an organism and the size of its genome was a bit of a puzzle or so-called **C-value paradox**. The space is saved in the genomes of less complex organisms because the genes are more closely packed together.

Bacterial Genomes

In prokaryotes, such a nucleus is absent, however, in many bacteria a area central part of the cell is distinguished from the rest called **nucleoid**. It is here that the majority of the DNA resides. In *E. coli* the nucleoid contains a single double-stranded circular piece of DNA. However, this piece of DNA is very large, having a molecular weight of approximately 2.8×10^9, with 4.2×10^6 base pairs and a length of 1.4 mm. To accommodate such a relatively large molecule inside the cell, the DNA is supercoiled. Packaging of the DNA also requires the assistance of proteins, some of which resemble the histone family of proteins, as will be discussed latter.

Plasmids

A plasmid is a replicon (unit of genetic material capable of independent replication) that is *stably inherited* (maintained without specific selection) in an extrachromosomal state. Jacob Schaeffer and Wollman (1958, 1960) coined the term *episome* for supernumerary element, which can exist either independently of bacterial chromosome or integrated into it. Thereafter, various types of other conjugation factors or sex factors were discovered. These factors determine the conjugational ability and transfer the genetic material to recipient cell in *E. coli* K-12 strain. Lederberg (1952) used the word plasmids for these extracellular and autonomously reproducing genetic structure. They are circular, double stranded molecules of DNA and exist independently of chromosomal DNA in bacterial cell. The genes associated with plasmid determine various biological characters in bacterial cell. The number of genes in plasmids varies from 3-4. They have no role in viability or growth of bacteria. Their function is additional to the functions of chromosomal genes. Two types of plasmids have been identified:

- **Conjugative plasmid:** It carries genes that promote the transfer of plasmids from host cell to a recipient cell by conjugation.
- **Non-conjugative plasmid:** It cannot promote its own transfer by conjugation.
- **Structure of plasmids:** They are circular dsDNA molecules and appear as

super helical coil. Each super helical turn consists of 400-600 base pairs. The twisted arrangement is known as covalently closed circular (CCC) DNA. When the closed circular DNA opens, it appears like cleavage or nicking DNA strands.

Types of Plasmids

Bacteria are hosts to small, extra chromosomal genetic elements called plasmids. Plasmids are dispensable to the cell under ordinary conditions of growth. Their presence is detectable when the genes they carry confer new properties on the host, and they are generally named for these properties. About 9 types of plasmids are known, they are: (1) Transfer and sex factor, (2) R-plasmids, (3) Plasmids conferring pathogenicity to mammals, (4) Col plasmids, (5) Degradative plasmids, (6) Mercury's-resistance plasmids, (7) Tumour inducing plasmids in *Agrobacterium tumefaciens*, (8) Cryptic plasmids, (9) Staphylococcal plasmids.

Transfer and sex factors: They are conjugative plasmids and determine their own transfer in bacteria and have the character to promote transfer of other genes from the donor to recipient cell at the time of conjugation. Those conjugative plasmids, which cause transfer of chromosomal genes during conjugation, are termed as sex factors. It is extrachromosomal genetic element and was known as sex factor F (for fertility in *E. coli* K-12). The chromosomal fragment or genes, which are transferred to the recipient cell, then joins with its chromosome.

Sometimes exchange between DNA segments of plasmids and chromosome takes place after a break on the both strands where the nucleotide sequences are similar. This results in insertion of plasmid into the chromosome. A bacterial cell which contains chromosomal DNA + plasmid DNA rings is known as *Hfr* (high frequency of recombination) cells.

All plasmids discovered to date are circular, double-stranded DNA molecules. Their molecular weights range from 3×10^6 to 1×10^8, which is sufficient to dose for 5-160 average polypeptides. Plasmids contain 3 to 4 genes. Most of the plasmids used as vector are derived from psc 101 to $EcolR_1$ plasmids by addition or deletions. pBR^{322} is one such popular derived plasmid vector having unique sites for restriction enzymes, which are available for insertion of DNA fragment. Shuttle vectors are generally employed which can replicate in more than one types of hosts. Generally, plasmids with 2 genes for different antibiotic resistance are used:

- to identify bacteria that carry plasmid, and
- to distinguish chimeric plasmid (recombinant plasmid) from the parental vector.

Thus, chimeric plasmid is resistant to one antibiotic while parental plasmid is resistant to two antibiotics. Multicopy plasmids are more suitable since 10 to 30 copies of one plasmid in a cell along with inserted gene will give an amplified response. Addition of chloramphenicol often affects new rounds of chromosome replication while plasmid replication is unaffected. This makes isolation of plasmid easier.

1. **Sex factors**: These mediate chromosome transfer by the mechanism described below. The most widely studied is F, the sex factor found in *E. coli* D12.
2. **Col factors**: These carry genes that cause their hosts to produce **colonies**, proteins that are lethal toxins for coliforms bacteria. Most members of this group are small (less than 10 megadaltons of DNA), are present in the cell in many copies (20-100), and are nonconjugative- lacking the gene system mediating self-transfer.

3. **Resistance (R) factors**: These carry genes conferring on the host cell resistance to various antimicrobial agents, such as antibiotics. A single plasmid, for example, may carry separate genes for resistance to streptomycin, chloramphenicol, tetracyclines, and sulfonamides. In some cases it has been possible to dissociate the plasmid into several smaller ones: an element called resistance transfer factor (RTF), carrying the genes governing the intracellular transfer process; and separate elements called **R determinants**, carrying the resistance genes. In other cases, the various elements remain tightly linked, and the entire plasmid is then referred to as an **R factor**.
   a) **Penicillinase plasmids of staphylococci**: These plasmids carry a gene that causes the cell to produce a potent penicillinase, thus rendering it resistant to penicillin. They differ from R factors in that they are not capable of transfer by conjugation. They can be carried from cell to cell, however, by phage mediated transduction.
   b) **Degradative plasmids of *Pseudomonas***: These plasmids carry sets of genes determining the enzymes of catabolic pathways, such as the enzymes for the degradation of camphor, toluene, octane, or salicylic acid.
   c) **Virulence plasmids**: A number of plasmids carry genes whose products contribute to the relative pathogenicity of the host cell. These plasmids include the enterotoxin and colonization antigen plasmids of enteropathogenic *E coli* strains and a staphylococcal plasmid carrying a gene for exfoliative toxin.

As will be discussed below, plasmids share many properties with bacterial viruses (phages). They are of major clinical significance, not only because they may carry genes for resistance to therapeutic drugs and for virulence factors but also because some of them mediate gene transfer- a process that leads to the emergence of strains with new combinations of antigenic and virulence properties.

Replication of Plasmids

Plasmid DNA replicates while maintaining a supercoiled, circular state. Replicating plasmid DNA can be isolated in the form of **relaxation complexes**, in which the DNA is bound to proteins that appear to provide the following functions:

1. Binding of the DNA to the membrane replicator site;
2. Nicking and unwinding of the strands to permit replication; and
3. Resealing of the nicks. Replication is bi-directional in some plasmids and unidirectional in others.

Plasmids regulate their own replication, such that each plasmid exhibits a typical copy-number ratio (ratio of plasmid copies to chromosome copies in the cell). In general, the small nonconjugative plasmids have high copy-number ratios whereas the large conjugative plasmids have copy number ratios closer to 1. Plasmid replication is unusually sensitive to inhibition by such agents as acridine dyes and ultraviolet light; by using these agents at threshold doses, cells can be cured of their plasmids.

Even in plasmids having a copy-number ratio of 1, partition between daughter cells following replication is highly efficient. This is affected by a plasmid DNA site called *par*, which is the functional equivalent of the eukaryotic chromosomal centromeres. It may act by binding to a cell membrane site or, alternatively, by associating with the host chromosome.

Incompatibility of Plasmids: Plasmids can be classified into a number of incompatibility groups; 2 members of the same group cannot coexist in the same cell. This phenomenon may involve competition for a specific attachment site in the cell membrane or may reflect the action of group-specific repressors. Members of the same incompatibility group are closely related as indicated by the extensive hybridization of their DNAs.

Self-Transfer of Plasmids

Gram-negative bacteria: Most of the plasmids of gram-negative bacteria are conjugative: they carry the genes (called the ***tra* genes**) mediating their own transfer by the process of cell conjugation. There are 12 or more *tra* genes arranged in an operon; some of these code for the production of the **sex pilus**.

Plasmid transfer in gram-negative bacteria begins with the extrusion of a sex pilus, a protein thread several times the length of the cell. The tip of the sex pilus adheres to gram-negative cell walls.

Binding of the recipient cell to the donor pilus requires the presence of specific receptor sites on the recipient cell's surface. In certain conjugation deficient mutants, one of the major proteins of the outer membrane is missing and the lipopolysaccharides are altered, indicating a role for both of these components in pair formation.

Following specific pair formation, the plasmid undergoes a special type of replication called **transfer replication**, one parental strand passing into the recipient and the other remaining in the donor cell. Complementary strands are synthesized in the donor and recipient simultaneously with transfer. The daughter molecules are circularized by ligase action immediately after transfer replication is complete.

Gram-positive bacteria: Plasmid genes have determined several antibiotics produced by members of the genus *Streptomyces*, and some of these plasmids are transferable from one streptomycetes to another. The process resembles conjugation in that direct hyphal contact is necessary, but the molecular details of the process are not understood. The best known such plasmid is SCPI, which carries the genes for the biosynthetic pathway producing the antibiotic methylenomycin. SCPI also carries the genes responsible for transfer by a mechanism, which has some similarities to that of plasmid-mediated chromosome transfer in gram-negative bacteria.

Plasmid-mediated conjugation also occurs in members of the gram-positive genus *Streptococcus*. In *Streptococcus lactis*, the ability to ferment lactose is conjugally transmitted as a plasmid-borne β-galactosidase (*lac*) gene. A series of conjugative plasmids have been analyzed in *Streptococcus faecalis*, carrying genes for hemolysin, bacteriocin, and single or multiple drug resistance. These plasmids can mobilize other (nonconjugative) plasmids as well as chromosomal markers.

Sex Pheromones: An unusual feature of the *S faecalis* mating system is the production by recipient cells of specific **sex pheromones**- diffusible proteins that stimulate donor cell aggregation (with each other and with recipient cells) and, if the donor cells are pre induced by the pheromone, increase the frequency of donor plasmid transfer as much as a million-fold. When a recipient cell acquires a given plasmid, it ceases to produce the pheromone specific for that plasmid but continues to excrete pheromones that plasmid but continues to excrete pheromones that act on donor cells harbouring other conjugative plasmids.

Recombination

Plasmids undergo crossing over with each other and with the host chromosome, depending on the extent of their base sequence homologies or on the presence of transposable elements. Since both plasmids and chromosome are circular, an odd number of crossovers serve to integrate the 2 DNA structures, which then replicate as a single unit. An even number of crossovers, on the other hand, brings about an exchange of segments.

A plasmid capable of integrating with the bacterial chromosome is called an **episome**. When integration occurs, a double replicon is formed bearing both a chromosomal and a plasmid replicator site. In some cases, replication continues to start at the chromosomal replicator; in others (*e.g.*, at nonpermissive temperatures in mutants temperature-sensitive for DNA synthesis), replication of the entire structure is taken over by the plasmid replicator, a phenomenon known as **integrative suppression**.

Cell Properties Determined by Plasmid Genes

Drug resistance: In gram-negative bacteria, genes governing resistance to such drugs as neomycin, kanamycin, streptomycin, chloramphenicol, tetracyclines, penicillins, and sulfonamides are found on one or another plasmid in various combinations. In the gram-positive staphylococci, genes governing resistance to such agents as penicillin, erythromycin, and heavy metals (*e.g.*, Hg^{2+} and Co^{2+}) are found on plasmids. Genes conferring resistance to the same agents may also be found on the chromosome, but in such cases they do so by different mechanisms. Most plasmid-governed resistance is mediated by enzymatic inactivation of the drug (*e.g.*, by acetylation or phosphorylation), whereas chromosome-mediated resistance usually reflects a lowered affinity of its target molecule for the drug. These findings are compatible with the fact that plasmids are (by definition) dispensable to the cell: Only chromosomal genes can confer resistance by structurally altering the binding site for the drug, since the genes determining the structures of indispensable cell components must themselves be indispensable.

Virulence: Enteropathogenic strains of *E coli* of porcine or human origin cause diarrhoeal illnesses by the liberation of enterotoxins. Two types have been recognized: a heat-liable toxin (LT) and a heat-stable toxin (ST). Plasmid genes determine both. Other plasmids of *E coli* carry genes determining surface hairs (pili) that serve as "colonization antigens" only strains possessing these pili can adhere to host epithelial cells and establish themselves in sufficient numbers to cause disease.

Plasmid-borne genes can contribute to host cell virulence in other ways. The colicinogenic plasmid Col V, for example, determines enzymes that synthesize cell-associated, hydroxamate-containing iron sequestering compounds which are induced in media containing low concentrations of iron. It is believed that invasiveness of symbiotic bacteria depends heavily on the ability of the bacteria to compete with their mammalian host cells for iron; most *E coli* strains isolated from bacteremias carry Col V, suggesting a role for the Col V -determined iron-sequestering system in host cell virulence. The invasiveness of the human pathogen *Yersinia enterocolitica* has also been shown to be plasmid-determined, although in this case the mechanism is not known.

Production of antimicrobial: Anti-microbial agents include antibiotics, which are the products of metabolic pathways, and polypeptide toxins. Plasmid genes encode a number of these agents, including some antibiotics of *Streptomyces*, bacteriocins (such as colonies), and microcins- oligopeptides produced by certain strains of *E coli*.

Other properties: As discussed above, plasmids are known that encode enzymes of special catabolic pathways (in *Pseudomonas*), enzymes of nitrogen fixation (in *Klebsiella*), and tumorigenicity for host plants (in *Agrobacterium tumefaciens*).

- ***Relation to Viruses:*** Bacterial viruses possess all of the properties described above for plasmids; a Pseudomonas phage has even been found to promote conjugation. The major difference thus appears to be the ability of phages to form mature, protein-coated virions that can be liberated and passed to other cells through the medium. Their many similarities suggest a close evolutionary relationship between phages and plasmids.
- ***Clinical Significance:*** The ease with which plasmids can transfer from cell to cell and the strong selection that chemotherapy has exerted for drug resistance have combined to produce striking results. In Japan, for example, the frequency of R-governed multiple-resistance Shigella strains rose from 10-20% in 1955 to 80% in 1968. In England, multi-resistant Salmonella typhimurium first appeared in 1961 and rose to 21% of all S typhimurium isolates by 1964.

In general, 60-90% of resistance markers in the gram-negative pathogens are carried on transferable plasmids. Although the experimentally determined rate of transfer of resistance *in vivo* is very low, epidemiological evidence indicates that such transfer accounts for the rapid rise in incidence of drug-resistant strains of gram-negative pathogens.

A common method for cloning DNA molecules is to cleave both plasmid and insert DNA with the same restriction endonuclease. The sticky ends created by enzyme can be sealed easily with phage T4 DNA ligase. T4 DNA ligase can also be used to join the blunt-ended DNA molecules together. Sticky end or cohesive end joining is more efficient and advantageous because foreign DNA can be retrieved easily as restriction sites (say, for $EcoR_1$ enzymes) are created on both sides of inserted DNA.

Bacteriophages can also be used as vectors. λ-Phase of *E. Coli* is normally used. The amount of DNA that can be packed in phage head has to be 80% to 105% of its normal size for encapsulation to occur, hence there is limitation for quantity of external DNA that can be inserted in the phase vector. About 20% of non-essential portion of original phase can be removed to make room for foreign DNA to be inserted. In insertion and transfer to the host the procedure comprises: (i) allow the virus to undergo lytic cycle first; (ii) get more viruses; (iii) prepare chimeric phages; (iv) allow it to undergo lytic cycle; (v) more chimeric phages obtained.

As pBR322 plasmid or phages are vector for *E. coli* cells, similarly, a range of vectors is now available for *Bacillus subtilis*, *Streptomyces* spp. and *Saccharomyces cerevisiae*.

Transfer of Foreign Gene through Vector to Appropriate Host (Cloning Organism): When foreign DNA is ligated (joined) to the vector, the recombinant vector is to be transferred to a suitable host. This is done by transformation of competent cells by treating it with cold $CaCl_2$ in the case of plasmid vectors and transfection in the case of phage vectors. This cloning organism should be deficient in the major pathway of DNA recombination (*i.e.* rec A-minus). This will reduce the possibility of undesirable recombinations. The cloning organism should preferably lack restriction enzymes that can degrade foreign DNA. Mini cells lacking in major chromosome but having all other cell machinery are suitable for testing expression and there will be no interference from the products of chromosomal expression in such cells. In eukaryotic cells, primary and secondary tissue cultures of African green monkey kidney cells have been used for recombinant DNA experiments.

E. coli was used and is still very useful as a cloning organism. *Saccharomyces cerevisiae* is also used, as it is safer, nonpathogenic, not living in human being and is close to human being (eukaryotic). *Bacillus subtilis* is a competent cloning organism when it is starved of nutrients. Many other bacteria and *Streptomyces* spp. can only be transformed when they are converted into protoplasts by removing their cell walls. So is the case with yeasts also, in which $CaCl_2$ and PEG treatment is given to facilitate protoplasts for the uptake of DNA.

Yeast (*Saccharomyces cerevisiae*)

For example, in *S. cerevisiae* genome, the chromosome III contains 26 genes thought to code for proteins and two coding for transfer RNAs (tRNAs), short molecules involved in reading the genetic code during translation. These 28 genes take up 66.4% of the 50-kb sequence.

1. **Relatively few of the yeast genes are discontinuous**. In this segment of chromosome III none of the genes are discontinuous. In the entire yeast genome there are only 239 introns, which is a remarkably small number compared with individual genes can have more than 100 introns.
2. **There are fewer genome-wide repeats.** This part of chromosome III contains a single LTR element, called Ty2, and four truncated LTR elements called delta sequences. These five genome-wide repeats make up 13.5% of the 50-kb segment. When all 16 yeast chromosomes are considered the total amount of sequence taken up by genome-wide repeats is only 3.4% of the total.

Yeast genome is much more economical and compact. It has fewer introns. The spaces between the genes are relatively short with much less space taken up by genome-wide repeats and other noncoding sequences.

Important Features of Prokaryotic Genomes

1. There are no introns in the genes present in this segment of the *E. coli* genome. In fact *E. coli* has no discontinuous genes at all and it is generally believed that this type of gene structure is absent in prokaryotes with a few exceptions, mainly among the archaea.
2. The infrequency of repetitive sequences. Prokaryotic genomes do not have anything equivalent to the high-copy –number, genome-wide repeat families found in eukaryotic genomes. They do, however, possess certain sequences that might be repeated elsewhere in the genome, examples being the **insertion sequences** ISl and ISl86 that can be seen in the 50-kb segment. These are examples of **transposable elements** (*sequences that have the ability to move around the genome and to transfer from one organism to another, even sometimes between two different species*)

Importance of Prokaryotic Genome in Research

Genome sequencing represents the frontier of molecular biology. Its territory was inaccessible just a few years ago. It has innovative approaches and a lot of sheer hard work. The major goal of molecular biology is to obtain the complete sequences of a many genomes as possible. Considerable effort is being devoted to a wide range of organisms. Following are the reasons for developing activity devoted to genome sequences:

1. The genome sequences are the key to the continued development of our knowledge of molecular biology, genetics, biochemistry, cell biology and physiology, etc.
2. A catalog containing a description of the sequence of every gene in a genome is immensely valuable, if at first the functions of many of the genes are unknown.
3. They help to catalog sequences (which they contain) of the coding parts of every gene, it will also include the regulatory regions for these genes.
4. The genome sequence therefore opens the way to a comprehensive description of the molecular activities of living cells and the ways in which these activities are controlled.
5. Gene catalogs also aid the isolation and utilization of important genes, such as those human genes responsible for inherited disease, or bacterial genes whose protein products have industrial value.
6. The genes can be isolated from a genome even if the complete genome sequence is not known.
7. It is easy to obtain a copy of the desired gene if the sequence of its genome is already known, so that the gene can simply be withdrawn from the catalog.
8. The genome of all higher eukaryotes contains extensive amounts of noncoding DNA. It is assumed that most of the noncoding DNA has no function, but perhaps this is because we do not know enough about the role of noncoding DNA. This is a matter of further research.

Transposons

Genomes of bacteria are not static, but may have quite large changes taking place. This is because of sections of DNA that have the capacity to move around. Such pieces of DNA are called **Transposable element (transposon).** The shift of a gene or chromosome segment to a new position of the chromosome called **transposition**. Transposons exist in different forms, the first to be discovered being the **insertion sequences** (IS). These are lengths of DNA that can be inserted into a target gene within the genome. For example, DNA may be able to move from the main DNA molecule of bacteria to be inserted into a plasmid.

Composite transposons are very similar except that they contain two insertion sequences, which flank a length of DNA. Isolating a eukaryotic gene by **transposon tagging** involves inserting into target DNA, fractionating fragments of the latter on southern blots and hybridizing the transposon with a probe. Usually such insertion sequences have at either end a short length of DNA known as an **inverted repeat**, *i.e.* this small length of DNA has the same sequence if read in either direction along the 5'-3' strand. Between these inverted repeats is a gene, which codes for an enzyme, **transposase,** which catalyses the transposition event. Cleaving out the transposon, together with flanking DNA, reveals the adjoining sequences of a gene. The probes are made for these adjoining sequences to find the fragment having gene of interest. Presence of transposon is confirmed by altered phenotype. This method was first employed to isolate *white* locus in *Drosophila*. The mutants with *white-apricot* eyes harboured a *copia* retrotransposon as well as accompanying *white* locus. Tn3 transposons are slightly more complicated. This class of transposon is not flanked by insertion sequences but is still able to move around because the transposon contains a gene coding for transposase.

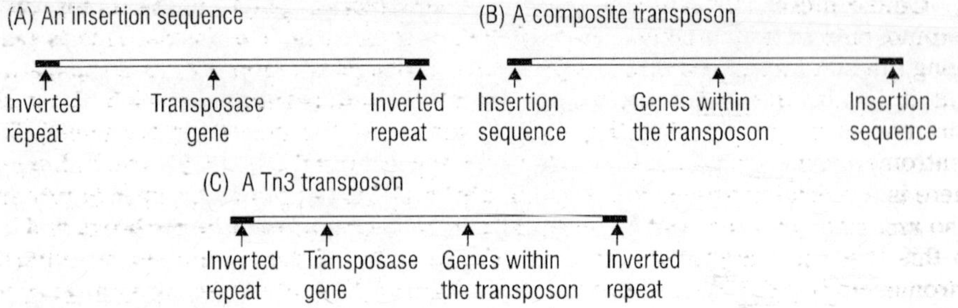

FIGURE 2.19: The classes of transposons.

Genomes of Eukaryotes

The term **chromosome** was proposed by Waldeyer for the individual threads within the cell nucleus. In eukaryotes the DNA is partitioned, each nucleus containing several DNA molecules, each of which helps to make up a chromosome. Chromosomes thread is visible in the prophase of mitosis and meiosis and sometimes at interphase. Also the finest unitary chromosomal thread that is optically visible; for example two chromonemata can often be observed to comprise a **chromatid**. **Chromosomal chimaera** is the chimaera the components of which do not have the same chromosome number.

The DNA is linear in all eukaryote nuclei, and in most nuclei there are two copies of each gene. This situation is referred to as the **diploid** complement, while certain cells. For example the sex cells of an individual, will contain only one copy of each gene and are therefore called **haploid**. Lastly, not all the DNA in eukaryotes is contained within the nucleus. Other organelles within the cells, such as mitochondria and chloroplasts, also contain their own complement of functional DNA.

The epression lampbrush chromosome describes the appearance of the chromosomes at the diplotene stage of meiosis in the oocytes of some amphibia, when the chromatids extend from each chromosomes to form lateral loops.

The small genomes in eukaryotes may only be 10-20 thousand kb, while the largest may be 120 million kb. Chromosome number is also very varied. Fruit flies have 23. However, it has become apparent that vast amounts of many eukaryotic genomes are redundant, *i.e.* not encoding gene products. For the human genome it has been estimated that only 2-3% is actually coding DNA. Of course, if **mutations** take place in the rest, it might mean that there is little or no consequence.

DNA in eukaryotes is packed as chromosomes which are composed of a length of DNA, which is in association with proteins. The proteins which contain a coloured prosthetic group bound either covalently or noncovalently called **chromoproteins**. One of the most important families of protein here is the **histones**. These are very basic proteins, having a relatively high content of the amino acids lysine, arginine and histidine, and they are very conserved in their sequence between different species. To date, there are five histones (H1, H2A, H2B, H3 and H4) have been characterized. They vary in molecular mass from approximately 11 kilodaltons (H4) to 23 kilodaltons (H1).

The DNA and histones are wound up into a complex structure known as the **nucleosome** and then nucleosomes are associated together, along with the DNA of course, into a chromatin fibre.

Centromere (L. *centrum*: center + Gr. *meros*: part) is the point on a chromosome to which spindle fibers attach during nuclear divisions. This is point along the chromosome where it is joined to its daughter chromosome in replication, and it is also the point of attachment of the **microtubules,** which draw the chromosomes apart so that they can be placed in the new daughter nuclei. The centromere exists along the DNA where there is a special DNA sequence. In humans there is a repeating sequence called the **alpha DNA.** In both cases, special proteins also associate with the DNA to form a structure known as the **kinetochore,** and it is to this that the microtubule attaches. The position of the centromere in different chromosomes is different. According to position of the centromere chromosomes are following types:

- **Metacentric:** Centromere is in the center of the chromosome.
- **Telocentric:** Centromere is close to one end.
- **Acrocentric:** Centromere is nearer to one end.

The ends of chromosomes are known as the **telomeres.** The functions of such areas appear to include the protection of the ends of the DNA, the prevention of DNA joining, and aiding in the replication of DNA. One again, the DNA has a special sequence associated with it here, in this case multiple repeating of a short sequence, and the telomere also has association with special proteins not found elsewhere in the chromosome. Telomere has recently come to prominence in the press because their length is thought to change with age.

The position of the centromeres in chromosomes helps researchers to pair up the copies of chromosomes in diploid cells, and such analysis may be useful in identifying individuals who contain too many chromosomes, as in **Down's syndrome** where the patient has an extra chromosome 21, or **Klinefelter's syndrome** where individuals have an extra X sex chromosome (being XXY instead of XY), or when a chromosome is missing, as in **Turner's syndrome** where an individual has a sex chromosome missing and therefore is referred to as being XO.

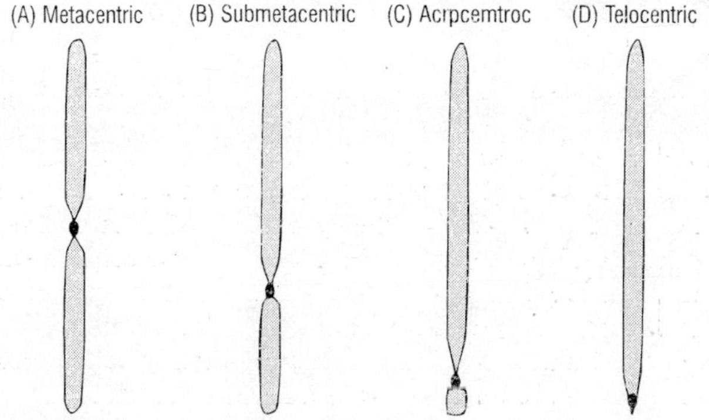

FIGURE 2.20: The positions of centromeres on chromosomes.

DNA Outside the Nucleus

Certain cellular organelles contain their own genomes, which are not only active but also vital to cellular function. Expression of the gene of such organelles is interesting as it will be seen that many of the proteins encoded here are parts of large and important protein complexes, the other polypeptides in the complexes being encoded by the nuclear genome.

Mitochondria

Mitochondrin (Gr. *mitos*: thread + *chondros*: cartilage, or grain) is an organelle that occurs in eukaryotic cells and contains the enzymes of the citric acid cycle, the respiratory chain, and oxidative phosphorylation. A mitochondrion is bounded by double membrane. **Mitochondrial DNA (mtDNA)** a circular piece of DNA consists commonly of a closed cricle of double-stranded DNA, of between 5 and 30μm in length, comprising 15-20 kilobases in most animals (longer in higher plants) and including about 50 gene sequences, of which about one-half code for transfer RNA.

Chloroplasts

Chloroplasts of plants contain a circular DNA genome. The presence of DNA and ribosomes in chloroplasts was first demonstrated in 1962. Our present knowledge of the organization of genetic information in chloroplasts is based on the application of molecular cloning and nucleotide sequencing technologies. Restriction mapping and cloning confirmed the double-stranded circular nature of the chloroplast DNA (plastome). The size of the plastome varies between 120 and 160 kbp (kilobase pair) in land plants; the average molecular mass of the plastome is about 1×10^8 kDa. To date, the entire genome sequence has been determined for the cloned chloroplast DNAs of three plant species, *viz.* tobacco, liverwort and rice, and the sequences for defined segments of many other chloroplast genomes have been completed. These studies indicate that the chloroplasts probably code for all of their tRNA (transfer RNA), rRNA (ribosomal RNA) molecules, or many of the proteins in the photosynthetic electron transport chain and in the ATP synthase. The remainder of the electron transport chain proteins and some in the ATP synthase complex are encoded by the nuclear genome, synthesized in the cytoplasm, and imported into the chloroplasts.

Proteomics of Chloroplasts

Defining Proteomics: Proteomics is the large-scale study of proteins, usually by biochemical methods. The word proteomics has been associated traditionally with displaying a large number of proteins from a given cell line or organism on two-dimensional polyacrylamide gels. In 1990s, biological mass spectrometry, Matrix assisted laser desorption/ionization – Time of fright (MALDI-TOF.MS), and Electrospray ionization mass spectrometry (ESI-ms/ms), emerged as powerful analytical method that removed most of the limitations of protein analysis. Today, the term proteomics covers much of the functional analysis of gene products or *functional genomics*, including large-scale identification or localization studies of proteins and interaction studies. Therefore, Proteomics is the study of all the expressed proteins of an organism. The information that proteomics studies can provide includes expression levels, post-translational modifications, sub-cellular localizations, protein-protein interactions, and protein-nucleic acid interactions.

Proteomics already has become an important tool for drug discovery and the analysis of yeast and *E. coli* protein expression patterns; however, it has not been widely applied in plant biology. The total proteome of higher plants is estimated to consist of ~21,000 to 25,000 proteins and chloroplast contain 10 to 25% of this total, an illustration of the central importance of the chloroplast for the plant cell.

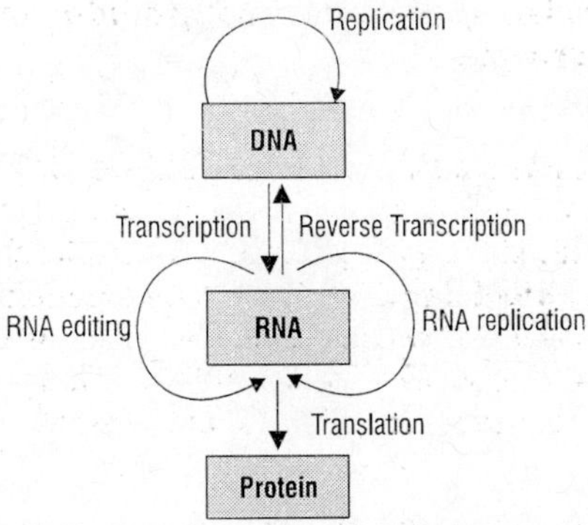

FIGURE 2.21: Flow of genetic information from DNA to RNA up to formation of protein.

GENETIC CODE

The genetic code is the message sent by the genetic material (DNA) of the cell through RNA to translate the synthesis of proteins. There are 64 possible triplets for the genetic code. Each triplet (*i.e.*, 3 units or bases) specifies the synthesis of one amino acid after translation. The code appears to be universal in the sense that any organism uses the same code triplets to synthesize amino acid and proteins through the aid of m RNA.

The code was determined by the use of two kinds of *in vitro* systems:

1. Synthetic polymers, each containing a mixture of two different nucleotides were used as message for the synthesis of polypeptides 'in vitro', by analyzing the ability of different polymers to stimulate the incorporation of different amino acids, many codons could be described.
2. Synthesis nucleotide triplets were used to stimulate the binding of specific t RNA molecules to ribosomes in vitro.

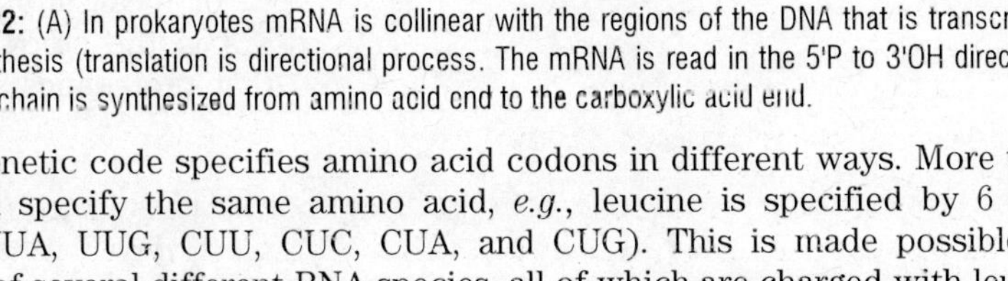

FIGURE 2.22: (A) In prokaryotes mRNA is collinear with the regions of the DNA that is transcribed. (B) Protein synthesis (translation is directional process. The mRNA is read in the 5'P to 3'OH direction, and the peptide chain is synthesized from amino acid end to the carboxylic acid end.

The genetic code specifies amino acid codons in different ways. More than one codon can specify the same amino acid, *e.g.*, leucine is specified by 6 different codons (UUA, UUG, CUU, CUC, CUA, and CUG). This is made possible by the existence of several different RNA species, all of which are charged with leucine but each of which has a different anticodon. In some cases a given anticodon can match either of two codons, which differ only in the 3rd nucleotide (*e.g.*, UUU, and UUC). The smallest number of code words is 1 for methionine (AUG) and there are two for aspartic acid (GAU and GAC), 3 for isoleucine (AUU, AUC and AUA) and 4 for serine

(UCU, UCC, UCA and UCG). If there is a change in the bases of the codon and this change does not affect the code words of the amino acid, then the product will not be altered or affected, *e.g.*, if the code words from DNA came for lysine as AAG and AAG instead of AAA and AAG than lysine will be synthesized normally because AAG is still another triplet for lysine.

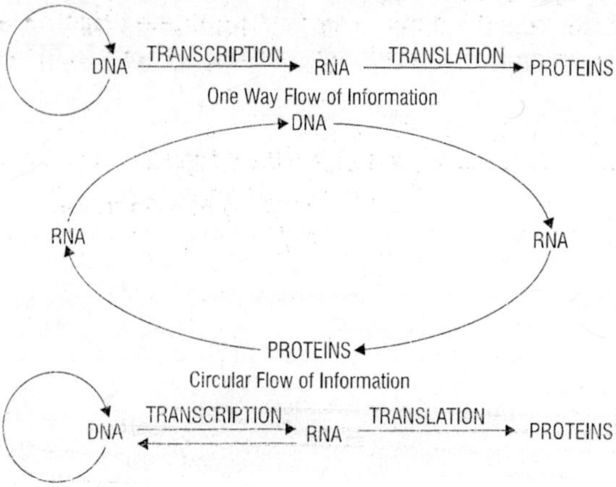

FIGURE 2.23: Flow of information from DNA to RNA and synthesis of protein.

First Letter	Second Letter: U	C	A	G	Third Letter
U	UUU } Phe	UCU } Ser	UAU } Tyr	UGU } Cys	U
	UUC } Phe	UCC } Ser	UAC } Tyr	UGC } Cys	C
	UUA } Leu	UCA } Ser	UAA Stop	UGA Stop	A
	UUG } Leu	UCG } Ser	UAG Stop	UGG Trp	G
C	CUU } Leu	CCU } Pro	CAU } His	CGU } Arg	U
	CUC } Leu	CCC } Pro	CAC } His	CGC } Arg	C
	CUA } Leu	CCA } Pro	CAA } Gln	CGA } Arg	A
	CUG } Leu	CCG } Pro	CAG } Gln	CGG } Arg	G
A	AUU } Ile	ACU } Thr	AAU } Asn	AGU } Ser	U
	AUC } Ile	ACC } Thr	AAC } Asn	AGC } Ser	C
	AUA } Ile	ACA } Thr	AAA } Lys	AGA } Arg	A
	AUG Met	AGC } Thr	AAG } Lys	AGG } Arg	G
G	GUU } Val	GCU } Ala	GAU } Asp	GGU } Gly	U
	GUC } Val	GCC } Ala	GAC } Asp	GGC } Gly	C
	GUA } Val	GCA } Ala	GAA } Glu	GGA } Gly	A
	GUG } Val	GCG } Ala	GAG } Glu	GGG } Gly	G

FIGURE 2.24: Presentation of 64 codons of mRNA.

Research work done by Nirenberg, Holley, and Khorana established the basis for deciphering the so-called **genetic code**. Just as DNA from very diverse biological sources usually contains only the four nucleotides A, T, G and C, proteins from diverse sources are commonly made up of only 20 amino acids (the building blocks of proteins). The question arises, how only four nucleotides code for 20 amino acids. That is how long a sequence of nucleotides, and which arrangements of the nucleotides, was necessary to code for 20 amino acids?

Mathematically, that all possible combinations of four bases, taken one or two at a time, could account for only four or sixteen amino acids respectively; taken as triplets (**codons**), (4^3) or 64 arrangements could be possible. This is more than enough to code for the 20 amino acid. However, the triplet code also provided for more than one code for amino acid. There are few codons, which cannot code for amino acids and are called **missense codons**. They are considered as the punctuation's for the genetic alpha or code. The finding that more than one codon could code for a given amino acid is known as **degeneracy** in the genetic code.

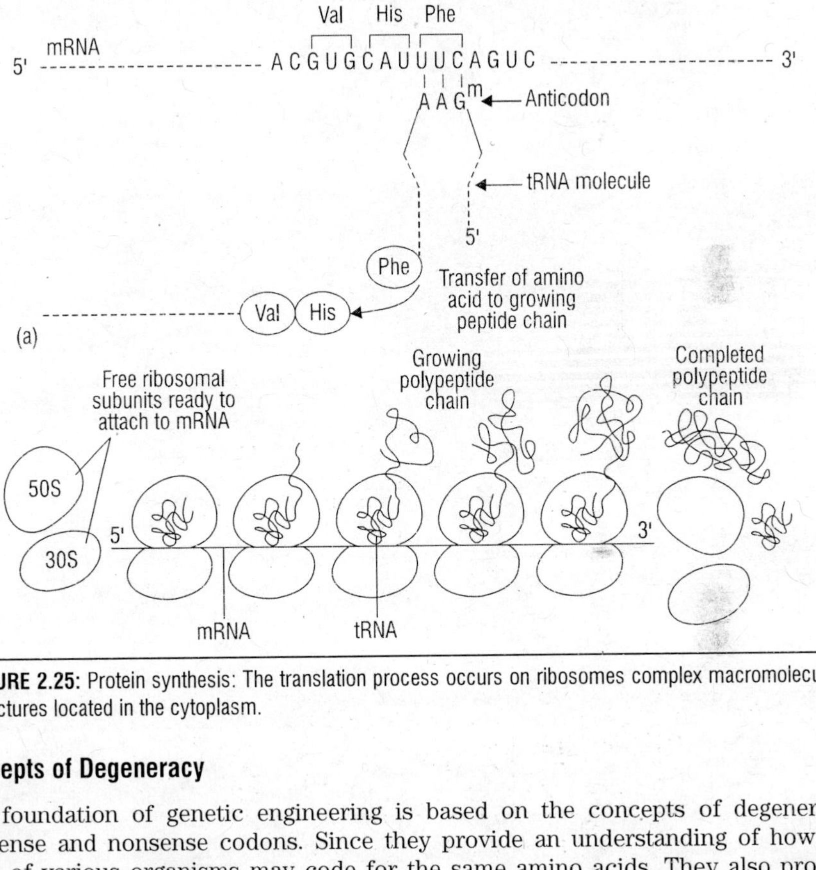

FIGURE 2.25: Protein synthesis: The translation process occurs on ribosomes complex macromolecular structures located in the cytoplasm.

Concepts of Degeneracy

The foundation of genetic engineering is based on the concepts of degeneracy, missense and nonsense codons. Since they provide an understanding of how the DNA of various organisms may code for the same amino acids. They also provide numerous ways to code not only for the composition but also for the unique arrangements or sequences of amino acids in the diverse proteins of those organisms. The genetic engineering researches have the potential, specifically rearranging, inserting, deleting, synthesizing, or transferring DNA. Such studies also include the knowledge now, where, and when genes function? **Genes** are defined as discrete sequences of DNA, which code for given biological molecules such as structural proteins and enzymes.

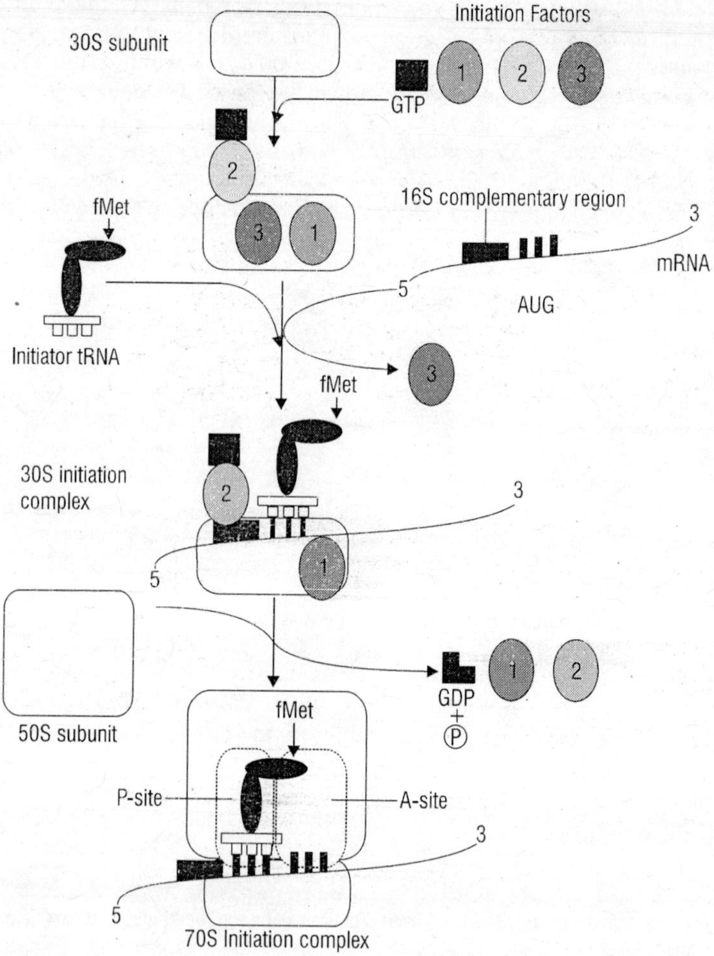

FIGURE 2.26: Initiation of protein synthesis in prokaryotes (*E. coli*).

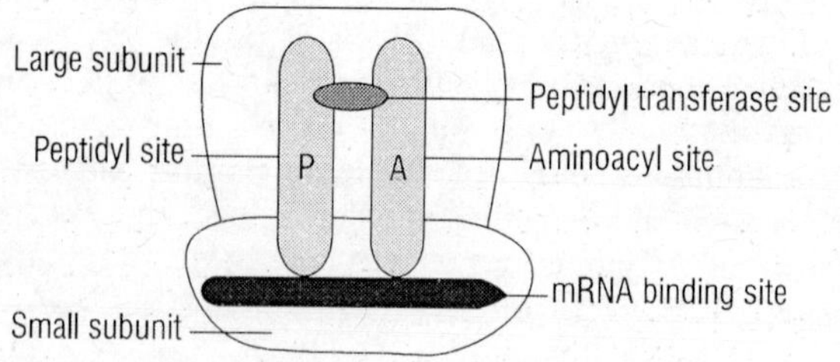

FIGURE 2.27: Structure of ribosome.

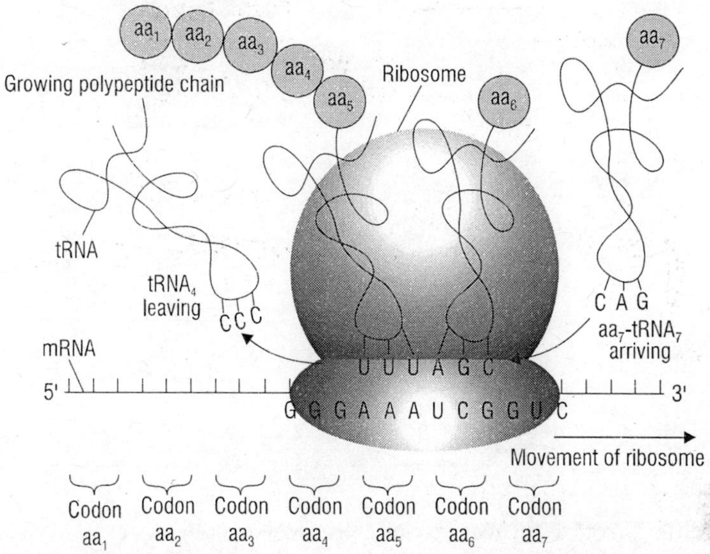

FIGURE 2.28: The translation of mRNA into protein. (a) Insertion of a single amino acid into the polypeptide chain. This is a highly diagrammatic representation of the process of translation. The codons in the mRNA are recognized by the anticodon loop on the tRNA. In this case a UUU codon is interacting with a phenylalanine tRNA. In all such interactions the last two nucleotides of the anticodon loop in the tRNA are the direct complement of the cognate codon in the mRNA. The third residue in the anticodon loop is often a 'non-standard' base, in this case, a methylated guanosine. The base in the third position is called the wobble base because it has the ability to pair with more than one base in the third position of the codon. Thus this phenylalanine tRNA is able to pair with either a UUU or a UUU phenylalanine codon. The enables a cell to utilize fewer tRNAs. (b) Orientation of a tRNA molecule relative to the large and small ribosomal subunits in the 3 main binding states designated A/A, P/P, and E.

DNA Encodes Genetic Information

DNA usually encodes genetic information in all living cells. It has complementary strands of opposite polarity, which are wrapped around each other to form a double helix. Each strand is composed of a phosphate-sugar backbone with one of the four different bases, adenine, guanine, cytosine or thymine, covalently attached to sugar residue. A complex of base, sugar and phosphate is called a **nucleotide;** the polynucleotides constitute a strand. The bases pair by non-covalent hydrogen bonds. Adenine forms two hydrogen bonds with thymine, and cytosine forms three hydrogen bonds with guanine. This specificity of base pairing allows the precise duplication of DNA, and enables it to act as the repository of genetic information.

During **DNA replication,** the helix is unwound and each strand acts as a template for the synthesis of a complementary strand. New strand is formed in 5' to 3' direction. This reaction is enzymatically catalyzed by DNA polymerase. In opposite polarity (3' to 5' direction), a series of discontinuous short pieces (**Okazaki fragments**) are formed, which are subsequently joined up by the enzyme DNA ligase.

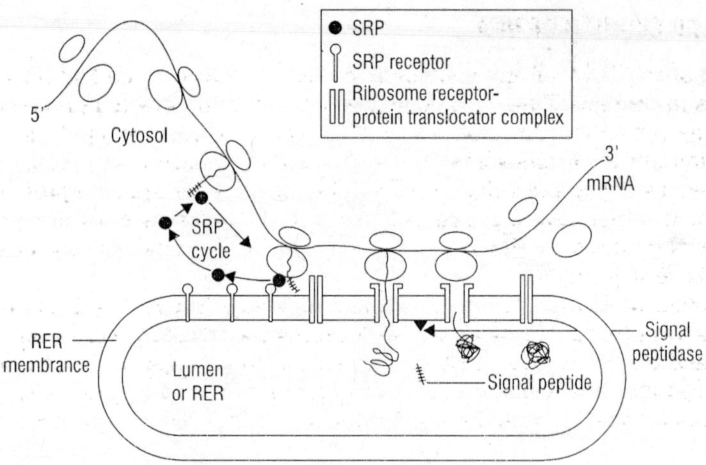

FIGURE 2.29: Protein secretion in eukaryotes.

RNA differs from DNA in containing a ribose, rather than a deoxyribose sugar and uracil base in place of thymine. There are three different classes of RNA, messenger RNA, ribosomal RNA and transfer RNA, all of which are transcribed from DNA templates. mRNA is the carrier of genetic information and forms only a few per cent of the total cellular RNA.

DNA can be linear or circular. Viruses, unlike cellular organisms, have a variety of genome structures, linear or circular, single-stranded or double-stranded, and DNA or RNA. Some viruses, such as the SV40 DNA tumour virus, have a genome of double-stranded DNA.

The genome of a prokaryote cell, such as *E. coli* consists of a gigantic circular molecule of DNA. The DNA molecule found within eukaryotic mitochondria is also circular, although the normal chromosomal DNA is linear.

A circular double stranded DNA molecule in which each strand is intact is termed closed circular DNA. If one of the two strands is broken, the molecule is termed as open circle. The open ends when join to regain circular structure, it supercoils. This property of circular DNA is technically important, because open and closed circular forms can be separated from one another by virtue of the super coiled nature of the latter molecule.

The genetic information within DNA directs the production of the structural proteins and enzymes, which build the cell. Production of proteins (or protein synthesis) is a two step process *viz.* transcription and translation. Transcription is production of RNA by copying the genetic information in DNA. It is fundamentally similar to DNA replication, except that only one of the two DNA strands is copied.

The nucleotide sequence of mRNA is read as a series of triplets (Genetic code). Each codon specifies the insertion of a particular amino acid into the growing peptide chain. This is then translated into the language of protein with the help of 20 naturally occurring amino acids.

Prokaryotes and eukaryotes use essentially similar mechanisms to decode the information contained within their DNA; however, they differ greatly in cell structure and in the size and organization of their genome.

MOLECULAR CLONING OF DNA

Only part of the DNA of any genome is directly involved in coding for amino acid sequences in proteins. Other noncoding regions function in such processes as DNA replication, recombination, the control of gene expression, and the structural organization of the chromosome. In many cases, this is accomplished by short base pair sequences in the DNA that serve as binding sites for specific proteins or RNA molecules; in other cases, it seems likely that recognition sites are provided by secondary structures in the DNA, formed by internal base-pairing in regions of repeated base sequences.

To obtain definitive information concerning such processes, it is necessary to perform a **functional analysis of DNA structure**: Specific segments of DNA of known base pair sequence must be altered and rearranged in known ways, then reintroduced into host cells or put into *in vitro* systems to determine the effects of the changes on specific functions. Such functional analysis has been made possible by 3 major technical advances: (1) the ability to determine the complete base-pair sequence of DNA molecules (**DNA sequencing**); (2) the ability to synthesize DNA sequences 20 or more base sequences in length (performed by automatic machines); and (3) the ability to carry out the **molecular cloning of DNA**. These techniques not only permit the functional analysis of DNA structure but also make possible the production in large quantities of almost any desired gene product, *e.g.*, otherwise scarce hormones, enzymes, and antigens.

Restriction Enzymes

The name restriction enzyme is derived from the genus and species of bacterium from which it is isolated. The first letter of the genus name and first two letters of the species are combined to form the enzyme name. This is followed by a strain designation if needed. In many instances, a bacterial strain contains more than one restriction endonuclease. When this occurs, each enzyme is assigned a Roman numeral. Thus, *Bam* HI was the first enzyme activity reported from *Bacillus amyloliquefaciens* strain H.

Structurally, most restriction enzymes reported in purified form are composed of two equal subunits with molecular weights of 20,000- 25,000 or single polypeptides with molecular weights of 30,000-35,000.

Enzyme activities can be differentiated from each other by their characteristic patterns of digestion of small viral DNAs. The DNA from bacteriophage Lambda is the most widely used substrate for screening restriction enzymes. Because it's often difficult to determine a characteristic pattern from a Lambda digest, smaller DNAs, such as the replicative form of bacteriophage ϕX174 and of SV40 are also used as substrates. The resulting DNA digest is displayed on agarose or polyacrylamide gels and visualized by staining with Mcthylene Blue Plus™ or ethidium bromide.

Sequence-specific, or Type II, endonucleases are commonly described as restriction enzymes. In contrast with nonspecific or Type I enzymes, Type II endonucleases generate producible nucleotide fragments from specific DNAs. They cleave double-stranded DNA by hydrolyzing two phosphodiester bonds (one per strand) within defined nucleotide sequences. Over 1500 H.O. Smith and collaborators have discovered enzymes since the first report, with a variety of bacterial cells as their source.

A given sequence in DNA is recognized and can be cleaved by more than one restriction enzyme. The term *isoschizomers* describes a group of enzymes that recognize the same sequence in DNA. In such cases, the representative enzyme that is used most commonly is selected on the basis of ease of purification and stability in purified form. The sequences recognized by these enzymes are for the most part centrosymmetric *palindromic* sequences that are usually hexamers, pentamers, or tetramers. Several Type II enzymes recognize DNA at a specific site and hydrolyze phosphodiester bonds at a defined distance from that site. An example of this group of enzymes is BglI, which recognizes a sequence containing two groups of specified residues separated by completely unspecified residues - GCCNNNNNGGC; it, therefore, generates DNA fragments with

Endonucleases are enzymes that hydrolyze phosphodiester bonds at internal locations within a polynucleotide chain. Exonucleases, by comparison, break phosphodiester bonds sequentially, starting at one free end of a polynucleotide and working towards the other. Restriction endonucleases cleave duplex DNA only at specific sites, producing double strand breaks. They generally cut to the 5' side of the phosphate, resulting in breaks, which are amenable to the DNA ligase repair process, suggesting that such accidental nicking and repair may happen in nature.

DNA Fingerprinting

DNA typing (also called DNA profile analysis or DNA fingerprinting is a recently developed method that allows for the unambiguous identification of the source of unknown DNA samples. The method has become very important in forensic biochemical laboratories where it has been used to provide evidence in paternity and criming cases. In contrast to the more conventional methodologies, such a blood typing, which can only exclude a suspect, DNA fingerprinting, can provide positive identification with great accuracy.

DNA fingerprinting involves the electrophoretic analysis of DNA fragment sizes generated by restriction enzymes.

MAPPING GENOMES BY GENETIC TECHNIQUES

Genetic mapping uses genetic techniques such as crossbreeding and pedigree analysis to construct genome maps. The basis of genetic mapping is the calculation of recombination frequency by linkage analysis. Genetic analysis of bacteria requires gene transfer from one cell to another. Genes were originally used as markers but these are now supplemented with DNA markers such as RELPs, SSLPs and SNPs. These techniques involve much more than just methods for sequencing DNA molecules.

Limitations

1. Even with the most sophisticated technology it is rarely possible to obtain a sequence of more than about 750 bp in a single experiment. This means that the sequence of a long DNA molecule has to be constructed from a series of shorter sequences. One approach is to break the molecule into fragments, determine the sequence of each one, and use a computer to search for overlaps and build up the master sequence. This is done by shotgun method in prokaryotic genomes (The shotgun approach on its own is inappropriate for larger and more complex genomes).
2. The shotgun method may lead to errors when repetitive regions of a genome of a genome are analyzed. When a repetitive sequence is broken into fragments many

of the resulting pieces contain the same, or very similar, sequence motifs. It would be very easy to reassemble these sequences so that a portion of the repetitive regions was left our or even so that two pieces of the same or different chromosomes were mistakenly connected together.

Shotgun Technique

The DNA molecule is broken into small fragments, each of which is sequenced. Searching for overlap between the sequences of individual fragments assembles the master sequence. In practice, an overlap of several tens of base pairs would be needed to establish that two sequences should be linked together. The DNA molecule contains two segments of repetitive DNA. Each made up of many copies of the motif GATTA. When the sequences are examined, two fragments from different parts of the DNA appear to overlap. If the error is not recognized then the central segment of the DNA molecule will be left out of the master sequence. If the two repetitive DNA segments were on different chromosomes, then the sequences of these chromosomes might be mistakenly assembled.

Once a genome map is available, the sequencing phase of the project can proceed in either of two ways.

1. **By the clone containing approach:** The genome is broken into manageable segments, each a few hundred kb or a few Mb in length, which are then sequenced individually, usually by the shotgun method. Once the sequence of a segment has been completed, it can be positioned at its correct location on the map.
2. **By a directed shotgun approach:** This strategy uses the distinctive features on a genome map as landmarks to aid assembly of the master sequence from the huge numbers of short sequences obtained by the shotgun approach.

With both approaches, the map provides the framework for carrying out the sequencing phase of the project.

Genetic and Physical Maps

Genetic mapping is based on the use of genetic techniques to construct maps showing the positions of genes and other sequence features on a genome. There are two conventional methods for genome mapping:

The technique, for prokaryotes, includes crossbreeding experiment. Physical mapping uses molecular biology techniques to examine DNA molecules directly in order to construct maps showing the positions of sequence features including genes.

Markers for Genetic Maps

Genes are very useful markers but they are by no means ideal. Mapped features that are not genes are called DNA markers as with gene markers, to be useful a DNA markers. As with gene markers, to be useful a DNA marker must exist in at least two allelic forms. There are three types of DNA sequence feature that satisfy this requirement. Genetic mapping is based on the principles of inheritance as first described by Gregor Mendel in 1865 (Orel, 1995).

Genes are segments of segments of DNA molecules. They are the abstract entities responsible for the transmission of heritable characteristics from parent to offspring. To be useful in genetic analysis, a heritable characteristic had to exist in two alternative forms or phenotypes. This approach was fine in the early days but geneticists soon realized that there are only a limited number of visual phenotypes whose inheritance can be studied, and in many cases the analysis is made less easy because more than one gene affects a single physical feature.

A genome, consisting of a linear DNA molecule of 2.5 Mb. It has been mapped and the positions of eight markers (ABCDEFGH).

On the left, the clone counting approach starts with a segment of DNA whose position on the genome map has been identified because it contains markers A and B. The segment is sequenced by the shotgun method. The master sequence placed at its known position on the map.

On the right, the directed shotgun approach involves random sequencing of the entire genome. This result in pieces of contiguous sequence, possibly hundreds of kb in length. If a contiguous sequence contains a marker, then it can be positioned on the genome map.

Microbes (bacteria and yeast) have very few visual characteristics. A big advantage of these markers over visual phenotypes is that many of the relevant genes have multiple alleles. The problem is made worse by the fact that only a fraction of the total number of genes exists in allelic forms that can be distinguished conveniently. Gene maps are, therefore, not very comprehensive. We need other types of markers.

TABLE 2.2: Typical biochemical markers used for genetic analysis of *Saccharomyces cerevisiae*

Marker	Phenotype	Method by which cells carrying the marker are identified
ADE2	Requires adenine	Grows only when adenine is present in the medium
CAN1	Resistant to canavanine	Grows in the presence of canavanine
CUP1	Resistant to copper	Grows in the presence of copper
CYH1	Resistant to cyclocheximide	Grows in the presence of cyclocheximide
LEU2	Requires leucine	Grows only when leucine is present in the medium
SUC2	Able to ferment sucrose	Grows if sucrose is the only carbohydrate in the medium
URA3	Requires uracil	Grows only when uracil is present in the medium

Restriction Fragment Length Polymorphisms (RFLPs)

RFLPs were the first type of DNA marker to be studied. Restriction fragments are produced when a DNA molecule is treated with a restriction endonuclease, which is a type of enzyme that cuts DNA molecules at defined sequences. For example, the restriction endonuclease *Eco*RI cuts double-stranded DNA at:

5'-G A A T T C – 3'

3'-C T T A A G – 5'

and at no other sequence. This sequence specificity means that treatment of a DNA molecule with a restriction enzyme should always produce the same set of fragments. This is not always the case with genomic DNA molecules because some restriction sites are polymorphic, existing as two following alleles:

1. Allele displaying the correct sequence for the restriction site and therefore being cut when the DNA is treated with the enzyme.
2. Allele with a sequence alteration so the restriction site is no longer recognized.

In order to score an RELP, it is necessary to determine the size of just one or two individual restriction fragments against a background of many irrelevant fragments. This is not a trivial problem: an enzyme such as *Eco*RI, with a 6-bp recognition sequence, should cut DNA approximately once every $4^6 = 4096$ bp and so would give almost 750 000 fragments when used with human DNA. Fortunately, there are techniques that enable individual fragments to be detected.

Southern hybridization was the first technique used to type RELPs. Agarose gel electrophoresis and the ones being studied detected by hybridization probing separate the DNA fragments resulting from restriction from one another.

The **polymerase chain reaction** or PCR is now more commonly used because it s faster than Southern analysis. In PCR, the region of DNA containing the RELP is amplified into multiple copies before the DNA is treated with the restriction enzyme. Now the RELP can be treated with the restriction enzyme and can be visualized by staining an agarose gel of the restriction fragments with ethidium bromide, which is a less sensitive detection method than hybridization probing.

Note that these techniques directly detect both alleles of an RELP: this means that (as with other DNA markers) the alleles are codominant.

Simple Sequence Length Polymorphisms (SSLPs)

SSLP are arrays of repeat sequences that display length variations, different alleles containing different numbers of repeat units. Unlike RFLPs, SSLPs can be multiallelic as each SSLP can have a number of different length variations. There are two following types of SSLP:

1. **Minisatellites**, also known as variable number of tandem repeats (VNTRs), in which the repeat unit is a few tens of nucleotides in length.
2. **Microsatellites** or simple tandem repeats (STRs), whose repeats are much shorter, usually di, tri or tetra nucleotide units. We met two Microsatellites in Chapter 1 when we looked at a typical 50-kb segment of the human genome.

Southern Hybridization

In Southern hybridization, a collection of restriction fragments is transferred from an agarose gel to a nylon membrane and the specific ones being studied are detected by hybridizing probing. As well as its use in RELP mapping. It has many applications in other procedures that require identification of specific restriction fragments, for example to check the identity of a cloned fragment.

Agarose gel electrophoresis separates linear DNA molecules, such as restriction fragments, according to their sizes. If there are only a few fragments in the digest then each one forms a separate band that can be seen after staining the gel with ethidium bromide. If there are more than about 50 fragments then the bands merge together into a smear and individual fragments cannot be seen. Instead, the fragments are transferred to a nylon membrane, simply by placing the membrane on the gel and allowing buffer to soak through, taking the DNA from the gel to the membrane where it becomes bound. One can buy an expensive machine to do this, but is simpler to use a pile of paper towels.

A **hybridization probe** is a labeled DNA molecule whose sequence is complementary to the target DNA that we wish to detect. Because the probe and target DNAs are complementary they can base pair or hybridize. Detecting the signal given out by the label attached to the probe therefore identifies the position of the target restriction fragment on the membrane. The probe could be a synthetic Oligonucleotide or it could be a cloned DNA fragment. For detecting an RELP, the probe is usually a cloned DNA fragment that spans the polymorphic restriction site.

DNA CHIP AND ITS TECHNOLOGY

The gene expression studies are useful in determining the function of a genes. However, there is a serious limitation of the current technique like monitoring gene expression, namely via Northern blots, because one can analyze expression of only *one gene at a given time.* DNA chips allows simultaneous and *en masse* analysis of hundreds and thousands of genes (DeRisi and Brown, 1997, *Science*, **278**: 68-686; Ferea and Brown, 1999, *Curr. Opin. Genei. Dev.* **9**: 715-722). In fact, it has become possible to analyze expression of all the genes of an organism such as yeast on a single chip. This technology has been given various names like, *lab-on-a-chip, array-of-hope*, or *revolution on a square cm.*

Structure

A DNA chip is a wafer of silicon, 2 cm^2 or less in area, carrying many different oligonucleotides in high-density array. The DNA to be tested is labeled with a fluorescent marker and pipetted on to the surface of the chip. Hybridization is detected by examining the chip with a fluorescence microscope; the positions at which the fluorescent signal is emitted indicating which oligonucleotides have hybridized with the test DNA. Many SNPs can therefore be scored in a single experiment (Wang *et al.*, 1998).

A DNA chip carries a large number of DNA probes, each one with a different sequence and each at a defined position on the surface of the chip. The probes can be synthetic oligonucleotides or other short DNA molecules such as complementary DNAs. In the earliest technology, the oligonucleotides or cDNAs were spotted on to a glass microscope slide or a piece of nylon membrane to form a micro array. With this approach only, relatively low density can be achieved, typically 6400 spots as an 80 × 80 array in an area of 18 mm by 18 mm. To prepare really high-density arrays a more sophisticated technology was needed. The answer has been to synthesize oligonucleotides *in situ* on the chip surface, which in turn has required an advance in the methodology used for preparing oligonucleotides, as shown in the Figure 2.30. The normal method involves adding nucleotides one by one to the growing end of oligonucleotides, the sequence determined by the order in which the dNTP substrates are added to the reaction mixture. If used for synthesis on a chip, this method would result in each Oligonucleotide having the same sequence. Instead, modified dNTP substrates are used, ones that have to be light activated before they will attach to the end of a growing Oligonucleotide. The dNTPs are added one after another to the chip surface, photolithography being used to direct pulses of light at individual positions in the array and hence determine which of the growing oligonucleotides will be extended by addition of the particular dNTP added at each step.

DNA chips are designed to allow many hybridization experiments to be performed in parallel. Their main applications have been in the screening of polymorphisms such as SNPs and comparing the RNA populations of different cells. They also have potential in novel DNA sequencing methodologies.

A density of up to one million oligonucleotides per cm^2 is possible (Ramsay, 1988), so if used for SNP screening half a million polymorphisms can be typed in a single experiment, presuming there are oligonucleotides for both alleles of each SNP. A DNA chip is not complicated to use. The chip is incubated with labeled target DNA to allow hybridization to take place. Which oligonucleotides have hybridized to the target DNA is determined by scanning the surface of the chip and recording the positions at which the signal emitted by the label is detectable. Radioactive labels can be used with a low-density micro array, signals being detected electronically by phosphor imaging. The does not provide enough resolution for a high-density chip, so with these it is necessary to use a fluorescent label. The fluorescent signal is detected by laser scanning or, more routinely, by fluorescent confocal microscopy.

Under highly stringent hybridization conditions, a stable hybrid occurs only if the oligonucleotide is able to form a completely base-paired structure with the target DNA. If there is a single mismatch then the hybrid does not form. To achieve this level of stringency the incubation temperature must be just below the melting temperature or T_m of the oligonucleotides. At temperatures above the T_m, even the fully base-paired hybrid is unstable. At more than 5 °C below the T_m, mismatched hybrids might be stable. The T_m for the oligonucleotide shown in the figure would be about 58 °C this is calculated from the formula T_m = (4 × number of G and C nucleotides) + (2 × number of A and T nucleotides) °C.

CHAPTER 3

Applications of Genetic Engineering

Genetic engineering, recombinant DNA technology, genetic modification / manipulation (GM) and gene splicing are terms that apply to the direct manipulation of an organism's genes. Genetic engineering is different from traditional breeding, where the organism's genes are manipulated indirectly. Genetic engineering uses the techniques of molecular cloning and transformation to alter the structure and characteristics of genes directly. Genetic engineering techniques have found some successes in numerous applications. Some examples are in improving crop technology, the manufacture of synthetic human insulin through the use of modified bacteria, the manufacture of erythropoietin in hamster ovary cells, and the production of new types of experimental mice such as the oncomouse (cancer mouse) for research.

The term genetic engineering was coined in Jack Williamson's science fiction novel *Dragon's Island*, published in 1951, two years before James Watson and Francis Crick showed that DNA could be the medium of transmission of genetic information.

Genetic engineering has unlimited scope for application, which include technologies that cater to human health and prosperity. The goal of plant, animal and microbial genetic engineer is to improve the quality and yield of products.

Biological Molecular Markers Assisted Breeding

Molecular markers are the most advanced tools of genetic research. Breeders have used phenotypic markers to follow segregation of genes but most of the agronomic characters are not associated with scorable phenotypic characters. Discovery of restriction enzymes that cleave DNA at sequence-specific sites, have evolved the molecular marker technology by splicing any specific segment of DNA and the traits associated with it. Genetic analysis methods for morphological markers are few. Application of molecular and biochemical markers may help breeders to tag agronomic traits and to screen those at early stages of growth.

The DNA molecular markers exist in every genotype; their number may vary from hundreds to thousands. They are stable makers and are independent of plant growth stage and external environment. As a result, molecular markers can be scored using DNA from seedlings and plants at any stage of growth in any environment.

For example if a set of markers established for high starch/protein, a breeding population could be screened for that character even at the seedling stage. Interdisciplinary research is required to establish molecular markers, associated with the traits of agronomic or market interest.

In this chapter, various applications have been fragmented into three major subdivisions *viz.* transgenic plants, transgenic animals and miscellaneous applications.

The term 'transgenic' is used to describe plants and or animals which have had DNA introduced into them by means other than transfer of DNA from a sperm cell to an egg. The DNA transferred by these non-sexual processes may be DNA from same species, from other plant or animal species or even from a prokaryote. Today many transgenic plants as well as animals have been engineered by the scientists with special beneficial properties.

TRANSGENIC PLANTS

Up till 1980s, production of transgenic plants was restricted mainly to tobacco, petunia or tomato of the family solanaceae. However, now in more than 40 dicot species transgenic plants have been successfully produced. The production of transgenic plants has now been extended to several monocotyledons like wheat, maize, rice and oats.

In higher plants transgenic plants have been developed using different methods in:

1. **Herbaceous dicotyledons:** *Actinidia* sp. (kiwi), *Apium graveolens* (celery), *Arabidopsis thaliana*, Armoracia sp. (horse radish), Beta vulgaris (sugarbeet), Brassica napus (oilseed rape: canola), *Brassica oleracea* (cauliflower), *Brassica oleracea* var. *capitata* (cabbage), *Brassica rapa* (syn. *B. campestris*). *Carica* papaya (papaya). *Chrysanthemum* sp. (chrysanthemum). *Cichorium intybus* (chicory). *Cucumis melo* (muskmelon). *Cucumis sativus* (cucumber). *Daucus carota* (carrot). *Dianthus caryo*phyllus (carnation). *Digitalis purpurea* (foxglove). *Fragaria* sp. (strawberry), *Glycine max* (soybean), *Glycyrrhiza glabra* (licorice), *Gossypium hirsutum* (cotton), *Helianthus annuus* (sunflower), *Ipomoea batatas* (sweet potato), *Ipomoea purpurea* (morning glory), *Lactuca sativa* (lettuce), *Linum usitatissimum* (flax), *Lotus corniculatum* (lotus), *Lycopersicon esculentum* (tomato), *M. varia*, *Medicago sativa* (alfalfa), *Nicotiana plumbaginifolia* (wild tobacco), *N. tabacum* (tobacco), *Petunia hybrida* (petunia), *Pisum satium* (pea), *Rosa* sp. (rose). *Solanum melongena* (eggplant), *Solanum tuberosum* (potato), *Vaccinium macrocarpon* (crtanberry), *Vigna aconitifolia*, *Vitis vinifera* (grape).
2. **Woody dicotyledons:** *Populus* sp. (poplar), *Malus sylvestris* (apple), *Pyrus communis* (pear), *Azadirachta indica* (neem), *Juglans regia* (walnet).
3. **Monocotyledons:** *Asparagus* sp. (asparagus), *Dactylis glomerata* (orchard grape), *Secale cereale* (rye), *Oryza sativa* (rice), *Triticum aestivum* (wheat), *Zea mays* (corn), *Avena sativa* (oats), *Festuca arundinacea* (tall fescue).
4. **Gymmosperms**: *Picea glauca* (white spruce)

ENGINEERED RESISTANCE AGAINST HERBICIDE

The development of crop plants that are tolerant to herbicide is an important approach to control weeds. Most of the modern herbicides interfere with amino acid biosynthesis in plants. Once the mode of action of a herbicide is established, the transfer of resistance to the herbicide can be done by two different approaches: (1) The first approach is modification of the target side. (2) Detoxification of herbicide. Transgenic plants carrying the genes for herbicide tolerance has been produced in tobacco, petunia, tomato, potato, *Populus* etc.

Modification of the Target

This approach has been made for developing resistance against atleast three herbicides *viz.* glyphosate, sulphonyl urea and imidazolinones.

Resistance against Glyphosate

Glyphosate, an active component of round up herbicides, is used as non-selective post-emergence herbicides. It is suggested that glyphosate inhibits aromatic amino acid biosynthesis by competitive inhibitor of enzyme 5-enol-pyruvyl shikimate-3 phosphate synthase [EPSPS]. EPSPS catalyzes the synthesis of phenylalanine, tyrosine and tryptophan. The aro A gene which codes EPSPS has been isolated and sequenced from *E. coli*, *Salmonella typhimurium* and *Arabidopsis thaliana*.

There are two possible methods for producing glyphosate resistant plants by genetic engineering:

1. Transfer of a glyphosate sensitive EPSPS under the control of a powerful promoter causing over expression of the protein and/or
2. Transfer of gene which codes a mutated, glyphosate resistant EPSPS. cDNA of the EPSPS gene with 35 S cauliflower mosaic virus promoter was constructed and the transformed petunia cell lines with this construct exhibited 40-fold increase in EPSPS activity.

An alternative method is insertion and expression of mutated bacterial aro A gene coding for glyophosate resistant EPSPS. The source of the *aro-A* gene was a mutagenized strain of *S. typhimurium* or *E. coli* and was transferred to tomato and/or tobacco. Transgenic tobacco plants, showing tolerance to commercial levels of glyphosate are field tested in USA.

TABLE 3.1: Mechanisms of action of different herbicides and basis of achieving resistance against them in transgenic plants

Active principle of herbicide	Inhibited pathway	Target product	Use	Basis of resistance
Amino acid biosynthesis inhibitors				
Glyphosate (Roundup)	Aromatic amino acid biosynthesis	EPSPS	Broad spectrum	Over-expression of EPSPS gene; bacterial aroA gene
Sulphonylurea and Imidazolinones	Branched chain amino acids	ALS	Selected crops	Mutant ALS gene
Phosphinothricin (Basta)	Glutamine	GS	Broad spectrum	Gene amplification; bar gene; detoxification
Photosynthesis inhibitors				
Atrazine (Lasso)	Photosystem II	Qb (32 kDa protein)	Selected crops	Mutant PsbA gene; GST gene; detoxification
Bromoxynil (Buctril)	Photosynthesis	-	Selected crops	bxn gene; detoxification

Resistance against Sulfonylurea and Imidazolinone Herbicides

The herbicidal action of sulfonylureas and imidazolinones is based on their ability to inhibit non-competitively an enzyme of branched-chain amino acid biosynthesis, acetolactate synthase (ALS). ALS is the first enzyme in the biosynthetic chain resulting in the synthesis of the branched chain amino acids valine, leucine and isoleucine.

Mutated strains resistant to sulfonylureas have been obtained from bacteria, fungi and plant cell cultures. The resistance of all these mutants can be attributed to possession of mutated forms of the ALS. Transgenic tobacco plants expressing a mutant ALS gene from tobacco or *Arabidopsis*, were produced that were tolerant to sulfonylurea herbicides.

Resistance against Phosphinothricin

L-Phosphinothricin (PPT) is a naturally occurring amino acid with herbicidal activity and is active ingredient of herbicide 'Basta'. PPT is a potent inhibitor of glutamine synthase and thus causes rapid increase in ammonia concentration in plants. This leads to death of plant cell. 'bar' gene from *Streptomyces hygroscopicus* encodes phosphinothricin acetyl transferase enzyme that acetylates the free-NH_2 groups of phophinothricin and renders it inactivates the herbicide Basta. This 'bar' gene with CaMV 35S promoter has been transferred to tobacco, tomato and potato plants using *Agrobacterium* Ti plasmid vector system. The transgenic plants have been tested for 'Basta' resistance.

Resistance against Atrazine

Atrazine is another herbicide, which inhibits photosynthesis. A 32kDa protein, Q_B is responsible for herbicide binding and is encoded by psb A gene. The DNA sequences of psb A are highly conserved in different plants. More than 20 weed species have developed resistance to atrazine herbicides, for example, *Amaranthus hybridus*.

Detoxification or Degradation of Herbicide

This approach is based on selective use of herbicide, which will kill the weeds and not the crop. A number of detoxifying enzymes have been identified in plants as well as microbes. Few examples are given here: *(i) glutathione-S transferase* or GST (in maize and other plants): It detoxifies the herbicide atrazine; *(ii) nitrilase*: It is coded by gene bxn in *Klebsiella penumoniae*, and it detoxfies the herbicide bromoxynil, and *(iii) phosphinothricin acetyl transferase* or PAT (coded by *bar* gene in *Streptomyces* and transgenic plants using the *bxn* gene from *Streptomyces* spp).: It detoxifies the herbicide PPT (L-phosphinothricin). Transgenic tomato plants using the *bxn* gene from *Klebsiella ozaenae* and *bar gene* from *Streptomyces*, as well as, transgenic potato, oilseed rape (*Brassica napus*) and sugarbeet using *bar* gene from *Streptomyces* have been obtained and were found to be herbicide resistant. Other crops for engineered herbicide tolerance include soybean, cotton and corn.

ENGINEERED RESISTANCE AGAINST PEST

Pests and insects cause severe damage to our crops and thus use of insectides and pesticides is a common measure. With genetic engineering, crops can now be protected with insects without applying any synthetic chemical. More than 30 crop species have been successfully transformed including corn, cotton, soybean, and rice with insecticidal properties.

For transgenic plant production with pest resistance properties, two major approaches have been developed: a) the introduction of protein delta endotoxins from Bt and, b) introduction of protease inhibitors in plants.

Bacillus thuringiensis Endotoxins

The entomocidal bacterium *Bacillus thuringiensis*, upon sporulation normally produces a parasporal crystalline toxin. When ingested by a susceptible insect, a combination of the high pH and proteinases of the insect midgut solubilizes the crystal and yields active toxin. The effects of the toxin occur within minutes of indigestion, leading to disruption of insect's midgut cells. Bt toxin activity has been found against many species of insects within the orders of Lepidoptera, Diptera and Coleoptera.

These delta endotoxins are very specific in their action and are safe insecticides, but their use is limited due to high production cost and due to instability of crystal proteins when exposed in the field.

The above toxin gene (*ht2*) from *B. thuringiensis* has been isolated and used for *Agrobacterium* plasmid mediated transformation of tobacco, cotton potato and tomato plants. These transgenic plants were resistant to the feeding damage of *Manducta sexta* larvae (tobacco horn worm), a pest of tobacco. Experiments of feeding the larvae of *M. sexta* on leaves of these transgenic plants showed 75%-100% mortality of the larvae, while the control plants carrying no transgenes were severely damaged.

Pseudomonas Flourescens that Secretes Bt Toxin

The cystalline protein toxin produced by *Bacillus thuringiensis* var. *israelensis* is toxic to the larval stage of several mosquitoes and black fly species. Normally this toxin is produced by fermentations of *B. thuringiensis* and the toxin is sprayed onto crops. Scientists have produced genetically engineered *Pseudomonas fluorescens* living in the roots of corn plants. This bacterium can secrete Bt-toxin to kill black cutworm.

Field tests using transgenic insect resistant plants were also conducted with tobacco and tomato and may be used for commercial cultivation in the near future.

Protease Inhibitors

Protease inhibitors are proteins with antimetabolic activity against wide range of insects. Such inhibitors are widely distributed within the plant kingdom and can accumulate to high levels in seeds and storage organs. Other major advantage of protease inhibitors is their inactivation with cooking.

In cowpea (*Vigna unguiculata*), trypsin inhibitor (CpTi) level was shown to be responsible for its resistance to attack by the major storage pest of its seeds (*i.e.* bruchid beetle = *Callosobruchus maculatus*) A variety of insects have shown to be toxic to CpTi. This CpTi gene was joined with a CaMV 35S promoter and one marker gene with the transgene and was used to infect tobacco leaf discs. *Agrobacterium* was used for transformation and the transgenic tobacco plants express a high level of CpTi. The CpTi gene in transgenic plants is stably inherited and there is no serious 'yield penatly'. Thus like Bt toxin, CpTi can also be used as a protectant against insect attack in transgenic plants. However, extensive field trials are necessary before releasing these transgenic plants to the farmers.

Gene for other Insecticidal Secondary Metabolites

The production of secondary metabolites by plants can also implicate the resistance to insect attack. However, biosynthesis of each of these metabolites involves many steps, each controlled by a separate gene. Furthermore, these genes are tissue specific in expression. These features make the production of transgenic plants difficult in this case. Utilizing these facilities, transgenic plants with insect resistance due to secondary metobolites will be available in the near future.

ENGINEERED RESISTANCE AGAINST VIRAL INFECTION

Over seven hundred plant viruses are recognised causing various diseases and significant crop losses. Due to the lack of 'viricides', the practical control depends on methods that prevent or restrict virus infection. Various strategies have been applied for protecting viral infection; few are described here like:

Cross Protection

If susceptible strain of a crop is inoculated with a mild strain of a virus, the susceptible strain, as a result, develops resistance against more virulent strains. The phenomenon is known as **cross protection.** This method has been used to reduce yield losses in crops like tomatoes against **tomato moisac virus** (TMV), in potato against **potato spindle tuber viroid** and in citrus against **citrus tristeza virus**. In most cases of cross protection, the symptoms of infection are delayed, and even the replication of virus is suppressed, although eventually the severe strain may be able to overcome the protection.

The disadvantages of practicising cross protection includes

1. Possibility of mutation in inducing mild virus strain.
2. Possibility of synergism between inducing virus and another unrelated virus.
3. Possibility of unnecessary spread of mild virus causing threat for future yield losses.
4. Possibilities of some yield losses due to mild strain. Transgenic plants have been produced in tobacco, tomato, and potato with single gene using a broad spectrum of plant viruses.

Coat Protein Mediated Protection

Coat protein - mediated resistance to viruses has been one of the successes of plant genetic engineering. Coat protein gene from tobacco mosaic virus (TMV), a positive strand RNA virus, has been transferred to genome of tobacco plants. In the transgenic plant, expression of coat protein (CP), as well as, low and delayed infection was observed when inoculated with TMV. However, in such transgenic plants, coat protein gene should be constitutively expressed and may thus have effects on the nutritional value of plants. Subsequently Cp genes isolated from different plus strand RNA plant viruses have been cloned into plant expression vectors and transferred to various crop plants like tobacco, tomato and potato, using *Agrobacterium* mediated plant transformation system. Potatoes have been produced which have coat protein genes and are tolerant in field tests to both potato virus X (PVX) and potato virus Y (PVY). A target DNA coding for a component of TMV replicase enzyme, was also transferred to tobacco plants, conferring resistance to TMV.

Antisense RNA Mediated Protection

Antisense constructs also generate protection against RNA and DNA viruses. Transgenic tobacco plants expressing antisense transcript (antisense - coat protein gene) were protected from CMV infection.

Transgenic tobacco plants with Nucleocapsid (N) gene, CaMV 35S promoter and a leader sequence (to enhance expression) showed expression of N-gene. Such transgenic plants were resistant to tomato spotted wilt virus. (TSWV) TSWV is a negative strand RNA virus with RNA joined firmly to the nucleocapside protein.

Satellite RNA Mediated Protection

Satellite RNAs are associated with specific strains of some plant RNA viruses, though they are unrelated to viral genome. These extragenomic RNA species depend on a helper virus for replication. Some satellite RNAs are known to attenuate the symptoms of their helper virus. Thus satellite RNA might be used to protect crop plants against the effect of CMV infection. The nature of protection in transgenic plants by satellite RNA is different from coat-protein protection.

Defective Interfering Mediated Protection

Defective interfering (DI) particles are deletion mutants of genomic viral sequences, which depend on their parent virus for replication. Like satellite RNAs, DI particles can attenuate the disease symptoms of their helper virus by interfering with its replication. Artificial DI molecules of TMVY, TMV and BMV have been constructed and inserted in plant protoplast *e.g.*, deletion mutants of BMV RNA 2 exhibited reduced replication of MBV RNA1 and RNA2 in barley protoplasts.

Replicase Mediated Protection

It has been discovered that transgenic tobacco expressing part of replicase gene of TMV strain was highly resistant to this and closely related strains.

Currently, atleast three approaches are available to broad spectrum resistance. The first is based on the replication and cell-to-cell movement of virus. Second approach relies on the transgenic expression of antivirus protein of non-plant origin including antibodies. The third approach is based on genetic manipulation of natural viral defences in plants.

ENGINEERED RESISTANCE AGAINST FUNGAL PATHOGEN

Genetic engineering has opened vistas with isolation of resistance genes and gene transformation methods to develop transgenic plants. Resistance to fungal palthogen is achieved by isolating and transferring fungal resistance genes to the desired susceptible crop. Compounds toxic to fungus can also be used to produce transgenic plants as done in case of tobacco. Antifungal proteins like **endochitinase** and **ß-1,3-endoglucanases** are thought to inhibit fungal growth. Transgenic tobacco plants with endochitinase CH5B gene with Ca MV 35S promoter exhibits reduced seedling mortality when grown in presence of *Rhizoctonia solani*.

TABLE 3.2: Some pathogens for which resistance has been transferred in some crop plants

Pathogen	Disease	Resistance gene	Source of gene	Transgenic crop
Pseudomonas syringae	Wild fire	Acetyl transferase gene	-	Tobacco
Alternaria longipes	Brownspot	Citinase gene	Serratia marcescens (soil bacterium)	Tobacco
Rhizoctonia solani		Chitinase gene	Bean	Tobacco
Phytophthora infestans	Late blight	Osmotin gene	Potato	Potato

GENETIC ENGINEERING AND PLANT LIPIDS

Plant lipids are major components of the human diet and are present in plants as storage oil. Engineered vegetable oils have been tested as field trials. A high stereate phenotype has been engineered in rapeseed by antisense approach. Stearoyl-acyl carrier protein (Stearoyl - ACP) desaturase is a chloroplast enzyme which catalyzes the first desaturation step in seed oil biosynthesis, converting stearoyl-ACP to oleayl-ACP.

This coding region of the gene for rapeseed desaturase was fused in an inverted position to the napin storage protein promoter and to the promoter of seed-specific acyl carrier protein gene, and then introduced into rapeseed. This reduced the activity of desaturase enzyme in engineered plant resulting in increased levels of stearate in seeds (upto 40% of the total fatty acids), with corresponding decrease in oleate. Due to tissue specific expression of antisense RNA, integrity of membrane lipids in leaf remained unaffected.

Length of fatty acids can be manipulated with thioesterase enzyme, which is responsible for the accumulation of short chain fatty acids in triglycerides. The gene has been cloned and expressed in developing seed of *Arabidopsis*, where it caused the accumulation of C12 storage lipids. It is useful for application in confectionery production.

The field of storage lipid modification via the engineering of the fatty acid biosynthesis enzymes promises to be a very fertile one that will contribute to production of healthier food and of chemical feed stocks.

GENETIC ENGINEERING AND STORAGE PROTEINS

Human nutrition requires a balanced source of amino acids and the amino acid balance of many plant products is unsatisfactory. Genetic engineering may be carried out in crops making following three approaches: (a) expressing a desirable and heterologous storage protein, (b) increasing the level of a desirable, but little expressed, endogenons protein and, (c) suppressing the expression of antinutritional proteins.

A heterologous species of sulphur-rich storage protein in Brazil nut containing 18% methionine and 8% cysteine has been expressed in tobacco and rapeseed. In transgenic tobacco, **phaseolin** gene has been expressed, leading to accumulation of methionine rich phaseolin.

Another approach for increasing amino acid synthesis is by engineering of a rate-limiting enzyme. For example, in a tobacco mutant lysine overproduction was caused by a lysine-insensitive **dehydro-picolinate synthase**. Forty fold increase in free lysine has been obtained by expression of a bacterial dehydropicolinate synthase in plant chloroplasts.

Genomic clones encoding two subunits of soybean **ß-conglycin** (7S protein) genes were transferred into petunia plants. The temporally regulated expression of these two genes in transgenic plants mimics their temporal regulation during soybean embryo development. The gene encoding for 42 kDa potato storage protein, **patatin** was introduced into tobacco. Stable synthesis of patatin protein was confirmed in the heterologons environment. Furthermore, transgenic tobacco possessing the 5' and 3' flanking sequences of the bean ß-phaseolin gene fused with 15 kDa *zein* gene could synthesize up to 1.6% of total seed protein as zein. Thus, zein is deposited and accumulates in vacuolar protein bodies of the tobacco embryo and endosperm.

GENETIC ENGINEERING FOR NITROGEN FIXATION

Transfer of Nif-Genes from *Klebsiella pneumoniae to E. coli*

Klebsiella pneumoniae is a non symbiotic nitrogen fixing bacterium. R.A. Dixon and

J.R. Postgate (1972) transferred nif-genes of *K. pneumoniae* into *E. coli* cells by conjugation. The transgene in the new host produced functional nitrogenase system. The nif-genes of *K. pneumoniae* have been introduced into several other organisms, *e.g. K. aerogenes*, *Salmonella typhimurium*, *Erwinia herbicola*, *Serratia marcescens*. These organisms are genetically modified and are now able to fix atmospheric nitrogen.

Transfer of *Nif*-Genes of Eukaryotic Organisms

Nif-genes from Rhizobium have been transferred to *Agrobacterium tumefaciens*. The expression of transferred gene has been successful in cereal crops like wheat, paddy etc. through the Ti-plasmids of *A. tumefaciens*.

Transfer of Nod-Genes to Increase Host Range

Cloned nod-genes of *Rhizobium leguminosarum* that nodulate pea have been transferred to *R. phaseoli* (this normally nodulates bean). The transformed *R. phaseoli* can now nodulate pea plants also.

Plants that Produce Plastic

Chris Somerville and coworkers have evolved a transgenic *Arabidopsis thaliana* to polyhydroxy butyrate (PHB). It is a natural and totally biodegradable plastic material. In future, plastic producing sugar beet and potatoes could also be produced. These scientists have isolated two genes from a bacterium *Alcligenes eutrophus* which produced PHB in nature and accumulates it as a coating. These two genes were inserted separately into two *A. thaliana* plants with the help of *Agrobacterium tumefaciens*.

MISCELLANEOUS APPLICATIONS

The knowledge of genetic engineering has been exploited in industries to deliver products and processes of economic and social value. Products of biotechnology include organisms and substances made by it that are consumed directly as such or serve as components for other industries. The actinomycetes or soil microorganisms that produce the plethora of miracle drugs - the **antibiotics** have also been added to the list. The new techniques permit harnessing of single cells to produce non-native gene products from exogenously supplied genes. Industrial use of single cells and enzymes for the production of stated products may require special tailoring of the cells for adaptation to mass-scale production processes.

The pharmaceutical and chemical industries were the first to exploit the gene engineering technology. A futuristic application is envisaged in the field named 'bioelectronics' or 'bionics'. The potential of biological material to serve as extra-sensitive conductors, sensors, and support matrices for semiconductor molecules is already being explored. The drugs and pharmaceuticals may be synthesized in heterologous cells or in animal cell lines that produce them. For instance, human chorionic gonadotropin (HCG), erythropoietin and calcitonin synthesizing cell lines have been reported. Of these, only HCG is successfully used for commercial production. The drugs and pharmaceuticals that are candidates for the genetic engineering are: (i) hormones, (ii) growth factors, (iii) blood-derived factors, (iv) enzymes, (v) antibiotics, (vi) immunoproteins, (vii) immunodiagnostics, and (viii) DNA probes for molecular diagnosis.

CHAPTER 4

Enzymes in Genetic Engineering (Nucleic Acid Enzymology)

Prior to 1970, there was simply no method available for cutting a duplex DNA molecule into discrete fragments. Discovery of DNA metabolizing enzymes allowed scientists to contemplate and initiate genetic engineering. All recombinant DNA research developed from the ability to *cut* DNA molecules at defined sequences. In other words, it was based upon the discovery of type II restriction enzymes. The isolation of the first enzymes (Hind II and Hind III) was a result of an interesting discovery by Ham Smith and his coworkers that *Hemophilis influenzae* extracts contained activities that cut large DNAs into defined fragments. It gave rise to Recombinant DNA research. In addition, an entire industry developed with the prime purpose being discovery, characterization, purification and marketing of over 100 different site-specific restriction enzymes.

The bringing together of DNA fragments to form covalently linked chimeric molecules is the basis of recombinant DNA research; it is crucial in genetic engineering. This is accomplished by ligation catalyzed by DNA ligase, an enzyme whose discovery predated that of restriction enzymes.

Before 1970 the existing dogma in molecular biology was that genetic information transfer occurred from DNA to RNA, and from DNA to RNA and then to protein. The proof that RNA-to-DNA information transfer did occur rested on the discovery and characterization of reverse transcriptase by Temin and Baltimore. Reverse transcriptase allows us to generate DNA copies (cDNA) of mRNA subsequent to cloning. The generation of cDNA, containing direct protein coding information is the usual step in cloning of eukaryotic genes.

Perhaps the most revolutionary and in many respects the most simplistic molecular biological technical development is PCR (polymerase chain reaction). PCR is a straightforward application of DNA polymerase to permit the test tube binomial amplification of specific DNA sequences. The discovery of type II restriction enzymes demonstrated the immense power and utility of site specific DNA cleavage reagents.

Several manufacturing processes in major industries are totally dependent of enzyme action (*e.g.* renin in cheese making). Enzyme from microbial, plant and animal sources are all of commercial importance.

The microbial enzymes are the most important in industrial purpose. Many bacilli produce the enzyme proteases which are mainly used in detergents. Proteases make meat and fish tender. Other important enzymes are as follow:

1. **Glucose Oxidase:** This converts glucose to gluconic acid which is an industrial chemical and is also used extensively in diagnostic test for measuring blood sugar.
2. **Renin**, used in cheese production.
3. **Papain**, an enzyme derived from papaya plant and added to animal feeds as a

meat tenderizer.

4. **Glucose isomerase** converts glucose to fructose
5. **Pepsin**, an animal protease used in the manufacturing industry.
6. **Urokinase** is used as an anti-thrombotic agent in treatment or pulmonary embolism.
7. **Asperaginase** used in cancer chemotherapy
8. **Tyrosine hydroxylase,** which converts tryosine into DOPA which is specific against Parkinson's disease.

STORAGE OF DNA AND HANDLING OF ENZYMES

DNA can be stored in TE buffer (pH 8.0) or in sterile distilled water at -20 °C. Frequent freezing and thawing of DNA should be avoided to prevent breaks and nicks.

Enzymes should be stored in their original packing in the freezer at –20 °C and should never be placed on the counter top except in an ice bucket for short 1-2 minute intervals when pipetting is to be carried out. The assay buffers are supplied along with enzymes by the manufacturers and should also be stored at -20°C. Sterile double distilled water should be used for dilution during the preparation of reaction mixtures (restriction endonucleases) or mastermixes (for PCR). Enzymes should be handled very carefully to avoid contamination. Separate, fresh sterile pipette tips should be used for each job.

RESTRICTION ENDONUCLEASES

The term restriction endonuclease was coined by Lederberg and Meselson (1964) to describe *the nuclease enzymes* that destroy (*restrict*) any foreign DNA entering the host cell. These enzymes have been classified into three different types *viz.*, Type I, Type II and Type III. In gene manipulation technology, restriction endonucleases are popularly called molecular knives or molecular scissors or molecular scalpels.

Types of Restriction Enzymes

- **Restriction Enzyme: Type I:** These enzymes interact with an unmodified recognition sequence in double strand DNA and then attach to long DNA molecule. After travelling far distance between 1000 to 5000 nucleotides the enzyme cleaves only one strand of the DNA at an apparently random site, and creates a gap of about 75 nucleotides in length. This kind of enzyme is not useful for gene manipulation, because their cleavage sites are non-specific. Type I enzymes bind to target sites, after which they are released from fully methylated sites, complete the methylation of hemimethylated sites, or move along DNA from non methylated sites to cleave the molecule elsewhere. Type 1 can simultaneously hold 2 different sites on DNA creating a loop in nucleic acid. The type I restriction enzyme consists of there types of subunit. The Eco K enzyme has the slreucliest R_2 M_2 S. The R subunit is responsible for restriction, the M subunit for methylallen and the S subunit, the enzyme's binding to DNA may be succeeded by either restriction or modification.
- **Restriction Enzyme: Type II:** These enzymes are used for gene manipulation studies and unlike Type I, they recognize a particular target sequence in a double-strand DNA molecule. They cleave the polynucleotide chain within, or near that sequence to give rise to discrete DNA fragments of *defined length* and

sequence. They require Mg^{2+} ions for restriction.

- **Restriction Enzyme Type III:** These enzymes cleave double stranded DNA at well defined sites. They require ATP, Mg^{2+} ions and have very partial requirement for S-adenosyl-methionine for restriction. They have intermediate properties between Type I and Type II.

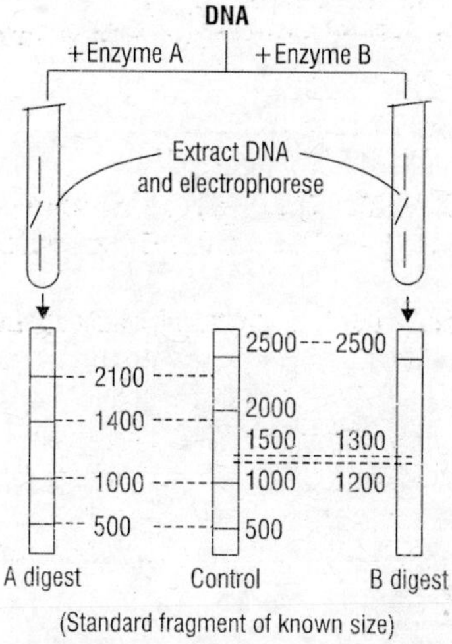

FIGURE 4.1: Clevage of DNA by two restriction endonucleases A and B into fragments which can be separated by agarose gel electrophoresis.

Naming of Restriction Endonucleases

About 350 restriction endonucleases have been isolated from more than 200 bacterial strains. Large number of these enzymes has called for a uniform nomenclature. A system based on the proposals of Smith and Nathans (1973) has been followed for the most part. This includes:

1. Each enzyme is named by a three-letter code.
2. The first letter of this code is derived from the first epithet of the genus name.
3. The second and the third letters are from the species name.
4. This is followed by the strain number. If a particular strain has more than one restriction enzyme, these will be identified by Roman numerals as I, II, III etc.
5. A general name endonuclease R may be added. For example, EcoRI enzyme is derived from E. coli carrying antibiotic resistance plasmid (RI).

Target Sites of Restriction Endonucleases

A restriction endonuclease enzyme of type II recognises a specific recognition site (base sequence) on the DNA and will make a cut at this site only. These target sites are 4 to 6 nucleotides long and exhibit palindromic symmetry (rotationally symmetrical), *i.e.* nucleotide pair sequences are same reading forward or backward from a central axis of symmetry, like the nonsense phrase *AND MADAM DNA*.

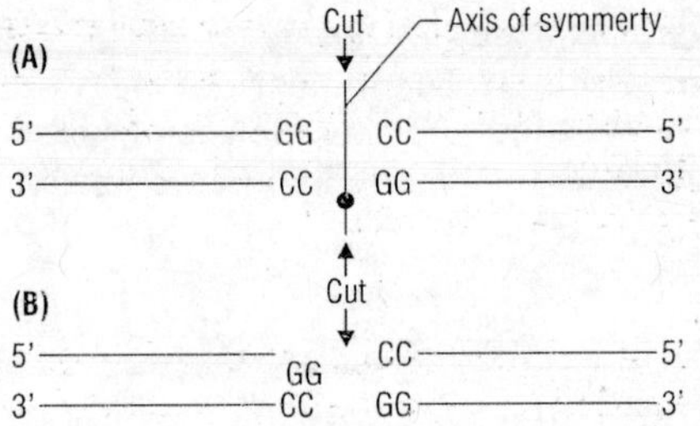

FIGURE 4.2: (A) The target site for RE Hae III. Arrows indicate the sites where the cuts will be effected. (B) The target site after the cut. As a result of this the ends are blunt, that is protruding unpaired bases.

TABLE 4.1: Recognition sites for some restriction enzymes

Microorganisms	**Enzyme**	**Recognition sequence and recognition site**
Acetobacter aceti	Aat II	GACGT↓C
Bacillus caldolyticus	Bcl I	T↓GATCA
Chromatium vinosum	Cvn I (Sau I)	CC↓TNAGG
Escherichia coli RY 13	Eco RI	G↓AATTC
Escherichia coli R 245	Eco RII	↓CC (A/T) GG
Haemophilus influenzae Rd	Hind II Hind III	GTPy↓PuAC A↓AGCTT
Klebsiella pneumoniae OK 8	Kpn I	GGTAC↓C
Nocardia opaca	Nop I (Sal I)	G↓TCGAC
Nostoc	Nsp BII	C(A/C) G↓C(T/G) G
Streptococcus faecalis	Sfa I (Hae III)	GG↓CC
Streptomyces albus	Sal PP (Pst I)	GTGCA↓G
Streptomyces albus	Sal I	G↓TCGAC
Xanthomonas oryzae	Xor II (Pvu I)	CGAT↓CG
Xanthomonas badrii	Xba I	T↓CTAGA

Note: Recognition sequences are written from 9-3', only one strand being given, and the recognition site is indicated by an arrow. Bases within parentheses signify that either base may occupy that position.

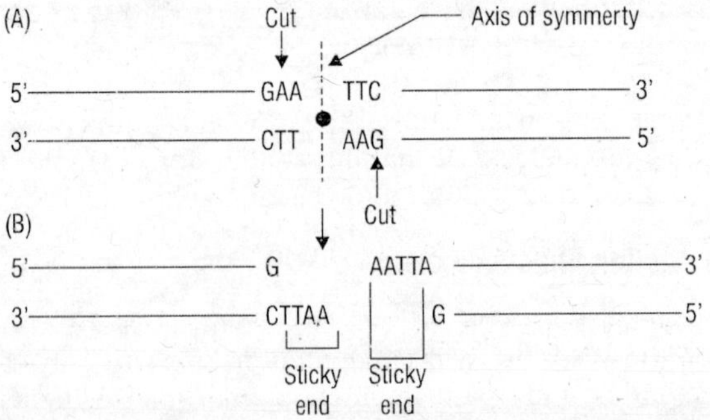

FIGURE 4.3: A. Diagram showing the recognition site of the restriction endonuclease EcoRI. This enzyme makes a cut in the sugar - phosphate back bone between the nucleotides with bases guanine and adenine on both the polynucleotide strands (shown by arrows). This leads to the formation of DNA fragments with sticky ends (B).

The term *palindromic* has also been applied to sequences such as 5'-AGCCGA-3'-TCGGCT- which are palindromic within one strands. X-ray crystallography of enzyme-DNA complex suggests that endonuclease acts as a dimer of identical sub units and that the palindromic nature of target sequence reflects the two fold rotational symmetry of the dimeric protein.

Nature of the Cut Ends

The restriction enzymes cut DNA molecules by cleavage, this action occurs in in two styles, (i) blunt-end style and (ii) sticky-or cohesive-end style.

Enzyme	Recognition site	Cleavage product
Hae III	-GG↓CC-	-GG CC-
Sma I	-CC↑GG-	-CC GG-
Sma I	-CCC↓GGG-	-CCC GGG-
	-GGG↑CCC-	-GGG CCC-

Blunt-end Style: Certain restriction endonucleases (*e.g.* Hae III, Sma I) make cuts across both strands of DNA at the same position. The utility of this style during the joining of DNA fragments is that any pair of ends may join together, irrespective of sequence. This is especially useful for those researchers who are interested to join two defined sequences without introducing any additional material between them. Following Table presents blunt-end restriction sites.

Enzyme	Recognition Site	Cleavage Product
Eco RI	-G↓AATTC- -CTTAA↑G-	-G AATTC- -CTTAA G-
Hind III	-A↓AGCTT- -TTCGA↑A-	-A AGCTT- -TTCGA A-

Sticky- or Cohesive-end Style: In this style the restriction enzymes (*e.g.* Eco RI, Bam HI, Hind III) make single-strand cut some nucleotide pairs apart in the opposite strands of DNA, and so generate fragments with protruding termini (ends). These DNA fragments can associate by hydrogen bonding between overlapping termini, or the fragments can circularize by intramolecular reaction, and for this reason the fragments are said to have sticky-or cohesive-ends.

Host Controlled Restriction and Modification

Certain strains of bacteria are immune to bacteriophages. This is called **host controlled restriction**. The restriction is due to these restriction endonuclease enzymes which could recognise and split specific loci in the foreign DNA. Thus these enzymes prevent or restrict the survival of foreign DNA in the host. This is analogous to an immune system.

All restriction sites in host chromosome of a bacterium is protected from its own restriction endonuclease due to a modification system. This helps in preventing suicidal self-degradation. Such modification occurs by methylation of specific bases in the recognition sequence of the endonuclease. The enzymes involved in such modification are called **methyltransferases**. These enzymes methylate adenine (add a methyl group) in the N-6 position and cytosine either in the N-5 or N-4 position and produce N-6 methyl adenine and 5 or 4 -methyl cytosine respectively. Unmodified foreign DNA entering the cell is degraded by the host restriction system. As both enzymes, methyltransferases and endonucleases recognise the restriction site, they are together called *restriction* and *modification system.*

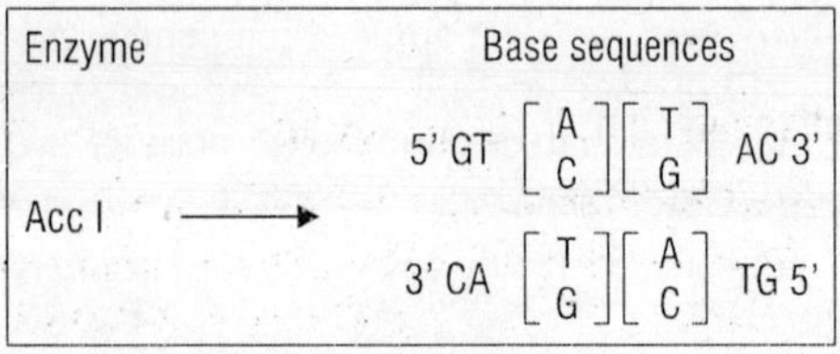

Above enzyme is isolated from Acetobacter alcoaceticus

Star Activity

Star activity is exhibited by several restriction endonucleases where they show relaxation in specificity of sequence under non-optimal conditions. In such condition, endonucleases even recognize other alternative base instead of a specific base.

Non ideal ionic strength buffers, high glycerol concentration (more than 5% v/v) and high enzyme concentration have been shown to alter the DNA recognition sequence for several endonuclease enzymes.

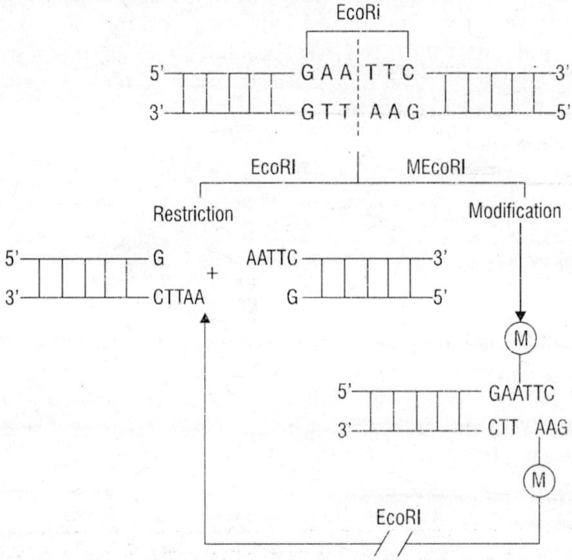

FIGURE 4.4: EcoRI restriction and modification system m=methyl group.

Isoschizomers

Isoschizomers are restriction enzymes which are isolated from different organisms but recognise identical base sequences in the DNA. For example, Asp 718 and Kpn I have identical recognition sites:

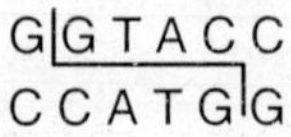

Source of Asp 718 is Achromobacter species 718, *Source* of Kpn I is Klebsiella pneumoniae OK 8

Some pairs of isoschizomers cut their target at different places (*e.g.* Sma I, Xma

D).

Restriction Endonucleases in Genetic Engineering

In gene cloning experiments DNA molecules have to be cut in a very precise and reproducible fashion. Thus, endonucleases play an important role in cutting the desired gene as well as cleaving the vector. The required DNA fragment from a large DNA molecule should be cleaved in a precise manner for further genetic manipulations. A particular restriction endonuclease can recognise and bind to specific base sequence of the DNA and then will cleave it. It is highly reproducible and can be programmed according to DNA sequences of required gene and particular endonuclease identifying and cleaving it.

Cutting the Vectors

The function of a vector DNA molecule is to carry a gene of interest to a second organism where it can express itself. During this process the DNA to be cloned is integrated with the plasmid. Hence each vector molecule should be cleaved with same restriction site at a single position to open the circular form so that the new DNA can be inserted at these complementary sites.

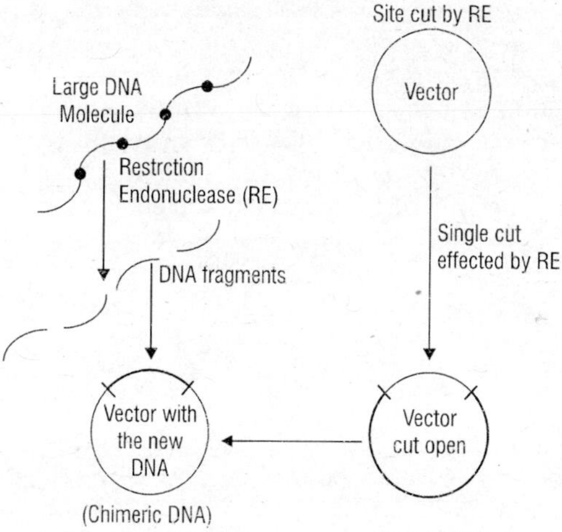

FIGURE 4.5: Diagram to explain the need for restriction endonucleases (RE) in the gene cloning experiments. The vector and the large DNA molecule are cut by the same RE.

If foreign DNA is introduced into *E. coli* host, it may be attacked by restriction systems active in the host cell. Because restriction provides a natural defence against invasion by foreign DNA, it is usual to employ a K restriction deficient *E. coli* K12 strain as a host in transformation with newly created recombinant molecules. This will eliminate the possibility that the in coming sequence will be restricted.

LIGASES

Although cutting DNA precisely is very useful for DNA analysis, its full potential is only revealed when *the fragments produced are joined together to give a new structure, known as recombinant DNA*. This joining, or *ligation* is achieved by the use of a DNA ligase enzyme. The most common ligase is isolated from the bacterial virus (T4 phage). Thus DNA ligases is a group of enzymes which mediate annealing, sealing or joining of DNA fragments. Primarily, these enzymes are involved in the repair of DNA where sealing or union of DNA fragments takes place. DNA ligases also play active part in processes like DNA replication and recombination. These enzymes are widely used in genetic engineering for the production of hybrid DNA. Since ligases join DNA fragments or seal the nicks chain, they are called molecular sutures.

Activity of Ligases

If two different DNA preparations are treated with the same restriction enzyme to give fragments with sticky ends, these ends will be identical in both preparations. Thus, when the two sets of fragments are mixed, base pairing between sticky ends will result in the coming together of fragments which were derived from different molecules. There will, of course, also be pairing of fragments derived from the same molecule. Such pairings are transient, owing to the weakness of hydrogen bonding between the few bases in the sticky ends, but they can be stabilised by the use of DNA ligase, which forms a covalent bond between the 5'-phosphoryl at the end of one strand and the 3'-hydroxyl of the adjacent strand. T4 polynucleotide ligase catalyzes the end to end joining of DNA duplexes at the base paired end. This reaction could occur intermolecularly or intramolecularly. Researches confirm that intermolecular mode is correct.

The ligation reaction, which is *driven by ATP*, is often carried out at 4 °C to lower the kinetic energy of molecules. This reduces separation of paired sticky end and are later stabilised by ligation. However, long reaction times are needed to compensate for the low activity of DNA ligase in the cold.

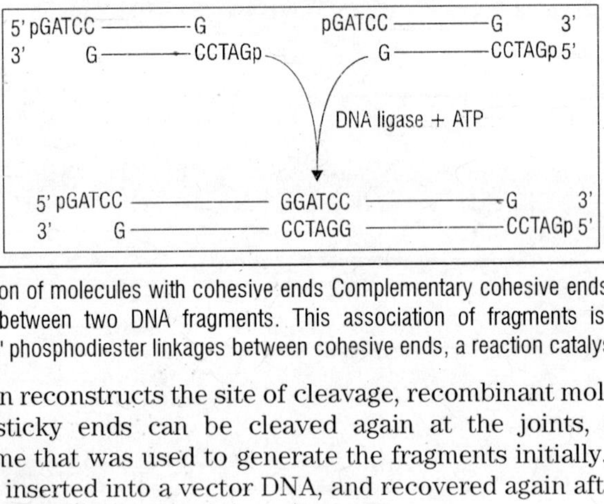

FIGURE 4.6: Ligation of molecules with cohesive ends Complementary cohesive ends basepair, forming a temporary link between two DNA fragments. This association of fragments is stabilised by the formation of 3' to 5' phosphodiester linkages between cohesive ends, a reaction catalysed by DNA ligase.

Since ligation reconstructs the site of cleavage, recombinant molecules produced by ligation of sticky ends can be cleaved again at the joints, using the same restriction enzyme that was used to generate the fragments initially. Consequently a fragment can be inserted into a vector DNA, and recovered again after cloning of the recombinant molecule.

Blunt-Ended Ligation

Lengths of blunt-ended DNA can be ligated, but, since there is no base-pairing to hold fragments together temporarily, concentrations of DNA and ligase must be high. However, blunt-ended ligation is a useful way of joining together DNA fragments which have not been produced by the same restriction enzyme, and which therefore, probably have incompatible sticky ends. These ends are removed prior to ligation, using the enzyme *S1 nuclease*, which digests single-stranded DNA.

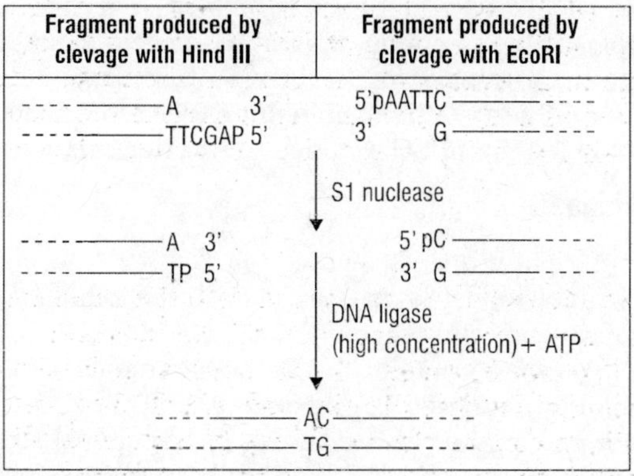

FIGURE 4.7: Production and ligation of blunt ends. Different blunt-ended fragments cannot be held together temporarily by base-pairing between cohesive ends, and so both DNA and ligase must be used at high concentrations to increase the chances of two DNA fragments occupying the ligase active site simultaneously.

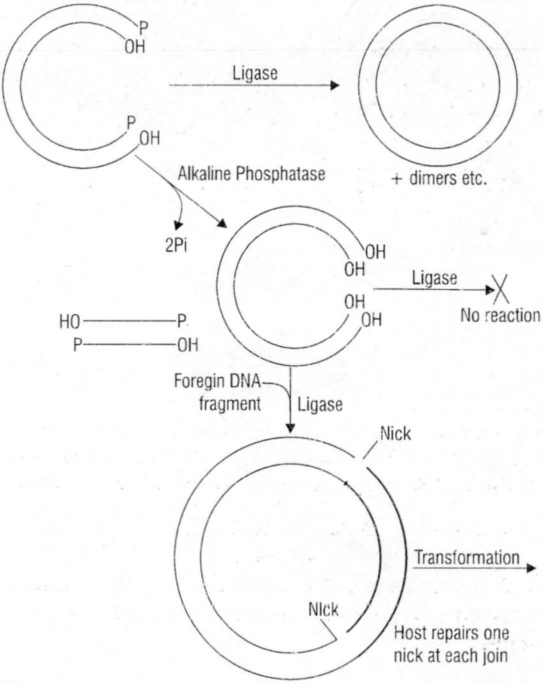

FIGURE 4.8: Application of alkaline phosphatase treatment to prevent recircularization of vector plasmid without insertion of foreign DNA.

Source of DNA Ligases

DNA ligases are isolated from *E. coli* and phage T4. The enzyme isolated from *E. coli* is a polypeptide chain with a molecular weight of 75 kDa. It needs NAD^+ as cofactor. The ligase obtained from T4 bacteriophage is 68 kDa. It requires ATP as a cofactor and a source of energy. For routine laboratory requirement, T4 DNA ligase is obtained from an induced lysogen of lambda T4 lig phage. This enzyme has the capacity to ligate a variety of cohesive and blunt ended DNA fragments. The enzyme concentration is kept higher and PEG is added to reaction mixture for stimulation.

Applications of DNA Ligases

1. Genetic engineering experiments involve joining of DNA fragments to produce recombinant DNA molecules. Ligases are used in the joining process.
2. Ligation of vector and inserting recombinant DNA.
3. Ligation of linkers or adapter molecules at the blunt ends of DNA fragment.
4. Sealing nicks in double stranded DNA.

Ligase requires 3'-OH and $5'\text{-}PO_4^{3-}$ group for ligation. This requirement can be advantageous as:

- Self ligation of DNA can be prevented by dephosphorylation (using alkaline phosphatase) of intended donor fragments prior to ligation.
- Dephosphorylation of vector DNA will prevent recircularization of the vector in cloning procedure.

ALKALINE PHOSPHATASE

Alkaline phosphatase catalyses the removal of the 5'-terminal phosphate residues from nucleic acids (RNA, DNA and ribo-and deoxyribonucleotide triphosphates). This enzyme is a dimeric glycoprotein with a molecular weight 14,000. It is made up of two identical or similar subunits each with a molecular weight of 69,000. It is a zinc containing enzyme with four atoms of Zn^{2+} per molecule.

Applications of Alkaline Phosphatase

1. Linearized cloning vectors can be prevented from recircularizing by dephosphorylation with alkaline phosphatase.
2. The free 5'-OH can be phosphorylated with polynucleotide kinase and $\Upsilon\text{-}^{32}P$ ATP to produce ^{32}P end labelled nucleic acids.
3. Enzyme is used for mapping and finger printing studies.

POLYNUCLEOTIDE KINASE

Polynecleotide kinase catalyses the transfer of the terminal phosphate group of ATP to the 5'-hydroxylated terminal of DNA or RNA. This enzyme is frequently used to end-label nucleic acids with ^{32}P. This can be accomplished by any method among following:

1. Forward Reaction: Transfer of labelled ϒ-phosphate from [$\Upsilon\text{-}^{32}P$] -ATP to the free 5'-hydroxyl group of substrate.

$$5'\ OH\text{-}DNA^{+}\ [\Upsilon\text{-}^{32}P]\ ATP\ 5'\ ^{32\rightarrow}PO\text{-}DNA + ADP$$

2. Substrates that do not have a free 5'-hydroxyl requires prior dephosphorylation by alkaline phosphatase.
3. Exchange Reaction: First, the terminal 5'-phosphate is transferred from substrate to ADP present in the reaction mixture. Then, the labelled ϒ-phosphate from [ϒ-

^{32}P]-ATP is transferred to free hydroxyl group of substrate.

$$5'\text{-PO-DNA} + \text{ADP} \rightarrow 5'\ \text{HO-DNA} + \text{ATP}$$

$$5'\text{-HO-DNA} + [\Upsilon\text{-}^{32}\text{P}]\text{-ATP} \rightarrow 5'^{32}\text{PO-DNA} + \text{ADP}$$

Applications of Polynucleotide Kinase

Polynucleotide kinase is used to label 5'-termini of DNA and RNA with [Υ^{32}P] ATP by phosphorylation of 5'-hydroxyl groups or by the exchange reaction. This 5'-terminal labelling is used in mapping of restriction sites, DNA or RNA fingerprinting, hybridization studies and sequence analysis of DNA.

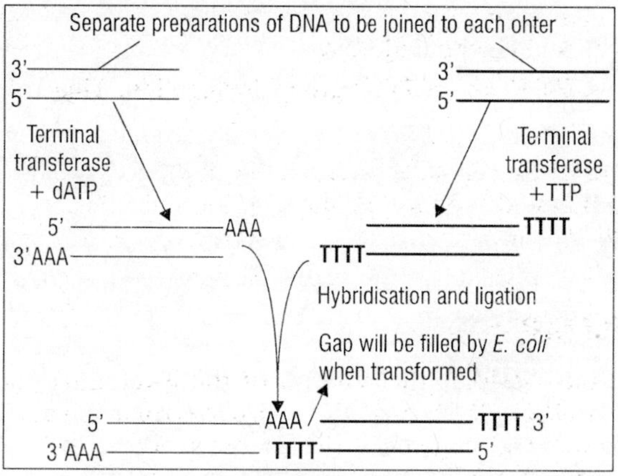

FIGURE 4.9: Homopolymer tailing. One DNA preparation is given poly (dA) tails at its 3' ends, the other receives poly (T) tails. These tails will hybridise with each other when the two preparations are mixed, and ligation can be used to stabilise this association. If the tails are long enough, hybridisation will be so stable that ligation is not needed.

TERMINAL DEOXYNUCLEOTIDYL TRANSFERASE

Terminal deoxynucleotidyl transferase catalyses the repetitive addition of mononucleotide units from a deoxynucleoside triphosphate to the terminal 3'-hydroxyl group of a DNA molecule. This enzyme has a molecular weight of 32000 and consists of two subunits each with a molecular weight of 26500 and 8000. The enzyme is purified from calf thymus.

Application of Terminal Transferase

1. Terminal transferase is used to add homopolymer tails to DNA fragments. Using a technique called homopolymer tailing, sticky ends can be built up on blunt-ended molecules. For example, one preparation of DNA could be treated with the enzyme terminal transferase in the presence of dATP, resulting in the addition of a poly (dA) chain to the 3 end of each strand. The other preparation would then be given 3'tails of poly (T), using the same enzyme with TTP. On mixing, there would be base pairing between complementary sticky ends, which could then be ligated. An attractive feature of this method is that ligation will not occur between fragments from the same preparation.
2. It is used for 3'-end labelling of DNA fragments.

3. Terminal transferase can also be used for addition of single nucleotides to the 3'ends of DNA for in vitro mutagenesis.

Purine and pyrimidine polymerization rates, by using this enzyme, depend on the inclusion of Mg^{2+}, Mn^{2+} or Co^{2+} in the reaction mixture.

S1 NUCLEASE

S1 Nuclease is a single strand specific endonuclease which cleaves DNA to release 5'-mono and 5'-oligo nucleotides. Double stranded DNA, double stranded RNA and DNA-RNA hybrids are resistant, however, very large amounts of enzyme can completely hydrolyze double stranded nucleic acids. The enzyme *hydrolyzes single stranded regions* in duplex DNA such as *loops and gaps*. S1 nuclease can also cleave single stranded areas of superhelical DNA at torsional stress points where DNA may be unpaired or weakly hydrogen bonded. Once the superhelical DNA is nicked, S1 can cleave the second strand near the nick to generate linear DNA. The enzyme is a monomeric protein with 3800 daltons molecular weight. It requires Zn^{2+} for its activity, and is relatively stable against denaturing reagents such as urea, SDS and formamide. The optimum pH required lies between 4-4.5

Applications of S1 Nuclease

1. S1 nuclease is used to analyse DNA-RNA hybrid structures to map transcripts.
2. It can be used to remove single stranded tails from DNA fragments to produce blunt ends.
3. Hairpin loop structures formed during synthesis of double stranded cDNA is digested by this enzyme.
4. It is also used for DNA mapping.

DNA POLYMERASE I, HOLOENZYME

It has 5' exonuclease activity in addition to DNA synthesis. This bifunctional activity enables the enzyme to use nicks or gaps in double stranded DNA as a starting point for DNA synthesis. The 5'-exonuclease activity degrades that DNA strand which is complementary to the template strand and thus forming nick. DNA synthesis begins at 3'-end of nick and produces a new strand of DNA complementary to the template. The net result is the movement of nick along the template strand (nick translation) until all the DNA complementary to the template strand (starting from the site of the origin of nick to the 5'-end of the template strand) is replaced.

Applications of DNA Poly I

1. Enzyme is used with radioactive or biotinylated nucleotides to prepare labelled DNA of high specific activity.
2. DNA polymerase can also catalyze de novo DNA synthesis.

DNA POLYMERASE I, KLENOW FRAGMENT

Treatment of DNA polymerase I holoenzyme with protease results in production of two proteins fragments. The larger fragment is also known as Klenow fragment does not exhibits 5'-exonuclease activity (5'-exonuclease activity is exhibited by intact enzyme). This Klenow fragment is used to synthesize DNA when there is no need of removing the DNA strand, which is complementary to the template strand.

Applications of Klenow Fragment

1. In DNA sequencing by dideoxy-method.
2. For production of second strand of cDNA.
3. Radiolabelling by filling in 5'-single stranded extension on double stranded DNA.
4. Mutagenesis of DNA with synthetic oligonucleotides.
5. In labelling the DNA by random primer method.

T4 DNA POLYMERASE

T4 DNA polymerase lacks 5' exonuclease activity but has a very active 3'-exonuclease action. This allows radiolabelling of DNA fragment by replacement synthesis. In this method it acts on both the 3'-end of double stranded DNA resulting in long 5'-single stranded extensions. DNA complementary to these single strands are synthesized with deoxynucleoside triphosphase enzyme in the presence of radiolabelled compounds.

Applications of T4 DNA Polymerase

1. Useful in generating 5'-single stranded ends.
2. The enzyme can also be used in radiolabelling of DNA.

Taq DNA Polymerase

Taq DNA polymerase is isolated from the thermophilic bacterium *Thermus aquaticus*. This enzyme has the highest DNA polymerase activity at a pH of 9 and temperature around 75 °C. DNA polymerase activity is resistant to incubation at high temperatures like 95 °C. This enzyme consists of a single polypeptide chain with a molecular weight of 95,000. It lacks 5'to 3' and 3'to 5' exonuclease activities. The highly thermostable DNA polymerase from *Thermus aquaticus* (Taq) is ideal for both manual and automated DNA sequencing because it is fast, highly progressive, has little or no 3'- exonuclease activity and is active over a broad range of temperatures.

Applications of Taq Polymerase

1. It can be used in DNA sequencing studies.
2. It is used in 'Polymerase chain reaction (PCR)' as it can withstand high temperatures.

Ribonuclease (RNAse H)

RNase H is an endonuclease that degrades the RNA portion of the RNA - DNA hybrids.

Applications of RNAse H

1. RNase H is the key enzyme in the cDNA cloning procedure. Here it is used to remove the mRNA from the RNA - DNA hybrid.
2. Used to detect the presence of RNA-DNA hybrids.
3. Used to remove poly (A) tails on mRNA.

REVERSE TRANSCRIPTASE

Reverse transcriptase is an enzyme isolated from Avian myeloblastosis virus (AMV). It is an RNA-dependent DNA polymerase. This enzyme requires DNA primer complementary to the RNA template, as well as, presence of Mg or Mn for initiation of transcription. Reverse transcriptase mediates the conversion of genetic information present in single stranded molecule of RNA into a double stranded molecule of DNA. This enzyme has two sub units. The enzymatically active forms of the purified enzyme are α, ß and α.ß. The molecular weight of the α subunit is 68,000 and that of ß-subunit is 92,000. The mature α.ß form is the most active form of AMV reverse transcriptase. It has several enzymatic activities such: as RNA-directed DNA polymerase, DNA-dependent DNA polymerase and RNase-H activity.

The α-subunit contains the polymerase activity. It also has the RNase H activity which has the ability to degrade the RNA in DNA : RNA hybrids. This exonucleolytic activity of RNase-H can proceed either from the 5'- or the 3 terminus.

Applications of Reverse Transcriptase

1. The in vitro synthesis of cDNA from mRNA and other RNA molecule using reverse transcriptases has become a very important tool in molecular genetic. Moreover reverse transcriptase also contains a DNA-dependent DNA polymerase activity. This activity is responsible for second-strand formation in cDNA synthesis when this enzyme is used as a polymersing agent. This activity is inhibited by the addition of actinomycin-D.
2. Reverse transcriptase mediates the conversion of genetic information present in single stranded molecule of RNA into a double -stranded molecule of DNA.

Poly (A) Polymerase

Poly (A) polymerase plays an important role in *in vitro* gene manipulation techniques as it catalyzes the addition of AMP units to the 3'end of RNA.

Deoxyribonuclease I

Deoxyribonuclease I (DNase I) is an endonuclease which digest either single or double stranded DNA, producing a mixture of mono - and oligonucleotides. DNase I hydrolyzes each strand of double-stranded DNA independently and at random. Addition of Mg^{2+} ensures random cleavage while Mn^{2+} gives cleavage nearly at the same place on both strands. The enzyme is derives mostly from bovine pancreas.

Applications of DNAse I

1. This enzyme is useful for a variety of applications including nick translation, DNA footprinting, bisulfite mediated mutagenesis and RNA purification.
2. Several enzymes are today commercially available for gene cloning experiments.
3. These enzymes have enabled the scientist to design and engineer the gene and thus produce desired specification.

CHAPTER 5

Gene Cloning Vectors

Genetic engineering can be defined as transfer of DNA between hosts (or species) by *in vitro* enzymatic manipulations. This implies that the DNA to be transferred will be duplicated in the new host. Since most DNA fragments are incapable of self-replication in *E. coli* or any other host cell, an additional segment of DNA, capable of autonomous replication, must be linked to the fragment to be cloned. This autonomously replicating fragment is the **molecular cloning vector** and, by definition, plays a central role in recombinant DNA technology. Most cloning vectors were originally derived from naturally occurring extrachromosomal elements such as bacteriophage and plasmids.

Stanley Cohen and co-workers first reported the use of bacterial plasmids as molecular cloning vectors. Since that initial report thousands of cloning vectors have been constructed, and their versatility in terms of cloning sites, host-range, and function appears to be limited only by the ingenuity and imagination of the inventor. Whereas insertion of foreign DNA fragments into pSC101 was limited to a single restriction enzyme cleavage site and to *E. coli* as a host, most vectors currently in use carry multiple restriction-enzyme cleavage sites and have been modified for use with most common laboratory microorganisms. Many vectors now include dual origins of replication that enable them to be shuttled between hosts as dissimilar as *E. coli* and human cells.

Specialized vectors are now available that enable the investigator to; (1) identify and isolate regulatory DNA sequences such as promoters and terminators; (2) identify open translational reading frames; (3) overproduce useful RNAs and proteins; and (4) determine the nucleotide sequence of genes and segments of DNA. Primarily, a cloning vector is necessary as carriers of the cloned gene. Without a vector, a DNA molecule introduced into a cell would be diluted out by cell division and eventually lost.

There are a number of features common to all cloning vectors as:

1. The vector must be able to replicate in the host cell. Thus, it must have a replication origin. Replication origin is a sequence element which is recognized by the host cell's replication machinery and hence the vector can be amplified in the host cell.
2. Vector must contain a selectable marker for identification and isolation of subpopulation of bacteria containing vector. Actually, efficiency of transformation is very low and only or minority of cells in the population take up and retain the exogenous DNA. Marker in vector helps in identifying transformed bacterial colony.
3. Most commonly used vectors contain a short DNA sequence with many closely placed restriction enzyme cleavage sites. It is known as multicloning site (MCS) or polylinkers. These MCS can also be chemically synthesized in a vector and are very helpful during foreign gene insertion. Any two sites within an MCS can be simultaneously cleaved with the help of range of restriction enzymes and that too without excising the vector sequences.

PLASMIDS

A *plasmid* is a *replicon* (unit of genetic material capable of independent replication) that is *stably inherited* (maintained without specific selection) *in an extrachromosomal state*. Most of the plasmids are not required for the survival of in which they reside. In many cases, however, they are essential under certain environment, such as in the presence of an antibiotic such as chloromphenical, ampicillin, tetracycline,

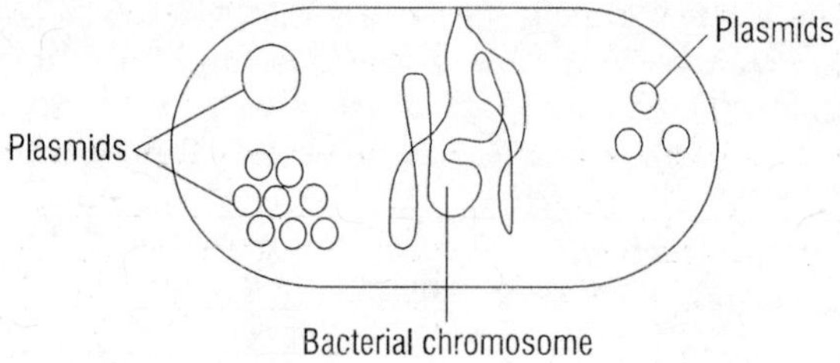

FIGURE 5.1: Bacterium showing chromosome and plasmids.

kanamycin etc. In *Rhizobium leguminosarum*, the genes for nitrogen fixation and nodule formations are located in plasmid.

Replication of Plasmids

The independent replication of plasmids is due to the presence of certain sequences acting as the origin of replication. The smaller plasmids use the DNA replicative enzymes of the host cells. Larger plasmids carry genes that code for special enzymes necessary for their replication. Under certain conditions, some plasmids may integrate into the bacterial chromosome. They are called episomes or integrative plasmids. At this stage they replicate along with the bacterial chromosome.

TABLE 5.1: Various sizes of some plasmids

Plasmids	Size (Nucleotide length in kb)	Organism
pBR345	0.7	E. coli
pBR 322	4.363	E. coli
Col E1	6.36	E. coli
F	95	E. coli
TOL	117	Pseudomonas putida
pTiAch 5	213	Agrobacterium tumefaciens

Size of Plasmids

The size of the plasmid varies from less than 1.0 kb to more than 200 kb. Smaller plasmids are much desirable for gene cloning experiments. Larger plasmids are less in number whereas smaller ones are more in number.

Copy Number

The number of molecules of a plasmid found in a single bacterial cell is termed as copy number. It ranges from 1 to more than 50 per cell but this number is specific for a given plasmid residing in bacterial cell.

Amplification of the Plasmid

The copy number of a plasmid can be increased manifold. This process is called **amplification** of the plasmid DNA. This property is exploited to increase the plasmid copy number. When the bacterial culture is at its exponential phase chloramphenicol is added to the medium. This arrest chromosomal DNA replication (and cell division). The culture is then incubated for another 12 hrs for the plasmid molecules to replicate. This increases the number of plasmids per cell. Sometimes the plasmid copy numbers may reach to several thousand.

Types of Plasmids

Plasmids can be categorized on the basis of number of copies per cell as,

1. Relaxed plasmids, which are normally maintained at multiple copies per cell, and
2. Stringent plasmids, which have a limited number of copies per cell.

Plasmids with larger copy number are more useful for gene cloning experiments.

Plasmids can also be classified as conjugative and non conjugative plasmids, depending on whether or not they carry a set of transfer gene called the ***tra*** genes. These ***tra*** genes promote bacterial conjugation. Generally conjugative plasmids are of high molecular weight and are present as 1-3 copies per cell, whereas non-conjugative plasmids have low molecular weight and are present in multiple copies, *i.e.*, 20-25 copies per cell.

Isolation of Plasmid DNA

Plasmids which are very common in bacteria are not so common in eukaryotic organisms. The best known eukaryotic plasmid is the 2μ circle that occurs in many strains of the Yeast, *Saccharomyces cerevisiae*.

Gene cloning and related experiment require pure plasmid DNA. Various methods have been used for the purification of plasmids. Usually these methods involve following main steps:

1. Growth of bacterial and plasmid amplification.
2. Breaking the bacterial cells to release their contents.
3. Treatment of bacterial cell extracts to remove all components except the DNA.
4. Separation of Plasmid DNA from the chromosomal DNA.

The bacterial strain containing required plasmid is grown usually on LB medium (Luria Bertani medium). LB medium contains trypton (10 g/l), yeast extract (5 g/l) and sodium chloride (10 g/l) and pH of the medium is adjusted to 7.5. Late long cultures are then transferred to LB medium containing appropriate antibiotic with small amount of chloromphenical for 12-16 hours incubation.

Isolation of DNA from such bacteria culture can be done by very gentle cell lysis, using lysozyme and then detergent, followed by clearing the lysate by centrifugation. Centrifugation sediments (the high molecular weight DNA - predominantly chromosomal) and cell debris leave small plasmid molecules and RNA in supernatent. Undamaged plasmid is particularly compact, since it is supercoiled as a consequence of having slightly too few turns of double helix per unit length. Further purification of the plasmid can be achieved by **caesium chloride density gradient ultracentrifugation** of the nucleic acid preparation in presences of ethidium bromide. Ethidium bromide causes unwinding of DNA as it binds to it, simultaneously producing a decrease in its buoyant density. Since supercoiled plasmid DNA can unwind to only a very limited extent, it will not bind the dye and have a higher density than other types of DNA (latter binds to dye). Because of this density difference, plasmid DNA can be separated from other DNA by isopycnic ultracentrifuge

Criteria for Plasmid Cloning

The following criteria are used to design an ideal cloning vector:

1. A plasmid vector should be small and should contribute as little as possible to the overall size of the recombinant molecule. Low molecular weight (small) plasmids are easy to handle, present in multiple copies and do not get damaged during isolation.
2. It should be well characterized with respect to gene number, location and should contain single cleavage sites for a large number of restriction endonucleases located in one or the other genetic marker. During insertion of a foreign DNA into plasmid vector, latter should be linearized (thus single cleavage site should be present). Presence of more than one site will break the plasmid into two or more fragment, which is avoided.
3. The plasmid should have the ability to confer readily selectable markers (phenotypic trait) on the host cells that can be used to distinguish the transformed cells from the non-transformed ones.
4. The plasmids should be easily propagated in the desired host so that the number of recombinant DNA molecule can be amplified.
5. It should have a large number of copies.
6. A plasmid vector should have an additional genetic marker that can be inactivated by insertion of the foreign DNA, so that the inactivated gene may help in distinguishing the cells harbouring recombinant molecules on the basis of a readily altered phenotype.

These properties provide maximum flexibility in terms of cloning different types of restriction fragments. In addition to these properties one should also keep in mind following characters when designing future molecular cloning vectors.

1. The vector should use, whenever possible, dominant genetic markers that can be expressed in a wide range of hosts. Cm^R (dominant genetic marker) do not restrict the vector to a particular genetic background. Covenient and quantitative assays for all vector markers should also be available.
2. Partitioning sequences such as par or cer should also be incorporated into the vector to ensure efficient segregation of plasmids to the daughter cells.
3. Incorporating a mechanism for controlling vector copy number will greatly increase the versatility of the vector. Plasmid vectors in which the RNAI (inhibitor) transcript is placed under the control of an inducible promoter are available. With these vectors, plasmid copy number can be lowered when RNAI is induced.
4. Since a number of recombinant DNA techniques require single strands of DNA, a vector with single-strand synthesis capability is desirable. This can be most easily achieved by incorporating the fd, f1, or M13 origin of replication along with the vector origin.
5. Because of its simplicity, a positive (direct) selection scheme for recombinant transformants is more desirable than the commonly used insertional inactivation method. The latter process usually requires the screening of large numbers of

clones to identify a few recombinant molecules.

CLONING VECTORS BASED ON BACTERIAL PLASMIDS

Bacteria are the common source of plasmids. For the sole purpose of cloning experiments, new plasmids with specific features are constructed *in vitro*. Such artificial plasmids are superior and efficient. The most popular plasmid vector thus obtained is pBR 322.

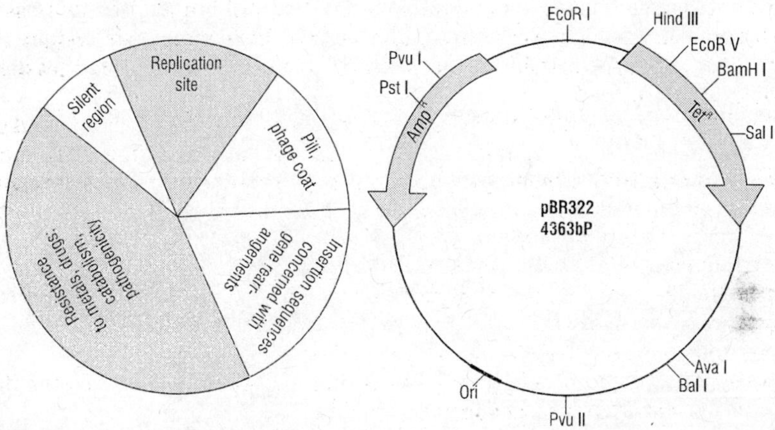

FIGURE 5.2: The plasmid pBR322 amp^R and tet^R are genes for resistance to ampicillin and tetracycline, respectively; ori is the origin of DNA replication. Some unique sites of cleavage by a selection of restriction endonucleases are indicated (*e.g.*, *EcoR* I, *Cla* I).

Plasmid pBR322

pBR322 is an artificial plasmid, which is regarded as the 'work house' of gene cloning laboratory. Its DNA is derived from there different but naturally occurring plasmids. The DNA sequence of entire plasmid has been mapped and published.

Size of pBR322	2.9 M Da or 4363 bp
Prepared from	E. coli strain RRI
Unique sites	Within the gene: Ampicillin resistance: Pst I, Pru I, Sca I Tetracycline resistance: Bam HI, Bsp MI, Eco RV. Nhel, Nru I, Sal I, Sph I, Xma III
Other unique sites	Aat II, Ava I, Bal I, Bsm I, Bsp M II, Cla I, E co RI, Hind III, Nde I, Pvu II, Ssp I, Sty I, Tth 111 I.

pBR322 has restriction sites for over 20 restriction endonucleases and it contains genes that give resistance against antibiotic ampicillin (Amp^R) and tetracyclive (Tet^R). Hence cloning in pBR322 at any of the sites within these two genes will result in insertional inactivation of either of these genes.

Nomenclature

The plasmids are named on the basis of certain criteria. This can be explained with the help of pBR322. In this plasmid,

p-	denotes that it is a plasmid

BR-	indicates the laboratory in which the plasmid was originally constructed, BR stands for Bolivar and Rodriguez who constructed this plasmid.
322-	It is a number given to distinguish this plasmid from others developed in the same laboratory. For example, there are plasmids pBR 325, pBR 327, pBR 328, pBR 345 etc.

Origin of pBR322

The plasmid pBR322 was constructed by using three different naturally occurring plasmids. The ampicillin resistance gene was derived from RSF 2124. The tetracycline resistance gene was taken from pSC 101. The origin of replication was obtained from pMB1 which is related to the plasmid ColE.

Advantages of pBR 322

The plasmid pBR 322 is an ideal cloning vector. It is the most common plasmid used in gene cloning experiments due to the following reasons:

1. The plasmid is much smaller than a natural plasmid, since this makes it more resistant to damage by shearing, and increases the efficiency of uptake by bacteria during transformation.
2. Since this plasmid is small, foreign DNA upto 6 kb in length can be inserted into this plasmid.
3. It has two antibiotic resistance genes namely Amp^R and Tet^R with unique restriction sites. Insertion of a new gene at a site in any one of these marker genes will inactivate the marker gene. This helps in the selection of E. coli cells harbouring recombinant plasmids.
4. pBR 322 has relaxed origin of replication (its multiplication is not tightly linked to cell division). So in presence of chloromphenicol its number may increase to 1000-3000.
5. This plasmid is used as a raw material to construct several other useful plasmids or other cloning vectors.
6. Single restriction sites for various enzymes, is present around the plasmid, which can be used to open the circle at a specific point prior to insertion of foreign DNA.

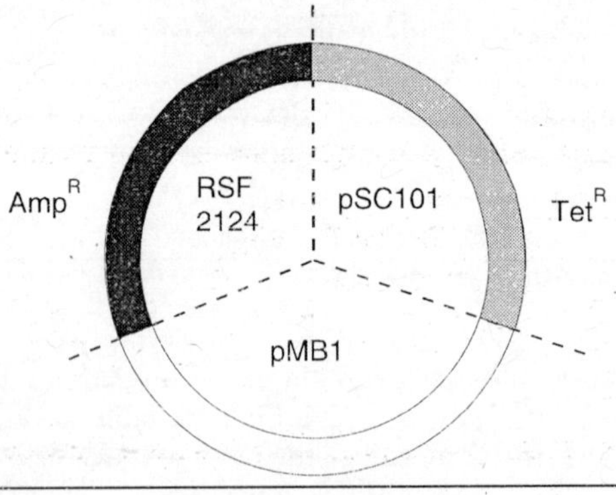

FIGURE 5.3: Diagram showing the origin of the plasmid pBR 322.

Though pBR 322 has been proved to be a useful and effective vector, it also has few disadvantages. Several derivatives with improved efficiencies have been constructed. Some disadvantages related with pBR 322 are as follows:

1. **Instability:** pBR 322 is lost in continuous culture (and in batch culture to a

limited extent) in the absence of selective pressure. This may create problems for the large-scale fermentation of recombinant bacteria for investigative or commercial purposes. However, to overcome this problem at least partially, derivatives containing the partition sequences have been constructed.

2. **Copy number:** Because of its relaxed mode of replication, pBR 322 is present in approximately twenty copies per chromosome. This multicopy feature can produce a gene dosage level that may be too low or too high for a particular experimental condition. For example, low-copy-number plasmids are preferred when regulatory elements are being analyzed, whereas a high copy number is desired when attempting to overproduce the product of a cloned gene. To overcome this limitation, some high-copy-number derivatives of pBR 322 and some derivatives with controllable copy number have also been constructed.
3. **Availability of cloning sites:** Although pBR 322 has twenty-one unique restriction sites, only eleven can be used to insertionally inactivate the antibiotic resistance genes. Another three unique restriction sites fall within the origin region and therefore cannot be used for cloning purposes without impairing plasmid replication. Several pBR-derivative vectors with multiple cloning sites have been constructed to enhance cloning versatility.
4. **Detection schemes:** Convenient, reliable, and quantitative assays for AP^R and Tc^R gene expression are not available. Consequently, a number of pBR 322 derivatives with improved selectable markers have been constructed. These include resistance to high tetracycline concentrations and resistance to neomycin, kanamycin and thiostrepton.
5. **Host range limitation:** Although pBR 322 was originally constructed as an E. coli vector, it can replicate in a few instances in other Gram-negative hosts like Serratia marcescens. Since the AP^R and Tc^R determinants on pBR 322 are known to function in a variety of organisms, the host range of this plasmid has been broadened by the construction of bifunctional plasmids called **shuttle vectors**.. Shuttle vectors can replicate in two different organisms because they contain two origins for DNA replication.

COL E1 PLASMID DNA

Bacterial strain containing Col E, plasmid produce Colicin E1, a protein that inhibits the growth of other *E. coli* strains. Col E1 plasmid also imparts immunity to low level of colicin E1 for strains carrying the plasmid. Colicin immunity can be tested by challenging stains with Colicin E1:

Size	4.4×10^6 Da or 6,600 bp
Isolated from	E. coli strain 600
Unique sites	With the gene for Colicin production - Ava I, Eco RI, Sac II, Sca I, Sma I.

Col E 1 Amp Plasmid DNA

This strain carries col E1 Amp and produces colicin. It has colicin immunity and is amplicillin resistant.

Size	7.3×10^6 Da or 10,900 bp
Isolated from	E. coli strain KP245
Unique sites	Within Colicin gene- EcoRI, Sma I
Other Unique sites	Bam HI

pBR 325 Plasmid DNA

This is a derivative of pBR 322 which confers resistance to ampicillin, tetracycline and chloromphenicol.

Size	4.0 M Da or 6,000 bp
Isolated from	E. coli strain HB101
Unique sites	Within the gene
Ampicillin resistance	Pst I, Pvu I
Tetracyclin resistance	Bam HI, Eco RV, Nru I, Sal I, Sph I
Chloromphenicol resistance	Eco RI
Other unique sites	Ava I, Bal I, Bcl I, Cla I, Hind III, Nde I.

pMB9 Plasmid DNA

Size	3.5 M Da; Approx 5300 bp.
Isolated from	E. coli strain RRI.
Unique sites	
(1) Within the gene	for tetracycline resistance BA MH I, Hind III, Sal I.
(2) Other unique sites	Eco RI

Confers tetra cycline resistance and colicin immunity.

pTZ Plasmids

A versatile cloning vector containing F1 and pBR322 are origins of replication allowing replication of the episomal DNA in ds or ss form. For ss replication, helper phage M13 K07 is required. pTZ also feature the multiple cloning sites from pUC 18 or pUC 19 to facilitate cloning. The ß-galactosidase gene provides easy identification of recombinant colonies by color detection when employing X-Gal (5-bromo, 4-chloro- 3-indoyl -ßD-galactopyranosidase) in the growth medium.

The T7 promoter, located within ß-galactosidase gene, serves as a template for *in vivo* or *in vitro* synthesis of specific RNA transcripts from cloned DNA. The *in vitro* synthesized RNA may be used as a hybridization probes.

Ampicillin resistance may be utilized for additional selection for plasmid containing colonies.

Size	2880 bp
Unique sites	within β-galactosidase gene- ampicillin resistance gene xmn I, Sca I.

pUB110 Plasmid DNA

Size	3.0 x 10^6 Daltons Approx. 4500 bp.
Isolated from	Bacillus subtilis strain BD170
Comments	This Staphylococcus aureus plasmid replicates in Bacillus subtilis. The plasmid confers resistance to kanamycin.
Unique sites	
Within gene for kanamycin resistance	Bgl II
Other unique sites	Bam HI, Eco RI, Xba I.

BACTERIOPHAGE VECTORS FOR *E. COLI*

The cloning of single genes is usually best carried out using plasmids, since the insert will rarely be larger than about 2 kb. But, for cloning of larger pieces of DNA (*e.g.*

during gene library construction), these plasmids are not suitable as larger inserts increase the plasmid size, making the transformation inefficient.

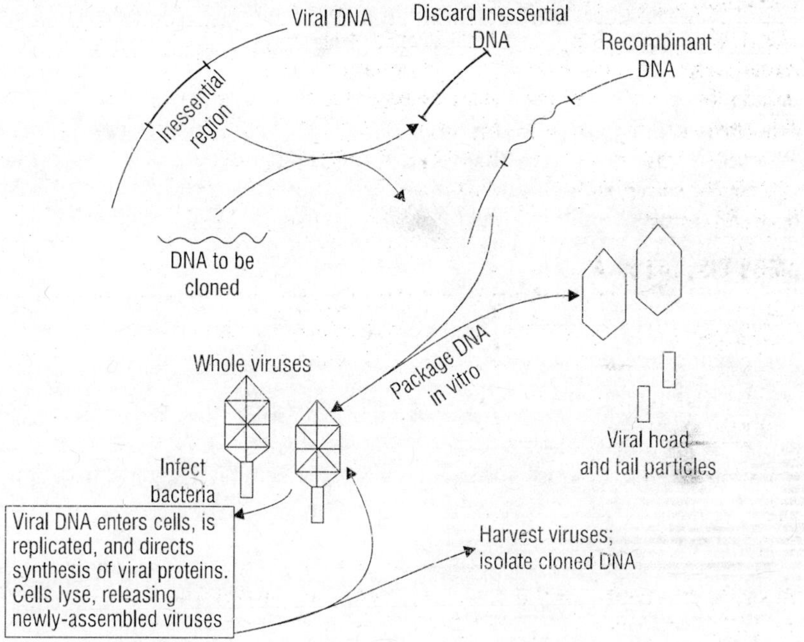

FIGURE 5.4: Cloning DNA in the bacteriophage λ. Inessential DNA is cut out of the λ DNA using restriction enzymes and is separated from essential DNA fragments by electrophoresis. Essential DNA and DNA to be cloned ligated and packaged in empty head particles, and tails are added to give infective viruses.

Large molecules can be injected in host bacterial cell by viral particles (bacteriophages). Commonly used bacteriophages are M13, f1, fd and λ phage.

Phage λ as A Vector

A commonly used vector is that of the λ phage. It is of 49 kb in length. For the cloning of long DNA fragments, up to about 20 kb much of the inessential λ DNA is removed and replaced by the insert. The recombinant DNA is then packaged within viral particles *in vitro*, and these are allowed to infect bacterial cells, which have been plated out on agar. Since the DNA is injected into the cells, a very high efficiency of transformation can be obtained. Once inside the cells, the recombinant viral DNA is replicated. All the genes needed for normal lytic growth are still present in the DNA, and therefore, multiplication of the virus takes place by cycles of cell lysis and infection of surrounding cells, giving rise to *plaques* of lysed cells on a background, or *lawn*, of bacterial cells. Cloned DNA can be recovered from the viruses in these plaques.

There are two kinds of λ vector which differ in size of they accept, λ replacement vectors and λ insertion vectors. These are described below:

Lambda Replacement Vectors

Lambda replacement vectors contain a restriction site for phage propagation in suitable bacterial host. Remaining part of lambda genome is removed and is replaced by foreign DNA. Ligation is performed at a ratio of arms to target that favours the formation of very long concatemers, in which vector and target molecules are interspersed.

In most replacement vectors (*e.g.* EM BL 4) the internal region that is replaced by the target contains a gene that renders the phage inviable in an appropriate *E. coli* host. Vector molecule containing target DNA and those without target DNA can be selected by infecting host. Recombinant phage in which the internal region is replaced by target DNA is viable and is mostly used for cloning eukaryotic DNA fragments.

Lambda Insertion Vectors

When cloning into an insertion vector, the phage DNA is cleaved with a restriction enzyme that cuts it only once, and the target is inserted into this site. No phage DNA is removed, therefore, much lower size of DNA can be inserted. In commonly used vector λ gt 10 the E col RII cloning site is in a gene which is deleterious to phage replication in certain host strains. This allows selection against non-recombinant phage.

Filamentous Phages as Cloning Vector

It included Ff class of filamentous phages, including strains f1, fd and M13, which infect *E. coli* cells displaying *E. coli*. These Ff virions are long and thin and contain a closed loop of single stranded DNA. Because the phages readily accept inserts of foreign DNA and they supply one strand of that DNA in an easily isolated form, vectors based on Ff phages have become standard choice.

M13 BACTERIOPHAGE

M13 is a filamentous bacteriophage of *E. coli*. It is 870 nm long and 6 nm wide. It has a protein coat (capsid) made up of three kinds of capsomeres. These filamentous single-stranded DNA phages infect cells by adsorbing to and entering through F pili; thus, these phages only infect F^+ or Hfr cells, not F^- cells. Lastly, these phages do not lyse the host cells (releasing progeny phage plus bacterial DNA from the ruptured cells) like phage λ during the lytic cycle. Instead, the progeny viruses are extruded through the layers of the cell membrane and cell wall without major interference with cell growth. Infected cells will continue to grow and extrude thousands of progeny virus particles, each containing a single-stranded genome to the medium. Because the virus particles are very small relative to the size of the host bacteria, the host cells can be removed by low-speed centrifugation.

The virus particles can be collected from the supernatant suspension by high-speed centrifugation, and their single-stranded DNA molecules can be isolated by simple phenol-chloroform extractions. The same DNA strand of the virus is always packaged; it is called the "+" strand (its complement is the – strand). The packaged + strand has the same *sense* as the mRNA; its nucleotide triplets correspond to the mRNA codons, but with T in place of U.

Major features of the M13 life cycle are illustrated in Figure 5.5. Packaging of single strands of phage DNA in progeny phage provides a neat biological purification of single-stranded DNA. Importantly, this will be true for a foreign gene cloned in the viral chromosome just as for the phage genes themselves. This property is exploited for its use as vector.

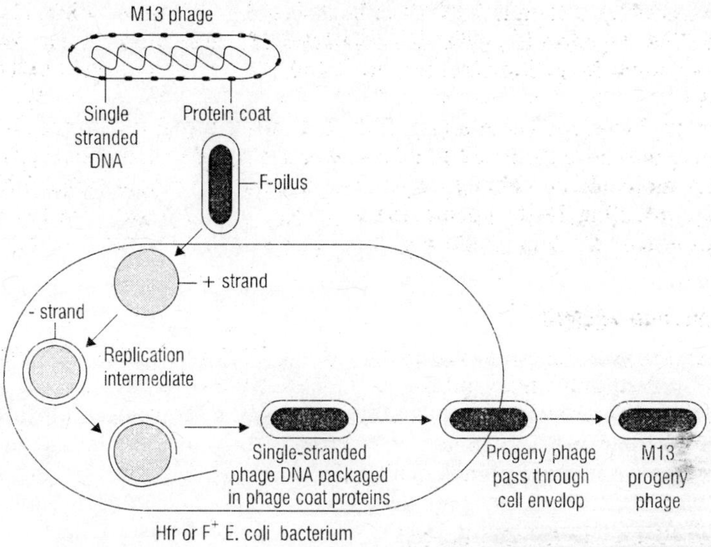

FIGURE 5.5: Simplified diagram of the life cycle of bacteriophage M13. The genetic information of the virus is stored in single-stranded DNA packaged within a long threadlike or filamentous virion. The virus enters the cell through an F pilus. The coat proteins are removed from the DNA, and it replicates by the rolling circle mechanism. Progeny single strands of DNA are packaged in new coats, and the progeny virions are extruded through the cell envelope without killing the host cell. The replicating DNA molecules are shown as relaxed circles; in reality, they are supercoiled throughout the duplication process.

Genetic Organisation of Wild Type Bacteriophage M13

The DNA of wild type M13 bacteriophage is single stranded and circular. It is 6407 bases long it has 10 genes that are closely packed. All these genes are essential for the replication of the phages. There is a segment of 507 nucleotide intergenic sequence (IS) which contains origin of replication (OR).

This intergenic region can be manipulated for cloning without disrupting the origin of replication. Hence the wild M13 phage has limited use in gene cloning experiments. The size of the phage particle is decided by the size of the phage DNA. Upto six times the normal length of M13 DNA can be packaged (J. Messing et al 1981).

Construction of M13 Based Vectors

In M13 phage DNA, the intergenic sequence is the only region which can be manipulated for cloning. As this region has only two restriction sites (Asa I and Ava II), wild type phage is phage is not an efficient vector. However, IS can be modified to introduce additional restriction sites. A few such vectors are discussed below:

M13 P1 and M13 MP2

The gene lacZ' (refer box) is introduced into the wildtypes IS to get the M13 mp1 phages. This produces blue plaques on X-gal agar plates. The LacZ' gene does not have any restriction site. However, it has a hexanucleotide sequence, GGATTC near the start. If the second G residue is substituted by an A residue, this sequence becomes an Eco RI site. GAATTC. This conversion is done by invitro mutagenesis. Now this phage is called M13 mp2. The lacZ' gene now has a slightly altered base sequence. Due to this, the enzyme ß-galactosidase encoded by the lacZ' has asparagine instead of aspartic acid in the fifth position. This change does not affect the activity of the enzyme. This can be tested X-gal agar where the plaque gives a blue colour.

The M13 mp2 is the simplest cloning vector derived from M13 phage. In the unique Eco RI site of M13 mp2 any foreign DNA with Eco RI sticky ends can be inserted. This insertion inactivates lacZ' (insertional inactivation). The recombinant phages fail to produce blue plaques on X-gal agar, instead, they produce clear plaques.

M13 MP7

M13 mp7 is a derivative of M13 mp2. When a polylinker is inserted into the Eco RI site of lacZ' gene; the M13 mp2 becomes M13 mp7. The polylinker is designed in such a way that it does not inactivate the lacZ' gene.

It has the Eco RI sticky ends and has restriction sites for Bam HI Sal I and Pst I. Thus M13 mp7 is a more complex vector with four possible insertional sites. Foreign DNA with corresponding sticky ends can be inserted into these sites. The recombinant M13 mp7 phage cannot produce blue ploaques an X-gal agar plates due to insertional inactivation of lacZ' gene. They produce clear plaques.

When M13 mp7 is cut with Eco RI, Bam HI, Sal I or Pst I, the entire polylinker or a part of it is excised. Foreign DNA with the corresponding sticky ends can be inserted to produce recombinant M13 mp7. Insertion of foreign DNA will inactivate the lacZ' gene and the production of galactosidase is prevented. This will be shown by the formation of clear plaques an X-gal agar by the recombinant phage DNA.

M13-Plasmid Hybrid Vectors

Hybrid vector contain component from both plasmids and phage chromosomes. These vectors replicate in *E. coli* as normal double-stranded plasmids until a **helper phage** is provided. After addition of the "helper" phage, they switch to the phage mode of replication (rolling circle replication like that observed for phage øXI- and package single strands of DNA in phage particles. The helper phage is a mutant that replicates its own DNA inefficiently, but provides viral replication enzymes and structural proteins for the production of plasmid DNA molecules that are packaged in phage coats.

PUC 118 AND PUC 119

The phage-plasmid "hybrid" vector pUC 118 and pUC 119 are a pair of vectors that are essentially identical except that the regions into which foreign DNAs are inserted are present in opposite orientations (turned end-for-end) relative to the rest of the genes of the vector. Thus, if a foreign DNA is inserted into a specific restriction site in both vectors, one vector will package one strand of the gene, and the other vector will package the complementary strand of the gene. Therefore, both strands of the gene can be isolated, sequenced, subjected to site-specific mutagenesis, and so on. The vectors were designated pUC for plasmid, University of California (where the first pUC vectors in the series were constructed by J. Messing and J. Vieira), and 118, 119 to distinguish them from earlier members (lower numbers) of the series. Vectors pUC 118 and pUC 119 differ from earlier vectors in the pUC series by the addition of the origin of replication from phage M13. This permits pUC 118 and pUC 119 to replicate either:

1. as a double-stranded plasmid in the absence of helper phage or
2. as a single-stranded DNA that is packaged in M13 phage coats and extruded from the cell in the presence of helper phage.

In the absence of *helper* phage, replication is controlled by the plasmid origin of replication. The pUC vectors called pBR322 by a series of directed modifications. The pUc vectors, like pBR322, contain an origin of replication initially present in plasmid ColE1. In the presence of "helper" phage, replication of pUC 118 and pUC 119 is directed by the M13 phage origin of replication that has been added to these plasmids.

The important features of the pUC 118 and pUC 119 cloning vectorare the following:

1. small, supercoiled, covalently closed circular DNA-thus, easily isolated and manipulated in vitro;
2. carry the amp^r gene as a selectable marker-thus, only bacteria harboring a plasmid will grow on medium containing ampicillin'
3. high copy number, up to 500 copies per bacterium-thus, large yields of DNA from small cell cultures;
4. carry a polycloning region containing a variety of restriction enzyme cleavage sites-thus, many different types of restriction fragments can be inserted without modification;
5. the polycloning region interrupts the coding region of the 5' end of the E. coli lac z gene-thus, colonies harboring plasmids with foreign DNA inserts can be distinguished from those carrying plasmids with no insert by a simple color test;
6. the lac z gene is under the control of the lac promoter-thus, genes inserted in frame (codons in proper reading frames can be expressed to produce β-galactosidase-foreign protein fusion products'
7. carry a plasmid origin of replication-thus, replication of the vector, DNA produces large numbers of double-stranded plasmid DNAs in the absence of "helper" phage;
8. carry a phage M13 origin of replication-thus, production of single-stranded DNA and packaging if this DNA in phage ocats in the presence of "helper" phage; and
9. the polycloning regions are present in pUC 118 and pUC 119 in opposite orientations-thus, if pUC 118 packages one strand of a cloned gene, pUC 119 will package the complementary strand.

Different members of the pUC vector series contain different, but related, sets of restriction enzyme cleavage sites. The polycloning regions of pUC 118 and pUC 119 contain 10 clustered restriction enzyme cleavage sites. Some of these sites are substrates for two or more different restriction enzymes.

The utility of the pUC vectors is greatly enhanced by a simple color test that allows one to distinguish cell harboring plasmids with foreign DNA inserts from those horboring plasmids with no insert. The basis of this color indicator test is the functional inactivation of the 5' segment of the lac z gene present in the vector by the insertion of foreign DNA into the polycloning region.

THE PEMBL8 CLONING VEHICLE

The pEMBL8 cloning vehicle is constructed by transferring a 1300 bp fragment of the genome of M13 phage into the pUC8 plasmid. This piece of M13 genome has the signal sequence recognised by the enzymes that convert the ds M13 DNA into a ssDNA molecule. So the pEMBL8 molecules are also converted into single stranded DNA molecules and these will be secreted as infective phage particles. When pEMBL8 vector is used, the *E. coli* cells should also be infected with an intact M13 particle. This will act a helper phage by providing necessary enzymes and phage coat proteins. Since pEMBL8 is derived from pUC8 it has the polylinker at the necessary lacZ' gene. Hence it has the advantages of pUC8 plasmids and that of the M13 phages:

1. Foreign DNA fragments with two different sticky ends can be inserted at the multiple cloning site on the lacZ gene.
2. Recombinant pEMBL8 genome can be packaged into the capsid of M13 phage.
3. The phage particles containing the recombinant pEMBL8 genome are as efficient as the wild type M13 phages in their ability to infect E. coli cells and then in the expression of the foreign gene.
4. Recombinant pEMBL8 genome can be easily screened using the medium containing X-gal.

COSMIDS

Cosmids are hybrid DNA molecules and can live a dual life. Their plasmid part enables them to replicate as it has origin of replication. Plasmid part also helps in selection due to the presence of marker gene. Cleavage site is located in the marker gene. Their lambda part (*cos* sequences) allows them to be packaged in a phage coat and to be transduced to a recipient by the lambda infection machinery. It has no genes for viral proteins, therefore, viral particles are not formed in the host. Host cell lysis is also absent. The vector cosmids ligate passenger DNA to increase the size of packaging and thus becoming stably packaged. This requirement is the basis for the size selectivity used for cloning.

Two cosmids are described below:

Cosmid pHC79

It is specially suitable for the cloning of large DNA fragments (upto 40 kb) in connection with an *in vitro* packaging system. It is 6.5 kb in size and contains part of the pBR 322 sequence and a fragment of L-phage DNA containing the cos region. The cos region is required for packaging into phage heads. The pBR 322 segment has the genes for Ampicillin and Tetracycline resistance.

Cosmid pJB8

This cosmid is 5.4 kb in size. It has ampicillin resistant genes of plasmid pBR 322 and the cos site derived from L -phage DNA.

Two facts are considered in using a cosmid for gene cloning in *E. coli*:

1. The enzymes that package the DNA molecule into the viral coat need only the cos sites in order to function.
2. The invitro packaging reaction will take place not only with phage genomes, but also with any DNA molecule that has cos sites separated by 37 -52 kb of DNA. In

other words, the protein coat of L phage can accommodate any fragment of DNA that ranges between 37-52 kb (5-105% of the length of the wild type L DNA) provided, this fragment lies between two cos sites.

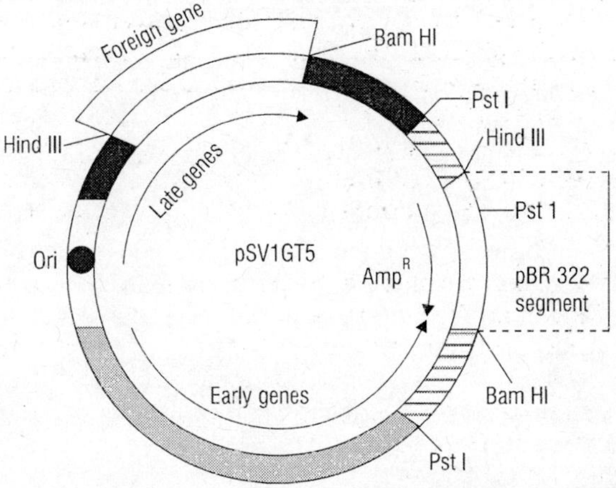

FIGURE 5.6: Gene map of pSV1GT5 vector it is constructed by inserting a 4 kb segment of the plasmid pBR322 into SVGT5. This segment codes for lactamase and contains the origin of replication of pBR322. This vector can be used as a shuttle vector.

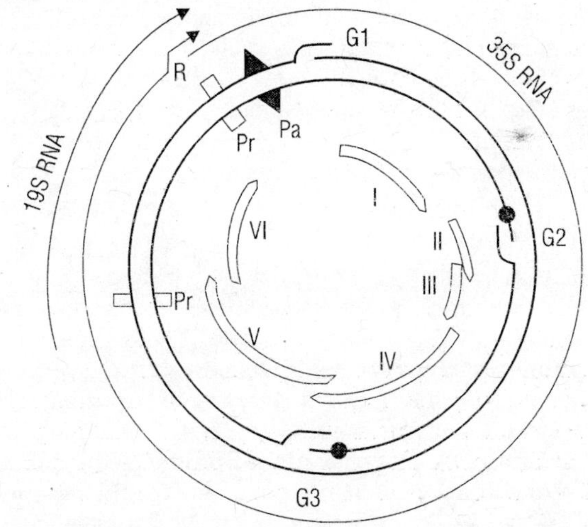

FIGURE 5.7: Diagram of the circular double stranded DNA of CaMV showing the three gaps: G1, G2 and G3 (after D. Grierson and S.N. Covey, 1988. Plant Molecular Biology, Blackie and Son Ltd., Glasgow).

Cloning Using a Cosmid Vector

Cosmids are used as gene cloning vectors in connection with the *in vitro* packaging system. Cloning with a cosmids is carried out as follows:

1. A suitable cosmid is selected. The cosmid pJB8 is used for explaining the

procedure.
2. The cosmid is cut at the restriction site with an appropriate restriction enzyme (Bam HI). Thus the cosmid is made into a linear form. Fragments of foreign DNA prepared using the same restriction enzyme are ligated with the linear cosmid DNA.
3. The foreign DNA segments will join with the opened up cosmids to form recombinant molecules. Ligation occurs in such a way that concatemers of recombinant cosmids are formed.
4. Concatemers of recombinant cosmid molecules will now be packaged in vitro into L phage heads.
5. Recombinant cosmids will be packaged into L phage heads. The resulting phages are infective. During packaging, unit lengths are cut out at the cos sites. In the phage heads the recombinant cosmid will remain linear.
6. When these phage particles infect bacterial cells the recombinant cosmids will be transferred into the bacterial cells.
7. Inside the bacterial cell, the linear recombinant cosmid DNA becomes circular by base pairing at the cos ends. Thereafter it replicates as a plasmid. The foreign gene may express.

VECTORS FOR PLANT CELLS

Several vector systems are used for the introduction of foreign genes into plant cells. Among them, the Ti-plasmid of *Agrobacterium tumefaciens* and a few plant viruses such as Caulimoviruses and Geminiviruses are the most important ones.

Caulimoviruses are a group of plant viruses which have double stranded DNA. These have a very narrow host range. One such virus is Cauliflower Mosaic Virus (CaMV). This virus infects plants of the family Cruciferae. The Caulimoviruses are isometric particles and are 50 nm in diameter. The cells of the infected plants accumulate virus containing proteinaceous inclusion bodies (viroplasms). These regions are regarded as the sites of virus assembly.

The Chromosome of CaMV

The DNA of the CaMV particles is a circular double stranded molecule. It is 8024 pb long. It has three discontinuities (gaps) at specific sites on each strand. One strand of the DNA has only one gap. The other has two gaps. These gaps have short regions of overlapping DNA produced by strand displacement.

The DNA of the CaMV has a small amount of covalently linked RNA. The function of this RNA is not known. The free genome of the CaMV is infectious and it has no tissue restriction. It has six genes. Gene1 produces the factors needed for the cell to cell spread of the virus. Gene II is responsible for the production of the aphid transmission factor. Gene III encodes a virion structural protein. Gene IV produces the coat protein. Gene V produces the enzyme reverse transcriptase. Gene VI produces the inclusion body protein.

Multiplication Cycle of CaMV

The CaMV enters the host cell. Immediately after entry, the coat proteins are shed and the DNA molecule enters the nucleus of the host cell. Inside the nucleus the single stranded overiaps at the gaps are digested and the gaps are then sealed. This circular DNA molecule becomes super coiled and associates with the host proteins to form a minichromosome. This minichromosome acts as a template and produces mRNA under the direction of the host RNA polymerase II. Two major RNA transcripts, 19S RNA and 35S RNA, are produced. The 19S RNA is the mRNA for the gene VI which encodes the subcellular inclusion bodies. The 35 RNA is genome length. The genome length 35S RNA comes out of the nucleus. It is suggested that it functions as a polycistronic mRNA for the synthesis of viral proteins to III. Another possibility is that subgenomic mRNA, that can express viral genes (with the exception of gene VI) are formed.

The 35S RNA also functions as a template for the synthesis of the minus strand DNA will be the template for the plus-strand synthesis. Thus a new complete viral DNA is synthesised.

The circular DNAs are finally assembled into viral particles, which can move from cell within the host plant. During the life cycle of CaMV, its DNA does not integrate with the host DNA. This virus also does not cause cell lysis.

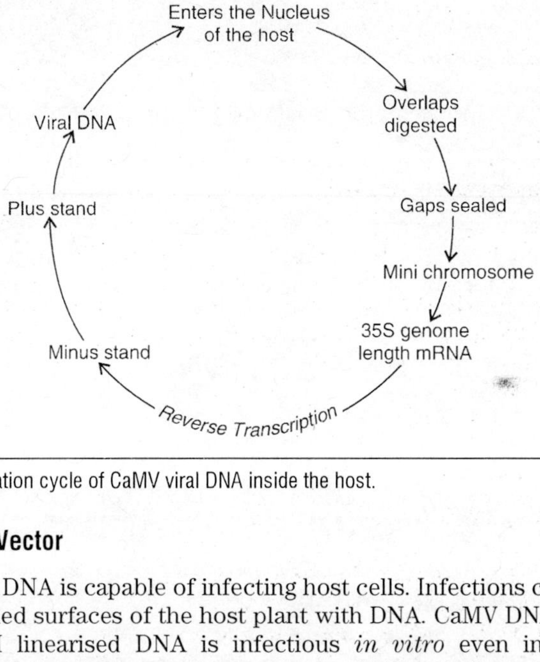

FIGURE 5.8: Replication cycle of CaMV viral DNA inside the host.

CaMV as a Gene Vector

The naked CaMV DNA is capable of infecting host cells. Infections can be initiated by inoculating abraded surfaces of the host plant with DNA. CaMV DNA has a single Sal I site. The Sal I linearised DNA is infectious *in vitro* even in the absence of religation. Recircularization occurs in the plant cell. The viral particles assembled in the host cells have the ability to spread from cell to cell. Thus it is a systemic virus. Above features are the advantages for considering CaMV as cloning vectors. Plant cells infected by the CaMV can be cultured *in vitro* to produce clones. This is useful for the plants that are propagated vegetatively.

Limitations

The use of CaMV as gene vector has limitations. The CaMV envelope does not accommodate larger DNA than the normal size. Hence foreign genes that are inserted into its genome cannot be packaged.

The genes of CaMV are closely packaged and it also lacks long non-essential sequences that could be replaced by foreign genes. If DNA longer than few hundred nucleotides is inserted the infectivity is destroyed. However, a small foreign DNA having the bacterial dhfr gene (dihydrofolate reductase) replacing the gene II, has been successfully expressed in plants.

The promoter sequences of the DNAs of CaMV are very efficient. These promoters are isolated and are used to construct vector systems in which foreign genes are efficiently expressed.

SHUTTLE VECTORS

Certain vectors can replicate in different host systems for example, in *E. coli* and in yeast. Such vectors are called shuttle vectors. For this purpose shuttle vectors carry different origins of replication which are characteristic for different host systems.

Yeast Episomal Plasmids (YEPs)

Yeast episomal plasmids (YEps) are shuttle vectors. They can replicate in *E. coli* and also in yeast. pJDB219 is an example. It is an artificial plasmid and has the following segments.

1. the 2 μm circular plasmid of yeast.
2. the entire pBR 322 sequence.
3. the selectable LEU2 gene of the yeast chromosome. This will also carry an origin of replication.

The 2 μM Plasmid

It is a plasmid found in several strains of yeast, Saccharomyces cerevisiae. It is 6 kb in size and has a copy number between 70 and 200. It replicates autonomously using several enzymes provided by the host cell and the proteins coded by its own genes.

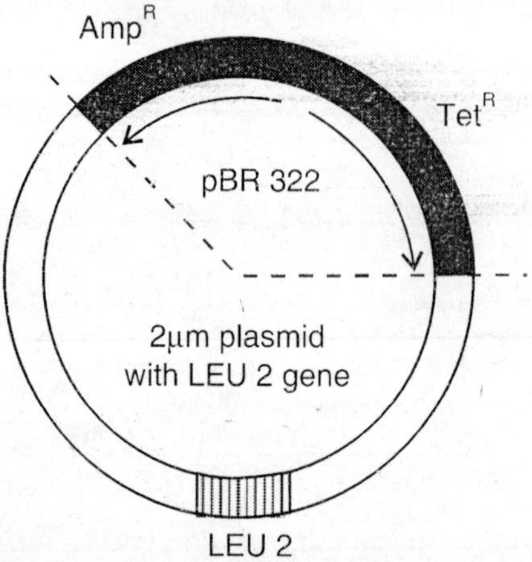

FIGURE 5.9: Structure of an yeast episomal plasmid (YEp), pJDB219 (after T.A. Brown, 1990. Gene cloning: An introduction).

Leu2 Gene

LEU2 gene is an yeast chromosomal gene that codes for isopropyl malate dehydrogenase. It is one of the enzymes involved in the conversion of pyruvic acid to leucine. When this gene is used as a selectable marker, the host yeast must be a mutant that has a non-functional LEU2 gene. Such strains are called leu2. These cells are unable to synthesise leucine and will grow only if this amino acid is added to the growth medium. However, yeast cells transformed by the YEp containing LEU2 gene can grow in the growth medium lacking leucine. Thus the transformed yeast cells (transformants) can be selected.

The pBR 322

It is the bacterial plasmid. It has two marker genes: the ampicillin and tetracycline resistance genes. It has its own origin of replication. Hence initial gene manipulation experiments can be done with *E. coli*.

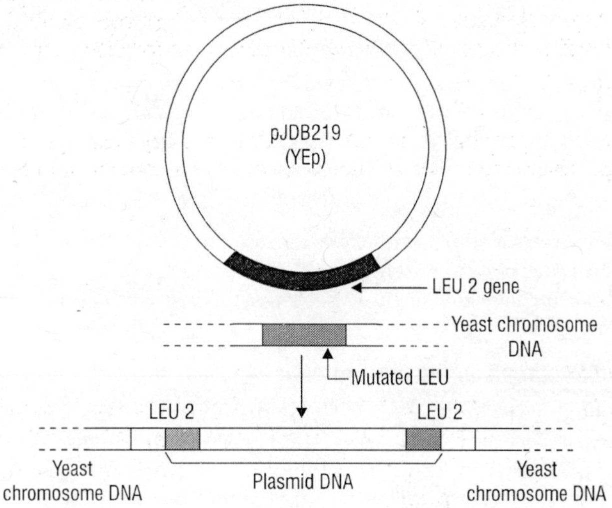

FIGURE 5.10: Homologous recombination between the LEU2 gene of pJDB 219 (an YEp) and the mutated LEU2 gene on the yeast chromosome. This leads to the insertion of this plasmid into the yeast chromosome.

The YEp vector is episomal in nature as it can integrate with one of the yeast chromosomes. Integration occurs by homologous recombination between the LEU2 gene and the yeast mutant LEU2 gene. This results in the insertion of the entire YEp into one of the yeast chromosomes. The plasmid may remain integrated or it may be excised later.

If one plans to clone a particular gene in yeast, the initial cloning experiment is done with *E. coli*. The recombinants are selected. The recombinant plasmids are then purified and introduced into yeast where the new gene will express itself.

YAC VECTORS

Large DNA segments can be cloned in yeast artificial chromosomes (YACs). YACs are linear DNA segments that contain all the molecular components required for replication in yeast: (i) a replication origin known as an autonomously replicating sequence (ARE), (ii) a centromere and (iii) the telomeres (the ends of linear chromosomes). They are also called minichromosomes. DNAs of several hundred kb (200-400 kb) can be introduced into YACs and successfully cloned. Example, pYAC2.

Expression Vectors

The primary function of a vector in DNA Recombinant Technology (DNART) is to carry a gene of interest into a recipient cell. When such a transfer is successful, the foreign gene should be expressed in the recipient cell. Some times, the foreign gene in the recipient cell may not be expressed. This may be due to the following reasons.

1. Transcription of the gene did not occur due to the absence of an effective promoter.
2. A terminator sequence to terminate transcription may be absent.
3. The initiation codon for the particular protein is absent.
4. The mRNA lacks a suitable Shine-Dalgarno sequence (in the case of prokaryotes).

Hence the vectors are constructed in such a way that they contain suitable expression signals. Such vectors are called expression vectors. A foreign gene carried by an expression vector into the recipient cell will have complete expression, *i.e.*, the gene will be transcribed into mRNA and then translated into the protein (gene product). Several expression vectors are constructed to suit the needs.

There are two main strategies for the construction of expression vectors:

1. Vectors which can allows the synthesis of a fusion protein (hybrid protein) having vector and insertion sequences.
2. Vectors that can synthesise pure proteins exclusively encoded by the inserted gene (foreign gene).

Vectors For the Synthesis of Fusion Proteins

The foreign gene inserted into a vector gene in such a way that the reading frame of the vector gene is conserved. During transcription the hybrid mRNA is formed. Transcription is initiated by the promoter of the vector gene. The hybrid mRNA is translated to yield a hybrid protein consisting of vector and foreign proteins. Translation begins from the start codon of the vector gene and ends at the stop codon of the foreign gene. The fusion protein is then cleaved to release the foreign protein.

Vectors For the Synthesis of Pure Unfused Foreign Protein

There are vectors that can produce only the proteins encoded by the foreign gene. Such vectors will be constructed by linking a suitable and strong prokaryotic promoter, a bacterial Shine-Dalgarmo sequence and the start codon infront of a desired structural gene. This will allow the synthesis of the corresponding gene product as a pure unfused protein.

pSV240 is an example for this kind of expression vector. This vector is designed to express SV40t - antigen gene. This vector is derived from pBR 322 to which the lac promoter, the S/D sequence and the start codon is linked infront of the SV40 -t antigen gene.

The lac promoter allows transcription of SV40-t antigen gene. The mRNA thus produced has the S/D sequences, the start codon AUG for translation and the codons for SV40 t- antigen. This mRNA is translated into t-antigen.

From the above two examples, it is clear that a foreign gene introduced into a host genome should have the following components for proper expression.

1. A suitable vector
2. A terminator sequence to terminate transcription.
3. Sequences to give Shine-Dalgarno sequence on the mRNA (if the gene is to be cloned in bacteria).
4. The start codon to initiate translation.

5. A stop codon to terminate translation.

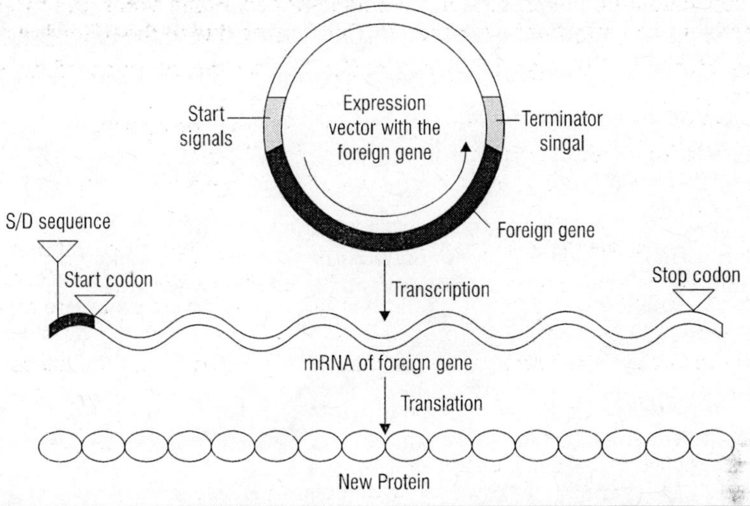

FIGURE 5.11: Expression vector with the foreign gene and its expression signals S/D sequence-Shine-Dalgarno sequence.

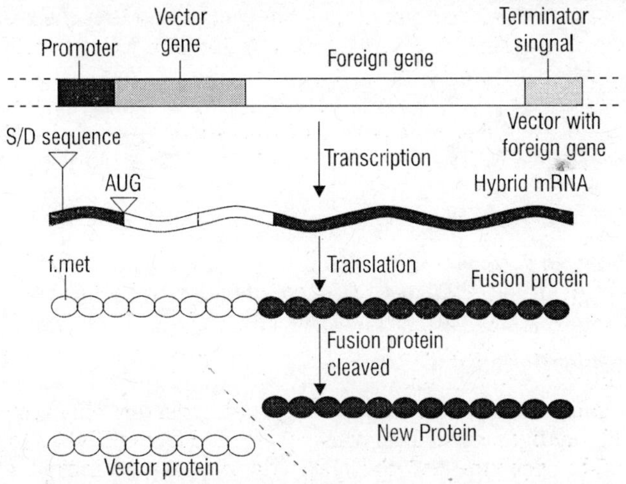

FIGURE 5.12: Expression vector for the synthesis of fusion protein.

GENE CARTRIDGES

Purified DNA fragments which may be a control region, a gene for a protein or another sequence are readily available. Such fragments are called gene cartridges. These genetic fragments are very useful for plasmid construction. Some gene cartridges and their parent plasmids are given in the following Table.

TABLE 5.2: A few gene cartridges, their size and the parent plasmids from where the gene cartridges are purified are given. The restriction enzymes with which the DNA segment is excised are also given.

Gene Cartridge	Size (Base pairs)	Parent Plasmid
trp Promoter (Hind III/Bam HI)	90	pDR720
tac Promoter (Hind III/Bam HI)	91	pDR540
pUC-13 multiple cloning site (Hind III/Eco RI)	45	pUC13
Tet^R (Eco RI/Ava I)	1427	pBR322
Amp^R gene/Ori (Eco RI/Puv II)	2296	pBR322

The ampicillin resistance gene cartridge consists of 2296 bp Eco RI/Pvu II fragment of pBR 322. This fragment contains the β- lactamase gene and the origin of replication. It is used as a primary fragment in plasmid construction.

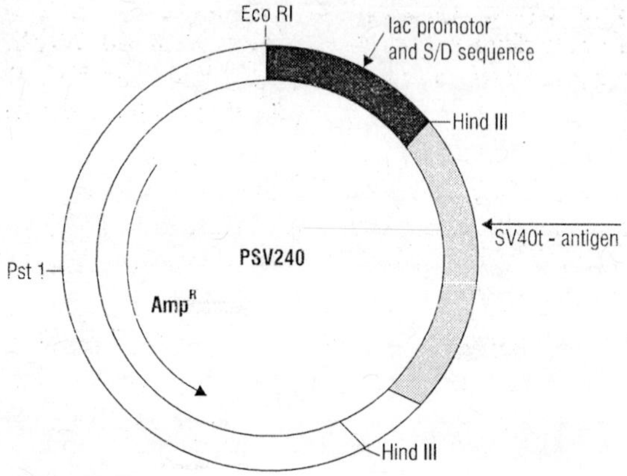

FIGURE 5.13: Expression vector for SV40 t-antigen. Restriction sites of a few endonucleases are shown.

Synthetic Regulator Sequences

Synthetic prokaryotic control sequences are useful in constructing vectors for gene expression. These products are useful in combination with the gene catridges to design vectors. Some of them are given below:

Universal Translation Terminator

It is a self-complementary 16- base oligodeoxynucleotide containing a 5' d (TAA) -3' stop codon in all the three reading frames:

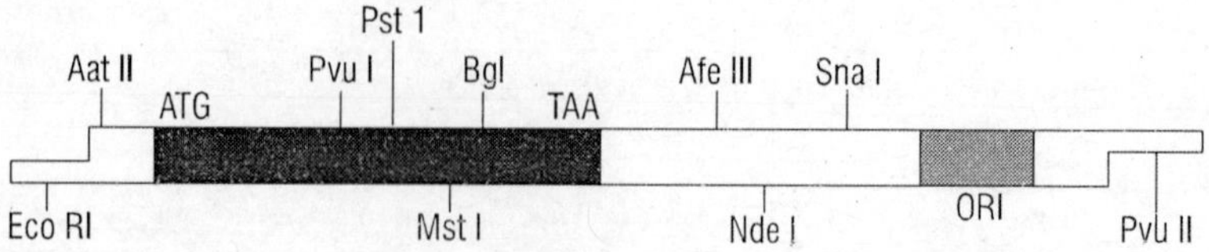

FIGURE 5.14: The ampicillin resistance gene cartridge having the β-lactamase gene (black) and the origin of replication (hatched). It has the Eco RI/Puv II sticky ends.

Portable Translation Initiation Sites (PTIS)

It is a double-stranded DNA equivalent of a prokaryotic RNA translation initiation site. The PTIS contains a five base Shine - Dalgarno (S/D) sequence with a 3' adjacent poly (A) tract followed by an initiator ATG codon eight bases from the S/D region. These features are required for translation. Each PTIS has specific sticky ends, with the help of which it can be ligated into a vector.

5' - d [G C T T A A T T A A T T A A G C] - 3'
3' - d [C G A A T T A A T T A A T T C G] - 5'

FIGURE 5.15: Base sequence of a portable translation initiation site (PTIS) having the S/D site and the start codon. It has Hindi III/Bam HI sticky ends.

Trp A Transcription Terminator

It is a 28 base pair trp a transcription terminator. It is a very efficient rho independent terminator. This sequence is essential in the stable cloning of DNA fragments carrying strong promoters. These sequences can also eliminate any read-through transcription which may lead to the over production of unwanted plasmid encoded proteins.

5' - d [AG CCC GCC TAATGAGC GGGC T T T T T T T T]3'
3' - d [TC GGG CGG ATTACTCG CCCG A A A A A A A] 5'

FIGURE 5.16: Base sequence of trp a transcription terminator.

CHAPTER 6

Recombinant DNA Technology

Recombinant DNA technology deals with isolation and manipulation of genes. Before nucleic acids can be cut or otherwise manipulated, they must be either isolated and purified or artificially synthesized. The isolated genes are also sometimes sequenced for a better understanding of its structure that needs to be manipulated. In this chapter we will discuss the methods available for isolation, sequencing and synthesis of genes.

ISOLATION OF TOTAL CELLULAR DNA

DNA is very easily damaged by shear forces; even rapid stirring of solution can break even with high DNA molecular weight into much shorter fragments. Consequently, DNA is recovered from cells by gentlest possible method of rupture, in the presence of EDTA to chalate the Mg^{2+} ions needed for DNase activity. Cell walls, if present, are digested enzymatically (*e.g.* lysozyme treatment of bacteria) and the cell membrane is solubilised using detergent. Cell disruption is performed at 4 °C using autocloved glassware and solutions to destroy DNase activity.

After release of nucleic acids from the cells, RNA can be removed by treatment with ribonuclease (RNase). The other major contaminant, protein, is removed by shaking the solution gently with water-saturated phenol, or with phenol/chloroform mixture, either of which will denature protein but not nucleic acids. Centrifugation of the emulsion formed by this mixture produces a lower, organic phase, separated from the upper aqueous phase by an interface of denatured proteins. The aqueous solution is recovered and deproteinised repeatedly, until no matter is seen at interface. Finally, the deproteinised DNA preparation is mixed with ethanol and allowed to precipitate out in freezer. After centrifugation, the DNA pallet is redissolved in a buffer containing EDTA for protection against DNases and this solution can be stored at 4 °C for at least a month. DNA solutions can be stored frozen, but repeated freezing and thawing tends to damage long molecules by shearing; so preparation in frequent use are normally stored at 4 °C.

This procedure is suitable for total cellular DNA. If the DNA from specific organelle or viral particle is needed, it is best to isolate the organelle or virus before extracting its DNA. Now we will discuss several basic techniques related with gene isolation and identification.

NUCLEIC ACID HYBRIDIZATION

If a double-stranded DNA molecule is exposed to high temperature, or to very alkaline conditions, then the two strands will come apart. The molecule is said to have become denatured. The temperature at which denaturation occurs is termed as melting temperature or T_m. If the denatured DNA is returned to a temperature below its T_m, or to neutral pH when alkali was used to denature it, each strand will, after a time, find its complementary strand. The two strands will 'zipper' back together to re-form a double-stranded DNA molecule. This ability of complementary sequences to anneal, or hybridize, to one another is called nucleic acid hybridization. This techniques helps in determining the gene structure and in identifying molecules which contain same sequences of nucleotides. In a complex mixture of nucleic acid molecules, nucleic acid hybridization technique helps in separation of complementary sequence.

When employed analytically, hybridization is normally performed using one labelled sequence, termed the probe, and an unlabelled sequence called the target. **Probe** is a short synthetic oligo deoxyribonucleotide which is complementary to target DNA sequences. Target DNA may be obtained from total cellular DNA preparations. The probe is labelled by incorporation of either radioactively labelled nucleotides or with some chemicals (described later). The probe is the known, pure species in the hybridization and the target is the unknown species to be identified.

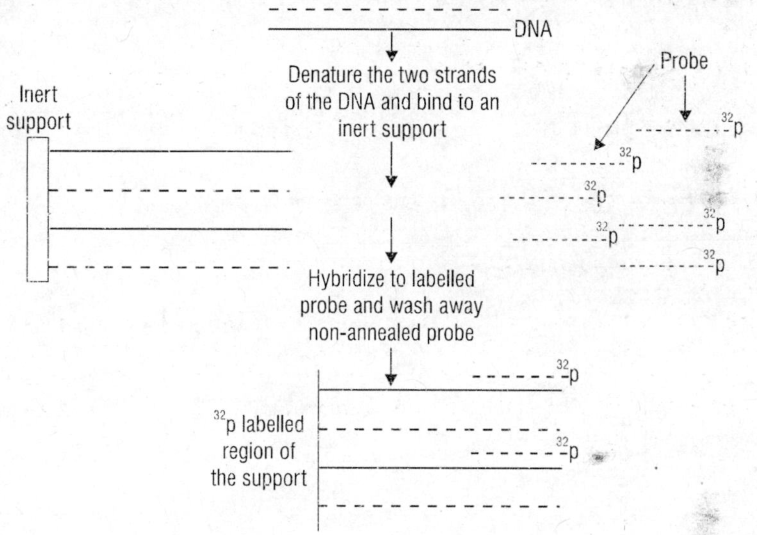

FIGURE 6.1: The principle of hybridization using an inert support. The target DNA is most often localized to one part of the support and, in most cases, the aim of the hybridization experiment is to identify this region. The probe is prelabelled by some method, most often by the incorporation of radioactivity. After hybridization, the annealed probe is detected by autoradiography.

The target will most often form part of a mixture of unrelated nucleic acid sequences. The probe is usually added in considerable excess over the target, and its concentration determines the rate of reaction. Hybridization reaction time is extended to ensure complete reaction. The target and probe can be hybridized to each other in solution, or alternatively the target can be immobilized on an inert support such as nitrocellulose. When the target is immobilized the rate of annealing is greatly reduced.

The rate of hybridization depends upon the DNA concentration, the concentration of salt in the solution and the temperature. Hybridization reactions are normally performed at 10-20 °C below the T_m of the duplex. Under any given conditions of ionic strength and temperature, the T_m of a duplex also depends on the base composition of the annealed partners.

Hybridization involving RNA is performed in the presence of formamide as RNA cannot withstand higher temperatures. Formamide disrupts hydrogen bonding and thus reduces the effective T_m of the duplex, allowing annealing to occur at a lower temperature (*e.g.* 37 °C).

METHODS FOR LABELLING NUCLEIC ACIDS

For identification of hybridized nucleic acid duplexes, labelling of probe or target is necessary. As probe is short synthetic oligonucleotide it can be easily labelled. A ^{32}P isotopic label can be added to the 5' hydroxyl group using polynucleotide kinase to a probe (Table 6.1). Alternatively, labelled nucleotides can be incorporated at the 3' end using terminal transferase. Because label is added at only one place within the oligonucleotide, such end-labelled probes contain relatively little radioactivity per unit weight of DNA. This low specific activity limits their sensitivity as probes. If a high specific activity probe is required, then some method of uniform labelling must be used. Here the probe sequence is copied along part or all of its length using DNA polymerase and labelled nucleoside triphosphate.

TABLE 6.1: Some methods of *in vitro* labelling of nucleic acids

Labelling method	Enzyme used	Template	Product	Structure at end of reaction*	Specific activity
5' end labelling	Polynucleotide kinase	DNA or RNA	DNA or RNA	d.s. or s.s.	Low
3'end labelling	Large (Klenow) subfragment of E. coli DNA polymerase-1	DNA	DNA	d.s.	Low
3'end labelling	Terminal transferase	DNA or RNA	DNA or RNA	s.s.	Low
Nick translation	E. coli DNA polymerase-1	DNA	DNA	d.s.	High
Random priming	Klenow subfragment of DNA polymerase-1	DNA or RNA	DNA	d.s.	High
In-vitro transcription	Bacteriophage (e.g. T7) RNA polymerase	DNA	RNA	s.s.	High

*d.s. - double stranded; s.s. - single stranded.

METHODS OF LABELLING NUCLEIC ACID AND PROBES

There are five basic methods for labelling nucleic acids. These are: nick translation, primer extension, methods based on RNA polymerase, end labelling methods and direct labelling methods.

Nick Translation

This is done by making single-strand cuts (**nicks**) in the double-stranded DNA molecule by brief exposure to a dilute solution of an endonuclease (usually deoxyribonuclease I of *E. coli*). DNA polymerase I is then used in the presence of at least one radioactive precursor (*e.g.*, Â-^{32}P-dATP) to "translate" the nick along the molecule in the 5' to 3' direction. This occurs by the concerted action of the 5'→3' polymerase and the 5'→3' exonuclease activities built into DNA polymerase I. The 5'→3' polymerase adds nucleotides to the 3'-OH terminus at each nick, while the 5'-phosphate terminus at the nick. The net result is that a nonradioactive strand of DNA is replaced by a radioactive strand (Figure 6.2). The DNA is then denatured and used as a radioactive probe in hybridization experiments (Southern blots, northern blots, etc.).

Nick translation can be used with a variety of labels to generate probes suitable for most hybridization applications. It is also appropriate for the generation of biotinylated probes (described later).

A major advantage of nick translation over other uniform labelling methods is its flexibility with respect to probe size, specific activity and concentration. It is particularly suitable for the production of large quantities of probes and for use in multiple hybridization techniques and/or where a high probe concentration is required.

Primer Extension Method

Primers are synthetic oligodeoxyribonucleotides which are complementary to specific regions of known vector DNA. Some commonly used primers are M13 sequencing primer, pBR322 primer etc. The 3' termini of these primers serve as initiation site for template dependent DNA synthesis by enzymes like DNA polymerase I.

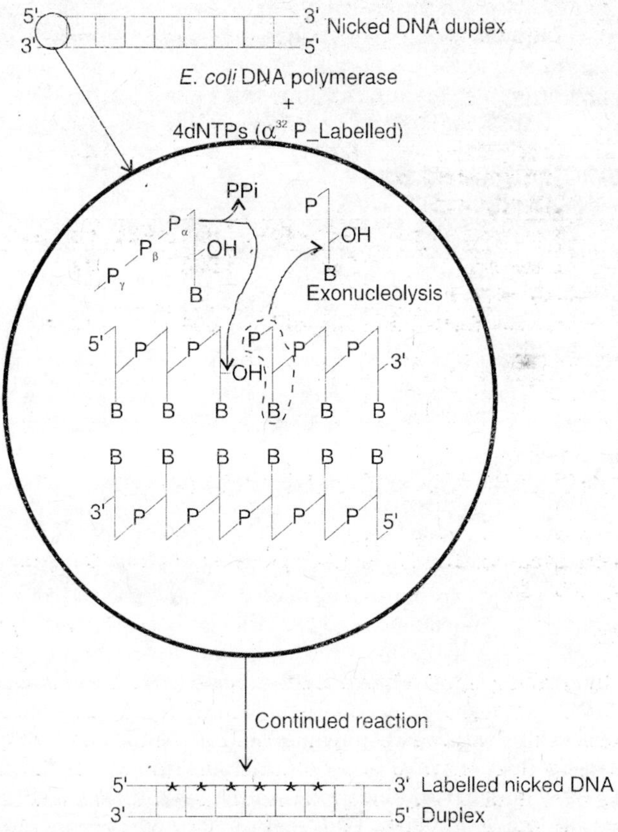

FIGURE 6.2: ^{32}P-labelling of duplex DNA by nick translation. Asterisks indicate radiolabelled phosphate groups.

DNA polymerase works by extending a short double-stranded region made by annealing an oligonucleotide primer to the single-stranded template. Thus this method of uniform labelling requires a primer which matches the probe sequence. Radiolabelling of primers can be done with two methods.

If the probe sequence is not known then random oligonucleotide labelling can be used (Figure 6.3). It is often in the case when natural cellular DNA is used. These primers are made by adding a mixture of all four bases at each step in the chemical synthesis reaction. The DNA is denatured and the two complementary strands are copied in the presence of labelled primers as well as, nucleoside triphosphates. The polymerase used is Klenow fragment derived from DNA polymerase-I of *E. coli*. Chance homology ensures that these primers anneal to the separated DNA strands at many points along their length, thus providing a base for polymerase to initiate DNA synthesis. This is only one of several uniform labelling methods.

The second method uses a unique primer to restrict labelling to a particular sequence of interest. In the primer extension method it is essential to use a polymerase lacking a 5'→3' exonuclease activity otherwise degradation of the primer will occur. Both the Klenow fragment of *E. coli* DNA polymerase I, which lacks the 5'→3' exonuclease activity and reverse transcriptase have been used successfully.

An advantage of random priming method is that is may be used to label relatively impure DNA. In primer extension method, there is not synthesis of DNA and labeled nucleotides are incorporated in concentrations. It is an ideal method for situations where high specific activity and low probe concentration are frequently employed.

Methods Based on RNA Polymerases

RNA polymerases catalyzes the synthesis of RNA from nucleoside triphosphates using a DNA template. Thus they can incorporate labelled ribonucleotides into RNA during transcription if such labelled nucleotides are provided to it. If a specific site of a vector or DNA is transcribed in such way, RNA probes (or transcripts) of defined length and sequence can be obtained.

Initially RNA probes were obtained from RNA polymerase from *E. coli*. This enzyme when used *in vitro* exhibited very little template and promoter specificity and therefore produces transcripts which have been initiated and terminated at random. Today, RNA polymerases from a number of phages have been used, which possess a high degree of specificity. Thus transcription can be limited to sequences cloned downstream of an appropriate promoter.

RNA probe's specific activity is determined solely by the specific activity of labelled nucleotide and moreover such probes are need not to be denatured before hybridization. These probes are more sensitive than nick translated probes because of avoidance of probe reannealing during hybridization (as RNA-RNA hybrids are more stable than RNA-DNA hybrids). A further advantage of RNA probes is that non specifically bound probe can be removed with RNase A. RNase A is very specific for single stranded RNA.

The only difficulty with RNA polymerase-based-labelling is that a specific promoter is read by RNA polymerases before transcripting the downstream. This promoter has to be subcloned and inserted into the vector. However, once an insert has been cloned into such a vector, DNA probes may still be prepared using nick translation or random primer labelling.

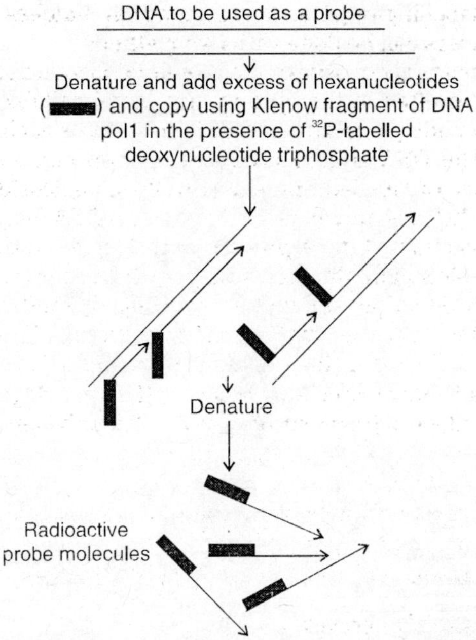

FIGURE 6.3: The principle of random primed (oligo-) labelling. The DNA to be used as a probe is denatured by heating and mixed with hexanucleotides of random sequence which then act as primers for DNA synthesis.

END-LABELLING OF NUCLEIC ACIDS

A wide variety of techniques is available for introducing label at either the 3' or 5' ends of linear DNA or RNA. Usually only a single label is introduced at the terminus. Nucleic acid can be 5' end labelled using T4 polynucleotide kinase. The enzyme catalyzes the transfer of the γ-phosphate of ribonucleoside 5'-triphosphate donor to the 5'hydroxyl group of a poly- or oligo-nucleotide or even to nucleoside-3-triphosphate. Radiolabelled phosphate group is donated by [γ^{32}-P] ATP to DNA or RNA containing a 5'-hydroxyl terminus. This is termed as forward reaction.

If 5'-phosphate group is present in DNA or RNA, then it is removed with alkaline phosphatase. This reaction is driven by excess ADP which causes the enzyme to transfer the terminal 5'-phosphate from DNA to ADP (Figure 6.4). This is known as exchange reaction. The DNA is rephosphorylated by transfer of labeled γ-phosphate from [γ^{32}-P] ATP.

The major advantages of 5'-end labelling are:

1. Both DNA and RNA can be labelled.
2. Oligonucleotide can be conveniently labelled *e.g.* for detection of mutants following site-directed mutagenesis.
3. Location of labelled group is known.
4. Very small fragments can be labelled.
5. Restriction digest fragment can be labelled.

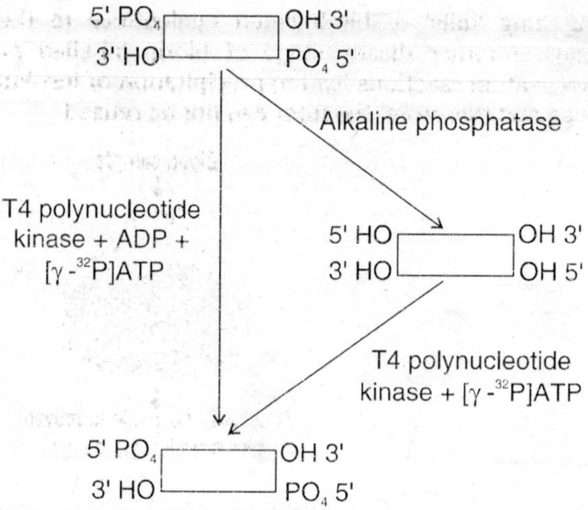

FIGURE 6.4: The 5'-end labelling reaction using T4 polynucleotide kinase.

DNA fragments also can be labelled at their 3'end by using terminal deoxynucleotidyl transferase, however, this method is not of wide use.

CHOICE OF LABEL

There are two technical parameters, resolution and sensitivity, which determines the success of probe application. High degree of resolution is required to known the relative position of a nucleic acid fragment. High sensitivity is necessary because sequence of interest may be present at low abundance.

Other factors are probe stability, safety and ease of use. Broadly labels can be categorised into radioactive and non radioactive types.

Radioactive Labels

These labels have wider applications as they can be easily detected with autoradiography. Their detection gives two important information, firstly about occurrence of hybridization between probes and target DNA and secondly about their position. Radioactive methods using ^{32}P are easily detectable. They are used often.

Non Radioactive Labels

A number of non radioactive labels for probes are available but biotin is widely used.

Biotin Labelled Probes: Biotinylated probes are prepared through a nick-translation reaction by replacing nucleotides with biotinylated derivatives. After hybridization and washing, detection of hybrids is done by adding avidine and going through a series of cytochemical reactions which finally give a blue colour whose intensity is proportional to the amount of biotin in the hybrid. There are several advantages of using biotinylated probes. For major advantages of using biotinylated probes are: (a) assays employ non- toxic materials, with longer half-life (b) can be prepared in advance in bulk and stored at -20 °C for repeated uses (c) detection of hybrids is much faster than by radioactive probes. A limitation of this technology is that biotinylated sites are limited, thus decreasing the intensity of signal. It has been solved by adding long 'tails' of biotinylated nucleotides to the probes through enzymatic methods. Another disadvantage of biotin labelled probes is that the cytochemical visualization reactions lead to precipitation of insoluble material which can not be removed and therefore, the filter can not be reused.

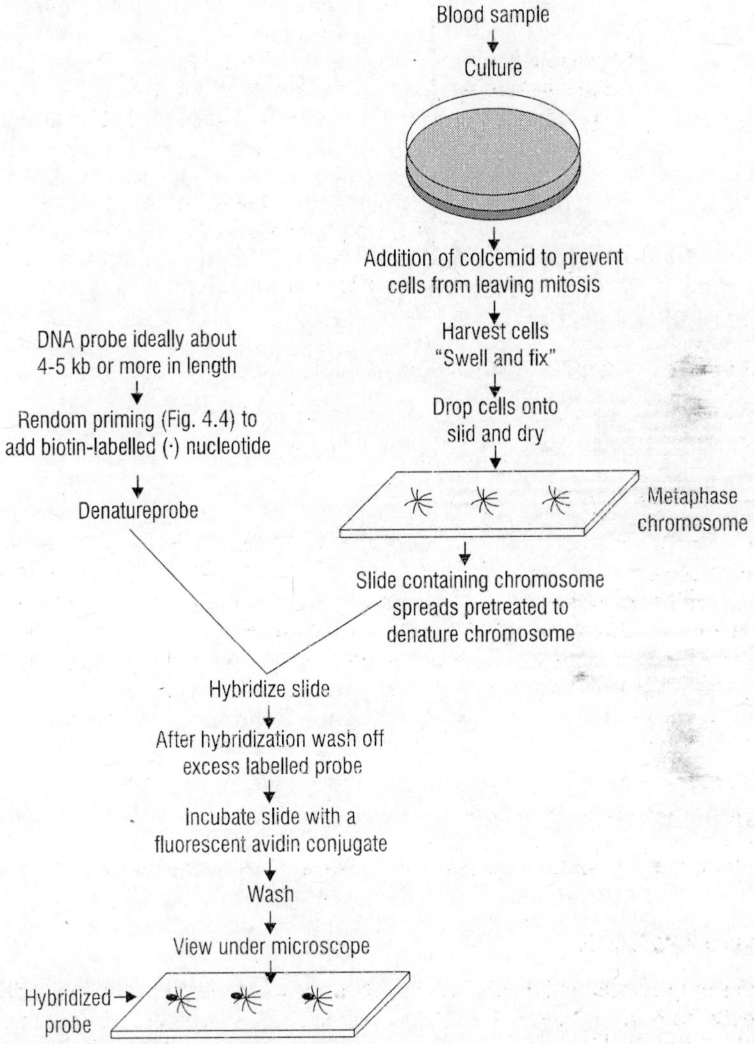

FIGURE 6.5: FISH is used where gene mapping is done with *in-situ* hybridization. It uses a non-radioactive labelling system involving biotin attached. When viewed under special filters the specific sites of DNA probe can be seen on a chromosome.

Digoxigenin Labelled Probes: Another method is to label DNA with digoxigen-labeled deoxyuridive triphosphate (dig-ÂUTP). After hybridization to the target DNA the hybrids are detected by enzyme-linked immunoassay using an antibody conjugate *e.g.* anti digoxigenin alkaline phosphatase. Enzyme reporter molecules with enzymes can also be used as label.

Alternatives to Biotin and Digoxigenin Labeling: Other ligands (*e.g.* hapten determinants, 2, 4-dinitrophenol, arsenate derivatives, etc.) are attached to specific proteins that can be tagged with enzymes or fluorescent molecules. It is possible to monitor many probes simultaneously by using several different ligands since each ligand would yield a different signal. A chemiluminescent (light emitting) probe system has also been developed in which two different probes complementary to a continuous segment of DNA hybridize to adjacent of a gene. The first label is a chemiluminescent complex which emits light at a specific wavelength. This emission excites the label molecule on the second probe to emit light at a different wave length which can be detected using a photomultiplier device. The processes called non-radioactive energy transfer, and can occur only if the two probes hybridize correctly and the two labels are close to each other.

THE MAJOR DISADVANTAGE OF BIOTIN, AND OF OTHER NONRADIOACTIVE LABELS, IS LOW SENSITIVITY IN COMPARISON TO RADIOACTIVE LABELS MAPPING GENES ON SPECIFIC CHROMOSOMES

One of the most important applications of nucleic acid hybridization is construction of genetic maps. This helps in determining the chromosomal location of individual genes. There are three commonly used methods that differ in the degree of resolution they afford viz somatic cell hybrids, *In situ*, hybridization and genetic linkage mapping.

Somatic Cell Hybrids

Somatic cell hybrids are prepared by fusing together human and rodent cells using reagents, such as polyethylene glycol or Sendai virus. The reagents help in membrane fusion. The resulting hybrid cells are then grown in culture medium containing selective agents which allow only the hybrid cells to grow. In hybrids produced using human and rodent cells the rodent chromosomes are retained, while the human chromosomes are lost. This random chromosome loss occurs during continued culture and shows no apparent selectivity for individual human chromosomes.

In Situ Hybridization

In this technique a labelled DNA probe is hybridized to metaphase chromosome. The position of hybridization is visualized at the light microscope level. Metaphase chromosomes are liberated from cells and bound to the surface of a cover slip. The DNA within the chromosomes is denatured in such a way that the individual chromosomes remain visually identifiable. The probe is labelled, either by incorporation of a ^{3}H-nucleotide or non-isotopically. The chromosomes are incubated with the labelled probe for many hours and, after hybridization, the excess unbound probe is washed away and the annealed probe detected.

The signal is detected using a fluorescent molecule thus is called fluorescent *in-situ* hybridization (FISH). It is more sensitive than radiolabelling and can be used to give a fairly precise position of hybridization.

Thus FISH is particularly useful for determining the respective locations of two markers on the same chromosome. The two probes are labelled with different immunologically labelled adducts and a single hybridization reaction is performed. The two probes are then detected using fluorochromes which emit at different wave lengths when excited by UV light, such as rhodamine (red fluorescence) and fluorescein (green fluorescence). This technique has been used for probes which are separated by few hundred kilobases of DNA on same chromosome. The FISH technique can also be applied to interphase nuclei, which allows accurate ordering of probes along a chromosome when they are separated by no more than 20-30 kilobases.

Transposon Tagging

Isolating a eukaryotic gene by transposon tagging involves inserting into target DNA, fractionating fragments of the latter on southern blots (described later in this chapter) and hybridizing the transposon with a probe. Cleaving out the transposon, together with flanking DNA, reveals the adjoining sequences of a gene. The probes are made for these adjoining sequences to find the fragment having gene of interest.

Presence of transposon is confirmed by altered phenotype. This method was first employed to isolate *white* locus in *Drosophila*. The mutants with *white- apricot* eyes harboured a *copia* retrotransposon as well as accompanying *white* locus.

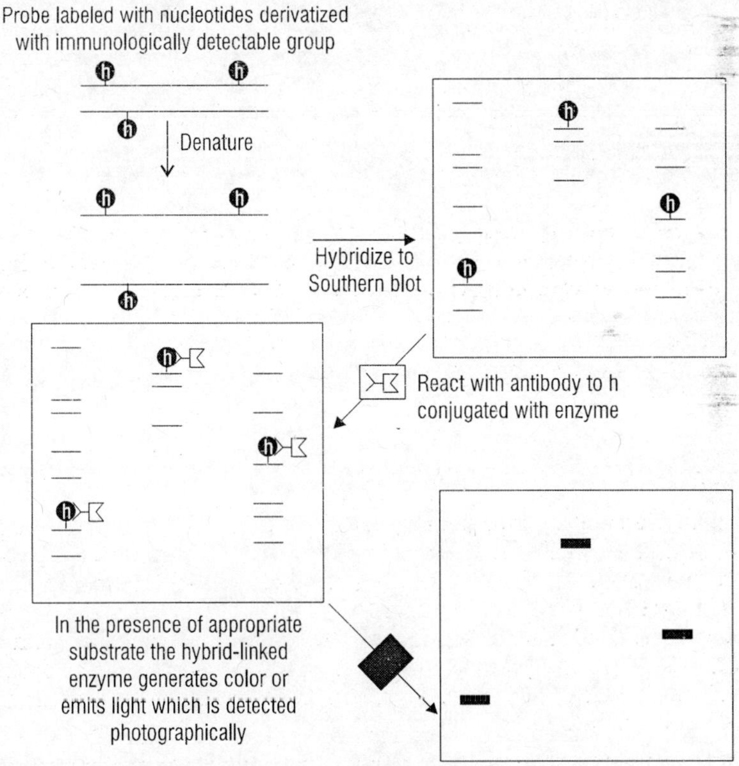

FIGURE 6.6: The principle of non-radioactive detection methods for in-situ hybridization.

Genetic Linkage Mapping

This form of mapping is used to construct genetic linkage maps of individual chromosomes and also to localize genes involved in genetic disease. Genetic linkage analysis relies on an ability to estimate the frequency of crossing over (recombination) that occurs between homologous chromosomes during meiosis. The closer two genetic markers are to each other then the lower is the chance that they will be separated during meiosis. The statistical probability that two markers are linked is measured as the logarithm of the odds (Lod). A Lod score of 3 is usually taken as the threshold of significance, while a Lod score below -2 suggests that the two loci are not linked. Lods between -2 and +3 are not significant.

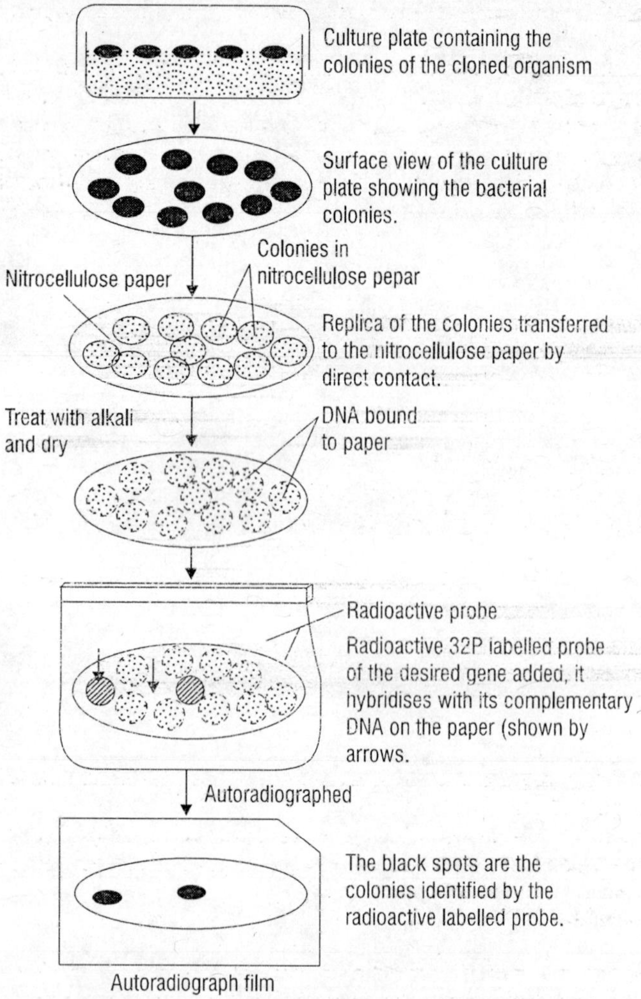

FIGURE 6.7: Colony hybridization to identify the clones containing the DNA of interest.

GENOMIC LIBRARY

The complete set of cloned fragments of DNA of an organism is known as **genomic library** or **gene library**. Such a library contains all or most of the genes present in the cell or the organism. It is difficult to identify a particular gene from an organism and then clone it. Hence the organism's entire genome as DNA fragments is cloned and the clone containing the sequence of interest is identified.

Cloning experiments can be divided into two types (1) those where the cloned DNA segment is of unknown composition and function and, (2) those where the cloned DNA segment is of known composition and function. In the first approach the entire cellular DNA has to be fragmented into clonable size by either digestion with restriction endonucleases or, mechanical sheering.

These experiments with randomly cloned fragments are known as 'shot gun cloning experiments'.

The chromosomal DNA of the organism of interest is isolated. It is then treated with a known restriction enzyme to obtain DNA fragments of clonable size. The fragments are cloned using appropriate cloning vectors in any organisms like bacteria, virus or yeast. For identification, a marker gene is inserted while multiplying in vector. Hybridization of such genes can be carried out by two major techniques *viz.* colony hybridization and plaque hybridization depending on the type of vector used.

Colony Hybridization

Once a genomic library or cDNA library is available, gene sequence can be isolated by colony hybridization techniques. It involves replica plating the colonies formed by transformed cell into nitrocellulose filter and their *in situ* hybridization with a radioactive probe. This method was first developed by Hogness and Grunestein (1975). Procedure is described in following steps:

1. The cloned yeast colonies, bacterial colonies or phage plaques to be tested are transferred from the culture plate on to a nitrocellulose filter paper by replica plating (Figure 6.7).
2. The filter with the colony replicas is treated with NaOH to lyses the cells/phages and to denature DNA.
3. The filter is then baked to fix the DNA.
4. It is then treated with a radioactive ^{32}P labelled single stranded DNA probe that is complementary to the ssDNA of interest.
5. The filter is washed to remove the unbound excess probe, dried and then autoradiographed.
6. The DNA fragments hybridized with the radioactive probe can be detected on the autoradiograph film.
7. This indicates that the cells in the corresponding colonies contain the desired gene. The colony is taken out from the master culture plate for mass culture.

Plaque Hybridization

This technique is applicable where a chimeric phage particles are carrying the gene of interest. In such a situation, a bacterial lawn is infected with a mixture of chimeric phage particles (*i.e.* the library) and a large number of plaques develop overnight. These plaques can be treated just like the colonies in colony hybridization to identify and isolate the chimeric phage particle carrying the gene of interest. Two new techniques have shown their potential in gene isolation and characterization. They are chromosome walking and chromosome jumping. Let us have a small account on both of these techniques.

Chromosome Walking

Identification of fragments with overlapping sequences may be a key to the reconstruction or characterization of large chromosome regions. This is achieved by the technique popurlarly described as chromosome walking.

The technique of chromosome walking involves the following steps:

1. From the genomic library a alone of interest (identified by a probe is selected.
2. One end of the clone is subcloned.
3. The subcloned fragment of the selected clone may be hybridized with other clones in the library and a second clone hybridizing with the subclone of the first clone is identified due to presence of overlapping region.
4. The end of the second is then subcloned and used for hybridization with other clones. This helps in identifying a third clone having overlapping region with the subcloned end of the second clone.
5. Identified third clone is also subcloned and hybridized with clones in the same manner and the procedure may be continued.
6. Restriction map of each selected clone is prepared and compared to know the region of overlapping, so that identification of few overlapping restriction sites resembles the walking along the chromosome or along a long chromosome segment.

Regions of chromosomes approaching 1000 kb have been mapped following the above technique. Restriction maps of entire chromosomes can be prepared in this manner following the technique of chromosome walking.

Chromosome Jumping

In order to bring the molecular marker close to the gene of interest, *chromosome jumping* approach has been utilized. This technique can be described in the following steps:

1. The distance of 'jumps' or 'hopsize' (*e.g.* 100 kb or 200 kb) i s determined.
2. Genomic DNA molecules in the range of selected size are selected through pulsed-field gel electrophoresis.
3. For circularization of DNA segments, ligation between two ends of each long linear DNA molecule is allowed using T4 ligase).
4. These circular DNA circles are digested with EcoRI.
5. Phage vector Ch3A lac, is also cut with EcoRI and used for cloning small DNA fragments.
6. Such cloned DNA fragments represent the jumping library, which can be plated on a bacterial host and screened through the technique of plaque hybridization.

The technique of chromosome jumping helps in narrowing the gap between the gene and available molecular markers. After several cycles of chromosome jumping followed by cloning the regions broximal to the gene, it will be possible to approach very close to the desired gene capable approached and cloned. The gene for **cystic fibrosis** has recently been isolated using this technique.

CLEAVING DNA WITH RESTRICTION ENZYMES

After locating gene of interest in colony or on chromosome, the DNA is extracted and cleaved with enzymes. Most restriction enzymes cleave DNA molecules in a site specific manner. The genomic DNA from an individual organism is digested with either a single or more restriction enzymes. This results in fragmentation of DNA molecules with variation in length. These fragments are known as restriction fragment length polymorphisms or RFLPs. Since restriction enzymes cut DNA in a sequence specific manner, every homologous DNA molecule will be cut at exactly the same sites. This allows to isolate large quantities of specific DNA fragments for subcloning and isolating the DNA sequence of interest.

The sizes of the restriction fragments can be determined by polyacrylamide or agrose gel electrophoresis. It also helps in separation of various RFLPs. Here few electrophoritic and blotting techniques are described.

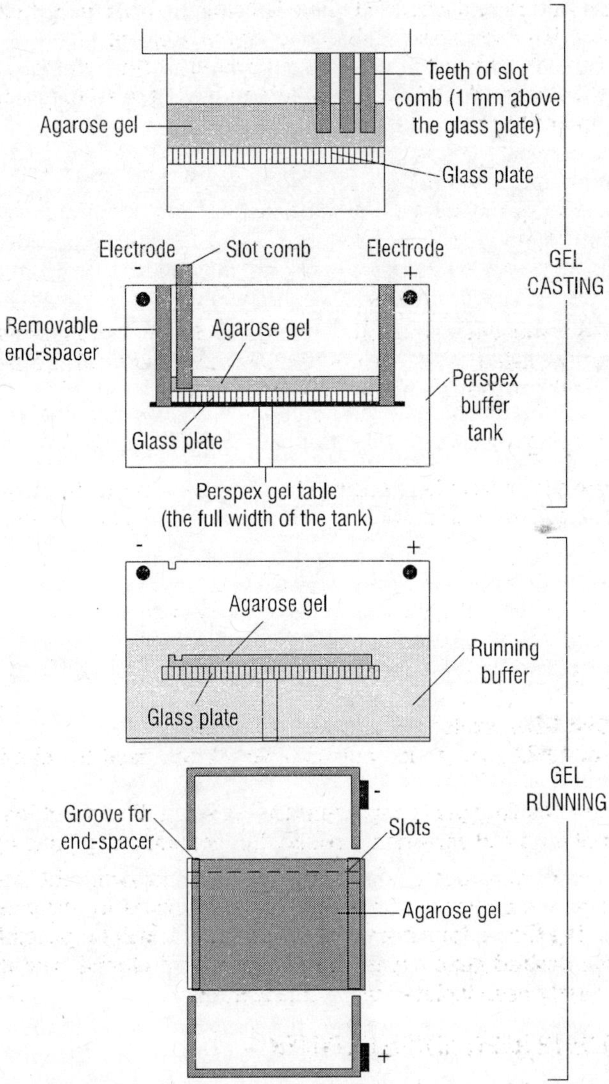

FIGURE 6.8: Agarose gel electrophoresis.

Gel Electrophoresis

Nucleic acid molecules can be distinguished by differences in their chain length, and study of gene organization and expression includes nucleic acid hybridization with a chain length measurement.

DNA and RNA have a net negative charge. At neutral pH therefore, these molecules migrate towards the positive terminal when placed in an electric field. This process of electrophoresis is performed in an agarose or polycrylamide gel. Nucleic acids are loaded into slots in the gel and allowed to migrate towards the positive terminal. The pores in the gel act to sieve the molecules. Therefore, the mobility of a particular nucleic acid species depends on its length. All the molecules of a particular size move at approximately the same rate through the gel, forming a band which gradually increases in width during electrophoresis because of diffusion. The size of the molecules can be estimated by running DNA molecules of known size in a parallel track on the gel, and determining their migration position relative to the species of unknown size.

Polyacrylamide has a smaller average pore size than agarose and so is effective at separating molecules of 10-1000 nucleotides in length (1000 nucleotides is termed 1 kilobase or 1 kb), with very high resolution. The larger pores in agarose allow it to resolve much bigger molecules, up to 100 kb in length. However, the separated molecules migrate as a wider band so that the resolution (*i.e.* the ability to separate molecules which differ only slightly in size) is lower with agarose than with polyacrylamide. In pulsed-field gel electrophoresis (PFGE) the electrical field across the gel is repeatedly switched back and forth between two or more directions. This allows very long DNA molecules, several million base pairs in length, to be separated, since very big molecules change direction less rapidly as they move through the agarose gel.

After gel electrophoresis, the nucleic acid molecules must be detected. They can be visualized directly by including ethidium bromide in the polyacrylamide or agarose gel. This dye binds to double-stranded nucleic acids by intercalating between adjacent base pairs, and emits a red fluorescence when exposed to UV radiation. As little as 5-10 ng of DNA can be detected. If the nucleic acid molecules are radioactively labelled, then individual resolved species can be detected by autoradiography.

BLOTTING TECHNIQUES

Analysis of DNA by Southern Blotting

In 1975, E. M. Southern invented a procedure to identify the locations of genes and other DNA sequences on restriction fragments separated by gel electrophoresis. The essential feature of this technique is the transfer of the DNA molecules separated by gel electrophoresis to a nitrocellulose or nylon membrane.

The DNA is denatured either prior to or during transfer by placing the gel in an alkaline solution. After transfer is complete, the DNA is immobilized on the membrane by drying or UV-induced cross-linking to the filter. A radioactive DNA (*probe*) containing the sequence of interest is then hybridized or annealed with the immobilized DNA on the membrane. The probe will anneal to form a double helix only with complementary DNA molecules on the membrane. Nonannealed probe is then washed off the membrane, and the washed membrane is exposed to X-ray film that detects the presence of the radioactivity in the bound probe. After the autoradiogram is developed, the dark bands show the position(s) of DNA sequences that have hybridized with the probe.

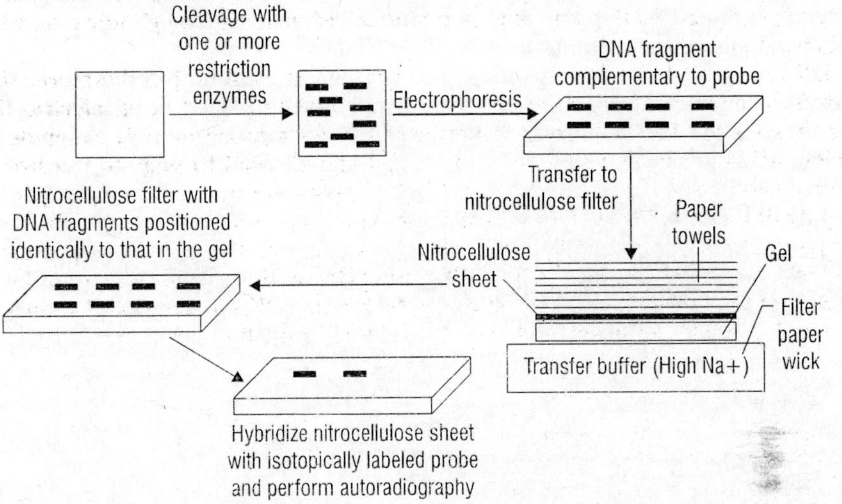

FIGURE 6.9: Southern blotting method of analyzing DNA segment that share homology with a nucleic acid probe.

The ability to transfer DNA restriction fragments or other DNA molecules that have been separated by gel electrophoresis to nitrocellulose or nylon membranes for hybridization studies and other types of analyses has proven to be extremely useful. Such transfers of DNA to membranes are called Southern blots after E. M. Southern, who developed the technique.

Analysis of RNAs by Northern Blot Hybridizations

As DNA molecules can be transferred from agarose gels to nitrocellulose or nylon membranes for hybridization studies, RNA molecules can also be separated by agarose gel electrophoresis similarly and transferred for analyses analyzed. Such RNA transfers are used routinely in molecular genetics laboratories and are called *northern blots* as it is the mirror image of the Southern blotting technique.

The northern blot procedure is essentially identical to that used for Southern blot transfers however, degradation by RNA molecules are more sensitive to degradation by RNases. Thus, gloves must be worn at all times to prevent contamination of solutions with RNases on one's fingers. In addition, all glassware must be baked overnight to inactivate RNases, and all chemical reagents must be baked or be highly purified to ensure that they are RNase-free. RNase molecules are extremely stable enzymes; they are not inactivated by boiling or other treatments that would totally destroy most enzymes. Most RNA molecules contain considerable secondary structure. Therefore, they must be kept denatured during electrophoresis to separate them on the basis of size. Denaturation is accomplished by adding formaldehyde or some other chemical denaturant to the loading buffer and the electrophoresis running buffer. After transfer to an appropriate membrane, the RNA blot is hybridized to either RNA or DNA probes just as with Southern blots. Now an alternative to nitrocellulose, DBM or diazobenzyloxymethyl paper is used. It may be reused several times for different probes, without appreciable loss of nucleic acid signal.

Northern blot hybridizations are extremely useful in studies of gene expression. They can be used to determine whether a particular gene is transcribed in all tissues of an organism or only certain tissues. They can also be used to study the temporal pattern of expression of individual genes during growth and development. Major disadvantage with northern blot hybridizations is that it only measure the accumulation of RNA transcripts. but explains nothing about why the observed accumulation occurs.

Analysis of Proteins by Western Blot Techniques

Polyacrylamide gel electrophoresis has been used as an important tool for the separation and characterization of proteins.

Since many functional proteins are composed of two or more subunits, individual polypeptides are separated by electrophoresis in the presence of the detergent sodium dodecyl sulfate (SDS), which denatures the proteins (Figure 6.10).

After electrophoresis, the proteins are commonly detected by treating with Coomassie blue or silver stain. However, the separated polypeptides in the gel can also be transferred to a nitrocellulose membrane, and individual proteins can be detected by using specific antibodies. This transfer of proteins from acrylamide gels to nitrocellulose membranes is called western blotting and is performed by using an electric current-so-called *electroblotting*. After transfer, a specific protein of interest is identified by placing the membrane with the immobilized proteins in a solution containing an antibody to the protein. Nonbound antibodies are then washed off the membrane, and the presence of the initial ("primary") antibody is detected by placing the membrane in a solution containing a "secondary" antibody. This "secondary" antibody reacts with immunoglobulins (the group of protein containing all antibodies) in general. The secondary antibody is conjugated to either a radioactive isotope (permitting autoradiography) or an enzyme that produces a visible product when the proper substrate is added. The western blot procedure is a very powerful tool for identifying and characterizing specific gene-products.

Dot Blots and Slot Blots

Another variety of Southern or Northern blots is dot blots or slot blots. In dot blots, cloned or purified extract of DNAs is tested by spotting them adjacent to each other on a nitrocellulose membrane. DNA blots thus produced are immobilized and denatured so that they are bound on the membrane as single stranded DNA blots. The membrane is then hybridized with readioactively labelled probe (DNA or RNA). The dot representing sequence related to probe will light up by autoradiography. The intensity of the dot will indicate the relative concentration of a sequence related to the probe in the DNA sample used for a particular dot. No steps involving digestion with enzyme, gel electrophoresis or transfer from gel to membrane are needed in this technique. Dot blot are useful in screening viral genomic RNA, RNA transcripts and especially in samples where restriction sites are not considered.

Sometimes, an apparatus is used for placing spots on the membrane, through slots made in this equipment. The spots made thus are in the form of oblong slots rather than round blots. These slots are used just like dot blots and are described as slot blots.

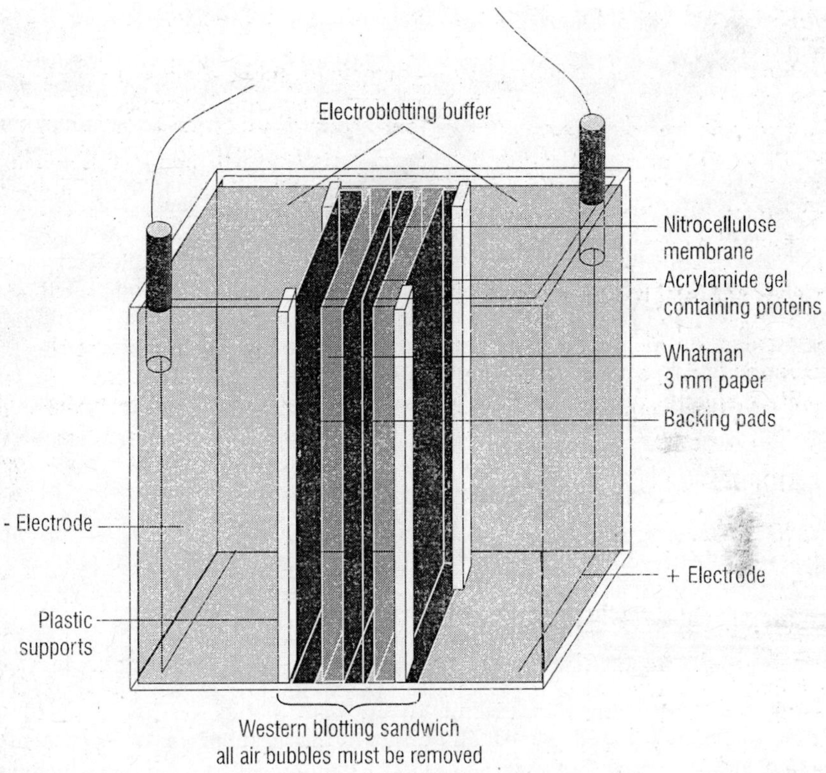

FIGURE 6.10: Diagram of a typical Western blotting or electroblotting apparatus. An electric current is used to transfer the proteins from the gel to the nitrocellulose membrane placed next to it in the blotting sandwich. All other components of the sandwich function to provide gentle but firm support; tight contact between the gel and the membrane is essential for good transfer. All bubbles must be carefully removed from the sandwich to assure uniform flow of current and complete transfer of all proteins.

DETECTION OF RFLPS

A RFLP can be demonstrated using the following steps:

1. Extract and purify DNA from several individuals which may differ in some respects among themselves.
2. Digest DNA samples with a restriction endonuclease.
3. Subject each DNA digest to gel electrophoresis separately, but on the same gel slab.
4. The DNA fragments of different lengths resulting from digestion can be separated by gel electrophoresis, but the differences in the distribution patterns of fragments in several DNA samples due to digestion by several endonucleases can not be detected directly. This is because the number of fragments is large and the range in size is rather continuous, such that they form a continuous smear on the gel. Electrophoresis is, therefore, followed by the following steps.
5. Fragments are transferred from gel to nitrocellulose filters using the technique of **Southern blotting**.
6. The filters with small fragments, fully or partially homologous to the probe, can

be detected by autoradiography after hybridization.

With a sufficient number of digests, it is possible to deduce the origin of each band on the gel, that is, which enzyme or combinations of enzymes have generated it. This yields a restriction enzyme cleavage map or restriction map. Obtaining such a map is very often essential first step in analyzing a piece of DNA of unknown structure. Another method is by labelling with probe followed by autoradiography. Since DNA clones having repetitive DNA may hybridize with many fragments, they will give a smear on autoradiography. Therefore, unique DNA sequences are generally used as probes for detecting RFLPs. The DNA fragments hybridizing with the probe, can be visualized by autoradiography, and will be called RFLPs at the phenotypic level. RFLPs can be studied in a set of related species, using a random or a specific DNA probe. The similarities and differences be used to infer phylogenetic relationships. This has been done in a number of cases, both in plants and in animals. RFLPs have also been used to prepare chromosome mops in humans mice, fruitfly, maize, tomato, lettuce and rice.

DNA SEQUENCING

Restriction enzyme mapping and Southern blotting help establish the gross organization of a piece of DNA, and allow the approximate position of sequences of interest to be determined. The next step in analysis is normally to determine the nucleotide sequence.

Methods for Analyzing DNA Sequence

Our present ability to sequence essentially any DNA molecule is the result of four major developments. (1) The most important breakthrough was the discovery of restriction enzymes and their use in preparing homogeneous samples of specific segments of chromosomes. (2) A second major advance was the improvement of gel electrophoresis procedures to the point where DNA fragments that different in length by a single nucleotide could be resolved. (3) The development of gene cloning techniques greatly facilitated the preparation of large quantities of a particular gene or DNA sequence of interest for use in sequencing studies. (4) Finally, two different approaches to the rapid sequencing of DNA molecules (e.i. by chemical degradation and by chain termination) were developed in the period from 1974 to 1977.

Sequencing by Chemical Degradation

Determination of DNA sequence depends upon the resolution obtained from polycylamide gels which are run in the presence of denaturant *e.g.* urea. If two single-stranded DNA molecules, identical in sequence over most of their length but differing in just one base on one of the two molecules, are subjected to electrophoresis they will be separated. In the chemical degradation procedure a DNA restriction fragment is isotopically labelled with P at either its 5' or its 3' termini and each of the two strands is separated and isolated. The DNA is then partially modified with chemical reagents specific for the different bases, and cleaved at the modified nucleotides. This generates a set of molecules differing in length but with the same isotopically labelled terminus. These fragments are subjected to denaturing gel electrophoresis in parallel slots of high resolution gel, and the sequence of the DNA can be deduced from the resulting autoradiogram.

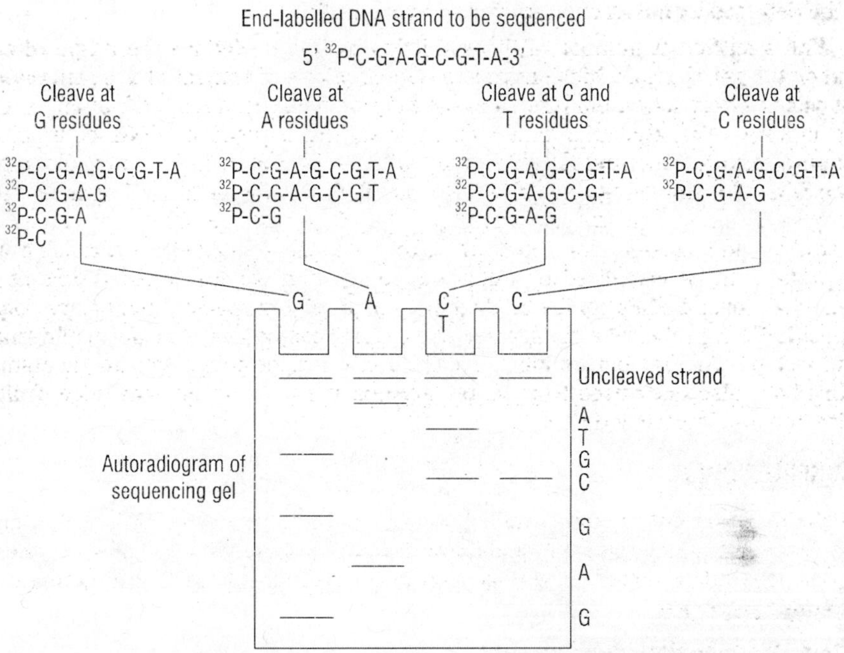

FIGURE 6.11: DNA sequence analysis by the chemical degradation (Maxam and Gilbert) technique.

Sequencing by Chain Termination

In practice the chemical degradation procedure has been replaced by chain termination method. In this procedure DNA is synthesized rather than degraded, but the principle is similar to the chemical method. DNA polymerases function by adding a primer, a short synthetic oligonucleotide, to pre-existent DNA strand, to provide a fixed 5' terminus for the growing chain.

The reaction is performed in the presence of chain terminators. These nucleotide derivatives act as blocking group at their 3' hydroxyl terming and once there are incorporated into the growing chains, they prevent further addition of nucleotides. For example, it dideoxy GTP, is mixed with unmodifies GTP and the other three nucleoside triphosphates, terminates at a subset of G residues in the newly synthesized strand. Four parallel reactions are run with dideoxy radiolabelled nucleoside triphosphates of all four kinds are included. The nucleotide sequence of the template strand can be deduced by comparison of the pattern of autoradiographic bands in the four lanes of the gel.

A suitable template for single-strand DNA sequence analysis can be created by inserting the double-stranded template DNA into the genome of a bacterial virus which naturally packages only one of the two strands into viral particles. Another method is denaturing of double-stranded DNA template by treatment with alkali. An excess of primer is added before re-annealing occurs, so that primer will compete with the complementary strand for annealing to the template. This is a preferable method over insertion of DNA into viral vector.

DNA sequence analysis using chain terminators is best performed using a single-stranded template. This allows the primer to be free accessible to the template.

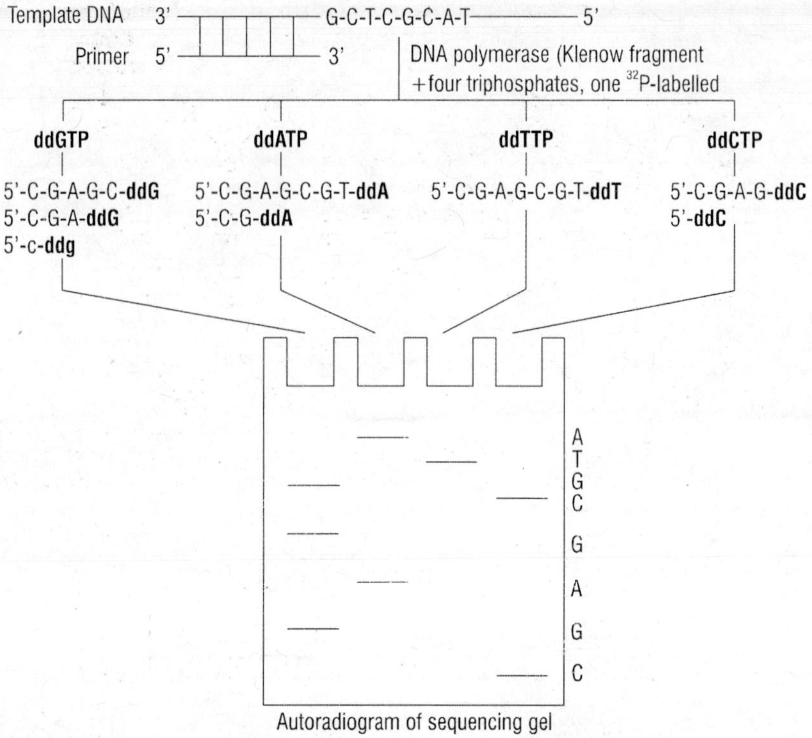

FIGURE 6.12: DNA sequence analysis by the chain termination (Sanger) method.

The major disadvantage of double-stranded DNA sequence analysis is the presence of competing complementary strand. This leads to a higher level of sequencing artifacts, like presence of more than one band. In such situation it may be impossible to decide, which is the correct residue at that position. Artefacts of this kind are not restricted to double-strand DNA sequence analysis; some level of artefacts is a universal problem in sequence analysis.

The DNA sample then re-sequenced using another primer, or by using the other strand (*i.e.* the strand which is complementary to that used in the original analysis) as template.

Even when a single-stranded DNA, molecules with more than 500 nucleotides, clearly it is not possible on a polyacrylamide gel to resolve when the molecules are larger than about the nucleotides. This sets the upper limit to the length of sequence to be determined. One way to extend from a known into an unknown region of sequence is to synthesize an oligonucleotide primer which is complementary to a tract near the end of the region whose sequence has already been established. In this way it is possible to 'walk' along a sequence, at each step synthesizing a new primer which is used to extend the region of known sequence. Alternatively, it is possible to delete sequences enzymatically from the template at a position downstream of the annealing site of the primer, to generate a deletion series. The nucleotide sequence of a set of such molecules can be used to deduce the sequence of the intact template.

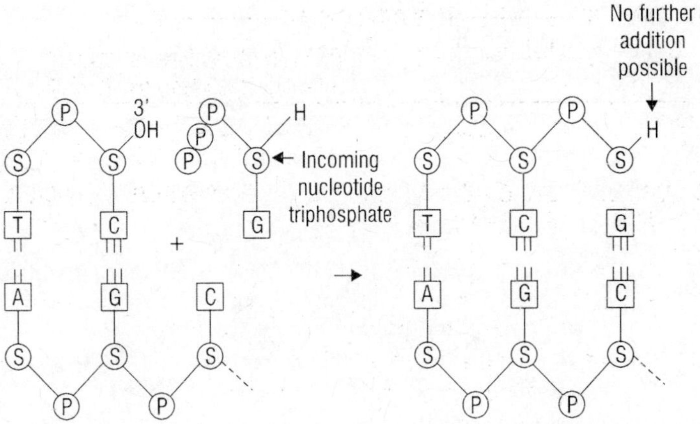

FIGURE 6.13: The chemical basis of sequence analysis using chain terminators. This is a representation of a reaction in which a dideoxy G residue incorporated into the growing chain blocks further incorporation.

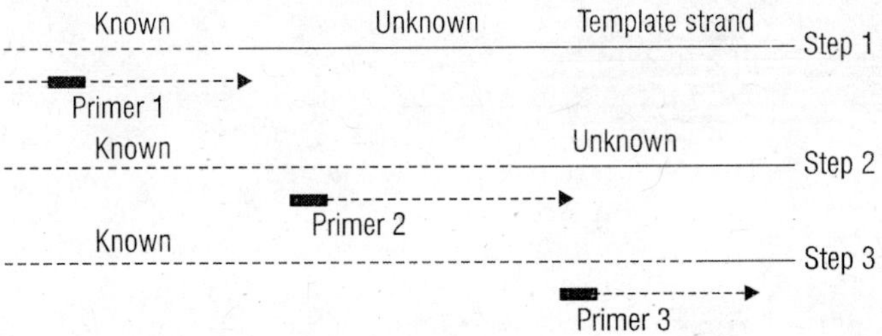

FIGURE 6.14: DNA sequence analysis by *primer walking*.

By determining the sequence of both strands of a DNA molecule, and confirming that the two deduced sequences are perfectly complementary, it is possible to detect and eliminate artefacts generated in the reactions or during electrophoresis. When this check is performed, DNA sequence can be established with a very high degree of accuracy.

Direct DNA Sequencing Using PCR (Also Called Ligation Mediated PCR=LMPCR)

Polymerase chain reaction (PCR) has also been used for sequencing the amplified DNA product. This method of DNA sequencing is faster and more reliable and can utilize either the whole genomic DNA or cloned fragments for sequencing a particular DNA segment. The DNA sequencing using PCR involves two steps: (i) generation of sequencing templates (double stranded or single stranded) using PCR and (ii) sequencing of PCR products eight with the thermolabile DNA polymerase or with the thermostable Taq DNA polymerase. Thus the DNA sequencing method using PCR eliminates the need of cloning the DNA in single stranded DNA phage vector *i.e.* M13. Although double stranded DNA product of PCR can be utilized for sequencing, this may cause difficulty due to reassociation after denaturation thus preventing the sequencing primer from annealing to its complementary sequence to allow extension. To reduce this problem, either a variant of the standard method for sequencing double stranded DNA is employed or single stranded DNA templates are produced following **asymmetric PCR** earlier discussed in Chapter 4.

A number of thermolabile DNA polymerases have been used for sequencing of *in vitro* amplified DNA. Alternatively, **Taq polymerase** (thermostable enzyme) used for PCR can also be used for sequencing reaction. In either case, Sanger's synthetic method involving incorporation of dideozynucleotide (ddNTP) for chain termination is used for sequencing. However, Maxam and Gilbert's chemical degradation method can also be used.

In Sanger's method, as usual, four mixtures ar prepared, each using one of the four ddNTP. The sequencing primer is labelled with ^{32}P and the mixtures with amplified DNA, Taq polymerase and appropriate buffer are incubated at 70 °C for 5 min. The reaction is stopped by addition of formamide stop solution in each tube and mixtures are run on polyacrylamide sequencing gel to obtain the ladders, which can be read by computer or manually. This method using PCR helped in automation of DNA sequencing.

Automated DNA Sequence Analysis

Using the chain termination method, DNA sequencing can be mechanized to make the process rapid. In a conventional sequence reaction described above four separate singlestrand extension reactions are performed, with each containing a different chain-terminating dideoxynucleoside triphosphate. The radiolabelled reaction products are separated on four separate tracks of a polyacrylamide gel. In machine-based sequencing a single reaction is run, with each of the four dideoxynucleoside triphosphates containing a different fluorescent label.

When excited by an argon laser, the fluorescent labels emit light at a different wavelength. The same chain-termination reactions are carried out; however, it is no longer necessary to run the products in separate lanes of a gel. The reaction products are mixed and run in a single lane in a gel and as the different length fragments pass the laser each fluorescent label gives a unique signal which is stored in the computer.

Machine-based DNA sequencing is beginning to change the speed and scope of sequencing projects dramatically. The first complete genomic sequences were those of simple viruses such as the SV40 tumor virus, containing around 500 based of DNA. Recently, the DNA sequence of over 106 000 bases of DNA from human chromosome 19 was determined in a few months using DNA sequencing machines. The sequence of a significant fraction of the *E. coli* genome has been established, the entire sequence of yeast chromosome 3 is known, and there are plans eventually to determine the sequence of the entire human genome.

MECHANICAL SHEARING OF DNA

In addition to digestion DNA with restriction endonucleases to produce discrete fragments, there are a variety of treatments which result in non specific breakage. Non specific endonucleases and chemical degradation can be used but the only method that has been much applied to gene manipulation involves mechanical shearing.

The long, thin threads which constitute duplex DNA can not be easily broken by shear forces in solution. Intense sonication with ultrasound can reduce the length to about 300 nucleotide pairs. More controlled shearing can be achieved by high-speed stirring in a blender. Breakage occurs essentially at random with respect to DNA sequence. The termini consist of short, single-stranded regions which may have to be taken into account in subsequent joining procedures.

TRANSCRIPT MAPPING TECHNIQUES

Analyzing the nucleotide sequence of a piece of DNA is a necessary preliminary to understanding its precise organization and function, but is not normally sufficient for these purposes. Because eukaryotic gene transcripts are subjected to a complex series of post-transcriptional processing events, the structure of a gene can be understood only by correlating the organization of the genomic DNA with the organization of its mRNA transcript. This has required the establishment of sophisticated cloning and mapping techniques which can, when used in conjunction, give a complete description of the structure of a gene.

It is possible to isolate, by gene cloning, the double-stranded DNA copies of individual mRNA sequences. These cDNA clones will normally contain a DNA copy of the poly(A) sequence at the 3' terminus. Hence, by determining which strand of the cDNA clone contains a poly(A) tract at one end, it is possible to identify the coding strand of the cDNA clone. Provided a sufficient length of sequence has been established to make their presence statistically likely (in practice 300-500 nucleotides), termination codons will occur in two of the three potential coding frames, ruling them out as translational open reading frames (ORFs).

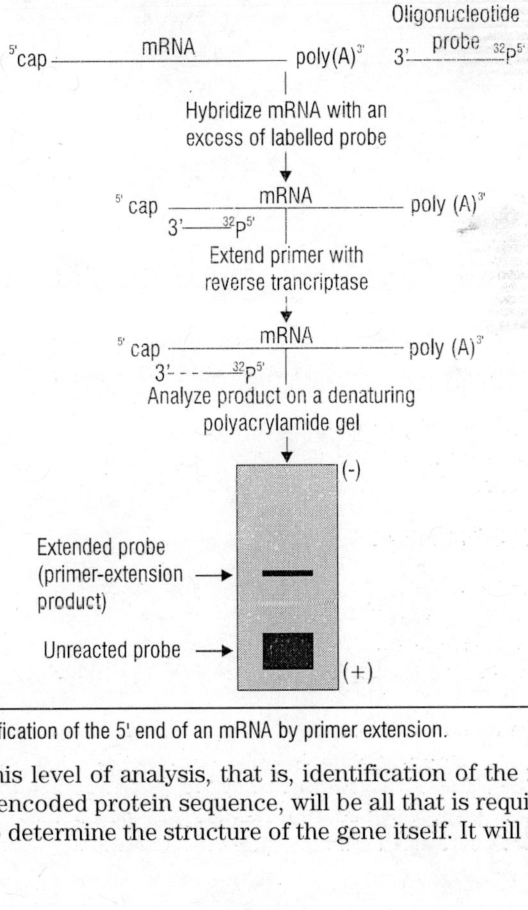

FIGURE 6.15: Identification of the 5' end of an mRNA by primer extension.

Sometimes this level of analysis, that is, identification of the reading frame and deduction of the encoded protein sequence, will be all that is required. However, it is often desirable to determine the structure of the gene itself. It will have been isolated as part of a genomic clone. This will contain the gene and a variable amount of flanking DNA depending upon the method of cloning used.

By correlating the sequence of the gene with the sequence of the mRNA deduced from the cDNA clone, it is possible to identify the site of poly(A) addition and the positions of introns. However, technical limitations in the cDNA cloning procedure ensure that the cDNA clone will not normally contain sequences derived from the extreme 5' terminus of the mRNA. There are two potential methods to determine the position of the 5' end, primer extension and S1 mapping.

Primer Extension

In primer extension, a short oligonucleotide complementary to a sequence tract near to the 5' end of the mRNA is annealed to the mRNA. This is then used to prime synthesis with the enzyme reverse transcriptase. This enzyme produces a DNA copy of the mRNA (a cDNA) which extends to the 5' terminus of the mRNA. By correlating the length of the cDNA primer extension product with the sequence of the genomic DNA, it is possible to deduce the start site of transcription.

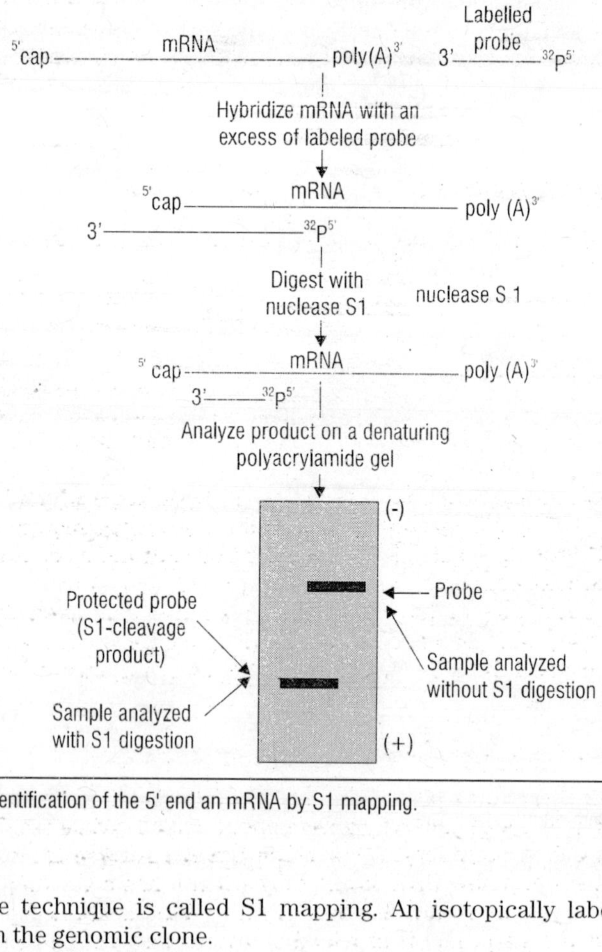

FIGURE 6.16: Identification of the 5' end an mRNA by S1 mapping.

S1 Mapping

The alternative technique is called S1 mapping. An isotopically labelled probe is generated from the genomic clone.

This probe is complementary to the mRNA over a region encompassing part or all of the first exon, and extending upstream of the region where the cap site is expected to be located. The cap site may have already been putatively localized using primer extension. The probe is annealed to the mRNA and digested with an enzyme which destroys single-stranded nucleic acids but leaves double-stranded molecules intact. In early experiments an enzyme called nuclease S1 was generally used, and the name S1 mapping has been retained, even though other nucleases are now sometimes used.

During digestion, the 3' proximal region of the probe, which has no complement in the mRNA moleculeand which therefore remains single-stranded, is degraded. A molecule is generated which is the complement of the region between the cap site and the position at which the 5' terminus of the probe annealed to the mRNA. Again, by determining the length of this molecule it is possible to infer the position of the cap site.

These two techniques are often used in parallel to determine the cap site. They are both subject to artefacts, but of different kinds. Therefore if both methods agree, it greatly increases confidence in the assignment of the cap site. If the hybridization is performed with an excess of probe, the amount of primer extension or nuclease-resistant product is proportional to the amount of primer extension or nuclease-resistant product is proportional to the amount of complementary mRNA. Both techniques can therefore be used an alternative to Northern transfer to quantitate mRNA levels.

SYNTHESIS OF CDNA FROM MRNA

Complementary DNA can be prepared by isolating mRNAs from tissues which are actively synthesizing proteins, like roots and leaves in plants, ovaries or recticulocytes in mammals etc. Isolated and purified mRNA can then be directly used to synthesise complementary DNA strand using the enzyme reverse transcriptase. This results in a DNA/RNA hybrid. The RNA part of the hybrid is then removed with alkali. Thus a single-stranded DNA is generated which can act as the template for the synthesis of its complementary strand in the presence of DNA polymerase. The double stranded DNA molecule thus formed is called complementary DNA (cDNA), as it is synthesised complementary to the mRNA (Figure 6.17). In the prokaryotes the double stranded cDNA will be identical to the gene (DNA) from which the mRNA is formed. But, most of the eukaryotic genes contain intervening sequences (introns) which interrupt the coding sequences. Hence, the cDNA of the eukaryotic cells and their native DNA are not colinear.

As bacterial genes do not have the intron - exon organisation found in the eukaryotic genes they find the expression of eukaryotic genes in them (bacterial) difficult. Therefore one has to depend upon cDNA of eukaryotes, which does not have introns, for cloning.

Preparation of Double-Stranded cDNA

The mRNA that is specific for a particular kind of protein is isolated and purified. All naturally occuring mRNAs of eukaryotes have about 200 adenylate residues at their 3'-termini. This is called polyadenylate tail. The enzyme reverse transcriptase can mediate the synthesis of a new DNA strand only when it has a growing point in the form of a pre-existing primer, which is base paired with the mRNA template and has a free 3' OH group. Such a primer is provided by hybridizing a short complementary oligo (dT) molecule with the poly adenylate (poly-A) sequence.

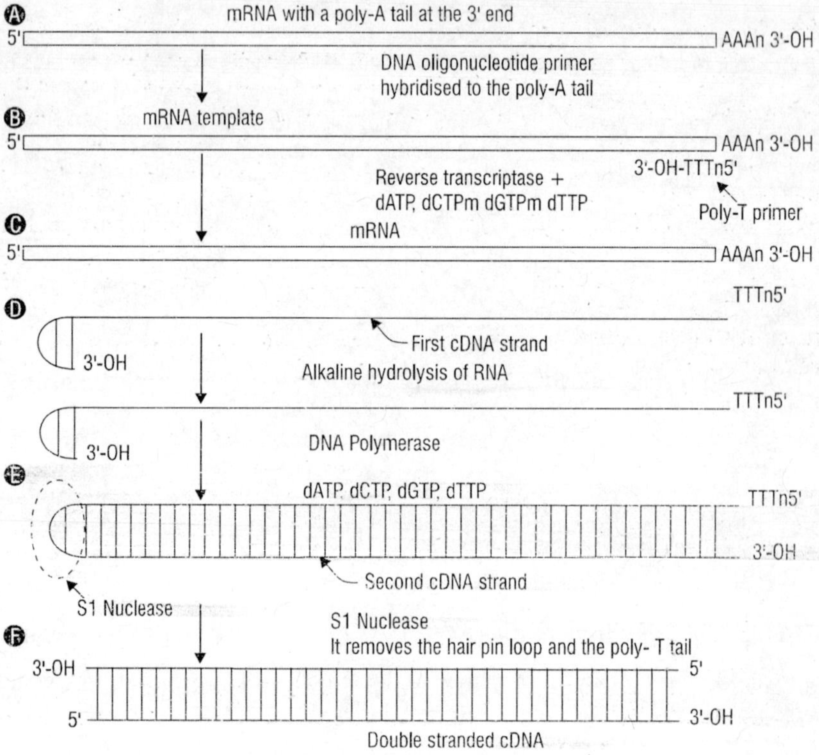

FIGURE 6.17: Synthesis of double stranded cDNA from an mRNA.

The 3'OH end of the poly-T primer is made double strandard by reverse transcriptase forming RNA-DNA hybrid. The RNA strand of this RNA - cDNA hybrid is digested by alkaline hydrolysis (DNA is resistant to alkali). At the 3'-OH end of the newly formed single stranded cDNA, a hairpin is formed which is stabilised by base - pairing. This hairpin, which has a 3'-OH free end acts as a self-priming structure. Forming second strand of the cDNA in the presence of the fragment of the *E. coli* DNA polymerase-1 (Kornberg enzyme) and the four deoxynucleotide triphosphates.

The enzyme reverse transcriptase or T4DNA polymerase can also be used for the synthesis of the second strand of cDNA. The synthesised double strandede DNA is treated with the single-strand specific nuclease S1. This enzyme digests the curved region of the hair pin and any polynucleotide tails. Thus, finally a double stranded cDNA molecule is formed. This DNA can now be inserted into a suitable vector and can be further cloned in the desired host.

Complementary DNA of a given mRNA is inserted into a suitable vector can then be cloned in a host. The cDNA is blunt ended. It has no cohesive ends that are complementary to the cohesive ends of any of the vectors. This is overcome by homopolymer tailing. Once inside the host cell, the cDNA in the hybrid will express the gene(s) it carries.

cDNA Library

Complementary DNAs (cDNAs) of the genome of an organism can be synthesised and cloned to generate a cDNA library. Thus, cDNA library is a collection of cDNA clones of an organism. The starting material for the synthesis of cDNA is the mRNA. Hence the resulting cDNAs will represent the mRNAs present in the cells from where these mRNAs were isolated. In the case of multicellular organisms there is specialisation of individual cells. For example, a mammal is made up of a large number of cell types: brain cells, mammary cells, blood cells, liver cells, cells of the pancreas, nerve cells etc. Each type of cell will contain the same complement of genes. However, only a particular set of genes will be expressed in a given type of cell. Other genes will remain silent. Only those genes that are expressed are transcribed into mRNA. Hence the cDNA clones of this type of cell will be only a selection of the total number of genes in a cell. Hence for such organisms, cDNA clones of different cellare prepared.

SEARCHING FOR GENE USING COMPUTERS

Although the series of analyses described above are necessary ultimately to establish the organization and mode of expression of a particular gene, genes can be sought by less laborious means using computer programs. These searches for regions of a DNA sequence which look like coding regions flanked by the signals that direct gene transcription and processing of their RNA products. This procedure is of greatest value when large regions of genomic DNA for which cDNA clones are not available are being analyzed. It is thus an essential part of the Human Genome Project.

One of the principles, that of searching for long ORFs (= open reading frames), has already been described. Although the sequence (the Kozak sequence) that precedes the ATG initiation codon is only weakly conserved between different genes it can provide helpful guides to the start site of translation. The start site of transcription often lies downstream of a TATA box, and it is also possible to search for the consensus binding sites of other transcription factors.

RNA processing signals can also be used to help establish the likely gene organization. The sequence that signals polyadenylation is well conserved, and splice junctions have a consensus sequence comprising an almost perfectly conserved core (5' GU----AG 3'), with moderately well conserved flanking sequences.

Identification genes by analysis of DNA sequences is an evolving science. The structures of new genes are constantly adding and the sophistication of the search programs is increasing. The databanks exists which contain many thousands of gene sequences *e.g.* Genbank and the EMBL. Although some scientists initially submit their gene sequence data to one rather than other, the two organizations that compile the databases then exchange data.

CHAPTER 7

Genetic Engineering Techniques

By harnessing nature's methods of gene transfer, scientists have been able to genetically alter a number of common crops, creating new varieties that are better suited to farmer's needs. Certain crops respond more readily to biotechnology than others. One of these crops is canola. Already, several new varieties of canola have been developed through genetic engineering.

Special techniques in genetic engineering allow scientists to produce new varieties of plants with selected characteristics. These new varieties are known as transgenic varieties.

When two plants are crossbreed, they each contribute all of their genetic information to the new plant. The new plants that result from this breeding may receive almost 50,000 pieces of genetic information from their "parents" and could have thousands of new characteristics. Sometimes the desired characteristic is lost amongst the thousands of extra genes and the trait plant breeders are looking for may not be able to express itself in the plant.

TRANSGENIC TECHNIQUES

Genetic engineering overcomes the limitations of traditional breeding and allows scientists to use new traits from many kinds of plants and other living things such as fish, insects, bacterium and even humans.

Because all organisms use the same genetic language, different kinds of organisms can understand each other's genetic code. If a new gene is introduced to another organism's cells, that cell will begin to produce that gene's particular protein and will display the new trait directed by the gene.

There are four basic steps to creating a transgenic plant:

1. First, biotechnologists isolate a gene, which has the recipe for the characteristic that the new plant must have.
2. Second, a vector is chosen which can carry the new gene into the plant's cells.
3. Third, the gene is clipped from its chromosome and loaded onto the vector (usually bacteria), which acts like a genetic gun that shoots the gene into the cell.
4. Fourth, once the gene has been delivered into the cell it travels into the chromosome strand.
5. After it is shot into the cell, the new gene becomes part of the plant's recipe book. All of the new plants, which are produced from the altered plant will pass on the gene to their offspring.

STEPS FOR DEVELOPING NEW CROP VARIETIES

Genetic engineering to enhance a crop variety involves most if not all of the following steps. The process can take several years, but often moves much more quickly, especially as the various techniques become perfected. In any case, the process is still faster than transferring genes through conventional plant breeding, if that is even possible for the particular desired trait.

Step 1: Finding a plant or other organism showing the desired characteristics.

Step 2: Identifying the gene controlling that trait and its location on a chromosome. In recent years, scientists have been working to produce genetic maps of the chromosomes of many species, including humans, livestock, crops and potentially useful microorganisms. (These are often referred to as genome projects, genome being the term used to refer to an organism's entire genetic complement.) Through this process of genetic mapping, scientists have been able to determine the location of many specific genes on the chromosomes of different species and to determine their respective functions.

Step 3: Marking the genes, so that their presence can be detected quickly and simply. Identifying where a gene is located on a chromosome and confirming that it has been isolated or transferred is done through a process called marker-assisted selection. Specific genes or segments of DNA, called markers, are used to mark the location of the genes to be transferred. Markers that can be detected easily and that appear to always be associated with the desired trait are chosen for this process.

To some extent, marker genes have been used in conventional plant breeding for many years. Plant breeders observed that certain traits almost always appeared together as plants were cross-bred and their offspring tracked through the generations of selection required for development of crop variety. Such sets of genes are said to be linked. By choosing easily detectable marker genes that were linked to desirable traits that were more difficult to measure, plant breeders were able to speed the process of incorporating desirable traits into new varieties. As they identify where each marker occurs on a chromosome, and how close it is to a specific gene, scientists can create maps of the markers and genes on specific chromosomes.

Step 4: Isolating the genes from the rest of the DNA so that only the desired information will be transferred. Scientists are able to isolate individual genes using enzymes that cut DNA at specific sites along the DNA strand.

Step 5: Producing large numbers of the gene and introducing the desired gene into cells of the organism to be enhanced. One common means of transferring genes into plants is by employing the natural ability of some bacteria to alter the DNA of organisms, which they infect. These bacteria have the ability to inject a segment of their DNA into that of an infected cell, thereby affecting its behaviour. For example, the common soil bacterium, *Agrobacterium tumefaciens*, causes a disease called crown gall in susceptible plants by inserting its genes into a plant's DNA. The bacterial genes disrupt the genetic code of the plant's cells in the infected area causing them to grow into an abnormally shaped mass called a gall. Scientists have discovered ways to use this ability of *A. tumefaciens* to transfer genes between species in the laboratory. *A. tumefaciens* and some other bacterial species produce small, circular pieces of DNA called plasmids. Plasmids function independently of other bacterial DNA and can enter cells of other organisms, carrying genetic information with them that then merges with that of the host cell.

To transfer genes from one cell to another, researchers use an enzyme to cut a gap in a bacterial plasmid. They then insert a gene from the donor DNA strand into the plasmid. Because the cut ends of both the plasmid and the donor gene segment are chemically 'sticky,' they attach to each other or recombine to form a plasmid containing the new gene (hence the name, recombinant DNA [rDNA] technology). The recombined plasmid now carries the gene that can result in the expression of the new trait when transferred into a plant cell by the plasmid.

Once a gene is inserted into a plasmid, it can be introduced into a bacterium that is easily reproduced in the lab (*e.g.*, *E. coli*). When the altered bacteria multiply, the plasmid containing the desired gene is also copied or cloned in every cell. Because bacteria grow quickly, this method makes it possible to make millions of copies of the desired gene in a short period.

Using the appropriate enzymes, the plant genes are then extracted again from the bacteria and inserted into the plasmids of *A. tumefaciens*. Finally, the altered *A. tumefaciens* is mixed with the target plant cells, where the engineered plasmid enters the target plant cells. The 'foreign' gene is then incorporated into DNA of some of the target plant cells.

Step 7: Identifying which plant cells now contain the desired gene, through the use of markers as described above.

Step 8: Growing the altered cells into full plants, using a process called tissue culture, to confirm that the desired trait is expressed properly.

Step 9: Using traditional plant breeding techniques to transfer the trait into a usable variety.

BACTERIA: NATURE'S GENETIC ENGINEERS

As far back as 1869, the Swiss scientist Fredrick Meischer discovered and isolated DNA, the substance inside the cells of any organism, which contain the genetic "blueprint" controlling all of its characteristics. Like his contemporary Gregor Mendel, who first established the principles of heredity, Meischer's discovery was largely ignored by the scientific community of his time. It was in the mid-1920s that the British pathologist Frederick Griffith learned that the pneumonia-causing bacterium he was studying was capable of transforming its basic characteristics. His experiments showed that a harmless strain of bacteria could transform into a lethal one. Several decades later, researchers discovered that viruses living in the bacteria are the agent of its genetic transformation from one type to another. The scientists observed that bacterial and viral DNA can integrate, and then *ferry* genes between different kinds of bacteria.

Bacteria and Gene Transfers in Plants

Crown galls form on a plant at the site of a fresh wound when the wound is infected by a common soil bacterium. Although at the time they didn't understand the genetic science involved, the researchers were observing the activity of *Agrobacterium tumefaciens*, which is capable of inserting its genes into plants. The foreign genes can then *hijack* the genetic code of the plant, making it a better host for the bacteria. What Smith and Townsend did come to realize was that the cell mechanisms of all living things, whether plant or animal, are fundamentally the same. This discovery later made it possible to apply the process of gene transfer, first observed in the plants changed by *A. tumefaciens*, to the modification and improvement of many plants useful in agriculture. In time, this was accomplished by finding a way to delete the genes that cause the crown gall disease and substitute other genes that produce desirable traits. Scientists found that they could harness this unusual ability of *A. tumefaciens* to carry out gene transfers in the lab.

How Bacteria are used to Modify Plants

Once scientists have discovered the genes responsible for the trait they want to introduce into another plant, they face several difficult problems in transforming the target plant.

1. **First** they must accumulate enough pure DNA needed to genetically alter a number of target plant cells.
2. A **second** problem is finding a way to deliver genes through the walls of the cell and into the nucleus. After all, the cell is designed by nature to keep foreign material out.

Several ways have been found to solve these problems, but one of the most useful methods harnesses bacteria to increase the amount of DNA as well as to *deliver* genes through cell wall and into the nucleus.

How Do They Do It?

Scientists have discovered that a number of enzymes (as described previously), complex organic substances originating in living cells, can be used as tools to *cut* genes from plants. Some 300-400 enzymes are now available for use in biotechnology. Different enzymes are used to cut and isolate specific genes. Once scientists have discovered and isolated the genes that control a desired trait in a plant (such as resistance to a disease), they have to find a way to replicate or clone enough exact copies of the genes to transform a large number of cells from the target plants.

Their first step is to take the genes responsible for a desired trait from a plant and insert them, using enzymes, into a plasmid taken from a common type of bacterium called *E. coli*. Plasmids (as discussed previously) are very important in biotechnology because they are the basis of gene cloning. Once a gene is inserted into a plasmid, the plasmid can be reintroduced into the bacterial cell. When the altered bacteria are grown in a culture (a medium that promotes rapid growth), the plasmid containing the desired gene is copied or cloned in every cell. Because bacteria grow quickly, this method makes it possible to make millions of copies of the desired gene in a short period. Using enzymes, the plant genes are now removed from the *E. coli* plasmids and inserted into the plasmid of *A. tumefaciens*, the soil microorganism that can move foreign genes into plant cells.

Finally, the altered *Agrobacterium tumefaciens* is mixed with the target plant cells. The bacteria ferry the engineered plasmid into the target plant cells. The "foreign" plant gene is then incorporated into the plant cell's DNA. New plants can be grown directly from these modified cells in a special growth chamber. Some of the plants grown from these cells will have the trait specified by the new gene. By growing the plants, scientists can now test to see which of the plants have been genetically transformed.

Three gene-transfer techniques have been developed to such a stage of reproducibility and practical applicability that they can be recommended for future practical work. These are *Agrobacterium-mediated* gene transfer, *ballistic* gene transfer, and *direct* gene transfer to *protoplasts*. These are additional technique that have yielded confirmed transgenic plants and that show some promise for future development, such as *microtargeting*, *microinjection*, *electroporation* into tissues, and *whiskers*. These techniques are described to a smaller extent and the literature citations will support further reading. There is a further group of techniques for which unequivocal evidence for the production of transgenic plants is still missing such as the pollen tube-pathway, and for which the reader is referred to a more detailed assessment (Potrykus, I.).

The transgenic crop plants obtained by *Agrobacterium*-mediated transformation are: *Medicago sativa, Malus pumila, Prunus armeniaca, Asparagus officinalis, Populus tremula, Hordeum vulgare, Phaseolus vulgaris, Lotus corniculatus, Ribes nigrum, Dianthus* sp. *Caryophyllus, Citrus, Daucus carota, Brassica oleracea, Apium graveoleus, Cicer arietinum, Cichorium endivia, Chrysanthemum* sp., *Gossypium hisutum, Zea mays, Vaccinium macrocarpon, Cucumis sativus, Festuca rubra, Festuca arundinacea, Linum usitatissimum, Gerbera hybrida, Vitis* spp., *Actinidia chinensis, Lactuca sativa, Cucumis melo, Brassica juncea, Avena sativa, Brassica napus, Dactylis glomerata, Dendrobium* sp., *Carica papaya, Passiflora edulis, Pisum sativum, Arachis hypogaea, Carya ovata, Lolium perenne, Solanum muricatum, Petunia hybrida, Prunus domestica, Populus sp., Solanum tuberosum, Boehmeria nivea, Oryza sativa, Secale cereale, Sorghum bicolor, Glycine max, Fragaria x Anannassa, Stylosanthes humilis, Trifolium subterraneum, Beta vulgaris, Saccharum officinarum, Helianthus annuus, Liquidambar siyraciflua, Cyphomandra betacea, Physalis ixocarpa, Lycopersicon esculentum*, etc.

AGROBACTERIUM MEDIATED GENE TRANSFER

For genetic transformation in plants *Agrobacterium tumefaciens* (a soil bacterium) is used. It transfers T-DNA into plant genome. Foreign genes are inserted in T-DNA through *Ti*-plasmid, co-transferred and integrated in the host genome. Only some sequences of T-DNA in *cis*-position are required for its transfer. By deleting T-DNA encoded genes and adding selectable markers a *disarmed plasmid vector* is prepared without disturbing endogenous balance. Disarmed strains with *Ti*-plasmid can be used to produce transgenic plants.

Plant-Transformation Vectors

These vectors are designed on the basis of naturally occurring gene-transfer mechanisms. They are widely employed in plant molecular biology and in the genetic engineering of plants. Chilton (1993) described these vectors as *poor man's vector*. They are used for gene delivery to higher plants.

Advantages of Vector

(1) They are convenient and efficiency. (2) They allow the transfer of large segments of DNA with minimal rearrangements. (3) They are the integration of small numbers of copies of genes into plant chromosomes. (4) Foreign genes delivered by this method are usually transmitted to progeny plants in Mendelian manners. (5) In the Ti-plasmid, the genes responsible for the transfer of T-DNA are clustered together in a region. The transfer process is active even when the virulence genes and the T-DNA are located on separate replicon in an A. tumefaciens cell. (6) In the widely used binary system, a Ti-plasmid services as helper; providing the virulence functions, and artificial T-DNA, which contains a selectable marker gene and other genes of interest, is placed on a second, small plasmid, which is often referred to as binary vector (An *et al.*, 1998). (7) In dicotyledonous plants the systems of Agrobacterium mediated transformation have been well established for many. However, monocotyledonous plants (cerea/grasses) were originally outside, the host range of A. tumefaciens.

GENE CLONING

Gene cloning is a technique, where an isolated single copy of a gene is cloned to obtain its indefinite identical copies. In gene cloning, we introduce a vector containing the desired gene into the host cell.

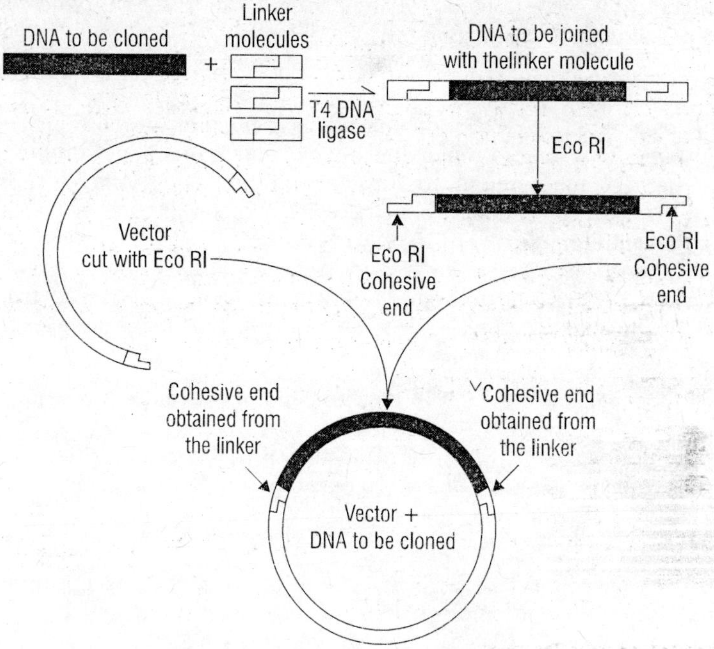

FIGURE 7.1: Linker molecules containing Eco RI cleavage site are joined by T4 DNA ligase to both the ends of blunt-ended DNA-to-be-cloned. Cohesive ends are then generated by cutting with Eco RI. This DNA is then inserted into a vector molecule cut by the same restriction enzyme.

Cloning can be done in bacterial host (e.g., *E. coli*) or in eukaryotes (e.g., yeast). Basically, cloning involves four steps:

1. The vector DNA is cleaved with one or more restriction enzymes;
2. The DNA to be cloned, the target or insert is joined to the vector, generating a recombinant molecule;
3. The recombinant DNA molecules are introduced into the host bacterial cell. The host cell is said to be transformed by the introduction of such vector molecule;
4. Transformed colony is selected and amplified.

Another method of amplifying the desired gene is PCR, which offers this possibility in test tube. The two methods PCR and gene cloning are complementary techniques. Molecular cloning of a PCR product is now commonly used to isolate and manipulate genes.

Creating Recombinant DNA

Recombinant DNA molecules are produced by inserting a foreign DNA segment into the DNA molecule of a vector. This involves joining of the broken ends of vector DNA with the two ends of sequence to be cloned. These recombinant DNA molecules (also called as rDNA molecule) are subsequently cloned. There are three methods of joining fragments *in vitro*. The first uses ability of DNA ligase to join the cohesive ends produced by certain restriction enzymes. The second depends on the ability of

T4 ligase to form phosphodiester bonds between blunt-ended fragments. The third utilizes the enzyme terminal deoxynucleotidyl transferase to synthesize homopolymeric tails at the ends of fragments. The three enzymes and their mechanism of joining DNA are separately dealt below.

DNA Ligase

The sticky ends created by restriction enzyme have the nick after a few base pairs in opposite strands. DNA ligases repair these nicks and forms intact duplex (also see chapter 3). The optimum temperature for ligation of nicked DNA is 37 °C, but at this temperature the hydrogen-bonded joint between the sticky ends is unstable. Thus temperature is kept in range of 4 to 15 °C.

This technique has the advantage of regenerating two restriction sites in recombinant DNA. Thus, the foreign DNA segment can be retrieved from cloned DNA copies by cleaving again with the same enzyme. The disadvantages within this technique include:

1. The cohesive ends of foreign DNA may join end to end and self-circularize before getting inserted in vector.
2. The recognition site, particularly in sequence to be cloned, may not lie at a convenient position so that sometimes only a part of gene is inserted.

T4 DNA Ligase

The *E. coli* DNA ligase can not catalyse ligation of blunt ends except under special reaction conditions of macromolecular crowding. Such blunt end ligation can be done with T4 DNA ligase. T4 DNA ligase can join the broken blunt ends of two DNA molecules irrespective of the sequences. The disadvantage of this technique is that any two broken ends may join including those belonging to same DNA molecule. However, blunt-ended ligation is a useful way of joining together DNA fragments, which have not been produced by the same restriction enzyme and therefore probably have incompatible sticky ends. These ends are removed prior to ligation using the enzyme S1 nuclease, which digests single stranded DNA.

Blunt ligation is most usefully applied where blunt-ended fragments are joined via *linker* molecules (described later). The linker molecule can be ligated to both ends of foreign DNA to be cloned, and then treated with restriction enzyme to produce sticky ended fragments. The vector molecule is also cut with same restriction enzyme. Finally, the foreign DNA is ligated to vector via linker created sticky ends. These linkers also help in excising and recovering the foreign DNA (gene of interest) after cloning and amplification in host bacterium. Here a brief account on various types of linkers is given.

Linkers

They are self complementary synthetic oligonucleotides, which contain restriction endonuclease recognition sites. They may be used to clone DNA fragment into plasmids or other vectors.

These blunt ended linkers are first phosphorylated using polynucleotide kinase and labelled or unlabelled ATP molecules. These are then ligated to the blunt ended DNA fragment using T4 DNA ligase. The DNA fragment is finally treated with restriction enzyme to generate sticky ends and ligated into vector which has been cut by the same enzyme.

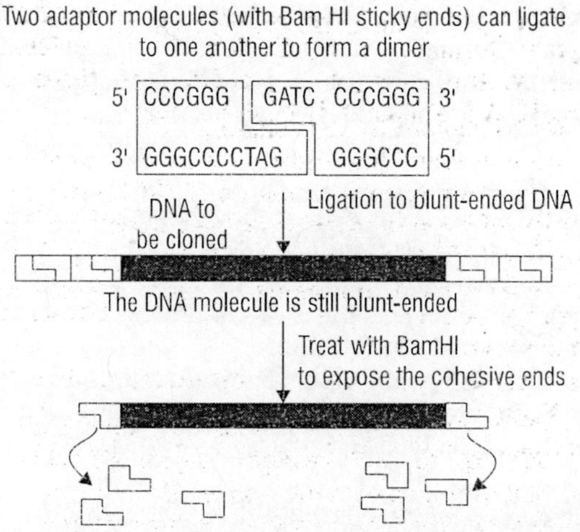

FIGURE 7.2: Digram to explain the problems associated with the use of adoptor molecules. A. Two adoptor molecules with Bam HI cohesive ends have ligated to each other to form a dimer. B. Such dimer of the adoptor molecules can ligate to a blunt-ended DNA molecule. The DNA molecule thus obtained is still blunt-ended. C. The cohesive ends are recreated by treatment with Bam HI.

Stop Linker

They are 5'-phosphorylated double-stranded synthetic oligo-deoxynucleotides which can be cloned into an expression vector to ensure transcription termination. Such linkers contain stop codons in each reading frame from both directions. Each stop linker contains an SspI restriction site, which can be used to screen clones for linker insertion.

Adaptors

They are linkers, which contain more than one restriction enzyme recognition sites. They are used to insert new restriction sites into cloning vectors or to join restriction fragments to vectors with incompatible cohesive ends.

Double-Linkers

In some plasmid vectors like pUC8, duplex cDNA molecules can be cloned. This is done by double-linker approach, in which different linker molecules are added to the opposite ends of the cDNA. This is an advantageous method as: (1) Orientation of inserted DNA is fixed. (2) Vector re-closure without insertion of foreign DNA can be done. (3) Efficient for cloning of cDNA obtained from rare mRNA molecules. (4) Better than homopolymers where expression from vector-borne promoter is desirable.

Terminal Transferase

Besides adding cohesive ends or linkers, blunt ended DNA fragment and vector can also be ligated. This technique makes use of producing and annealing complementary homopolymer sequences. An enzyme, terminal transferase (purified from calf-thymus), is used to synthesize homopolymeric extensions. Using precursor dGTP, poly dG is added at both the 3'cut ends of vectors while poly dC is added to

5'cut end of foreign DNA. The vector and clone can then be joined by annealing the poly dG with poly dC tails and then ligating them using DNA ligase enzyme. The cloned sequence can be retrieved by using Pst I restriction enzyme. The method works out the chances of reannealing between the two cut ends of same DNA molecule or of two similar DNA molecules, thus is advantageous.

CLONING IN BACTERIA AND EUKARYOTES

Cloning in Bacteria

After ligation of target into vector, the recombinant DNA is multiplied in a host. Various bacterial strains are available as host. Most common prokaryotic host is *E. coli*, which is also termed as **workhouse of genetic engineering**. In this technique the recombinant DNA is subjected to *in vitro* packaging and used to transform bacteria for its amplification. The host bacteria are modified and selected on the basis of high transformation efficiency. The type of bacterial host is selected on the basis of plasmid vector. Various bacterial hosts commonly employed are:

1. Gram positive bacteria *e.g.*, E. coli: host for plasmids only.
2. Gram negative bacteria *e.g.*, Bacillus subtilis: host for plasmid, phages and cosmid vectors.

Chimeric DNA is inserted into bacterial cells to create transformed bacterial cells. Colonies of transformed cells are selected and used for multiplication in suspension cultures. The recombinant DNA is retrieved and isolated from the host cell when required.

Cloning in Eukaryotes

E. coli is workhouse of genetic engineering but the chromosome structure and gene expression in prokaryotes and eukaryotes differ radically. Therefore, *E. coli* offers limitation to its use in cloning eukaryotic genes. The split genes can not be correctly expressed in prokaryotic host as latter do not have introns and thus splicing of mRNA can not take place. Therefore, eukaryotic cells are used to clone and express eukaryotic genes.

Among eukaryotes, DNA cloning has been done in yeast, mouse and some plant species. Yeast has following attractions as host for genetic engineering: (1) Short doubling time (90 minutes). (2) Can be maintained in either a haploid or diploid state. (3) Can be grown on simple defined media and auxotrophs can be selected. (4) The wall can be removed and foreign DNA entry can be facilitated with PEG and $CaCl_2$ mixture. (5) Confers extra-chromosomal replication of chimeric DNA just as plasmids in E. coli.

The simplest kind of yeast vector contains a selectable marker such as TRP1, joined to plasmid vector. TRP1 encodes an enzyme in the tryptophan biosynthetic pathway and when introduced into TRP^- cell by DNA transformation, it renders the cell capable of growth in absence of added tryptophan. Vector used is a hybrid or shuttle type. When transformed into yeast, such a vector integrates into the yeast genome by recombination and makes the transformed yeast selectable on the basis of growth in absence of added tryptophane. Mammalian RNA transcripts are not spliced in the yeast cell nor the mammalian proteins are glycosylated correctly.

In animal cells like mouse cells, special animal viruses are used as cloning vehicle. Simian virus 40 (SV40) with foreign DNA can be transcribed and translated in mouse kidney. Retroviral vectors are used for transformation of mammalian cells.

These animal viruses comprise single stranded RNA genome, gene of interest and G418R gene for resistance against protein synthesis inhibitor G418.

AMPLIFICATION OF DNAS BY POLYMERASE CHAIN REACTION (PCR)

The major scientific development of year 1989, as named by prestigious journal *Science* was **Polymerase Chain Reaction** (PCR). Kary Mullin is the inventor of PCR who revolutionised the method of DNA analysis in both research and clinical laboratories.

The PCR, is an extremely powerful new procedure that allows one to make million fold copies of a selected DNA sequence in a genome. PCR can be used to clone a given DNA sequence *in vitro* without using living cells during the cloning process. However, the procedure can only be applied when the nucleotide sequence of at least one short DNA segment on each side of the 'region of interest' is known. The PCR procedure makes use of synthetic oligonuclotides complementary to the known sequences spanning the region of interest to fatch *enzymatic amplification of this segment of DNA in the test tube.*

PCR may eventually replace gene cloning technique. This technology is much easier and requires much smaller quantity of DNA (in ng) whereas for cloning, DNA needed in microgram (µg) quantities.

Procedure

The PCR procedure involves three steps, each repeated many times to produce cycles of amplification.

- **Step 1:** The genomic DNA containing the sequence to be amplified is denatured by heating.
- **Step 2:** The denatured DNA is annealed to an excess of the synthetic oligonucleotide primers.
- **Step 3:** DNA polymerase is used to replicate the DNA segment between the sites complementary to the oligonucleotide primers. The primer provides the free 3'-OH required for covalent extension; the denatured genomic DNA provides the required template function. These three steps (denaturation, primer binding and DNA synthesis) represent a single PCR cycle.

The products of the first cycle are replicated for further amplification. This reaction can be performed many times to supply unlimited copies of amplified DNA. Repetition is made possible by regular denaturation of freshly synthesized double stranded DNA molecules by heating it to 90-98 °C.

At this temperature, the two strands separate. Once the double stranded DNA is made single stranded, it is mixed with two primers and is cooled to 40-60 °C.

This allows the primers (which are in excess) to bind to their complementary strands through renaturation followed by replication with DNA polymerase. The cycle is repeated many times until the desired level of amplification is achieved.

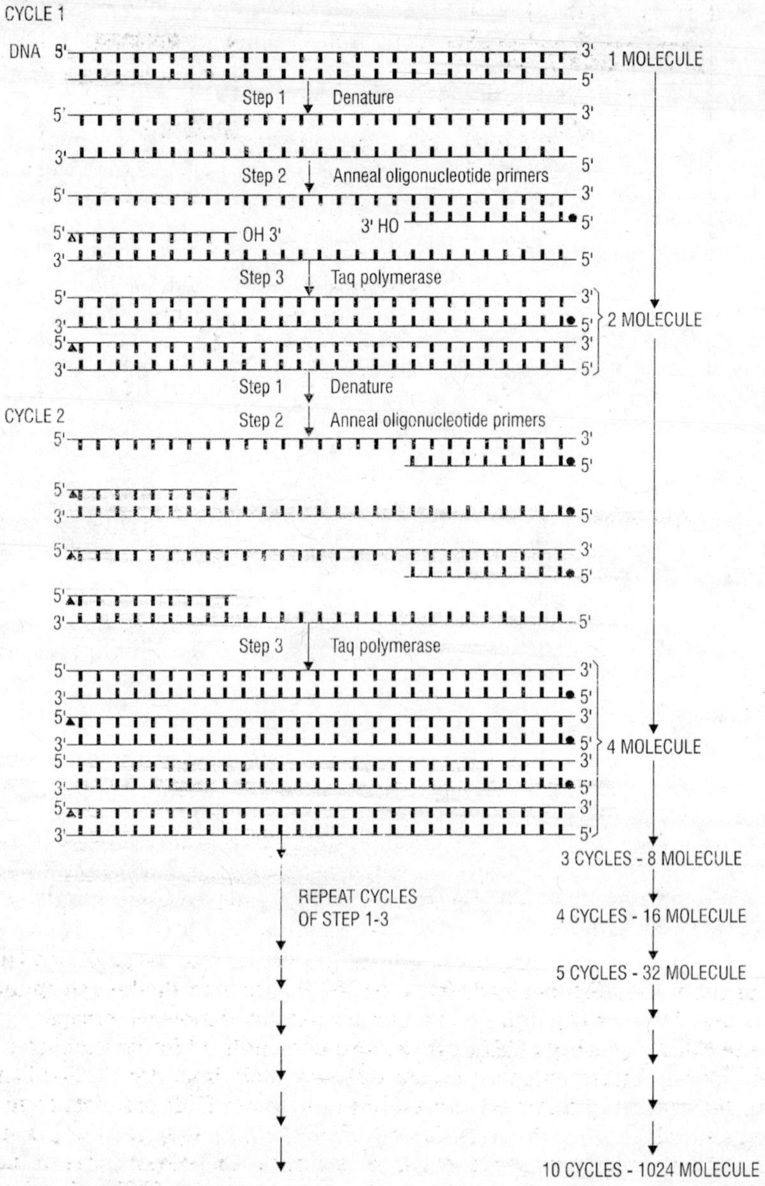

FIGURE 7.3: Diagram illustrating the use of PCR to amplify DNA molecules *in vitro*. Each cycle of amplification involves three steps: (1) denaturation of the genomic DNA being analyzed, (2) annealing of the denatured DNA to chemically synthesized oligonucleotide primers with sequences complementary to sites on opposite sides of the DNA region of interest, and (3) enzymatic replication of the region of interest by Taq polymerase.

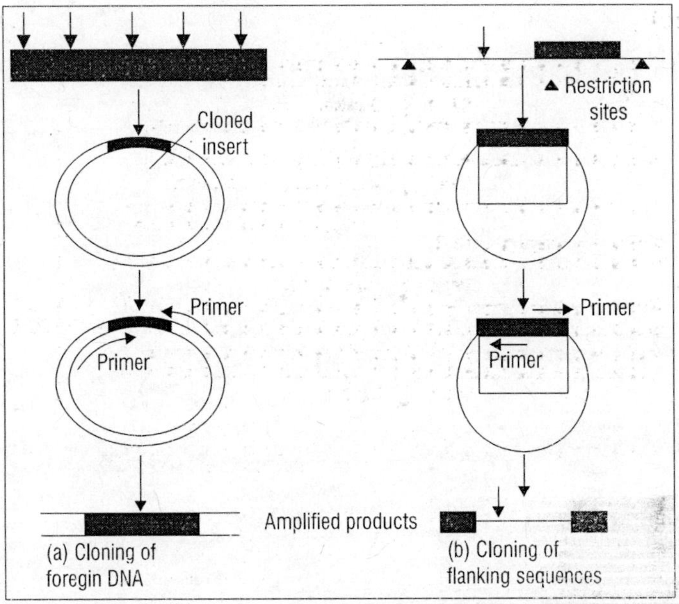

FIGURE 7.4: Inverse PCR (a) amplification of genes using flanking vector sequences as primers; (b) amplification of sequences flanking the gene, using sequences at the two ends of the gene as primers.

Applications of PCR

During the last few years, with the improvement of PCR protocols and due to the availability of automatic thermal cyclers commercially, the applications of PCR have increased manifold. Some of the applications are listed here.

Study of DNA Polymorphism Using PCR: DNA polymorphism is amplified using PCR and can be used for study. Loci either with known DNA sequence or at random sites, both can be amplified. PCR can be used to study RFLPs as well as RAPDs. Loci with poly (A), poly (G), poly (TC) and poly (TG) etc., known as short tandem repeats or simple sequence repeats (SSR) can also be amplified with PCR. Some of the these SSR loci such (CA), or (GT)n occur in the human genome with many copies. SSRs can be utilized in preparing saturated molecular maps.

Gene Tagging Using PCR: PCR has also been utilized for developing molecular markers closely linked to specific genes of economic importance. For instance in tomato, 144 random primers were used to produce 625 PCR products from a set of near isogenic lines. Near isogenic lines (= NIL's) differ only for the presence and absence of a specific gene for *Pseudomonas* resistance. Atleast three of these PCR products were present in one and not in the other of a pair of NIL's showing linkage with *Psedomonas* resistance gene (Pto). These PCR products could be mapped close to Pto.

PCR for Confirming the Presence of Transferred Gene: When a chimeric gene is transferred to cultured cells or organisms, primers can be designed to conduct PCR for amplification of the gene sequence so transferred. This technique allows the confirmation of transfer and maintenance of the gene of interest.

DNA Fingerprinting Using PCR: DNA fingerprinting is use in forensic medicine for identification of criminals and disputed parentage. Some characterized sequences of microsatellites are being used for designing primers. PCR allows amplification of DNA from individual hairs, stains of blood or seminal fluid having partially degraded DNA. Characterization of individuals with such small amount of DNA could not be done earlier.

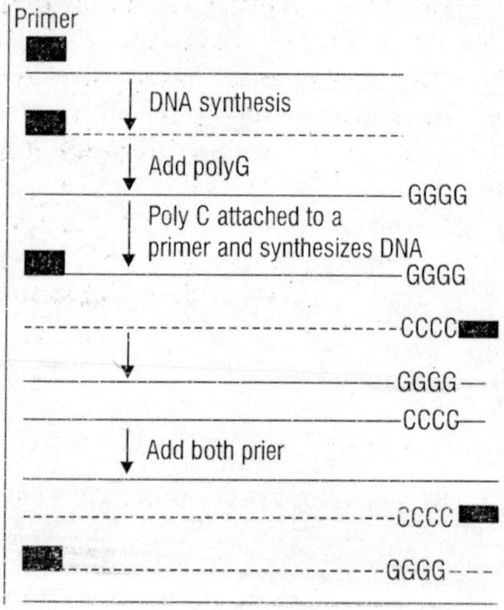

FIGURE 7.5: Anchored PCR, using a single primer in the first cycle.

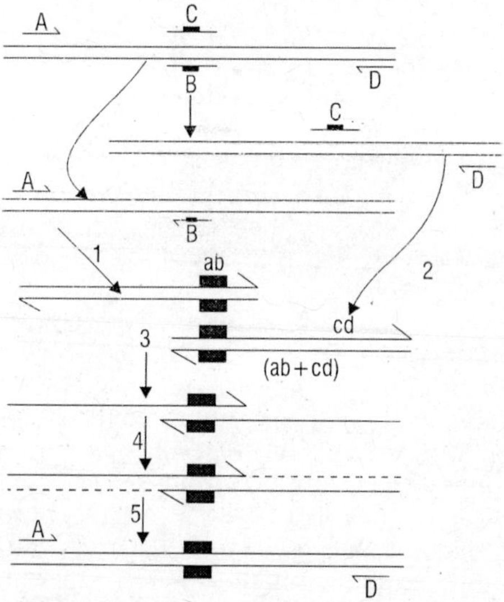

FIGURE 7.6: Introduction of mutation at an internal site using overlap extension (two pairs of primers A & B and C & D are used. B and C represent internal sites and overlap each other).

PCR in Gene Therapy: In gene therapy experiments, the transfer and presence of a marker gene for neomycin resistance (NeoR) could be detected in the blood of patients, even after 60 days, although the frequency of marked lymphocytes gradually decreased necessitating a second transfusion of such marked cells.

Similarly, ADA (adenosine deaminase deficiency) gene was transferred for therapeutic purposes and PCR was used to detect the presence of this gene. Thus PCR proves to be of immense help in monitoring a gene in gene therapy experiments.

PCR technologies thus provide shortcuts for many cloning and sequencing applications. These procedures permit scientists to obtain definitive structural data on genes and DNA sequences when very small amounts of DNA are available. One important application involves the diagnosis of inherited human disease, especially in cases of prenatal diagnosis, where very limited amounts of fetal DNA are available. A second major application occurs in forensic cases involving individual identities. No criteria can provide more definitive evidence of identity than DNA sequences; after all, other phenotypic traits are controlled by the expression of these DNA isolated from small blood samples, sperm, or even individual human hairs. Thus, PCR DNA printing experiments are likely to play a major role in legal cases involving disputed identity.

GENE TRANSFER TECHNOLOGY

Gene transfer is of basic as well as applied interest. It enables to study the structure and function of isolated genes via modification, reintroduction and subsequent analysis of their function in transgenic plants, cell lines or even cell populations. Besides these, transfer of specifically designed hybrid genes to plant genomes creates novel varieties with designed characters.

Gene transfer in plants can be accomplished by sexual and asexual methods. Asexual methods include:

1. Non-specific gene transfer by protoplast techniques.
2. Specific gene transfer methods.

In animals, gene transfer is done using egg and cultured stem cells or by specific gene transfer.

Sexual Method

Gene Transfer Using Pollen or Pollen Tube: Pollen grains are treated with heavy dose of X-ray which pulverizes chromosomes. The pollen, if able to pollinate, assures incorporation of changed chromosomes into daughter progeny. It is assumed that DNA can be taken up by the nuclei or reach the zygote through the pollen tube pathway. Both these approaches have been tried, though several problems exist in this method like presence of cell wall, nucleases, callose plugs in pollen tube etc.

Incubation of Dry Seeds, Embryos, Tissues or Cells in DNA: This method has been tried in many cases and expression of defined genes has been witnessed. In all the cases, plant cell walls work as efficient barriers, thus DNA uptake can be enhanced by PEG or electroporation or by any other device.

Asexual Methods

Non Specific Gene Transfer: Fusion of protoplasts to form somatic hybrid and partial hybrids are the knwon methods. The most direct method of gene transfer to plant cells is the uptake of plasmid DNA but at present its application relies on the availability of isolated genes. Agronomic traits are not coded for by single genes but rather by families of interacting genes. Thus, there is an interest in techniques which allow the transfer of large blocks of intact DNA encoding polygenic traits.

Protoplast membranes may be induced to fuse with nucleated or mitotically inactivated protoplasts to form hybrids; they may be induced to take up isolated nuclei or chromosomes; or they may be fused with bacterial spheroplasts, or liposomes.

Protoplast fusion may be carried out with three different methods; by using chemicals, by an electric field or by using a U.V. laser microbeam. Electrofusion is reported to be free of cytotoxicity, associated with chemical fusagen such as polyethylene glycol (PEG) or polyvinyl alcohol (PVA). Electrofusion appears superior to laser fusion as former is commercially available and affordable for a typical biological laboratory while this is not presently true for the laser microbeam. Furthermore, the number of hybrids that can be produced in a given time is much higher using electrofusion.

Foreign DNA can be directly introduced into mammalian cells. Firstly, DNA is precipitated with $CaCl_2$ and then this precipitate is mixed with the cells to be transformed. The DNA will be taken up by the cells. Inside the cell, the new DNA fragments get ligated to give a concatamer, which is then integrated into the nuclear DNA as one single piece. The integration occurs at random sites. In order to select the transformed cells several marker genes are also introduced along with the genes to be cloned. The marker genes will be linked with the genes of interest prior to integration into the host genome. One such marker is the neomycin resistance gene, which would normally inhibit protein synthesis.

FIGURE 7.7: Direct transfer to leaf protoplasts and regeneration of transgenic plants in tobacco (*Nicotiana tabacum*). (A) Freshely isolated leaf protoplasts of tobacco treated with polyethylene glycol and plasmid DNA bearing a chimeric *npt2* gene as selectable marker; (B) selection of kanamycin-resistant transformed colonies from protoplasts in bead-type culture; (C) shoot differentiation from tobacco calli obtained from transformed protoplasts (D) rooting of transformed (left) and untransformed (right) shoot from protoplasts on selective medium; (E) fertile transgenic tobacco plants obtained from protoplasts.

Specific Gene Transfer: Specific gene transfer in plants is mostly done with *Agrobacterium* species having natural biological delivery system. There are several other techniques developed recently for introducing cloned genes into plant cells. These are categorized as artificial delivery system transferring gene directly. Some examples of artificial delivery systems are direct DNA uptake, electroporation, fusion with liposomes etc. Unlike with *Agrobacterium* species mediated gene transfer (where cells with intact cell walls and tissue explants can be used), artificial delivery systems can be applied to protoplasts only.

The basic pre-requisites for successful gene transfer are:

1. selectable marker gene, which could be expected to yield a clear phenotype in transformed cell clones;
2. expression signals, which are independent of physiological state of host cell;
3. precise linkage of the protein-coding region of the selectable gene to the expression signals. This will guarantee the expression of hybrid gene in the host genome;
4. DNA stretches on both sides of the hybrid gene for its integration into the host genome without disrupting the gene construct;
5. an absolutely tight selection protocol for presumptive transformants; and
6. where of artificial delivery systems are utilized, the protoplast system taken should have routine high plating efficiency and plant regeneration capacity.

BIOLOGICAL DELIVERY SYSTEM

To date, *Agrobacterium. tumefaciens* mediated transformations have been in wider practice and a much broader range of transgenic plants have been produced with this technique. It is a method of choice for routine production of transgenic species since it can transform regenerable tissues with relative ease.

Agrobacterium tumefaciens: An Important Vector for Genetic Engineering

Agrobacterium tumefaciens is the most important tool in the genetic engineering of plants (the Ti plasmid of the soil bacterium *A. tumefaciens*). This bacterium is the causative agent of crown gall disease of dicotyledonous plants only (unable to develop gall in monocotyledonous species).

The name refers to the galls or tumours that often form at the crown (junction between the root and the stem) of infected plants. Since the crown of the plant is usually located at the soil surface, this is where a plant is most likely to be wounded (*e.g.*, due to a soil abrasion from the plant blowing in a strong wind) and infected by a soil blowing in a strong wind) and infected by a soil bacterium such as *A. tumefaciens*. However, *A. tumefaciens* can infect a plant and induce a tumour at any wound site.

In the normal disease process the bacterium enters the plant at the site of a wound. The infection often occurs at the crown, but it may involve an upper part of the stem, the petiole, or the leaf. The bacterium attaches to the wall of a cell and transforms the cell. Infected cells proliferate at the site of infection, forming a tumor or gall. The tumor can be fatal to young plants if it grows big enough to crush the vascular system, although often the tumor is merely debilitating and unsightly. Transformed cells also have the ability to grow in culture on a medium that lacks the hormones auxin and cytokinin. Finally, transformed cells produce opines, such as octopine and nopaline. These are chemicals that are formed from two amino acids. Argenine and alanine form octopine, and argenine and glutamine produce nopaline. Octopine and nopaline are not found in normal plant cells.

Infection of Agrobacterium tumefaciens

During the infection of a wound site by *A. tumefaciens*, two key following events occur:

1. The plant cells begin to proliferate and form tumours.
2. They begin to synthesize an arginine derivative called an opine.

The synthesized opine is usually either nopaline or octopine depending on the *A. tumefaciens* strain involved.

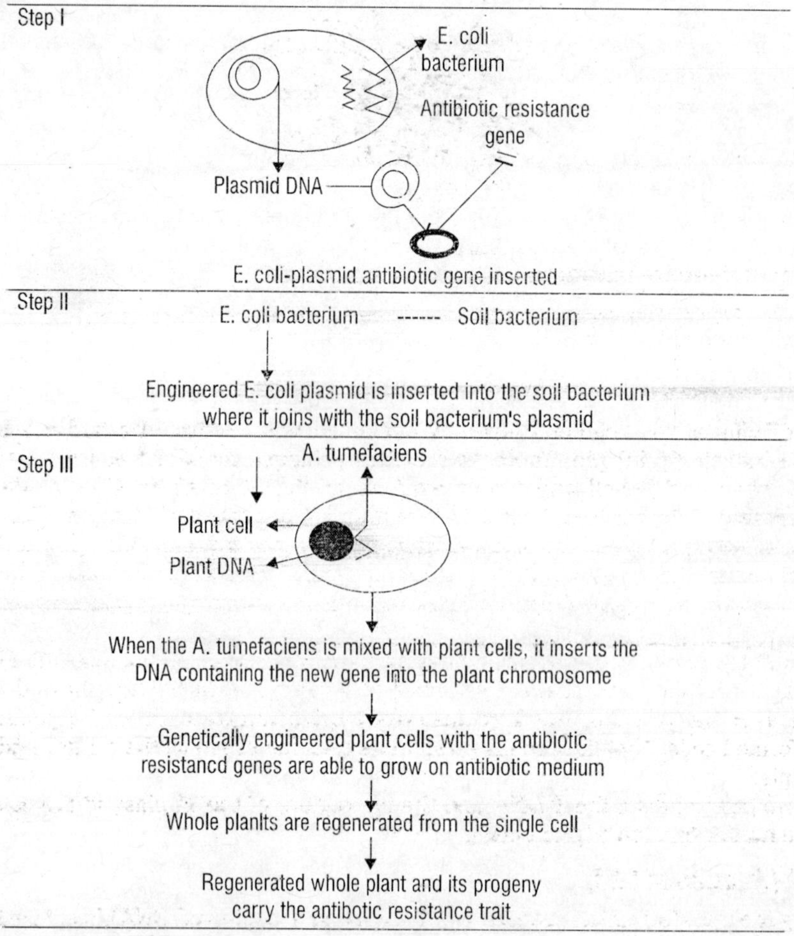

FIGURE 7.8: Various steps (I-III) used in plant genetic engineering system.

These opines are catabolized and used as energy sources by the infecting bacteria. Interestingly, *A. tumefaciens* strains that induce the synthesis of nopaline can grow on nopaline, but not on octopine, and vice versa. Clearly, an interesting interrelationship has evolved between *A. tumefaciens* strains and their plant hosts. *Agrobacterium tumefaciens* is able to divert the metabolic resources of the host plant to the synthesis of opines, which are of no apparent benefit to the plant, but which provide sustenance to the bacterium.

Genetic Information Needed For Crown Gall Development (Ti Plasmid)

The ability of *A. tumefaciens* to induce crown gall disease in plants is controlled by genetic information carried on a large (about 200,000 nucleotide-pairs) plasmid called the Ti plasmid for its tumor-inducing capacity.

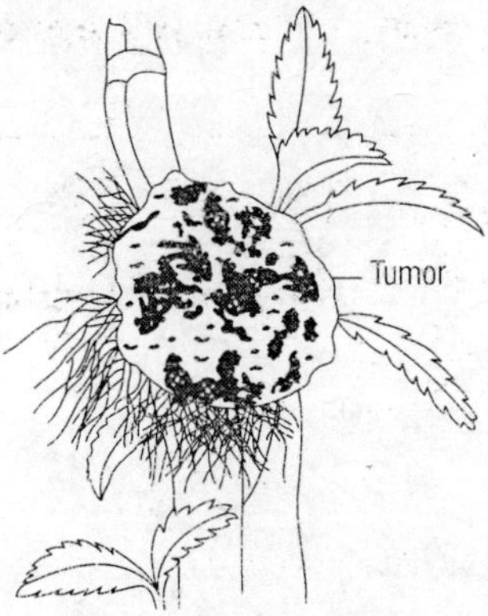

FIGURE 7.9: A plant tumor induced by Agrobacterium tumefaciens.

Tumour-Inducing Principle

Armin Braun at Rockefeller University explained that the bacteria had provided a tumour-inducing principle. The nature of this principle remained obscure until the 1970s, when Jeff Schell and his co-workers at the State University of Ghent in Belgium found that virulent bacteria all contain a large circular DNA plasmid. When strains of bacteria lose the plasmid, they lose the ability to infect plants. When bacteria regain a plasmid, they regain virulence. Further experiments by Rob Schilperoort's group in Leiden, Holland, demonstrated that many of the genes that control

Tumour characteristics (morphology, opine synthesis) lie on the plasmid. Finally, Mary-Dell Chilton et al. at the University of Washington in Seattle showed that a segment of the plasmid, the T (transferred) DNA, integrates into the genome of transformed cells. The plasmid (Ti plasmid) is thus identified as the tumour-inducing principle.

Two components, the T-DNA and the *vir* region, of the Ti plasmid are essential for the transformation of plant cells.

T-DNA (Transferred DNA)

During the transformation process, the T-DNA (for Transferred DNA) is excised from the Ti plasmid, transferred to a plant cell, and integrated (covalently inserted) into the DNA of the plant cell. The available data indicate that integration of the T-DNA occur at random chromosomal sites; moreover, in some cases, multiple T-DNA integration events occur in the same cell. In nopaline-type Ti plasmids, the T-DNA is a 23,000-nucleotide-pair segment that carries 13 known genes. In octopine-type Ti plasmids, there are two separate T-DNA segments.

Some of the genes on the T-DNA segment of the Ti plasmid encode enzymes that catalyze the synthesis of phytohormones (the auxin-IAA and the cytokinin isopentenyl adenosine). These phytohormones are responsible for the tumorous growth of cells in crown galls. The T-DNA region is bordered by 25-nucleotide pair imperfect repeats, which are required in cis for T-DNA excision and transfer. The deletion of either border sequence completely blocks the transfer of T-DNA to plant cells.

FIGURE 7.10: *Agrobacterium*-mediated gene transfer and regeneration of transgenic plants in pea (Pisum sativum). (A) cocultivation of leaf and shoot explants of pea with *A. tumefaciens* strain bearing Ti-plasmid with chimeric *hpt* gene as stable marker; (B) Selection of transformed pea callus on hygromycin-containing proliferation medium; (C) induction of shoot formation from transformed pea callus; (D) *in vitro* growing transformed pea plant; (E) adult transgenic pea plants growing in soil under greenhouse conditions; (F) fertile transgenic pea plants obtained from *Agrobacterium*-mediated gene transfer.

Vir Region (For Virulence)

The *vir* (for virulence) region of the Ti plasmid contains the genes required for the T-DNA transfer process. These genes encode the DNA processing enzymes required for excision, transfer, and integration of the T-DNA segment. *vir* genes can supply the functions needed for T-DNA transfer when located either *cis* or *trans* to the T-DNA. The *vir* genes are normally expressed at very low levels in *A. tumefaciens* cells growing in soil. However, exposure of the bacteria to plant cells or exudates from plant cells induces increased levels of expression of the operons containng the vir genes. Surprisingly, this induction process is very slow for bacteria, taking 10 to 15 hours to reach maximum levels of expression. The phenolic compounds like acetosyringone have been purified from plant exudates and shown to act as inducers of the *vir* operons. Thus, the induction process can now be studied *in vitro* by using these purified inducer molecules.

Disarmed Ti Vectors

When the T-DNA region of the Ti plasmid of *Agrobacterium tumefaciens* is transferred to plant cells and becomes integrated in plant chromosomes, the potential use of *A. tumefaciens* in plant genetic engineering seems to be obvious. The foreign genes can be introduced into the T-DNA region and, hopefully, these genes can be transferred to the plant with the rest of the T-DNA segment. In fact, this works very well. All the available data indicate that any DNA inserted any where between the T-DNA border sequences is transferred to plant cells and integrates in plant chromosomes with the rest of the T-DNA. The problem is that the transformed plant cells that have received the T-DNA from a wild-type Ti plasmid lose their normal control of cell division and form tumours. This oncogenicity of T-DNA renders wild type Ti plasmids incompatible with the goals of most gene-transfer experiments.

Vectors

A shuttle vector is commonly used, which can replicate in *E. coli* (where recombinant manipulations can be easily handled), and then transferred into *A. tumefaciens* in preparation for transfer into plants. There are two basic modes of maintenance of the shuttle vectors in *Agrobacterium*:

1. either by integration into Ti plasmid by recombination at a region of DNA homology
2. or, by autonomous replication in trans to the Ti plasmid.

The former type of vector is referred to as *cis* or integrating vector while the latter is called a *trans* or binary vector.

Selectable markers are required to recognize the transformed cells and on other hand, suppress the growth of wild type cells. This helps in identification of transformed cells, which are in small proportion.

Limitations: *A. tumefaciens* based gene transfer is hampered by host range limitations, which are especially disturbing when aiming at gene transfer into cereals or other graminaceous monocots.

Artificial Delivery Systems

Escape from host range limitations can be made by transferring the genes *directly* without using any biological vectors, into plant cells. Cell wall constitutes an effective barrier for DNA molecules to pass; naked plant cells, the 'protoplasts', have been found ideal experimental system to study vectorless gene transfer. Various artificial delivery systems are given here.

GENE TRANSFER USING PARTICLE BOMBARDMENT TECHNIQUE

The first genetically engineered plants were produced in middle 1980s (Horsch et al. 1985) and developed interest of genetic engineers in the production of transgenic plants for both basic and applied work. The major efforts were in the development and refinement of methods for transgenic plant production and also in the isolation and characterization of useful gene for introduction into plants. Through gene transfer, plants have already been produced that contain genes for disease and insect resistance, and modified fruit and grain quality. Particle bombardment genes transfer (or biolistics) is a method of transferring genes. Biolistics has been used to transform a large number of different plant species (reviewed by Christou 1994), as well as some animals, fungi, and bacteria.

The basic principle of particle bombardment for gene transfer is to use high velocity microprojectile to incorporate the introduced genes. The outer cell layers are penetrated in order to introduce genetic material into living cells.

History

Biolistics (a combination of *biological* and *ballistics*), is a method in which high-velocity microprojectiles are used to deliver exogenous genetic material into plant tissue. It was developed, and first described by John Sanford in collaboration with Ted Klein, Ed Wolf, and Nelson Allen (Sanford et al. 1987). This method of particle acceleration has been described as the *particle gun, the gene gun, the bioblaster*, and the *microprojectile bombardment method.* The important aspects of biolistics are:

1. It is a direct gene transfer method.
2. It does not require biological vector.
3. It has been used successfully to transform cells that were once impossible to transform by other means.
4. DNA delivery appears to be genotype and tissue independent.
5. With this technique, the microprojectile is shot through the physical barriers of the cell.
6. There are no biological limitations to DNA delivery.
7. Transformation via the biolistics method is simple and safe.

Applications of Biolistic

1. The utility of the Biolistic method is broad and the technology can be used for basic studies on transformation.
2. Modifications of gene expression.
3. Understanding essential components of genes.
4. The production of transgenic plants of economic value.

Particle Gun Design

Several particle guns have been designed in various laboratories. The basis of all of these designs is to coat DNA onto small dense particles and accelerate the particles towards a target tissue. The particles usually consist of either gold or tungsten.

Gold particles are chemically inert. They do not produce cytotoxic effects. They are more uniform in size than tungsten particles. However, the cost of gold particles may limit their accessibility and the more affordable tungsten particles are sufficient for most studies.

Tungsten particles are somewhat phytotxic and tend to be more variable in size than gold particles. Ideally the particles used for bombardment should have good initial affinity for the DNA, yet freely release it once in the cytoplasm or nucleus of the target cell.

Preparation of DNA Coated Microprojectiles

1. Wash gold or tungsten particles and mixed them with plasmid DNA.
2. The DNA is bound on the particles using either ethanol or $CaCl_2$ precipitation methods.
3. Spermidine may be added to the mixture, possibly protecting the DNA from degradation and/or altering its conformation.
4. After precipitation, the particles may be washed, resuspended and either dried or stored on ice as an aqueous suspension until use.

Use of Macrocarrier

Many of the particle guns utilize a macrocarrier. They support or carry the particles and gun is accelerated along with the particles towards the target. The macrocarrier is usually retained by a stopping plate or screen before it collides with the target, whereas the particles continue along their course. In most cases, the particles are accelerated under partial vacuum in a vacuum chamber to reduce air drag.

The penetration of particle is controlled by modifying the intensity of the explosive burst. It is done by changing the distance that the particles must travel to reach the target tissue or by using different sized particles.

Gene Gun

The original gene gun described in the literature used DNA-coated tungsten particles in an aqueous slurry loaded on the end of a small plastic bullet, which served as the macrocarrier. The plastic macrocarrier was placed into a 0.22 caliber barrel in front of a gun powder cartridge. Once the cartridge was fired, the plastic bullet was propelled towards a solid stopping plate containing a small opening in the center. The microprojectiles continued through the hole towards the target tissue while the macrocarrier was retained. Both the stopping plate and the macrocarrier were discarded afterwards. The initial blast from the gunpowder cartridge necessitated frequent cleaning of the chamber and the target variations in results were common with this device, this first unit was used successfully by a number of different laboratories.

Modified bombardment devices have been developed. They are: (1) Helium-Modified Bombardment Device, (2) Accel Particle Gun, (3) Particle Inflow Gun, (4) Microtargeting Device, and (5) Helios Gene Gun.

FIGURE 7.11: PDS 1000 particle gun.

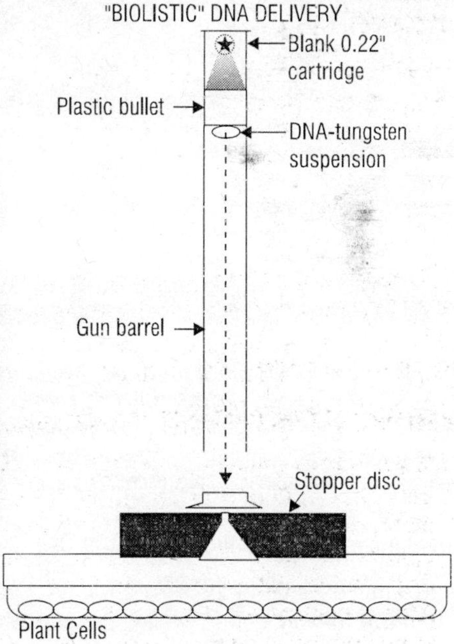

FIGURE 7.12: The gene gun.

Factors Affecting Particle Bombardment-Mediated Transformation

1. Particle bombardment is a physical process of DNA introduction.
2. After the DNA-coated particles are introduced, there are numerous factors that influence gene expression and the subsequent recovery of transgenic plants.
3. These factors are resulting in the expression and eventual integration of the foreign DNA. For successful transformation via particle bombardment, the plasmid DNA should be carefully designed and selected, while special attention also needs to be placed on the nature, state and receptivity of the target tissues.

FIGURE 7.13: Microprojectile bombardment of cultured immature zygotic embryo and regeneration of transgenic plants in wheat (*Triticum aestivum*): (A) Cultured immature zygotic embryo of wheat before incroprojectile bombardment; (B) microprojectile bombardment precultured wheat embryos after proliferation and transfer to regeneration medium in absence of selective agent; (C) phosphinothricin-resistant regenerating callus obtained from precultured immature zygotic embryos bombarded with microprojectiles coated with plasmid DNA bearing a chimeric *bar* gene as selectable marker; (D) methotrexate-resistant plantlet regenerated from precultured immature zygotic embryos bombarded with microprojectiles coated with plasmid DNA bearing a chimeric *dhfr* gene as selectable marker; (E) Transformed (center) wheat platlet obtained from microprojectile bombardment using a chimeric *bar* gene as selectable marker and untransformed controls (left and right) after transfer to phosphinotricin-containing rooting (left); (F) *in vitro* growing methotrexate-resistant wheat plantlets from microprojectile bombardment using a chimeric *dhfr* gene as selectable marker; (G) fertile transgenic wheat plants from microprojectile bombardment to precultured immature zygotic embryos.

Components of the Introduced Plasmid DNA

The introduced plasmid DNA(s) typically contains the necessary plasmid backbone (allows growth and selection in the bacterial host), plant marker genes and the gene(s) of interest.

The *plant marker genes* can be selectable markers (which allow growth of transformed plant cells in the presence of a selective agent) and/or scorable markers (reporter genes). The genes themselves are composed of the promoter, coding region and terminator. Introns, enhancers and attachment regions are defined regions of additional DNA that can be used to enhance, modulate or stabilize gene expression.

Selectable Marker Genes: The selection of proper marker genes of choice is critical for the successful recovery of stably transformed tissues. The selectable marker allows the transformed cells to proliferate in the presence of a selective agent while nontransformed cells either do not grow or multiply at a much reduced rate. Selectable marker genes may be either antibiotic or herbicide resistance genes. The resistance genes can act either by modifying the selective agent itself to inactivate it or by producing an insensitive from of the normal target of the selective agent.

Selectable Marker Gene: Nptii: It is most commonly used selectable marker gene.

1. It imparts resistance to the antibiotic kanamycin.
2. The NPTII gene product is neomycin phosphorylation, which inactivates the antibiotic by phosphorylation.
3. Other antibiotics that are commonly used with selectable marker genes in plants include hygromycin, phleomycin and gentamycin.

Selectable Marker Gene: *Bar* Gene: It is most commonly used herbicide resistance marker gene.

1. It is typically used with species of the Gramineae.
2. The bar gene encodes phosphinothricin acetyl transferase, which inactivates phosphinothricin herbicides by acetylation.
3. The bar gene can be used with bialaphos of glufosinate; again, selection of the proper herbicide must be empirically determined as with antibiotics.
4. Other commonly used herbicide resistance genes impart resistance to glyphosate, sulfonyl ureas and dalapon.

Reporter Genes: β-glucuronidase (GUS) is the most widely used reporter gene for plant transformation.

1. The GUS gene has proven to be very useful in monitoring transient expression in a number of species.
2. Plant tissues could be evaluated at various times following bombardment by reporter genes whose expression can be monitored without causing tissue damage. Such a system could greatly reduce the effort and time involved in selection of stable transformants.
3. The firefly **luciferase gene** is a nontoxic reporter gene that has been successfully used to monitor gene expression in plants. After activity bombarded tissues are treated with luciferin (substrate) solution, luciferase activity is documented using either X-ray film.
4. Luciferase activity can also be assayed using extracts of plant tissue that are incubated with the luciferin substrate.
5. The detection techniques for luciferase severely limit the flexibility of using this reporter gene.

Introns

1. The introns are present between the promoter and coding region of a gene.
2. They significantly affect gene expression. Monocotyledonous species, in particular the Graminae, show significant enhancement of gene expression when using introns.
3. Introns may act by stabilizing mRNAs, thus leading to greater amounts of

translation products.

4. Introduction of different introns between the cauliflower mosaic virus 35S promoter and GUS gene caused significant enhancement of transient gene expression in maize. The degree of expression varied depending on the intron.

Promoter Analysis

The use of reporter genes such as GUS or GFP under control of strong promoters (*e.g.*, CaMV 35S) allows for optimization of transformation efficiency of crop plants. Particle bombardment also provides a rapid and convenient means for evaluation of promoter strength, analysis of the function of different regions of promoters, and for examination of tissue specificity of gene expression. The promoter either in its entirety or with various deletions/mutations is fused to a reporter gene and introduced into the target tissue. This approach has successfully been used in a number of different species.

Codon Usage

The ability to introduce genes into plants from nonplant sources had led to the realization that genes from different organisms can be processed very differently with respect to their expression when compared with have native plant genes (Diehn, *et al.*, 1996). Unaltered DNA from nonplant sources may contain DNAs that are recognized by plants as signals for splicing or polyadenylation. Changes for codon usage resulted in a 300-fold increase in expression levels of a synthetic Bt gene.

Target Tissue

A variety of different plant tissues have been used as targets for particle bombardment-mediated transformation. Selection of the appropriate target tissue is dependent on the nature of the research. For rapid gene expression studies, various plasmid constructions can be introduced into different tissues and transient expression can be quickly analyzed to assess promoter activity without the production of stably transformed plants (IIDA et al. 1995). Almost any tissue can be used for transient expression studies as long the cell wall is penetrable by the DNA-coated particles. The choice of the appropriate target tissue, physiological state of the plant material, and pre- and postbombardment treatments are critical to the successful regeneration of stable transformants.

Embryogenic Cultures

Embryogenic cell cultures have been very useful for the production of stably transformed plants. Particle bombardment of embryogenic maize and wheat cultures was used to generate the first transgenic plants of these species. Embryogenic cultures provide a reliable source of tissue for optimization of bombardment conditions and can be used for year-round production of transgenic plants.

Shoot Apical Meristems

Shoot meristem cells are most effective target for production of stable transgenics. Theoretically, introduction of DNA into would result in the production of chimeric plants, where the transformed cells would directly give rise to germ-line tissue and the introduced DNA would be passed on to the progeny. This approach could potentially avoid or reduce tissue culture manipulations but there are many problems with shoot meristem bombardment.

In sunflower, bombarded shoot apices of particles alone (no DNA) was done and then inoculated the tissue with *Agrobacterium*. In this case, particle bombardment was used as a method to wound the target tissue for transformation via *Agrobacterium* rather than for direct DNA introduction itself. Although the resultant plants were chimeric for the introduced gene(s), it is important to note that many of the transformation events were germ-line and transgenic progeny were recovered.

Other Target Tissues

Particle bombardment can be used to introduce DNA into any target tissue that is penetrable by the DNA-coated particles. The other tissues that have been subjected to particle bombardment include leaves, pollen, styles, cereal aleurone cells and tassel primordial.

Tissue Treatment

One treatment that greatly influences gene expression is osmotic conditioning. Osmotic conditioning can be both pre- and post-bombardment. Tissues are subjected to either partial drying in a laminar flow hood or cultured in a medium containing an osmotic agent such as mannitol and sorbitol at relatively high concentration (~0.4 M). Osmotic treatment can enhances both transient expression as well as significantly increase stable transformation. The osmotica may act by causing plasmolysis of the target cells that lessens or eliminates extrusion of the protoplasm in cells that are penetrated by particles.

Other media additives are silver thiosulfate along with mannitol. They increase GUS expression in bombarded scutellar tissue of wheat, presumably by reducing the negative effects of wound ethylene. Inclusion of abscisic acid with an osmoticum (myo-inositol) increased trnsient GUS expression 1 day after bombardment of *Picea* embryogenic cultures.

The Fate of the Introduced DNA(s)

Although particle bombardment has been used for DNA delivery to plant cell for some time, it is still nuclear what happens to the majority of DNA that is introduced. Transient expression studies indicate that large numbers of cells can receive the particles resulting in approximately 10,000 GUS-positive cells per bombardment. In cells that transiently express the introduced DNA, particles are most often seen either in or directly adjacent to the nucleus.

Recombination: Plasmid DNA which is introduced into plant cells via particle bombardment undergoes recombination with other plasmid molecules as well as with the host chromosomal DNA. Recombination occurs whenever new gene arrangements are formed through exchange, elimination or insertion of DNA. Plasmid DNA can either insert cleanly into plant chromosomal DNA as a single entity or large linkages of plasmids can form and subsequently integrate (the full range of intermediate combinations is possible). Although the exact fate of DNA introduced via particle bombardment is not clear, it appears that plasmid DNA molecules rearrange or recombine with each other to yield linkages of both whole plasmids and plasmid fragments.

Position Effect: The expression of the introduced gene(s) is dependent on the nature of the DNA as well as the final physical arrangement of the foreign DNA in the plant genome. The influence that adjacent, native plant DNA has on expression of the introduced DNA is called *position effect*. If the foreign DNA integrates in a region of DNA that is active, the introduced gene may be expressed at relatively high levels. If the introduction occurs in a region that is not transcriptionally active, gene expression may be reduced.

Co-Suppression: A reduction in expression of a gene resulting from the introduction of multiple copies of the gene is called *co-suppression.* Co-suppression is useful in some situations when a reduction in expression of a native gene is desirable. Unfortunately, co-suppression is also observed as an undesirable product of particle bombardment-mediated transformation when multiple copies of the same gene are introduced.

Scaffold Attachment Regions: To stabilize gene expression in transgene plant tissue, Scaffold attachment regions (SARs; also known as matrix attachment/associated regions, MARs) have shown some utility. SARs are regions of DNA, which were isolated based on their ability to bind to the nuclear scaffold. For transformation, the SARs are ligated to the flanking regions of the gene of interest.

Targeted Recombination Systems in Plants: In order to have better control on the expression of the introduced DNA(s), it would be beneficial to predict or *direct the site integration.* This can be accomplished through either *agrolistic transformation* or homologous recombination.

Agrolistic Transformation or Homologous Recombination: For agrolistic transformation, plant tissues are bombarded with plasmids that contain some of the DNA excision components from the *Agrobacterium* gene transfer system. Approximately 20% of agrolistically transformed plant cells contained precisely defined DNA inserts that would be expected for *Agrobacterium*-mediated transformation.

For targeting using homologous recombination, genes could potentially be placed in certain areas of the genome based on sequence homology between the introduced and the genomic DNA. Although targeted or homologous recombination is fairly well-characterized in some organisms, it has not been well-studied in higher plants. Very little is known about native plant recombinases with most recombination studies in plants relying on information and genes that are available from nonplant systems.

Homologous Recombination Systems: Two homologous recombination systems have been evaluated in plants.

1. Cre-lox system from bacteriophage P1
2. FLP/FRT system from yeast

In these systems, a target site containing specific DNA sequences must be introduced specific recombinase, a second piece of DNA using transformation. Following activation with a specific recombinase, a second piece of DNA replaces the target DNA through homologous recombination.

GENE TRANSFER BY MICROINJECTION TECHNIQUE

Intranuclear microinjection is a direct physical approach that overcomes many of the biological and other obstacles. Originally developed for animal cells, it is now applied to plant cells also. The microinjection technique uses a fine capillary needle to deliver DNA precisely into cells (even nuclei of cells) in such a way that the cells are not killed but survive the treatment and can develop further into clones.

For transformation, microinjection systems are designed for speed and operational simplicity as these factors govern the total number of cells that can manipulated. To facilitate rapid injection rates, protoplasts with partially reformed cell walls can be attached to solid support (glass coverslips or slides etc.) with poly-L-lysine or artificially bound substrate without damaging the cells. After one day in culture, the cell walls of protoplasts are firm enough to provide support and protection yet they can be easily penetrated with micropipettes worth 0.5-10 μm diameter tip). Each protoplast is microinjected, segregated and transferred to optimal condition to obtain transformed cell line. An alternative method employs a blunt holding pipette to hold each protoplast under suction and segregating it directly into microdrop culture after microinjection.

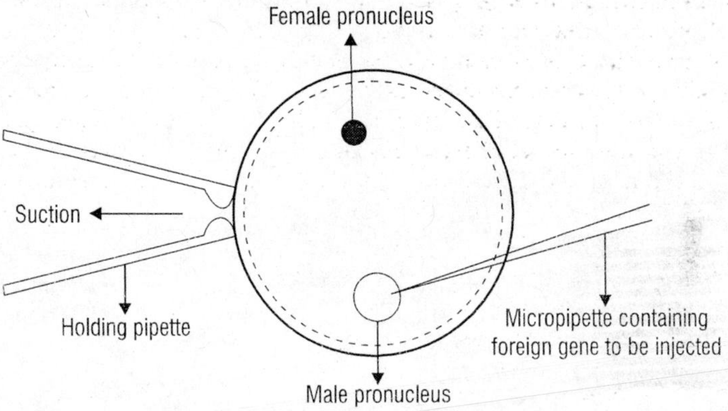

FIGURE 7.14: Microinjection system.

Several advantages are associated with the microinjection technique. First of all, the amount of DNA delivered per cell is not limited by the technique and can be optimized. This improves the chance for integrative transformation. Secondly, the delivery is precise, even into the nuclei of the target cell, again increasing the chance for integrative transformation. Thirdly, the small structures can be injected containing only a few cells and with high regeneration potential, for example, microspore derived and zygotic proembryos. Lastly, it is a direct physical approach and therefore host-range independent.

However, there are some major drawbacks like, only one cell is targeted per injection and the handling requires specialized skill and instrumentation. Is hundreds of injections can be performed per working day, low transformation rate is yet not a serious disadvantage.

Applications of Microinjection Technique

Different applications of microinjection technique in plant science have been reported. Some experiments dealt with the introduction of fluorescent dyes into differentiated cells to study intracellular transport. Efforts have been made to microinject microorganisms into suspension cells. Attempts to transfer chromosomes or even cell organelles have been made. A common feature to these experiments is low numbers of manipulated cells.

DNA has also been microinjected in mice and fish. In mice, foreign DNA is injected into the mole pronucleus, residing in fertilized ovule. The injected zygotes are cultured *in vitro* to blastocysts and then placed inside a foster mother. This technique has been used to introduce rat growth hormone gene. Transgenic fishes have been obtained in many species like carp, cat fish, gold fish, salmon, Tilapia, rainbow trout and Zebrafish. As the male pronucleus is difficult to locate in fishzygote, the DNA is injected into cytoplasm of fertilized ovule within first few hours of after fertilization. As the fishes undergo external fertilization, transfer of embryos into foster mothers is not needed. Transformed embryos are instead hatched in trays. Various gene transferred into fish are human or rat growth hormone, chicken delta-crystalive protein, *E. coli* β-galactosidase gene, *E. coli* neomycin resistance gene, *E. coli* hygromycin resistance gene, winter flounder anti freeze protein (AFT) gene, and, cDNA of rainbow trout growth hormone. Cytoplasmic microinjection is a tedious and time consuming procedure and is unsuitable for mass gene transfer.

The Technique

The macroinjection technique involves the use of injection needles with diameters far wider than cell diameters for delivering DNA into wound sites within tissues. However, at the same time it destroys those cells which are in direct contact with the injected DNA. To integrate, the DNA must gain entry to intact cells adjacent to the wound site.

There are a variety of problems associated with experiments that require DNA passage through single, double (in the case of pollen) or even many cell walls. The uptake of DNA across cell walls is a very rare event. Majority of DNA molecules applied get attached to cell walls before they have a chance to enter the cell. Penetration is further reduced by subsequent presence of cell wall. Moreover, DNA does not normally move from cell to cell. Thus, recombination occurs at relatively low frequency by this method. Microinjection has been mostly applied to ovule, embryos and other tissues

Lipofection

The use of liposomes for transformation of transfection system is called lipofection. Liposomes, as defined by Bongham, in 1965, are special type of lamellar phase in which water is self contained and the lipid molecules are disposed in bimolecular layers attached by their non-polar interfaces.

Liposomes possess many properties akin to those of biological membranes. They are easy to manipulate, their lipid contents can be varied at will and many substances may be trapped inside the interlamellar spaces. They are found to be ideal carrier systems and are now used in genetic engineering to deliver foreign DNA molecules into a desired cell.

DNA or RNA, encapsulated in liposomes, can be transferred into plant protoplasts by either direct fusion with the naked plasma membrane or through endocytosis of the liposome. Although it is efficient in terms of DNA encapsulation and transfer, the method once again requires protoplasts and its application is limited to species for which protocols are available for protoplast regeneration. Foreign macromolecules, for example impermeant fluorescent dyes, RNA and DNA, can be introduced into walled plant cells by an alternative strategy which involves encapsulation of the desired probe into liposome that can be pressure-injected into the vacuole. There are two advantages of this method. First of all, the liposome protects the DNA from being damaged by the acidic pH and proteases present in the vacuole. Secondly, when liposomes are constructed from material that is compatible with the lipids of the tonoplast, liposome-tonoplast fusion occurs (Madore *et al.*, 1986) and so the encapsulated DNA should be successfully delivered into the cytoplasm.

Liposomes would appear to offer the following advantages as vectors for gene delivery into plant cells:

1. Enhanced delivery of encapsulated DNA by membrane fusion.
2. Protection of nucleic acids from nuclease activity.
3. Delivery into a variety of cell types besides protoplasts entry through plasmodesmata.
4. Delivery of intact small organelles.
5. Protect the genetic material from immunogenic reaction (liposomes are non-immunogenic).
6. Composition of lipid can be manipulated to confer specific properties to liposomes.

The use of liposome for delivery of gene was first described for delivering polio virus RNA. Later liposomes were used in combination with polyethylene glycol for delivery of plasmid DNA into tobacco protoplast.

SILICON CARBIDE FIBER-VORTEX (SILICON WHISKERS)

Silicon carbide forms microscopically small needles (silicon whiskers) that can be used to perforate plant cell walls and plasmalemma of suspension cells or protoplasts. Advantages of the silicon carbide fiber-mediated transformation method over other procedures includes the ability to transform walled cells (thus avoiding protoplast isolation), relative ease of the procedure, and very low equipment costs.

Technically, the method is very simple: a mix of whiskers and plant cells in a small test tube is shaken. This method involves a mixture of plasmid DNA encoding a selectable or screenable marker gene, silicon carbide fibers, and tissue of the species to be transformed in an Eppendorf tube. Mixture is vortexed to facilitate cellular penetration by enhancing frequent and forceful intercellular collisions. DNA deliver in this system is presumably due to cell wall penetration by DNA coated silicon carbide fibers. The silicon carbide fibers apparently act as microinjection needles facilitating DNA delivery.

Only Eppendorf tubes and a vortex is sufficient equipment. This opens the way for DNA diffuse into the cells (Kaeppler *et al.*, 1992). Although, details of the mechanisms by which silicon carbide wiskers work work is unclear, stable transformation with maize has been recently published (Frame *et al.*, 1995). The overall efficiency of the wiskers approach is between one-fifth and one-tenth that of conventional microprojectile shooting, but is advantage would be its *low tech* character, dispensing with any sophisticated or expensive instrumentation. Currently, only maize has been transformed and a highly regenerating system was used. It remains an open question whether the whiskers approach will be useful in organized tissue.

A procedure has been recently developed for the injection of DNA into *Zea mays* and *Nicotiana tabacum* tissue cultures using silicon carbide fibres.

SONICATION

The latest method developed uses ultrasound to facilitate the uptake of nucleic acids into plant cells. By this technique, plant protoplasts and cells in suspension and intact pieces of plant tissue can readily be transformed. The protoplasts, suspension cells or small pieces of tissue are suspended in a few ml of sonication medium in a microcentrifuge tube. Plasmid DNA (and possibly carrier DNA) is then added and after rapid mixing the samples are ready for sonication.

The pulses of ultrasound are delivered by ordinary machines. The microtip (normally tapered) is immersed 2-3 mm into the suspension and pulses of selected intensity and duration are delivered. The cells are finally transferred to fresh growth medium.

There are two possibilities for permeabilization of cell and uptake of DNA. Firstly the violent collapse of activation bubbles, generating high-pressure and high-temperature shock waves could possibly cause localized rupture of the plasmalemma and lead to uptake of exogenous solute. This may be followed by re-establishment of membrane integrity. The second hypothetical possibility may be the existence of a critical hydrostatic pressure at which the intrinsic membrane potential is sufficiently high to induce mechanical breakdown of the membrane (60-100 MPa) in a hyperbaric chamber. Consequently, it is possible that either the high oscillating pressure generated by the ultrasonic field and/or the high-pressure shock waves originating from collapse cavitation could produce such higher hydrostatic pressures that reversible membrane breakdown would occur.

This method has been applied for transferring plasmid DNA into protoplasts, suspension cells and tissues of sugarbeet and potato.

ELECTROPORATION

This method uses an electrical pulse to introduce DNA into cells. By exposure to brief electric shock, the cells become temporarily permeable to DNA. If the required DNA fragment is kept in direct contact with the protoplast membrane, the entry of DNA molecules into the cells is facilitated.

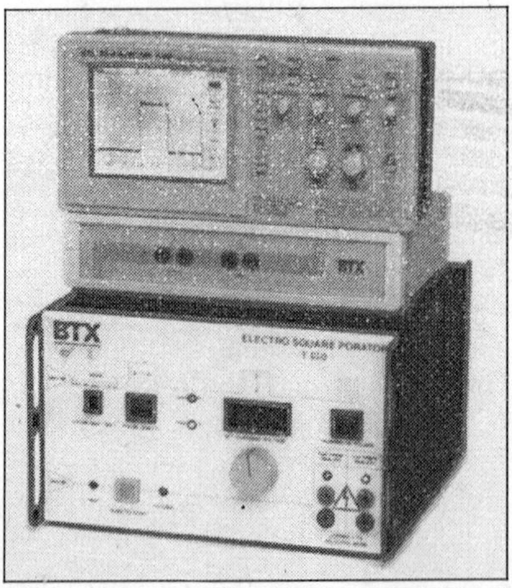

FIGURE 7.15: Electroporation apparatus.

Successful DNA transfer through this technique has been shown in bacterial, yeast, fungal, plant and mammalian cells. Among plants, successful gene transfer using electroporation method has been reported in protoplasts of tobacco, petunia, maize, rice, wheat and sorghum. In carrot, maize and tobacco protoplasts, bacterial CATgene with different plant promoters has been introduced and efficiently expressed. Electroporation is applicable to both monocot and dicot protoplasts.

It has been recently hypothesized that the mechanism of DNA entry into the cell during electroporation may be either due to unspecific membrane process, or it may be specifically mediated by permease. The activation of permease may be due to high electric field, and thus, may lead to thinning of membrane. Hole may be created as a result and stabilized by a favourable dipole interaction with the electric field. Various advantages of electroporation have been listed. It is a convenient, simple, fast and efficient method applicable to a wide range of plant protoplasts and involves low cell toxicity.

The main disadvantage of electroporation is its requirement for protoplasts and therefore a system where regeneration of these protoplasts to calli or whole plants have been established. Consequently, it may not be applicable to some plant systems. Recently an electroporation system using organized and easily regenerable tissues such as immature maize embroys has been developed.

POLY-CATION MEDIATED DNA UPTAKE

Direct DNA uptake by protoplasts can be stimulated by using hydrophilic, long chain polycations such as polyethylene glycol (PEG), poly L-lysine, poly L-ornithene or DEAE-dextran with or without metal ions such as Zn^{2+}, Li^{+}, Cs^{+}, Rb^{+}, K^{+}, Na^{+}, Ca^{2+} or Mg^{2+}. The technique is efficient and can be applied virtually to every protoplast system and for transfer of even small quantities of DNA.

Polyethylene-glycol is an extremely hydrophilic molecule and it removes 'free water' when placed in a solution. Free water indicates such molecules, which interact with charged (usually ionic) molecules soluble in water.

Thus, under high PEG concentration (15-25%), ionic macromolecules such as DNA can no longer stay in solution and get precipitated. The protoplast membrane as well as DNA is normally negatively charged, and therefore, charge repulsion is obvious. This repulsion limits the interaction between DNA and protoplasts. At very high concentration, PEG seems to minimize charged repulsion effects thus stimulating DNA uptake by endocytosis without any gross damage to protoplasts. Studies have been conducted with *Petunia*, *Nicotiana*, rice, maize etc. In these experiments, PEG was used in combination with pure Ti plasmid or calcium phosphate precipitated Ti plasmid mix with a carrier DNA. Mechanism of cross membrane transport in presence of PEG is still to confirm.

DNA-uptake may be enhanced as a result of the interaction of the polycations at one or more of the following levels:

1. Protection of the exogenous DNA against nuclease degradation.
2. Increase in the permeability of the plasma membrane.

DNA transformation by using the polycation "polybrene" (hexamidethrine bromide) is new, although similar techniques have been used for several years in the transformation of animal cells. The major advantages of the polybrenc technique are the following:

1. It is less toxic than other polycations
2. The high transformation efficiency allows very small quantities of plasmid DNA to be used, thus it is relatively easy to introduce only one sequence of a genome. Even with quite high plasmid concentrations only one or a few copies of the plasmid are integrated and concatamers of integrated plasmid are rarely observed.
3. Since no carrier DNA is used to integrate plasmid DNA into the host genome thus, the sequences surrounding the site of integration can be analysed.

a) The transformation frequency appears to be independent of nature of plasmid (supercoiled or linear).
b) The polybrene method can be used for both stable and transient expression.

CA-DNA CO-PRECIPITATION METHOD

The basis of the Ca-DNA technique is the formation of a co-precipitate of plasmid DNA with calcium phosphate, formed by adding $CaCl_2$ to a solution of DNA in phosphate buffer. On contact with protoplasts, the co-precipitate is transferred across the plasma membrane in a calcium requiring process; and in order to encourage the endocytotic uptake of the precipitate, the protoplast/Ca-DNA complex is treated with polyvinyl alcohol and high pH calcium. This method was first used for plant transformation by Hain et al. (1985). He used a tobacco leaf protoplast system.

ULTRASONICATION

Gene transfer by ultrasonication is the latest and simple method, where, plant protoplasts, cells in suspension and intact pieces of plant tissues can be transformed. The target cells are suspended in sonication medium in a microcentrifuge tube. Carrier DNA is added and microtip (generally tapered) is immersed in the sonication medium. Pulse of selected intensity and duration are delivered by the ordinary homogenizing machines. Transformed cells are finally transferred for selection.

There are two hypotheses for permeabilization of membrane by sonication method. First assumes that reversible localized rupture of plasmalemma results in is due to violent collapse of activation bubbles which results in generating high-pressure and temperature shock waves to plasmalemma. The second hypothesis predicts the existence of critical hydrostatic pressure responsible for reversible mechanical breakdown of membrane.

This method has been used in tobacco, wheat and sugar beet. In tobacco, transgenic plants were obtained at 22% frequency with ultrasonication. Ultrasound transformation is unique among existing methods because of its versatility as plant protoplasts, cell in suspension and intact pieces of plant tissue can be readily transformed. This feature, along with the fact that the equipment for ultrasound transformation is simple, cheap and multifunctional should allow for substantial future applications.

UV LASER MICROBEAM

A new method of introducing exogenous gene materials into cells is laser microbeam irradiation. DNA can be incorporated into whole plant cells and has been successfully applied to tobacco. DNA enters the cell through a self-healing hole made with a laser microbeam.

There are several advantages to this method. A laser beam can be used inside of tissues, cells and organelles, thus increasing the rate of transformation and the speed of operation. Wide controllability of the laser beam intensity, flexibility in optical manipulation wide choices for laser wave length and pulse width are other advantages. It is also applicable to cells with hard walls. Its wide application in the field of cell biology is the ability to transfer cytoplasmic material. Finally, future versions of this system are expected to be more automated which should greatly increase output as well as the success rate.

This technique can be used for genetic manipulation of plant tissue, individual cells, protoplasts and organelles. Furthermore, it permits selective fusion in a part of a subcellular organelle present inside a single living cell.

A number of techniques exist today for transferring genes into plant protoplasts and cells. Most of these techniques use protoplasts because the cell wall is not sufficiently permeabilized for DNA uptake. As protoplasts of many species are often difficult to regenerate efficiently into fertile plants it can not be applied to any system. These techniques can be preferably used as an analytical tool, for example, in testing the function of gene constructs.

Moreover, most of the systems require sophisticated and costly equipment. In addition, it does not allow the combination of both accurate quantitative estimates of gene expression and efficient generation of transgenic plants.

However, successful gene transfer has been reported in few systems using above techniques, and much research in the context is still in progress.

PROBLEMS INVOLVED IN GENE TRANSFER

Expression System: Adequate expression of gene is essential with high expression at right time and in a particular tissue. For high expression strong promoters like 35-S promoter of Cauliflower Mosaic Virus (CaMV) is used which has a wide host range. More specific promoters are required for tissue specific attachment regions (SAR's) are used to increase expression. SAR's acts by forming loops in chromatin structure thereby reducing gene silencing in cells having limited number of transgenes. But high amount of m-RNA may not have corresponding amount of product.

Cellular Localization: Abiotic stress causes injury to membrane (by formation of reactive oxygen intermediates) affecting membrane bound process finally influencing metabolism of plant. It is desirable to locate membrane modifying, osmoprotectant producing or radical scavenging enzymes to defined organelles. Transit peptides are required to ensure correct localization of enzymes expressed. Typical transit sequence used to direct polypeptides to chloroplast is from small subunit of Rubisco.

Proteolysis, Protein Folding and Prosthetic Group Acquistion: Short polypeptides after expression may undergo proteolytic degradation. This can be avoided by processing and folding of proteins by co-expression of chaperon proteins in transgenic plants especially in case of large enzymes. Oxygen radical metals like, Fe, Zn, Cu, Mn, Therefore, the metal ions should be present in adequate amount.

Precursor Availability: Amount of precursor has a great effect on product formation. Precursor can be extracted from environment or synthesized in cell from existing metabolic pathways.

Inhibitory Environments: Intracellular conditions in transgenic plants (pH, temperature, ionic strength) affect foreign proteins. It is usually operated during varied environmental conditions. Therefore, the introduced gene should be taken from closely related plant.

CHAPTER 8

Expression of Induced Genes

Genetic Engineering in plants includes formation of recombinant DNA, its introduction into cells or protoplasts and more importantly expression of the foreign genes. After introduction of foreign gene, complete plants are regenerated from transformed cells or tissues. Regenerated plants are then examined for expression of gene constructs. It is a lengthy process, involving selection and bulking of tissues for analysis of integrated genes. This duration can be avoided by studying the 'transient expression' of the constructs introduced directly into protoplasts. In this approach, foreign DNA is added to protoplasts by gene transfer method and these protoplasts are cultured for 1-2 days. The protoplasts are then harvested and assayed for products encoded by the introduced (but not necessarily integrated) genes. This confirms the incorporation of required gene into the protoplast.

FACTORS AFFECTING GENE EXPRESSION

Over expression of genes involved in the control of rate of biosynthesis can increase oil content. In some cases, introduction of additional copies of endogenous gene may interfere withgene expression, thereby rather than enhancing the gene product. This phenomenon is called ‘co-suppression’. Lowering gene expression by the use of antisense RNA has been successful in reduction of polygalactouronase levels in tomatoes.

Regulation of Gene Expression

Lipids are essential components of plant membrane and serve other structural roles in all tissues of plants. Species that accumulate novel fatty acids in seed oil largely limit their presence to storage lipids. Thus, seed specific expression is desirable such that the structural lipid metabolism is not effected. Specificity even within seed (endosperm, cotyledons) may be required.

During development seed enters the maturation phase showing cell elongation and accumulation of storage reserves. It is a stage of maximum oil synthesis. Genes intended to alter fatty acid synthesis must be expressed during maturation phase when oil accumulation rates are maximum.

Regulatory sequences for the genes expressed in seeds during various stages could be used to express foreign genes in seeds. Genes for major storage proteins have been isolated and regulatory sequences from many of the genes have been tested in transgenic plants. Genes for major storage proteins have been isolated and regulatory sequences from many of the genes have been tested in transgenic plants. Genes isolated from oil synthesis which might be expected to contain regulatory sequences are those encoding ACP (acyl carrier protein) from *Brassica napus* and *B. campestris*.

Genes expressed during seed development have been characterized including seed storage protein (napin and cruciferin). Regulatory elements from *B. campestris* genes have been characterized and expression cassettes have been developed that will be useful in expression of genes for modification of oil synthesis. Napin gene regulatory sequences are preferred as it is expressed earlier and corresponds to the period of oil accumulation in *Brassica*. Napin is encoded by a multigene family in *B. napus* and *B. campestris*. The upstream regulatory sequence of one of these genes, *gNa* is used to express a tagged napin gene in transgenic *B. napus*. Other genes isolated from *B. campestris* are *BcNA1*. ACP genes are *1Bcs* and *Bce4*. Coding region an regulatory for these genes have been isolated.

Napin 5' 1.75 Kb	**S Bg Px**	**Napin 3' 1.26 Kb**

FIGURE 8.1: Gene expression cassette for foreign gene expression in developing rapeseed. 5' promoter and 3' terminator. Letters between 5' and 3' refer to unique restriction sites of inserting foreign genes.

S=SalI, Bg=Bg12, P=Pst1, X=XhoI

Bce4 napin cassettes show higher average levels of expression as compared to ACP. It is also seen that promoters are regulating GUS expression in tissue specific manner. Choice of promoter may be an important factor for maximum phenotypic expression.

Dates show that TAG composition is determined by pool of fatty acyl Co.A available during TAG synthesis. Therefore, to modify TAG in transgenic oil seeds, one has to modify make up of acyl Co.A pools available to the TAG synthesizing enzymes.

The expression cassettes can be utilized for expressing various genes in transgenic rape seed that is genes involved in lipid biosynthesis but basic lipid metabolism in other tissues is not affected. Similar genetic engineering of novel oil composition in other oil seeds like soyabean, maize can be expected in future.

REPORTER GENE FOR TRANSIENT EXPRESSION

A reporter gene is added to gene of interest before its entry into the target cell. With the help of reporter genes, information on aspects of gene constructs such as the relative-level and tissue specificity of expression can be obtained.

Reporter genes are frequently introduced into genetically modified plants for identifying and tracking genetic modification as they tag the transformed cells. They find more use where the genetically modified plants cannot be regenerated from single cell and direct selection is not feasible or effective.

The important features needed in reporter gene include its low background activity in plants and absence of any detrimental effect on metabolism. The gene product should have moderate stability *in vivo*, so that down regulation of gene expression as well as gene activation can be detected.

β-Glucuronidase Gene

The β-Glucuronidase (GUS) gene, encoded by the Uid A locus of *E. coli*, is most popular reporter gene used in plant transformation. The product of this gene *i.e.* enzyme β-glucuronidase breaks down glucuronides giving a coloured reaction. A blue coloration develops in the cells due to the reaction, thus expressing the gene. GUS activity can be quantified by excitation with light at 360 µm and monitoring fluorescence at 460 µm. Its presence can be detected *in situ*, inside the plant tissue, used either as thin section or in any other form. Several glucuronides which can be used as substrates, include β-nitrophenyl glucuronide (PNPG), 5-bromo, 4-chloro, 3-indolyl glucuronide (BCIG), naphthol As-BI glucuronide (NAG) and resorufin glucuronide (REG).

Luciferase Gene

This gene can be used as reporter gene and for transient gene expression. The activity of luciferase gene fusion can be assayed in transformed plants by their ability to grow in dark. The enzyme luciferase differs in bacteria and *Photinus pyralis* (firefly). While in bacteria, it consists of two peptide subunits coded by gene lux A and lux B, in case of firefly it consists of single polypeptide coded by a gene lux. The enzyme luciferase uses different substrates for luminiscence in these two systems. When the source of the gene is bacteria, the substrate used is an aldehyde (decanal) which is supplied exogenously with FMNH2. Alternatively when the source is firefly, luciferin (a heterocyclic carboxylic acid) is used as a substrate in the presence of ATP and oxygen. It generates oxyluciferin and yellow green fluorescence.

Chloramphenicol Acetyl Transferase Gene

This gene, isolated from *E. coli*, is primarily used as reporter gene and not as marker gene. As this gene is not present in mammals and higher plants, gene construct introduced in them can be detected by chloramphenicol acetyl transferase (CAT) assay. The enzyme uses acetyl Co A and, chloramphenicol (^{32}P) as substrates and helps in the transfer of acetyl group to chloramphenicol. Presence of acetyl-chloramphenicol can be detected through autoradiography. CAT gene is also used for identification of a number of regulatory sequences.

Nopaline (Nos) Synthase Gene

The disarmed Ti-plasmid obtained from *Agrobacterium tumefaciens* is used as a vector for gene transfer in dicot plants. The disarmed plasmid is without tumour causing region of TDNA. Hence it can not cause tumour. However, the border sequence and the nos gene are retained *e.g.* pGV3840. This plasmid is derived from the Ti-plasmid pTiC58. The nos gene codes for the enzyme nopaline synthase. Plant cells transformed using such a plasmid (pGV3840) will produce nopaline in their cells. The presence of nopaline can be identified by biochemical analysis. A positive result will show that cells are transformed.

Neomycin Phosphotransferase Gene (Npt II)

This gene is used both as selectable markar gene as well as reporter gene. This is the first marker to be used and is isolated from E. coli. This gene has been successfully used in many systems including mammalian cells and fungi. In solanacious plants such as petunia, tobacco and tomato, it provides an excellent, unambiguous selectable marker. For assay of the gene product (*i.e.* neomycin phosphotransferase), this enzyme is first fractionated using non-denaturing polyacrylamide gel electrophoresis (PAGE). Since the enzyme detoxifies kanamycin by phosphorylation, radioactively labelled ATP (^{32}P) is also used with it and incubated at 35 °C. The phosphorylation leading to incorporation of ^{32}P in kanamycin can be detected by autoradiography. Another method of enzyme assay is much easier. Dot blots of cell extracts are obtained on filter and this filter is incubated with substrate and finally autoradiographed to detect NPT II activity.

Anthocyanins

It utilises the C1, B and R genes, which code for trans-acting factors that regulate the anthocyanin biosynthetic pathway in maize seeds. The introduction of these regulatory genes into plants by microprojectile bombardment induces cell-autonomous pigmentations in non-seed tissues.

Dihydrofolate Reductase Gene

Another selectable marker is the mouse gene for dihydrofolate reductase. It encodes an altered protein that does not bind to methotrexate, a potent inhibitor of this essential enzyme. Petunia cells that contain and express this gene are able to grow on concentrations of methotrexate that completely inhibit the control cells.

For expression of these reporter genes, suitable promoters are added adjacent to the former.

PROMOTER ELEMENTS

One of the best studied plant promoters is the 35S promoters. This viral promoter produces the cauliflower mosaic virus 35S genomic RNA. In the early experiment approximately 1000 bp of promoter DNA were fused to various reporter genes. Analyses of protoplasts, transformed calli and transgenic plants demonstrated that the reporter genes with promoters were always expressed at high levels and were also insensitive to various endogenous and environmental cues (such as hormones, heat shock or light). The so called constitutive expression made the 35S promoters popular in dicot species. In monocot cells, the expression levels with the 35S promoter are 10 to 100 times lower than in dicot. A variety of promoters and other methods have been used to increase the level of expression of genes introduced into monocot cells. The incorporation of an intron into the transcriptional unit of the foreign gene increases gene expression in transformed monocot cells. The combination of the first intron of maize alcohol dehydrogenase 1 gene (Adh 1) and the CaMV 35S promoter have been used to control expression of the bar gene in transformed maize, oat and wheat. An alternative strategy is to include a modified maize Adhi sequence in the Emu promoter. This has been used in expression of neomycin phosphotransferase (npt II) gene in transformed rice and sugarcane. Finally, efforts have been made to isolate monocot promoters that show high level constitutive activity. The promoters of the genes for rice actin (Acti) and maize ubiquitin (Ubii) have been used to express the bar gene in transgenic wheat, barely and rice.

The direct transformation systems are most suitable for transient expression studies at present. However, the most successful and widely used system for stable transformation of plant is that based upon the Ti plasmid of Agrobacterium. In this method, the tissues are inoculated with Agrobacterium carrying the requisite vector having gene of interest. The next step is to select the transformed cells or tissues. This is facilitated by the presence of selectable marker genes available in vector.

MARKER GENE

A good selectable marker gene is one that provides resistance to a drug, antibiotic, or other agent that arrests the growth of normal plant cells (plant cells not harboring the marker gene). The selective agent should inhibit the growth of plant cells or kill them slowly. Agents that kill cells rapidly often result in the release of phenolic compounds and other substances (from the dead cells) that are toxic to the growth of the remaining, otherwise resistant cells. Various markers have been used for selection of transformed cells

Three marker genes among them are used more extensively, providing resistance to the antibiotics: (1) Kanamycin (and the related aminoglycoside G418, which are more effective growth inhibitor in eukaryotes), (2) Hygromycin, and (3) Methotrexate

Transformed system (tissues/organ) is placed on regeneration medium containing an antibiotic like **kanamycin** and transformed plants can be obtained directly. Cells, which are not transformed, die due to kanamycin. The heterogenous explant like calli or non-transformed tissue may escape initial selection. The leaf disc instead, exihibits the regeneration from edges, which is in contact with selective agents and thus, is a better alternative.

INACTIVATION OF FOREIGN GENE EXPRESSION

There are a number of conditions that can interfere with gene expression in transgenic plants. These include:

1. Poor recognition of promoter elements and differences in transcription efficiency between the source of the promoter and the transformed material.
2. Inefficient mRNA termination, polyadenylation, processing and/or stability.
3. Inefficient translation due to low rates of translation initiation and/or inappropriate codon usage.
4. Poor design of expression vectors, which might contain multiple repeated regions or multiple genes with opposite orientations leading to transcriptional interference.
5. Antisense-mediated gene inactivation.
6. Gene silencing by homologous sequence.

Transgene Inactivation and Methylation

Multiple copies of the transgene also suppress their expression. There is reverse correlation between gene copy number and expression level. Low expression is correlated with increased methylation of the transfer DNA. It is well established that methylated DNA is not or poorly transcribed. The most common DNA modification in plant cells is cytosine methylation at CG dinucleotides and CNG (were N can be any base) trinucleotides. Methyl-cytosine can interfere with protein-DNA interactions. This phenomenon has been observed with maize dihydroflavonol-4-reductase (DFR) gene in *Petunia* and with GUS transgene in tobacco.

Double Transformations and Gene Silencing

Introduction of a second T-DNA construct into tobacco already containing T-DNA also lead to the suppression of genes located on T-DNA first. Presence of second T-DNA leads to methylation of the genes of T-DNA first, thus resulting in their suppression. If T-DNA second is crossed out, the T-DNA first genes become demethylated and reactivated. It has been suggested that homology between the DNA sequences of the two T-DNAs, even though they are not transcribed, triggers the silencing.

Post-Transcriptional Gene Suppression

Supression of β-1-3-glucanase and chitinase transgene expression is only observed in plants that are homozygous for the transgene. The β-1-3-glucanase transgene suppression is the result of a post-transcriptional process and is observed only in homozygous and in haploid plants.

A number of issues still need to be addressed before transformation technology can be exploited fully in the agronomic improvement of plants. These include those that act to regulate the efficiency of transcript termination, transcript stability, post-transcriptional modification and translation efficiency. An increased understanding of these regulatory components in plants will prove profitable for achieving the regulated expression of foreign genes in transgenic plants.

CHAPTER 9

Gene Silincing and Antisense Technology

The instability of expression of the transgenes or even the endogenous genes.

Gene silencing in plants has provided interesting but intriguing insight and valuable information about gene regulation, especially when challenged by the alien interference. Earlier gene silencing was considered as a disappointment, now it turned as a new, academically interesting and commercially viable sector of genetic engineering.

A considerable variation has been found in the expression of transgenes in individual transformants, which is not due to copy number (Stam *et al.*, 1997). These transgenes are when inserted into plant they either promote the expression or suppression of homlogous genes. That means transgenes can inactivate expression of homologous genes. The suppression of homlogous genes is known as gene silencing. This phenomenon has been reported in various plant species, transformed with various genes and is a form of epigenetic modification. The inactive state is usually stable and in some cases is meiotically stable, but it is not permanent. The silent genes can undergo spontaneous as well as developmentally regulated reactivation by a process. It is called resetting.

The use of genetic engineering in plant breeding is a routine technique for crop improved around the world, specially for development of transgenic plants. This technique has developed many problems, as the introduced genes (transgenes) though properly introduced genes (transgenes) though properly integrated, do not always express fully. Frequently observed instability of transgene expression, commonly called **gene silencing**. It is not restricted only to the transgenes, as even the endogenous genes are subjected to this suppression after transfer of a homologous transgene. Gene silencing is the setback to the idea of commercialization of transgenic plants, and this was the challenge for molecular plant breeders to unravel the cause (s) of gene silencing.

The expression of the desired phenotype in which the alien gene has been introduced depends on various factors, the important factors are:

1. The transgene needs to be integrated at a site where is transcription is not suppressed by **cis-effect** of the neighboring sequences.
2. Its inaccessibility to the transcription and processing machinery in the packed chromatin of the interphase nucleus.
3. To ensure expression of the transgene, its transcripts have to be properly processed and transported to the cytoplasm where these need to be precisely translated and the products suitably modified for ultimate expression.
4. A minor alteration at any of these steps may lead to the absence of the expected characteristic or development of an unusual phenotype or inheritance.

REASONS FOR GENE SILENCING

The gene silencing in plants is a genetic control mechanism implicated in virus resistance, genome maintenance and developmental control. This concept was given by Vionnet and Baulcombe (1997). The signal molecule is likely to be nucleic acid. Probably, signal molecule could mediate sequence specific gene silencing by forming a base-paired or triple helical structure with the target RNA. A nucleic acid could move in plant using the channels involved in virus or viroid movement. Finally Hamilton and Baulcambe (1990) discovered that post-transcriptional gene silencing in plants is a nuclieotide sequence specific defence mechanism that can target both cellular and viral m-RNAs. They analyzed three types of transgene-induced PTGS and one example of virus-induced PTGS in plants.

In each case, antisense RNA complementary to the targeted mRNA was detected. These RNA molecules were of a uniform length, estimated at 25 nucleotides, and their accumulation required either transgene sense transcription or RNA virus replication. They suggested that the 25 nucleotide antisense RNA is likely synthesized from an RNA template and may represent the specificity determinant of PTGS.

To account for the sequence specificity and posttranscriptional natural of PTGS, is has been proposed that antisense RNA forms a duplex with the target RNA, thereby promoting its degradation or interfering with its translation. If these hypothetical antisense RNA molecules are of a similar size to typic mRNA, they would have been readily detected by routine RNA analyses. However, there have been no reports of such antisense RNA that is detected exclusively in plants or animals exhibiting PTGS. Nevertheless, PTGS-specific antisense RNA may exist, but may be too short for easy detection. Hamilton and Baulcambe (1999) carried out analyses specifically to detect low molecular weight antisense. RNA in four classes of PTGS in plants. They used five tomato lives, each transformed with a tomato 1-aminocyclopropane-1-carboxylate oxidase (ACO) cDNA sequence placed down stream of the Couliflower mosaic virus 35S promoter. Two lines exhibited PTGS of the endogenous ACO mRNA. Low molecular weight nucleic acids were purified from the five lines, were separated by denaturing polyacrylamide gel electrophoresis, blotted and hybridized to ACO sense (Antisense-specific) RNA probe.

They found that a discrete, ACO antisense RNA of 25 nucleotides was present in both PTGS lines but absent from the nonsilencing lines. 25-nucleotide ACO RNA of sense polarity and at the same abundance as the 25-nucleotide ACO antisense RNA was also present only in the PTGS lines.

Thus, Hamilton and Baulcombe (1999) used 25-nucleotide antisense RNA, complementary to targeted mRNAs, accumulates in 4-types of PTGS. They detected 25-nucleotide RNA in other examples of PTGS, and never detected 25-nucleotide RNA in the absence of PTGS. This correlation and the properties of 25-nucleotide RNA were consistent with a direct role for 25-nucleotide RNA in PTGS induced by transgenes or viruses. Twentyfive nucleotide RNA species also serve as molecular marker for PTGS. Their presence could be used to confirm their examples of transgene – a virus induced PTGS and perhaps also to identify endogenous genes that are targeted by PTGS in nontransgenic plants. They also suggested that 25-nucleotide antisense RNA species are not degradation products of target RAA because they have antisense polarity. A more likely source of these RNAs was the transcription of an RNA template. This was consistent with the presence of the 25-nucleotide PVX-infected cells that did not contain a DNA template.

An RNA-dependent RNA polymerase, as acquired by this model, is required for PTGS in *Neurospora crassa*. The precise role of 25-nucleotide RNA in PTGS remains to be determined. However, it has suggested that they are long enough to convey sequence specificity yet small enough to move through are components of the systemic signal and specificity determinants of PTGS.

TYPES OF GENE SILENCING

Homology-Dependent Gene Silencing

Homology-dependent gene silencing occurs very frequently when a number of copies of the transgene are integrated at the some locus or in different positions within the genome. This is described as the homology detection mechanism of plants, which leads to methylation of the multiple homologous copies. Though the mechanism of this process has not been completely understood, however, the available evidences suggest that methylation is mediated by transient pairing of the homologous sequences. This occurs more efficiently, if multiple copies are integrated as concatamers at the same locus as inverted or direct repeats. The inactivation of transgenes after crossing with the lines carrying *hypermethylated homologous sequences* may be one of the reasons for the same pairing mechanism. Not all genes are susceptible to this type of trans-inactivation, reflecting that the capability of detecting the homology at different chromosomal locations varies. The telomeric region shown to be favorable site for interaction with the homologous sequences.

Position Effects

The position of integration of transgene may influence subsequent gene expression. The gene integrating in the hypermethylated inactive regions of chromatin sometimes get methylated, thus, remain silence. The expression of transgenic, increases if it is integrated into an actively transcribed region.

Environmental Stress

Environmental stress may cause gene silencing. The silencing effect of the environmental stress can be duplicated in tissue cultures by addition of propionic acid or butyric acid. These acids induce hypermethylation. In transgenic petunias A1 gene of maize conferring a brick red color to the flowers. When these plants were grown in glass house, they produced exclusively brick red flower irrespective of the growing season. On the other hand, when these were grown under field conditions, they did not do so. The plants, which had produced brick red flowers during the early season developed weakly colored ones later. The change in color was found to be associated with methylation of the transgene.

The de nove methylation due to environmental stress may be due to sequence composition of the transgene which happens to be deviated from the adjacent regions. It may be a **natural defense mechanism** of the plants against foreign DNA followed by methylated and thus silenced. Based on AT contents, a common isochore structure has been deduced for plant genes. The AT contents of bacterial, monocot and dicot genes differ and therefore these have different isochore compositions.

Antisense Gene Silencing

Antisense gene silencing involves the inversion of the normal coding regions between the promoter and terminator sequences. As a result, rather than the sense strand, antisense strand is transcribed. The RNA so synthesized binds to the RNA transcribed from the normal gene. The resultant RNA-RNA complex cannot be translated into a functional protein. As a result gene expression is switched off. The **RNA duplex** is degraded by the normal cellular mechanisms.

Endogenous Genes Silencing by Co-Suppression

Endogenous genes are present in a cell and are prone to gene silencing. This takes place if transgene happens to be homologous to the endogenous gene, and is thus capable of transcribing mRNA of the same strandedness as the transcript of the endogenous gene. The effect has been termed as **co-suppression,** which requires co-ordinate transcription of both the endogenous and the introduced genes.

This kind of gene silencing has been studied in petunias. It appears due to the expression of chalcone synthase (CHS) gene. **Chalcone synthase** is a key enzyme in flavonoid biosynthesis. It is responsible for color of the flower. To have darker flowers, the genes are re-introduced in a flowering line of *Petunia hybrida* which produces deep violet flowers. However, instead of having the desired effect due to the expected over-expression of the gene, the progeny produced white or variegated flowers. The resultant **aberrant phenotype** may be due to inhibition in expression of the gene. The co-suppression may result because of the reintroduction of an endogenous gene leading to a significantly reduced expression or total switching off. Therefore, if development controls are introduced the silencing can be avoided.

The mechanism of co-suppression is still an enigma. However, it has been suggested that it is triggered by an ectopic interaction of the homologous genes, which results in the production of aberrant RNA (aRNA), in addition to the normal mRNA. The aRNA moleculaes are recognized by the cell and sequence-specific degradation is affected. This results in destruction of mRNA as well.

POST-TRANSCRIPTIONAL GENE SILENCING (PTGS)

In PTGS, promoters are active and the genes transcribed but m-RNA fails to accumulate. The transgene induced PTGS mechanism affects expression of the transgenes and of endogenous genes with which they share a considerable degree of sequence identity. The latter case is also known as co-suppression because the endogenous genes and the transgenes are silenced. Co-suppression was first observed with genes involved in flower pigmentation and in tomato fruit ripening. Silencing of the **Chalcone synthase** (Chs) genes in Petunia flowers occur post transcriptinoally.

Characteristics of PTGs

The reasons for this are not known exactly, but they seem to be related to transgene expression levels and the organization of the T-DNA inserts. Moreover silencing does not always occur in every cell of a particular tissue. In anthocyanin gene silencing, it is visible due to variations in colour patterns. In some systems, PTGS is developmentally regulated. Silencing of uid A, and of β-1, 3 glucanase transgenes in tobacco does not occur in young seedlings but starts between 2 and 6 weeks after germination, depending on the expression level of the transgenes.

Possible Mechanisms of Post-Transcriptional Gene Silencing

There is no universal of gene silencing, because of the complex and intricate nature of the expression pathway. The precise molecular mechanisms gene silencing is still needed. The possible role of PTGS and its identification can be observed by the reduction in accumulation of specific transcripts. This reduction may result from RNA instability (from activation of a sequence specific RNA degradation process). However, the exact reason is still unknown.

Model of Transgene Expression Level (RNA Threshold Level)

This model explains that the transgenes produce too much m-RNA that level exceeds a threshold thereby triggering a mechanism that specifically removes all homologous RNA's irrespective of their source this RNA threshold model gained support from observations whereby PTGS was correlated with highly expressed transgenes conferring viral resistance.

Plants that contain highly transcribed transgenes did not accumulate the transgenic mRNA's. They remain resistant to infection by homologous RNA virus. Plants, which normally contain lower levels accumulated transgenic RNA remain sensitive to a viral infection. Sometimes a virus infection is needed to induce the PTGS mechanism and resistance. This results in line with reaching the hypothetical RNA threshold level. Studies by Metzlaff *et al.*, (1996) of Chs cosuppression in *Petunia* transformante suggest that silencing requires active transgenes.

PTGS and Methylated Transgenes

The silencing may appear at both transcriptional and post-transcriptional levels. It is often accompanied by an increase in DNA methylation, especially in the former case. PTGS is frequently associated with methylated transgenes. Also Smith *et al.*, (1994) noticed that the viral transgenes of viral resistant plants were methylated more than those of sensitive plants. Despite this methylation, the promoters were active and the genes transcribed.

Methylation of an increased number of cytosine residues resulting in the formation of 5-methylcytosine moieties is a common feature of DNA found associated with transcriptionally inactive regions of chromation. The inactivation of transgenes is also due to increase in DNA methylation. Therefore, the ultimate effect (gene silencing) is preceded by DNA methylaiton however the causes leading to this event vary.

The direct evidences for a role of DNA methylation in PTGS was observed by English *et al.*, (1996). The PTGS *ed uid A* genes in tobacco plants were mentioned by by Hobbs *et al.*, (1990, 1993). These genes were more methylated near the 3' end of the gene were which included the polyadenylation region. This 3' region was required to prevent infection by the PVX *uid A* chimeric viruses, as if this part of the RNA is the target for the degradation of RNA. These findings show a link between DNA methylation and the RNA based silencing mechanism.

RNA Directed DNA Methylation (Rddm)

In tobacco transformants, it was found that transgenes composed of 3 or 4 tandemly arranged viroid c-DNAs in sense or antisense orientation and driven by the CaMV-35S promoter were methylated. This methylation was caused by the virold RNA's. A two copy and a Viroid cDNA construst which were unmethylated, became methylation had taken place indicate that the viroid RNA is responsible for the methylation of the homologous transgene DNA, rather than the transgene structure or intergration site. The process of its occurrence is unknown, but DNA-RNA hybrids are formed.

Elimination of Homologous Transcripts

If the PTGS mechanism is induced according the RNA threshold model, it shows that cells are able to measure levels of specific RNA's. In normal cells, if such activity functions monitoring RNA levels from endogenous genes, one would expect that it also establishes and maintains a certain steady state, RNA levels in transgenic cells. But the vast majority of the homologous RNAs are degraded. To speculate about the nature of this RNA degradation activity, Dougherty's group postulated a role for complementary RNAs (cRNA) synthesized by the plant encoded RNA dependent RNA polymerase (RdRP) in the cytoplasm. RdRP from tomato was recently characterized and it was known that *in vitro*; this enzyme synthesizes small RNAs from RNA templates. It is hypothesized that *in vitro* these c-RNAs hybridise to the complimentary m-RNAs which are then degraded by double stranded RNA specific RNAase. The appeal of the RdRP-cRNA model is that it explains the strong sequence specificity of PTGS.

PTGS of Endogenous Genes and the Presence of Specific Transgene Loci

PTGS is often associated with multi copy T-DNA looi (English *et al.*, 1996). How the organization of a transgene locus affects PTGS to explain this there are two possibilities.

1. A multi copy locus is prone to deliver the hypothetical aberrant RNA assumed to trigger the cytosolic RNA degradation machinery directly. This requires transcription of the transgenes. The aberrant nature of the RNAs might originate from read through transcription, abnormal RNA processing or transcription of a methylated template. When the RNA degradation machinery is activated, it eliminates all homologous RNAs.
2. The second possibility applies only to cases where the genome contains an endogenous homologoue. Given that barely transcribed Chs sense transgenes and promoterless transgenes are able to confer strong suppression of endogenous Chs genes. (Van Blokland *et al.*, 1994) a transgenes derived RNA plays a key role in this PTGS process. In line with the RdRP-cRNA model. The aberrant RNAs might be derived from the endogenous Chs genes. One possibility is that it occurs as a result of ectopic DNA pairing between the transgene locus and the endogenous gene(s). Based on the detection of elevated levels of unspliced Chs transcripts in nuclei containing silenced chs genes, this pairing may have changed features of the endogenous gene leading to an unpaired processing and / or transport of the RNAs. These transcripts may be intrinsically unstable and rapidly degraded, or may act as aberrant RNA causing the degradation of other homologous RNAs.

Not all transgene loci, may be able to pair ectopically with an endogenous gene.

ANTISENSE TECHNOLOGY

Calgene created in 1994 the first commercial transgenic plant, a long shelf life tomato, by the suppression of polygalacturonase activity due to an antisense gene. However, this Flavr Savr tomato variety was removed from the trade 3 years later, because of its disease susceptibility and its lack of productivity. Later, other tomato varieties with long storage qualities were obtained by the utilization of an antisense RNA inhibition of ACC synthase or ACC oxydase, two ethylene precursors.

The antisense technique was also used to reduce the lignification of woody plants, by blocking the enzymes involved in the precursor of lignin biosynthesis. Another interesting application wsa the induction of white flowers in petunia and in different other ornamental plants by the suppression of chalcone synthase activity.

This technology involves the reduction in gene expression by using RNA containing complementary sequences to a given portion of double helix transcribed into RNA it is always the same strand for a given gene. If a cloned gene is engineered so that only the opposite DNA strand is transcribed, the result will be "anti-sense RNA" with a sequence complementary to the normal RNA transcripts. Antisense RNA when synthesized in large amount will often hybridize with sense RNA (made by normal genes) thereby inhibiting synthesis of corresponding protein.

Like sense genes, antisense genes are also known to elicit post-transcriptional gene silencing. Suppression of gene activity by antisense genes has been used for inhibiting viral replication (Bejarano and Lichtenstein, 1992). Techniques of tomato expressing antisense RNA against protein encoded by Cl gene showed resistance to Tomato yellow leaf curl virus (TYLCV).

Antisense genes, initially found in Prokaryotes play a significant role in regulation of diverse and complex phenomenon like plasmid replication, regulation of phage reproduction etc. They play an important role in regulation of transgenic expression as well.

Formation of Antisense mRNA

1. Antisense mRNA can be produced accidentally if the transgene has been introduced in a transcriptionally active region where there is a promoter to initiate transcription from the coding strand of DNA.
2. Antisense mRNA can be transcribed if the transgenes are present with converging promoters in the construct such that if transcription over runs the termination signal. Small amounts of RNA would also be made from the other insert but in opposite direction.
3. Antisense m-RNA can also be produced by RNA dependent RNA polymerase.

Inhibition of Gene Expression by Antisense RNA

Antisense m-RNA can hamper gene expression in many ways:

It can block RNA production by inhibiting transcription that is antisense transcripts act in the nucleus by either interacting with DNA template to generate a triple helix or with nascent transcript and thus cause transcription termination.

It may also interact with the promoter region to repress transcription.

1. Gene expression can also be adversely affected due to interference of antisense RNA with m-RNA processing and transport.
2. Antisense RNA may disturb normal transport of m-RNA out of nucleus.
3. Antisense RNA also disturbs the regular flow of transcripts by forming hybrids with their target m-RNA.
4. In Prokaryotes antisense RNA complementary to the ribosome binding sites can inhibit translation while inhibition in Eukaryotes depends on the ability of antisense m-RNA to reach the cytoplasm.

Plants from Antisense Technology

Fruits Ripening Can Be Inhibited by Antisense RNA

During tomato ripening, two ACC synthase genes are expressed ie LE-ACC$_2$ & Le-

ACC_4. Expression of antisense RNA derived from LE-ACC_2 results in almost complete inhibition of m-RNA accumulation. The antisense phenotype can be reversed by treatment with ethylene or propylene.

Pigmentation in Flowering Plants

Pigmentation in flowering plants can be altered by this method. Chalcone synthase is key enzyme in flavonoid synthesis. It has been shown that constitutive expression of an antisense Chalcone synhtase gene *t* in transgenic *Petunia* and Tobacco results inaltered flower pigmentation. It was observed that there was reduction in levels of both m-RNA for the enzyme itself. The trait was stably inherited.

Production of Male Sterile Plants

Antisense RNA technology has been used for production of male sterile plants of *Brassica*. It has great potential as it will have applied values and will help to understand fundamental mechanisms of gene expression and development of organisms.

CHAPTER 10

Scope, Achievements and Hazards of Genetically Modified Crops

Genetically modified crops are widely grown all over the world. Most of these *first generation* products have specific agronomic traits designed to improve the efficiency of production. New varieties under test contain product quality or other higher value trails intended to provide specific benefits to end-user. Examples of such *second generation* traits to predict range of household, medical, industrial products that might become available in coming years.

Most transgenic plants are generated for basic research purposes, such as the evaluation of tissue-specific expression of genes, processing and secretion signals, and enhancer elements. A growing effort is being made to use transgenic plants for broader objectives. A wide variety of foreign products can be obtained from transgenic plants, not only proteins, but also all kinds of modified compounds through the expression of the appropriate enzymes or even catalytic antibodies. The production of plant biomass is inexpensive, the plant cell machinery can provide specific processing unavailable from microbial systems, the isolated products are free of bacterial contaminants, the plant seeds can be used as low-cost storage, and ultimately plants use sunlight as their source of energy. These facts make us believe that the production of foreign compounds in plants is becoming a competitive alternative system to traditional methods.

FUNGAL RESISTANCE

Plant diseases have been with us since agriculture began and intensification and continuous cultivation have resulted in increasing disease pressure. The epidemic spread of fungal diseases is controlled by various methods, like application of protective agrochemicals, breeding for resistance varieties and various crop husbandry techniques. Plant breeders have developed a large numbers of cultivars resistance varieties for fungal diseases. The breeding programmes are time consuming, therefore, keep pace with the rapid evolution of the pathogen. The use of agrochemicals by the farmers is costly and eventually less efficient due to the evolution of the pathogen. It is therefore, necessary to develop disease control measures as alternative to chemicals. It is a priority of scientists worldwide. Newly developed technologies in plant breeding such as isolation of resistance genes and gene transformation methods can be used to develop transgenic plants. Furthermore, there is an extensive search for genes that encode enzymes involved in the synthesis of toxic to fungi and for genes encode proteins with direct inhibitory effect on the growth of fungi.

Fungal diseases cause world wide economic losses. Although plants have natural resistance mechanism but pathogens have some hoe also developed ways to evade these defence mechanism. Bowles (1990) grouped the defence genes into following classes:

1. Genes synthesizing compounds involved in cell wall modification.
2. Genes encoding defence related proteins exhibiting anti microbial activities or catalyse the synthesis of products that retard microbial activity.
3. Genes encoding pathogen related (PR) proteins whose appearance is co related with defence responses.

In response to pathogenic fungi attack the plant synthesis defence related proteins which include amylase proteinase inhibitors, hydrolytic enzymes like chitinase and enzymes involved in synthesis of phytoalexine. Phytoalexins (secondary metabolism product) are low molecular weight antimicrobial compounds, which act as broad-spectrum antibiotics play an important role in arresting the growth of fungal pathogens. First phytoalexin to be identify and purified was pisatin from pea. It is predicted that plants able to make large amounts of foreign phytoalexins would be resistant to pathogens that could detoxify the new chemical structures.

A common natural mechanism of plant to resists fungal attack is secretion of the enzyme chitinase which attacks the cell wall of fungus. This enzyme chitinase is very stable, resistant to heat and inhibits fungal growth in-vitro.

Seeds of various cereals contain proteins that are toxic to some pathogens. For example, barley contains a ribosome inhibiting protein (RIP) that prevents peptide elongation. This protein while not toxic to plants, inhibits the growth of number of fungi. Using a chimeric capable of expressing barley RIP in stem and roots of tobacco. Logemann et al (1992) developed transgenic plants resistant to *Rhizotonia solani*.

Long Lived Fruits and Vegetable

Fruits and vegetables are spoiled due to ethylene formation that triggers fruit ripening. Ripening can be delayed in transgenic plants. Tomatoes become soft due to production of polygalaturonase (PG) which causes break down of pectin in cell. Flavour and colour are not effected by this enzyme. DNA in anti sense orientation was inserted by Calgene scientists. Transgenic tomato exhibit decreased PG level up to 99% thereby increasing shelf life.

Race-Specific Resistance Genes

True patho-systems of the cultivar/race depend on the presence and function of resistance genes in the host and a virulence genes in the pathogen. The genetic inter-dependence of host and pathogen determines the outcome of the interaction. It was first postulated in Flor's *gene for gene hypothesis*. The race-specific resistance is characterized by rapid and strictly localized cell death in the host (hypersensitive response) limiting the spread of the pathogen to non-infected tissues and preventing its propagation. Various approaches are being pursued for isolation and molecular characterisation of resistance genes including map-based cloning and transposon tagging.

Transposon Tagging

It leads to the isolation of a race-specific resistant gene from maize, the genetically defined HM1 locus' conferring resistance to race 1 of the fungus *Helminthosporium carbonum*. The derived amino acid sequence of the HM 1 genes shows similarity with the amino acid sequence of plant NADPH and NADH-dependent reductases and very likely the HM 1 gene product is responsible for detoxification of the HC-toxin. This pathogen-produced toxin mediates the specific pathogenicity of *H. carbonum* race 1 on maize.

After isolation of fungal resistance genes, they can be transferred to other cultivars/species to provide resistance to specific races of fungal pathogens. The resulting transgenic plant will remain susceptible to other races of the pathogens. Furthermore, the large-scale growth of new bred fungus-resistant cultivars is likely to lead to evolution of new virulent races, and the cultivation of crops as monocultures will promote rapid epidemic outbreaks.

Two-Component Systems for Non-Specific Resistance

The durable non-specific resistance was obtained by engineering plants which have hypersensitive response is elicited by a wide range of pathogens. They further proposes a model for transfer of the *avr* 9 gene from fungus *Cladosporium fulvum* into a tomato lines containing resistance gene Cf 9. The model proposes that in transgenic plant containing these two-component systems - a hypersensitive response will establish in many host/pathogen interactions, if expression of the avr 9 gene is put under control of a promoter, there is rapid and local transcriptional activation in response to a broad spectrum of pathogens. Upon isolation of the Cf 9 gene, the avr 9-Cf 9 system could be introduced as a cassette also into plants that lack Cf 9. The strategy requires that the avr 9-encoded elicitor is targeted to correct cell within the transgenic plants to give a functional interaction with Cf 9 genes product. The success of this concept is largely dependent on the availability of suitable promoter to direct *avr* 9 expressions.

Martini et al. (1993) developed a strategy for artificial generation of programmed cell death in transgenic potato, potentially limiting the spread of a wide range of fungal in the host tissue. A promoter fragment of potato PrP1-1 gene has been combined with barnase gene from *Bacillus amyloliquefaciens* encoding a highly cytoxic RNase. Rapid synthesis of this RNase in the vicinity of infection sites should initiate necrosis of host cell during early stage of compatible interaction and therefore, restrict the growth and propagation of biotrophic pathogenic fungi.

Compounds Toxic to Fungi

Microorganisms and plants produce low molecular weight antimicrobial substances. The plants produce phytoalexins and are often synthesized locally. They are accumulated after exposure to pathogens and/or stresses. In *Vitis vinifera* and *Picea sitchensis*, stilbenes are involved in protection against fungal challenge. Different biotic and abiotic signals have been shown to stimulate their accumulation. They activate genes for the key regulatory enzymes (phenylalanine-ammonia lyase and stilbene synthase) for their biosynthetic pathway.

Tobacco contains the precursors for the formation of stilbenes but lack the enzyme stilbene synthase. After transfer of a stilbene synthase gene from grapevine to tobacco transgenic plants expressed the foreign gene in response to treatment with fungal elicitor or infection with the broad range of fungal pathogen. The reduction of disease incidence on leaves directly correlated with amount of accumulated resveratrol with rapidity of stilbene synthase gene activation.

Anti-Fungal Protein

The characteristic features of fungal structure and cell metabolism represent potential targets for inhibitory agents. The constitutive or pathogen-inducible expression of genes encoding proteins with fungi toxic or fungistatic capacity in transgenic plants may enhance resistance to fungal damage in these plants.

Chitin and β-1, 3-glucans are structural polysaccharides of the cell wall of many fungi. The breakdown of these components by endochitinase and β-1, 3-endoglucanases may inhibit fungal growth. Four classes (1-4) of plant endochitinases have been described of which atleast three are present in tobacco. Three major classes (1-3) of β-1,3-endoglucanases are also found in this plant species. **Class 1** hydrolases are localised in plant vacuoles and exert a strong inhibitory effect on fungal growth *in vitro*. Inhibition is far more pronounced when mixtures of the two types of hydrolases are applied indicating that the proteins act synergestically. In contrast, class II hydrolases, which are similar to the class I hydrolases on the basis of their primary structure but are localised extracellularly, are not antifungal either alone or in combination with other proteins.

Broglie and coworkers (1991) combined the bean endochitinase CH5B gene encoding a class 1 protein, with the promoter region of the CaMV 35 S gene conferring high constitutive expression in a wide variety of plant cell type. In the non- infected stage, transgenic homozygous tobacco plants harbouring this chaemeric construct showed a 2 to 4 fold increase in the roots and 23 to 44 fold increases over control plants in chitinase activity in the leaves. For phytopathological evaluation, these plants were grown in the presence of *Rhizoctonia solani*. Seedling mortality or the loss of root fresh weight was clearly reduced in transgenic plants compared to control plants. When 35 S-chitinase plants were infected with the non-chitinous fungal pathogen *Pythium aphanidermatum*, no difference in survival was detected compared to control plants.

In contrast, Neuhaus and coworkers (1991) found that transgenic tobacco plants bearing a class I chitinase from tobacco under the control of the CaMV 35 S promoter did not reveal a substantial increase of resistance to the chitin- containing fungus *Cercospora nicotiana*, although most transformants expressed high level of enzymatically active chitinase in the intracellular compartment of leaves. This could indicate that factors other than chitinase appear to be limiting in defence against this pathogen.

The group of J. Ryals at CIBA-GEIGY, Research Triangle park (U S A) has reported on protection of transgenic tobacco plants against various fungal pathogens as a result of high- level expression of proteins associated with systemic acquired resistance (SAR) in this plant species. The majority of these SAR proteins belong to group of pathogenesis-related (PR) proteins. Their mRNA accumulates not only in pathogen- infected (primary) leaves but also in non-infected (secondary) leaves. The goal of this work is to achieve broad range protection against pathogen by over-producing combination of SAR proteins in transgenic crops.

Ribosome-Inactivating Proteins (RIPs)

Plant RIPs inhibit protein synthesis in target cells by N-glycosidic cleavage of 28 S rRNA (Stirpe *et al.*, 1992). Two types of RIPs exist-single chain type 1 proteins and type 2 proteins consisting of two chains can bind to cell surfaces. The best known is ricin and is most potent natural toxin. RIPs do not interfere with the functioning of self ribosomes but exert inhibitory activity towards fungal ribosomes. In *in vitro* assays a barley RIP has a lower antifungal activity than chitinase or B-1,3-glucanases from barley. However, a strong synergy is observed when barley RIP is mixed with either of these two hydrolases (Leah et al. 1991). Logemann et al. (1992) improved resistance to *R. solani* in transgenic tobacco. A barley type 1 RIP gene was put under control of the potato Wun1 promoter which mediates wound and pathogen- inducible transcription in the epidermis of leaf, stem and root from tobacco. R1 progeny showed an increased resistance to *R. solani*.

In the mean time, a large number of proteins with inhibitory effect on fungal growth *in vitro* have been identified from the plants. Among these are osmotin, which are produced in response to salt stress and cysteine-rich proteins of various origins. The function of these proteins in transgenic plants remains to be tested.

The transgenic plants show enhanced resistance against specific fungi, although such crops have not reached the market yet. New concepts have been developed to obtain broad range pathogen resistance, and these concepts will be worked out further in the next few years. Undoubtedly, the molecular basis of both pathogenicity and resistance will lead to the development of new strategies in the future.

ENGINEERED RESISTANCE AGAINST VIRUS DISEASES

Plant viruses cause varied diseases and significant crop losses due to the lack of proper *viricides*. Virus diseases are usually, controlled by using certified virus free planting material, by eradicating infected plants and by spraying chemicals against virus vectors. These measures are not very successful.

The genetic engineering of virus resistance into plants provides a direct and more efficient control of virus diseases. The engineering strategies are based on the introduction of a virus-derived or a virus-targeted sequence into the genome of a potential host plant. These sequences interfere with specific stages in the viral infection cycle.

The genomes of viruses consist of single or double-stranded RNA or DNA. The vast majority of pathogenic plant viruses (about 80 %) have genomes of plus strand (messenger sense) single stranded RNA but also viruses with minus sense or ambisense genomic RNA (TSWV), single-stranded DNA (geminiviruses) or double-stranded DNA (caulimo and badnaviruses) cause significant losses to crop plants. All viruses encode proteins involved in the replication of their nucleic acid. RNA viruses encode a putative RNA-dependent RNA polymerase, while double-stranded DNA viruses, which replicate via RNA intermediates code for reverse transcriptase. Single-stranded DNA viruses contain genes for enzymes necessary for replication via complementary DNA. Besides the replication enzymes, genome of most viruses also encodes a coat protein, which protects the viral nucleic acid during the transfer of virus particles from one plant to another. Additionally, many viruses synthesize proteins that facilitate their movement from cell to cell in the host plant and there are also several viral gene products with unknown function. To enable monocistronic translation, some viruses have divided their genome into segments, each representing a mRNA for one protein, others synthesize sub-genomic RNAs which are mRNAs for proteins encoded downstream of the 5- terminal cistron. Finally some viruses translate their genome into polyprotein, which is processed into functional proteins by virus-encoded proteases.

To engineer resistance into host plants the following strategies are currently under investigation:

Coat Protein-Mediated Protection (CPMP)

Coat protein-mediated protection concept is based on the observation of cross protection and was first used as a test of relatedness between viruses, but soon thereafter became a tool to control virus diseases in agriculture. A plant infected by a mild strain of a virus resists infection by other related strains, a phenomenon referred to as cross protection (Mckinney, 1939). The tobacco mosaic virus (TMV) coat protein (CP) is specifically involved in cross protection.

Coat protein-mediated resistance to viruses is done through plant genetic engineering. Several major crop plants have been engineered to resist important viral pathogens and, in some cases, the resistant plants have been in field trials for several years. Beachy (1986) introduced the TMV coat protein gene into the genome of tobacco plants. Transgenic plants expressing high levels of coat protein upon infection with TMV exhibited a delay in disease development. Subsequently, CP genes isolated from different single-stranded (plus) sense RNA plant viruses have been cloned into plant expression vectors and transferred into various crop plants (tobacco, tomato and potato) using the *Agrobacterium tumefaciens*-mediated plant transformation system.

The CPMP approach has been extended to cereals. CPMP is achieved by transforming plants with coat protein genes, under the control of CaMV 35 S promoter which mediated strong constitutive transcription in many cell types. The degree of resistance is correlated with amount of intact coat protein expressed in transgenic plants.

The introduction of non-functional transgenes is able to interfere with virus multiplication. Plant containing anti-sense coat protein RNA of CMV or PVX were protected against viral infection. High levels of resistance were obtained by introducing a coat protein cistron of PVY lacking a translational start signal. An anti-viral effect was also established by introducing untranslatable coat protein genes of TEV into tobacco plants. It has been suggested that resistance resulted from hybridization of the coat protein RNA to the minus sense replication intermediates of the viral RNA, thus inhibiting the production of infectious virus particles. The formation of RNA: RNA hybrids were also postulated as a mechanism inhibiting multiplication of TSWV, a virus with an ambisense RNA genome. Inhibition was mediated by the RNA of the nuleocapsid protein which encoded in viral complementary sense on a genome RNA fragment.

The results from these and several field trials demonstrate that CPMP might be very effective in preventing losses due to virus infection, but a large number of clones may need to be screened to identify the most resistant line. A better understanding of the mechanism (s) of CPMP should help to extend resistance beyond its current limitations.

Defective Interfering RNA/ DNA Protection

Defective interfering (DI) particles are deletion mutants of genomic viral sequences, which depend on their parent virus for replication. DIs RNAs have been described in animal virus systems, but only rarely in plant virus systems such as TCV, TBSV, CyRSV and TSWV. The occurrence of a DI viral DNA was reported for ACMV, a single-stranded DNA virus, which produces sub-genomic DNA particles.

Like satellite RNAs, DI particles can attenuate the disease symptoms of their helper virus by interfering with its replications. Thus, DI RNAs or DNAs may also be used as tools for genetic engineering of plants. There have been attempts to construct artificial DI molecules of TYMV, TMV and BMV. For example deletion mutants of BMV RNA 2 were shown to reduce the replication of BMV RNA 1 and 2 in barley protoplasts.

Satellite RNA-Mediated Disease Attenuation

Satellites are small extragenomic RNA species that depend on a helper virus for replication. Some satellite RNAs are known to attenuate the symptoms of their helper virus. Transgenic tobacco plants expressing the satellites of CMV or TobRSV were shown to be protected against severe effects of their respective helper virus. The expression of CMV satellite RNA also protected against the symptoms of infection with TMV, but not against a range of other viruses.

Anti-Sense RNA/ Ribozyme-Mediated Protection

Antisense constructs have generated protection against RNA and DNA viruses. Antisense coat protein genes mediate high level of resistance in PLRV. Huntley and Hall (1993) reported an antisense transcript of BMV RNA 3 intercistronic region interferes with viral RNA replication.

Ribozymes are RNA molecules catalyzing endonucleolytic cleavage reactions. Some viroids, virusoids and satellite RNAs perform self-cleavage reactions. Mostly, the cleavage site consists of a consensus structure, called the **hammerhead** motif. The nucleotide region directing the catalysis of cleavage reaction could be separated from the region where the cleavage occurs and the recognition of the target could be modified by changing the nucleotide sequence of the regions flanking the cleavage site. Steinecke et al. (1992) designed a ribozyme targeted against the mRNA of the npt gene, which was shown to reduce mpt gene expression when transiently expressed in tobacco protoplasts. A cleavage product of the NPT mRNA was detected.

Replicase and Protease-Mediated Protection

Golembowski et al. (1990) discovered that transgenic tobacco expressing part of replicase gene of TMV strain was highly resistant to this and closely related strains. In contrast, transgenic tobacco expressing functional AIMV replicase protein was not virus resistant and in barley protoplasts, intact BMV replicase did also not reduce virus replication. Longstaff et al. (1993) changed the conserved NTP-binding or polymerase motifs of the PVX open reading frame 1 RNA (encoding the putative viral replicase) rendering the viral genome non-infectious. The mutant genes were transformed into tobacco and were then shown to confer extreme resistance against PVX infection.

The recent report describing virus resistance in plant expressing protease genes of polyviruses suggest that this could be an additional new type of pathogen-derived resistance based on interference with the processing of the viral polyproteins. This possibility is not yet proved.

Movement Protein-Mediated Protection

The movement of viruses between cells is an attractive target for transgenic resistance mechanisms. It has been expected that resistance based on cell to cell movement might have broad spectrum effectiveness. There are reports that virus resistance in transgenic tobacco is mediated by a defective movement protein of TMV. It is shown that the dysfunctional protein responsible for resistance does not modify plasmodesmata. The movement of protein- mediated resistance was effective, at least partially, against virus of the TMV group that were only distantly related to TMV. Transgenic expression in tobacco of the BMV movement protein also conferred partial resistance to TMV. It might be considered that the movement-protein of BMV dysfunctional in tobacco.

Resistance through Transgenic Expression of Antiviral Proteins

There have been reports of virus resistance resulting from transgenic expression of genes encoding a single chain antibody against a virus encoded protein by constructing transgenic plants expressing single chain antibody gene. Tavladoraki et al. (1993) have shown specific protection against artichoke mottle crinkle virus. This report is the first example of resistance to pathogen attack through expression of transgenic antibodies directed against a structurally important epitope of a viral coat protein. The resistance conferred by transgenic expression of rat 2-5 oligo-A synthetase in potato plant is effective against two unrelated viruses PVX and TMV (Truve et al. 1993). Precisely how this resistance might operate is a mystery.

The pokeweed anti viral protein is a ribosome- inactivating protein similar to ricin and related proteins found in many plants. These proteins inactivate ribosomes by de-adenylation of ribosomal RNA and are thought to contribute to natural defense by serving as cellular suicide proteins. Normally, the proteins are located in the cell wall. They are released into the cell when the plasma membrane is broken by physical damage (when plants are penetrated by invertebrate vitrus vectors or when the cells are mechanically damaged in a manner that allows virus entry). A recent report (lodge et al. 1993) indicates that tobacco plants transformed to a virus-resistant phenotype by transgenic expression of the pokeweed anti viral protein.

Following are the approaches to broad spectrum resistance:

1. The first is based on the increasing molecular understanding of the function of virus encoded proteins mainly implicated in replication and cell to cell movement of virus.
2. A second approach relies on the transgenic expression of antivirus protein of non-plant origin including antibodies.
3. The third approach is based on genetic manipulation of natural viral defenses in plants.

Over the recent years, progress has been made towards identification of viral components that trigger these resistance mechanisms. In the near future there is good prospect that the resistance genes that control these defense mechanisms will be cloned and characterized. With the combined information about these host and viral components, it should be possible to design methods of manipulating the broad-spectrum component of the natural defense mechanisms.

HERBICIDE TOLERANCE GENES

Expression of foreign genes conferring herbicides in transgenic plants lead to high level of herbicide resistance. Herbicide tolerance can be obtained by following methods:

Herbicide Target Modification

Herbicide targets are proteins and their action is two folds: it either inhibits photosynthesis or amino acid biosynthesis.

Triazines are common herbicides which inhibit photosynthesis.

1. Triazines block electron transport in PS-II by binding to Qb protein present in thylakoid membrane encoded by psbA gene of chloroplast DNA.
2. Triazine resistant mutants having one altered amino acid have been identified from naturally occurring plants or microbial species.
3. Triazine resistance can be obtained by transferring the resistant chloroplast genome by sexual hydridization or by developing a chloroplast transformation system.
4. Tobacco cells were transformed by Agrobacterium vector having a pabA gene coding a triazine insensitive protein, fused to transist peptide of nuclear encoded chloroplast protein (Cheung *et al.*, 1998).

Triazines which inhibit amino acid synthesis:

1. Triazines affect amino acids biosynthesis, like sulphonyl reas, imidazolinones.
2. The target enzyme is acetolactate or ALS.
3. Mutant forms of ALS resistant to herbicides having one amino acid sequence have been identified and isolated.
4. Maize plant tolerant to imidazolines correlated with the presence of altered ALS has been produced.

Over Production of Target Enzyme

Glyphosate (Round up™) interferes with amino acid biosynthesis by inhibiting the enzyme EPSP (5-enol pyruvyl shikimate 3-phosphate synthase). High level herbicide tolerance has been obtained in plants by over production EPSP in chloroplast. *aro A* bacterial gene was transferred from *Salmonella typhimurium* into tobacco. Transformed plants showed resistance to glyphosate. Tolerance is dependant on *aro A* encoded bacterial EPSP.

Detoxifying Enzymes

Herbicides detoxifying enzymes inactivate herbicides before they are able to inhibit the target enzyme. The most successful example is the detoxification of phosphinothricine phosphate (Murakami *et al.*, 1986).

TABLE 10.1: Herbicide Resistant Transgenic Plants

Species Modified	Transgene Source	Transgene Product
Target modifications:		
Beta vulgaris	Arabidopsis thaliana	Acetolactate synthase
Nicotiana tobaccum	A. thaliana	Acetolactate synthase
Enzyme over production:		
Glycine max	Plant and microbial genes	Analogue of EPSP synthase
Enzyme detoxification:		
Brassica napus	Streptomyces hygroscopicus	Phosphinothricin

Insect Tolerance

Pesticides are often highly toxic to non-target organism. Transgenic plants can be developed that are able to protect themselves against insects by expressing insecticidal protein or a proteinase inhibitor gene. *Bacillus thuringiensis* produces insecticidal protein crystals during sporulation that are toxic to lepidopteran insects. Commercial insecticide of from bacteria is effective against 20 lepidopterans. Fischoff et al (1987) constructed chimeric genes containing 35-S promoter of CaMV and protein coding sequence of bacterium. Plant can be made insect resistant by introducing genes for certain protease inhibitors. Proteins as inhibitors conferring endogenous resistance to insect attack are common in higher plants. In addition, they have anti-metabolic activity in wide range of insects.

Coat Protein Genes for Virus Protection

Control of plant virus depends on methods that prevent or restrict its infection. Most successful method of producing virus resistant plant is to insert and allows expression of a viral coat protein genes. The principle is based on the observation that infection of a plant with one viral strain protects against super infection by another related strain. This phenomenon is called **Cross-protection**. It is assumed that the mild virus which infected the cell first, produces inhibit the uncoating of RNA of second virus thereby delaying or preventing the RNA expression and replication. Powel – Abel et al. (1986) were first to describe the expression of TMV coat protein when infected with TMV in transgenic tobacco. A C-DNA coding for TMA coat protein under the control of CaMV 35-S promoter was transferred to tobacco. Progeny showed delayed symptoms or no symptoms.

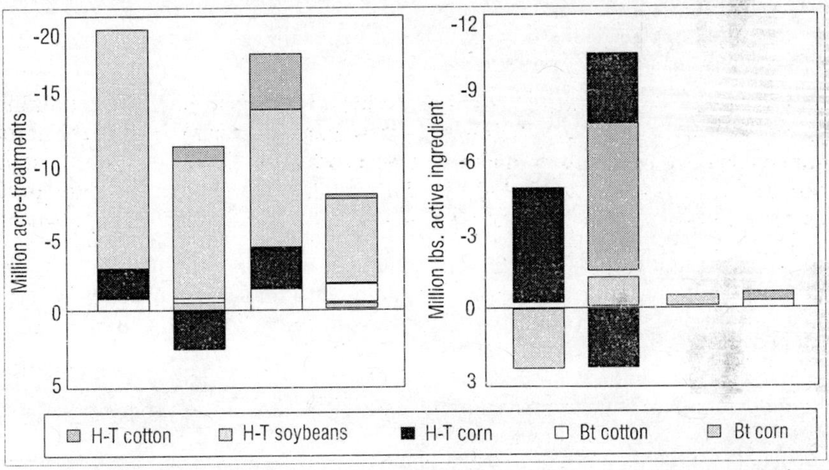

FIGURE 10.1: Reduction in pesticide use accompanies adoption of genetically engineered crops (Source: Economic Research Service, USDA, Agricultural Resource Management Study, 1997 and 1998).

Using a non structural gene from TMV strain U1, Golemboski et al (1990) were able to produce highly virus resistant transgenic tobacco plants. The chimeric gene used contained a CaMV 35-S promoter. Tansgenic plant showed complete resistance even when inoculated with high concentration of virus.

Virus resistance can be obtained via satellite RNA expression. Satellite RNA's are small RNA molecules encapsulated by plant viruses and packaged together with viral genome. Certain plant RNA viruses harbor these molecules. Such molecules are unable to replicate in dependently but require assistance from the virus. The transgenic plants which expressed the satellite RNA when infected with corresponding virus exhibit significant delaying symptom development compared to the plants devoid of gene coding RNA.

Light Regulated Genes

Many light regulated genes show tissue specific expression. Cis elements for tissue specific expression of light regulated genes have been investigated. Transgenic tobacco plants containing the chalcone synthase (CHS) promoter from *Antirrhinum majus* and NPT-II structural sequence was obtained. The transcription of a chimeric gene with promoter was shown to be light inducible in tobacco.

Antisense RNA

This technology involves the reduction in gene expression by using RNA. The proposed mechanism is the formation of ds RNA that is readily degraded than free m-RNA. Rothstein et al (1987) demonstrated inhibition of nopaline synthase (NOS) gene in tobacco. This method can be used to reduce ripening in fruits.

TRANSPOSABLE GENETIC ELEMENTS

Transposable genetic elements were discovered in maize (*Zea mays*) by Barbara McClintock. Although their ability to move, affect gene expression, and cause chromosomal rearrangements. McClintock's discovery was recognized with the award of a Nobel Prize. The study of maize transposable elements now extends from the corn field to in vitro mutagenesis of cloned DNA fragments. Transposable elements are also found in *Holobacteria*, *Saccharomyces cervisiae*, *Drosphilla melanogaster* (*hoho* element and *mariner* element)), *Xenopus* sp., *Antirrhinum majus*, etc.

The most striking property of maize transposable elements is their ability to sense developmental parameters. Elements transpose and promote genetic rearrangements at characteristic times and frequencies in the development of the plant. There are indications that the elements can be differentially expressed within the organism and that they can be preprogrammed to undergo changes in expression at specified intervals, in certain parts of the plant, or in different areas of a single tissue. McClintock originally gave them the designation controlling elements because she understood that such genetic elements were separate from a gene's structure, yet could impost a novel developmental pattern of expression on the gene.

Transposable Elements and Maize Development

The properties of maize transposable elements have facilitated the study of plant development. Insertion mutations are commonly unstable, and they revert during both plant and kerned development. Insertion mutations reduce or prevent gene expression, giving null or intermediate phenotypes. Reversion occurs by excision of the element, generally restoring gene function and the original phenotype. Hence, plants with transposable element mutations can be variegated.

The Genetic characteristics of Ac and Ds Elements

McClintock first identified the Ds element as a specific site of chromosome breakage or dissociation. Chromosome breakage at Ds did not occur spontaneously, but required the presence of a second genetic element, designated the **Activator**, for its ability to activate chromosome breakage at Ds.

Among the earliest strains with transposed Ds elements, McClintock identified one with a new mutation at the *c* locus on the short arm of chromosome 9. It was through the detailed genetic analysis of this mutation that McClintock understood the relationship between unstable mutations and transposition. She established that Ds, identified by its ability to break the chromosome, had transposed to the *c* locus in the mutant strain. The new mutation was stable in the absence of an *Ac* element, but reverted both somatically and in the germ line when an *Ac* was present. Germinal revertants of the *c* gene mutation no longer showed chromosome breakage at the locus, thus revealing that the instability of the mutation was attributable to the excision of the Ds element.

In subsequent studies on a variety of mutations, McClintock found that the Ac element could also cause insertion mutations. These differed from Ds mutations by their inherent instability. That is, an Ac insertion could spontaneously excise, while a Ds insertion could excise only the presence of an Ac element. She reported that not all Ds elements broke chromosomes and that chromosome breakage was rarely associated with an *Ac* insertion.

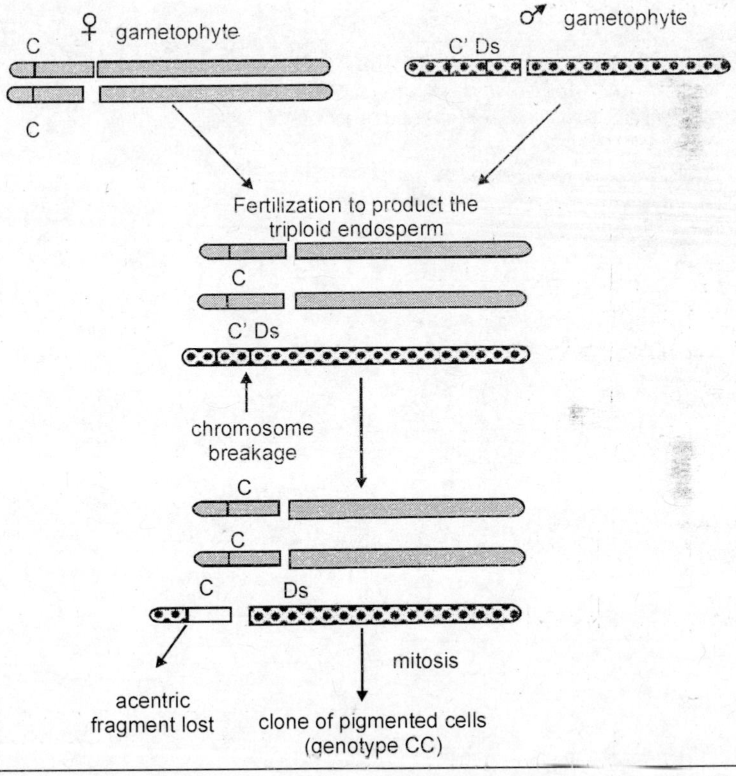

FIGURE 10.2: Chromosome breaking caused by the transposable element Ds in maize.The allel C' on the short arm of chromosome 9 produces normal pigmentation in the aleurone (of maize kernal), the allele C' inhibits this pigmentation (after Gardener *et al.*, 1991).

Furthermore, she reported that an Ac mutation could change directly into one that had the genetic properties of a Ds mutation, suggesting that at least some Ds elements might be mutant Ac's. Moreover, an Ac element could undergo reversible inactivation. When inactive, the Ac element behaved genetically as a Ds element, but differed from a true Ds element by its ability to return to an active form. The various genetic properties of the Ac and Ds elements are summarized diagrammatically.

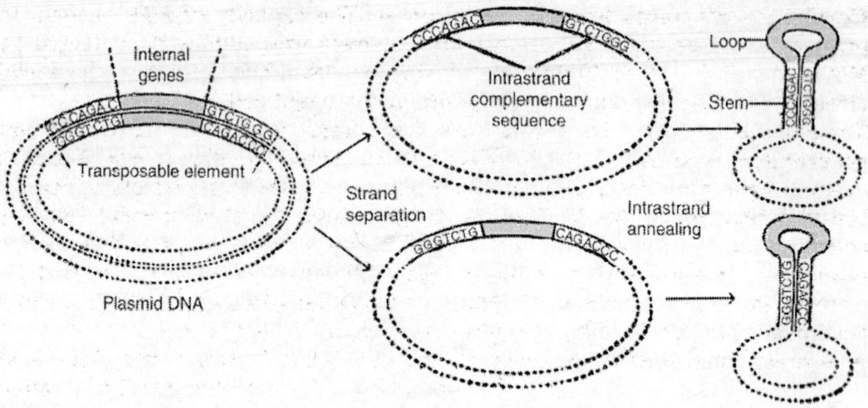

FIGURE 10.3: Presence of inverted repeats at the two ends of each strands of a transposon in a plasmid and the formation of characteristic stem and loop in each strand on strand separation due to denaturation. Stem and loop formation is an evidence for inverted repeats.

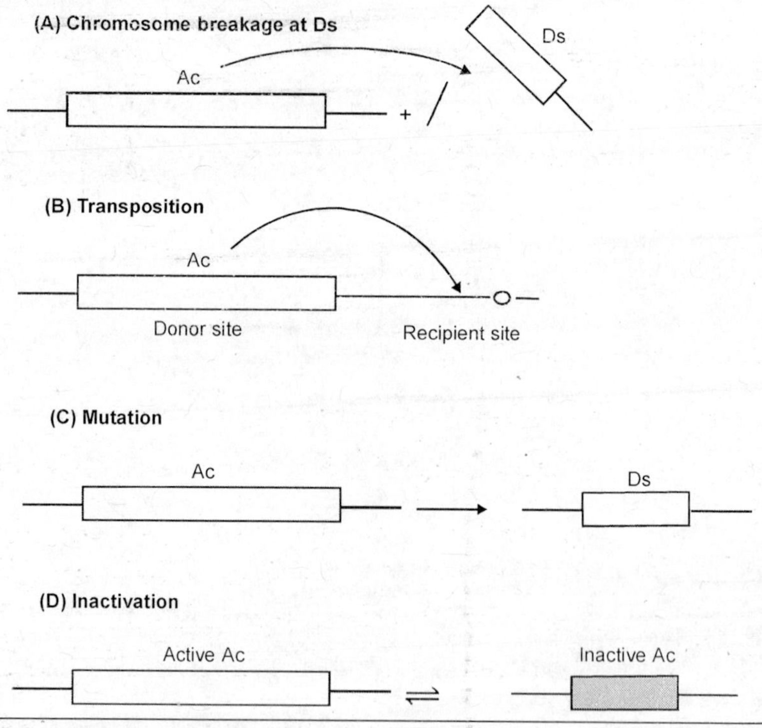

FIGURE 10.4: Genetic properties of *Ac – Ds* element family, Elements belonging to the *Ac-Ds* family can break chromosomes, transpose, mutate, and become reversibly inactivated.

The first Ac element was isolated from the *waxy* (*wx*) locus maize, which encodes an abundant starch-biosynthetic enzyme. The important characteristics of transposable elements are:

1. **Certain Ds elements break chromosomes:** The capacity of a *Ds* element to promote chromosome breakage and to transpose was initially documented by McClintock using a multiply marked chromosome. The initial chromosomal cleavage event occurs during or after chromosome replication.
2. **Transposition of Ds can be accompanied by chromosomal rearrangements:** Although Ds elements can undergo simple transposition events of the type described above for Ac, transposition of the chromosome-breaking Ds element that McClintock first identified and studied was frequently accompanied by chromosomal rearrangements. Indeed, she noted that a large proportion of kernels that showed phenotypic evidence of a transposed Ds element failed to germinate, suggesting that lethal rearrangements frequently accompany movement of the chromosome-breaking Ds element.
3. **A nontransposing Ds element:** McClintock identified several Ds mutations at the *sh* and *bz* loci which had the unusual genetic characteristic that the mutation reverted without apparent loss of the resident Ds element, as judged by the continued association of a Ds chromosome breakage site with the locus.

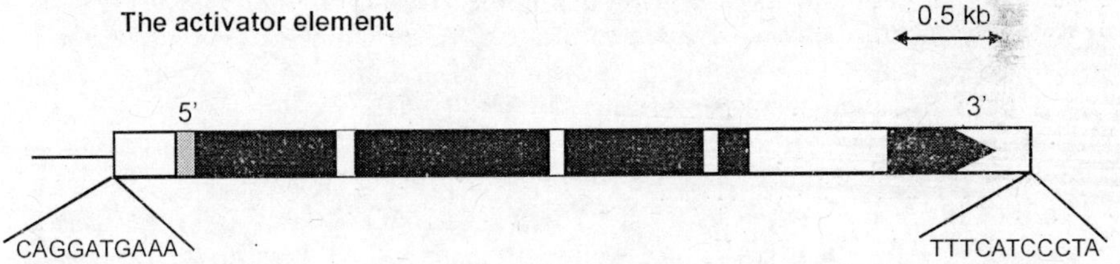

FIGURE 10.5: Structure of *Ac* element and several *Ds* elements. The *Ac* element is 4.6 kb in length and has 11 bp imperfect terminal Irs. The 5' and 3' ends of the *Ac* transcription unit are indicated, the left and right ends of the element are correspondingly dedignated the 5' and 3' ends. The shaded box represents the region of the element within which transcription starts sites map. The black filled boxes corrospond to exons, and the open boxex between them represent interons.

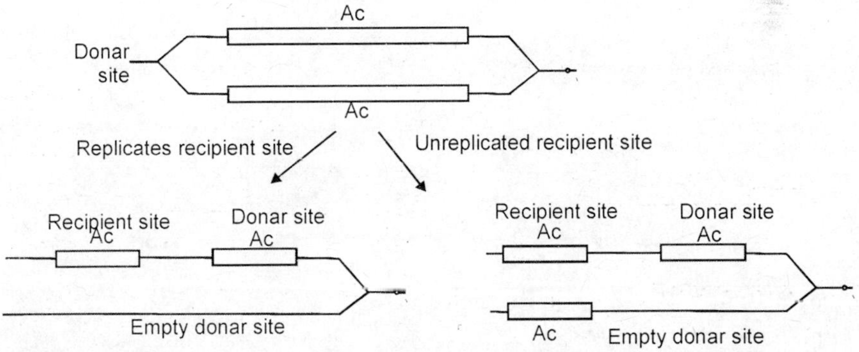

FIGURE 10.6: *Ac* transposition mechanism. As described in the text, the *Ac* donor and receipient sites are commonly on the same chromosome. *Ac* transposes from the donor site on one daughter chromatids to either unreplicated or a replicated recipient site.

The Molecular Mechanism of Transposition

The chromatid selectivity of transposition is disrupted by the double Ds element: Although nothing is known about the molecular mechanism of Ac transposition, important inferences can be drawn from the types of rearrangements that have been observed in strains with chromosome-breaking Ds elements. Ac transposition generally involves only one of the two replicated daughter chromatids, which implies an asymmetry in the recognition of parental strands by the enzymes involved in the chromosome breakage and rejoining events. The rearrangements that accompany movement of the double Ds element necessitate cleavage of both replicated daughter chromatids at the donor site and can result in the movement of both copies of the element. This suggests that the structure of the double Ds element interferes with the inherent strand asymmetry of the transposition process.

Could asymmetric cleavage sites determine strand selectivity?: Methylation of element sequences is implicated in the control of both transposition and expression of transposable elements in bacteria and in maize. Although there is no detailed information about the role of methylation in transposition of maize elements, it is known that transposition of Tn10 is more frequent from hemimethylated DNA than from fully methylated DNA.

Sequence other than termini are necessary for transposition: The first hints that there are sequences inside the elements' IRs that are critical to the excision process have come from experiments on Ac and Ds elements introduced into tobacco cells by *Agrobacterium tumefaciens* Ti plasmid-mediated transformation. Since the Ac element promotes its own transposition in tobacco cells, such experiments permit the analysis by in vitro mutagenesis of sequences involved in transposition.

Empty donor sites retain the target site duplication: Like most other transposable elements, the Ac and Ds elements generate a short duplication of target sequence upon insertion.

Ac encodes a transposase: There is evidence that an Ac-encoded gene product is involved in excision and transposition.

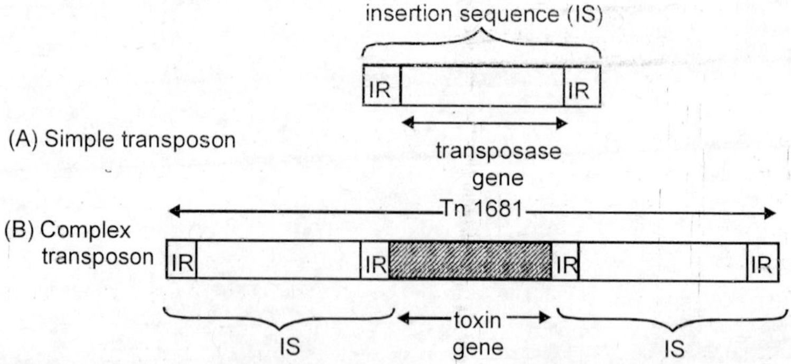

FIGURE 10.7: (A) A simple transposon (IS) carries only the genetic information necessary for transposition which is often enclosed by short regions of inverted repeat (IR) sequences, (B) The complex transposon (Tn) is composed of insertion sequences (IS) and contains genetic information in addition to that needed for transposition. In Tn 1681 transposon carries the gene for a heat-liable toxin.

Regulation of Ac transposition: The frequency and timing of Ac transposition, as well as expression of the element, are subject to genetic control. These aspects of Ac function are as yet understood only poorly or not at all at the molecular level.

Transposition is developmentally delayed as Ac copy number increases: The developmental timing of Ac transposition becomes progressively later as the number of Ac copies per genome increases. This manifests itself as a reduction in the frequency of a large revertant sectors produced by excision events early in development of the tissue.

Ac probably encodes a negative regulator of transposition: The simplest interpretation of the Ac dosage effect is that the element encodes a repressor of element expression that accumulates with increasing number of Ac elements. Several strains with Ds elements that arose from Ac elements by short internal deletions have been analyzed genetically for the ability of the mutant element to contribute to the dosage effect. The small deletions identified for the *wx-m9* Ds element and a Ds derivative of the Ac *bz-m2* allele suffice to render the element unable to contribute to the dosage effect. If the element's major transcript is its only transcript, then the corresponding protein is responsible for both the dosage effect and the element's *trans*-acting transposase activity.

Using Transposable Elements

Isolation of Maize Genes: Maize transposable elements belonging to all three of the families discussed here have been used in cloning maize genes. The first gene isolated using a transposable element was the *bz* locus, and its facile isolation demonstrated the feasibility of using elements to clone a gene whose product had not been identified, but which was marked by the insertion of a cloned and characterized transposable element.

An additional improvement in using transposable elements for gene isolation developed from the observation that most sequences homologous to *Spm* are methylated in maize genomic DNA, while some sites within active elements are not. This has permitted the use of methylation-sensitive restriction endonucleases in the identification and isolation of genomic DNA fragments corresponding to a gene with an active element. Although the high redundancy of the *Mu* element reduces its utility in gene isolation, its usefulness has recently been improved by combining the use of the element to identify Mu-containing genomic DNA fragments cloned from a strain with an insertion mutation at the *bz2* locus with the further screening of the cloned fragments for homology to mRNAs present in strains with a wild-type allele of the locus, but not in strains from which the gene was deleted.

Transposon Tagging of Maize Genes: The recent rapid progress in isolating maize genes with transposable element probes has been possible because of the availability of genetically well-characterized insertion mutations at many loci.

Maize Transposable Elements are Mobile in Other Plants: The observation that the maize Ac element transposes in tobacco cells when introduced on an *Agrobacterium* Ti plasmid has opened the possibility of using the well-characterized maize elements to tag genes in plants other than maize. The Ac element excises from the donor site on the T-DNA in up to 70% of transformed tobacco cells, implying not only that the element is efficiently expressed and its transcript is properly processed in a dicot, but that the dicot can provide any additional factors that are required for transposition of the maize element.

Transposable Elements and Evolution

Molecular studies on mutations caused by maize transposable elements have revealed that they contribute to genetic change at both fine and coarse structural levels. The insertions themselves can either abolish or, in essence, reprogram gene expression in development, and a chromosomal site that has experienced an insertion rarely returns to its previous sequence when the element transposes away. The mutations that result from the insertion and excision of transposable elements contribute to sequence diversity at he relatively fine resolution of a few base pairs. More extensive structural rearrangement of all types have also been associated with active transposable elements. Moreover, maize elements have the capacity to act in *trans* to promote excision and transposition of defective elements, as well as intraelement deletions and chromosomal rearrangements with endpoints at homologous insertions. Thus a single active element can make extensive contributions to genetic change throughout the genome.

An important recent insight into transposable element functions is that maize elements can undergo reversible, methylation-associated changes that affect both their ability to expression *trans*-acting functions and their ability to move in response to transposase produced by *trans*-acting elements. Equally important is the realization that active elements can inactivate themselves by intraelement deletions. Thus, the mutagenic effects of transposable elements are kept in check by both reversible and irreversible mechanisms, some and perhaps even all of which are element encoded. There is increasing evidence that elements interact with each other to influence both immediate expression levels and the heritability of expression and there is ample evidence that inactive elements can be activated by a variety of agents and manipulations that perturb genome structure. Thus, transposable elements increasingly emerge as a dynamic, environmentally responsive system of genetic change and genome reorganization.

SEED STORAGE PROTEINS

In legumes and most of the dicots, the major storage proteins are salt soluble globulins. In monocots, prolamines (alcohol soluble) and glutelins (acid-base soluble) are dominant seed proteins. Tissue specific expression of these genes has made it possible to clone and transfer these genes into various plants. Transgenic tobacco plants have been obtained by introducing 917Kbp soyabean DNA fragment containing lectin gene and at least four non-seed protein genes into tobacco genome.

BIOACTIVE PEPTIDES

Biologically active peptides are chemically synthesized or obtained by extraction from biological materials or by expression as fusion proteins in prokaryotic or eukaryiotic cells (Josephson and Bishop, 1988). Leu-enkephalin, a pentapeptide (YGGFL) with opiate activity has bee produced in *Arabidopsis* and oilseed rape as part of chimeric plant seed storage proteins.

The 2S albumins, or napin-like proteins, are formed by two subunits linked by disulfide bridges and are synthesized as prepropolypeptides, being co- and posttranslationally processed and stored in the protein bodies. The 2S albumins from different species are structurally very similar, but contain a region between the sixth and seventh cysteine residues that is highly variable. Vandekerckhove et al. inserted sequences encoding the neuropeptide leuenkephalin into the *2S1* gene from *Arabidopsis thaliana*, the variable region was substituted by the enkephalin peptide flanked by lysine residues to allow its cleavage from the remainder of the 2S albumin using a trypsin digestion. The small size of enkephalin probably produced a minimal disruption of the protein structure and allowed a stable, correctly processed hybrid protein. Seeds present the advantage of stable storage of proteins for long periods, but some plant seeds may contain contaminants that could cause purification problems.

HUMAN PROTEINS

Human serum albumin (HSA) has been expressed in transgenic potato. It is protein of broad clinical use and, consequently, of a high commercial value. In humans, it is synthesized as preproalbumin, released from the endoplasmic reticulum after removal of the prepeptide and proteolytically processed by a serine protease that cleaves the six residues of the propeptide. Similarly to HSA, secreted plant proteins contain NH_2-terminal signal peptides that are removed from the preprotein by a specific protease. The NH_2-terminal amino acid sequence analysis of purified HSA produced in transgenic potato plants showed that the processing of the protein depended on the type of signal sequence. The two signal peptides are capable of targeting HSA extracellularly. The HSA accumulated up to 0.02% of the total protein. The amount could probably be increased in tubers by using a tuber-specific promoter. HSA added to round untransformed potatoes did not show any degradation during the industrial process of starch extraction, as it was the protein obtained in the waste liquid fraction of the process. This observation suggests that transgenic starch tubers could well be used as an inexpensive source for protein production, provided that the levels of HSA could be increased. Human interferons (INFs) are small defense proteins related to resistance to viral infection. They are high-value proteins and have been clones and produced as recombinant proteins in bacterial and cultured animal cell systems. Interferon-like factors have been detected in virus-infected plants (Sela, I.), and some have been isolated by their affinity for antibodies against human interferon beta, although they do not show structural homology to the interferons. Human interferon β has been expressed in tobacco transgenic plants. It was detected by immunoblot analysis and extracts from positive plants inhibited the cytopathic effect of vesicular stomatitis virus in human Wish cells. Transgenic plants producing interferon-β could be used as an inexpensive system to produce the protein.

ENZYMES

They are used, soluble or immobilized in a wide variety of industries. They are isolated from the organisms that produce them or they are obtained as recombinant proteins. Transgenic plants may constitute an appropiate system to produce industrial enzymes. Hoekema's group has expressed *Bacillus licheniformis* α-amylase in transgenic tobacco. It is used in the starch-processing industry, and also in others, such as the brewing, baking, wine and juice, and detergent industries. *Bacillus licheniforms* α-amylase is the most commonly used in starch liquefaction because of its head stability and wide pH range of activity. The molecular mass of the enzyme produced in tobacco was 64 kDa; this value is higher than that of the *B. licheniformis* enzymes, which is only 55.2 kDa. This difference could be attributed to glycosylation in plants. Despite differences in glycosylation, the enzyme exhibited biological activity and had similar thermostability. Hoekema's laboratory has expressed *Aspergillus niger* phytase in transgenic tobacco. Phytase catalyzes the conversion of phytate (*myo*-inositolhexaphosphate) into inorganic phosphate and *myo*-inositol. Phytate is the main storage form of phosphorus in many plant seeds used as animal feed. A phytase from *A. niger* has been developed that functions well in the acidic conditions found in the gastrointestinal tract of these animals. Transgenic phytase seeds were tested *in vivo* by milling and subsequent addition to the basal diet of broilers.

ANTIBODIES

Of the variety of bioactive compounds expressed in transgenic plants, antibodies may offer the widest range of possible applications. Antibodies produced in plants possess all of the characteristics and are virtually indistinguishable from antibodies produced by hybridoma cells. Recently, it has been found that antibodies that possess catalytic capabilities can be isolated from mouse hybridoma. Genetically stable seed stocks of antibody-producing plants can be isolated and stored indefinitely at low cost; the seed stock can be converted into a harvest of any quantity of antibody within one growing season. Although tobacco has been used as the principal research tool to initiate the study of antibodies in plants, there may be more appropriate plants for production. A variety of common crop plants can be used as the production host. Acreages of perennial forage crops could be generated by clonal propagation or from seed and harvested numerous times in a growing season. The choice of species may depend on the quantity and nature of contaminants encountered during purification. Some candidates are alfalfa, soybean, tomato, and potato. Because large-scale production of antibodies is not yet commonplace, appropriate techniques for purification of hundreds or thousands of grams have yet to be perfected.

VACCINES

Plants represent a less expensive production system here, being most appropiate for oral vaccines that could be expressed in edible plant tissues. Hepatitis B surface antigen (HbsAg), which is used as vaccine against hepatitis B, has been successfully expressed in transgenic tobacco plants. Tobacco was transformed with constructs containing the sequence encoding for the HbsAg preceded by an enhanced CaMV 35S promoter and the 5'-untranslated leader of tobacco etch virus. The presence in transgenic leaf extracts of material that reacts specifically with monoclonal antibody against HbsAg was tested, and levels ranging up to 66 ng/mg of soluble protein were found. However, if these levels could be increased, the inexpensive plant-produced protein could be used in vaccination against hepatitis B.

INDUSTRIAL PRODUCTS

Plants can also be engineered to produce foreign metabolites by introducing genes coding for the appropiate enzymes that convert compounds that are normally present in the plant into products of higher commercial value. Cyclic oligosaccharides of six (α), seven (β) or eight (γ) α-1,4-linked glucopyranose molecules are used pharmaceutical industry as delivery system and in the food industry for flovor and odor enhancement and for removal of undesired compounds such as caffeine. Cyclodextrins are prepared *in vitro* by the action of the bacterial enzyme cylodextrin glycosyltransferase (CGT) on prehydrolyzed starch. The gene encoding cyclodextrin glysocyltransferase from *Klebsiella pneumoniae* has been cloned and has been expressed in transgenic potato. A tuber-specific promoter from a class I patatin gene was used to restrict expression of the enzyme to the tuber, which storage large amounts of starch, the CGTs substrate. Northern blot analysis of the transformants showed transcription of the chimeric gene, but no CGT was detected in tubers by immunoblot analysis. A potato tuber contains approximately 14% starch, of which 0.001-0.01% was converted to cyclodextrins. For the commercial production of cyclodextrins, this value should be increased to 1-10%. This might be possible by using stronger promoters and more efficient targeting signals.

Plastics are probably the most used materials in industry nowadays. Their uses creating environmental problems, because most of them need extremely long period to biodegrade. Therefore, growing efforts are being made to obtain inexpensive biodegradable plastics.

METAL RESISTANCE IN PLANTS

Metals like aluminium when present as ions poison plants roots by making cells rigid and unable to lengthen. *Arabidopsis* plant after rendom mutations (by chemicals) were screened for Al tolerance. One of the mutants coped with Al by secreting organic acids (citric acid and malic acid) which bound the ions outside cell forming respective salts and thereby inhibiting their entrance into root tip cell. The gene responsible is mapped to be present on first chromosome of *Arabidopsis*. The second type of mutant responded by increased flux of hydrogen ions into root tip, alkalinizing the medium outside root. Increased in external pH (0.15 unit) leads to formation of aluminium hydroxides and precipitates that failed to enter cell. Other metals like Cd and Cu produce free oxygen radicals. Plants cope with these metals by binding them in complex with peptides called phytochelatins. Experiments show that genes for a metal resistance enzyme called phytochelatin synthase from wheat, yeast and *Arabidopsis* enable yeast to survive a dose of Cd that kills control cells.

TRANSGENIC PLANTS WITH HIGHER STRESS TOLERANCE

To increase productivity it is necessary to increase tolerance against abiotic stresses. Environmental stress gene expression and permits isolation of stress related genes. Plants can be genetically engineered to improve stress tolerance. Many organisms have gene that enable them to survive in extreme environments and which can be introduced in higher plants. Stress relieving genes might encode enzymes involved in particular metabolic pathway. Thus stress responses help organism in adaptation by changing metabolic flow.

Reduction in water availability causes reduction and failing complete inhibition of photosynthesis. In condition when photosynthesis is impaired and chloroplasts are exposed to light there is photo reduction of oxygen forming products like peroxides, superoxides that damage membrane system. Antioxygen enzyme systems scavange reactive oxygen intermediates. The three common types of stress that plants face are:

Water Stress: Many plants depend on their ability to function under water scarcity. Abscissic acid (ABA) concentration effects yield under water stress condition. This forms an important criterion for drought resistance.

Temperature Stress: It includes heat tolerance, chilling stress and freezing stress. The reproductive stage is most sensitive to heat leading to floral abscission, pollen sterility and poor fruit set. Chilling is the most severe environmental stress that reduces germination and growth rate. Genetic resources for chilling tolerance have been found in maize. In crop plants considerable genetic variability occurs in freezing tolerance below zero degree centigrade. Frost hardiness is considered a quantatively inherited trait controlled by a complex interaction of several genes.

Salt Stress: Salinity causes water stress from the osmotic effects, mineral toxicity of salt and interruption of mineral nutrition of plants. Efforts to develop salt resistant varieties have been unsuccessful due to this multi partite nature of stress.

Strategy for Stress Tolerant Transgenic Plants: Basic steps involved in formation of stress tolerant plants by genetic engineering can be explained by following flower chart.

Properties/Characters Required for Improved Stress Tolerance: Stress tolerance can be improved by introduction of genes encoding enzymes that catalyze conversion of naturally occurring substrate into product with osmoprotective properties. Thus, properties that should be emphasized are:

Production of Osmoprotective Compounds: The ability of plant for accumulating low molecular mass osmoprotectants and osmolyts (amino acids, sugar alcohols) is a strategy to determine is resistance to environment stress. For example, mannitol (sugar alcohol) is produced in Arabdiopsis and tobacco by bacterial mltd gene encoding mannitol-1-dehydrogenase. Seeds of transgenic *Arabdiopsis* showed greater germination in high salt concentration.

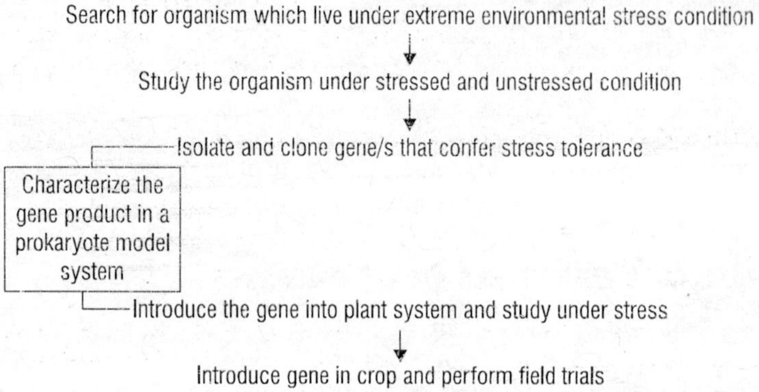

FIGURE 10.8: Basic steps involved in formation of stress tolerant plants by genetic engineering.

Improved Membrane Flexibility: Chilling sensitivity depends upon the unsaturation of fatty acids in plastid membrane. Presence of centrally positioned *cis*-double bonds in the membrane lipids lowers phase transition period to zero degree centigrade. By introducing enzymes catalyzing formation of *cis* double bonds in saturated fatty acids, chilling resistant phenotypes can be obtained.

Stress Induced Proteins: Transcription of genes encoding late embryogenesis abundant (LEA) proteins is activated during abiotic stress. The protective effect of these proteins was proved by introducing HVA-I gene, encoding three LEA proteins from barley to rice. Plants showed improved osmotic stress tolerance as indicated by delayed development of damage symptoms and improved recovery.

Scavenging Reactive Intermediates: Abiotic stress causes formation of reactive oxygen intermediates that cause oxydative stress by damaging membranes and macro molecules. Freezing and salinity resistant plants have well developed anti oxidant defences that scavange oxygen radicals. Mn-SOD c-DNA from *N. plumbaginifolia* has been introduced in alfalfa Field trial showed that yield and survival of transgenic plants was improved.

One approach for engineering stress tolerance may be to introduce genes from different stress responses to a single plant. It is important to target the location, control of time and level of expression and ensure precursor availability for each enzyme in order to avoid negative effects.

CHAPTER 11

Plant Tissue Culture: Principles and Methodology

Plant tissue culture is the technique of growing plant cells, tissues and organs in an artificial prepared nutrient medium static or liquid, under aseptic conditions. It has advanced the knowledge of fundamental botany, specially in the field of agriculture, horticulture, plant breeding, forestry, somatic cell hybridization, phytopathology and industrial production of plant metabolites, etc.

IMPORTANCE OF TISSUE CULTURE TECHNIQUE

All the cells in an organism carrry the same genetic information, yet show variations in expression. Our knowledge of cell and tissue cultures has been developing with full swing, specially in biotransformation, forestry, genetic engineering, morphogenesis, somatic hybridization, secondary metabolite production, hybridization, variety development and their conservation, maintaining pathogen free plants and rapid clonal propagation, totipotency, differentiation, cell division, cell nutrition, metabolism, radio biology, cell preservation, etc. It is now possible to cultivate cells in quantity, or as clones from single cells; to grow whole plant from isolated meristems and to induce callus or even single cell to develop into complete plant either by organogenesis or directly by embroygenesis *in vitro*.

The production of haploid through tissue culture from anthers or isolated microspores and of protoplasts from higher plant cells has served as the basic tools for genetic engineering and somatic hybridization. Tissue culture technique helps to propagate plants of economic importance such as orchids and other ornamental plants in large numbers by their meristem culture or by other *in vitro* methods. This provides them virus-free plantlets. Propagation of valuable economic plants through tissue culture based on the principle of **totipotency** (*every cell within the plant has potential to regenerate into a whole plant*).

In plant breeding, embryo, ovary and ovule culture as well as *in vitro* pollination have been employed to overcome morphological and physiological sterility and incompatibility. In recent years, plant tissue culture technique is in increasing use for producing haploids from anthers or isolated microspores, and of protoplasts from higher plant cells and the recognition of the potential of these materials in genetics and plant breeding. One of the most significant developments in the field of plant tissues culture during recent years are the isolation, culture and fusion techniques which have their special importance in studies of plant improvement by cell modification and somatic hybridization.

Plant tissue culture technique is a boon in the studies of the biosynthesis of secondary metabolites and provides an efficient means of producing economically important plant products (fine chemicals). Plant tissue culture also provides raw material to pharmaceutical, cosmetic and confectionary industries. Examples are berberine, ginseng, shikonin and vanilla.

TABLE 11.1: Land marks in plant tissue culture research*

Worker	Year	Contribution
G. Haberlandt	1902	Was first to culture isolated plant cells in vitro on artificial medium.
W.J. Robbins, W. Kotte	1922	Culture of isolated roots-organ culture.
P.R. White	1934	Demonstrated capability of indefinite culture of tomato roots (long periods).
R.J. Gauhtheret, P. Nobecourt	1939	First culture cambial tissues isolated from carrot.
P.R. White	1939	Callus culture of tobacco tumour tissue from interspecific hybrid of Nicotiana glauca x N. langsdorfii.
J. Van Overbeck	1941	Discovered nutritional value of liquid endosperm of coconut (coconut milk) for culture.
P.R. White, A.C. Braum	1942	Experiments on crown-gall and tumour formation in plant growth of bacteria-free crown-gall tissue
A. Caplan, F.C. Steward	1948	Use of coconut milk and (2,4-Dichlorophenolacetic acid) for proliferation of cultured carrot and potato tissues.
G. Morel	1950	Culture of monocot tissues using coconut milk.
W.H. Muir	1953	Developed technique for culture of single isolated cells (nurse culture method).
W. Tubecke	1953	Haploid cultures from pollen of gymnosperm (Ginkgo sps.)
C.O. Miller, F. Skoog	1955	Discovery of cytokinins, e.g. kinetin, as potent cell division factor
E. Ball	1955	Culture of gymnosperm tissue (Sequioa)
F. Skoog, C.O. Miller	1957	Predicted hypothesis that shoot and root initiation in cultured callus is regulated by the proportion of auxin and cytokinin in the culture medium
E.C. Cocking	1960	Enzymatic isolation and culture of protoplasts
G. Morel	1960	Development of shoot apex culture technique
G. Morel	1964	Use of modified shoot apex technique for orchid propagation
S.G. Guha, S.C. Maheshwari	1966	Cultured pollen and anthers can produce haploid embryos
J.P. Nitsch	1974	Culture of microspores of Datura and Nicotiana, to double the chromosome number, and to harvest seeds, from the homozygous diploid plants just within 5 months
R. R. Hendre and coworkers	1975	Established technique for obtaining virus free sugarcane, citrus, potato and cassava.
G. Melchers	1978	Production of somatic hybrid from fusion of protoplasts isolated from potato and tomato.
S. K. Mukherjee, S. Bhaskaran	1980	Isolated auxotrophic mutants for vitamin B components in Nicotiana.
A. Mascarenhas, V. Jagannathan	1982	Isolated spontaneous varients from wheat callus cultures.
K.A. Barton, W.J. Brill,	1983	Insertion of foreign genes attached to a plasmid vector into naked plant protoplasts
M.D. Chilton	1983	Production of transformed tobacco plants following single cell transformation or gene isertion
H. Kohn and coworkers	1985	Somatic hybrids in tobacco mediated by electrofusion.
E. Sundberg and K. Glemelius	1986	Somatic hybrids in Brassicaceae

Worker	Year	Contribution
R. Nadgauda, A. Mascarenhas	1986	Isolated and planted variants of sugarcane resistance to mosaic virus and turmeric plants of the variety `Tekurpeta' in the field.

*for details of more developments please refer to the work done by various researchers in the text.

TISSUE CULTURE RESEARCHES IN INDIA

In India, the significance of *in vitro* culture technique was realized quite early by Professor P. Maheshwari. He initiated investigation with complex tissues such as ovary, ovule, and control of fertilization. The initial exploratory work on these organs laid the foundation of several achievements in plant cell, tissue and organ culture in India. During 1956 to 1966, attempts were initiated to culture the pollinated ovaries of *Aerva tomentosa, Allium cepa, Althaea rosea, Anethum graveolens, Foeniculum vulgare, Hyoscyamus niger, Iberis amara, Linaria maroccana* and *Tropaeolum majus*. Success with the culture of pollinated ovaries made it possible to culture ovaries and ovules at even earlier stages. Cultured ovaries from pollinated flowers of *Zephyranthes* developed seeds with fully differentiated embryos. Excised ovules containing zygote and primary endosperm nucleus also matured into normal-looking seeds but were without fully differentiated embryos. The seeds were however always smaller than the natural seeds (M. Kapoor, 1959). The *in vitro* formed fruits of *Anethum* were larger than the *in vivo* fruits. Another important feature was the occurrence of polyembryony due to cleavage and/or budding of zygotic embryos, on a culture medium. Polyembryony is useful in the multiplication of plants producing a limited number of seeds. This is of a special significance in umbellifers because of low seed-set and germination.

The method of ovary and ovule culture is also appropriate for rearing hybrid seeds. In *Gossypium hirsutum*, Joshi (1962) was able to grow ovules with 12-celled proembryo and 500 endosperm nuclei to maturity. The hybrid ovules of a cross between *G. arboreum* and *G. hirsutum* could be grown to maturity and viable seeds were obtained.

Of considerable importance are the adventive embryos from nucellus, which genetically uniform, and reproduce the characters of the maternal parent. Excised nuclellus from micropylar-half of pollinated ovules of *Citrus microcarpa*, a polyembryonic species, proliferated on a medium and the callus differentiated *pseudobulbils* which, eventually, developed into plantlets (Rangaswamy, 1961). Embryogenesis from nucelli of unfertilized ovules of *Citrus sinensis* and *C. aurantifolia* is reported by Mitra and Chaturvedi (1972). The embryos arose from nucellar cells or the callus. It was demonstrated that the pollination/fertilization stimulus is not essential.

The organogenic potentiality of endosperm has been demonstrated by Johri and Bhojwani (1965) in *Exocarpus cupressiformis*. In *Scurrula* and *Taxillus*, shoot buds differentiated on a cytokinin medium, whereas auxin is also essential for *Dendrophthoe* and *Tolypanthus*. Continuously-growing tissue and organogenesis have also been observed in the mature endosperm of autotrophic taxa such as *Croton bonplandianum, Jatropha panduraefolia, Putranjiva roxburghii, Codiaeum variegatum, Santalum album, Oryza sativa, Nigella damascena, Euphorbia geniculata* and *Emblica officinalis*.

Khuspe et al. (1980) described methods for *in vitro* growth of immature hybrid embryos of *Carica papaya* x *C. cauliflora* and development of F_1 plants. The resultant seedlings could be transferred to pots and field. The culture of young floral primordia has provided a potential tool for understanding the morphogenic sequences leading to flowering. Studies in floral morphogenesis have been conducted in *Ranunculus sceleratus*, *Phlox drumondii*, *Kalanchoe pinnata* and *Browallia demissa*. In *Ranunculus* spp., cultured floral buds proliferated rapidly, and differentiated roots, shoot buds and embryoids. The buds developed into shoots terminating in a flower bud. Flowers were also born directly on the callus. Rarely, mature seeds were also formed. The embryoids passed through the stages comparable to *in vivo* embryogenesis. These plants also flowered *in vitro*.

The work on haploids provided a novel experimental system for speeding up of homozygosity, analyses of genetic combinations, and detection of mutations. In cultured anthers of *D. innoxia* (with uni- or bi-nucleate pollen), numerous embryoids emerged on Nitsch-medium. The embryoids germinated to form plantlets (Guha and Maheshwari, 1967). George and Rao (1979) induced triploids through anther cultures of *Physalis* spp. Direct microspore-derived embryos in anther culture of two cultivars of *Brassica juncea* have been demonstrated by Sharma and Bhojwani (1985). On B5-medium with 2% sucrose the embryos developed into plantlets. Anthers of *B. nigra* cultured on B5-medium developed callus and/or embryos. The most significant result is the *in vitro* flowering of these plants in 2-months-old cultures. Other examples of anther culture leading to the formation of pollen embryoids/plantlets are *Petunia axillaris* by Doreswamy and Chacko (1973), *Solanum melongena* by Raina and Iyer (1973), *Petunia obconica* by Bajaj (1981), and *Physalis ixocarpa*, *Datura innoxia* and *Petunia hybrida* by Chandra and coworkers (Chandra and Kothari, 1987). By anther culture technique, homozygous recombinants of *Hyoscyamus niger* with higher alkaloid content could be obtained. Such a technique has proved very useful in the improvement of crop plants. Haploids of cereals are used for one-step transfer of genotypes of inbred lines. For the induction and characterization of mutants also, haploids are used. The pollen grains are extensively used for the isolation of protoplasts. Shrivastava and Johri (1988) reviewed Indian contribution to morphogenesis and plant tissue culture studies (Indian Review of Life Sciences, 8:249). A. F. Mascarenhas has compiled a Hand Book of Plant Tissue Culture published by ICAR, New Delhi (Feb., 1993).

Majority of the private firms are involved in production of foliage, flowering plants (roses, etc.), and ornamentals. Few deal in plants like *Musa* (Banana), *Fragaria* spp. (Strawberry), Orchids and Tree species. They mostly cater to the foreign market. Some of these private laboratories are also involved in R & D work. But majority of the private tissue culture companies get the know how from a R & D institution either from India or abroad and put it in operation in mass produce the plant species.

PLANT TISSUE CULTURE: PRINCIPLES

The technique has developed around the concept that a cell is **totipotent** that is has the capacity and ability to develop into whole organism. The principles involved in plant tissue culture are very simple and primarily an attempt, whereby an explant can be to some extent freed from inter-organ, inter-tissue and inter-cellular interactions and subjected to direct experimental control.

The most common culture in plant tissue is **callus**, which is wound tissue composed of undifferentiated, highly vacuolated and unorganized cells.

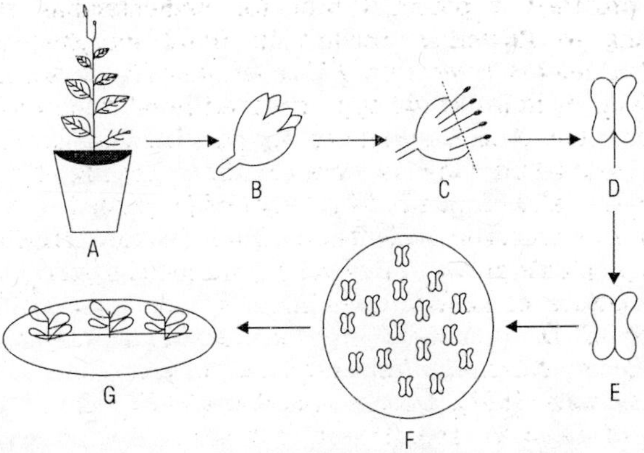

FIGURE 11.1: Diagrammatic representation of the anther culture protocol for tobacco. (A) Flowering diploid plant. (B) Floral bud excised from plant. Calyx and corolla re of approximately equal lengths. (C) Floral bud with calyx and corolla removed. Buds normally contain five anthers, which are shown still attached to filaments. (D) Isolated stamen with anther and filament. (E) Anther removed from filament. (F) Petri dish with cultured anthers. (G) Plantlets emerging from anthers.

Callus Culture

For raising the callus tissues, a tissue culturist must have clear understanding of some basic principles. A cell from any part of the plant like shoot apex, bud, leaf, mesophyll cells, epidermis, cambium, anthers, pollen, fruit etc., when inoculated in a suitable medium under aseptic laboratory conditions can able to differentiate and multiply. This results into the formation of an amorphous mass of cells known as **callus**, which can be induced to re-differentiate on appropriate medium to develop **embryoids** which directly develop into the plantlets, eventually giving rise to a whole viable plant.

The term **clone** (from the Greek *klon*, meaning: a slip or twig suitable for plant propagation) was suggested by Webber (U.S.A.) in 1903 to explain those plants which were obtained by a sexual reproduction; it is even applied to DNA multiplication (cloning of genes in bacteria). In strict scientific sense, cloning means *an organism obtained from a single cell through mitotic divisions.*

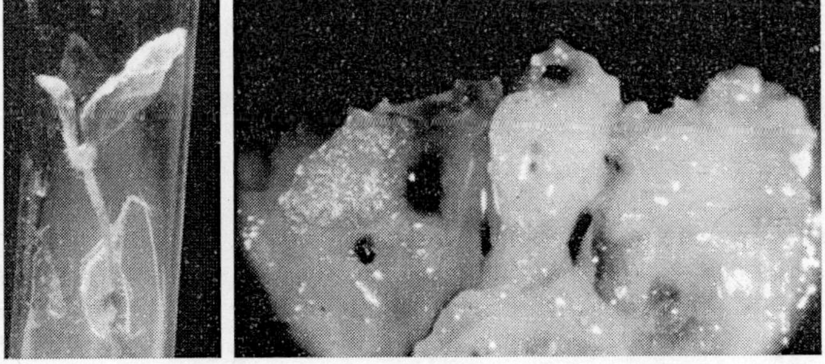

(A) (B)

FIGURE 11.2: (A) *In vitro* cultured plant material, (B) A callus.

Meristem Culture

When a meristem is cultured *in vitro*, then it produces a small plant bearing 5 or 6 leaves. This could be obtained within a few weeks. Then the stem is cut into 5-6 small micro cuttings, which under favourable conditions, become fully grown plants.

Organ Culture

A body of higher plants has complex inter-relationships between different organs like root, shoot, apical meristem, leaf primordia, floral buds, ovary, ovule, anther lobs, pollen grains, fruit, seed, etc. In this method a particular organ is isolated and cultured under laboratory conditions in a chemically defined medium where they retain their characteristic structures and other features and continue to grow as usual. In organ culture, organs are not induced to form callus, therefore, it differs from the callus culture where the organization of the intact tissues is lost.

This technique provides an experimental system to define the nutrients and growth factors that are usually received by the organ from other organs of the plant body and from surrounding environment. It also helps us in understanding the inter-dependence of organs with respect to various physical and chemical growth factors including growth hormones. Organ culture technique also provides the knowledge about the various problems of morphogenesis and the sites of biosynthesis of specific metabolites and growth compounds. It may be used as a tool for improvement of various economically important crops.

Organ culture may be grouped into two major categories: **vegetative organs** (root culture, leaf culture, and shoot tip culture) and **reproductive organs** (complete flower culture, isolated ovary culture, isolated ovule and embryo culture, pollen mother cell culture, seed and fruit culture).

THE CONCEPT OF TOTIPOTENCY OF CELLS

Some concepts in science become inherently acceptable long before their practicality is demonstrable. This was so in the concept of the totipotency of cells of higher plants. Even in the mid-twenties one encountered the tacit view that, apart from inherent practical difficulties, there was no theoretical reason why one should not rear a begonia plant from a single leaf hair cell. This view was traceable **first** to the then well recognized principle that as cells divide mitotically, they do so equationally to produce daughter cells in facsimile.

Secondly, the concept was due to G. Haberlandt's historic but then unsupported claim, expressed in 1902, that one day it should be possible to rear plants from isolated surviving cells of flowering plants. Haberlandt's insight was, in fact, the more remarkable because he even stated that out of surviving somatic cells artificial embryos would be reared asexually. In higher plants, embryos do develop in situ from appropriately stimulated somatic cells but without any prior sexual act. At the outset, the special significance of the fertilized egg in plants should be seen as restricted to its role as the genetically unique product of a fusion of male and female gametes. Having established the genetic constitution of a given individual, the zygote (or fertilized egg) really behaves developmentally as a very general kind of living cell- a cell with a built-in capacity to grow in an organ, the ovule, that fosters that growth. Moreover, as will be shown, and in a satisfying number of cases, isolated somatic cells may return to a simulated zygotic state and grow into embryos and to plants under the appropriately applied conditions which furnish the requisite nutrients and stimuli.

Contrasts Between Plant and Animal Cells

Some inherent differences between plants and animals are relevant here, for these go far to explain why the clonal development of individuals from somatic cells is intrinsically more difficult in animals than it is in plants. The new biology rightly emphasizes that the molecular basis of metabolism, whether of plants, animals, or bacteria, is essentially the same. The classical events are essentially the same from microorganisms to man. However, the differences in plants and animals are organized and provide their cells and organs in situ with the requirements for what they do?, where they are?; moreover, they profoundly affect the ability of animal cells to develop in isolation.

The green flowering plants are autotrophic and can live in an inorganic world. Even so, the non-green cells of plants, which are necessarily heterotrophic for carbohydrate, have such simple other requirements that they may often be grown (even though slowly) in tissue explants or organ cultures (for example, of roots) in a relatively simple, largely inorganic, medium. Plant cells remain capable of receiving their requirements from the outside world (CO^2 and H^2O, NO^3, SO^4, and PO^4 and mineral elements), where they are very dilute. They can survive in varied composition of their ambient media. Plants are bounded by a cellulose wall and so may utilize their turgor to maintain a thin protoplasmic lining around large enclosed vacuoles; this thin, living layer is, however, in easy contact with the outer air or medium with which the cells of plants are in constant interchange.

In contrast, higher animals are heterotrophic for a wide range of metabolites, and they are adapted to receive, digest, and assimilate their nutrients from complex sources and to distribute these via the blood in a complex way, without direct parallel in plants, to the cells and organs of the body. Moreover, the animal body creates and maintains within narrow limits an internal environment to which its living cells are exposed and which furnishes their requirements in relatively concentrated form. For example, a mammalian embryo develops from a fertilized egg, it rapidly establishes a complex nutrient supply with the parent via the placenta; or, in other forms, the embryo develops first a free living larval form at the expense of the nutrients prestored in the egg.

In higher plants the provision of nutrients to the embryos of higher plants in the embryo sac and ovule, via the endosperm for their attachment in the ovule via a suspensor serves a mere mechanical purpose, while the pro-embryo and its later formed cotyledons absorb nutrients and stimuli directly over their outer surfaces. Thus, if somatic plant cells can be induced to form immature embryos, it is very much simpler to provide for their nourishment externally than for embryos of higher animals, which need a blood supply.

This may well account for the fact that testicular teratomas of the mouse, lacking a blood supply, fail to develop. However, these structures do embark upon a simulated embryogeny and indeed similar asexual forms have long been known to occur in other animals. By contrast, and as will be shown below, proembryos of several plants which originate from free somatic cells can now be caused to form embryos, and plantlets by the thousands; this occurs even in isolation and in a limited volume of an appropriate aqueous solution which behaves, in this respect, like an artificial ovule or embryo sac.

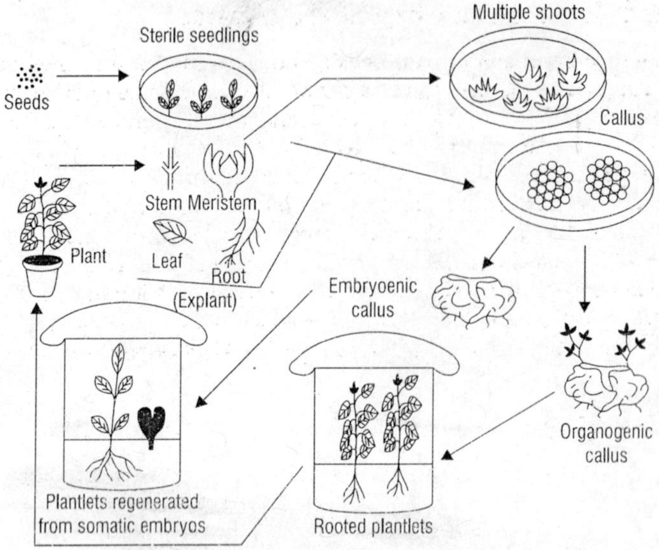

FIGURE 11.3: General presentation of steps used for plant tissue culture.

There is, however, another obvious reason why totipotent development from somatic cells is more feasible in plants than in higher animals. Such animals develop their organs early, they assign to them highly specialized functions and then integrate them by means of the circulating tissue of the blood, by a nervous system spinal cord, and brain, and by highly specialized hormones which are the product of discrete glands. Moreover, these developmental events in animals essentially occur but once. By contrast, higher plants create their organs repetitively and, often, virtually indefinitely. Plants do all this by arranging, in their growing regions, living cells which retain the essential characteristics of the plant and which, during development, depart from, or return to, the situation to be seen in the primary growing apices of shoot and root by relatively small and often easily reversible steps.

The Autonomous Organelles: Their Behaviour During Growth Induction and Morphogenesis

The stimuli that cause quiescent cells of carrot to proliferate and grow also affect all their organelles (mitochondria, plastids, dictyosomes, reticulum and polysomal aggregates of ribosomes in the ground cytoplasm) in various ways. The same stimuli affect the metabolism of the tissue and its ability to form residual or secondary biochemical products.

For example, deep orange-red and carotene-rich plastids occur in the carrot root, but, even so, they become bright green in explants cultured on coconut milk in the light. Combinations of light intensity and of temperature and of diurnally fluctuating light and temperature all have their effects on the pigmentation, but none have yet produced in free cells or proliferating explants the bright orange-red, carotene-rich cells of the normal carrot root. Thus, it is not only what the potentially totipotent cells are that determines what they will do, nor in fact how readily they may be caused to grow, but where, morphologically, they develop.

Sites and Modes of Action of Growth Regulating Substances

How the totipotent cells respond to the exogenous messages that they receive? It would be gratifying if, in response to the appropriate stimuli, the nuclear genes were to pour out messenger RNA's into cytoplasm and there stimulate the appropriate proteins and enzymes to cause the cells to do what they should, when and where they are. This mechanism, essentially bacterial in nature, may in due course be observed to operate in flowering plants, but, so far, attempts to demonstrate it have had meagre success. In fact, it seems as if carrot cells on a basal medium may possess all the idling mechanisms of protein synthesis and require only certain external chemical triggers, which have been described, to set it into directed motion. All this raises the question *whether plant cells really need to ask the permission of their nuclei*, in terms of activated or de-repressed genes, for every task they need to perform.

The Behaviour of Carrot Cells *in vitro*

The genetic inheritance of the zygote, transmitted at cell division to all the daughter cells, conveys to every organelle the inherent capacity to carry out its various functions. However, thereafter the autonomous organelles, each with their own genetic information, may be called into appropriate activity by the great array of simple substances which, singly or in combination, act as growth regulators; these release, wholly or in part, the inherent **totipotency** of angiosperm cells. Thus, there is a vast area open to exogenous chemical control over the responses of otherwise totipotent cells.

Clonal Development from Animal and Plant Cells

There is now good evidence that the nuclei of certain animal cells (*e.g.* of the intestinal wall of a tadpole) retain intact all the genetic information, but they only release this, as yet, in contact with the cytoplasm of an enucleated egg. Perhaps eventually the equivalent of the plant techniques here described may induce somatic cells of animals to embark directly upon an embryological development, and, perhaps, if this is done, they may even be furnished in some way with the equivalent of a parental blood supply.

Such steps present, however, obviously greater orders of difficulty, even if they do not constitute insuperable barriers to the free clonal development of higher animals from somatic cells. Thus, until these problems show signs of being resolved, it seems best to regard the free clonal growth of higher animals from somatic cells as a distant, even if it is a desirable, goal. Meanwhile, however, the techniques of clonal development of plants from free cells open up various technically rewarding possibilities, which are being pursued in this and many other laboratories.

PLANT TISSUE CULTURE: METHODS

The setting up of a tissue culture laboratory needs proper planning. It depends upon space availability, volume of work to be carried out and funds. Usually, the available laboratory space, is be divided into five distinct laboratory areas. These are: *Media preparation area/room, Aseptic transfer chamber area, Environmentally controlled culture room, Analytical room and Acclimatization room.*

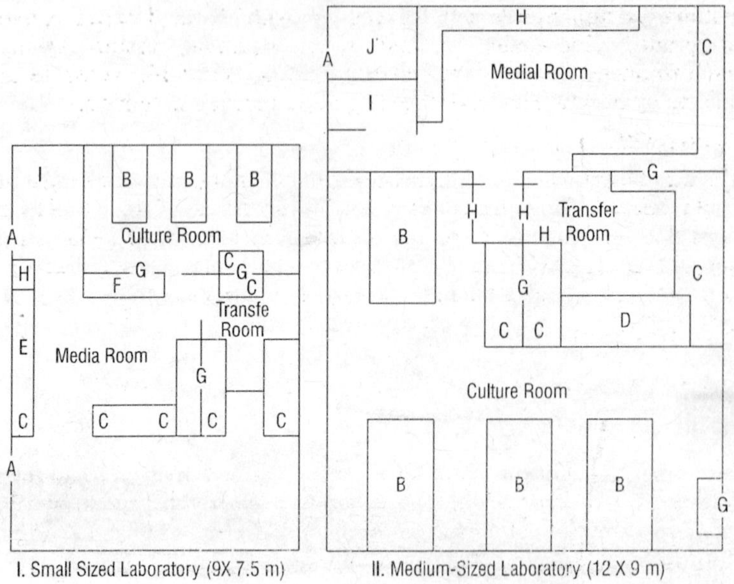

FIGURE 11.4: Various designs of tissue culture laboratory (A) entrance (B) shelves (C) counter (D) laminar airflow cabinet (E) sink (F) gas outlet/burner (G) window (H) refrigerator and deep freezer (I) store (J) conference room (K) library.

Media Preparation: Area/Room

Requirements: Laboratory tables or benches and revolving stools with adjustable height, Hot plate and magnetic stirrers, analytical loading single pan balance with precision of ± 0.001 g, weighing range 0.1 mg-180g, digital read out, Top pan loading balance for quick weighing, range 100 mg-500g capacity, sensitivity 0.1g, Refrigerator and freezer, Water purification and storage system, Glassware washing facility with proper drainage, Gas outlet, Electric hot-air oven range upto 250 ± 2°C and microwave oven, Digital pH meter, Range 0-14 pH, accuracy 0.1 pH temperature compensation 0-100°C, Autoclave preferably horizontal., Continuous supply of single and double distilled water

Cabinets or Shelves

For storing glasswares, plastic wares, chemicals, plugs and appliances required for media preparation are as follows:

Requirements: Culture tubes/conical flasks/petri dishes of various capacities, Measuring cylinders 25 ml, 100 ml, 500 ml, 1000 ml, Cotton for plugs/plastic caps (autoclavable), General glassware's/plastic wares of various capacities such as volumetric flasks, beakers, reagent bottles, pipettes, vacuum filtration system and glass rods.

Culture Media, Washing Powder/ Liquid Detergent, Disinfectants

Requirements: Powder or liquid detergents or wetting agents such as Tween-20, 70% alcohol and absolute alcohol. Glass distilled water, Stock solutions of nutrients of tissue culture media or ready-made/pre-mixed powdered media, Sucrose, Agar (tissue culture grade), Sterile culture vessels with distilled water, Chemicals of analytical grades (Inorganic, organic salts, vitamins, amino acids, growth regulators/hormones and activated charcoal), Coconut milk, yeast extract, malt extract, casein hydrolysate and extracts of potato, carrot and tomato.

Other Requirements

Spatulas, weighing butter paper/boats, stirring bars (magnetic) for magnetic stirrers and stirring retrievers, Brush (flask and test tubes), gloves (disposable 23 cm), mop (household), scoop, towels (household), wastebasket (large and medium), Service lines such as gas, water, electricity, vacuum pump and generator, A low bench/table/desk for culture evaluation and data recording.

Aseptic Transfer Chamber Area

Requirements: Laminar air-flow cabinets to provide constant flow of air across working area, Dissecting and stereo zoom microscopes and lens magnifier, Micro-dissecting scissors, scalpel handles with blades, forceps (various sizes), catheter trays, needles and inoculating loops, Gas outlet, vacuum facility, Tissue paper/filter paper, Sterilizer (dry heat with glass beads) and pipette dispenser (automatic).

Environmentally Controlled Culture Room

Requirements: Racks with light arrangements on timers and controlled temperature (25 ± 2°C) maintained with air cooler or by window air conditioners fitted with temperature indicators, Incubators having dark and light/dark photoperiod with controlled temperature, Rotary shakers of variable speed from 80-220 rpm to take 100 ml or 250 ml Erlenmeyr flasks with arrangement of lighting to provide an intensity of 2000 to 4000 lux, Lux meter to measure intensity of light in culture room, incubator and shaker.

The cultures are usually incubated at 25 ± 2°C under 16:8 light: dark photoperiod. The source of light for the cultures in racks should be make available with cool-day-light (fluorescent tube lights of 40 watts, 2000 lux). It is advisable to connect the controlled culture room with power generator for emergency power supply. Some space should also be kept for incubating cultures in continuous darkness.

Analytical Room

Requirements: Inverted microscope for bright field, dark field with compensating wide angle eye pieces, preferably with photo-micro graphic attachment, Colorimeter for chemical estimation such as chlorophyll, starch, nucleic acid, phenols, oxidising enzymes etc., Low speed centrifuge with continuous variable electronic speed control, chemical reagent racks for qualitative and quantitative chemical analysis, Viscosity meter, Gas outlet.

Acclimatization Room

The hardening chamber needs high illumination (4,000-10,000 lux) and high humidity (90-100%, through mist and fog systems). Humidity is required for conditioning tissue culture plants after taken out from rooting media and transfer to pots under greenhouse.

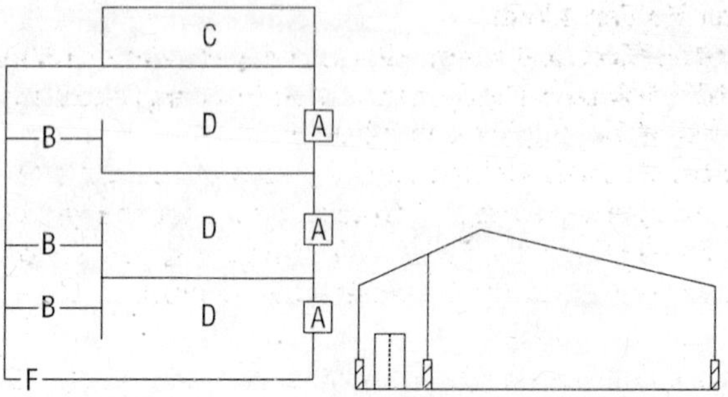

FIGURE 11.5: Design and elevation of greenhouse with three compartments having desert coolers. (A) Desert-cooler (B) Air-vents (C) Water tank (D) Greenhouse chamber (E) Entrance.

Miscellaneous Items

Requirements: Air conditioners, uninterrupted power supply (UPS) and emergency light, Bunsen burners, Permanent markers, tapes (autoclave indicator), tape label (self-adhesive), aluminium foil and parafilm, Fluorescent lamps/tubes, Trays and baskets for cultures, Plastic carboys to store water and other solvents, UV germicidal lamp, Metal racks to keep test-tubes in culture room, Gas lighter/match box, Fire saving, equipment and first-aid box etc., Filter paper, culture trays, culture boxes and culture tube racks.

To ensure the growth and development of an explant, it has to be provided with a suitable nutrient medium and proper laboratory conditions for culturing. These operations have to be carried out under aseptic conditions.

Specifications of Laboratory Equipments

The following laboratory equipements are required for tissue culture.

- **pH Meter (digital):** 230V 50Hz, single phase supply with combined pH electrode, range 0-14pH/0-1400mv, temperature compensation 0-100°C.
- **Balances:** Manual - single pan, capacity 100-200g, sensitivity 0.1mg. Electronic - top loading, precision €0.005g, range - 0 to 1200g.
- **Electric Hot Air Oven:** Thermostatically controlled, range 5°C to 250 ± 2°
- **Microscopes**
  - **Dissecting:** two lenses (eyepieces) 10X, 20X.
  - **Laboratory:** with facilities for bright field, dark field, phase contrast, wide angle eyepiece with photomicrographic attachment.
  - **Inverted:** Wide angle eyepieces, quintuple objective turret adjustable specimen 55 mm petridish holder and photomicrographic attachment.
- **Centrifuge** (low speed): Variable electronic speed control, speed indicator, Amp. meter, timer, dynamic break, 0 starting switch, 230V 50Hz.
- **Electric Autoclaves**
  - **Vertical:** with safety valves, pressure gauge, steam-release cock.
  - **Horizontal:** mounted to tubular stand, heavy hings
  - **Steamers:** With immersion heaters of ejection safety device, size: 31cm x 1 3cm x 10cm to 61cm x 20cm x 15cm.
- Filter Sterilization Equipment: Syringe filter holder: 2.5cm

- Pressure Filter Holder: 4.7cm
- **Manestry Stills:** Electrical water stills, 2 lit capacity/hr of 1.5 kw.
- **Double Distilled Water Equipment**: Built-in energy regulator all glass water stills, heat resistant boiling flask with heater.
- **Environmental Growth Cabinets:** Cabinet with controlled temperature, light and humidity, temperature range 4° to 45°C with timer to regulate photoperiods.
- **Gyratory Shakers:** Capacity: 50 to 1000 ml flasks, speed: 80 to 200 rpm.
- **Laminar Air-flow Cabinets:** Constant flow of purified air, sizes: 0.6m, 1.2 m and 1.8m.

The other miscellaneous equipments which are required for tissue culture are: air conditioners, arrow heads, bunsen burners, deep-freeze, dissecting needles, glasswares, forceps, florescent lamps/tubes, heaters, hot plates with magnetic stirrer, inoculation cabinets, metal trays and bowls (for transport of cultures), tubes, refrigerators, UV germicidal lamps, wooden or metal racks, etc.

ASEPTIC TECHNIQUE

In *in vitro* condition plant cells and microbes have basically same requirements. When the culture medium contains sugar (as carbon source) it attracts a variety of microorganisms, which grow fast than that of the cultured tissue in medium and they ultimately kill the plant cells. It is, therefore, necessary to have complete aseptic condition around the culture equipments, which prevents contamination of the culture medium. Following are the three main sources of contamination of the medium and the subsequent methods to check them:

1. The microorganisms may be present in the nutrient medium at the time of its preparation. These microorganisms can be destroyed by proper plugging and autoclaving the culture tubes or flask. The medium can be completely sterilized by maintaining it at 120° C for about 20 minutes at 15 lb pressure in the autoclave.
2. The explant (plant part to be cultured) may carry microorganisms with it, therefore, the plant part should be surface-sterilized by mercuric chloride (1 to 2%) or by sodium hypochloride solution for 30 minutes.
3. Precautions must be observed to prevent the entry of microorganisms when the plug of a culture is removed during transfer of the plant material to the medium or from one medium to another. The inoculation chamber may be sterilized by UV-radiations.
4. Correct pH of the medium is important. Highly alkaline or acidic pH affects the nutrient uptake in culture tissues. Therefore, the tissue culture medium is adjusted to a pH of 5.6 to 6.0 before autoclaving.
5. Semi-solid and liquid media are most commonly used for growing plant cells. A high concentration of gelling agent (agar-agar, gelatin, silica gel) makes the medium very hard and decreases the nutrient uptake by the tissues. Agar at 0.8% to 1.0% concentration is widely used.

STERILIZATION OF PLANT TISSUES

It is essential to remove dirt and debris from the plant tissue and should be washed in a weak detergent solution and rinsed several times with distilled water prior to sterilization. Some woody tissues, such as buds and twigs, are cleaned by immersing them briefly in a 70% ethanol solution, which wets and spreads over the tissue surfaces more effectively than a higher concentration alcohol solution.

- **Sodium Hypochlorite (NaOCl):** It is the most common chemical agent used to sterilize plant tissues (0.025%-0.25% NaOCl). Diluted household bleach can also be used for this purpose, which normally contains 5.25% NaOCl. It is equally effective and considerably less expensive.
- **Calcium hypochlorite (CaOCl):** It can be used as a substitute for NaOCl. CaOCl causes slightly less damage to plant tissues but tends to precipitate out of solution. To avoid the accumulation of CaOCl on the plant tissue surfaces, sterilization solutions should be filtered or decanted prior to use.
- **Hydrogen Peroxide (H_2O_2) Solution:** Plant tissues can also be surface sterilized using a H_2O_2 (3%-10%). It is much easier to remove from tissues than NaOCl and CaOCl.
- **Other Substances:** Plant tissue can also be surface-sterilized **by bromine water** (1%-2%), **silver nitrate** ($AgNO_3$ 1%) and **mercuric chloride** ($MgCl_2$ 0.1%-1%).

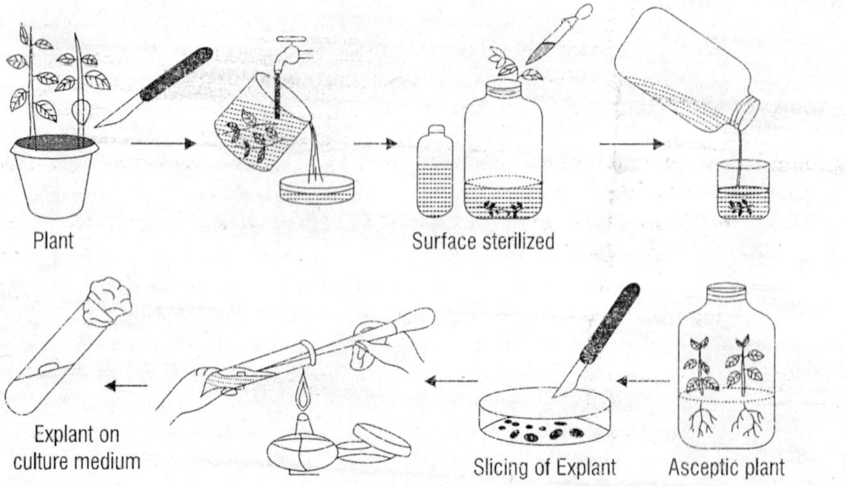

FIGURE 11.6: Diagrammatic presentation of the procedure for surface sterilization of plant material and inoculation of explant for culture.

Cleaning (Preparation of Glasswares/Plastic Wares (Autoclavable)

1. Clean the glasswares/plastic wares in 10% commercial detergent liquid or powder for 1 hr and then in HCl for 2 hr.
2. Remove the traces of detergent and acid by thorough washing with tap water
3. Rinse vessels with double distilled water and allow them to dry over night at room temperature.

Sterilization

1. Plug glasswares such as conical flasks or test tubes with non-absorbent cotton or cover by the plastic caps. Wrap the petri dishes with aluminium foil. Place forceps and scalpels in test tubes, plug the tubes with cotton or cover with aluminium foil. Plug the mouth end of the pipettes with cotton. Wrap them

individually in aluminium foil.
2. Autoclave glasswares and instruments at 121°C for 1 hr.

FIGURE 11.7: Portable autoclave.

3. For dry-heat sterilization, metal instruments should be sterilized in an oven at 140-160°C for 2 hr.
4. Filter sterilization for heat labile amino acids, vitamins, growth regulators, antibiotics, natural complexes should be through millipore filtration assembly using filter membranes of 0.45 or 0.22 μM porosity. Plug the receiver flask with cotton. Assemble the filtration assembly and wrap the filtration unit with paper or foil. Autoclave the receiver and filtration unit at 121°C for 1 hr. Attach the filtration unit with receiver flask with vacuum pump in a laminar flow bench pour solution to be sterilized into the filtration unit. Apply slight air pressure to start filtration. Transfer the desired volume to sterile flasks under laminar air-flow bench. Use a sterile pipette for drawing filter sterilized solution to autoclaved medium.

Surfactants

- **Tween 20 or Triton X-100:** These are scientific reagent-grade surfactants and are often added in low concentrations (0.05%) to chemical sterilization solutions. Their use ensure that the sterilizing agent come in contact with the entire plant tissue surface.
- **Stirring of the Tissues:** Good surface contact is also facilitated by stirring the tissues during sterilization.
- **Ultrasonic Bath:** It is an effective method to ensure good surface contact during sterilization treatment in an ultrasonic bath like those used to clean dentures.

This technique is particularly useful for sterilizing buds and woody tissues that have many small surface crevices and cracks.

After surface sterilization, minimum of three sequential rinses with sterile distilled water are recommended to remove any remaining chemical sterilizing agent.

Control of Bacterial and Fungal Contaminants by Antibiotics in Plant Tissue Culture

Antibiotics are used to reduce, control, or eliminate contaminants in plant tissue cultures.

It is suggested that antibiotics should not replace careful aseptic technique. Most antibiotics are heat-sensitive and cannot be autoclaved. They are usually dissolved in water or another suitable solvent, filter-sterilized, and added to autoclaved culture media that has cooled to 45 °- 50 °C. Falkiner (1990) suggested the list of antibiotics which are suitable for plant tissue culture.

FIGURE 11.8: Tissue culture / growth room with culture vessels.

TABLE 11.2: Antibiotic agents and their mode of action

Antibiotic	Mode of Action
Amino glycosides	Inhibit protein synthesis by interaction with 30S or 50S ribosomes.
Manamycin Neomycin Streptomycin	
ß-Lactams	Inhibit bacterial cell wall synthesis.
Ampicillin Carbenicillin Penicillin	
Chloramphenicol	Inhibits protein synthesis by acting on 50S ribosome.
Glycopeptides	Interfere with bacterial cell wall synthesis.
Vancomycin	
Macrolides and lincosamides	Inhibit protein synthesis by acting on 50S ribosome.
Erythromycin Lincomycin	
Polymixins	Attach to cell membrane and modify ion flux, resulting in cell lysis.
Polymixin B Polymixin E	
Quinolones	Interfere with DNA replication by inhibition of DNA gyrase.
Nalidixic acid, Norfloxacin, Ofloxacin	
Rifampicin	Interferes with mRNA formation by binding to RNA polymerase.

Antibiotic	Mode of Action
Tetracyclines	Inhibit protein synthesis by acting on 30S ribosome.
Trimethoprim and Sulphonamides	Inhibit synthesis of tetrahydrofolate.

TABLE 11.3: Gole and type of explant tissue

Goal	Explant Tissue
Bud culture	Apical and axillary bud
Meristem culture	Apical meristem
Micropropagation	Shoot apex or lateral bud or embryo
Root culture	Lateral roots from adult or seedling
Callus culture/ Somatic embryogenesis	Cotyledons, hypocotyle, stem, leaf, root, any part of seedling
Haploid culture	Anther and pollen

IN VITRO ENVIRONMENT

A piece of plant tissue taken out from original site of plant and transferred to an artificial tissue culture media for the growth or maintenance is called as **explant material**. The choice of tissue depends upon on ultimate goal of the tissue culture project. Any piece of the plant tissue can be used as an explant material. Various factors of an explant tissue source influence the culture on tissue culture media. These are:

1. Physiological and ontogenetic age of organ or tissue
2. Quality of source plant
3. Season in which explant tissue is obtained
4. Size of the explant
5. Aim of the culture

PRETREATMENT TO EXPLANT TISSUES PRIOR TO CULTURE

Many explant tissues specially woody tissues produce phenolics into tissues culture medium, which cause browning of explant material. Antioxidants such as L-ascorbic acid, free acid 0.1 g/l; citric acid, free acid anhydrous 0.15 g/l; L-cysteine HCl 0.05 g/l are commonly used for checking browning problem. The browning pigments are toxic to the plant growth in cultures. Best results are obtained when explants are treated with freshly prepared antioxidant solutions.

Procedure

1. Prepare the mixture of L-ascorbic acid (100 mg/l) and citric acid (150 mg/l) in double distilled water
2. Filter sterilize the solution through a 0.22 μm filter unit
3. Store the explant material in a cold antioxidant mixture and incubate explants in refrigerator at 0°C for 5-30 min. to allow the tissue to soak in antioxidant solution
4. Commercial bleach contains about 5% sodium hypochlorite and thus may be used at a concentration at 10-20%, which is equivalent to 0.5-1.0% sodium hypochlorite.

Sterilization Pocedures May Be Enhanced By

1. Place the material in a 70% ethyl alcohol solution before treating with another disinfectant solution. The use of a two step (two source) sterilization procedure

is beneficial.

2. Use of a wetting agent (Tween 20 or 80 respectively) is beneficial. It reduces surface tension and allow better surface contact.
3. Conduct the sterilization process under vacuum. This helps in the removing air bubbles and provides efficient sterilization process.

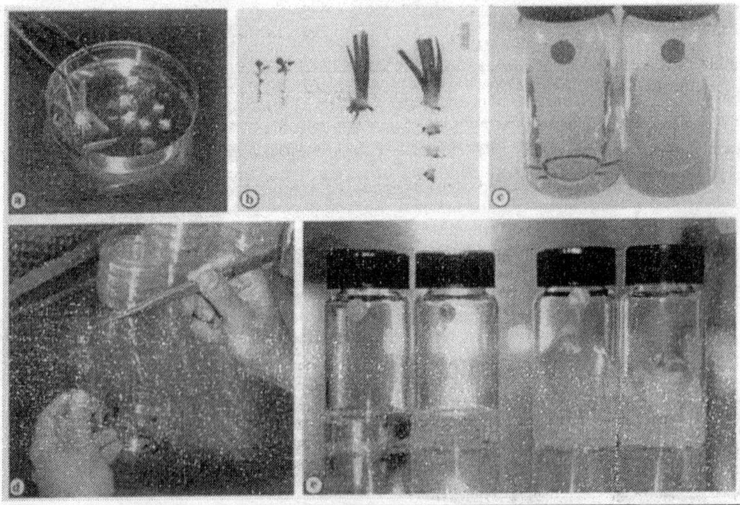

FIGURE 11.9: Culture indexing for cultivable contamination. (a) Aseptic technique is use to obtain tissue sections from the Stage I shoot culture. (b) Shoots with upright stems (left) are sectioned into nodal segments. The shoot tip is either cultured in the indexing medium or transferred to fresh Stage I medium. Cross-sectional stem disks are made from shoots with basal meristems (right). Scale base = 1 cm. (c) Indexing medium is prepared as a liquid and agar-solidified slants. (d) Several tissue samples are directly placed in the liquid indexing medium. (e) Clouding of inoculated liquid indexing medium is a positive indication of the presence of cultivable contaminants in the tissue sample. Development of colonies on the surface of the medium and/or halo in the medium where the tissue sample was stabbed indicated culture contamination.

TABLE 11.4: Commonly used disinfectants for plant tissue culture

Disinfectant	Concentration (%)	Exposure (min)
Calcium hypochlorite	9-10	5-30
Sodium hypochlorite	0.5-5	5-30
Hydrogen peroxide	3-12	5-15
Ethyl alcohol	70-95	0.1-5.0
Silver nitrate	1	5-30
Mercuric chloride	0.1-1.0	2-10
Benzalkonium chloride	0.01-0.1	5-20

Procedure

1. Wash explants in a mild detergent before treatment with disinfecting solution (exclude herbaceous material which may not need this treatment).
2. Within a few days, cells proliferate and a callus culture is obtained. In this, dividing cells form a layer of meristem and build a globular mass of non-dividing parenchyma. Alternatively, they may form small meristematic and build a

globular mass of non-dividing parenchyma. Alternatively, they may form small meristematic zones interspersed in non-meristematic regions, yielding a sort of nodulated callus.

Organogenesis is the development of adventitious organs or primordia (embryoid) from undifferentiated cell mass (callus) in tissue culture. It is controlled mostly by a balance between cytokinin and auxin. A relatively high ratio of auxin: cytokinin induces root formation in callus tissues whereas, a low ratio induces shoot formation. **Caulogenesis** is a type of organogenesis by which only adventitious shoot bud initiation takes place in the callus tissue. When it is applicable for root, it is known as **rhizogenesis**. Anomalous structures when develop during organogenesis is called **organoids**. The localized meristematic cells on a callus which give rise to shoots and/or roots is termed as **meristemoids**.

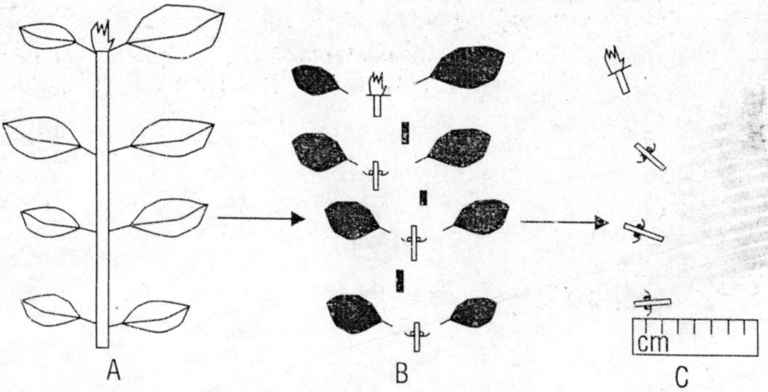

FIGURE 11.10: Diagram illustrating how to cut shoots (A) into single-node segments 2 to 3 cm long, removing the leaves (B), and keeping a small part of the petiole subtending the bud (C). Shaded sections are discarded.

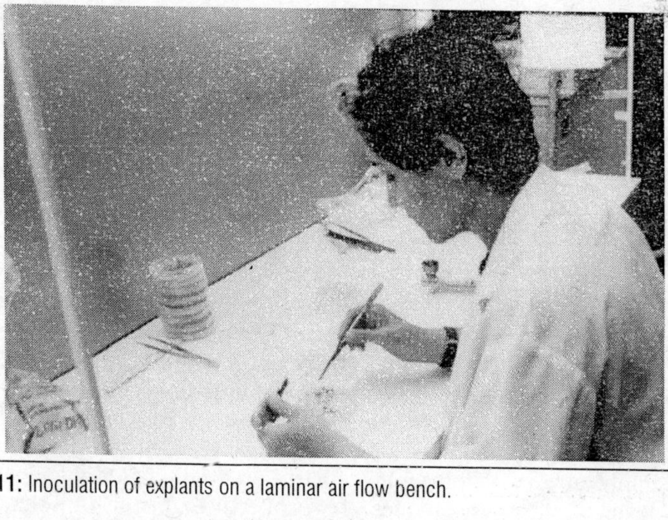

FIGURE 11.11: Inoculation of explants on a laminar air flow bench.

MICROPROPAGATION THROUGH ORGANOGENESIS

The principle of micropropagarion is based on the phenomenon that shoot tip when cultured on tissue culture medium, can develop large number of shoots identical to the parent plant.

The technology provides many advantages over conventional propagation methods such as product development in highly speedy manner, uniforming in product development, large population can be produced in small growing space, quick multiplication of elite and genetically engineered products, and *in vitro* storage of germplasm. The technique also helps in enhancing tissue culture products via specific product format, rooted or unrooted micro cutting, bulblets, and embryos, certified plant material free of pathogens and production can be obtained throughout the year, as most of the multiplication phase is completed under artificially controlled conditions.

MAJOR STAGES OF MICROPROGATION

↓

Selection of an elite mother plant

↓

Explant pieces

↓

Trimming

↓

Repid shoot or embyo formation

↓

Surface sterilization

↓

Washing

↓

Establishment of cultures on appropriate growth medium

↓

Transfer of multiplication medium

↓

Embryo shoots or plantlets transferred to sterilized soil or artificial medium by different gradual weaning processes (gradual reduction in humidity and nutrient levels)

FIGURE 11.12: Procedure of removing plant parts.

Through the use of auxin and cytokinin, hormonal control of organogenesis became feasible. Skoog and Miller (1957) demonstrated that the differentiation of root, shoot, and both root and shoot in tobacco pith tissue is the result of auxin-cytokinin ratio (*i.e.*, the differential regulatory role is concentration-dependent). A high level of cytokinin promoted shoot, and auxin root formation. An equal concentration of cytokinin: auxin resulted in callusing. However, the requirement of exogenous supply of growth hormones for differentiation is dependent upon the endogenous level of these substances. To prove the efficacy of somatic cells to behave as zygote, Reinert (1958) and Steward (1959) reported the first somatic embryogenesis from the tissues of carrot.

By culturing shoot tips of *Lupinus* and *Tropaeolum*, Ball (1946) raised complete plants, which could be transplanted. Shoot tip culture helped Morel and Martin (1952) to recover virus-free plants of *Dahlia* and, subsequently, in rapid multiplication of orchids.

CULTURE MEDIA AND PREPARATION

The success in cell, tissue and organ culture technology is related to the selection or development of the culture medium. As no single medium will support the growth of all tissue

Various media compositions which are frequently used for tissue culture. A literature search is useful for selecting the appropriate culture medium as a starting points in developing a medium for specific purpose such as callus induction, axillary bud proliferation, organogenesis, somatic embryogenesis, anther culture etc. A nutrient medium generally contains inorganic salts, vitamins, growth regulators, a carbon source and gelling agent. Other components added for specific purposes include organic nitrogen compounds, hexitols, amino acids, antibiotics and plant extracts. The Murashige-Skoog medium (MS) (1962), Revised Murashige-Skoog medium, White's medium (1963), Linsmaier and Skoog (LS) (1965), B5 (Gamborg et al, 1968), Nitsch and Nitsch (1969), Woody plant medium (Llyod and McCown, (1981), Somatic embryogenesis medium and derivatives of these media have wide applications for different plant species and for different culture objectives. The decision on using type of media for the metabolic needs of the cultured cells and tissues, is a major factor of success in plant regeneration process.

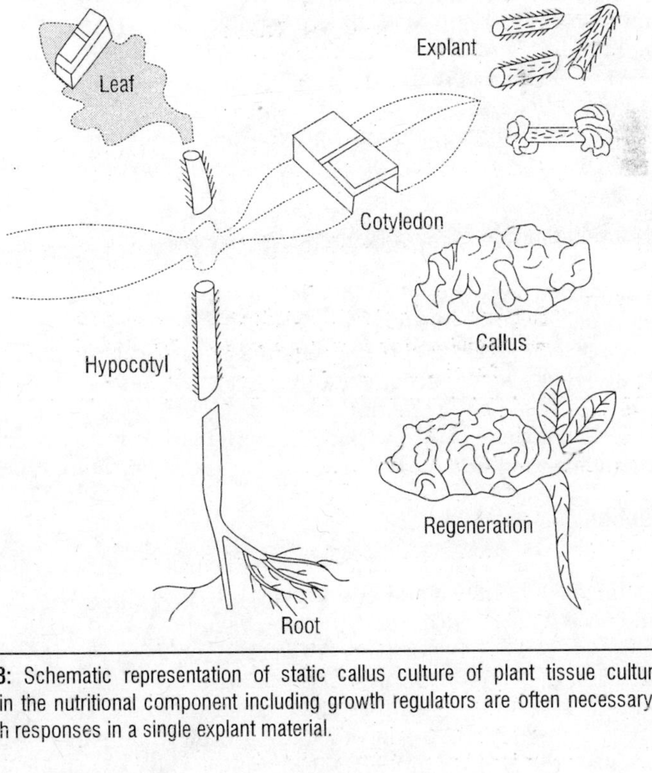

FIGURE 11.13: Schematic representation of static callus culture of plant tissue cultures therefore modifications in the nutritional component including growth regulators are often necessary for different types of growth responses in a single explant material.

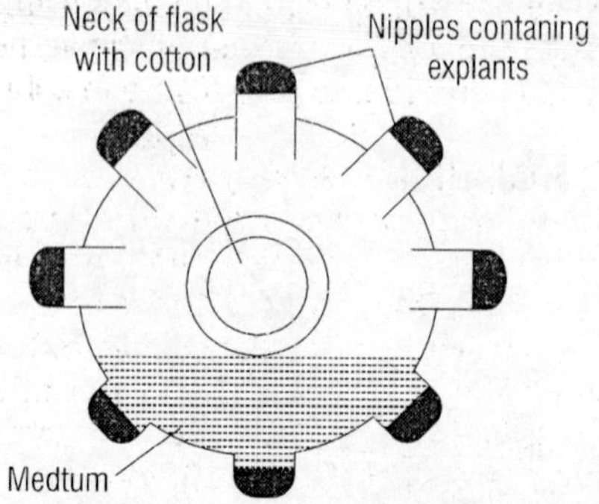

FIGURE 11.14: Tissue culture techniques are now practiced on a grand scale. Special nippled flasks have proved very useful for the liquid culture of single cells and cell clumps.

MEDIA COMPONENTS

Inorganic Salts

A relatively small number of mineral salts are used as component of media for plant tissue culture. The inorganic salt formulations can vary in various reported media, however MS formulation is most widely used with or without modifications. The distinguishing feature of MS inorganic salts is their high content of nitrate, potassium and ammonium in comparison to other salt formulations. The stocks are prepared at 100 X (times) the final medium concentration. Each stock is added at the rate of 10 ml per 1000 ml of medium prepared.

The Na-FeEDTA stock should be protected from light stored in bottle that is amber coloured or wrapped in aluminium foil. Concentrated salt stocks enhance the accuracy and speed of media preparation. Guidelines for maintaining stock solutions.:

1. All salt stocks should be stored in the refrigerator and are stable for several months
2. Always prepare stocks with glass distilled or demineralized water
3. Label the stock solutions clearly with date
4. Reagent grade chemicals should be used to ensure maximum purity
5. The nitrate stock usually precipitate out and must be heated until crystals are completely dissolved before using
6. Any stock showing cloudy or has bacterial or fungal growth should be discarded
7. Do not combine the stock to other stocks unless they are stable and compatible.

Plant Growth Regulators

The four classes of growth regulators are commonly used in tissue culture media *i.e.*, auxins, cytokinins, gibberellins and abscisic acid. The type of growth regulators and concentration used will vary according to the cell culture purpose.

An auxin (IAA, NAA, 2,4-D or IBA) is required for the induction of cell division and root initiation in cultured tissues. The auxins are mostly used in combination with cytokinins. The 2,4-D is used for callus induction where as IAA, IBA, and NAA are used for root induction. Auxin stocks are usually prepared by dissolving in ethanol, I N NaOH or 1 N KOH until crystals dissolved (not more than 0.3 ml/10 mg of auxin), rapidly adding 90 ml of distilled water and increasing the volume to 100 ml in a volumetric flasks. Though the auxins are thermostable, however IAA is destroyed by low pH, light, oxygen and peroxidases. The NAA and 2,4-D are most stable form of auxin.

The cytokinins (KN, BAP, 2iP and Zeatin) are adenine derivatives, promote cell division, shoot proliferation, organogenesis and somatic embryogenesis. They have essential role in differentiation and micropropagation of most plant species.

The cytokinin stocks are prepared in a few drops of In HCl and water to dissolve crystals. Gentle heating is usually required for complete dissolving of crystals. Bring the stock up to the desired volume by adding double distilled water in a volumetric-flasks. Cytokinin stocks can be stored for several months in the refrigerator. Cytokinins are thermostable during autoclaving in media.

The gibberellins are infrequently used in plant tissue cultures as it can inhibit callus growth but for meristem culture after shoot primordia formation are used in plant regeneration and elongation.

The stock solution of GA_3 can be prepared by dissolving in water and adjusting the pH 5.7. They are not thermostable therefore should be filter sterilized.

The abscisic acid is useful in embryo culture and somatic embryogenesis. Abscisic acid is heat stable but light sensitive. Stock solutions can be prepared in double distilled water and stored in coloured bottle in refrigerator. Dilution of stock solutions may be as per the requirement.

Vitamins: Vitamins have catalytic functions in enzyme reactions. The most commonly used vitamins in tissue culture media are nicotinic acid (B_3), thiamine (B_1) and pyridoxine (B_6). They are added in medium before autoclaving. The stocks are usually prepared in water at 100X or 1000X (10 ml per 1000 ml medium or 1 ml per 1000 ml medium) and stored in a freezer.

Carbon Source

The carbohydrates in form of sucrose or glucose (2-5% W/V), as a carbon source are essentially required in tissue culture as cells or tissues are generally not photosynthetically active. Lower levels of a carbohydrate may be used in protoplast culture but higher levels are required for embryo or anther culture.

Sugars undergo caramelization prolonged on autoclaving (too long period) and will react with amino acid compounds. Sugars are degraded and form melanoidin, which are brown, high molecular weight compounds that can inhibit cell growth.

Hexitols: Among hexitols, myo-inositol has been found very important ingredient in tissue cultures, it is considered as growth promoter in tissue cultures. This has an action like carbon source as well as vitamin like. Mannitol or sorbitol is good osmotica for protoplast isolation. It is water soluble and stock can be made up at the strength of 100 X (10 ml aliquots are used for 1000 ml medium).

Gelling Agent

In tissue cultures, washed or purified agar of TC grade or Difco-bacto agar grade is used. The agar must be kept in motion while dissolving otherwise it will burn on the bottom of the flask. The agar must be completely dissolved before it is dispensed into the culture vessels.

The agar can also be melted in a autoclave or in a foil capped Erlenmeyer flask for 15 min at 121 °C and dispensed aseptically into sterile containers by using laminar air-low bench before solidification of agar.

Amino Acids and Amides

The amino acids and amides are very important in tissue cultures specially for the morphogenesis. All L forms of amino acids are commonly used, as L-tyrosine can contribute to shoot initiation, L-arginine can facilitate rooting, and L-serine can be used in haploid embryos induction in microspore cultures. L-cysteine is used for controlling phenol leaching from explant tissues. Amides such as L-glutamine and L-asparagine can induce somatic embryogenesis.

Antibiotics

The various fungicides and bactericides are used in case plant explants on cultures excessively contaminated. These chemicals are toxic not only to contaminants but also to cultures or explant materials so restricted use should be made for additions into the culture medium. The antibiotics are soluble in water should be made fresh and be added to the medium. The antibiotics are soluble in water should be made fresh and be added to the medium after autoclaving by filter sterilization.

Natural Complexes

The natural complexes such as coconut (endosperm) milk (CM), yeast extract (YE), malt extract (ME), tomato juice, potato extract, casein hydrolysate (use enzyme digest) and fish emulsion are used in tissue cultures for various purposes. Addition of these complexes in the medium make the medium undefined, since variation in growth promoting or inhibiting compounds in these complexes.

Antoxidants: The antioxidants such as citric acid, ascorbic acid, pyrogallol, phloroglucinol and L-cysteine are used in tissue culture to reduce excessive browning of the explants. Adsorbents like PVP and activated charcoal are also used for checking excessive browning.

ADDITIONAL REQUIREMENTS

Quality of water, chemicals and natural complexes: Demineralized or double distilled water of high purity are used in making stocks and medium. Glass distilled water is most desirable and stored in clean containers.

Callus-Induction Medium

Murashige and Skoog medium	1.01
2,4-D	1.0 mg
Agar	8.0 g

Prepare 1 litre of standard MS medium. Add the 2,4-D and adjust the medium pH to 5.5 using 0.1 M NaOH. Dissolve the agar in the medium in a steam bath. Dispense the medium into culture tubes or vessels and autoclave for 20 min at 121 °C.

Chlorate Selection Medium

$MClO_3$	600.0 mg
$Ca(NO_3)_2$ $4H_2O$	118.0 mg
$MgSO_4$ $7H_2O$	19.5 mg
K_2HPO_4	19.7 mg
P-IV trace metal solution	3.0 ml

Dissolve the salts in 900 ml of distilled water. Add the P-IV trace metal solution and adjust the medium pH to 7.0. Add additional distilled water to make 1 litre of medium.

Chlorate Selection Medium Overlay

Chlorate selection medium	500.0 ml
Gel-rite ™ gelling agent	4.0 g

Slowly add the Gel-rite a little at a time to the chlorate selection medium while stirring the mixture with a magnetic stirrer. Set the mixture in a steam bath to dissolve the Gel-rite. Dispense 4 ml of the overlay medium into each culture tube; 4 ml should spread out as a very thin layer over the surface of the media in plates.

Embryo Culture Medium

Murashige and Skoog medium	1.0 l
Agar	8.0 g

Prepare 1 litre of standard MS medium. Adjust the medium pH to 5.5 using 0.1 M NaOH. Dissolve the agar in the medium in a steam bath. Autoclave for 25 min at 121 °C. Allow the medium to cool to 50 °C in a temperature controlled water bath. Pour the medium into sterile 100 mm petri plates.

L/10 Green Algae Medium

$Ca(NO_3)_2\ 4H_2O$	0.118/ g
$MgSO_4\ 7H_2O$	0.0195 g
K_2HPO_4	0.0197 g
P-IV trace metal stock	3.0 ml

Dissolve all of the salts in 1 litre of distilled water. Adjust the medium to pH 7.0 by adding 1 M HCl or 1 M NaOH.

Micropropagation Medium

Murashige and Skoog medium	1.0 l
Indolebutyric acid (IBA)	1.0 mg
Benzylaminopurine (BAP)	3.0 mg

Prepare 1 litre of standard MS medium. Add the IBA and BAP and adjust the medium pH to 5.5 using 0.1 M NaOH. Dissolve the agar in the medium in a steam bath. Dispense the medium into culture tubes or vessels and autoclave for 20 min at 121 °C.

Murashige and Skoog (MS) Medium

Macro salts	
NH_4NO_3	1.65 g
KNO_3	1.90 g
$CaCl_2\ 2H_2O$	0.44 g
$MgSO_4\ 7H_2O$	0.37 g
KH_2PO_4	0.17 g
Micro salts	
$FeSO_4\ 7H_2O$	27.80 mg
$Na_2EDTA\ 2H_2O$	33.60 mg
KI	0.83 mg
H_3BO_4	6.20 mg
$MnSO_4\ 4H_2O$	22.30 mg
$ZnSO_4\ 7H_2O$	8.60 mg
$Na_2MoO_4\ 2H_2O$	0.25 mg

$CuSO_4\ 5H_2O$ .... 0.025 mg
$CoCl_2\ 6H_2O$ .... 0.025 mg

Organic supplements

Myoinositol .... 100.00 mg
Nicotinic acid .... 0.05 mg
Pyrodoxine HCl .... 0.05 mg
Thiamine HCl .... 0.05 mg
Glycine .... 0.20 mg
Sucrose .... 20.00 g

Dissolve the salts and organics in 800 ml of distilled water. Adjust the medium pH to 5.7 by adding 1 M NaOH. Add additional distilled water to adjust the final volume to 1 litre.

Ms/C Medium

MS salts and organic supplements
IAA solution .... 8.0 ml
Kinetin solution .... 2.5 ml
Agar .... 8.0 g

Dissolve the salts and organics in 800 ml of distilled water. Add the IAA and kinetin solutions. Adjust the medium pH to 5.7 by adding 1 M NaOH or 1M HCl. Add additional distilled water to adjust the final volume to 1 litre. Add the agar and heat the medium on a hot plate or in a steam bath until the agar melts. Stir the medium occasionally until all agar is dissolved and the solution is clear. Do not let the medium boil. Dispense 8 ml aliquots in 20 × 150 mm culture tubes (approximately 120 tubes of medium).

Myriophyllum aquaticum Shoot-Induction Medium

Murashige and Skoog medium .... 1.0 litre
[2-isopentenyl] adenine (2iP) .... 2.0 mg
Agar .... 8.0 g

Prepare 1 litre of standard MS medium. Add the 2iP and adjust the medium pH to 5.7 using 0.1 M NaOH. Dissolve the agar in the medium in a steam bath. Dispense the medium into culture tubes or vessels and autoclave for 20 min at 121 °C.

M. aquaticum Stock Plant Medium

Murashige and Skoog medium 1.01
Agar .... 8.0 g

Prepare 1 litre of standard MS medium. Adjust the medium pH to 5.7 using 0.1 M NaOH. Dissolve the agar in the medium in a steam bath. Dispense the medium into culture tubes or vessels and autoclave for 20 min at 121 °C.

P-IV Trace Metal Solution

Na_2EDTA .... 0.750 g
$FeCl_3\ 6H_2O$ .... 97.0 mg
$MnCl_2\ 4H_2O$ .... 41.0 mg
$ZnCl_2$ .... 5.0 mg
$CoCl_2\ 6H_2O$ .... 2.0 mg
Na_2MoO_4 .... 4.0 mg

First dissolve the Na_2EDTA in 500 ml of distilled water, then dissolve the remaining metal salts. For greater accuracy, it may be easier to prepare 10 X concentration stock solutions of the Zn, Co, and Mo salts and add 1/10 of these stocks to the P-IV stock solution.

Pandorina ammonium Medium

NH_4Cl	27.0 mg
$CaCl_2$ $2H_2O$	100.0 mg
$MgSO_4$ $7H_2O$	19.5 mg
K_2HPO_4	19.7 mg
P-IV trace metal solution	3.0 ml

Dissolve the salts in 900 ml of distilled water. Add the P-IV trace metal solution and adjust the medium pH to 7.0. Add additional distilled water to make 1 litre of medium.

Pandorina Nitrate Medium

$NaNO_3$	35.0 mg
$CaCl_2$ $2H_2O$	100.0 mg
$MgSO_4$ $7H_2O$	19.5 mg
K_2HPO_4	19.7 mg
P-IV trace metal solution	3.0 ml

Dissolve the salts in 900 ml of distilled water. Add the P-IV trace metal solution and adjust the medium pH to 7.0. Add additional distilled water to make 1 L of medium.

Pandorina Hypoxanthine Medium

Hypoxanthine	68.0 mg
$CaCl_2$ $2H_2O$	100.0 mg
$MgSO_4$ $7H_2O$	19.5 mg
K_2HPO_4	19.7 mg
P-IV trace metal solution	3.0 ml

Dissolve the salts in 900 ml of distilled water. Add the P-IV trace metal solution and adjust the media pH to 7.0. Add additional distilled water to make 1 litre of medium.

Pandorina Uric Acid Medium

Uric acid	84.0 mg
$CaCl_2$ $2H_2O$	100.0 mg
$MgSO_4$ $7H_2O$	19.5 mg
K_2HPO_4	19.7 mg
P-IV trace metal solution	3.0 ml

Dissolve the salts in 900 ml of distilled water. Add the P-IV trace metal solution and adjust the medium pH to 7.0. Add additional distilled water to make 1 litre of medium.

Potato Dextrose Agar

White potatoes, sliced	250 g
Dextrose	20 g
Agar	15 g

Boil the potatoes in 500 ml of distilled water for 15 min until soft. Filter this mixture through cotton to remove most of the particulate matter. Dissolve the dextrose in 200 ml of the potato infusion. Add 800 ml of distilled water. Adjust the final pH to 3.5-4.0. Dissolve the agar in a steam bath or on a hot plate. Autoclave at 121 °C for 25 min.

Trypticase-Soy Broth Medium

Trypticase	17.0 g
Phytone	3.0 g
NaCl	5.0 g
K_2PO_4	2.5 g
Glucose	2.5 g

Dissolve the ingredients in 1 litre of distilled water. Adjust the medium pH to 7.3 by adding 1 M NaOH. Dispense 10 ml aliquots in 20 X 150 mm culture tubes. (approximately 100 tubes of medium).

Yeast Extract Broth (Yeb)

Yeast extract	1.0 g
Beef extract	5.0 g
Peptone	5.0 g
Sucrose	5.0 g
$MgSO_4\ 7H_2O$	0.5 g

Dissolve all the ingredients in 1 litre of distilled water. Adjust the medium pH to 7.0 by adding 1 M NaOH. Dispense and autoclave for 25 min at 121 °C.

Yeast Extract Indicator Medium (Yi)

Yeast extract	1.0 g
Lactose	10.0 g
Agar	20.0 g

Dissolve the yeast extract and lactose in 1 litre of distilled water. Adjust the medium pH to 7.0 by adding 1 M NaOH. Add the agar and dissolve it by heating the mixture in a steam bath or on a hot plate. Autoclave for 25 min at 121 °C.

Sterilization of Media

Tissue culture media are generally sterilized by autoclaving at 121 °C and 1.05 kg/ cm^2 (15-20 psi). The time required for sterilization depends upon the volume of medium in the vessel. Dispense medium in small aliquots whenever possible as many media components are broken down on prolonged exposure to heat. Medium exposed to temperatures in excess of 121 °C may not properly get or may result in poor cell growth.

TABLE 11.5: Minimum Autoclaving Time

Volume of Medium per Vessel (ml)	Minimum Autoclaving (min)	Volume of Medium per Vessel (ml)	Minimum Autoclaving (min)
25	20	500	35
50	25	1000	40
100	28	2000	48
250	31	4000	63

Minimum autoclaving time includes the time required for the liquid volume to reach the sterilizing temperature (121 °C) and 16 min at 121 °C. Times may vary due to differences in autoclaves. Validation with system is recommended. Several medium components are considered thermolabile and should not be autoclaved. Stock solutions of the heat labile components are prepared and filter sterilized through a 0.22 mm filter to sterile container. The filtered solution is aseptically added to the culture medium which has been autoclaved and allowed to cool to approximately 35-45 °C°. The medium is then dispensed under sterile conditions.

Use and Storage of Coconut Water

Coconut water has been shown to stimulate shoot proliferation in many species of plants. Coconut water is prepared from selected coconuts by filter sterilized and frozen prior to use. This precipitation should not effect the growth of the plant tissue. Coconut water can be divided into smaller aliquots, corresponding to standard medium batch size, and refrozen until needed. Coconut water should be used at a concentration of 5-20% (v/v).

RELATED PROCEDURES

Ultraviolet Light

UV light may be divided into three wave length groupings near UV (315-400 nm), mid range UV (280-315 nm) and far UV (200-280 nm). Maximal sensitivity in humans is at about 280 nm. Exposure to direct or indirect mid-range or for UV can cause acute eye irritation after a latent period of 2-24 hrs. Because retina is not sensitive to UV eye damage may result without the subject being aware of the exposure. Skin is also sensitive to UV which may cause for skin cancer. Hence protect your eyes and skin from the effects of UV irradiation by wearing goggles with side shields by clothing, and by limiting exposure.

Preparation of Phenol

All crystalline phenol must be redistilled at 160 °C to remove contaminants that cause or cross linking of DNA or RNA. Soon after distillation add 0.1% hydroxyquinoline. The melted phenol is extracted several times with an equal volume of 1.0 M Tris pH 8.0 followed by 0.1 M Tris pH 8.0 and 0.2% ß-mercaptoethanol, until pH of the aqueous phase is 7.6. Phenol is stored in aliquots at 4 °C under equilibration buffer for periods upto 1 month.

Phenol is widely used as a disinfectant and germicide. It is a dangerously toxic materrial that can produce poisoning when ingested, inhaled or absorbed trough the skin. The toxic effect include headache, dizzines, nausea, weakness, difficulty in breathing, unconciousness and death. Phenol is corrosive to skin, initially producing a softened area followed by severe burns.

1. If phenol is spilled on the skin, flush immediately with large amounts of water. Do not use ethanol.
2. If eyes are contaminated, wash them with running water for about 15 min, call for medical help.

Working with ^{32}P Labelled Compounds

ß-particles with an energy of 1.71 MeV (6.1 meter range in air) is emitted by ^{32}P. Hence ^{32}P labelled compounds must be handled carefully with much caution using shields. When ß particles hit targets, electromagnetic radiation known as

Bremsstrahlung is produced, the yield of which is directly proportional to the density of material used for shielding. Therefore, a low density material may be added to absorb the Bremsstrahlung emitted. Always ear gloves (two pairs if necessary), protect eyes and use dosimeters. Always cover the work area with absorbant papers and use survey meter to check spillage. Eating, smoking or drinking while handling radioactive compounds should be banned. Use special tape to label containers and tubes in which radioactive materials are kept. The maximum permissible burden of ^{32}P is 30 uCi but the maximum permissible burden for bone is only 6 μCi.

Silanization of Plastic and Glassware

Place the plastic and glasswares to be silanized in a desiccator. Add about 1 ml of dichlorodimethyl silane in a small container in the desiccator. Pull vacuum on the system until dichlorodimethyl silane boils. Close the system and allow to sit for about 2 hrs. Open the desiccator in a fume hood and allow to air out several hours. Rinse the plastic and glassware with water and autoclave.

10 X Restriction Endonuclease Buffers (Refrigerate)

Low .... 100 mM Tris-HCl (pH 7.5)
.... 100 mM $MgCl_2$
.... 10 mM Dithiothreitol (DTT)
Medium .... 500 mM NaCl
.... 100 mM Tris-Cl (7.5)
.... 10 mM DTT
High .... 1M NaCl
.... 500 mM Tris-Cl pH 7.5
.... 100 mM $MgCl_2$
.... 10 mM DTT

Preparation of Dialysis Tubing

Cut dialysis tubing into convenient length. Boil them for 10 min in a large volume of 2% sodium bicarbonate and 1 μM EDTA. cool and rinse thoroughly in distilled water and again boil for 10 min in distilled water. Cool and store inrefrigerator submerged in water. Just before use rinse with water. Wear gloves while handling the dialysis tubing.

Lengths and Molecular Weights of Common Nucleic Acids

Nucleic Acid	Number of Nucleotides	Molecular weight
LAMBDA DNA	48,502 (Circular, dsDNA)	3.0×10^7
pBR322 DNA	4,363 (ds DNA)	2.8×10^6
28SrRNA	4,800	1.6×10^6
23S rRNA	3,700	1.2×10^6
18S rRNA	1,900	6.1×10^5
16S rRNA	1,700	5.5×10^5
5S rRNA	120	3.6×10^4
tRNA (E. coli)	75	2.5×10^4

Standards

1 kb of ds DNA (sodium salt) .... 6.6×10^5 altons
1 kb of ss DNA (sodium salt) .... 3.3×10^5 Daltons
1 kb of ss RNA (sodium salt) .... 3.4×10^5 Daltons
The average MW of a deoxynucleotide base .... 324.5 Daltons

Common Conversions of Nucleic Acids and Proteins

I. Spectrophotometric Conversions

IA_{260} unit of ds DNA .... 50 mg/ml
IA_{260} unit of ss DNA .... 33 mg/ml
IA_{260} unit of ss DNA .... 40 mg/ml

II. Protein Molar Conversions

100 pmoles of 100,000 MW protein .... 10 mg
100 pmoles of 50,000 MW protein .... 5 mg
100 pmoles of 10,000 MW protein .... 1 mg

III. Protein/DNA Conversions

1 kb of DNA = 333 amino acids of coding capacity .... 3.7×10^4 MW
10,000 MW protein .... 270 bp DNA
30,000 MW protein .... 810 bp DNA
50,000 MW protein .... 1.35 kb DNA
100,000 MW protein .... 2.7 kb DNA

Half Life of Important Radioisotopes Used

Radionucleotide .... Half life
Tritium .... 12.43 years
Carbon-14 .... 5.730 years
Sulphur-35 .... 87.4 years
Phosphorous-32 .... 14.3 years

Problems and Possible Solutions in Plant Tissue Culture Work

Symptoms	Possible Causes	Possible Solution
Culture contamination	Source heavily infested/ infected with micro organisms Poor sterilization	Improve sterilization method (70% Ethanol, drop of detergent, antimicrobial agents) clean plant material/ select unexposed tissue.
Explant dies	Strong disinfectants.	Use weaker disinfectant/ change sterilizing agents
	Media too strong	Use 1/2 or 1/4 strength
	Wrong stage of growth	Obtain explants at different stage of growth
Culture blackens and dies	Contaminated by micro-organisms	Discard with care. Review sterile technique and sanitation
	Bleeding	Subculture immediately. Transfer more frequently Try different agar concentrations
	Agar problem	Check water purity Try different formula
	Water problem	
	Wrong formula media constituents	
Explant live but no growth	Dormant	Chill for a month
	Media too harsh	Use explant at different stage of growth
	Wrong formula	Lower salts and hormones try different formula
Culture live but no growth	Too cold	Increase temperature
	Wrong medium	Try different medium
Shoots tool long (leggy), and poor multiplication leaves are yellow, watery	Too little cytokinin	Increase cytokinin Change cytokinin/ auxin ratio
Leafy shoots too short	Hormones too strong	Decrease or omit hormones
No multiplication	Too little cytokinin	Increase cytokinin

Symptoms	Possible Causes	Possible Solution
	Needs chilling	Cold store 4-8 weeks
	Too cold	Run cytokinin/ auxin grid
	Requires dormacy period	Increase temperature Cold treat 3-8 weeks
Fat stems, small and pale leaves	Too much cytokinin	Decrease cytokinin/ increase auxin
Unwanted callus	Wrong hormones	Decrease or omit hormones Run cytokinin/ auxin grid
Leaves chlorotic	Contaminant	Index for contaminants
	Too hot	Decrease temperature
	Wrong formula	Try different medium
Leaves succulent (watery), virtrification, abnormal stem, embryos	Osmotic potential upset	Decrease temperature
	Too high cytokinin	Increase agar strength
	Wrong agar	Decrease hormones
	Culture too old	Try different agar
		Transfer more often
Premature rooting	Wrong hormone balance	Transfer more often
		Run cytokinin/ auxin grid
		Increase cytokinin/ decrease auxin
Red stems/ embryos/ cells	Stress	Change light and/ or temperature
		Lower sucrose content
		Increase nitrate (NO_3)
		Transfer more frequently
Non-friability of callus	Too much sugar Not enough NO_3 Culture too old Media composition Plant source	Using number of media having range of hormones. Select most rapidly growing callus. Change to liquid culture and after friable to agar medium.

Source: Bhansali, R. R. (1995)

INITIATION OF EMBRYOGENESIS IN SUSPENSION CULTURE

Steward and coworkers (1958) observed the initiation and development of embryos from differentiated tissue (somatic tissue). However, earlier researchers had already observed these formations in culture, without recognizing them as embryos.

These embryos are named as **somatic embryos**, and their origin is different from zygotic embryos, which result from the fusion of gametes. This phenomenon is also called adventive or **asexual embryogenesis**.

Somatic embryos closely resemble zygotic embryos in their structure, as well as in their physiological properties, especially with wild carrot. Nevertheless, the organization of these somatic embryos is generally more variable than that of zygotic embryos. Abnormalities in shape and size are frequent, and because of this variation they were, at first, called **embryoids**.

In contrast to buds, somatic embryos have a bipolar axis with an apical meristem and a root, and as they have no vascular connection with the mother callus, they are easily detached by the swirling action of the agitated medium.

Three types of medium are required to induce somatic embryogenesis in suspension.

1. The first medium is solidified by agar and contains auxin; this dedifferentiates thesomatic tissue and provokes initiation of embryogenic cells (primary culture).
2. The second medium, which is liquid and also contains auxin, ensures the multiplication of these cells.
3. The third medium, which is also liquid but without auxin, allows the cells to express their embryogenic potential.

It is not very easy to carry out culture in a liquid medium. When the tissue is inoculated, it sinks and rapidly dies because of lack of oxygen. To prevent asphyxia, the liquid must be agitated to dissolve air in the medium. The culture of somatic embryos in a liquid medium, however, has numerous advantages. The swirling medium naturally separates the embryos, which are then easily observed. Thus, the embryos can be fractionated according to their stages. They can be obtained in great quantity and used as a basis for a large-scale micropropagation.

Materials

1. Growth chamber for plant culture. Temperature (25 °C) and lighting are regulated. Lighting must be bright (5 W/m^2), discontinuous (16 h of lighting/d), and provided by Grolux fluorescent tubes (F36W/GRO). This growth chamber is optional, since plant material can also be collected from outdoors.
2. Culture room for tissue culture. Temperature has to be regulated at approximately 25 °C. Continuous light (1 W/m^2) can be supplied by ordinary fluorescent tubes placed above the rotary shaker.
3. Actively growing callus in tubes.
4. Culture medium: The mineral solution of Murashige and Skoog can be used for culture of somatic embryos. The solution described in chapter was evolved for the culture of zygotic embryos because of its low toxicity. It must have a pH of 5.5. In addition, it contains NH_4^+ and K^+ ions, which are considered to be promoters of somatic embryo growth.
5. For mature embryo-growth, use half-strength MS medium containing sucrose at 5 g/l.
6. Sieves (1-mm grid) made of stainless screens (tea sieves from hardware store) to fraction suspension culture and transfer only the smaller embryos into the new flask. Sieves can also be made with nylon mesh filtration cloth (industrial nylon mesh filter).
7. Subsequent plantlet development requires filter-paper bridge apparatus and small pots containing soil mixture.

Method

Generally, three steps are needed to obtain embryogenic suspension culture. First, embryogenic tissue is initiated by culture on an agar medium with auxin; it is then transferred to liquid medium with auxin, and eventually transferred into a liquid medium without auxin.

Initiation of Embryogenic Tissue

Growth initiation is better on solidified medium containing 2,4-D (1 mg/l). When the callus has developed the potentiality for embryogenesis, that is to say 5 wk at least after explant isolation, it is transferred to a liquid medium.

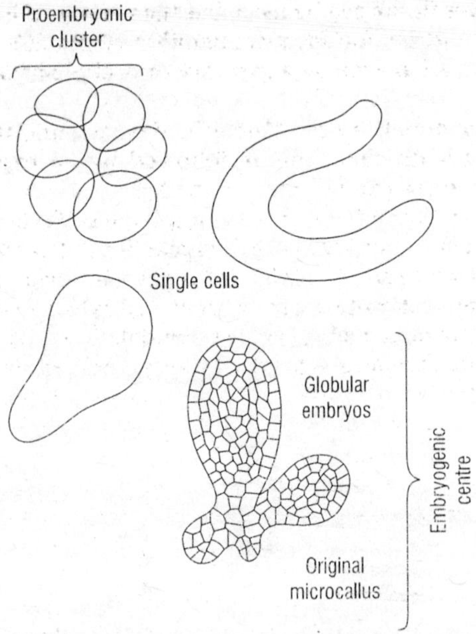

FIGURE 11.15: The embryogenic cells divide in the liquid medium and constitute proembryonic clusters. A certain number of new embryogenic centers will give rise to globular embryos of different sizes (wild carrot).

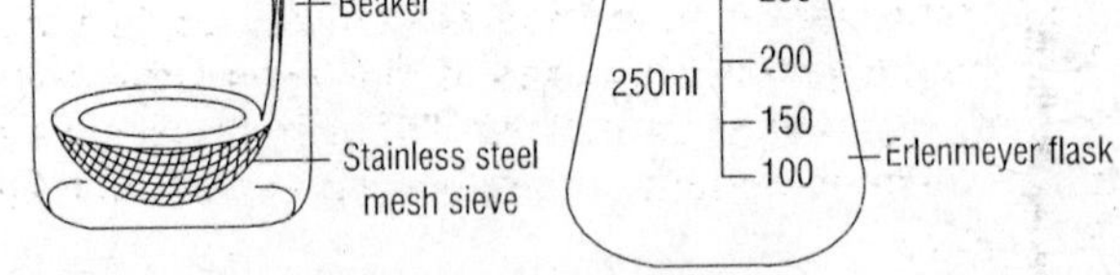

FIGURE 11.16: The metal sieve, on the left, is used principally to remove the larger embryos before transferring the embryonic population into a fresh medium. The nylon sieve, on the right, is used to obtain a homogeneous population of embryogenic cells and synchronize the different stages of embryo development.

ESTABLISHMENT OF EMBRYOGENIC SUSPENSION CULTURE

1. The callus should be removed from the culture tube with sterile forceps and transferred to a Petri dish containing filter paper.
2. Discard brownish parts of the callus, and inoculate a fragment of about 2 g in a 250-ml, Erlenmeyer flask containing 50 ml of medium.

3. Smaller Erlenmeyer flasks can be used, but the volume of liquid in relation to the size of the flask must be, for adequate aeration, about 20% of the volume of the flask. These flasks are placed on a gyrotory or orbital shaker and are agitated at 100-150 rpm.
4. When the plant material is first placed in the medium, there is an initial lag period prior to cell division. This is followed by an exponential rise in cell number. Finally, the cells enter a stationary stage.
5. In order to maintain the viability of the culture, the cells should be subcultured at the beginning of this stationary phase. It is reached in 2-3 wk, and the suspension has to be transferred to fresh medium at regular intervals within this period. In addition, a minimum density must be achieved when cells are transferred to fresh medium, to maintain embryogenic potential.
6. To subculture embryogenic suspension, wait several minutes until the cells are settled at the bottom of the flask and decant almost all the medium. Resuspend the suspension by gently rotating the flask, and transfer one-fourth of the entire population to fresh medium.
7. All these operations can also be carried out, under safer conditions, using a micropipet. In that case, when the cells have settled, aspirate almost all the supernatant above the cells. Then, aspirate one-fourth of the cell population and transfer it into a new medium.
8. A population of cells typically shows a wide range of proembryonic stages visible under the dissecting microscope. It is a mixture of single cells, proembryonic cell clusters, and new embryogenic centers and older embryos.
9. To obtain a certain degree of uniformity, it is necessary to sieve the inoculum when transferring the suspension.
10. The proembryo suspension is passed through a 200 mm sieve and then a 100 mm sieve. In the second sieve, differentiated embryos from the late globular stage are retained and may be examined, while proembryonic cells pass through.
11. When the suspension, which has passed the sieves, is settled decant most of the medium to obtain a suspension with a high density of cells.

Maturation of Embryos

When embryo expression and maturation are needed, the inoculum is transferred to a liquid medium having the same composition, but lacking auxin and glutamine. Cells express their embryogenic potentiality, and if the cells have not been carefully homogenized by sieving, a mixture size in 2 wk. These embryos can be dispersed, in a Petri dish, on an agar medium without auxin, but with small amounts of cytokinins (0.1 mg/l of BAP or zeatin).

When the embryos are mature, they are transferred to tubes on filter paper bridges. The medium is composed of Murashige and Skoog mineral solution diluted by half and containing a low concentration of sucrose (5 g/l). To stimulate the formation of leaves, the tubes must be well illuminated. When the plantlets are tall enough, with a large number of leaves and roots, they are transferred into pots with a mixture of peat, soil, and vermiculite for subsequent development. After their transfer, plantlets have to be protected from desiccation by covering the pots with plastic film for a few days.

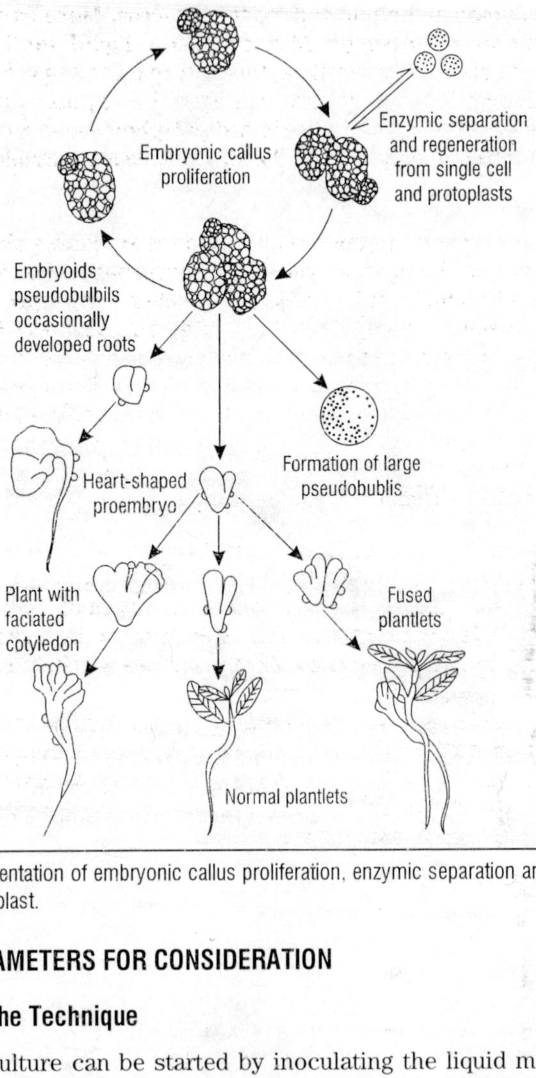

FIGURE 11.17: Presentation of embryonic callus proliferation, enzymic separation and regeneration from single cell and protoplast.

IMPORTANT PARAMETERS FOR CONSIDERATION

Simplification of the Technique

1. Suspension culture can be started by inoculating the liquid medium containing 2,4-D (1 mg/l) with an explant of differentiated tissue isolated directly from the plant.
2. The initiation of multiplication of cells requires the inoculation of a large amount of tissue- about 3 g for 100 ml of medium.
3. The dividing cells will gradually free themselves from the inoculum because of the swirling action of the liquid.

Different Causes of Failures (and Remedies)

Darkening of the Medium

In a number of cases, especially with explants isolated from woody plants, the liquid medium becomes dark after a few days. The radicle ends of the embryos turn brown, and the embryos rapidly stop growing and show necrosis.

Several procedures can help to reduce this process. More frequent transfer into fresh medium can prevent browning. After transfer to liquid, for the first days, when the proembryos are particularly sensitive, the culture must be performed in complete darkness. After this period, the culture can again be exposed to light. This lethal browning is the result of formation of oxidized polyphenols, so antioxidants, such as ascorbic acid and cysteine, may be used, but the results are variable.

No Appearance of Embryos

Not all plant species respond to culture and produce somatic embryos. Some plants give only adventitious buds, and others, no organogenesis at all. if a good experimental model is sought, it is preferable to select some species in families like Umbelliferae an Ranunculaceae, since they offer an easy way to obtain somatic embryogenesis. The explant has to be carefully chosen, since different regions of the plant body do not have the same embryogenic potential. Young material like zygotic embryos and reproductive tissue is an excellent source to initiate embryogenesis. For example, the diploid tissue of an immature anther of grapevine develops into somatic embryos.

Insufficient Number of Embryos

If a culture produces few embryos, suspending the cells in a plasmolyzing solution containing a high concentration of sucrose (1M) for a short time (45 min) is recommended. When these are replaced in normal conditions, somatic embryogenesis is efficiently promoted. The effect may be because of the rupture of intercellular connections and isolation of cells that are reinstated into the condition of the zygote.

Alterations of the composition of the medium can be beneficial. Some authors demonstrated that NAA (naphthaleneacetic acid) is sometimes better to initiate somatic embryogenesis than 2,4-D. Cytokinins like zeatin can help the embryos to mature. The addition of some amino acids like serine, proline, and glycine is generally considered to stimulate embryo growth.

CHAPTER 12

Protoplast Technology

Within the cell wall are the living contents of the cell, called the protoplast. These contents are bounded by a single, two-layered cell membrane. The protoplast contains the cytoplasm, which in turn contains various membrane-bound organelles and vacuoles, as well as the nucleus, which is the hereditary unit of the cell.

The field of tissue culture has expanded at such a rate that the time has now arrived for individual techniques such as protoplast culture to break off as their own individual areas.

Protoplasts are plant cells with a plasma membrane but without the cell wall. The absence of cellulosic cell wall permits advantages to fuse protoplast of similar or on different species and the fused product can generate into whole plants. This is called somatic fertilization or fusion of two vegetative cells to form hybrids.

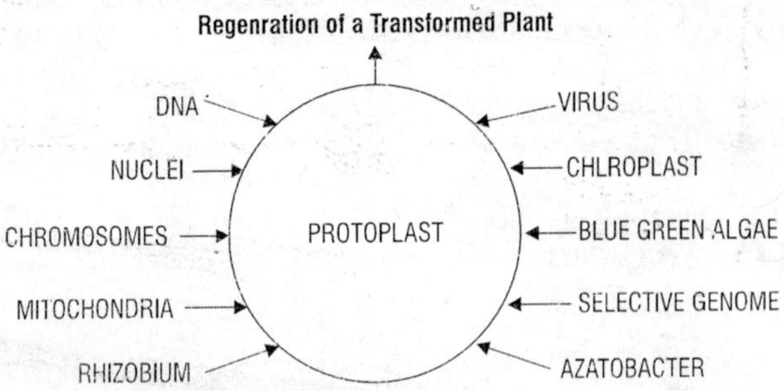

FIGURE 12.1: Hypothetical illustration for the uptake of different cell organelles and introduction of genetic material into plant protoplasts. This technique results into the regeneration of new plant bearing desired characters.

IMPORTANCE OF PROTOPLAST ISOLATION AND CULTURE

The isolation, culture and fusion of protoplast are one of the most fascinating fields of research. The techniques are important for the following reasons:

1. To develop novel hybrid plant through protoplast fusion, genetic engineering would continued to be an exciting area of research in modern plant biotechnology This technology holds great promises to synthesize a plant of desired characteristics.
2. This helps in crop improvement by somatic hybridization and cell modification.
3. The protoplast in culture can be regenerated into an entire plant.
4. The technique in future will be one of the most frequently used research tools for tissue culturists, physiologists, pathologists molecular biologists, cytogeneticists, and biotechno-logists.
5. It provides a tool for isolating protoplasts and exploring the possibilities of genetic engineering.

ISOLATION OF PROTOPLAST FROM VARIOUS PLANT PARTS

Plant tissues .... Young leaves, roots, stems
Flower parts .... Petal, reproductive organs
Callus/cells........ Friable callus tissues/cells
Suspension cultures .... Fast growing cells
Aseptically grown plantlets........ Leaves, stems, roots

Protoplast is the living material of the cell where as an isolated protoplast is the cell from which the cell wall is removed. Protoplasts can be isolated from almost all plant parts *viz.*, roots, leaves, fruits, tubers, root nodules, endosperms, crown gall tissues, pollen mother cells, pollens, pollen tetrads and cells of callus tissues grown *in vitro*. Protoplasts are isolated from cells by two methods:

1. Mechanical isolation, and
2. Enzymatic isolation

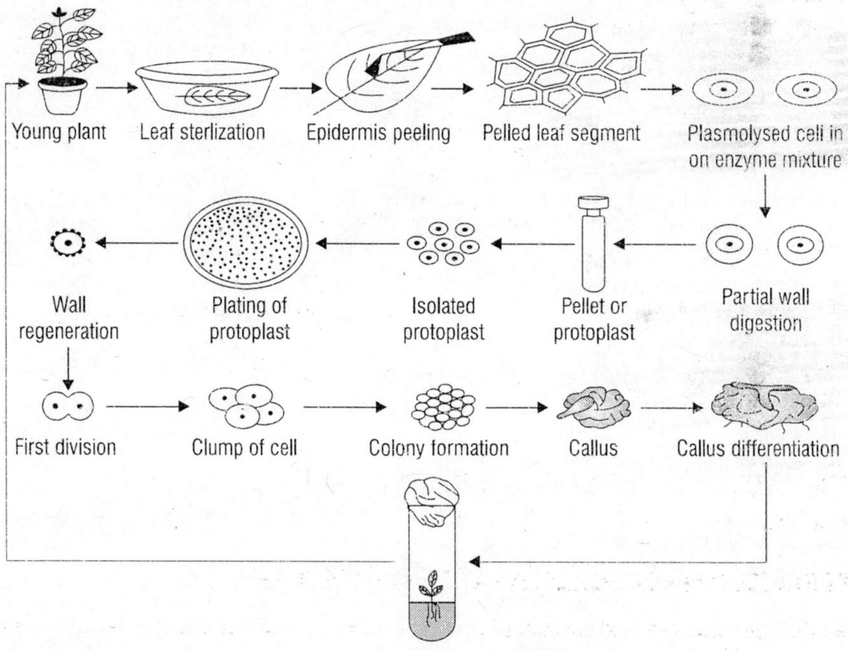

FIGURE 12.2: Systematic illustration of the technique used for isolation, culture and regeneration of plants from leaf protoplasts.

TABLE 12.1: Application of plant protoplast in fundamental research of plant sciences

1.	***Structure***	Cell wall, Plasma membrane, Organelle- structures and biosynthesis
2.	***Function***	Biochemistry, Photosynthesis, Absorption
3.	***Genetics***	Fusion, Organelle and DNA uptake
4.	***Plant Pathology***	Virus, RNA uptake, Pathotoxin
5.	***Differentiation***	Morphogenesis, Embryogenesis

Enzymatic Method

Enzymatic method is most often used in isolation of protoplasts from various plant parts. Enzymatic methods generate very large numbers of protoplasts in comparison to mechanical methods, but in some instances, the enzymes have deleterious effects on plant metabolism. However, the effects of enzymes used on protoplasts (which is unknown) are overlooked in this method. Enzymatic isolation of protoplast has some advantages over mechanical method such as: (i) cells is not damaged, (ii) Osmotic shrinkage of protoplast is much less.

Mechanical Method

Mechanical method, though not most often is in use, still has its merit. It is rarely used because it is an extremely tedious process that results in the yield of only very small numbers of protoplasts. The cells are plasmolysed, causing the protoplast to shrink away from the cell wall. The protoplasts obtained from this method are then cultured on suitable culture medium.

ENZYMIC ISOLATION OF PROTOPLASTS: METHOD

The starting material is sterile *in vitro* shoot cultures or any plant part. In these cases protoplasts are enzymically isolated in a two-step or a one-step method.

First: Isolated cells are prepared (maceration) by treating the leaf or other tissue segment with macroenzyme (a pectinase) in 13% mannitol. The isolated cells obtained from this incubation are purified by filtration through a nylon mesh.

Second: The protoplasts are prepared by incubating these isolated cells in 2 per cent cellulase for about 90 minutes. In the *one-step* method both enzymes (cellulase + pectinase) are used simultaneously. In *one-step* method 2 to 3 hours at 20 to 22° C is adequate to release significant numbers of protoplasts.

Isolation of Protoplast From Leaves: The process of isolating protoplasts from leaves involves a number of steps; these include surface sterilization, removal of epidermis, enzymic digestion and cleaning of the protoplasts.

For isolation, the physiological state of the leaves is extremely important. The leaves normally chosen for experimental purposes should be fully expanded and from young plants (vegetative state, *e.g.*, 10-14 weeks in tobacco). The lower epidermis is removed and is used to isolate epidermal and guard cell protoplasts. The remaining peeled leaf is used for isolation of mesophyll protoplasts. The isolation of protoplast involves four main steps which are as follows: (1) Surface sterilization of leaves, (2) Peeling off the epidermis and (3) Enzymatic treatment.

Method

1. Fully expanded young leaves are surface sterilized by dipping them into 70% ethanol for one minute and then in 2% solution of sodium hypochlorite for 20-30 minutes.
2. The leaves than washed three times with sterile glass distilled water to remove traces of sodium hypochlorite.
3. The subsequent steps to isolate sterile protoplast are taken up under aseptic conditions.
4. Lower epidermis of sterilized leaves in carefully peeled off and the stripped leaves are cut into small pieces.
5. Peeling off process is easier with flaccid leaves than those with turgid leaves.
6. The protoplast is generally isolated by two methods: (i) Direct Method and

Sequential Method.

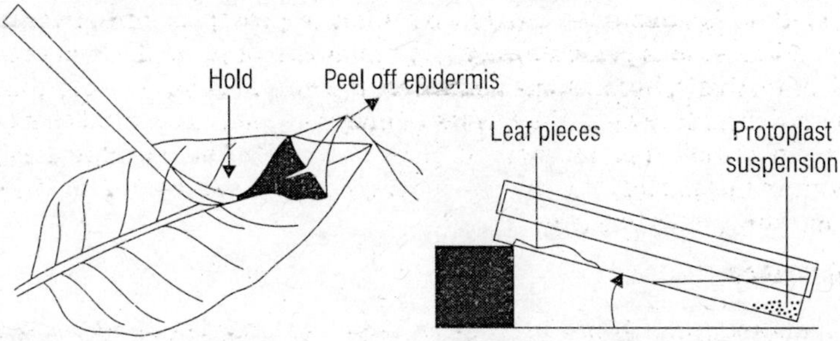

FIGURE 12.3: (A) Peeling off leaf epidermis. (B) Release of protoplasts from peeled leaf pieces after enzyme treatment.

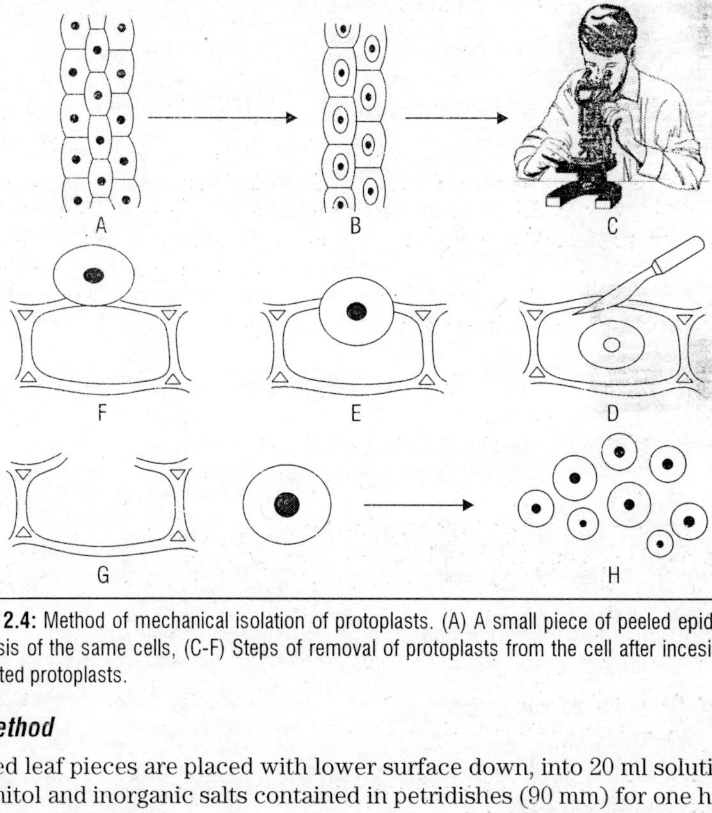

FIGURE 12.4: Method of mechanical isolation of protoplasts. (A) A small piece of peeled epidermis, (B) Plasmolysis of the same cells, (C-F) Steps of removal of protoplasts from the cell after incesion, (G&H) Free isolated protoplasts.

Direct Method

1. Peeled leaf pieces are placed with lower surface down, into 20 ml solution of 13% mannitol and inorganic salts contained in petridishes (90 mm) for one hour.
2. The mannitol-inorganic salt solution is pipette out with the help of Pasteur pipette and an enzyme mixture (20 ml) in mannitol (0.5% macerozyme + 2% Onozuka cellulase in 13% sorbitol or mannitol at pH 5.4) is added and incubated overnight (15 to 18 hours) at 20 to 22° C.
3. The petri plates are then gently agitate to facilitate the release of the protoplasts, pushing the larger pieces of leaf-material to one side with a sterile forceps and

keeping the petridish at an angle of 15 °C.

4. After sometimes protoplasts will settle down in the petridish and then protoplast-enzyme mixture is transferred to 15 ml screw-capped centrifuge tubes using Pasteur pipette.
5. Centrifuge the material at 100g for one minute. This process is repeated for 2 to 3 times and protoplasts are washed with 13% sorbitol solution.
6. For the final washing, 20% sucrose solution is used in place of sorbitol and centrifuged at 200g for one minute.
7. The cleaned protoplasts float and debris settles down.
8. The floating protoplasts are carefully pipette out with a Pasteur pipette leaving behind the remains of mesophyll cells.
9. This method is useful for the isolation of protoplast both from spongy and pallisade parenchyma.

Sequential Method

In this method of protoplast isolation cells are first separated and then transformed into protoplasts. This method is completed into two steps:

Step I. Isolation of Cells

1. The peeled leaf segments are placed into a petridish (140 mm) containing an enzyme mixture (mecerozyme 0.5%, potassium dextran sulphate 0.3% in 13% mannitol at pH 5.8).
2. The petridishes are put into a desiccator for vaccum infiltration of enzyme mixture for about 4 to 5 minutes, then transferred to a water bath at 25° C.
3. Agitate them slowly.
4. After 15 to 20 minutes the enzyme mixture is replaced by fresh one and is again incubated for one hour. By this process cells are completely separated from one another.
5. The isolated cells are filtered through a nylon mesh, then centrifuge at 100g for one minute.

Step II. Isolation of Protoplasts

1. Isolated cells are now treated with another enzyme mixture containing 2% cellulase in a 13% solution of mannitol at pH 5.4 for 90 minutes at 30°C and then centrifuged at 100g for one minute.
2. The supernatant is decant off and the protoplasts are washed three times with mannitol.
3. The protoplasts are finally cleaned with 20 to 25% sucrose solution. This method can be used for isolation of protoplasts from pallisad cells.

Isolation of Protoplast From Shoot Apex

The use of sterile shoot cultures as a starting material for leaf and stem protoplast isolation is popular. One key advantage is that the material is already sterile and does not have to be surface sterilized prior to incubation in the digestive enzyme mixture. Sterile shoot cultures are used as starting material in a wide range of plant species, from potato and tobacco, and a wide range of tree species.

Isolation of Protoplast From Root and Storage Organs

Protoplasts have been isolated directly from a wide selection of roots and storage organs. These include potato tubers, artichoke tubers, onion roots and root nodules.

The enzyme treatments are sometimes slower and often a more complex enzyme mixture is required.

Isolation of Protoplast From Pollen Grains

Pollen protoplasts have some advantages over the somatic cells being found in uniform in chromosome number (ploidy). Protoplast obtained from mature pollen could be used in the study of pollen ontogeny, mutation, somatic hybridization, cell modification and regeneration of haploids. Fusion causes the formation of a normal diploid instead of doubling the chromosome number (to tetraploid) of the new hybrid. It is also possible to regenerate haploid plantlets from isolated pollen protoplasts.

Pollen grain has highly sculptured and chemically complex cell wall. It is covered in a highly resistant coat of sporopollenin, as polymer of carotenoid esters and can be removed by a pretreatment with strong oxidizing solutions.

Pollen grains taken out of the anther lobes are sterilized with 2% sodium hypochlorite solution for 10 to 12 minute and subsequently washed 2 to 3 times with sterile distilled water. The concentration and combinations of the enzyme incubation to pollen grains depend upon their stage of development. Protoplasts are released in many ways described as follows:

Protoplast ooze out through germ pores due to dissolution of pecto-cellulosic membrane by enzyme action. The enzyme mixture used normally contains high concentrations of β-1,3-gluconase, which is capable of digesting both cellulose and callose.

1. Due to mechanical rupture of the exine.
2. By partial dissolution of the exine.

Isolation of Protoplast From Cultured Cells

Actively dividing cells in suspension cultures are proved as most suitable material for isolation of non-germ protoplasts in large amount. Moreover, protoplasts isolated from various somaclones can also be used by plant breeders as raw material for somatic hybridization and cell manipulation. Protoplast isolation through enzymatic activity from older plant parts is very difficult. Protoplasts have been isolated from suspension culture of many plant species like, carrot, rose, *Atropa* sp., sugarcane, etc. Protoplasts can be easily isolated from such cultures by treating the filtered suspension with 2 to 4% Onozuka cellulase in 0.6 M mannitol, for 4 to 6 hours at 32° C in a gently shaking water bath.

Other Sources: Protoplats have also been isolated from coleoptiles, flower petals, aleurone layers and plant cell tumours or galls. The basic isolation technology is the same in all cases.

METHODS OF PROTOPLASTS CULTURE

Laboratory Facilities

Protoplasts can be cultured in liquid as well as solid medium. Concentration of enzyme, intensity of light (300-3000 lux) and temperature (28-45° C) play vital role in protoplasts culture.

Enzyme Mixture and Osmotic Stabilizer (Osmotica)

The composition of the cell wall indictates that the digestion mixture should be able to degrade cellulose, hemicellulose and pectin, and in some cases callose. The number of commercial enzyme preparations available is somewhat limited and very often they are contaminated with a wide range of biologically active impurities of other enzymes- *i.e.*, proteases, nucleases and lipases. They have a degrading effect on the plasma membrane of the isolated protoplasts.

TABLE 12.2: Plant species in which protoplast have been successfully cultured

Source	Enzyme mixture used	Culture medium	Growth response
MESOPHYLL CELLS			
Brassica napus L.	Cellulase Onozuka P 1500 (0.5%) + Rhozyme HP 1500 (0.5%) + Driselase (0.5%) + Hemicellulase	B + NAA (10-6M) + BA(10-6 M)	Plants
	(0.5%)+ Driselase (0.5%)+ Hemicellulase		
	(0.5%) in sorbitol (4.5%)+ mannitol (4.5%)		
Cucumis sativus	Preplasmolysis in a salt medium and cellulase (0.3%) +pectinase (0.4%)+ PDS (0.5%) in 11% mannitol	Harad's medium (1973)	Cell clusters
Datura innoxia	Macerozyme (1%)+ cellulase Onozuka (3%) in 0.5M mannitol BAP (0.4 mg/l) + NAA (0.4 mg/l)	Durand et al. (1973)	Plants
Hyscyamus niger	Pectinol (0.02%) + cellulase Onozuka R 10 in KCl (2.5%) + MgSO (1%) + 0.6 M mannitol	Durand et al. (1973)	Callus
Nicotiana tabacum cv. *xanthi* (2x)	Macerozyme (0.5%) + cellulase Onozuka (2%) in NAA (3mg/l) + 6-BAP(1mg/l) + 0.7M mannitol	Nagata & Takebe (1971)	Plants
CALLUS			
Saccharum officinerum	Cellulase Onozuka 4S (5%) + glusulase (1.5%)+ sorbitol + 0.4M + glucose 5.5 mM	Mod. White's medium + yeast extract	Callus
STEM CALLUS			
Atropa belladonna	Cellulase R10 (1.5%) + in 0.5M sorbitol + NAA (2 mg/l) + kinetin (0.5mg/l)	Mod. MS +	Embryoids & plants
OVULAR CALLUS			
Citrus sinensis	Cellulase (1%) + pectinase (1%) + PDS (0.3%) in 0.14 M sucrose + 0.28M mannitol + 0.28M sorbitol	Murashige & Tucker's (1969) basal medium	Embryoids
PERICARP CALLUS			
Vitis vinifera	Cellulase Onozuka SS (2%) +	B5 + Casein hydrolysate	Callus

Source	Enzyme mixture used	Culture medium	Growth response
	meserozyme (1%) in 0.1M CaCl2 + 0.14M KCl + (2000 mg/l) kinetin + 0.2 mg/l) +NAA (0.1 mg/l)		
CROWN GALL			
Parthenocissus tricuspidata	Mecerozyme R 10 (0.01%)+ cellulase + NAA (0.1 mg/l) + Onozuka R 10 (2%) in 13% mannitol	Nagata & Tabeke (1971)	Callus

Following are the commercial enzyme preparations used for isolation of protoplasts.

1. Onozuka R10 cellulase (Kinki Yakult Biochemical, Nishinomiya, Japan)
2. Cellulase R10 (Kinki Yakult Biochemical, Nishinomiya, Japan)
3. Macerozyme R10, pectinase (Calbiochem-Behring, San Diego, California, USA)
4. Hemicellulase (Rohm and Hass Co. Philadelphia, PA., USA)
5. Driselase, cellulase, (Kyowa Hakko Kogyo Co., Tokyo, Japan)
6. Cellulysin, cellulase (Calbiochem-Behring, San Diego, California, USA)
7. Pectinase (Sigma, St. Louis, MO, USA)
8. Macerase (Calbiochem-Behring, San Diego, California, USA)
9. Rhozyme HP 150, Hemicellulase (Rohm and Hass Co. Philadelphia, PA., USA)

The enzyme mixture is normally dissolved in culture media together with an osmotic stabilizer. Calcium (2 to 10mM) is a necessary component and phosphate (0.5 to 2.0 mM) appears to stabilize the isolated protoplasts.

After the digestion of cell wall the isolated protoplast is subject to osmotic stress. If an osmotic stabilizing agent is not included in the medium the isolated protoplasts would take in water by the process of osmosis and would eventually burst as there is no cell wall to constrain the cells. The osmotic agents may be sugar, alcohols, sorbitol or mannitol (13% w/v). Sucrose can be used for this purpose. The concentration of osmoticum should not be high because it causes protoplast shrinkage.

Protoplast is cultured in liquid medium in Erlenmeyer flasks or in microchambers. Microchamber is prepared by placing two 22 mm^2 coverslips about 18-22 mm apart on a drop of heavy mineral oil on a slide. A drop of medium containing protoplasts is placed in between the two coverslips. A third coverslip is then gently placed on the medium and finally sealed with mineral oil or parafilm. Through this method protoplast can be cultured in a small amount and for a limited time.

PURIFICATION OF ISOLATED PROTOPLASTS

Protoplasts contain cell debris and broken cell organelles in medium. A number of methods have been used to separate the intact protoplasts from this surrounding cellular debris.

Sedimentation and Washing

1. The crude protoplast suspension in osmotically adjusted medium is decanted into a conical tip centrifuge tube.
2. It is centrifuged at low speed (50-100 x g/5 min). Under these conditions the intact protoplasts accumulate in the form a soft pellets in the tip of the tube.

3. The supernatant, containing the broken cells debris, cell wall, and cell organells etc., are then carefully pipetted off.
4. The pellets are then gently resuspended in fresh culture medium containing mannitol, and rewashed. This process is repeated two or three times.

Flotation

As intact protoplasts have a relatively low density as compared to other cell organelles, many types of gradients have been used that allow the protoplasts to float and for the sedimentation of cell debris.

A concentrated solution of mannitol, sorbitol or sucrose may be combined with the enzyme-protoplast mixture in a Babcock bottle and then centrifuged at low speed.

Protoplasts can be pipetted off from the top of the tube. The concentration of sucrose used for flotation varies from 0.3 to 0.6 M. The flotation method causes less loss due to damage than the pelleting and washing method. However, the high osmotic concentrations of solution may cause osmotic stress to the protoplasts, which may delay the wall formation or leads to eventual loss of the viability.

Other Purification Methods

Other more complex pelleting and flotation systems are also used for protoplast purification. Some workers have layered crude protoplast preparation of *Hyoscyamus muticus* onto 20% Percol (polymer of solicos). After centrifugation debris was in the lower half of the gradient and protoplasts floated to the top.

After obtaining a reasonably pure isolated protoplast preparation, it is important to determine what proportion of the protoplasts is alive and to be able to culture.

PROTOPLAST VIABILITY TESTING

In early days the viability of protoplast is determined by observing its cytoplasmic streaming, exclusion of Evans Blue dye, changes in protoplast size induced by changes in the level of osmoticum and measure of photosynthetic and respiratory activity. Most of these methods have proved to be rather unreliable for determining viability.

The most frequently used methods for estimation of viability is the use of fluorescein diacetate (FDA). As the FDA accumulates within the plasma membrane, viable protoplasts fluoresce green or white. Protoplast preparation treated with FDA (normally 0.01%) should be observed within 5 to 15 minutes, because after this period FDA dissociates from the membrane.

Another stain commonly used is **phenosafranine** (0.01%). This stain detects dead protoplasts, which turn red in the presence of the dye. Viable protoplasts remain unstained even after 2 hours of staining.

Isolated protoplast can be cultured in several ways of which agar-embedding technique in small petridish is commonly followed. In petridishes, embedding of protoplasts in solid agar medium is known as **plating of protoplasts**.

General Steps of Protoplast Culture

Dilute the protoplast culture medium ($1 \times 10_5$ protoplasts/ml) and transfer 2 ml of culture medium containing protoplasts in an airtight Petri dish. Add 1 ml of protoplast culture medium containing double agar concentration (1.6%) to each petri dish containing protoplasts in liquid. For this, melt the medium having agar and store at 30-35° C until required. Higher temperature is injurious to protoplasts. Mix gently but quickly by rotating petri dish. Allow the medium to set and seal petri dishes with parafilm. Incubate petri dishes down in an incubator at 25 ± 2° C with continuous illumination at 2000 lux. Protoplasts can also be cultured by suspension culture (without agar) and droplet culture method by placing of protoplast suspension containing protoplasts plate ($1 \times 10_4$ or $1 \times 10_5$ ml). Incubation procedure is same as described above.

The plated protoplast can be handled very easily and the agar medium gives good support to the protoplast. Though various techniques have been developed for the culture of plant protoplasts however, the style of the culture often depends upon the objective of the experiment.

CULTURE MEDIA FOR PROTOPLAST CULTURE

Protoplast Culture Media for PC I Group

F.5 Medium (Frearson et al., 1973)

Constituents	Concentrations (mg/l)	Constituents	Concentrations (mg/l)
$CaCl_2.2H_2O$	850.0	$ZnSO_4.7H_2O$	4.3
$CuSO_4.5H_2O$	0.025	BAP	1.0
$CoSO_4.7H_2O$	0.15	Biotin	0.05
$FeSO_4.7H_2O$	13.9	Folic acid	0.5
H_3BO_3	3.1	Glycine	1.0
KH_2PO_4	353.6	Mannitol	130,000.0
KI	0.498	Meso-inositol	100.0
KNO_3	525.0	NAA	2.0
$MgSO_4.7H_2O$	739.0	Nicotinic acid	5.0
$MnSO_4.4H_2O$	11.15	Pyridoxine HCl	0.5
Na_2EDTA	18.75	Sucrose	10,000.0
$Na_2MoO_4.2H_2O$	0.125	Thiamine HCl	1.0
NH_4NO_3	412.25	pH	5.8

Nagata and Takeba Medium (1971)

Constituents	Concentrations (mg/l)	Constituents	Concentrations (mg/l)
$CaCl_2.2H_2O$	220.0	Na_2EDTA	37.3
$CuSO_4.5H_2O$	0.025	$Na_2MoO_4.2H_2O$	0.25
$CoSO_4.7H_2O$	0.030	NH_4NO_3	825.0
$FeSO_4.7H_2O$	27.8	$ZnSO_4.4H_2O$	8.6
H_3BO_3	6.2	BAP	1.0
KH_2PO_4	680.0	Mannitol	130,000.0
KI	0.83	Meso-inositol	100.0
KNO_3	950.0	NAA	3.0
$MgSO_4.7H_2O$	1233.0	Sucrose	10,000.0
$MnSO_4.4H_2O$	22.3	Thiamine HCl	1.0
		pH	5.8

V 47 (Binding, 1974)

Constituents	Concentrations (mg/l)	Constituents	Concentrations (mg/l)

Constituents	Concentrations (mg/l)	Constituents	Concentrations (mg/l)
$CaCl_2.2H_2O$	735.0	BAP	0.4
$CuSO_4.5H_2O$	0.015	Biotin	0.04
$CoCl_2.6H_2O$	0.015	Folic acid	0.4
H_3BO_3	2.0	Glycine	1.4
KH_2PO_4	68.0	Glucose	99,000.0
KI	0.25	Mannitol	8,19,000.0
KNO_3	1480.0	Meso-inositol	10.0
$MgSO_4.7H_2O$	984.0	NAA	1.52
$MnSO_4.H_2O$	5.0	Nicotinic acid	2.0
Na_2EDTA	37.0	Pyridoxine HCl	0.7
$Na_2MoO_4.2H_2O$	0.1	Sucrose	1,70,000.0
NH_4NO_3	1444.0	Thiamine HCl	4.0
$ZnSO_4.7H_2O$	1.5	pH	5.8

Murashige and Skoog Medium

For protoplast culture, use MS culture medium as described for tissue culture supplemented with 13% mannitol (w/v).

Modified B5 Medium (Kartha et al., 1974)

Constituents	Concentrations	Constituents	Concentrations
+ Sorbitol	4.55% w/v	$CaCl_2.2H_2O$	0.0875%
Mannitol	4.55% w/v	2,4-D	2.3×10^{-6}M
d-glucose	0.25% w/v	BAP	10^{-6}M
D-ribose	0.125% w/v	NAA	10^{-6}M
N-Z anime	0.015% w/v	Calculated molarity	0.52

Protoplast Culture Media PC II Group

Media calculated under PC I Group with minor changes. The changes are: the concentration of mannitol/sorbitol present in media individually or in combination reduced by half. Concentration of agar in the medium is 0.8%.

Protoplast Culture Media PC III Group

Media described PC I Group with following minor changes:

1. Mannitol/sorbitol/D-glucose/D-ribose individually or in combination are omitted in the media.
2. The sucrose concentration in all media is adjusted to 2% w/v.
3. PC III Group media may be prepared with 1.6% or 0.8% agar depending on the mode of protoplast culture.

Composition of the digestion mixture, wash medium and regeneration medium used for isolation and culturing of protoplasts.

Digestion Mixture

Salts and Vitamins of Murashige & Skoog (MS)

Cellulysin 1.0%
Macerase 0.5%
Rhozyme 1.0%
$CaCl_2$ .... 4.5 mM (0.5 g/l)
Mannitol .... 0.3 M (54.7 g/l)
Sorbitol .... 0.3 M (54.7 g/l)

MES.. 0.3 mM (640 mg/l)
pH.. 5.7
Filter Sterilize Washing Medium (MS)
$CaCl_2$.. 4.5 mM
Sorbitol.. 0.3 M
Mannitol.. 0.3 M
pH.. 5.7

Autoclave Regeneration Medium (MS)		Vitamins, Sugar and sugar alcohols (pH 5.7)		Sugar and Sugar Alcohols (g/l)	
Sucrose	20 g/l	Nicotinamide	1.0	Fructose	0.125
2,4-D	0.5 mg/l	Pyridoxine HCl	1.0	Fibose	0.125
Kinetin	1.0 mg/l	Thiamine HCl	1.0	Xylose	0.125
Coconut water	2.0% (v/v)	D-calcium pantothenate	0.5	Mannose	0.125
Inositol	100 mg/l	Folic acid	0.2	Cellobiose	0.125
Casein hydrolysate	200 mg/l	p-aminobenzoic acid	0.01	Sorbitol	54.7
Sodium pyruvate	5.0 mg/l	Choline chloride	0.5	Mannitol	54.7
Citric acid	10.0 mg/l	Riboflavin	0.1		
Malic acid	10.0 mg/l	Ascorbic acid	1.0		
Fumaric acid	10.0 mg/l	Vitamin B12	0.01		

Agar Embeded Culture

In this method protoplasts may be allowed to regenerate a new cell wall in liquid culture before embedding or may be embedded directly after isolation. The original method of Nagata and Takebe for the isolated protoplasts is mixed with 1.0% agar-culture medium and maintained at 40 to 45° C. Small amount of the agar (liquid) protoplasts mixture is then poured into sterile petriplates.

Microchambers

This method is used for observation of plant cells. It is quite common. The number of possible designs of chamber is enormous. A chamber is constructed of a small plastic ring with a coverslip on top. The joints of the system are sealed with mineral oil. The simplest form is to hold a droplet between two coverslips with a ring of mineral oil around to form a seal. The mineral oil prevents evaporation of media; this can be a major problem with protoplast cultures as the osmotic concentration of the media rises. Another good sealing substance, which is easy to handle is clear nail polish.

Hanging Drop Cultures (HDC) Techniques

To avoid evaporation of the media while observing protoplast, this method is used. Drop can be placed in the depression of a specially prepared hanging drop-slide, which is then undersealed with a coverslip and oil, or the drops are placed on the lid of a petridish. The petridish contains mannitol solution to maintain the humidity. The dish is sealed with parafilm.

Multidrop Array (MDA) Techniques

This is a refinement and amplification of the hanging drop technique. Through this technique it becomes easier to screen a wide range of nutritional and hormonal factors rapidly (using a small amount of plant material, less than 1g of plant tissue). The system can be described as follows:

1. Prepare a dilution series of two variables A and B, so as to have tubes A_1 to A_{10}, B_1 to B_{10}, likewise 100 possible combinations can be prepared, i.e., A_1B_1, A_2B_2 ..... $A_{10}B_{10}$, etc.
2. To these 100 different media (1.0cm^3 each) add 0.1cm^3 of protoplast suspension prepared in basal media at 20 times the minimum planting density.
3. For each combination, *i.e.* A_1B_1, A_1B_2, etc. make, 49 drops + 4 control drops in order on the lid of a petridish and label the dish, *i.e.* A_1B_1.
4. To each drop add 20 μl of another variable media component previously prepared C-C7, 11-17. Thus each dish contains 49 different media combinations.
5. A total of 4900 different media compositions each inoculated with cells have thus been prepared on only 100 petriplates.
6. 20 cm^3 of mannitol is added to the base of the dish. The lid with attached droplets is inverted into position and the plates are sealed and incubated.
7. After a suitable incubation period the plates can be easily evaluated microscopically to determine which media combination, has given the most successful growth.
8. The best method for the culture of protoplast is by plating them in a medium containing 1.2% agar. In this condition, protoplasts grow best by good number of divisions and can be handled conveniently. Moreover, it could be observed under the microscope.

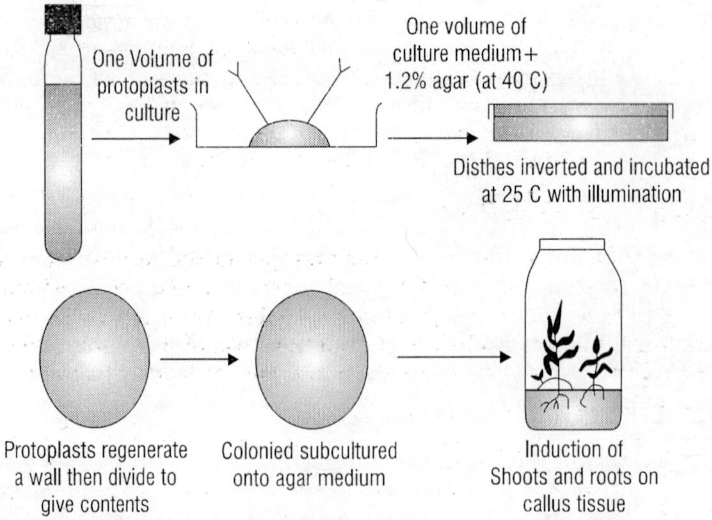

FIGURE 12.5: Diagrammatic presentation of culture of protoplast by agar embedding technique in small petridishes.

GROWTH AND DIVISION OF PROTOPLAST

For the growth and nuclear division, the regeneration of cell wall is not seems to be a prerequisite in protoplast culture. In *Convolvulus* sp. protoplasts undergo one or two nuclear division prior to cytokinesis. The same was observed in *Haplopappus* spp.

It has been observed that for the rapid growth of protoplasts frequent subculturing in mannitol free medium is necessary. Protoplasts donot grow in large colonies on high osmotic medium. Its growth gradually shows a downward trend which ultimatly inhibited altogether. The colonies, therefore, should be picked up along with small pieces of agar and then transferred on the top of another medium to avoid any damage to protoplasts by rough handling with the forceps.

Protoplast Culture: Regeneration of Cell Wall

In culture, protoplasts start developing a wall around itself within few hours and it takes only few days to complete the process. Wall materials are progressively deposited at the surface of the plasmalemma. The cellulose is deposited either between the plasmalemma and the multilamellar wall material or directly on the plasmalemma. The nature of biosynthesis of the cell wall depends on the plant material and the system of protoplast culture.

The newly built cell wall can be observed either by plasmolyzing the protoplast by transferring it in a hypertonic solution, or by staining the cell wall with **calcofiuor white** fluorescent stain (0.1%). However, electron microscopic studies and freeze etching studies have revealed much about the structure and progressive development of cell wall around the protoplast in culture medium.

1. Observe regularly the regeneration of cell wall, cell division and small callus formation under inverted microscope
2. Examine cell wall formation in protoplasts with a droplet of 0.1% calcofluor white R, American Cyanamid, Bound Brook, N. J. USA, in 0.4 M sorbitol solution on a slide. The cell wall regenerated protoplasts fluoresce
3. Small cluster of calli are observed after 2-3 weeks of culturing protoplasts
4. Subculture the cell clusters on a freshly prepared protoplast culture medium with or without 1/2 the intial mannitol and 0.8-1.6% agar.

Development of Callus/Whole Plant

Soon after the formation of wall around the protoplasts, the reconstituted cells show considerable increase in size and first divisions usually occur within 7 days. Subsequent divisions give rise to small cell colonies. After 2-3 weeks macroscopic colonies are formed which can be transferred to an osmotic free medium to develop a callus. The callus may be induced to undergo organogenic differentiation, or whole plant regeneration.

TABLE 12.3: Name of some of the families and species in which shoot differentiation of plant regeneration has been achieved from cultured protoplasts

Family	Species
Compositae	*Cichorium intybus, Lactuca sativa cultivars (L. serriola, L. saligna), Petasites japonicus, Senecio vulgaris*
Cruciferae	*Arabidopsis thaliana, Brassica campestris (B. carinata, B. juncea, B. napus, B. nigra, B. oleraceae var. capitata), Sinapis alba*
Cucurbitaceae	*Cucumis sativus*

Family	Species
Euphorbiaceae	*Manihot esculenta*
Gramineae	*Bromus inermis, Oryza sativa, Pennisetum americanum, Saccharum spp., Triticum aestivum*
Leguminosae	*Glycine argyrea, G. canescens, G. clandestina, G. max, Medicago arborea, M. coerulea, M. difalcata, M. falcata, M. glutiniana, M. hemicyla, M. sativa cultivars (M. varia), Psophocarpus tetragonolobus, Trifolium hybridum, T. repens, T. rubens*
Liliaceae	*Asparagus officinalis, Hemerocallis sp.*
Linaceae	*Linum usitatissimum, L. strictum, L. lewissii*
Magnoliaceae	*Liriodendron tulipfera*
Ranunculacea e	*Ranunculus sceleratus*
Rutaceae	*Citrus aurantifolia, C. grandis, C. limon, Citrus medica, C. paradisi, C. reticulata, C. sinensis*
Salicaceae	*Populus tremula, P. alba x P. grandidentata, P. nigra var. Butulifolia x P. trichocarpa*
Santalaceae	*Santalum album*
Solanaceae	*Atropa belladonna, Capsicum annuum, Datura metel, D. meteloides, D. innoxia, Hyoscyamus muticus, Lycopersicon esculentum, Nicotiana acuminata, N. alata, N. debneyi, N. glauca, N. langsdorffii, N. iongiflora, N. otophora, N. paniculata, N. plumbaginifolia, N. suaveolens, N. sylvestris, N. tabacum, Petunia hybrida, P. inflata, P. parodii, P. parviflora, P. violacea, Salpiglosssis sinuata, Solanum aculeatissimum, S. aviculare, S. brevidens, S. chacoense, S. dulcamara, S. etuberosum, S. fernandezianum, S. gilo, S. khasianum, S. luteum, S. lycopersicoides, S. melongena, S. nigrum, S. pennellii, S. phureja, S. phureja x S. chacoense, S. pinnatisectum, S. torvum, S. tuberosum cultivars (S. tuberosum tetraploid clones, diploid clones), S. uporo, S. viarum, S. xanthocarpum*
Ulmaceae	*Ulmus species*
Umbelliferae	*Daucus carota, Foeniculum vulgare*

DETERMINATION OF PROTOPLAST PLATING EFFICIENCY

Calculate the average number of cell colonies per cm^2 of the petri dish by using following formula:

$$\text{Plating efficiency} = \frac{\text{X x Area of petri dish x 100}}{\text{Number of protoplast plated/petri dish}}$$

$$X = \frac{S_1 + S_2 + S_3 + S_4 + S_5}{5}$$

X = Average number of cell colonies per cm^2 and S_1, S_2, S_3, S_4, S_5 = the number of cell colonies in 1 cm^2 of Petri dish.

TECHNIQUE FOR ISOLATION OF SUB-PROTOPLASTS

Subprotoplasts are fragments derived from protoplasts and do not contain the entire content of plant cells. **Cytoplasts** are subprotoplasts containing most or fractions only of the original cytoplasmic material but are lacking the nucleus. Subprotoplasts containing the nucleus are called **karyoplasts** or **miniprotoplasts**. In this case the nucleus is surrounded by only a small, amount of cytoplasm and the plasma membrane. The term **microprotoplast** was suggested for subprotoplasts containing not all but a few chromosomes. The term **microplast** was used to describe protoplast fragments containing only minor fractions of the cytoplasmic material surrounded by an inner membrane of the cell. In contrast to microplasts, subprotoplasts normally surrounded by the original outer membrane, the plasma membrane.

After obtaining satisfactory quantities of isolated intact and viable protoplasts, that are able to regenerate cell wall, undergo mitotic and cellular divisions and form a callus. The next important step is to regenerate a whole plant by suitable manipulation in culture medium.

HANDLING OF REGENERATED PLANTLETS

Plantlets regenerated by the process of embryogenesis or organogenesis is then used to transfer to non-sterile conditions. This can be very critical period when the plantlet is removed from sterile controlled environment and transplanted to the real world of agriculture. As the plantlet is moved to non-sterile conditions care must be taken to allow gradual release of these careful controls.

Anatomical analysis of these plantlets has shown that under these conditions often the cuticle (covering the leaf surfaces), is extremely thin and the root hairs are poorly developed. If these plantlets are suddenly move to a situation where they are subjected to water stress they would be unable to control their water balance adequately and will die. Both the plantlets should first allow to develop a good root system before transferring them *in vivo* conditions and care should be taken for least possible damage of the roots. If the plants have been grown on agar-solidified medium, this can be removed by gentle washing in a basin of warm water.

These plantlets are then carefully taken out from the test tubes or flasks and adhered agar medium is removed from them. The *in vitro* plants with roots are then carefully planted in small pots. The care is to be taken that roots should make quick and good contact with the potting mix because the plant may suffer water stress. The planting mix should be well balanced for water retention and sterile. Small, sterile peat pots (Jiffy pots) are excellent for this purpose.

PROTOPLAST FUSION

Plant protoplasts represent the finest single cell system that could offer exciting possibilities in the fields of somatic cell genetics and crop improvement. The isolated protoplasts are surrounded by plasma membrane only. The lake of the cell wall allows the plasma membrane of two or more protoplasts to come into intimate contact. The important aspect has been that incompatibility barriers do not exist during the cell fusion process at interspecific, intergeneric, or even interkingdom levels. Under certain conditions they will stick together rather like two soap bubbles. Later, if they are given an appropriate stimulus they will fuse together forming a single mass surrounded by a common membrane. Kuster was able to see occasional spontaneous fusion of protoplasts. However, with the development of enzymic methods for producing large numbers of isolated protoplasts, great interest has now been developed in the use of protoplast fusion (**somatic hybridization**) as a possible tool of plant breeding. Many people believe that protoplast fusion offers a useful tool to plant breeders to make crosses between sexually incompatible species for transfer of nuclear or cytoplamic characters. Protoplast fusion can be used to make crosses within species (intraspecific), between species (interspecific), within genera (intrageneric) and between genera (intergeneric).

Protoplasmic fusion permits the formation of cytoplasm containing organelle of 2 different parents like chloroplast of one parent and mitochondria of the other, but coexistence of a particular organelle like chloroplast of both the parents in a same cytoplasm usually does not persist due to sorting during mitotic divisions. Potoplasmic fusion is helpful in several graminae, solanaceae and cruciferae members to overcome sexual barriers, to produce plants with resistance to diseases or tolerance to selective herbicides, to produce somatic hybrids having efficient organelle system and widen to genetic base (Glimelius *et al.*, 1991). Protoplast system can be transformed by incorporation of pure DNA or calcium phosphate-DNA coprecipitate or DNA encapsulated in liposomes or by direct micro injection of DNA (Schlperoort and Wullems, 1983). The DNA uptake can be further enhanced under high pH or by heat shock treatment and / or by addition of polyethylene glycol, poly – 1 ornithine or polyvinyl alcohol.

By inactivation of nucleus of one parent and subsequent fusion with normal protoplasts or by fusion of normal and subprotoplasts or microprotoplasts or by fusion of normal and subprotoplass or microprotoplasts or by using mutants and anti metabolities it is possible to produce `cybrids' having nuclear genes of one parent and cytoplasmic genes of other parent. Cytoplasmic organelle like chloroplasts and mitochondria possess DNA, which control the expression of male sterility. (Levings *et al.*, 1980). Thus the production of cybrids will be helpful in seed propagated annual ornamentals to exploit hybrid vigour by heterosis breeding. It may also be possible to achieve postponement of pollen induced senescence in flowers.

General Steps of Protoplast Fusion

An efficient method employing polyethylene glycol (PEG) has found wide application in experiments on protoplast fusion. Many fusion inducing agents such as sodium nitrate, high Ca^{++}, high pH 10.5, high temperature (37°C) and polyvinyl alcohol have been used for fusion of protoplasts.

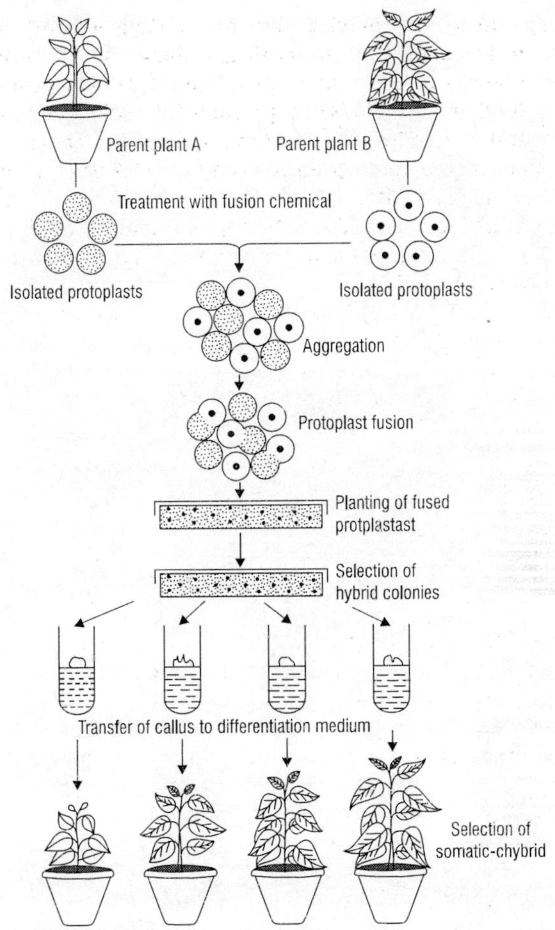

FIGURE 12.6: Diagrammatic presentation of fusion of protoplast from two different plant species and the regeneration of somatic hybrid plants.

Procedure

1. Place a drop (1 drop = 50 μl) of each protoplast suspension in sterile Petridish, gently shake the plate to ensure proper mixing of suspensions from callus or suspension culture with leaf protoplast. The concentration of each species should be about 1×10^5/ml before mixing.
2. Wait for 5 min to allow the protoplasts to settle to the bottom of petri dish
3. Slowly add 300-450 μl PEG solution to the edge of the protoplast suspension, then in the centre of the protoplast, and wait for 15 min
4. Add drop by drop 1 ml of 0.7 M mannitol solution to dilute the PEG solution
5. Raise one side of the plate and wash the protoplast clumps adhering to the plastic surface of plate upto with 9 ml of 0.7 M mannitol
6. Remove the PEG and mannitol residues from petri dish. Add a few drop of mannitol solution to the fused cells
7. After 5 min observe the fused product on the inverted microscope. The process

of adhesion or agglutination of protoplasts in various combinations can be seen
8. Study the fused and unfused protoplasts for the synthesis of cell wall, first cell division, formation of homokaryons/heterokaryons, frequency of multinucleate homokaryons from heterokaryons and mitotic index, cytologically examination under microscope.

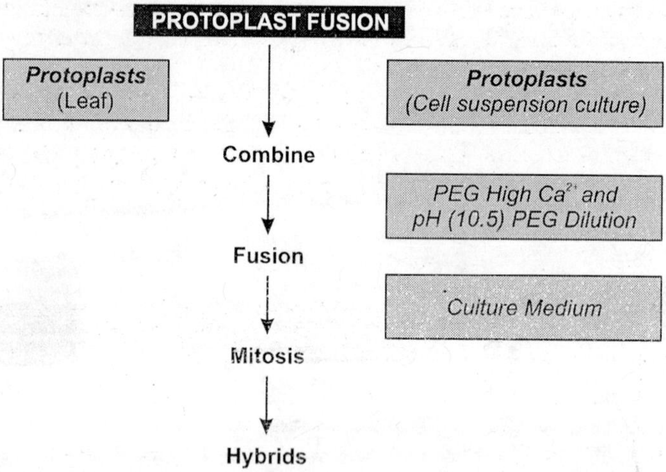

FIGURE 12.7: Presentation of stages in protoplast fusion and production of hybrids. 1 = Parental protoplasts, 2 = Aggulation adhesion.

The technique of protoplasts fusion has developed new vistas for the plant breeders where conventional methods failed or the plant species are incompatible. Protoplasts fusion results in somatic hybrids, the phenomenon is known as somatic hybridization. Protoplast fusion may be spontaneous or induced.

The protoplasts fusion may be of three kinds: (1) Spontaneous fusion, (2) Mechanical fusion. (3) Induced fusion.

Spontaneous Fusion: Only interspecific protoplasts have been found very often fusing through their plasmodesmata during enzyme treatment. Nearby protoplastsin a Perti dish have been observed to form large multinucleate (coenocytic) mass. Protoplasts of young leaves are prone to fuse spontaneously with one another.

Mechanical Fusion: The giant protoplasts of *Acetabularia* have been fused mechanically) This kind of fusion is not dependent uopn the presence of fusion-inducing agent. However, in this procedure protoplasts are likely to get injury.

Induced Fusion: This kind of fusion can be done with the help of (a) $NaNO_3$ treatment, (b) High pH/Ca^{++} treatment, (c) Polyethylene glycol (PEG) treatment, (d) Electrofusion. This method can bring together both intra- and interspecific protoplasts. For this, some inducing agent is necessary. The inducing agent is called **fusogens**. In animals **sendai virus** plays this role but in plants both physical as well as chemical methods are used.

Several chemicals like sodium nitrate, PEG, poly-L-ornithine, poly-D-lysine, cytocholasin B, protomine sulphate, lysozyme, glycerol, dimethyl sulphoxide, proteins and calcium ions at high pH have been used as fusogens. Kuster (1909) for the first time used sodium nitrate to plasmolyse onion protoplasts, which underwent fusion on deplasmolysis. Thereafter, Power et al. (1970) employed the same technique and successfully fused root tip protoplasts of maize and oat.

Keller and Melchers (1973) employed calcium ions at high pH (0.05 M CaCl $2H_2O$ in 0.4 M mannitol at pH 10.5) for fusion of tobacco protoplasts. They spinned the isolated protoplast in the fusion inducing solutions for 3 minutes at 50g and then kept the tubes in water bath at 37° C for 40-50 minutes nearly 20-50% protoplasts undergone fusion process.

The one most widely used fusogen is polyethylene glycol. The effects of PEG are not specific and it promotes the aggregation and fusion of protoplasts from the same or different species or intergeneric protoplasts.

Zimmermann has shown that if protoplasts are placed into a small culture cell containing electrodes and a potential difference is applied then the protoplasts will lie between the electrodes. Protoplasts fusion can be induced after applying extremely short, square wave electrical stocks. This method has become very popular for its highly controllable fusions property. It is possible to fuse two single protoplasts.

PROTOPLAST CULTURE: REGENERATION OF PLANTS

The idea that cell contains all the information necessary for the regeneration of a whole organism was given in the cell theory, proposed by Schwann. At that time, however, the technology did not exist to study regeneration of plants from any single cell other than a zygote, and even this developmental process takes place within plant body and not as an isolated single cell *in vitro*.

It has been a long practice to regenerate vegetative plants by taking stem cuttings. Haberlandt successfully regenerated whole plant from small meristematic pieces however he could not obtain any growth of a single cell system because of its inability to regenerate plants from single cell. This was not due to genetic reason, but due to lack of adequate nutrients in the medium. He further suggested the use of embryo sac fluids in the medium for such culture.

Protoplasts in culture regenerate cell wall around themselves to reconstitute cells. These cells in proper medium by repeated cell divisions form callus. Callus tissue by manipulation of the nutritional and physiological conditions can be induced to regenerate into the morphogenic form of plant.

About 100 plant species have successfully been regenerated from single cell or protoplast. Regeneration of plants from isolated cells or protoplasts is by one of two: (1) By Organogenesis, (2) By Embryogenesis.

Organogenesis

Organogenesis takes place from a callus and not directly from a single cell. When isolated protoplasts are put into culture under appropriate conditions of plant inoculum, medium and environmental factors they go through a set series of events: (1) Wall regeneration, (2) Early mitotic division and callus formation, (3) Organogenesis.

Embryogenesis

Plant tissue *in vitro* can induce to form somatic haploid embryos. Steward and coworkers first observed the phenomenon of somatic embryogenesis in carrot. Somatic embryos can be induced in cultural conditions from three different sources: (1) Vegetative cells of mature plants; (2) Reproductive tissues other than the zygote; and (3) Hypocotyls and cotyledons of embryos.

Embryoids are initiated in callus from small superficial clumps of cells associated with dense cytoplasm and large starch grains. The developing embryoids *in vitro* then pass through a sequence of growth stages that is exactly the same as seen in the development of a seed embryo.

Like cells, protoplasts are genetically unstable *in vitro*. Somaclonal variations have also been detected in the plants regenerated from protoplasts. Chromosomal variation has also been observed in plants regenerated from protoplasts. Shepard and his associates conducted detailed studies of plant regeneration from protoplasts of Russet Burbank potatoes. Significant variations were detected for growth habit, tuber colour, fruit production and tuber uniformity. Several of these traits are considered to be improved over the widely grown commercial variety. They further reported somaclones with resistance to early blight (*Alternaria solani*) and late blight (*Phytophthora infestans*). Our knowledge is insufficient to understand the mechanism of such instability in culture.

In *Nicotiana tabacum*, protoplast cultures were regenerated into cells and callus tissues. These calli were then transferred to fresh medium supplimented with IAA (4 mg/l) and cytokinin (2 mg/l). Calli differentiated into shoots and occasionally in roots within 3 to 4 weeks. The plantlets are then subsequently transplanted to pots.

Handling of Regenerated Plantlets

Plantlets regenerated by the process of embryogenesis or organogenesis are then used to transfer to non-sterile conditions. This can be very critical period when the plantlet is removed from sterile controlled environment and transplanted to the real world of agriculture. As the plantlet is moved to non-sterile conditions care must be taken to allow gradual release of these careful controls.

Anatomical analysis of these plantlets has shown that under these conditions often the cuticle (covering the leaf surfaces), is extremely thin and the root hairs are poorly developed. If these plantlets are suddently move to a situation where they are subjected to water stress they would be unable to control their water balance adequately and will die. Both the plantlets should first allow to develop a good root system before transferring them *in vivo* conditions and care should be taken for least possible damage of the roots. If the plants have been grown on agar solidified medium, this can be removed by gentle washing in a basin of warm water.

These plantlets are then carefully taken out from the test tubes or flasks and adhered agar medium is removed from them. The *in vitro* plants with roots are then carefully planted in small pots. The care is to be taken that roots should make quick and good contact with the potting mix because the plant may suffer water stress. The planting mix should be well balanced for water retention and sterile. Small, sterile peat pots (Jiffy pots) are excellent for this purpose.

PROTOPLAST CULTURE: UPTAKE OF FOREIGN MATERIALS

Isolated protoplast of plant cells have the remarkable property of taking up micro- as well as macromolecules like ferritin, polystrene, latex, protein, DNA, chromosomes, whole nuclei, chloroplasts and even virus and bacteria. This unique property of protoplast can be utilized for the incorporation of desirable traits into plants to get what we call *transferred* or *noval varieties* from wild ones.

Incorporation of Foreign DNA

Unlike transformation of bacteria by exogenous DNA, transgenosis in cells or protoplasts of higher plants are now possible and have been tried successfully in some plant species. Doy and his associates transformed haploid tomato callus culture by lambda phage. The transformed higher plant cells can grow on a medium containing galactose and lactose as the only carbon source that is considered to be due to phage DNA incorporation. This kind of transformation phenomenon is termed as **trasgenosis**. These studies have given a major break through in agricultural biotechnology.

Incorporation of Nuclei

Intra- and interspecific nuclear incorporation into protoplasts of *Nicotiana tabacum*, *Petunia hybrida* and *Zea mays* have been observed. These exogenous nuclei enter the protoplasts without any damage to plasmalemma. However, the role of these incorporated nuclei in the metabolism of protoplasts in culture is yet to be confirmed.

Incorporation of Chloroplasts

In addition to nuclear material and nuclei as a whole protoplast can take up certain cell organelles like chloroplasts, mitochondria etc. Transplantation of chloroplasts into albino plant species could solve a great physiological deficiency. Potrykus (1973), Bonner and Eriksson (1974) have reported the uptake of chloroplasts by albino *Petunia* and carrot protoplasts. Nass (1969) and Gills and Sarafis (1971) have incorporated spinach chloroplast into animal cell cultures. They have also reported that these chloroplast survive and remain matabolically active in animal cells. Transplantation of chloroplast in plant having insufficient or deficient photosynthetic system will have far- reaching implications in plant improvement programme.

Several methods for the induction of chloroplast into plant protoplasts have been reported, all of them depending either on some form of osmotic effect or on hypothesized changes in the charge pattern on the plasmalemma.

Bonnett and Eriksson used a method involving plasmolysis by polyethylene glycol (PEG) to induce uptake of *Vaucheria* chloroplasts by carrot protoplasts. A dense mixture of protoplasts and chloroplasts was made up to a volume of 0.5 ml with protoplast culture medium. A volume of 1.5 ml of the solution containing 3 ml of protoplast culture medium and 7 ml of a 56% aqueous solution of PEG was added to the protoplast-chloroplast mixture. The final concentration of PEG was about 30%, a concentration known to promote cell aggregation and cell fusion without reducing cell viability. After 10 min the mixture was diluted to 10 ml with a solution of 0.1 M $CaCl_2$ in 0.3 M sorbitol, and centrifuged for 3 min at 150x g. The pellet was resuspended in 10 ml of the same solution, recentrifuged and resuspended in 2 ml of the protoplast culture medium.

Incorporation of Cyanobacteria

Experiments have been performed to incorporate certain cyanobacteria or blue-green algae (*Gleocapsa*, *Anacystis*, etc.) in protoplast of higher plants. The method is used to co-incubate the algal preparation with the isolated protoplast preparation in the presence of 25% polyethylene glycol, when high Ca concentration is added the protoplasts begin to engulf the algal cells. The method of uptake has been shown to be by envagination of the plasma membrane.

Incorporation of Bacteria

Incorporation of nitrogen fixing bacteria (*Rhizobium*, *Azotobactor*) blue green algae and *nif*-genes into non-leguminous plants specially cereals is a important task in the hands of geneticists and agronomists. Davey and Cocking (1972) introduced a symbiotic nitrogen fixing bacterium (*Rhizobium*) in legume chloroplasts. These chloroplasts containing nitrogen fixing bacteria could be fused with non-legume chloroplast to impart the capability of nitrogen fixation in non-leguminous cash crops. *Agrobacterium tumefaciens* have been adapted to become efficient and reliable gene vectors for genetic engineering of dicotyledonous plants. *Chimeric*-genes have been constructed which upon transfer into differentiated plant cells allow the identification of DNA sequences involved in the regulation of gene expression. Recently, direct DNA transfer and expression of a bacterial gene in protoplasts of *Triticum monococcum* and *Nicotiana tabacum* have been reported; and in the case of tobacco transformed protoplasts were regenerated into plants which obeyed Mendelian law of inheritance.

Incorporation of Virus

Virus, an obligate parasite in nature enters the plant cells, leaving behind its protein coat only in those plant cells whose cells wall is damaged. The virus genome (RNA) enters the protoplasts of the cell and then multiplies in cytoplasm. Takebe and Otsukic (1974) reported that protoplasts can be infected by one or more than one virus. Cocking (1966) observed the uptake of TMV by tomato fruit protoplast.

The inclusion of these micro- and megamolecules in plant protoplasts has opened a new path to solve the genetic deficiency in economically important plants through biotechnology.

INCORPORATION OF NON-BIOLOGICAL MATERIALS

Incorporation of non-biological materials have been tried such as polystylene in to plant protoplasts. These type of studies have proved useful as a method of determining the maximum size of an object that can be engulfed by endocytosis. However, no direct biological value can be seen to these studies at the present time.

SELECTION OF FUSION HYBRIDS

Visual Selection

This method can be used to select fusion products of protoplasts that have distinct physical characters. For example, fusion between leaf mesophyll protoplasts of green colour and a cultured cell that have anthocyanin- containing red protoplast. A single fusion product between the two will have both chloroplasts and an anthocyanin vacuole together with two nuclei. The same method can be applied to fusions between leaf mesophyll and hyaline cultured cell protoplasts.

Obviously, the drawback with this method is that it is very laborious and only a very limited number of fusion products can be selected.

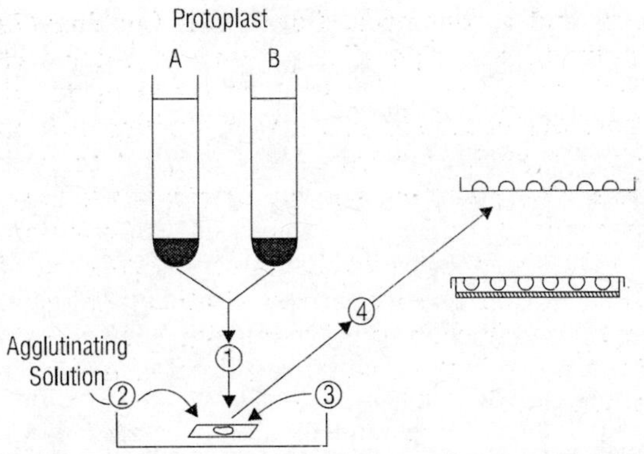

FIGURE 12.8: Typical protocol for protoplast fusion of potato using PEG. (1) Dilute protoplast mixture to 10^4 cells per milliliter in 0.5 M glucose, 3 mM $CaCl_2$, 0.7 mM KH_2PO_4, pH 5.7; (2) add 3 to 200 μl volumes of agglutinating solution (0.09 mM PEG 6000, 10 mM $CaCl_2$, 0.7 mM KH_2PO_4, pH 5.5); (3) add five 100-μl volumes of diluting solution (50 mM $CaCl_2$, 0.5 M glucose, 50 mM glycine buffer, pH 10.0); (4) wash cells with culture medium and culture in hanging drop suspensions.

Fluorescent Labels

1. In this method, fluorescent labelled dyes are used to detect fusion products.
2. If the two original protoplast cultures are pre-incubated for 12-15 hours, one in octadeconyl aminofluorescein and the other in octadecyl palamine B each group of protoplasts takes on a specific fluorescence colour. The dyes are non-toxic and do not affect viability, wall regeneration or growth.
3. After fusion of the protoplasts fusion products may be identified by their fluorescence characteristics under a fluorescence microscope.

Fluorescence Activated Cells Sorting

Protoplasts are fluorescently labelled as already described. After fusion three types of fluorescence can be found; two original fluorescence of the two parental populations and the fluorescence of the fused hybrids. A machine now exists to separate these populations. A droplet containing a single cell is held between two fluorescence detectors. If it is one of the two parent populations the machine charges two electrical plates, as the droplet falls it is deflected by the electrical charge. If the fluorescence is of the hybrid, no electrical charge is applied to the plates and the droplet fall vertically. Thus the protoplasts are automatically separated into the parent types and the fusion products. The fusion products can then be plated into an appropriate culture system.

Nutritional Selection

In some cases, Carlson et al. were able to separate fusion products by their ability to grow on a media that would not permit growth of the parent protoplast lines. For example hybrid of *Nicotinia glauca* and *N. langsdorfii* could be cultured in auxin free culture medium in contrast to its parents protoplast.

Drug Sensitivity and Resistance

Power and co-workers used sensitivity to actinomycin-D to select fusion products between *Petunia hybrida* and *Petunia parodii*. The two parental species are sensitive to actinomycin-D; however, the hybrid is resistant. Again it would be of great benefit to the field of somatic cell hybridization if a wider range of resistance mutants could be isolated. Some research groups are now attempting to produce large numbers of resistant mutants for use in protoplast fusion studies.

SOMATIC CELL HYBRIDIZATION OR CYBRID OR CYTOPLAST

Success in protoplast fusion between diversified plant species gave great impetus to geneticists and plant breeders though the technique has some shortcomings. Nevertheless, it has stimulated research activities in many laboratories around the world.

When two protoplasts fuse along with their nuclei true hybrid are formed. However, often the two nuclei will survive independently in the mixed cytoplasms, forming a heterokaryon. Chromosome loss can occur from one or both of the nuclei; if all the nucleus of one parent is lost, what is left is one nucleus in a mixture of both cytoplasms. This product is called a **cytoplast** or **cybrid**. Cybrids can also be prepared by fusing a normal protoplast with an enucleated protoplast. Presently, researchers are studying the use of cybrids to transfer resistance to some herbicides. This resistance character is carried on the chloroplast genome. Cytoplasmic male sterility can be controlled by transfer of the mitochondrial genome. The study of cybrids is also important for investigation of possible recombination within these extra-chromosomal genomes.

The scenario presented in this chapter gives an overall view of protoplast culture. The technique has unravelled the complexities of protoplast culture and its application to agricultural biotechnology. The protoplast technique is used in studies of plant cell genetics specially in somatic embryogenesis and transfer of genetic information by DNA uptake and organelle implantation. Though tissue culturists have developed many plantlets and new varients through this technique, care must be taken to achieve cost-effective results so that the *in vitro* technique of protoplast culture can be adapted for commercial exploitation of agricultural crops in general and plantation crops in particular.

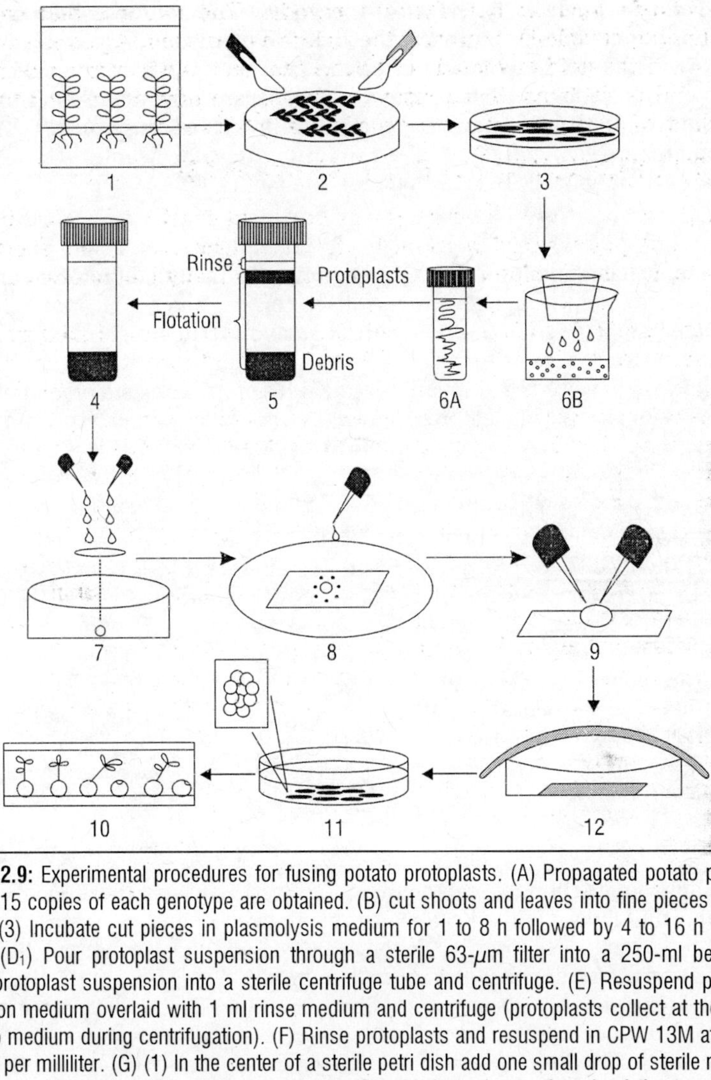

FIGURE 12.9: Experimental procedures for fusing potato protoplasts. (A) Propagated potato plantlets *in vitro* until 15 copies of each genotype are obtained. (B) cut shoots and leaves into fine pieces using two scalpels. (3) Incubate cut pieces in plasmolysis medium for 1 to 8 h followed by 4 to 16 h in enzyme medium. (D_1) Pour protoplast suspension through a sterile 63-μm filter into a 250-ml beaker. (D_2) Transfer protoplast suspension into a sterile centrifuge tube and centrifuge. (E) Resuspend pellet in 10 mL flotation medium overlaid with 1 ml rinse medium and centrifuge (protoplasts collect at the interface of the two medium during centrifugation). (F) Rinse protoplasts and resuspend in CPW 13M at a density of 1×10^6 per milliliter. (G) (1) In the center of a sterile petri dish add one small drop of sterile mineral oil; (2) position a sterile cover slip over the droplet; (3) add three drops of each of the two protoplast suspensions. (H) Fuse protoplasts by gradually adding six drops of Fusogen PEG 22.5 medium. (I) Wash protoplasts with Ca^{2+} washing medium. Replace washing medium with culture medium. (J) Incubate protoplasts in dim light at 25°C. (K) After 2 to 3 weeks embed multicellular colonies in medium with agarose. (L) Regenerate shoots and transfer to MS basal medium for rooting.

PROTOPLASTS FOR ISOLATION OF CELL COMPONENTS

The danger of erroneous interpretation of protoplast metabolism as truly representing intact cell processes is hardly encountered when the aim is merely the isolation of cell components. The objective of isolating such components as plasmalemma, nuclei, and chloroplasts from protoplasts, rather than from cells or intact tissues, is in most cases to obtain them by convenient methods which will cause the least destruction. Therefore, if the functionality of these components is of primary importance, the evaluation of the rate and quality of damage (*e.g.* in nuclei) as well as their unquestionable identification and purity (*e.g.* of plasmalemma) are important considerations. Most of the problems involved in the isolation of cell components from protoplasts are specific to plant cells because of the latter's rigid cell wall and their specific organelles, *e.g.* chloroplasts and vacuoles. These problems are very rare in animal cells but are common to plant cells.

Plasmalemma

Isolation of plasmalemma from cells of higher plants is a difficult task. It is hampered by two major factors: (a) high shear force used for cell homogenization will damage the plasmalemma (b) good markers are essential to identify the plasmalemma fraction. Therefore, protoplasts obtained from leaf mesophyll or from cell suspensions were isolated by enzyme treatment. Plant protoplasts bind concanavalin A (con A) is used as a plasmalemma marker.

Chloroplasts

Chloroplasts were first isolated from protoplasts by Wagner and Siegelman as a by-product of their isolated vacuoles. The protoplasts were ruptured osmotically by suspending them into a phosphate buffer containing Mg2+ and dithiothreitol. Chloroplasts were then separated on discontinuous sucrose gradients and were found to be photochemically active. Isolation of cereal chloroplasts is especially problematic, chloroplasts of these plants are obtained by suspending the protoplasts in an appropriately buffered osmoticum (containing bovine serum albumin and dithiothreitol) and passed through a 20μ nylon net. The chloroplasts are then collected by centrifugation without fractionation. Nishimura developed a new technique for spinach leaf protoplasts, using a syrings needle to rupture the protoplasts.

Mitochondria

Large number of mitochondria can be obtained from plant tissues and cultured cells. Some of the methods mentioned above for chloroplast isolation from protoplasts may also be useful for mitochondria and the two types of organelles can be separated from the same sample of plant materials. When 0.05- 0.1% bovine serum albumin is included and a sucrose gradient is employed for fractionation of the disrupted protoplasts, mitochondria will band quite sharply at a density of 1.18g. cm^{-3}, and they can be identified by their fumerase activity, while chloroplasts will peak at an appreciably higher sucrose density (1.22 g. cm^{-3}).

Vacuoles

Vacuoles are most fragile cell organells. Wagner and Siegelman reported that when protoplasts from various plant tissues are ruptured gently by transferring it into phosphate buffer, vacuoles could then be separated by a low-speed centrifugation and be further purified by layering over 5% Ficol containing 0.55 M sorbitol and 1 mM tris-MES buffer. The homogeneity of the vacuole preparation can be nicely demonstrated by the use of anthocyanin-containing tissues, in Tulipa petals.

The scenario presented in this chapter gives an overall view of protoplast culture. The technique has unravelled the complexities of protoplast culture and its application to agricultural biotechnology. The protoplast technique is used in studies of plant cell genetics specially in somatic embryogenesis and transfer of genetic information by DNA uptake and organelle implantation. Though scientists have developed many plantlets and new varients through this technique, care must be taken to achieve cost-effective results so that the *in vitro* technique of protoplast culture can be adapted for commercial exploitation of agricultural crops in general and plantation crops in particular.

CHAPTER 13

Micropropagation in Plants

Men have been vegetatively propagating superior plant material because of its beauty, growth form or yield for centuries. It is only during the past 20 years that micropropagation has been available to increase the levels of efficiency and control over these systems.

It is important, if one is to produce many plants from a single individual that the starting material be of the right clonal selection. For effective micropropagation plant must be in an active, vigorous, and healthy state. Micropropagation cannot be regarded as a rehabilitation phase for poor, sickly material; if it is poor and sick on its own roots, it is going to be equally substandard in culture.

ADVANTAGES OF MICROPROPAGATION

Micropropagation offers many advantages over conventional methods of plant propagation such as rapid largescale multiplication of true-to-type plants, through the year available technique, disease free plants, and conservation of space and time. Main methods of micropropagation are:

1. Micropropagation through shoot bud proliferation
2. Micropropagation through adventitious shoots
3. Meristem tip culture
4. In vitro tuberization
5. Somatic embryogenesis

This technique is an alternative method of vegetative propagation. and is applied with the objective of enhancing the rate of multiplication. The number of plant propagules that can be developed in a short time are extremely large.

A major advantage of micropropagation happens to be the minimum growing space is required in commercial nurseries. Several thousand million plants can be maintained inside vials on a shelf space built into a room of about 3 m × 3 m × 5m. This makes possible the propagation of clones on a commercial scale for large number of horticultural species (African violet, banana, eucalyptus, ferns, orchids, gloxinia, gerbera and rhododendrons).

Other Advantages of Micropropagation Methods

1. Millions of plants of the elite, productive types(s) can be produced.
2. All the plants are of the same physiological age and hence of uniform growth, otherwise, it is extremely difficult to obtain uniformity in vegetatively propagated material, unlike in the seed raised crops.
3. Planting material can be made free from viral and bacterial disease, which is especially important in vegetatively propagated species.
4. A large number of plants can be produced in a short time and space.
5. Cells grown in vitro may be used for biotransformation to a new chemical (drug).
6. Continuous and reliable sources of plants and products round the year

irrespective of seasonal variation.
7. Genetic and phenotypic uniformity can be maintained.
8. Induction of genetic variability and high yield of desired products (Bajaj et al., 1988).
9. Micropropagation is the only quick way to produce products developed by genetic engineering in the pharmaceutical industry. Again the advantage of using in vitro regeneration systems is the possibility to multiply the initial transformation event by cell proliferation and to select the transformed cell production.
10. Plant cells and tissues can be manipulated under cultural conditions so that chemical potentiality of specific phytochemicals can be induced (Staba, 1990).
11. Quality and desirability of the product can be maintained as the plantlets produced are free from bacteria, fungi and viruses.
12. This method can solve many fundamental problems associated with the biosynthetic pathway of phytochemicals.

The most popular use of micropropagation is as an alternative to the conventional methods of vegetative propagation with the objective of enhancing the rate of multiplication. Through this method, millions of plants can be produced from a small, even microscopic piece of plant tissue within a limited time. Such a prolific rate of multiplication cannot be expected by any of the *in vivo* methods of clonal propagation. Micropropagation is applied on a commercial scale on a wide range of ornamentals, bulbs and corms, flowering and pot plants, foliage plants, fruit and nut crops, vegetable crops, plantation and forest trees like:

Aglaonema	**Alpinia**	**Alstroemeria**
Ananus	Anthurium	Asperagus
Bambusa	Begonia	Carica
Coffea	Cordyline	Curcuma
Dalbergia	Dieffenbachia	Elettaria & Amomum
Eryngium	Eucalyptus	Ficus
Gerbera	Gladiolus	Hydrangea
Impatiens	Iris	Lilies
Maranta	Mimosa	Musa
Narcissus	Narcissus	Orchids
Philodendron	Rosa	Saccharum
Solanum	Spathiphyllum	Syngonium
Tamarindus	Vanilla	Vitis
Zingiber		

Advantages of Micropropagation over Traditional Methods

In vivo techniques have the following advantages over:

1. Certified virus free plants can be produced in large number.
2. It is possible to produce clones of some kinds of plants that are otherwise slow and difficult to propagate vegetatively.
3. Only limited space is required to maintain and produce large number of plants.
4. Plant material requires less attention between subcultures and there is no labour or material requirement for watering, weeding, spraying, etc. Micropropagation is most advantageous when costs less than traditional methods of multiplication.
5. Plants may acquire a temporary vigour through micropropagation, which makes

them more desirable to the grower than conventionally raised stock.
6. Predictability of yield and uniformity the product.
7. Production can be continued all the year round and is independent of seasonal changes.
8. Propagation is ideally carried out under aseptic conditions, free from pathogens. Once cultures have been started there should be no loss through disease and the plantlets finally produced should be free from bacteria, fungi and other microorganisms.
9. The rate of propagation is much greater than in micropropagation and many more plants can be produced in given time. This will enable newly selected varieties to be made available quickly and widely.

Disadvantages of Micropropagation

1. The changes of producing genetically aberrant plants may be increased.
2. The major disadvantage is the need for advanced skills, expensive production facility availability of specific systems for each species and variety, labour intensive and high cost of the propagules.
3. The plants derived from the cultures are not initially able to produce their own requirement of organic matter by photosynthesis and have to undergo a transitional period before they are capable of independent growth.
4. The young plants produced through micropropagation are more susceptible to water loss in an external environment. They therefore have to be hardened in an atmosphere by slowly decreasing the humidity and increasing the light.

COMMERCIAL USES OF MICROPROPAGATION

Micropropagation is used for production of various commercial of planting material. Micropropagation helps in rapid multiplication of plants and a large numbers of plants can be produced quickly. Most of the systems involve subculture every 30-45 days. The plant material at least doubles at each subculture. There is a gestation period (range from 6-12 months) between the start of the culture procedure and the production of plantlets in quantity. Since cultures are grown under controlled conditions (in an incubation room at 20-25°C and specific photoperiod, say 16 hr/8 hr light/dark photoperiod), the plant production can go on without any influence of the variations in the climate outside. It has rapid propagation potential, therefore, the stock area can be considerably reduced. Micropropagation also helps in producing disease-free planting material very rapidly. Micropropagation can also be used for introducing new species and varieties in large numbers for commercial plantations. Moreover, the plant production can be programmed in such a way that seasonal peaks in the demand are correctly met or a steady year round demand is adequately taken care of. By selecting the stock plants the quality of the planting material can be enhanced and maintained, in micropropagation. It is the answer for the propagation of difficult to root species. Micropropagated plants are grown under aseptic conditions that are without soil, fertilizer (biological and inorganic) and climatic influences can be freely moved between countries without fear of spreading diseases.

MATERIALS FOR MICROPROPAGATION

The starting material for a micropropagation programme is a shoot tip, not necessarily as small as the meristematic apical dome, but something a little larger with leaf primordia already developing around it. This material must initially be surface sterilized. Any tissue affected by exposure to sterilized material is trimmed and the remaining material placed on one of a variety of different media. Since it is initially unknown which medium will be suitable for a specific variety or species involved. Concentration of growth regulators should be adjusted in order to allow the plant tissue to initiate into culture. This is the *establishment phase* of the tissue *in vitro* conditions and can take, in some species, as long as 3 or 4 months, usually it can be completed within a few weeks. Under the optimal conditions the small shoot tip will initiate to grow in normal way, giving rise to a small, unrooted shoot in culture.

The initiated shoot, after a suitable period in the initiation medium can be subcultured such that nodal sections of the shoot are placed onto a multiplication medium. This medium differs from the initiation medium in that it contains higher levels of cytokinins, which are likely to give rise to precocious shooting of the axillary buds. The normal period between subcultures is 3 weeks and during this time the number of shoot tips available for subculture multiply as a result of breaking of nodal axillary buds anywhere from 2 to 12 times. Thus, after the 3 weeks on multiplication medium, somewhere on an average of about 5 shoot tips can be placed onto fresh medium, and these in turn will multiply 5 times in the subsequent 3 weeks, and thus micropropagation has led to a 25-fold increase in the plant material available over a total of 6 weeks.

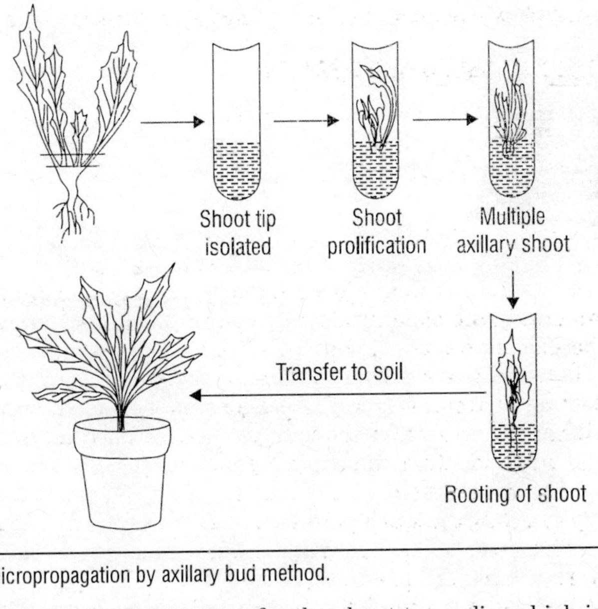

FIGURE 13.1: Micropropagation by axillary bud method.

For rooting in micro-shoots, transfer the shoot to media, which is rich in auxins and will allow the induction of *in vitro* roots. The roots formed *in vitro* are usually different morphologically than that of normal. They are be slightly swollen and brittle, and upon transfer to the soil new roots develop by the plant; before any extensive growth of the shoot can occur and the initial *in vitro* roots die back. This lag in the establishment of the plants can be critical and certainly costly to a grower. It can be avoided by the direct rooting of the micropropagated shoots into a natural or artificial potting mix. If the micropropagated shoots are treated as micro-cuttings, and placed in artificial potting mix maintained at high humidity, roots will develop within 2 to 3 weeks. These are normal physiological roots and not like the *in vitro* roots mentioned above. There is no lag phase when the material is potted on. It represents important part in the overall strategy of plant establishment.

Once the micropropagated plants are satisfactorily rooted in soil or soil substitutes, they must be weaned to a normal humidity level. During the rooting process they are maintained at close to 100% humidity, and this does not allow the normal development of cuticle and stomatal activity associated with drier conditions. The rooting normally takes place under reduced light. After rooting plants are exposed to full sunlight. This is done slowly for a period of 7 to 10 days. Such small plants are now autonomous, photosynthesizing and can fixed carbon. During the rooting phase under the reduced lighting conditions, they are living on carbohydrate reserves built up during micropropagation period *in vitro*. Once this weaning process is completed, the hardened can be incorporated into normal growing systems for their further development.

The investment in commercial tissue culture business will depend to a large extent on cost of the laboratory set-up, type of plant to be propagated and the skill involved. It is advisable that a commercial nursery man start with those crop species for which published methods are available.

Plant Health

Good plant health is the major advantage in the development of elite mother stock material for both the herbaceous ornamental producer and the woody plant grower. Before micropropagation, plant material can be put through stringent tests to bacterial and virus index. The presence of fungal contaminants or pathogens can also be detected and eliminated prior to micropropagation. Thus, the plants produced by the system can be certified as being disease indexed, and they represent clean, elite mother stock material for future conventional propagation methods.

Germplasm Storage

The concept of a tissue bank (a collection of valuable breeding or growth material) in a relatively confined space under controlled environment conditions is particularly attractive for plant breeders. Many plant breeders wish to maintain specific breeding or hetrogenous individuals in the field or greenhouse for subsequent years for testing or seed production. Micropropagation techniques applied to these materials allow them to over winter the material in the safety of a controlled environment and also give rise to the potential for multiplying up individuals for specific crossing or testing.

This elimination of the seasonal nature of much breeding and growing work has been another advantage often suggesting with respect to micropropagation. However, a word of caution is necessary here - although it is possible to micropropagate plant species throughout the year, in the case of biennial species requiring vernalization, it is necessary to do the micropropagation at a suitable time of the year to allow the tissue to become vernalized for flowering for next year.

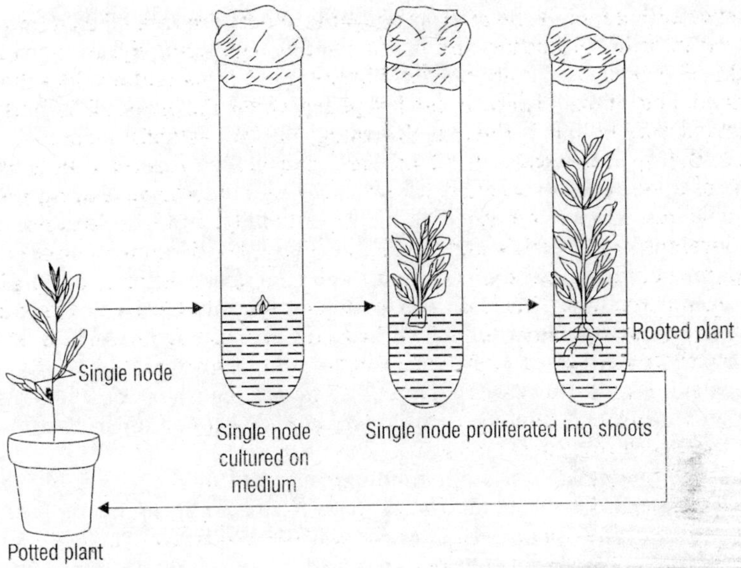

FIGURE 13.2: Micropropagation by single node culture method.

TYPES OF MICROPROPAGATION

Micropropagation through Shoot Bud Proliferation

Mass propagation through axillary and apical shoot bud proliferation is the common and reliable technique. Explants are obtained from actively growing or dormant plants. The buds are collected from plants growing in the field or greenhouse. Such buds are less contaminated.

Method

1. The leaves are removed carefully to minimize damage to the stem.
2. An initial thorough wash under tap water, then the buds are washed in a very dilute detergent solution.
3. It is followed by sterilization in dilute mercuric chloride or sodium or calcium hypochlorite solution containing a drop of wetting agent, *viz.*, Tween-20 or teepol etc.
4. Rinse them for several times in sterile water before transferring on to the nutrient medium.
5. For actively growing shoot tips quick dips in ethanol is practiced (Lane, 1978).
6. The aseptic cultures are then transferred to proliferation medium with a hormonal combination.
7. The shoots obtained by this method are then transferred to rooting medium under in vitro conditions.
8. The well-rooted plants are transferred to green house for acclimatization.
9. This method helps to increase multiplication rate of a plant (approximately 10,000 times) by two methods:
   a) The axillary buds present in the explant and in the newly developing branches are stimulated to develop into branches (an axillary bud is present

in the axil of each leaf), this is achieved by a relatively higher concentration of a cytokinin in the medium (enhanced axillary branching). After suitable each axillary branch is excised and transferred to a fresh appropriate medium for enhanced axillary branching. The branches may be transferred to a rooting medium and subsequently transferred to soil.

b) This method is applicable to those plant species where enhanced axillary branching cannot be achieved (each axillary bud/shoot tip develops into a single shoot). Nodal cuttings (each containing a single node) are excised from these stems and cultured for further multiplication.

The other company, which entered ornamental tissue culture is Indo-American hybrid seeds, Bangalore. The lab was set up in consultation with Sunki Pvt. Ltd. (Australia). Now, they are at their own and have orders for the supply of 6 million ornamentals like lilies, Alpine and Mimosa. The company also proposes to come up with diagnostic kits, for disease indexing and go in a big way in genetic engineering. Successful micropropagation protocols have been developed for fruit crops such as strawberry, cherry, apple, etc.

Forest resources in India are getting depleted day by day due to deforestation. One-sided approach to agriculturalization, urbanisation, industrialization have resulted in miserable dis-balance to forest land. This calls for immediate and urgent efforts to start tree improvement programmes. In this regard tissue culture has great potential. Today, protocols for *in vitro* mass production of some important forest trees such as *Tectona*, *Tamarindus*, *Poplars*, Teak and Bamboo are available.

Micropropagation work on spices is being done at Kerala Agricultural University and Calicut University. The important spices are cinnamon, clove, and nutmug. Cinnamon referred to as queen of spices has considerable export earnings, is propagated vegetatively as well as through seeds. Since it is a cross pollinated crop, seed progenies show variations and hence vegetative propagation through tiller is carried out. However, the rate of multiplication is slow and only 3 tillers are produced per plant per year. Through micropropagation, rate of multiplication has been shown to be more than 30 per cent over open pollinated seedlings.

Biotechnology division of Bhabha Atomic Research Centre (India) has standardized protocols for Banana. Field performances of these plants have been encouraging with vigorous growth, early maturity and increase in yield.

Palms are usually propagated through seeds except date palm, which is propagated through seeds as well as vegetatively by off shoots. Seedling derived plants often show a lot of variation which affects the total yield. Hence the mass multiplication of high yielding clones from elite palms through tissue culture is advantageous.

Pulses, grain legumes and oil seeds form an important constituent for food, fiber and oil for human and animal population. Sustainable development and improvement in these crops is vital for feeding the millions. Application of tissue culture in legume is difficult proposition. However, recent successful regeneration of whole plants from variety of legumes including pigeonpea and chickpea has paved the way for successful application of these techniques for genetic improvement and mass multiplication of these important crops. The successful protocols developed for regeneration and transformation can be used for productivity.

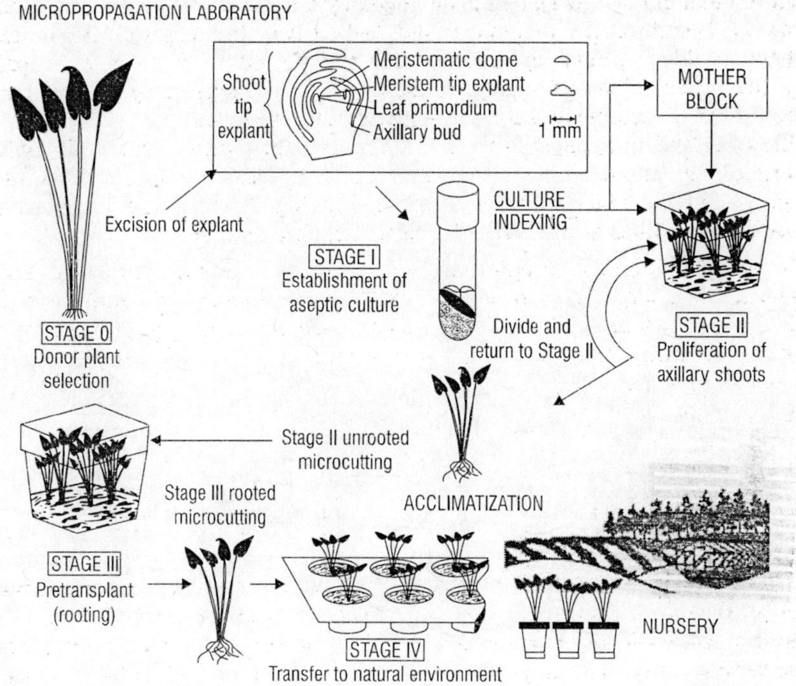

FIGURE 13.3: Micropropagation stages for production by shoot culture.

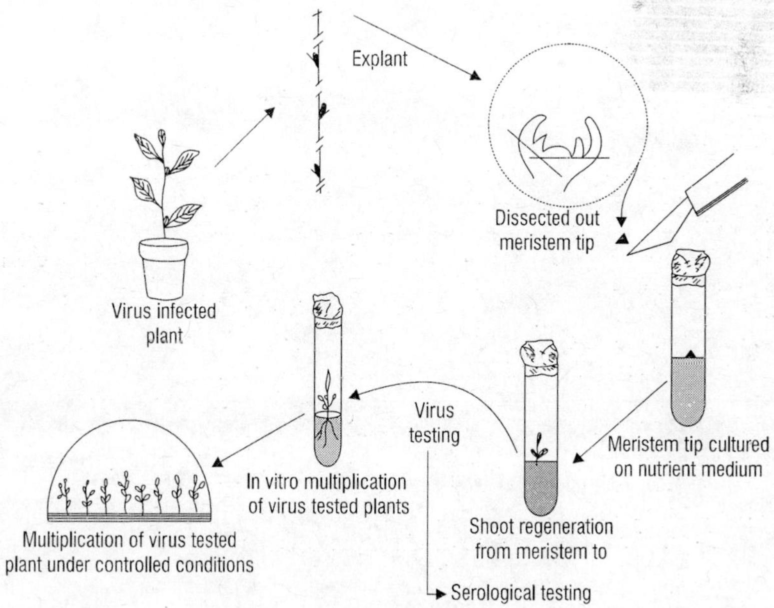

FIGURE 13.4: Diagrammatic representation of meristem tip culture.

Micropropagation through Adventitious Buds

Adventitious buds arise on plant parts other than in normal leaf axils. Propagation by direct induction of adventitious shoots on stems, leaves, bulbs, scales, corms, tubers and rhizomes of intact plants, is a common method. The adventitious shoot buds may develop either (a) directly from the cultured explant or (b) indirectly from the callus generated from the explant. Thus factors, namely explant and growth hormones in the culture medium, control the induction of adventitious buds and subsequent shoot formation. Deliberate induction of adventitious buds may also be done by an organogenic phase in an undifferentiated tissue such as callus. Callus tissue is the form of culture in which adventitious meristems are usually induced and from which plant regeneration is initiated. However, in this type of micropropagation, frequency of genetic changes, resulting from mitotic abnormalities, is often increased. This type of micropropagation also involves usual stages: (1) Explant culturing and establishment, (2) shoot multiplication, (3) rooting, and, (4) hardening of micropropagated plants and transplantation.

Adventitious shoot prediction has been used successfully for ornamental and herbaceous horticultural crops. Bulbs and corms grown adventitiously from meristems at the base of leaves and can be continuously propagated by adventitious shoots proliferation.

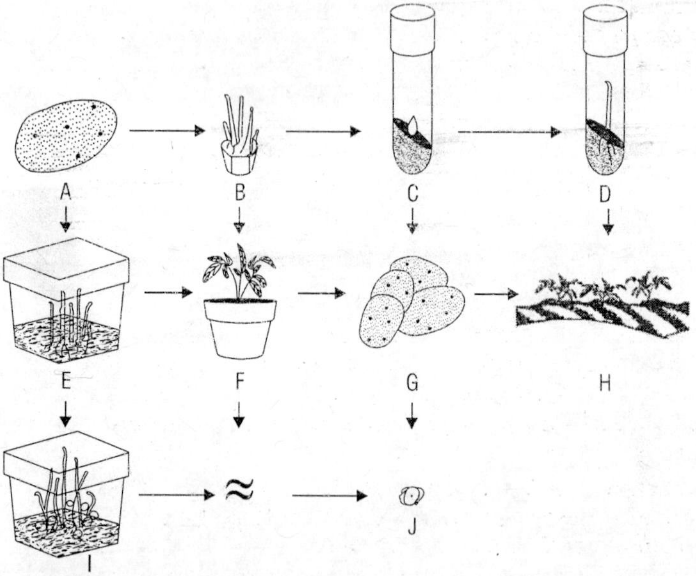

FIGURE 13.5: Diagrammatic representation of potato micropropagation by node culture and micro-tuber production. (A) Tuber obtained from a multi-generation pathogen-infected field potato population; (B) meristem tip explants excised from sprouted tuber sections; (C) establishment of meristem tip in culture; (D) culture is SPT and indexed for other contaminants; (E) shoots determined to be specific pathogen free are propagated by node culture to increase numbers; (F) microcuttings are rooted and acclimatized ex vitro; (G) tubers produced ex vitro from STP plants are used as planting stock; (H) field planting of STP seed tuber; (I) shoots may be transferred to a microtuber induction medium and promotive conditions; (J) microtubers produced are stored or used as STP seed tubers for field planting.

Meristem Tip Culture

Meristem tip refers to the region of shoot apex lying distal to the youngest leaf primordia, whereas shoot apex includes meristem tips plus a few sub-adjacent leaf primordia. Meristem tip culture is a method in which shoot meristem (meristem tip) is cultured *in vitro* with a few leaf primordia. The meristem when cultured *in vitro* on a suitable medium, differentiates into whole plants identical to the parent plant. Ball (1946) was the first to obtain rooted plants of *Tropaealum majus* and *Lupinus albus* from excised shoot apical dome.

Meristem tips are carefully excised from shoot tip. Shoot tips taken from *in vitro* growing plant material need not to be sterilized. The shoot buds or tips are excised from field grown plant material. The bud is taken under stereozoom microscope. Meristematic region at the apex is gradually uncovered by gradually removing the scales, immature leaves and pubescence with the help of very fine needles and blades. Then the apical meristem was gently removed from parental tissue by giving a horizontal cut at the base and cultured on solid medium supplemented with growth regulators, which induce plantlet regeneration.

Though, meristem culturing has been extensively used for vegetative propagation of many crops and fruit trees, it is mainly employed to obtain virus free plants since in infected plants the apical meristems are generally either free or carry a low concentration of viruses. The question need to be answered is why the meristems escape the viruses and how meristem culture leads to the production of virus free plants. Various reasons, explaining the use of meristem culture to obtain virus free plants, have been proposed. The most plausible explanation appears to be that there is a competition in a meristem between cell production and virus multiplication. Another explanation is the virus deactivating system in the plant body if any has higher activity in the meristems than in any other region. Absence of vascular system and plasmodesmata in the meristem greatly hinders the transport of virus particles.

In vitro Tuberization

Another method of mass propagation is the *in vitro* tuberization. The tuberization *in vitro* can be induced by culturing axillary shoots of potato to a culture medium supplemented with cytokinins and growing the cultures under an 8 hours photoperiod, at 22° C. *In vitro* produced tubers or minitubers have the following advantages:

1. A continuous year round production in large quantities.
2. This enables an easy shipment and convenient supply of material.
3. They can be stored for several months.
4. In vitro tuberization provdes an opprotunities to carryout an year round operation with year round scheduling according to the market demand.

It has been estimated that higher yields of the order of 5-6 times was obtained by *in vitro* tuberization over conventional methods. Similar, *in vitro* tuberization can also be induced in tropical tuber crops like *Dioscorea alata* (Yam) by culturing them under controlled conditions.

Somatic Embryogenesis

Somatic embryogenesis is the development of embryos from immature embryos and other somatic tissues cultured *in vitro* on defined media or from cells cultured in suspension. It is a process by which embryo like structure appears to recapitulate the typical stage in the embryogenesis of a zygote, which ultimately give rise to whole plants. Such types of embryos are referred to as somatic embryos since they are formed from sporophytic or somatic cells, in contrast to gametophytic or gametic cells. Somatic embryogenesis was first described in carrot (*Daucus carota*) by Reinert, 1958 and Steward *et al.*, (1958). This phenomenon has been observed in over 200 species (Ammirato, 1983).

Somatic embryogenesis can be induced from a variety of explants such as leaf, floral parts, young inflorescences, anther, immature embryos, nucellus, anthers etc. Both zygotic and somatic embryos share similar ontogeny passing through globular, heart shaped, torpedo and cotyledonary stages in the case of dicotyledons; globular, scutellar and coleoptilar stages for monocotyledons; embryonal suspensor mass, globular, torpedo and cotyledonary for conifers. There are two different routes for somatic embryogenesis.

Direct Somatic Embryogenesis

Somatic embryos arise directly from a cell or tissue without an intermediary phase of callus.

Indirect Somatic Embryogenesis

Somatic embryos arise from callus. The process of somatic embryogenesis normally takes place in following two stages:

1. **First**, the induction of cells with embryogenic competence referred to as proembryonic cell masses or clumps, proembryos etc. in the presence of high auxin.
2. Second, the development of embryogenic masses or proembryos into embryos in the absence or lower concentrations of auxins. Several factors such as cultural medium, growth regulators, carbon source, development stage of the explant and cultural conditions influence somatic embryogenesis.

Mass propagation through somatic embryogenesis, can best be achieved using suspension cultures. Mass propagation of some of the ornamental species and vegetables like celery and carrot, which quickly form somatic embryos in suspension culture, has been adopted on commercial scale. Date palm has successfully been multiplied through somatic embryogenesis and some of the commercial tissue culture labs have already exploited this technique. Tissue culture of oil palm is commercially important and is cloned at present on large scale through embryogenic cultures. Protocol for mass propagation of oil palm through somatic embryogenesis is now available in many labs. Plant produced through somatic embryogenesis had more uniform growth than seedling derived plants. It is estimated that higher yields of the order of 30 per cent and improved oil quality would be obtained by cloning palms possessing the desired characters.

In addition to their use in mass propagation, somatic embryos have been recently used to prepare synthetic seeds by their encapsulation in an appropriate matrix. Early reports in this case have been in carrot, celery and alfalfa. The main thrust idea is to prepare a simple delivery system by which the embryos survive sowing process, develop further and finally germinate. Although the technique is quite recent, it offers many advantages on a commercial scale. The resultant plant population, which originates from the synthetic seed will be uniform. The direct delivery of somatic embryos will save many subcultures to obtain plantlet from regenerated embryos. The encapsulated material could be packed with pesticides, fertilizers, nitrogen fixing bacterial and even microscopic parasite destroying worms. Thus, an artificial or synthetic seed may be defined as an analoguous to a true seed in which a somatic embryo is encapsulated with a coating material, which can be a thin or thick covering. There is another term `conversion' which is generally used in literature alongwith artificial seeds. Conversion is defined as the germination (elongation of radicle) of a somatic embryo followed by the development of a vigorous root system. The root is directly connected to a shoot.

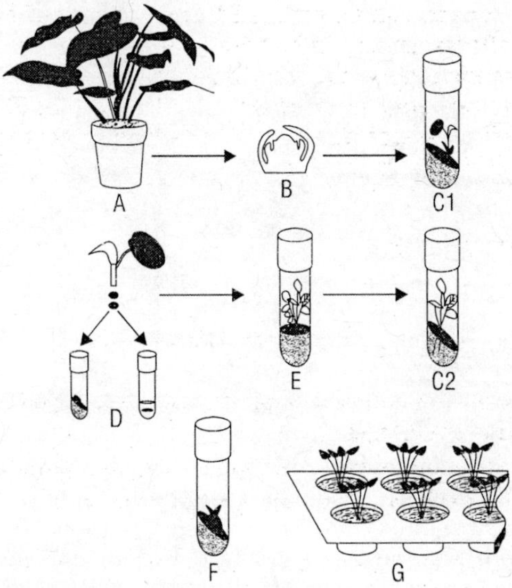

FIGURE 13.6: Diagrammatic representation of the *Syngonium* shoot culture laboratory exercise protocol. (A) Nodal and terminal vine tip explants are obtained from potted plants and then surface disinfested. (B) Successive inner ieaf layers are removed to isolate the meristem and shoot tip explants. (C) Primary explants are inoculated onto SEM (C1) and SMM (C2). Growth responses are compared after 6 weeks of culture. (D) Thin basal stem cross sections, excised from 6-week-old shoots generated on SEM, are cultured in both liquid and agar-solidified AC Broth for 7days to screen for the presence of cultivable contaminants. (E) Shoots are transferred to SEM. (F) Cultures screening positive for contaminants are discarded. Sterile cultures are transferred to SMM and cultured for 4 weeks. (G) Microcuttings are rooted and acclimatized ex vitro (Stage IV).

However, to start programmes on synthetic seeds, several basic studies are to be conducted. The plant should have the capacity to produce large number of somatic embryos over a long time period. The next step is to synchronize the development of somatic embryos since somatic embryos usually develop asynchronously from a cell mass comprising embryogenic tissue.

Two types of artificial seeds have been reported in literature: **desiccated** and **non-desiccated**. It varies from species to species whether a somatic embryos is to be dessicated or not since in soybean conversion has been improved from 30 per cent to 60 per cent in desiccated somatic embryos whereas conversion was reported 59 per cent in *Triticum*, which was less than achieved with non desiccated embryos.

Somatic embryos have successfully encapsulated in hydrated gels. The most practical encapsulation system has been found to be dripping of two per cent sodium alginate from a separatory funnel into a 100 mM calcium nitrate solution. The moment sodium alginate drops emerges at the tip of the funnel, a somatic embryo is inserted. These encapsulated embryos are complexed in calcium salt for about 20 minutes after which these are rinsed in water and stored in a closed container. The capsules containing somatic embryos, generally dry out, within 24 hours if these are not placed in air tight containers. The coating material is desirably packed with nutrients, hormones and biofertilizers.

Artificial seed research has successfully been done in Banana, sandalwood, in some cereal crops *viz.*, barley, rice and finger millet. The production of synthetic seeds in rice might be useful in the propagation and delivery of high yielding, individual hybrids.

So far the most advanced synthetic seed system has been developed for alfalfa where direct field planting has been accomplished. Despite the fact that somatic embryogenesis has been achieved for many plant species the efforts are called for research on somatic embryogenesis in valuable crop plants. Synthetic seed technology in years to come would certainly find its application in Agriculture, Forestry and Horticulture.

METHODS OF MICROPROPAGATION (GENERAL)

Shoot tip is the starting material for micropropagation, which is surface sterilized then trimmed and the remaining material placed on one of a variety of different media. The selection of specific medium is necessary with special reference to concentrations of particular growth regulator. This is the phase for acclimatization of the tissue to the *in vitro* conditions, which requires about 3 or 4 months and varies from species to species. Under the suitable laboratory conditions the small shoot tip grows well in a normal fashion, giving rise to a small, unrooted shoot in culture.

The initiated shoot can, after a suitable period on the initiation medium, be subcultured so that the nodal sections of the shoot are placed onto a multiplication medium. This medium differs from the initiation medium in that it contains higher levels of cytokinins, which are likely to give rise to precocious shooting of the axillary buds. The normal period between subcultures is 3 weeks and during this time the number of shoot tips available for subculture will multiply as a result of breaking of nodal axillary buds anywhere from 2 to 12 times. After 3 weeks on multiplication medium, somewhere on an average of about 5 shoot tips can be placed onto fresh medium, and these in turn will multiply 5 times in the subsequent 3 weeks, and thus micropropagation has led to a 25-fold increase in the plant material available over a total of 6 weeks. Rooting of above cultured micro-shoots can occur in two ways. One can transfer the shoot to media rich in auxins, which will allow for the induction of *in vitro* roots. In some species it is necessary since they need to be actively induced to root.

Which Material should be used?

1. The starting material for a micropropagation programme is a shoot tip, not necessarily as small as the meristematic apical dome, but something a little larger with leaf primordia already developing around it.
2. This material must initially be surface sterilized.
3. Any tissue affected by exposure to sterilize material is trimmed and the remaining material placed on one of a variety of different media.

Stages of Micropropagation

1. Selection and sterilization of elite plants
2. Establishment of axillary buds in culture
3. Multiplication in culture
4. Rooting of in vitro plants and transfer to compost

Materials

Stage I: Selection and Sterilization of Elite Plants: The selected elite stock plants should be visibly free from any sign of disease, stress, or surface blemishes. This material is grown in an environmentally controlled growth cabinet or clean glasshouse. It should be tested for the presence of specific viruses by using ELISA techniques. It is used for identification of viruses. Sterilization is done by using 70% ethanol plus four drops of surfactant (manoxol)/100 ml solution at room temperature or 2% chloros plus four drops of surfactant (manoxol)/100 ml solution at room temperature should be used.

Stage II: Establishment of Axillary Buds in Culture: 1mm diameter sterile Petri dishes containing approximately 10 ml of medium 1 or 85 mm diameter sterile Petri dishes containing approximately 25 ml of medium should be used. Use incubator or environmentally controlled growth chamber allowing environmental conditions of 20-24 °C (depending on variety or species), a 16-h photoperiod, and a light intensity of 4000-6000 lux.

Stage III: Multiplication in Culture: 1 ml sterile jars containing approximately 30 ml of medium 2 or medium 3. Environmental conditions as described for Stage II.

Stage IV: Rooting of *in vitro* Plants and Transfer to Compost: 1 ml sterile jars containing approximately 50 ml of medium 4, Propagation trays, plastic bags, or seed trays covered with glass sheets or a misting or fogging system, 50 mm diameter pots containing compost (3:2, peat: sand) supplemented with nutrients.

For potato (Solanum tuberosum) these are:

Osmocote	57 g
Sulphated potash	21 g
Epsom salts	28 g
Frit 252 A	14 g
Lime	170 g
Phosphate per 300 l peat sand mix	85 g

Methods

Stage I: Selection and Sterilization of Elite Plants

1. Use a clean sharp blade, carefully excise axillary buds of the desired variety and store in distilled water until enough buds have been obtained.
2. Commercial preparations of M&S and B5 salt (minus sucrose glutamine and hormones) are available in packets that make up 1 l of media.
   a) pH adjusted using. 1M HCl and 0.1M KOH before agar added and prior to autoclaving.
   b) The amount of agar needed varies depending on the brand used.
   c) Varying the hormones allows the above media to be used for axillary bud culture of a wide range of species.
   d) The practical should be conducted in a laminar flow bench.

3. Put a maximum of 20 buds into a sterile test tube.
4. Fill to the brim with ethanol solution and leave for 1-1.5 min.
5. Decant the ethanol.
6. Fill to the brim with chloros solution, replace the top, and agitate at 120 strokes/min for 12 min, either manually or with a shaker.
7. Decant the chloros solution and refill with sterile distilled water.
8. Rinse in sterile distilled water 3x.
9. Store in sterile distilled water until reedy to continue (not longer than 2h).

Stage II: Establishment of Axillary Buds in Culture

1. Empty the water plus axillary buds into an empty sterile Petri dish, for ease of handling.
2. Place up to 4 buds in a 50 mm Petri dish or 10 buds in an 85 mm Petri dish containing medium 1.
3. Make sure that the base of the bud is stuck firmly in the medium.
4. Take care that the bud is not buried.
5. Seal the Petri dish with laboratory sealing film, ensuring adequate gaseous exchange by puncturing the film 2-4x with a fine sterile needle.
6. Transfer to growth room or incubator, and leave for between 1 week and 2 months depending on the variety.

Stage III: Multiplication in Culture

1. When shoot extends, cut internodes, and transfer apical cutting and internodal cuttings to sterile jars containing medium 2 or 3.
2. Make sure that the basal portion of the stem is firmly pressed into the medium without burying the explant.

TABLE 13.1: Amounts of Chemicals (gL^{-1} or $mg\ L^{-1}$) in Media used in axillary bud culture of *Solanum* species based on either Murashige and Skoog medium or Gambourg B5 medium

Chemicals	Medium 1 (M&S)	Medium 2 (M&S)	Medium 3 (B5)	Medium 4 (M&S)
NH_4NO_3	1.65 g	1.65 g	-	1.65g
KNO_3	1.9g	1.9 g	2.5g	1.9g
$CaCl_2$ $2H_2O$	0.44 g	0.44g	0.15g	0.44g
$MgSO_4$ $7H_2O$	0.37g	0.37 g	0.25g	0.37g
KH_2PO_4	0.17g	0.17 g	-	0.17g
$(NH_4)_2SO_4$	-	-	13.4g	-
$NaH_2PO_4.H_2O$	-	-	0.15g	-
FeNa EDTA	36.7 mg	36.7 mg	40.0 mg	36.7 mg
H_3BO_3	6.2 mg	6.2 mg	3.0 mg	6.2 mg
$MnSO_4.4H_2O$	22.3 mg	22.3 mg	10.0 mg	22.3 mg
$ZnSO_4.7H_2O$	8.6 mg	8.6 mg	2.0 mg	8.6 mg
KI	0.83 mg	0.83 mg	0.75 mg	0.83 mg
$Na_2MoO_4.2H_2O$	0.25 mg	0.245 mg	0.25 mg	0.25mg
$CuSO_4.5H_2O$	0.025 mg	0.025 mg	0.025 mg	00.025 mg
$CoCl_2.6H_2O$	0.025 mg	0.025 mg	0.025 mg	0.025 mg
Nicotinic Acid	0.50 mg	0.50 mg	1.0 mg	0.50 mg
Thiamine HCl	0.10 mg	0.10 mg	10.0 mg	0.10 mg
Pyridoxine HCl	0.50 mg	0.50 mg	1.0 mg	0.50 mg
Glycine	2.0 mg	2.0 mg	-	2.0 mg

Chemicals	Medium 1 (M&S)	Medium 2 (M&S)	Medium 3 (B5)	Medium 4 (M&S)
Sucrose	20.0 g	20.0 g	20.0 g	20.0 g
Inositol	0.1 g	0.1 g	0.1 g	0.1 g
Glutamine	0.1 g	0.1 g	0.1 g	-
BAP (6-benzyl-amino purine)[4]	0.25 mg	0.25 mg	0.25 mg	0.25 mg
GA3 (gibberellic acid)[4]	0.1 mg	-	-	-
NAA (1-napthalene-acetic acid)	-	-	-	0.05 mg l^{-1}
pH	5.64	5.64	5.64	5.64
Agar (Difco Bacto)	8.0 g	8.0 g	8.0 g	8.0 g

Stage IV: Rooting of in vitro Plants and Transfer to Compost

1. Cut off the top 5 mm of in vitro plant (apex plus 2 or 3 nodes).
2. Transfer to medium 4. (12 plants/250 ml jar).
3. Leave for 3-5 d until 3 or 4 small, study roots approximately 5 mm long are visible.
4. Remove each plantlet carefully from the jar, removing as much agar as is possible without harming the root structure.
5. Transfer to damp compost in 50 mm pots.
6. Keep in high humidity conditions 12-24 h (propagator, plastic bag, misting, or the like).
7. Transfer to the glasshouse, preferably placing on top of capillary matting. Shade from direct sunlight.
8. When the plants are approximately 70 mm high and have begun to lose their juvenile characteristics, they should be hardened off and transferred to larger pots or to the field.

IMPORTANT CONSIDERATIONS AND PRECAUTIONS

Problems and Contamination in Culture

Contamination by Bacteria and Fungi: Bacteria (*Pseudomonas* sp., *Erwinia* sp. and *Bacillus* sp.) are the major causative factor of contamination during large-scale micropropagation of some plants. These slow-growing bacteria contaminants and persist even after initial surface sterilisation of explants. Such contaminants may persist for many generations without being noticed and cause reduction in vigour or chlorosis in propagated plantlets. Addition or antibiotics or fungicides to the culture medium may control the infection by microbial contaminants but for propagation of plants normally infected with latent or symptomless types of viruses or mycoplasmas, it is necessary to maintain stock of plants of them which are disease-free. Surface sterilization should remove most contamination. Frequent scrutiny of cultures should allow healthy buds to be transferred to fresh medium if occasional contaminated buds are seen. Alternatively, placing fewer explants in smaller Petri dishes reduces the problem and infected plants can then be discarded. The use of antibiotics to suppress bacterial or fungal infections is generally ineffective.

Contamination by Viral Pathogens: The danger can be minimized by testing for infections using known viruses, before initiating the culture. Once in culture, viral pathogens generally do not produce any symptoms, but are rapidly spread by axillary bud cultures. The smaller the piece of tissue used to initiate cultures, the less risk there is of transferring viral infection. To reduce this risk to a minimum, meristems can be used to initiate cultures.

Browning of the Medium: This kind of problem is commonly found during micropropagation of woody perennials. This occurs due to the accumulation of inhibiting substances in the growth medium specially during initiation of cultures. Explants from adult tissues of these species often produce excessive amounts of phenolic substances, which turn the medium dark brown. Such a medium is toxic to the tissues and inhibits their growth. Quick transfer of explants to a fresh medium at short intervals could alleviate this problem in orchid bud cultures. Browning of the medium may also be prevented by dissecting explant tissues under the surface of liquids or by incorporating ascorbic acid or citric acid in culture media. For teak tissue cultures, polyvinyl pyrrolidone has proved an effective amendment to the culture medium. Certain phenolic compounds *e.g.*, phloroglucinol (PG) have been found essential for shoot multiplication and rooting in a number of rosaceous cultivars. PG (found in the xylem sap of apple) is known to promote shoot multiplication and rooting in Pissardi plum and *Cinchona*.

Precautions For Sterile Culture: Use a laminar flow bench, and swab down the bench, roof, and sides with disinfectant. Always wear gloves (thin latex gloves are best), and swab gloves and bench surface frequently during any experimental work. Sterilize and flame all instruments before use. Finally, avoid passing anything over the top of opened containers.

1. **Stage I:** Choose as juvenile a tissue as possible to initiate cultures. Do not try to sterilize too many different genotypes at once. Start with 1 or 2, and build up to about 6. Problems of contamination and toxic effects of the sterilant increase with increased numbers of genotypes being treated simultaneously.
2. **Stage II:** Condensation can be a problem in Petri dishes. This can be minimized by stacking the Petridishes and rotating the position of each dish in the stack daily. The intensity of light reaching each culture does not appear to be critical at this stage, although light is necessary.
   Gibberellins tend to produce elongated, abnormal looking shoots. These revert to normal growth when transferred to medium that does not contain gibberellins. Callusing will occur around the base of the bud; only shoots that can be clearly seen to have derived from extension of the preexisting axillary bud should be transferred. Adventitious shoot formation in callus tissue generally produces high levels of variation and is the basis for producing somatic variants.
3. **Stage III:** Murashige and Skoog medium and Gambourg B5 medium are those most frequently used in the culture of axillary buds. They often need to be modified, mainly by varying the vitamins and growth regulators, depending on the species or variety being used.
   If the intent is to use the axillary bud cultures as a source of protoplasts, then all media need to be made up using distilled deionized water or water of equal purity other additions may also have to be made to the culture medium.
   Vitrification can be a serious problem in in vitro cultures. In this condition, the shoots tend to elongate and look glassy, the leaves become reduced or malformed, and if not treated the culture will die. The causes of vitrification are not fully understood. However, the risk of vitrification can greatly reduced if there is adequate gaseous exchange between the culture and the external environment which is achieved by piercing laboratory film seals or by loosening jar lids slightly.
4. **Stage IV:** Rooting and transfer of plants to compost can be difficult. If the auxin level is too high, subsequent root development after transfer to compost is

reduced. Some species can be transferred to compost without a rooting step. Some fruit tree species need a dark treatment as well as additions of auxin for successful rooting to take place (5). The transition from culture to compost is critical. High humidity must be maintained, but care must be taken not to waterlog the compost. If plants are transferred to the field, they need protection from wind damage, drought, and birds.

Once the micropropagated plants are satisfactorily rooted in soil or soil substitutes, they must be grown to a normal humidity level. During the rooting process, they require about 100% humidity, which inhibits the normal development of cuticle and stomatal activity associated with drier conditions. The rooting normally takes place under conditions of reduced lighting; therefore, the plants must not be exposed for the first time to full sunlight. This is done slowly for a period of couple of weeks. This procedure will develop small, autonomous and photosynthesizing plants. During the rooting phase under the reduced lighting conditions, they live on carbohydrate reserves built up during micropropagation period *in vitro*. Once this weaning process is completed, the hardened can be incorporated into normal growing systems for their further development.

COMMERCIAL ASPECTS OF MICROPROPAGATION

About thirty companies in the country who are setting up plant tissue culture facilities for micropropagation. More than a dozen are already exporting tissue cultured plants and also selling in the domestic market. Recently one of the State Seed Corporations-the Maharashtra State Seed Corporation (MSSC) has set up a tissue culture facility for micropropagation of banana at Akola in Vidarbha. The SPIC facility near Coimbatore is going to be the largest such facility in Asia. Tissue cultured planting material is available for *Elettaria cardamomum*, *Amomum subalatum* (Cardamom), *Musa* spp. (Banana), *Fragaria* spp. (Strawberry), *Carica papaya* (Papaya), *Pyrus malus* (Apple), *Prunus persica* (Peach), Lilies, *Rosa* spp. (Roses), *Dianthus* spp. (Carnations), *Gerbera*, *Eucalyptus*, *Tectona grandis* L (Teak), *Populus deltoids* (Poplars) and *Bambusa* spp. (Bamboo). Tissue culture Cardamom plants have given over 29.5% increased yield were conducted in three States Karnataka, Tamil Nadu and Kerala. Tissue cultured banana plants matured uniformly and a month earlier in comparison to the plants raised by suckers in the experimental plantings of BARC and MSSC.

The Department of Biotechnology established two large facilities for tissue culture propagation of forest tree species, one at the National Chemical Laboratory (NCL), Pune and other at the Tata Energy Research Institute (TERI), New Delhi. Both these units have transferred over 3.5 lakh plants to the Forest Department in the State of Haryana, Rajasthan, Uttar Pradesh, Maharashtra, Karnataka, Andhra Pradesh and Tamil Nadu. They cover an area of 200 ha. The initial growth parameters show a distinct advantage of the tissue cultured plants. Quantitative data on cost-benefit ratio would be available in few years. Dr. A. F. Mascrenhas from National Chemical Laboratories, Pune and Dr. Vibha Dhawan from TERI are here and will give you more details.

Cost of tissue cultured plants would always be higher. Ultimately the success will depend on the cost-benefit ratio for each species. This is most crucial for any commercial activity. What can be the profitably sold in the market will attract investment from the business community ? Scientists, in general, have no or very little knowledge of the market and hence identification of the right 'product' which is most important should be done in consultation with the industry. So far, the export market is largely for the ornamentals, especially the foliage plants and also floriculture. Globally the floriculture market is supposed to be Rs 750 Billion. In considering the cost-benefit ratio, the social and environment benefits for which it is difficult to assign a monetary value are equally important. This is specially true in forestry and agro-forestry.

Large Potential Market

There is a large potential for horticultural plants in domestic market, spices, and vegetatively propagated crops like sugarcane, potato, etc. Good planting material enhances the productivity but only to a limited extent. Good management, good agronomy, pest and disease control are equally important. All this would lead to good production. At present, India have the advantage of low cost manpower which is attracting the foreign companies to India for buy-back arrangements with local companies. Abroad, tissue culture research is aiming at automation and robotics. This may, in future, take away the advantage we have in India, at present.

Futuristic Outlook of Micropropagation

The transformation of self-sufficient agriculture to commercial and industrial agriculture and on to agribusiness will be the future task for Indian economy. Agri-exports are going to contribute a large share in countries foreign trade. In the eastern region you already have the large tea and jute industries. Genetic wealth of the fruit crop in the region can be realized for economic growth. The potential of the region for growing high value orchids and other ornamental plants in yet to be exploited. The role of tissue culture laboratories in the University and Colleges is in the budding stage. It can be enlarged into production oriented training units. They can accept contractual work for the propagation of specific plants from industry and nurseryman. This would provide opportunity to earn while gaining practical experience for the Botany students. All the same time they will also be exposed to the working of the industry. In the area of plant tissue culture and micropropagation, though we have the competence, knowledge and essential infrastructure, but still we have to go far to develop standard low cost technology to gain a source of immense wealth for India.

CHAPTER 14

Somatic Embryogenesis

Somatic embryogenesis is the process by which the somatic cells or tissues develop into differentiated embryos, and each fully developed embryo is capable of developing into a plantlet (young or miniature plant). Embryos can be obtained either directly from cultured explants (the organized structures, for example, leaf, hypocotyl, stem and other plant parts) and anthers (or pollen) or indirectly from callus (an unorganized mass of parachymatous tissue derived from explant culture as a result of wound response) and isolated single cells in culture. The process of embryogenesis involves various stages of differentiation and development such as proembryo, globular, heart-shape and torpedo embryo.

In fact, somatic embryogenesis is essentially similar in structure, function and biochemistry to that of zygotic embryogenesis (embryo derived from fertilized egg cell- the zygote), and somatic embryos share many characteristic features with zygote embryos; for instance, both are bipolar structures and originate from a single cell and do not show vascular differentiation. Nevertheless, somatic embryos are large in size and sometimes show more than two cotyledons (**pluricotyledony**) as compared to zygote embryos, which are smaller in size and exhibit two cotyledons (in case of dicots). Significantly, a large number of embryos potential use in volume and rapid micropropagation of high value crops, including crops propagated by seeds. Despite its potential, this method has not yet been commercialized, except in case of oil palm *(Elaeis guineensis)*.

More recently, the embryos derived from somatic cells (mostly) or pollens are being utilized in the preparation of artificial seeds, which appear to be of great value in plant propagation programme.

There are several differences between the two pathways of regeneration: a bipolar somatic embryo arises from a single cell and shows no vascular connection with the maternal tissue or explant; in fact in develops a closed radicular end. In organogenesis, on the other hand, the origin is multicellular and the monopolar structure develops procambial strands, which establish a connection with the pre-existing vascular tissue dispersed within the callus or the cultured explant.

The main difference between embryogenesis and organogenesis can be appreciated at the theoretical level. Normally, organogenesis is a property of the somatic tissues, whereas embryogenesis pertains to the reproductive tissues.

The properties of a reproductive tissue, which are acquired, *in vivo*, during the phase transition that occurs when a vegetative meristem becomes a floral bud, are acquired by the somatic cells *in vitro* through a process which is normally called **acquisition of totipotency**, but whose molecular mechanism is far from being understood.

Somatic embryogenesis has been described in more than a hundred species and it is likely that with the passage of time more, hitherto recalcitrant species, will be made to exhibit this potentiality. Of the several factors that affect the induction of somatic embryogenesis, foremost are the genotypes of the starting material, origin of the explant and media composition, particularly with respect to hormones.

CARROT AS A EMBRYOGENIC SYSTEM

There are now a number of embryogenic systems that work satisfactorily but carrot, the first to be described, is still the best. A number of embryogenic lines of carrot have been maintained in suspension cultures, in some cases for more than ten years. When hormones are removed from the medium and the cell concentration is lowered, these lines start the embryogenic programme that leads to a plantlet through the morphologically defined stages of *globular*, *heart* and *torpedo-shaped* embryos.

SOMATIC AND ZYGOTIC EMBRYOS

Somatic embryos show a few differences from a zygotic one. In the initial stages, the suspensor is less developed in somatic embryos (perhaps a reflection of its uselessness under *in vitro* conditions).

However, an important difference is that whereas the zygotic embryos after forming embryonal axis, with the apical meristems, prepare for dormancy, the somatic embryos do not undergo desiccation and dormancy and embryogenesis goes on from initial cell to plantlet without interruption. *In vivo*, development is similar to somatic embryogenesis up to the torpedo stage. Later, development of somatic embryos, particularly the developmental programme of the meristems, follows a path, which, in a sense, shows more analogies with organogenesis.

TOTIPOTENCY AND ROLE OF AUXIN

A tissue explanted *in vitro* consists of several cell types. The explant is treated with growth regulators so that its cells (or, rather, a fraction of them capable of responding to hormonal stimuli) de-differentiate and start to proliferate. In the presence of an auxin, after several days (sometimes weeks) a population of small, compact cells emerges in this tissue, which can be hand-picked or concentrated by a process of differential centrifugation through a Ficoll gradient.

Proembryogenic Masses and Role of Auxin

Those small, compact cells divide in an asymmetrical way and their daughter cells, sticking together, give rise to typical cell clumps, which have been called proembryogenic masses (Halperin, 1966) or **embryogenic clusters** (McWilliam *et al.*, 1974). From these proembryogenic masses develop embryos upon dilution of cells and removal of hormones. Totipotency once acquired, is a long-lasting capacity in the sense that a cell population that has acquired this property can be subcultivated in the presence of auxin for months and years and yet retain the capacity to generate embryos upon removal of the hormone.

Acquisition of Totipotency

It is clearly one of the most critical steps in somatic embryogenesis. However, the details of the process are not known. Treatment with auxin at high concentration is needed to cause de-differentiation and to elicit totipotency; carrot plantlets regenerated via somatic embryogenesis give rise to adventive embryos directly from the epidermal cells of the stem, but this has never been observed in the plants originated from zygotic embryos.

Various types of auxins have been used for this purpose, *viz.*, the natural auxin IAA and the synthetic ones NAA and 2,4-D. The latter is the most efficient and the most commonly used auxin for the promotion of somatic embryogenesis in carrot tissue cultures.

The natural auxin (IAA) at a low concentration (10^{-6} M) causes its polar and induces the adjacent cells to become specific for its transport; at a higher concentration (10^{-5} M), however, polar transport is switched off and IAA slowly diffuses in all directions (Goldsmith, 1982). In nature, a shift from low to high concentration of auxin (as it may occur on cutting a root and, thus, disrupting the communications and increasing the concentration of IAA in the cells of the wound) causes a block in polar transport and, thus, favours the onset of morphogenetic processes (for example, from callus to a new root). Other examples of re-programming that require the presence of auxin are gall formation and induction of tumours.

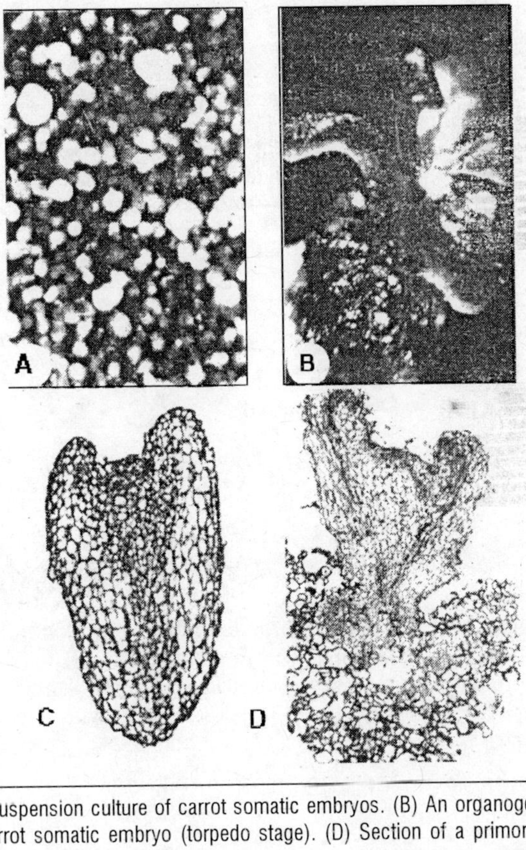

FIGURE 14.1: (A) Suspension culture of carrot somatic embryos. (B) An organogenic callus of tomato. (C) Section of a carrot somatic embryo (torpedo stage). (D) Section of a primordium arising from an organogenic tobacco callus.

LoSchiavo et al. (1989) found a positive correlation between the level of added auxin and the level of methylation in DNA. Among the auxins, 2,4-D can reach the highest intracellular concentration as free auxin, and is also the most efficient in promoting hypermethylation and in morphogenetic activity.

If instead, auxin is retained in the medium, the embryogenic progression stops somewhere before globular stage. The point of arrest is more or less typical of each cell line. Therefore, there will be carrot lines which proliferate showing various stages from undifferentiated cells to globular embryos and others showing only undifferentiated cells and PEM (**pro-embryogenic masses**). It should be noted that auxin affects differentiated cells of an explant by inducing de-differentiation on one hand and formation of embryo primordia (PEM) on the other. This apparent contradiction can be understood if one considers that once PEM are formed they become insensitive to auxin. Auxin sensitivity is then regained at a later stage (post-globular) when the embryos, in the presence of auxin, will stop their differentiative programme and revert back to unorganized tissue.

Experiments on embryogenesis in the presence of TIBA (2,3,5 tri-iodobenzoic acid), a drug that blocks the polar transport of auxin from the cells with consequent increase in the intracellular hormonal levels revealed that during the PEM-globular stages the embryos do not produce auxin, because embryogenesis proceeds normally up to globular stage embryos. Thereafter, the embryos start callusing, which can be explained by assuming the production of IAA, block of its transport, internal accumulation, and callus formation. Hence, after the globular stage the embryos start producing auxin and become sensitive to it and, thus, behave like the somatic tissue (LoSchiavo, unpublished results).

Expression of the Programme in the Absence of Auxin

The onset of embryogenesis leads to a profound rearrangement of the cell metabolism. Such studies are usually made by comparing unorganized callus tissue with embryos. The rate of protein synthesis as well as the rate of poly $(A)^+$RNA synthesis increases in embryos. Also, DNA synthesis and polyamine levels increase. Tubulin genes were also found to expressed at higher levels during embryogenesis. Lipids also show a certain amount of developmental variation.

Methylated Cytosine Level and Development

At the DNA level, changes in the level of methylated cytosine were recorded as a function of the developmental stage. As soon as the hormones are removed (the act that operationally marks the onset of embryogenesis) there is a sudden demethylation that may interest up to 30% of the sites. Then, with progress in the embryogenic process, the level of methylated cytosine goes up again and reconstitutes the level typical of the starting cell population. This methylation is, in part at least, site-specific so that DNA fragements from a genomic DNA library can be used as probes to analyze development-associated variations in cytosine methylation. The development-associated variations were found and, moreover, the pattern of methylation may, in turn, be associated with RNA transcription as measured in Northern blots.

THE GENETIC APPROACH OF SOMATIC EMBRYOGENESIS

The Need

1. Somatic embryogenesis is studied because it is an interesting process, liable to produce results of economic interest.
2. The field of plant embryogenesis is not well developed and somatic embryogenesis looks a promising model system.
3. Somatic embryos provide an interesting tool. It makes possible to mutagenize a cell population, make it to embryogenize and look for mutants of conditional type, *e.g.* temperature-sensitive mutants.

4. The seed embryos, being wrapped in various coats, are not amenable to microsurgery as in case of animal embryos. Moreover, for biochemistry a large number of synchronized embryos is needed and this is not so easy to obtain, particularly if one is interested in early embryonic stages.

This has been done with or without mutagenic treatment, starting from haploid or diploid cell lines, using 24-25 °C as permissive temperature and 31-32 °C as non-permissive one.

The formation of **transgenic plants** and the use of **artifical seeds**, which are the main applications of this technique are so well established.

THE PROCESS OF SOMATIC EMBRYOGENESIS

Induction of the Embryogenic State

Induction of the embryogenic state in differentiated explants often requires extensive proliferation through unorganized callus cycles, death or disruption of surrounding explant cells, and/or high levels or a synthetic auxin such as 2,4-dichlorophenoxyacetic acid (2,4-D) or picloram. Plasmolysis of explant cells was also shown by Wetherell (1984) to enhance somatic embryogenesis in wild carrot (*Daucus carota*). These factors are presumed to alter the epigenetic state of cells, and may be related in their ability to disrupt the cell-cell interactions required to maintain coordinated patterns of development. The role of cell isolation in induction of somatic embryogenesis was reviewed by Williams and Maheswaran (1986). Smith and Krikorian (1989) showed that breakage or wounding of zygotic embryos at explanting led to formation of somatic embryos on a hormone-free medium. Constituent cells of the damaged tissues were presumably released from positional or chemical restraints and were thus able to express their innate embryogenic potential on a medium permissive for growth. A similar observation was made for *Dysosma pleiantha* by Chuang and Chang (1987). Embryogenic callus was induced from wounded zygotic embryos, while intact embryos failed to respond. Cell isolation is manifest early in somatic embryogenesis by the formation of a cuticle.

In embryogenic cultures, each proembryonic group of cells becomes separated from surrounding cells by thickened, cutinized walls on the outer surface (Williams and Maheswaran, 1986).

Direct somatic embryogenesis, especially in the absence of exogenous auxin, is normally associated with a relatively brief developmental period between the time of cotyledon initiation and the beginning of seed maturation. During this time, embryonic cell division appears to directly clone the existing early embryonic epigenetic state.

Even within this developmental window, some differentiation away from the embryogenic state may be inferred from the nature of structures produced by cellular proliferation. In flax (*Linum usitatissimum*), late cotyledonary stage embryos produced numerous accessory cotyledons in addition to well, formed somatic embryos (Pretova and Williams, 1986).

Developmental gradients within a zygotic embryo are also evident by their response to different auxins. For example, in soybean (*Glycine max*) the tissue that preferentially produces somatic embryos in response to the auxin. When the stronger 2,4-D is used as the inducing auxin, somatic embryos are initiated from a more extensive subset of cotyledon cells.

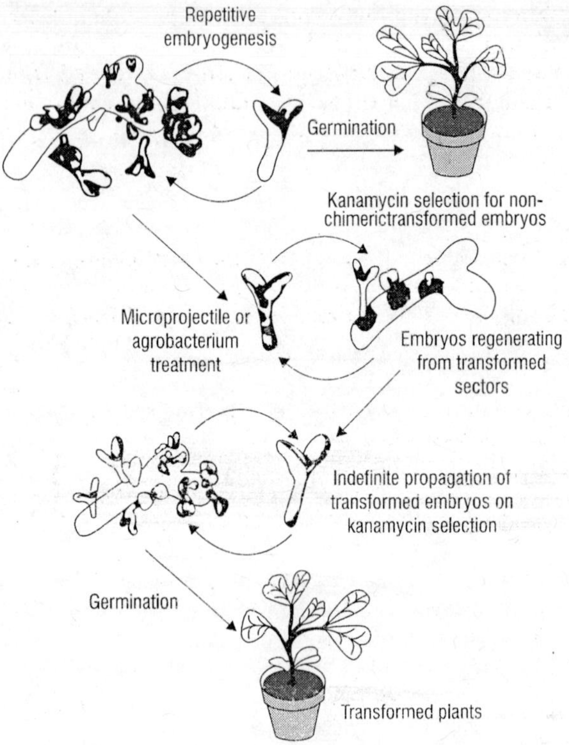

FIGURE 14.2: Recurrent embryogenesis and its use in genetic transformation and mass propagation. Although new embryos can form from older embryos at any stage of development, this example depicts recurrent embryogenesis occurring from cotyledonary stage embryos. Developing embryos can be exposed to *Agrobacterium* or bombarded with microprojectiles, transforming individual epidermal cells. As the embryo continues to grow and develop, transformed cells give rise to patches of transformed tissue from which transformed embryos develop on selection medium. In this example, kanamycin is used as the selection agent, but several other agents could be used, depending on the vector used in transformation. As long as the cycles of recurrent embryogenesis are maintained, transformed or nontransformed embryos can be propagated indefinitely.

Starting with a culture of embryogenic cells in the form of proliferating proembryonic masses, the process of regeneration requires, the initiation of bipolar differentiation to produce cotyledons, shoot apex and root pole, and then, in sequence, maturation of embryos, germination or conversion to plantlets, and transfer of plants out of culture into soil.

RECURRENT EMBRYOGENESIS

It is also known as repetitive, accessory, proliferative, or secondary embryogenesis. The power of embryo cloning techniques and their exploitation for mass propagation, metabolite production, or genetic transformation has recurrent embryogenesis as their basis. It also occurs when primary somatic embryos fail to mature normally into plantlets and instead give rise to successive cycles of embryos, most commonly from superficial cells of the cotyledons or hypocotyl. The process is probably homologous with the proliferation of globular proembryos in standard embryogenic cultures, differing only with respect to the stage at which integrated control of development is lost.

Expressions of recurrent embryogenesis are best viewed as a continuum, with proliferation of globular PEMs or early globular stages at one extreme, and the development of early embryogenic stages on bipolar embryos or germinating plantlets at the other extreme.

Problems

Recurrent embryogenesis may become a problem if it cannot be controlled when germination and normal growth are required. Where it can be stimulated or prevented, it offers the advantage of greatly facilitating mass propagation.

Maintenance

The maintenance of recurrent cycles of somatic embryogenesis can be spontaneous as is the case with alfalfa (*Medicago sativa* L). The cycles are maintained in the absence of growth regulators.

More frequently, however, the initiation of recurrent cultures requires that the developing embryos be locked into a developmental stage beyond which they cannot proceed, thereby repeating a cycle. This can be achieved by initial exposure to a very high auxin concentration such as 40 mg/l of 2,4-D, followed by maintenance of the recurrent system using a lower level of auxin, such as 5 mg/l of 2,4-D, which prevents the transition from proembryonic to embryonic development.

Auxin vs Cytokinin for Induction of Embryogenesis

Although a majority of studies have employed auxins, particularly 2,4-D and NAA, for the induction of somatic embryogenesis from immature embryonic explants, cytokinins have also been used as inducing agents in some instances. When young cotyledonary embryos of white clover (*Trifolium repens*) are explanted and exposed to the cytokinin BAP (6-benzylamino purine), the hypocotyl responds with the formation of somatic embryos. When 2,4-D is used instead of BA, it is the cotyledons that form somatic embryos. Likewise, pea (*Pisum sativum*) shows a positive response from hypocotyl cells in the presence of cytokinin, but it is the cotyledon cells that respond in the presence of auxin. Genotype, tissue type, and developmental stage may all be determining factors in the comparative ability to respond to auxin or cytokinin.

HOW TO OBTAIN EMBRYOS FROM EMBRYOGENIC CULTURES?

As stated earlier, a removal or decrease of the auxin concentration in the growth medium can break the cycle of **continuous proliferation** of PEMs, and permit embryos to develop to maturity.

Brawley et al. (1984) showed that in globular somatic proembryos of carrot (*Daucus carota*), ionic currents flowed inward at the site of the future shoot and out at the site of the future root pole. These currents were identified as being largely a K^+ influx and H^+ efflux. Similar ionic currents have been detected around haploid embryos forming from immature pollen grains of tobacco.

In carrot somatic embryogenesis, electrical polarity is accompanied by asymmetry in the distribution of activated **calmodulin**. Timmers et al. (1989), after using fluphenazine fluorescence, showed that polarity in the distribution of activated calmodulin already exists in the globular proembryogenic masses before morphological polarity is visible. Activated calmodulin concentration remains higher in the region of the root pole. During the later stages of bipolar development, fluphenazine fluorescence is also strong in the region of the forming shoot apex. Polarity in development of somatic embryos has also been detected as asymmetry in DNA synthesis by Nomura and Komamine (1986).

In direct somatic embryogenesis from immature zygotic embryos, suppression of normal polarity may play a role in embryo induction. Zygotic embryos in which growth of the main axis is weak or suppressed are more likely to give rise to somatic embryos from superficial cells.

EMBRYO MATURATION AND THE DEVELOPMENT OF GERMINABILITY

Auxin Levels

It is essential that for germination a embryos must have functional shoot and root apices with the activity of meristematic growth. **High auxin** levels can inhibit development and growth of the shoot meristem if young proembryos are not transferred to a low-auxin or zero-auxin medium after induction. Activated charcoal may be added to the medium to remove excess auxin from the somatic embryos. At **low auxin** levels, shoot meristem formation is usually achieved early after the initiation of cotyledons, so that under inappropriate culture conditions, germination can occur prematurely to give weak or inviable plantlets.

Sucrose Level

For production of vigorous plantlets, a period of embryonic growth and maturation is needed before germination. This can be achieved by culturing at sucrose levels of 3 to 6%, although progressively increasing levels up to 40% have been used for some species. High concentration of sucrose in the medium may cause osmotic desiccation in the embryos, however, for some species, efficient conversion to plantlets also requires the imposition of temporary desiccation before germination. This procedure, which mimics seed maturation *in vivo*, may be necessary to trigger metabolic processes needed for germination and seedling growth. The gradual reduction in osmotic potential through desiccation of mature somatic embryos of wheat (*Triticum aestivum*) improved germination percentages has also been reported.

Heat Shock Treatment

The vigor of the plantlets from dried somatic embryos remains greater than that of plantlets derived from embryos. Heat shock treatment induced a degree of desiccation tolerance in alfalfa somatic embryos that was equivalent to that conferred by ABA treatment but did not have detrimental effects on subsequent growth of plantlets.

ABA Levels

Ammirato (1974) showed that ABA at 10^{-7} M prevented precocious germination of somatic embryos of caraway (*Carum carvi*) in suspension. Ammirato (1983) later reported that the same level of ABA had a similar effect on suspension-cultured carrot somatic embryos, producing embryos more similar to their zygotic counterparts than those grown without ABA. Based on these results, he proposed that regulation of embryo maturation by ABA might be used to facilitate large-scale batch cultures, mechanized planting, artificial induction of dormancy and incorporation into artificial seeds.

The role of ABA in initiating the accumulation of storage reserves has not been ruled out, especially as the initiation of reserve accumulation coincides with the highest levels of endogenous ABA. The role of ABA in the initiation of reserve accumulation has also been observed. They found the presence of ABA essential for the stimulation of storage **protein accumulation** in somatic embryos of interior spruce (mixtures of *Picea glacua*, and *P. engelmannii* and their hybrids).

Water Saturation

Plantlets grown *in vitro* in water-saturated atmosphere show reduced development of cuticular waxes and abnormal stomatal function. On removal from culture, losses of such plantlets can be high if they are not protected from transpirational water loss while roots and normal leaves are developing. Acclimatization of culture-grown plantlets remains a problem in commercial micropropagation, since plantlets must usually be subjected to progressively reduced humidity over a period of week. Somatic embryogenesis offers some hope of avoiding or minimizing acclimatization problems if embryos can be removed from culture at physiological maturity and germinated under normal growing condition.

GENETIC CONTROL OF EMBRYO CLONING

The capacity to undergo somatic embryogenesis from immature zygotic embryos is under some degree of genetic control. This control appears to be the result of a low number of genes, and is, therefore, highly heritable and amenable to selection. Consistent with the observation that low numbers of genes are responsible for regeneration capacity. Regeneration capacity appears to consist of two major parameters, which are commonly measured in the literature.

1. The first is the frequency of explants, which regenerate.
2. The second is the average number of somatic embryos formed per regenerating explant.

The mass propagation and genetic transformation of crops are most likely dependent on the breeding and development of germplasms with a high capacity to undergo recurrent somatic embryogenesis. Once capacity for regeneration has been backcrossed into elite lines and agronomically superior cultivars, embryo cloning techniques will finally be sufficiently efficient to play an important role.

Genotype is one of the factors that influences regeneration from cell culture, however, very little is known about the genetic components of somatic embryogenesis from immature zygotic embryos. The genetics of regeneration of alfalfa is especially well documented and individual genes have been identified and named.

Genetic Variability

Genetic variability for regeneration via somatic embryogenesis has been documented for a wide variety of species, including soybean, maize, rice, barley, wheat, etc. Genetic control of regeneration capacity is largely additive and highly heritable in maize, rice, and wheat.

Cytoplasmic Effects

Cytoplasmic effects have also been important in maize, rice, wheat. In these crops cytoplasmic effects are sufficient to necessitate careful selection of maternal parents to ensure regeneration success. Non-embryogenic callus can be derived from embryogenic callus initiated from immature zygotic embryos of the cultivar Chinese Spring. The use of defined cytogenetic stocks has made it possible to further elucidate the nature of the genetic control of regeneration in wheat.

APPLICATIONS OF SOMATIC EMBRYOGENESIS

The high-volume multiplication of embryonic propagules is the most commercially attractive application of *in vitro* somatic embryogenesis. As commercially conceived, the system involves harvesting maturing embryos from a continuously proliferating embryogenic culture of elite genotype, and converting the harvested **clonal embryos** to **seedling** transplants or synthetic seeds for delivery to the grower. Although the induction of normal embryo physiology, scale-up of culture volume, and design of field delivery systems have so far prevented industrial applications, recent intensive work on synthetic seed systems shows commercial promise.

Mass Propagation

Somatic embryos have powerful advantages for mass propagation in comparison to both conventional clonal propagation methods (*e.g.*, rooted cuttings, grafting) and other *in vitro* regeneration systems (*e.g.*, micropropagation).

One advantage of propagation via somatic embryogenesis is the very high multiplication rates possible with many embryogenic systems. Unlimited numbers of embryos can be generated from a single explant. It depends on type of plant species.

In comparison, multiplication by rooted cuttings is limited to the amount of material available from the mother plant, and for most species, micropropagation also is characterized by relatively low multiplication rates. A second advantage of somatic embryogenesis is that, for many species, both growth of the embryogenic tissue and development of the somatic embryos can be carried out in liquid medium, making possible the handling of enormous numbers of embryos at one time.

Drew (1980) estimated that one liter of a carrot suspension culture contained 1.35 million somatic embryos. Thus, in comparison to rooted cuttings and micropropagation, somatic embryos offer the potential for high volume large-scale propagation systems that can be translated into significant labor savings. Even greater economics of scale may be possible if bioreactor and continuous culture technologies can be applied to embryogenic systems.

Plants derived from somatic embryos are less variable than those derived via organogenesis. This may reflect an intolerance of somatic embryos to mutations in any of the numerous genes that must be necessary for ontogeny to be successfully completed. In contrast, vegetative meristems may be more tolerant to mutations and epigenetic changes.

Probably the most obvious advantage of somatic embryogenesis in comparison to other clonal propagation methods is the fact that the product is an embryo. The morphological and physiological similarity of somatic embryos to zygotic embryos means that they are almost complete propagules in themselves, with embryoinc roots, shoots and leaves (or at least cotyledons) and, most importantly, the programme to make a complete plant. Thus, unlike other clonal propagation systems, no separate shoot growth or rooting steps are required for plantlet production, again providing savings in labor.

Unlike organogenic or axillary branching systems, many embryogenic systems produce discrete embryos, and thus require no physical separation from mother tissue or other embryos in order to be handled, which once again means savings in labor.

Over the past few years, some of these special characteristics of somatic embryogenesis have been examined for possible commercialization purposes. The potential for somatic embryos to be grown in large volumes in continuous culture and employed as direct-delivered propagules has received much attention.

Scale-up Potential

The fact that both the growth of embryogenic cells and subsequent development of somatic embryos can be carried out in **liquid medium** gives somatic embryogenesis the potential to be combined with engineering technology to create large-scale mechanized or automated culture systems. Such systems are capable of producing huge numbers or propagules with low labor inputs. With the application of this technology, costs per propagule have the potential to be reduced to the point where they may be competitive with seed-derived plants, depending on the crop.

Use of Bioreactors

The first report of large-scale embryogenic cultures described an attempt to grow carrot cells in 20-liter carboys, which resulted in the formation of few embryos. The biological/mechanical system most often described for application to embryogenic systems is the stirred-tank bioreactor, a mass culture system originally developed for microbial fermentations, but more recently adapted for growing plant cells on a large scale.

A major problem with adapting these bioreactor designs for use with plant cells is the high shear that stirring generates in these systems. **Air driven bioreactors**, with lower shear levels, have been tested as possible alternatives to the stirred-tank design, and have supported successful growth of a number of plant cell types. Air-lift bioreactors gave slightly higher yields of alfalfa somatic embryos compared to **propeller-stirred bioreactors** or cultures grown in flasks on a shaker.

To date, the application of bioreactor technology has apparently not met its potential to produce hundreds of thousands of clonal embryos capable of growing into plants. To improve the capability of bioreactors to produce competent embryos, a group of researchers has recently developed a kinetic model of carrot somatic embryo development in suspension culture by monitoring substrate utilization, culture growth and embryo development over the time course of an embryogenic culture.

Protoplast Culture

Embryogenic callus and suspension cultures, as well as somatic embryos themselves have been employed as a source of protoplasts for a range of species. The logic of this approach is that isolation of protoplasts from cells or tissues that are themselves regenerable will likely yield protoplast cultures capable of forming whole plants.

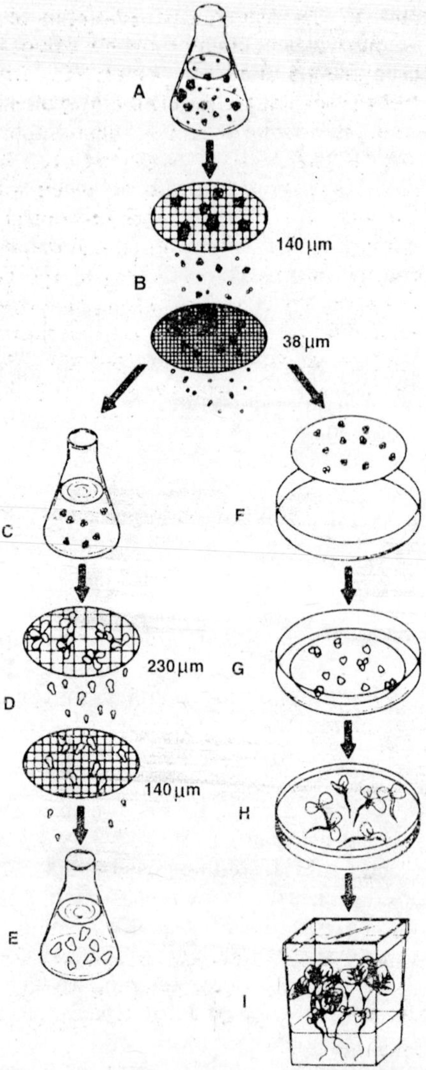

FIGURE 14.3: Fractionation/synchronization of embryogenic yellow-poplar suspension cultures for mass propagation. A Embryogenic suspension are grown in shaken flasks of liquid induction medium. B. PEMs are fractionated on stainless steel sieves, saving the fraction that passes through 140 µm, but not 38 µm mesh. C. Saved fraction is cultured for one week in liquid basal medium. D. Globular stage embryos are fractionated again to eliminate clusters and free cells, saving the fraction that passes through 230 um, but not 140 µm mesh. E. Globular stage embryos are cultured an additional 7-10 days in basal medium to obtain synchronous heart-torpedo stage embryos. Alternatively, following the first fractionation, F. PEMs are immediately placed on filter paper, which is then plated on semisolid basal medium. G. PEMs are cultured on filter paper/basal medium for 12-14 days to obtain synchronous, mature embryos. H. mature embryos are transfered to basal medium without filter paper to promote germination. I. Germinants are transferred to plantlet development medium, from which plantlets are ready for transfer to soil mix in 6-8 weeks.

Earliest application of the regenerative potential of protoplasts isolated from embryogenic material was made with embryogenic carrot suspension cultures.

Since then in three groups of plant species, *viz.* graminaceous species, citrus species, and forest trees (especially conifers), embryogenic cultures have proven to be especially valuable in providing a source of regenerable protoplasts.

In the Gramineae, regeneration of callus or even sustained cell divisions in mesophyll-derived protoplasts could not be achieved following methods that had previously proven successful with mesophyll protoplasts of solanaceous species. Although there were many reports of sustained cell divisions in protoplasts isolated from nonmorphogenic cell suspension cultures of the Gramineae, the protoplast-derived calli failed to undergo morphogenesis. Therefore, Vasil and Vasil (1980) turned to embryogenic cultures derived from immature embryos of pearl millet (*Pennisetum glaucum*) as a source of protoplasts. These protoplasts could be cultured to give rise to cell masses, from which embryoids and eventually plantlets could be regenerated. Similar success was subsequently reported using embryogenic suspensions of several other graminaceous species.

Embryogenic citrus suspension cultures have not only provided a source of regenerable protoplasts, but also made possible the production of interspecific and even intergeneric somatic hybrid plants. Interspecific somatic hybridization in citrus was first achieved by Kobayashi et al. (1988). They fused protoplasts isolated from an embryogenic suspension culture of navel orange (*Citrus sinensis*) cultivar Washington with leaf protoplasts of satsuma mandarin (*Citrus unshiu*) cultivar Hayashi. Interspecific somatic hybrids have since been produced between number of citrus species using similar techniques.

The ability to isolate protoplasts from embryogenic cultures of forest trees has had a large impact on regeneration studies for this group of plants, in particular coniferous species. Although a few researchers reported the growth of protoplasts isolated from conifer cotyledons, leaves, or suspension cultures to the colony or even callus/suspension stage.

The development of embryogenic callus and suspension cultures proved to be the key to the production of morphogenic protoplasts in coniferous.

Embryogenic cultures have also been shown to be a valuable source of regenerable protoplasts in some hardwood forest tree species. Rao and Ozias-Akins (1985) isolated Protoplasts from embryogenic cell suspension cultures derived from proliferating shoot segments of a 20-year-old sandalwood tree (*Santalum album*). The protoplasts could be cultured to form embryogenic cell aggregates, somatic embryos and eventually plantlets.

Similarly, embryogenic suspension cultures of yellow poplar provided protoplasts capable of regenerating whole plants via embryogenesis.

EMBRYO CLONING AND GENE TRANSFER

Regeneration in several species, especially tress and large-seeded legumes, is limited to regenerationn via direct somatic embryogenesis from immature zygotic embryos. The embryos form directly on the original explant tissue. If callus is present, it grows concomitantly with the somatic embryos. The embryos do not originate from it, thereby bypassing any opportunity that a callus phase provides to sort transformed cells from non-transformed cells. Confounding the problem is the fact that these somatic embryos may have originated from groups of cells rather than from single cells within the explant.

As current **gene transfer techniques** transform single cells, not clumps of cells, the recovery of **chimeric embryos** consisting of transformed and non-transformed tissues is virtually assured. Whereas the absence of a callus phase is the main factor that has limited genetic transformation in these species, this barrier has been overcome by the use of recurrent embryogenesis.

In **recurrent embryogenesis**, a cycle is initiated whereby somatic embryos continuously proliferate from previously existing somatic embryos. The cycles of embryo proliferation effectively substitute for a callus phase. Even if a chimeric embryo is obtained in the first cycle of regeneration, it becomes possible to obtain a non-chimeric embryo from the patch of transformed tissue on the original embryo. The recurrent embryos appear to have an epidermal or subepidermal origin. The recurrent embryos have single cell origins. Consequently, if a transformation technique is applied to a primary somatic embryo instead of a zygotic embryo, it should become possible to obtain totally transgenic somatic embryos, and this has, in fact, been observed for walnut.

The nature of recurrent embryogenesis also makes it ideally suited to particle gun mediated transformation (Klein *et al.*, 1987). Instead of relying on *Agrobacterium* to mediate the transfer of genes into plant cells, the particle gun literally shoots into plant cells DNA that has been precipitated onto particles of a heavy metal.

SOMATIC EMBRYOGENESIS IN TREES

The technique and pattern of the development of somatic embryogenesis in tree species differs, depending on wheather the species is angiospermous or coniferous (Gymnsperms). Conifer somatic embryogenesis is analogous to zygotic cleavage polyembryony and for most examples, depends on an *in vitro* proliferation of non-callus, suspensor-like cells derived from mature or immature zygotic embryos. In *Picea abies*, the cells, known as the embryonal suspensor mass (EMS), proliferate on BM-1 medium containing high concentrations of kinetin. Differentiation of ESM to cotyledonary-stage, somatic embryos occurred on BM-1 medium containing 10 per cent of the original kinetin. However, few somatic embryos have been converted to whole plants.

Somatic embryogenesis in angiosperm tree species is either analogous to adventive in crassinucellate angiosperms, nuclear polyembryony as in *Citrus*, or adventive zygotic polyembryony as in immature zygotic embryos of *Juglans*. The key tissue culture manipulation in a number of species was the use of immature zygotic embryos or nucellar tissue as the original explant source. The cell proliferation stage in tissue culture is in the form of an undifferentiated callus.

Somatic embryogenesis has, also been obtained from non-zygotic explant tissue (coffee leaf), suggesting that somatic embryogenesis may be obtained from sexually immature tree, zygotic embryo or ovule tissue is not available, thus it accelerate the process of tree genetic engineering.

Difficulties in developing somatic embryogenesis systems for tree species are similar to those for herbaceous species. However, tree species may also exhibit a unique set of tissue culture-dependent variabilities. Genetic variation may be higher for tree species than cultivated herbaceous species. The size of the genome is quite large for many trees, which is particularly important for genetic engineering. A further limitation for tree improvement using genetic engineering is that mature material must be collected from the field rather than from a controlled environment.

In addition, the problem of ecotypic or physiological variation from individual to individual is much greater due to the overall heterozygosity of most tree species. These additional variables further increase the potential difficulty of developing repeatable somatic embryogenesis in tree species.

For the production of artificial seeds in tree species, the recovery of plants (conversion) is crucial. Possibly, mango is the first tree species for which the viable artificial seeds have been produced. *Citrus* and coffee which already have reasonable conversion frequencies.

For the production of artificial seeds in tree species, the recovery of plants (conversion) is crucial. Possibly, mango is the first tree species for which the viable artificial seeds have been produced. *Citrus* and coffee, which already have reasonable conversion frequencies.

CHAPTER 15

Somaclonal and Gametoclonal Variant Selection

In plant cell, genetic variability develops spontaneously during tissue cultures. The term *somaclonal variation* was introduced by Larkin and Scowcroft (1981). Plant variant obtained from tissue culture is called **somaclones**. Evans et al (1984) coined the term **gametoclonal** variation for variant clones specifically raised from gametic or gametophytic cells. Occurrence of somaclonal variation in regenerated plants is considered a rule rather than exception.

Studies concerning different aspects of somaclonal variation are important for several reasons.

1. **First**, it is hailed as a novel source of genetic variation. However, successful utilization of somaclonal variation heavily depends upon its systematic evaluation and judicious utilization in breeding programmes. This necessitates appropriate experimentation.
2. **Second**, somaclonal variation is of interest as a basic genetic process, since it contradicts the concept of **clonal uniformity**. The cells and tissues which are expected to produce true to type plants through the processes of de-differentiation, division and re-differentiation, possibly perceive the whole process as stress, as a result of which the genome, known for its plasticity, restructures itself to modulate the expression of genes as demanded by the in vitro conditions.
3. **Third**, somaclonal variation is unwanted when the objective is micropropagation of elite genotypes or genetic transformation, which partly involve tissue culture. Under such circumstances, prevention or at least minimization of variation is of utmost importance. To achieve this, the frequency, nature and magnitude of somaclonal variation in relation to manipulation of media components, explant source, culture conditions etc. should essentially be understood.

Majority of studies undertaken on somaclonal variation are confined to early generations of somaclones. Therefore, information on the nature, inheritance pattern and stability of morphological and molecular changes expressed in the advanced generations of somaclones is lacking.

The different aspects of somaclonal variation investigated so far are as follows:

1. Generation of variation
2. Characterization of variants for morphological traits.
3. Analysis of biochemical and chromosomal basis of variation.
4. Relating the variations to alterations in DNA.

GENETIC VARIATIONS AND CROP IMPROVEMENT

Genetic variation appears during or after culture *in vitro*. It may occur in undifferentiated cells, isolated protoplasts, calli, tissues and morphological traits of regenerated plants. Variant selected in tissue cultures have been referred as **calliclones** (from callus culture), or **protoclones** (from protoplast culture) The change occurs because of variation in chromosome number and structure. Cytological heterogeneity in cultures develops due to the following reasons:

1. The expression of chromosomal mosaicism or genetic disorders in cells of the initial explant. The chromosomal mosaicism may be pre-existing mosaicism (polysomaty - the phenomenon of polyploidisation of body cells) in explants used for culture initiation, or by nuclear fragmentation associated with first cell division of callus initiation or endoreduplication or endomitosis occurring during culture initiation and/or abnormalities of the mitotic process leading to aneuploidy.
2. new irregularities brought about by culture conditions.

Somaclonal variation is causes problem for plant propagationists, since their objective is to reserve a specific plant genotype. While for plant Geneticists somaclonal variation is a valuable source of new genetic information. It leads to crop plant improvement and a deeper understanding of the biochemical and molecular basis of inheritance.

Somaclonal variation is one of the aspects of tissue culture technology and is widely recommended for crop improvement specially of desired traits for the salt, drought, temperature and disease tolerance. The method refers to heritable changes, which accumulate in the callus from a somatic explant and express in the progeny of *in vitro* regenerants obtained from callus. Even though relative data from deliberatly designed experiments is not available, indications of possible advantages of somaclonal *vis-a-vis* induced mutagenesis are:

1. The frequency of variation seems to be far greater than the yield of induced mutations.
2. The changes are very subtle and may not involve drastic altration in the genetic background.
3. Somaclonal variation occurs for trait of both nuclear and cytoplasmic origin. The variation of cytoplasmic genes obtained by this method is a distinct advantage.

In wide crosses somaclonal variations provide a mechanism of gene introgression. Immature embryos of the wide cross can be callused and plants with the introgressed desired genes (or gene complex) are selected among the regenerants of their progenies.

WHY VARIATIONS OCCUR?

Variants may also arise as a result of more suitable changes due to single gene mutations in cultures which have cells apparently showing no karyological changes. Recessive mutations are not detected in plants regenerated *in vitro* from any cell or tissue, but expressed in progeny. This shows that variants are the mutants. Single gene mutation responsible for somaclonal variation relates to transposable elements. Transposon-induced changes have been observed in maize, tobacco and wheat. Somaclonal variation may also be due to changes caused by mitotic crossing over in regenerated plants. Such changes may also occur due to changes in organelle DNA, isoenzyme and protein profiles *e.g.*, in wheat, potato, maize, barley and flax, etc. Changes in cytoplasmic genome have also been observed in somaclones.

THE MECHANISM OF SOMACLONAL VARIATION

According to Bhaskaran (1985) variations in somaclons occur due to the following reasons:

1. The pre-existing genetic variation in the explant tissue,
2. The spontaneous mutation which can accumulate during the many division cycles that cells of the explant go through before differentiating into an in vitro plant. The recessive mutations will naturally require a method by which they can express even diploid cells. Somatic crossing over followed by segregation is a likely mechanism, for the homozygosity and thus phenotypic expression of the recessive.
3. Numerical and structural changes in chromosomes during in vitro growth.
4. Intracellular mutagenic agents produced during in vitro growth.
5. Activation of transposable elements or **jumping genes**, are genetic entities which have the locus at which they get integrated is matured.

Agriculturists are very hopeful about practical advantages of somaclonal variations and they are waiting when this technique is fully integrated with the conventional plant breeding procedures.

SOURCE MATERIAL AND CULTURE CONDITIONS

Plant cell, tissues and somatic embryos developed from various explant sources for generating somaclonal variation. Explants are generally taken from any tissue, namely leaves, internodes, ovaries, roots and inflorescence. The source of explant has often been considered a critical variable for somaclonal variation. Initiation of callus and suspension cultures as described in previous chapter.

Determination of Cell Number

Take an aliquot of suspension and filter off the cultures through a wire mesh (300 mm). Note the volume of the filtrate (F) containing single cells and small clumps and place the drop of this suspension to haemocytometer to determine the number of cells by the equation

$$N = \frac{P \times 100 \times F}{.01\,mm}$$

Where, N = total number of cells and clumps, P = number of cells in the squares of the haemocytometer, F = volume of the filtrate.

FORMS OF SOMACLONAL VARIATION

Many different forms of somaclonal variation arise. The most common forms include point mutations, chromosomal aberrations, and increase or decrease in the number of nuclear chromosomes. It is important to realize that not all forms of variability that arise *in vitro* are heritable. Some morphological and biochemical variants are due to physiological effects and are not exhibited in subsequent generations.

DETECTION AND ISOLATION OF SOMACLONAL VARIANTS

There are several different approaches to detecting and isolating somaclonal variants from cultured plant cell populations.

1. Morphologically distinct cells such as non-photosynthetic (non-green) cells or

cells that accumulate anthocyanins and other plant pigments are detected visually.

2. To isolate herbicide- and antibiotic-resistant variants, plant cells are simply grown on media containing of the wild-type cells in a culture.
3. The surviving cells are then sub-cultured and retested for growth on herbicide or antibiotic supplemented medium.
4. Through this method one can eliminate any remaining wild-type cells that may have inadvertently survived the first round of selection.

Somaclonal variation induced in morphological traits has been developed in Sugarcane, Potato, Tobacco, Rice, Oats, Maize, Brassica, Pelargonium, Pineapple, Tomato, etc.

Those somaclonal variants that cannot be detected visually or selected directly are isolated by indirect means.

Those auxotrophic plant cells which unable to survive in absence of specific nutrient supplements not required by sensitive cells, which will not survive at temperatures above or below a certain threshold. This threshold will not affect normal wild-type cells. In absence of the necessary nutrient supplement or when grown at excessive temperatures, these cells become very weak and at this weakened state, these cells assimilate exogenously supplied cytotoxic compounds (arsenate, bromodeoxyuracil, or fluorodeoxyuridine) at lower rate than that of wild-type cells. Thus, treating a cell culture under restrictive growth conditions with one of these substances will tend to favor short term survival of the weaker auxotrophic or temperature-sensitive cells.

MUTAGENESIS AND SOMACLONAL VARIATION

Mutagenic agents (chemical and physical) are used to produce particular heritable forms of somaclonal variation *e.g.*, ultraviolet (UV) radiation, ethyl-methane sulfonate (EMS), nitrosuguanidine, and sodium azide, etc.

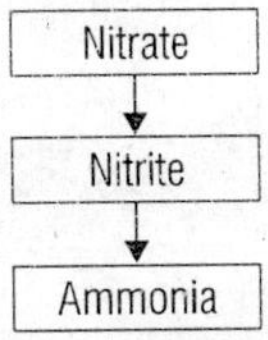

FIGURE 15.1: The biochemical reduction of nitrate to ammonia.

UV radiation induces dimer formation between adjacent thymine residues in DNA. This produces lesions that cause frameshift mutations and base pair substitutions during DNA replication. EMS and nitrosoguanidine are alkylating agents that cross link and sever DNA molecules, often resulting in gross DNA alterations. In contrast, sodium azide induces single base pair substitutions or deletions, resulting mostly in small point mutations.

SOMATIC GENETICS OF NITROGEN METABOLISM

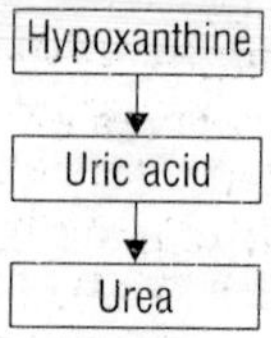

FIGURE 15.2. The biochemical reduction of hypoxanthine to urea.

Plant cells in culture medium can metabolize ammonium, nitrate, and nitrite sources of inorganic nitrogen. The cells use ammonium directly while the nitrate is first reduced to nitrite (enzyme nitrate reductase, NR) and then nitrite is reduced to ammonium (enzyme nitrite reductase NiR). NR needs a molybdenum-containing cofactor (MoCo) for proper enzyme activityas follows:

For isolation of variants, which unable to utilize nitrate, plant cells are grown on chlorate-supplemented media. Chlorate is a close analog of nitrate and will be reduced to chlorite, a patent cytotoxin that accumulates internally and eventually kills the cell. Certain metabolic mutants can survive chlorate treatment. Some of these mutant cells carry mutations affecting NR expression or assimilation. Other mutations may affect MoCo expression or chlorate assimilation.

Method for Isolation of Desired Variant Cells for NaCl -Tolerant from Callus/ Suspension Cultures

1. Semi-solid liquid media is prepared and NaCl (500 mg/l) is added to the medium, pH is adjusted at 5.6. Distribute the medium in 30 ml aliquots into 150 ml flasks or 50 ml aliquots into 250 ml flasks and grow the callus on NaCl containing medium. Select the granular friable callus for further subculture.
2. 1 g of callus is inoculated to each 250 ml flask containing 50 ml of liquid medium then incubate the cultures on a gyratory shaker (100 rpm) for 21 days at 25 ± 2 °C.
3. Pass the cell suspension through a stainless steel wire mesh (300 μm) and collect filtrate in 15 ml centrifuge tubes. Examine the filtrate for single cells and small aggregates (5-20 cells). Centrifuge the filtrate at 100 g for 5 min and discard the supernatant, add 5 ml of the sterilized medium to the pellet to obtain a cell suspension, and maintain the cell density of the suspension about $0.5\text{-}2.5 \times 10^5$ cell/ml. Add to the flasks containing with or without NaCl.
4. Incubate the cultures at 100 rpm at 25 ± 2 °C and centrifuge the cultures grown in control and NaCl (500 mg/l) at 100 rpm for 5 min.
5. Transfer the pellets to fresh medium of the same composition. Incubate at 25 ± 2 °C for 21 days and repeat these steps for 2-3 times to get a good growth rate of the NaCl tolerant cell line
6. Grow cultures on 1000 mg/l NaCl and follow the same steps, as carried out at 500 mg/l NaCl till a salt concentration beyond which the cells cease to grow. It is suggested that the salt concentration should be increased gradually by repeating steps
7. Regenerate variant cells into whole plants. Transfer 0.5 ml of cell suspension onto the surface of the regeneration medium gelled with agar by a wide mouth graduated sterile pipette.

8. In case of callus, inoculate 500 mg piece onto the surface of the organ/shoot forming medium having 500 mg/l NaCl
9. In most of the plant species, the differentiation of shoots and roots occurs on different media. Hence once the shoots are obtained, they are transferred to the rooting medium. Transfer the selected NaCl tolerant plantlets to soil.
10. Use NaCl solution to water the salt tolerant plants. The concentration of NaCl should be the same as used in the regeneration medium. This procedure can also be used to develop tolerant plants of alkali, high temperature, drought, disease, herbicide can be developed by using in vitro selection system.

APPLICATIONS IN PLANT BREEDING

Somaclonal variation and gametoclonal variation are the important sources of introducing genetic variations that could be of value to plant breeders. Single gene mutation in the nuclear or organelle genome usually provides the best available variety *in vitro* which has a specific improved character. Somaclonal variation are used to uncover new variants retaining all the favourable characters along with an additional useful trait, *e.g.*, resistance to diseases or an herbicide. These variants can then be field-tested to ascertain their genetic stability. Gametoclonal variation is induced by meiotic recombination during the sexual cycle of the F_1 hybrid, results in transgressive segregation to uncover unique gene combinations.

Various cell lines selected *in vitro* and plant regenerated through it prove potentially applicable to agriculture and industry specially resistance to herbicide, pathotoxin, salt or aluminium, useful in the synthesis of secondary metabolites on a commercial scale, etc.

Examples of gametoclonal variation has been developed in *Brassica napus*, *Hordeum vulgare*, *Nicotiana sylvestris*, *N. sylvestris* (several cycles) and *N. tabacum*, *Oryza sativa*, *Saintpaulia ionantha and Secale cereale x S. vavilotrii* raised from gametophytic tissue cultures.

TABLE 15.1: Aspects of improvement desired in some crop plants through somaclonal variation

Crop plants	Improvement desired
Cereals	
Rice	Tungro virus and leaf hopper resistance
Wheat	Quality, high temperature tolerance
Sorghum	Borer and shoot fly resistance
Maize	Delinking of phytohormone effect from reproductive development
Legumes	
Pigeon-pea	Resistance to pod borer, fusarium wilt, high protein content
Bengal gram	
Oilseeds	
Groundnut	Resistance to Cercospora, Fusarium, Aspergillus flavus
Rapeseed	Male sterility, low pungency combined with insect resistance
Sunflower	Self compatibility, resistance to *Alternaria* leaf blight, *Rhizoctonia*, *Fusarium* complex
Cotton	Insect resistance to gossypol free lines
Vegetables	
Potato	Virus and *Phytophthora* resistance
Tomato	Resistance to disease
Fruits	

Crop plants	Improvement desired
Grapes	Resistance to disease, short duration
Citrus	Higher solid content, increased shelf life
Watermelons	
Other (s)	
Sugarcane	Resistance to disease, short duration
Castor	Mutants with high fatty acids; oleic acid, ricinoleic acid

The techniques used for development of somaclonal and gametoclonal variation are relatively easier than recombinant DNA technology and is the appropriate technology for genetic manipulation of above cited crops.

CHAPTER 16

Gynogenesis and Crop Improvement

Gynogenesis or **haploid parthenogenesis** are frequently used terms which describe the possibility of obtaining haploid plants derived from female gametophyte. Spontaneous induction of haploid plants *in situ* have been known since 1922, when Blakeslee described this phenomenon in *Datura*. Spontaneous haploid induction is today regarded as a rare event of limited practical use. The main progress in induced haploid production has been made since 1964, when Guha and Maheshwari described the first successful *in vitro* haploid induction by means of anther culture.

As reviewed by Yang and Zhou (1982) as a result of this finding, studies of haploid induction from female gametophyte were neglected for about a decade. Later, gynogenesis was again frequently studied in several agricultural plants, and successful induction of gynogenic haploids has currently been reported in several species or genera. In most cases, gynogenesis is used in plants where androgenesis has failed. In some other studies gynogenesis is favoured over androgenesis on the basis of its higher genetic stability. Such, for instance, has been well studied in tobacco but little evidence exists to support the conclusion that this phenomenon is expressed also in other species.

Methods of inducing haploid plants via gynogenesis can be divided into two categories. The first is *in situ* induction by irregular pollination, which can be assisted by *in vitro* rescue of haploid embryos, and the second is *in vitro* cultivation of unpollinated female reproductive organs. Irregular pollination methods can be divided into pollination with pollen of the same species with or without selected haploid inducer genes, to pollination with pollen from wild relatives or other genera, and to pollination with irradiated pollen of the same species. *In vitro* culture methods include the culture of unpollinated ovules, placenta attached ovules, ovaries or whole flower buds.

The number of reports on gynogenesis differ among species. Only on a few do a relatively large number of published papers exist, while in others, only one or very few references could be found. In this paper different techniques are analysed on a limited number of better studied plant species.

GYNOGENESIS INDUCED BY IRREGULAR POLLINATION *IN SITU*

Induction of parthenogenesis *in situ* is mainly limited to the use of irregular pollination. There is only limited evidence that a chemical toluidine-blue can be used as a haploid inducer. A positive effect of toluidine-blue has been described for Populus but was not successful in *Vitis* and apple. All other efficient approaches use pollen as an inducer of haploidy.

The first possibility is to use the pollen of the same species, so as to provide an actually legitimate pollination, but the genotype of the pollen parent includes specific genes which may cause an increased percentage of haploid embryo development. The mechanism of induction is not yet completely analyzed but it has been suggested that maternal haploids result after the failure of fertilisation, and the consequent development of a reduced egg cell into the embryo. In some species, parthenogenic seeds can be recognized as twin seeds, where one is haploid and another normal diploid. There are also reports of haploids being detected on the basis of the morphology of the seedlings, in pear for instance described haploid genotypes as smaller, having shorter internodes, slender stem and narrow thin leaves. Maize is a typical example of haploid induction as result of legitimate crossings. Several approaches have been tested to induce a higher percentage of haploid seeds in maize.

The second possible approach is pollination of the studied species with wild relatives or with other genera of cultivated crops. This technique mainly requires *in vitro* embryo rescue to ensure the survival of induced haploid embryos. We shall analyse the specificity of this technique on the examples of wheat, barley and potato.

Potato is another plant species in which haploids are induced by means of wide crosses, only the mechanism of induction is different. It was recognized that crosses among commercial tetraploid varieties and the wild diploid relative *Solanum phureja* used as male parent can result in reducing the ploidy of tetraploid *Solanum tuberosum* to diploid level. In some genotypes of *Solanum phureja*, irregular meiosis occurred, resulting in only one sperm nucleus, which can therefore fuse with the egg nucleus or embryo sac nucleus, resulting in up to 40% diploids. Such diploid potatoes can be used for breding purposes, including alien germplasm introgression or selection on diploid level, but such plants are not homozygous.

A the third possible approach is the use of irradiated pollen of the same species for provoking haploid embryo development, which can be further grown on plant until maturity, or more often be recovered by *in vitro* culture.

Haploid induction in apple by the use of irradiated pollen was studied by Huang and Lespinasse. Their method, as published in several articles uses the following procedure. Pollen should be collected from a donor plant (clone RR) that carries a homozygous dominant marker gene coding for anthocyanin production in whole plant organs. Gynogenic production has also been studied in melon by several groups.

DEVELOPMENT OF USEFUL CROP VARITIES

Even when successful, interspecific and intergeneric transfers made by sexual methods are laborious and time-consuming; moreover, other problems must be solved before a genotype useful for crop production is obtained. Even after 6 backcross generations in an interspecific gene transfer, the natural processof recombination frequently will not separate tightly linked genes. This means that undesired traits that affect crop quality, yield, or adaptation may be carried along with the desired gene. Even if the desired gene is successfully separated from linked deleterious genes, its inheritance and expression may be unpredictably altered in the new genetic background. Le Deneuf and Sauton (1994) claimed that irradiated pollen induces stenospermocarpy (fruit development after embryo abortion) in melon, but they cannot clearly determine whether early embryogenesis is gynogenic or abnormally zygotic. In any case, the efficiency of haploid induction using this method is high enough to be routinely used in plant breeding programmes (Dore, 1994).

GYNOGENESIS INDUCED BY *IN VITRO* CULTURE OF UNPOLLINATED FEMALE REPRODUCTIVE ORGANS

Cultures of unpollinated ovules, ovaries or flower buds have ben successfully used to induce haploid plants in several crops. The first successful induction was performed by San Noeum 1976 in barley. This technique was subsequently efficient in several other species In comparison to gynogenesis induced by the use of irregular pollinations, *in vitro* culture of unpollinated female reproductive organs has the advantage that no hybrid plants can develop from legitimate pollination but regenerants can be induced from other sporophytic tissues, so confirming the haploid origin is still required. For the induction of unpollinated female reproductive organs, the most important elements are the composition of media and the genotype used.

Allium cepa and *Beta vulgaris* are the most studied plant species, in which gynogenesis is induced by *in vitro* culture of unpollinated female reproductive organs.

Beet cultivars are mainly triploid, resulting from crosses of tetraploid and diploid lines. Since beets are allogamous with expressed high inbreeding depression, the resulting hybrids are relatively heterogeneous. Approaches have therefore been tested to produce gynogenic haploid plants induced from ovule cultures. Hosemans and Bossoutrot (1983) succeeded in regenerating the first 17 plants from cultured unpollinated ovules. The basal medium was MS, several growth hormones were tested, and sucrose ranged from 2 to 8%. In a subsequent study, the same authors (Bossoutrot and Hosemans 1985) tested three other basic media supplemented with 1 mg l^{-1} BA and 3% or 8% sucrose. As a result, they achieved 0.2% regeneration of gynogenic plants.

Haploid induction from unpollinated ovules, ovaries or flower buds in *Zea mays, Triticum aestivum, Hordeum vulgare, Oryza sativa, Fagopyrum esculentum, Nicotiana tabacum, Cucurbita pepo, Solanum tuberosum, Beta vulgaris, Helianthus annuus, Allium cepa, Allium porrum, Allium tuberosum, Petunia hybrida, Gerbera jamesonii* and *Morus indica.*

Generalisation of successful approaches for efficient *in vitro* induction from unfertilized female reproductive organs is difficult, since results differ even within studies of the same species. Choice of macro and micro elements is very different, practically all media, which are frequently used in tissue culture procedures have been found to be successful for induction of gynogenesis. Similarly, hormonal requirements differ even among genotypes of the same species. Like in androgenesis gynogenic plants can be induced in very low frequencies even on no hormone media, but generally hormones are needed for induction step and sometimes (in lower doses) also in regeneration step. In most cases auxins (especially 2,4-D) are efficient in the first induction period, but also other hormones can have the same inducing effect. Requirements for carbohydrates are very important what is again similar to androgenesis, but beneficial effect is mainly limited to higher dose of sucrose, while other carbohydrates like maltose were not so efficient. The same is true for cold pretreatments, where attempts to use it for improved haploid induction have almost always been unsuccessful. Embryo sac should in most cases be at mature developmental stage. In this case a very few exceptions are reported. This situation is therefore also different from androgenesis, where immature pollen grains are used.

ORIGIN OF GYNOGENIC REGENERANTS AND METHODS OF CHROMOSOME DOUBLING

The origin of gynogenic regenerants has been studied in several species. It seems that the main source of haploid embryogenesis s the egg cell. Such development has been confirmed in sunflower with the additional observation that also other reduced cells such as the antipodals, can divide but no organized structure occurred in this case. The egg cell, synergids and antipodal cells of sunflower could be induced to undergo sporophytic development. Similarly in *Beta* viable gynogenic embryos originated only from the egg cell. It seems that the main problem in studies of gynogenic origin is that a high frequency of induction should first be achieved to enable the detection of dividing cells and their developmental pathway.

General to all gynogenic approaches is a need to double the genome from a haploid to doubled haploid state. Plant species differ in endogenous potential for chromosome doubling. While in some plants like apple and pear, spontaneous chromosome doubling occurs very frequently, in others like onion, beet, barley, wheat, maize, melon and tobacco, spontaneous chromosome doubling is mainly limited to 10% or less. Several approaches have been used for induced chromosome doubling. Colchicine has been far the most widely used chemical. In addition to previously known applications of colchicine on plants *in situ*, several techniques exist for applying colchicine *in vitro*. Colchicine is for the most part included in the media, where concentration and duration of treatments differ. Xu et al. (1991), for instance, found a 0.05% to 0.5% colchicine supplemented medium with additional vibration effect to be optimal for doubling haploid sugarbeet shoots, while Hansen et al. (1994) found the exposure of beet ovules to 0.4% colchicine for 5 hours in liquid medium to be optimal. Since colchicine is known to have a potential mutagenic effect, other chemical agents have been tested for efficiency for genome doubling and in relation to genetic stability. While Oryzaline has been recognized as a stronger inhibitor of spindle formation than colchicine (Verhoeven *et al.*, 1990) and has been efficiently used in doubling chromosomes of several species, the use of another herbicide trifluralin has only been recently proposed (Eikenberry, 1994) as being highly efficient in canola.

CONCLUSIONS

It has been shown that gynogenesis is already an efficient tool for induction of haploid plants. Technically, approaches differ more than those applied for androgenesis. In some plants, such as sugarbeet, onion, sunflower, melon and others, gynogenesis is already used in plant breeding programs, while for some others induction frequencies should first be improved. Gynogenesis should always be used to produce (di) haploid lines in dioecious plants like asparagus or hop, where hybrids are crosses among male and female plants. In asparagus, such system has already been applied for breeding new varieties while success in induction of gynogenesis in hop is at the moment still limited. In future, experiments should, therefore, be focused on finding the most appropriate low labour intensive method that would yield the highest number of (di) haploid lines regardless of genotype. The genetic stability of gynogenic lines should also be evaluated including comparisons among androgenic and gynogenic origin of haploids.

CHAPTER 17

Synseeds or Synthetic Seeds

THE NATURAL SEED

The seed stage of seed plants represents a unique developmental phase of the spermatophyte lifecycle, and as such involves structures, not characteristic of other stages of development. The essential structure of seed is defined as a *ripened ovule consisting of an embryo and its coats*. Anatomically a seed consists of some old or parental sporophyte tissue *viz.*, the seed coats, which are derived from the integument's and nucleus: some endosperm, which may be either gametophytic tissue or fertilized tissue: and the embryo, the new young sporophyte. The normal seed contains materials which it utilizes during the process of its germination. These substances are frequently found in the endosperm. Thus endosperm may contain variety of stored materials such as starch, oils, proteins etc. In some plants, however, the reserve food material is present in cotyledons.

DEVELOPMENT OF THE CONCEPTS OF TISSUE CULTURE AND ARTIFICIAL SEEDS

P. R. White is acknowledged as the father of tissue culture in the United States. He was the first to grow excised root tips of tomatoes (*Lycopersicon*) in continuous culture. When new material is started in culture, grown *in vitro* (literally, in glass), it develops very small juvenile shoots, which are reminiscent of seedlings. A plantlet continues to produce and maintain small stems and leaves throughout its duration in culture. This is fortunate because most mature material would be too unwieldy for micropropagation to succeed in a test tube. After multiplication in culture and when transferred to soil outside the laboratory, the plantlets will produce leaves of normal size and assume the mature features of the plants from which they originated.

When plants are multiplied vegetatively- as distinguished from those grown from seeds- whether by tissue culture or by cuttings, all the offspring from a single plant can be classified as a clone. This means that the genetic make-up of each offspring is identical to that of all the other offspring and to that of the single parent. On the other hand, plants propagated by seed, resulting from sexual reproduction, are not clones because each seed (and the resultant plant) has a unique genetic make-up- a mixture from 2 parents, different from either parent and different from one seed to another. The term *cloning*, with respect to tissue culture, refers to the process of propagating in culture large numbers of selected plants with the same genotype (the same genes or hereditary factors) as their respective parent plant.

The liquid cell suspension cultures have particular significance for the mass production of cells. One common source of cells for cell suspension is from friable callus, although specific cells, such as from leaf mesophyll (the thin, soft tissue between the upper and lower epidermis of the leaf), are also grown in suspension. Cells in suspension can form embryoids (somatic embryos) in the process of embryogenesis. Embryos may multiply and/or be induced to form plantlets in the process of morphogenesis. Many hybrid plants produce embryos that do not mature to viable seeds. These embryos can be rescued, removed from the seed at immature stage, and then grown in culture.

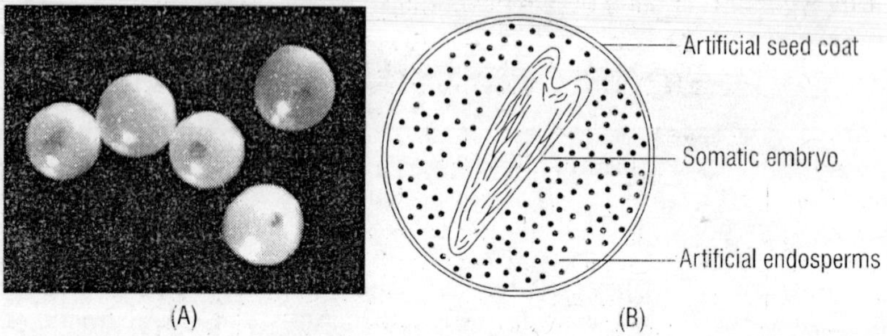

FIGURE 17.1: (a) Photograph of synthetic seed. (b) Capsule gel with hydrophobic membrane, the (A) artificial seed coat, (B) somatic embryo, (C) artificial endosperms.

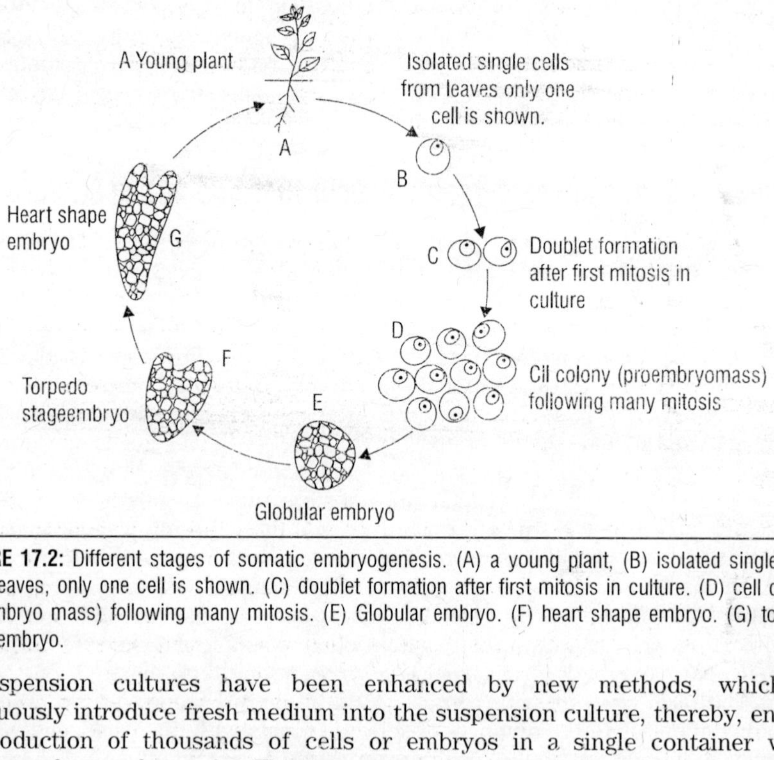

FIGURE 17.2: Different stages of somatic embryogenesis. (A) a young plant, (B) isolated single cells from leaves, only one cell is shown. (C) doublet formation after first mitosis in culture. (D) cell colony (proembryo mass) following many mitosis. (E) Globular embryo. (F) heart shape embryo. (G) torpedo stage embryo.

Suspension cultures have been enhanced by new methods, which can continuously introduce fresh medium into the suspension culture, thereby, enabling the production of thousands of cells or embryos in a single container with a minimum of manual transfer. This is one way that tissue culture can compete with the plentiful seed production in nature.

Interest in anther and pollen culture- the tissue culturing of anthers or pollen to obtain haploid (cells with half the normal number of chromosomes of vegetative cells) clones- is spurred by the practical applications of such haploid cultures. Haploid (n) plants are sterile, but if the chromosomes duplicate, either spontaneously or by induction, the plants will be diploid (2n, which is normal for the vegetative state), and their progeny will be true to form. Considering the fact that it takes several generations of inbreeding to obtain a pure line by conventional means, it is little wonder that plant breeders are interested in anther culture.

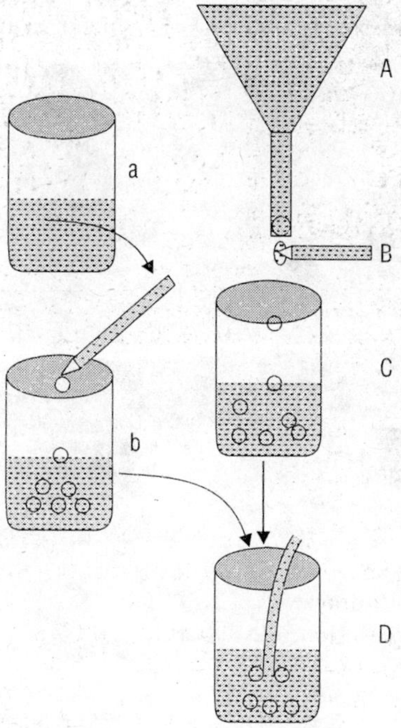

FIGURE 17.3: Preparation of artificial seeds via encapsulation with calcium alginate beads using a droping method. Alginate (2%) is either mixed with somatic embryos (a) or poured in a separatory funnel (A), droping of alginate beads along with embryo into a bath of calcium nitrate (100 mM) solution (b) or a single embryo is inserted into alignate drop using a plastic pipet having 4mm inside diameter (B), falling of alginate beads into a bath of calcium nitrate (C) and washing of the capsules in water (D). Diargram modified from Redembaugh *et. al.* 1991.

Street (1977) advocated the problem of reliability in embryogenesis. According to him morphogenic competence is determined from the time of culture initiation, such that there is the need to have an initiation medium that will ensure that the competent cells are involved in callus formation. Sunderland (1977) demonstrated that the production of hundreds of morphologically uniform embryos from *Datura* and *Nicotiana* pollen.

Robert Lawrence (of Union Carbide) started to develop various methods for cloning forest trees. It was difficult for him to produce hybrids for crops such as celery and lettuce. This group focused on delivery of somatic embryos using fluid drilling technology (Lawrence, 1981) and using polyoxyethylene to form seed tapes or sheets. Lawrence and Walker's groups came together at a symposium workshop, Advances in Methods of *In Vitro* Cloning for Large Scale Propagation of Plants, held September 21-22, 1981 at the W. Alton Jones Cell Science Center in Lake Placid, New York. They discuss the various concepts like how low-cost, high-volume propagation system can be developed for vegetable and agronomic crops using somatic embryos and delivered by fluid drilling (in a seed tape, or as an artificial seed). The Lawrence group (then at Agrigenetics) subsequently began to use alginate for encapsulating carrot and celery somatic embryos (Lutz, et al. 1985). Because their encapsulation results with alginate were similar to those at Plant Genetics, they focused on the problems of somatic embryo physiology. In this way, they were successful in obtaining germination of carrot somatic embryos in vermiculite in a growth chamber.

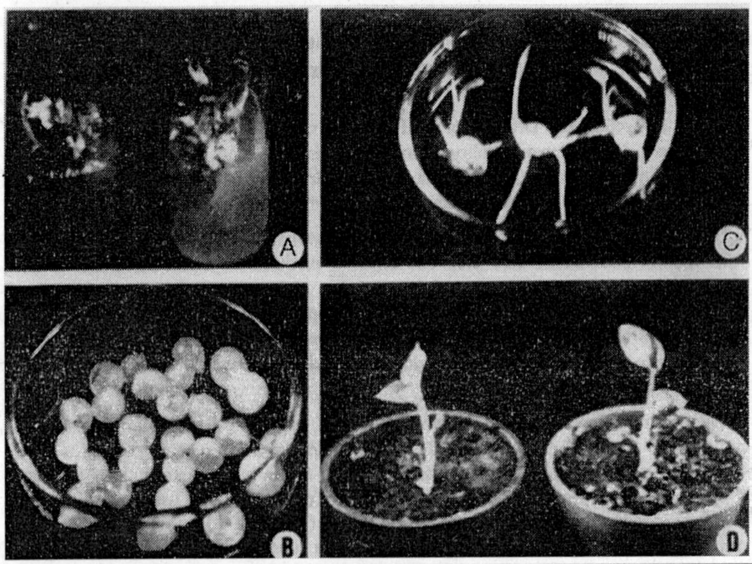

FIGURE 17.4: Encapsulation of shoot tips of cardamom. A - multiple shoot cultures. B - Shoot tips encapsulated in 3% sodium alginate matrix, C - emerging shoot roots from the encapsulated shoot tips and D- plantlets derived from encapsulated shoot tips paper cups. (After Rao et. al, 1997).

Drew (1979) was active in developing methods to commercially propagate crops using somatic embryos. He suggested delivering carrot somatic embryos in a fluid drilling system, but was able to produce only three plants from carrot embryos on a carbohydrate-free medium. He could not get success in producing many plants through this system. He faced a crucial problem and found the very slow rate of development of plantlets derived from culture.

Kitto and Janick (1982) coated clumps of carrot embryos, roots, and callus with polyoxyethylene. Some embryos survived the coating process as well as a desiccation step.

The early assessments of Murashige and Street (1977) on the difficulty of somatic embryogeny are still valid today. The quality and fidelity of somatic embryos are the limiting factors for development and scale-up of artificial seeds.

Interestingly, artificial seeds prepared from shoot buds can also be used for plant propagation, and this was reported by P.S. Rao's group from BARC, Bombay. Rice is the world's most important food crop and a primary food source for more than one third of the World's population. This crop has received considerable attention in biotechnological research programmes. Research on artificial seeds in rice is still in infancy and this technology through somatic embryogenesis would offer a great scope for large scale propagation of superior, elite hybrids (Brar and Khush, 1994). P. S. Rao and his associates have reported high frequency somatic embryogenesis from indica rice cultivars (Suprasanna *et al.*, 1995) and utilized this embryogenic system for the production of artificial seeds.

TABLE 17.1: Important crop plants in which artificial seed production and plant conversion has been demonstrated

In vitro propagules for encapsulation	Crop
Somatic embryos	Alfalfa, Celery, Brinjal, Carrot, Brassica, Lettuce, Sandalwood, Rice, Horse radish
Axillary buds/ Adventitious buds	Mulberry, Eucalyptus, Vitis
Shoot tips	Banana, Cardamom, Carum carvi

Since then the induction of somatic and/or pollen embryogenesis has been reported in a wide array of plants, including several crop plants such as rice, wheat, triticale, maize, pearl-millet, sorghum, sugarcane, potato, sweet potato, eggplant, lettuce, carrot, alfalfa, soybean, cucumber, *Brassica* species, asparagus, coffee, tobacco and cotton. However, the production of high quality and uniform embryos (which is very important for the preparation of artificial seeds) has been limited to only certain crops like carrot and alfalfa.

Somatic embryogenesis has, also been obtained from non-zygotic explant tissue (coffee leaf), suggesting that somatic embryogenesis may be obtained from sexually immature tree, zygotic embryo or ovule tissue.

Difficulties in developing somatic embryogenesis systems for tree species are similar to those for herbaceous species. However, tree species may also exhibit a unique set of tissue culture-dependent variabilities.

USES AND LIMITATIONS OF ARTIFICIAL SEEDS

Plants are traditionally propagated either by seeds or the vegetative propagules like stem cutting. Now most plants can be multiplied through tissue culture techniques, particularly shoot tip culture (clonal micropropagation).

Micropropagation through artificial seeds may be commercially exploited on a large scale, generating millions of plants in a few days, and this may become a profitable multibillion rupees industry in near future. This technology would be feasible and even competitive economically with the seed method.

Artificial seeds offer the possibility of a low-cost, high-volume propagation system that will compete with true seeds and transplants. Most likely, the technology will first be used with hybrid vegetable crops such as celery or with high-value flower and ornamental species. Because of the relative ease of producing large numbers of somatic embryos, artificial seeds will be applicable for monoculture as well as mixed genotype methods of agriculture. The artificial seed coating also has the potential to hold and deliver beneficial adjuvants such as growth-promoting rhizobacteria, plant nutrients and growth control agents, and pesticides.

Potential Uses of Artificial Seeds

1. Delivery Systems.
2. Reduced costs of transplants.
3. Direct greenhouse and field delivery of elite, select genotypes, hand-pollinated hybrids, genetically engineered plants, sterile and unstable genotypes, large-scale monocultures, mixed-genotype plantations.
4. Carrier for adjuvants such as microorganisms, plant growth regulators, and pesticides Protection of meiotically unstable, elite genotypes.

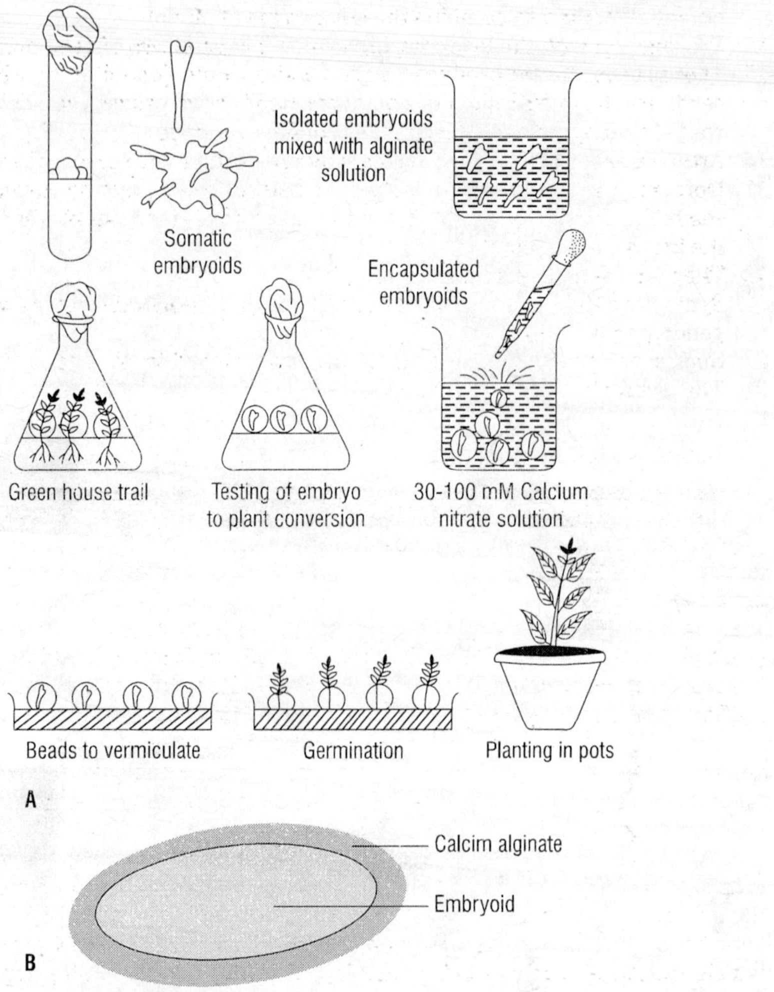

FIGURE 17.5: (A) Flow diagram presenting the procedure of synthetic seed production. (B) Cross section of synthetic seed.

5. Analytical Tools.
6. Comparative aid for zygotic embryogeny.
7. Production of large numbers of identical embryos.
8. Determine role of endosperm in embryo development and germination.
9. Study of seed coat formation.
10. The synthetic seeds so developed are breed true.
11. There are potential advantages of artificial seed technology specially for tree genetic engineering.
12. The artificial production of seeds has already been obtained successfully in Zea mays, Apium graveolens, Daucus carota, Lactuca sativa, Madicago sativa, Brassica spp., Gossypium hirsutum, Velerina sp., Santalum spp., etc.
13. The encapsulation of somatic embryos (hydrated or desiccated) provides a

potential method to combine the advantages of clonal.
14. Propagation with the low-cost, high-volume capabilities of seed propagation.
15. These seeds can be produced within a short time (one month) whereas natural seeds are the end product of complex reproductive process and breeders have to wait for a long time for development of new varieties.
16. Artificial seeds can be produced at any time and in any season of a year.
17. Dormancy is the common feature of natural seeds, but by means of artificial seeds the dormancy period can be reduced to a great extent, thereby shortning the life cycle of a plant.
18. They are useful in preserving germplasm.
19. Synthetic seeds are applicable for large scale monocultures as well as mixed genotype plantations.
20. Such seeds give the protection of meiotically unstable, elite genotypes.
21. The synthetic seeds provide us knowledge to understand the development, anatomical characteristics of endosperm and seed coat formation.

Both these propagation methods have **certain limitations** such as the need of intensive labour, rooting of regenerated shoots and transplantation, slow and smallscale multiplication. Micropropagation has some additional problems like the need of acclimatization of tissue culture derived plants before they are transferred into field conditions (hardening) because of their tenderness due to the absence of lignification and low cuticle formation. By contrast, plant propagation via artificial seeds has several advantages over classical methods as well as micropropagation (with shoot tip culture). The advantages of this technology include the rapid and large-scale multiplication, minimal labour and low cost propagation. In addition, artificial seeds can be directly delivered to the field, thus eliminating transplantation and tissue hardening steps. They can also be provided with various kinds of adjuvants like plant growth regulators, useful microorganisms and pesticides to tailor a field-specific, plantable unit for a desired crop. However, the genetic uniformity is maintained in all these propagation methods.

Artificial seed technology can be very useful for the propagation of a variety of crop plants, especially crops for which true seeds are not used or readily available for multiplication (*e.g.* potato) or the true seeds are expensive (*e.g.* cucumber and geraniums), hybrid plants (*e.g.* hybrid rice) and many vegetatively propagated plants which are more prone to infections (*e.g.* day lily, garlic, potato, sugarcane, sweet potato, grape and mango).

This newly emerging technology would also be useful for multiplying genetically engineered plants (transgenic plants), somatic and cytoplasmic hybrids (obtained through protoplast fusion techniques), sterile and unstable genotypes. Besides, artificial seeds would be useful material for preservation of desirable elite genotypes (cryopreservation). They would also be valuable tools in experimental research to study the process of zygotic embryogenesis and understanding the role of endosperm in normal embryo development and germination.

Synthetic seed technology offers many useful advantages on a commercial scale. The resultant plant population from the synthetic seed will be uniform and the direct delivery of somatic embryos will save many subcultures to obtain plantlets from regenerated embryos. The encapsulated embryos could also be packed with pesticides, fertilizers, nitrogen fixing bacteria and even microscopic destroying worms.

ESTABLISHMENT OF CALLUS CULTURE

↓

Induction of Somatic Embryogenesis

↓

Maturation of Somatic Embryos

↓

Encapsulation of Somatic Embryos

↓

Evaluation of Embryoid and Plant Conversion

↓

Planting in Fields/green House

FIGURE 17.6: Schematic presentation of steps of synthetic seed production.

At the Biotechnology Division of BARC, research on the development of protocols for synthetic seeds using somatic embryos, axillary buds and shoot tips is in progress in five economically important plants, sandalwood, rice, mulberry, banana and cardamom. The following pages describe the results obtained in this direction.

The artificial seed systems coupled with artificial intelligence and microcomputer systems like the most advanced robots which can mimic the motions and functions of a living being (*i.e.*, automated encapsulation) would tremendously increase the efficiency of encapsulation and production of artificial seeds, and revolutionize the plant propagation method in the years ahead.

This technology is gradually moving towards the commercial propagation of high value crops. However, there is a great need for refinement of this technology by the tackling of certain technical problems such as the need to produce high-quality and high-fidelity somatic embryos, and to avoid the genetic instability and variability of tissue culture derived plants (somaclonal variation, which is not preferred for crops where true-to type plants are important). These problems can be overcome if the process and regulation of somatic embryogenesis and origin of somaclonal variation are well understood. Intensive research is being carried out in several laboratories to address these vital issues. Further, the understanding about the storage, transport, handling, growth habit and harvest index of artificial seeds is essential. Similarly, the efforts to increase the output of embryos/plants per gram callus tissue of input (mass balance) and conversion frequency of artificial seeds are also needed. If all these problems are rectified with technical progress, no doubt this novel method can become valuable tool in agriculture to propagate crop species.

Although synthetic seed research is being carried out in many laboratories, the principle limitation for commercialization has been the somatic embryogenesis. Despite the fact that somatic embryogenesis has been achieved for many species. During the last decade for many of the important, high value genotypes, somatic embryogenesis has not been reported. Therefore there is a need to shift the focus on somatic embryogenesis in valuable crop plants. Research on encapsulation of axillary buds, shoot tips or any other propagules should be taken up. Equally important is the need to develop new synthetic seed coatings for encapsulating embryos and other vegetative propagules. Synthetic seed technology in years to come would certainly find its application in plant propagation and delivery of tissue cultured plants.

PRODUCTION OF SYNTHETIC SEEDS

Synthetic or artificial seeds are the living seed-like structure derived from somatic embryoids *in vitro* culture after encapsulation by a hydrogel. *The preserved embryoids are termed as synthetic seeds.* Somatic embryoids are identical with zygotic enbryos and give rise to plants only under controlled laboratory conditions. Somatic embryoids are without seed coats. *In vitro* embryoid develops from callus tissue and their induction is initiated by somatic embryogenesis supplimenting the medium with auxin and cytokinins in proper ratio.

Such seeds are contaminated with microbes and desiccate quickly when they are subjected to field conditions. Therefore, to get rid from this problem, they are encapsulated by protective gel like **calcium alginate**. These encapsulated embryoids can resist unfavourable field conditions without desiccation. These seeds so developed behave like a true seed and are used as a substitute of natural seeds. They can also be sown directly in the greenhouse or in fields.

Encapsulation or Coating of Synthetic Seed

Encapsulation is necessasry to produce and to protect synthetic seeds. The encapsulation is done by various types of hydrogels which are water soluble. The gel has a complexing agent which is used in varied concentrations.

The encapsulation or coating of carrot and celery somatic embryos is done by polyoxyethylene (Polyox) and dried the embryo in polyox mixture.

TABLE 17.2: Various type of hydrogels

Gel (Concentration) (% w/v)	Complexing Agent Concentration (μM)
Sodium alginate (0.5-5.0)	Calcium salts (30-100)
Sodium alginate (2.0) with Gelatin (5.0)	Calcium chloride(30-100)
Carragenan (0.2-0.8)	Potassium chloride
Locust Beam Gum (0.4-1.0)	Ammonium chloride (500)

Two standard methods have been used for encapsulation of somatic embryos.

Gel Complexation via a Dropping Procedure

The most useful encapsulation system is to drip two per cent LF60 sodium alginate from a separatory funnel into a 100mM calcium nitrate solution. As the sodium alginate drops from at the tip of the funnel, the somatic embryos are inserted. The encapsulated embryos complex in calcium salt for 20 min, after which they are rinsed in water and then stored in a air tight container otherwise the capsule will dry out within 24 hour. It is a slow method of seeds production.

Automate Encapsulation Process

Automate encapsulation process is the recent and quick method of artificial seed production. An encapsulation machine can be used successfully to encapsulate somatic embryos, *e.g.*, for alfalfa. Blank alginate capsules were planted in Speeding™ trays using a vaccum seeder. The blank capsules are planted in the field using a Stanhay planter. However, for the rapid drying and the thickness of the alginate capsules, a hydrophobic coating is required for mechanical handling. For coating, an Elvax 4260 Copolymer™ (Dupont), is suitable for producing a slow-drying, nontacky coating which allows embryo conversion Based on this system of production of artificial seeds the cost factor is not high for most of the cash crops.

Alginate or carrageenan is also used for artificial seed production, *e.g.*, of carrot, asparagus, Norway spruce, etc. Mascarenhas (India) reported the encapsulation of *Eucalyptus* somatic embryos. He obtained 50 per cent germination from such seeds. Alginate artificial seeds are spherical and transparent. The alginate capsule is generally non-inhibitory.

Mass Balance Concept

An additional concept that has greatly aided the improvement of artificial seed performance is *mass balance*. Mass balance considers the amount of tissue at the beginning of the experiment (or production run) and the number of high quality plants produced at the end of it. Simply emphasising the number of embryos per gram of fresh callus or the number of embryo-producing calli is not adequate. In fact, treatments that lead to higher numbers of embryos may actually produce fewer superior quality of embryos than another protocol. At this time, the artificial seed package, consisting of a calcium alginate bead coated with a hydrophobic Elvax polymer, appears to be sufficient.

Steps of Commercial Artificial Seed Production

The following steps are needed for commercial synthetic seed production:

1. Production of embryogenic tissue from transformed cells or tissue.
2. Large-scale production of synchronous somatic embryos.
3. Maturation of somatic embryos.
4. Non-toxic encapsulation/coating process.
5. Artificial endosperm/megagametophyte, depending on species.
6. Storage capability of artificial seeds.
7. High frequency, direct green house/nursery field conversion, depending on production requirements.
8. Low genetic and epigenetic variation.
9. Appropriate expression of engineered trait.
10. Artificial Seed Propagation
11. Artificial seed propagation could potentially reduce the time needed to insert a desirable gene into a productive forest, as compared to using seed as the propagation method. A considerable advantage would be to eliminate or minimise the requirements for seed production using the following process:
12. Production of large-scale embryogenic tissue from genetically engineered cells;
13. Concurrent plant regeneration, confirmation of transformation, and *progeny* testing;
14. Cryogenic storage of potential superior lines;
15. Scale-up production and maturation of somatic embryos;
16. Encapsulation of somatic embryos as artificial seeds;
17. Either greehouse / nursery establishment, growth, and transplanting into the field or direct seedling.
18. The final stage will be the evaluation of production plantations for increased yield/ performance due to engineered trait.

Unlike herbaceous species, the growth and maturity of trees far exceed the time required for tissue culture manipulations. If the engineered trait is expressed only in the mature tree and is not stable during meiosis, then mass clonal propagation would be accomplished only through tissue culture methods (or, by traditional relatively low-volume ramet production).

Cryopreservation of desirable genotypes is one of the key components for artificial seed propagation of tree species. It retains the genetic gains from genetically engineered tree species without having to establish clonal orchards. Once the progeny tests are completed, then embryogenic tissue corresponding to the superior clones can be thawed for rapid scale-up production via somatic embryogenesis.

Although the use of artificial seed technology should be extremely valuable for the rapid introduction of genetically engineered material into production of forests.

Hydrogel Encapsulation of Artificial Seeds

Water soluble hydrogels have been found suitable for making artificial seeds. Two methods have been used to coat somatic embryos: gel complexation via a **dropping procedure** and **molding**.

Redenbaugh et al. (1986) mixed alfalfa somatic embryos with sodium alginate (2% w/v) and dropped them into a calcium nitrate solution (100 mM). Surface complexation began immediately and the drops were gelled completely in 30 minutes. Alternatively, the embryos could be mixed in a temperature-dependent gel such as Gel-rite™, placed in the well of a microtiter plate, and gelled as the temperature was lowered. Somatic embryos from several crops have been encapsulated in alginate with plants recovered *in vitro*.

TABLE 17.3: Useful gels for encapsulation of somatic embryos

Gel	Conc. % w/v	Complexing Agent	Concentration (mM)
Sodium Alginate	0.5-5.0	Calcium Salts	30-100
Sodium Alginate with Gelatin	2.0	Calcium Chloride	30-100
Carrageenan with	0.2-0.8	Potassium or Ammonium Chloride	500
Locust Bean Gum	0.4-1.0	Temperature lowered	
Gelrite	0.25		

The crops encapsulated in calcium alginate beads are Apium graveolens L., Brassica species, Daucus carota L., Gossypium hirsutum L., Lactuca sativa L., Medicago sativa L. and Zea mays L.

Initially, the effect of encapsulation was difficult to assess because of the overall poor quality of the somatic embryos. Although visually normal embryos were produced (*i.e.* bipolar, root and shoot axis, cotyledons), the germination and continued development of the embryos was very inconsistent. In fact, the use of germination (root elongation and emergence) as an efficacy assay was found to be unsuitable when shoot production and further growth was not observed concomitantly. Consequently, the approach for developing artificial seeds was shifted away from one focused on somatic embryogenesis (initiation of embryo formation) to one of somatic embryogeny (initiation, development, and maturation of embryos).

The concept of somatic embryogeny and the production of high quality embryos is not one that is widely followed by many researchers who have either focused on the production of a somatic embryogenesis system that results in some plant recovery or who have interest only in the study of the early stages of embryogenesis. This focus separated from an emphasis on producing mature, true-to-type, high quality embryos can possibly lead to conclusions based on abnormal somatic embryogenesis. To overcome this problem and to achieve high quality embryo production for scale-up of artificial seeds, measure the embryo response in terms of embryo-to-plant development or *conversion*. Essentially, embryo conversion frequency is the percent of the somatic embryos that produce green plants having a normal phenotype. This assay has been critical for developing conditions and media that select for uniform plant production. Following are the events, which are associated with the process of embryo-to-plant conversion.

1. Germination (radicle elongation)
2. Development of a vigorous root system
3. Growth and development of the shoot meristem
4. Production of true leaves
5. A direct shoot-to-root connection
6. Absence of hypertrophy of the hypocotyl
7. Minimization of callus growth in the hypocotyl
8. A green plant with a normal phenotype

SYNTHETIC SEED AND FOREST TREES

The use of biotechnological approaches in forestry may be greatly enhanced and considerable time could be saved by using artificial seed technology. Plain steps in genetic engineering of tree species focus on transformation, followed by traditional forest seed production and tree evaluation are as under:

1. Regeneration of genetically engineered tissue;
2. Confirming presence and expression of engineered gene;
3. Bulking up propagules through vegetative propagation or seed production;
4. Greenhouse/nursery establishment and growth;
5. Seed orchard establishment with concurrent progeny testing, including evaluation of the engineered trait;
6. Seed orchard roguing;
7. Seed production in seed orchards and;
8. Either nursery production with transplanting into the field or direct seedling.
9. The final stage will be the evaluation of plantations for increased performance due to the engineered trait.

SOMATIC EMBRYOGENESIS AND SYNSEEDS

Somatic embryogenesis in many woody species is less successful than other methods of micropropagation. The earliest report of somatic embryogenesis in a coniferous tree is that for spruce *Picea abies*. Since then, somatic embryogenesis has been reported in several other *Picea* species. Mainly immature, and occasionally mature embryos were used successfully in conifers, yielding somatic embryos and plantlets. Although the number of species that can be propagated through this method has been increasing, the percentage of recovery for plantlets remains relatively low. Studies of somatic embryo formation in pines show that they can arise either in the conventional manner, as for spruce, or by a process termed somatic polyembryogenesis, as found with sugar and loblolly pines. The resulting embryos elongated and formed numerous cotyledons in a repetitive and true-to-type polyembryonic process. In the loblolly pine, the somatic embryos thus produced developed transplantable plants. The rate of somatic embryo formation has been improved recently, making it commercially viable for some species. Procedures for induction of somatic embryogenesis and subsequent conversion of the embryos to artificial seeds have been developed in a limited number of spruce and pine genotypes, such as Norway spruce and loblolly pine, with treated embryos being stored for further use as artificial seeds.

CHAPTER 18

Animal Cell and Tissue Culture

INTRODUCTION

The foundation of animal cell and tissue culture was laid at the beginning of the present century, when cell could be shown to survive and divide *in vitro*. The actual beginning of animal cell and tissue culture was however, made by Ross Harrison (1907), by using frog as a source of tissue. Alexis Carrel (1912) used tissue and embryo extract as culture media. For about 50 years, mainly tissue explants rather than cells were used for culture techniques, although later after 1950s, mainly dispersed cell cultures were utilized. Similar to plants, for animal if the explant maintains its structure and function in culture, it is described as an organotypic culture irrespective of the tissue from which it was derived, it is described as a histotypic culture.

The animal tissue culture is a technique is which the tissue/cells are taken out from an animal's body and grown, and maintained in laboratory in a suitable medium. It is only in the past few decades that man with the immense knowledge and techniques of science at his command has been able to venture into the deep bionomics of cell and learned more and more about its applications to the well being of human beings. Tissue culture is not a science but an art made up of a wide range of activities, which made a rough distinction between fundamental and applied research. At present, tissue culture is an indispensible tool, particularly in the fileds of medical and agricultural sciences.

ADVANTAGES AND DISADVANTAGES OF TISSUE CULTURE METHODS

There are several advantages and disadvantages of animal tissue culture, therefore, this technique should not be used indiscriminately.

Advantages

1. The behaviour of cells in culture can be interpreted and regulated properly.
2. There remains homogeneity of cell types (achieved through serial passages)
3. It is economical because smaller quantities of reagents are needed than *in vitro*.
4. The legal, moral and ethical questions of animal experimentation are avoided.

Disadvantages

1. It needs controlled physiochemical environment (pH, temperature, osmotic pressure, O_2, CO_2, etc.)
2. It is ten times more expensive for same quantity of animal tissue; therefore reasons for its use should be compelling.
3. Unstable aneuploid chromosome constitution
4. Controlled and defined physiological conditions (constitution of medium, etc.) are needed

PRIMARY AND ESTABLISHED CELL LINES

A piece of tissue from the organism is usually quite complex and may contain, besides the specialized cells of the tissue, connective tissue cells, a variety of blood cells and reticuloendothelial cells. When a culture is first set up, these all survive for at least a day or two. In usual culture conditions many cells begin to migrate almost immediately.

The first cells to do this are often macrophages, followed by fibroblasts, which migrate in a radial manner from the explant. Many of the specialized cells, however, remain immobile in the connective tissue stroma. Nerve cells, for example, usually remain in the explant although axons may migrate out from it.

The subsequent fates of these cells vary enormously. Many of them are quite short-lived, *e.g.*, most of the blood cells die and disappear from the culture within two or three days. Other cells, such as neurons and muscle cells, frequently persist in culture, sometimes for months without dividing at all and then eventually die too. Still other cells begin to divide rapidly and continue to do so for sometime. However, many of these also die after a period, which varies from weeks to months. If the cells multiply repeatedly for a long time, they can often be *passaged.* First obtaining the cells in suspension and then inoculating this into a new culture vessel along with fresh medium usually achieve this. As soon as cells have been *passaged* in this way the culture is designated as **primary cell line.**

Primary cultures is used advantageously because of:

1. The expense and inconvenience of maintaining a established cell stocks is obviated.
2. They are particularly suitable for vaccine production since the probability of *in vitro* transformation of cells to malignancy is minimized.
3. Massive quantities of tissue can be obtained conveniently for short-term studies.
4. The are hardy and can be sustained well in media of relatively simple composition.
5. Their degree and range of sensitivity to viral infection may exceed that of the common established cell lines.
6. The use of primary cell cultures has following inherent disadvantages:
7. The may be contaminated with latent viruses (*e.g.*, foamy virus in monkey kidney tissues).
8. Long-term experiments concerning the biological properties of cells can not be carried out.

Mixed populations of cells may confuse interpretation of experimental findings (Merchant *et al.*, 1964).

Frequently, primary cell lines go on dividing at quite a high rate for a long time and can be passaged repeatedly. Even after quite a large number of passages, some primary cell lines cease to proliferate and die out. However, sometimes cell lines can be cultured for such a long time that they apparently have developed the potential to be sub-cultured indefinitely *in vitro.* Such cell lines are called **established cell lines.** As a general rule, a line is not designated an established cell line unless it has been sub-cultured at least 70 times at intervals of 3 days between subcultures.

Transition from primary cell line to established cell line is smooth and gradual in some instances but in others it arises from a primary cell line by a dramatic event called **cell alteration** or **transformation.** During this alteration, in the primary cell line, a few rapidly growing colonies of transformed cells appear, which quickly outgrow the rest of the culture and become the predominant cell type. The established cell lines arising in this way often differ in many respects from the primary cell lines from which they are derived. All primary cell lines at first have the normal number of chromosomes, whereas, established cell lines almost invariably have an unusual number. There are some interesting species differences in the stability of cells. The human fibroblasts is a classical example of a particularly sable primary cell lines; it never undergoes spontaneous transformation to an established cell line (although they can be transformed by treatment with certain tumour viruses). On the other hand, mouse fibroblasts almost invariably undergo a smooth transition to form established cell lines.

Established cell lines behave in a remarkably similar manner irrespective of their origin.

1. They have short doubling timings, of the order of 12 to 20 hours.
2. They are invariably aneuploid.
3. They have similar nutritional requirements, whatever their origin.
4. They grow to much higher densities than primary cell lines.
5. They do not usually show much evidence of spatial orientation.
6. It is rare for them to show obvious specialized functions.
7. They will often grow from dilute inocula.

Most of them can be established in suspension cultures, whereas, it is exceptional for primary cell lines to grow in suspension.

KINETICS OF CELL GROWTH

Established Cell Lines

Cells in culture display very much the same type of growth pattern as microorganisms. In particular, they show the classical growth demonstrated by cultures of bacteria, yeast and protozoa. The culture exhibits following phases:

1. **Lag phase:** This is the phase when practically no growth occurs and may last for some hours to a few days before growth commences.
2. **Logarithmic (log) phase:** During this phase growth proceeds steadily with the population doubling every 15 to 20 hours in the case of fast growing cells
3. **Stationary phase:** At the end of log phase maximum population is reached and the growth becomes stationary.

During log phase, the cell population increases according to the formula:

$$N = N_0 2kt$$

$$i.e., \log N = \log N_0 + Kt \log^2$$

(where, N_0 = initial inoculum, N= cell number at `t' hours, and k is a regression constant).

The factor kt is actually equal to the generation number (n), *i.e.*, the number of generations involved in the increase by doubling at each generation from N_0 to N. It follows that the mean generation time (T), the time for the population to double, is the inverse of K, *i.e.*, T = 1/k).

The quation can, therefore, be written:

$$\log N = \log N_0 + n \log^2$$

$$n = (\log N - \log N_0)/\log^2$$

Since $1/\log^2 = 3.32$, this can be written in the form

$$n = 3.32 (\log N - \log N_0)$$

This calculation assumes that all cells in a population divide and they do so at approximately the same rates. In instances where a fraction of the cells does not divide or where cells may even be dying in large number, this calculation applies only to the dividing fraction.

The growth rate of cultured cells is not necessarily always the same. It may vary to some extent from one cell strain to another but in particular it varies considerably with environmental conditions such as pH, temperature and osmotic pressure.

Primary Cell Lines

Primary cell lines do not behave in quite the same ways as established cell lines. When established cell lines have become stationary the medium in which they have been grown is usually inadequate for maintenance of a fresh inoculum of cells. However, it can often be observed that cultures of primary cell lines stop growing before the medium is exhausted. The reason for this is a phenomenon called **contact inhibition**, which was first described by Abercrombie and Heaysman. They observed that when certain kinds of normal cells, mainly fibroblasts, came into contact they were immediately immobilized. This is the very common property of primary cell lines. Not only is cell movement affected by contact inhibition; cell division, DNA synthesis, RNA and protein synthesis are much reduced or eliminated when a cell sheet becomes confluent. When primary cell lines become transformed, one of the most outstanding features of the transformed cells is the absence of great diminution of contact inhibition. This is the reason why transformed cells grow to higher densities and pile up on each other. The effect of contact inhibition on the kinetics of growth of primary cell lines is that they exhibit ideal kinetics only when in a very dilute inoculum. As soon as small sheets of cells are formed contact inhibition takes effect and growth slows progressively.

Interaction among Cells

Besides contact inhibition, the most interesting interaction is the ability of like cells to recognize and adhere to each other. Holtfreter showed that when amphibian embryonic cells were disaggregated in calcium and magnesium free salt solution and the separated cells were then allowed to mix together, they first adhered in a random manner and then sorted themselves out into groups of like cells. Eventually the entire embryo was reconstructed. Moscona demonstrated the same phenomenon with mammalian and avian cells.

There are two different schools of thought, one of which postulates a kind of intercellular cement which sticks like cells to each other and the other of which suggests that the adhesion phenomenon is an intrinsic property of the cell membrane themselves.

GENETICS OF CULTURED CELLS

Primary cell lines usually retain their diploid karyotype. Transformed cell lines show a great variation in karyotype. Shortly after transformation the incidence of tetraploid cells increases; aneuploid cells then make their appearance and stable established cell lines commonly have an aneuploid daryotype with a wide spread of chromosome numbers. The emergence of aneuploidy is apparently due to nondisjunctive cell division.

Later on, in the established cell lines the morphology of the individual chromosome also changes; it is because of chromosome breaks, fusion and translocations, *e.g.*, many mouse cell lines contain metacentric chromosomes, whereas, it is typical of the mouse that all the chromosomes are normally acrocentric. Mutant cells also arise in the tissue culture.

Metabolism

In cultured cells, the metabolism of glucose proceeds by way of glycolytic and Krebs pathways as in the tissues of the intact organism. However, many cells show a marked tendency to accumulate lactic acid and keto-acids in the medium. Cultured cells have very variable needs for oxygen and considerable part of the energy requirements can be met by the breakdown of 6-carbon carbohydrate such as glucose to 3-carbon compounds such as lactic acid and pyruvic acid, a process which requires no oxygen. Cells can be grown in the complete absence of oxygen for rather short periods of time.

Tissue culture cells can synthesize lipids from simple chemical substances such as acetate. It is not known whether fats themselves can be taken up from the medium and stored. Some cells are capable of synthesizing cholesterol.

Cultured cells can build nucleic acids readily from simple compounds in a medium (such as formate, glycine and bicarbonate). They possess all the enzymes necessary for this purpose.

ANIMAL CELL AND TISSUE CULTURE

Animal cell cultures have many applications including their use as model systems for biochemical, physiological and pharmacological studies and the production of growth factors, blood factors, monoclonal antibodies, interferons, enzymes, vaccines, and hormones.

The major problem associated with the isolation of free cells and cell aggregates from organs is that of releasing the cells from their supporting matrix without affecting the integrity of the cell membrane. Various methods have been employed to achieve this goal.

Mechanical Technique

This includes the forcing of the tissue through cheese or silk cloth or shaking the tissue with glass beads in an appropriate buffer. This technique causes considerable cell damage and results in a low cell yield.

Biochemical Technique

This technique has largely overcome the problems caused by mechanical dissociation. Collagenase and hyaluronidase in a calcium free medium have been used for hepatocyte isolation. The liver is thinly sliced and then incubated with the enzymes.

TABLE 18.1: Some examples of the applications of animal cell and tissue culture

Cell type	Process investigated
Monocytes and macrophages	Pinocytosis and phagocytosis
Blood lymphocytes	Karyotype analysis for detection of genetic defects in humans
Normal and transformed fibroblasts	Surface adherence properties of normal and malignant cell membranes
Kideny tubule epithelial cells	Differentiation of monolayers; electrical and vectorial transport of solutes; monoclonal antibody production
Myeloma cells and ß-lympohcytes	Purification and characterization of specific membrane proteins e.g. α-and ß-adrenergic receptors, dopamine receptors
Kidney epithelial cells	To investigate relationship between membrane polarity and budding properties of envelope RNA viruses
Transformed leucocytes, fibroblasts and either lymphocytes or lymphoblastoid cells	Cells are infected with Sendai virus to produce À, ß, and interferon respectively
Transformed Hela cells, mammalian cells	Radiation therapy and the design of radiosensitisers and radioprotectors
Mouse fibroblasts	Acute and chronic toxicity testing and metabolism of xenobiotics; vaccine production
Primary monkey kidney cells	Production of poliovaccines; hormone secretion
Fibroblasts, mammalian brain cells	To identify chemicals capable of including chromosome aneuploidy

Animal cells may be broadly subdivided into:

1. Those which remain viable only when attached to a solid substrate (*e.g.*, primary cultures, normal diploid fibroblast cell strains), and
2. Those that will proliferate in fine suspension (*e.g.*, human tumour cells, Hela cell lines and hybridomas).

The material, to which cell stick must be non-toxic, sterilisable and preferably transparent, so that the cells may be observed under microscope. The surfaces, which have been used successfully include plastic, glass, teflon tubing and DEAE-sephadex. Cells may be detached from such surfaces by mild trypsin digestion.

ANIMAL TISSUE CULTURE MEDIA

Culture Media Containing Naturally Occurring Ingredients

In spite of vast use of chemically defined media in tissue culture, it is still necessary in most undertakings to depend on naturally occurring substances derived from the organism. The various kinds of such media which are in used. These are as follows:

(i) blood plasma, (ii) blood serum, (iii) tissue extract and (iv) complex natural media.

Blood Plasma

Tissue culture was first conducted by Harrison (1907) in clotted frog lymph. Burrows (1910) substituted a coagulum prepared from chicken plasma. After many years it was found that plasma provided a complete nutrient in which cells could survive and multiply slowly for extended periods under conditions that resembled in many respect those found in body. Plasma is still being used to advantage for the following purposes:

1. To provide a nutritive substrate and a supporting structure for many types of cultures, just as it also provides a matrix for new cells during the repair of injury in the body.
2. To provide a means of conditioning the surface of glass for better attachment of cells.
3. To provide a means of protecting cells and tissues from excessive traumatic damage during subculture.
4. To provide some degree of protection from sudden changes in the environment at times of fluid change.
5. To provide localized pockets of conditioned medium around cells.

For culture work, plasma from the adult chicken is preferred to mammalian plasma because it forms a clear, solid coagulum even when diluted several times. Mammalian plasma is either too opaque for good optical work or else it fails to produce solid clots.

The plasma is obtained by centrifugation of whole blood before coagulation takes place. The tissue is then placed in a small quantity of the plasma and coagulation encouraged by addition of a small amount of tissue extract or thrombin. This is done because the cells in culture require a solid support for continued growth and activity. In case of fowl the blood is obtained from the wing, heart or carotid artery. In case of mammals it is obtained from carotid artery and heart.

Blood Serum

Blood serum (*plasma minus fibrinogen*) with or without other nutritive substances may be used either as the entire culture medium or as the fluid phase of a medium consisting partly of a plasma coagulum. For many years it was assumed that whole serum was toxic, that plasma was useful only as a supportive structure and that the nutritive requirements of the cells were supplied by the embryo extract that was usually added to the medium. Eventually, however, it was found possible to cultivate tissues in serum alone without plasma or tissue extract.

In 1928, des Ligneris reported the successful cultivation of many mammalian tissues in diluted serum and later Parker (1933, 1936) cultivated chick tissues in serum. Simms (1936), and Simms and Sanders (1942) introduced an ultrafiltrate of serum that was used as a basal medium for many purposes including the propagation of viruses. Fischer and co-workers (1948) stressed the importance of the low molecular weight growth factors provided by serum. As some of the more elaborate chemically defined solutions were developed, it was found that they had to be supplemented with 10 to 20 per cent serum to provide completely adequate medium for the continuous propagation of established cell lines and freshly explanted tissues for extended periods. Harris (1959) concluded that medium 199 and NCTC-109, as well as the simpler basal medium of Eagle (1955) are all deficient in one or more factors that occur in serum dialysate and are essential for the growth and maintenance of chick skeletal muscle fibroblasts. Thus serum does provide some of the growth factors or some of the physical conditions, or both, that are presently lacking in synthetic media.

Preparation of Chicken Serum

The fluid plasma from which the serum is prepared should be completely coagulated. The plasma is coagulated deliberately by adding to each tube a drop or two of embryo tissue extract or an equivalent amount of thrombin and leaving the tubes to incubate for several hours at 37 °C. The coagulated plasma is broken up into fragments and it is ground in a mortor with sterile quartz sand. After grinding the serum is separated by centrifugation.

Preparation of mammalian serum

The mammalian blood is left at room temperature for an hour. The clot is removed by a glass rod and then centrifuged for 30 minutes at 3000 rpm and the serum is separated.

Serum Free Media

The use of serum in culture media is not so common because it has following disadvantages:

1. The quality of serum varies from batch to batch and deteriorates within one year. Therefore, every batch of serum needs fresh testing.
2. If more than one cell type is used, each may require different serum batch, therefore, many batches are to be maintained and co-culturing may be difficult.
3. The demand of serum usually exceeds the supply for a variety of reasons.
4. When cell culture is used for downstream processing to recover cell products, the presence of serum is an obstacle to purification;
5. Serum increases the cost of the medium.
6. Serum may stimulate undesirable growth and may even inhibit growth in some cases.

Advantage of Serum Free media

1. It has the ability to make a medium selective for a particular cell type, since each cell type appears to require a different recipe.
2. It has high degree of purity of reagents and water.
3. It needs high degree of cleanliness of all apparatus.

How to Develop Serum Free Media?

1. A known recipe for a related cell type may be used.
2. Individual constituents of the serum may be altered, until the medium is optimized.
3. The development and assessment constituent is a time consuming process. Sometimes it takes about three years for development of a new medium.
4. In the second approach, an existing medium like **RPMI 1640** or **Ham's F12** or **DMEM (Dulbecco's modified minimal essential medium)** is taken and a shorter list of constituents like selenium, transferrin, albumin, insulin, androgen, hydrocortisone, estrogen, etc. is used for manipulation.

Tissue Extracts

Carrel (1912) discovered that embryo tissue extract had remarkable powers of promoting cell growth and multiplication in cultures of connective tissue cells from chick embryo heart. Since Carrel's experiments, there have been many attempts to determine the chemical nature of the substances responsible for the stimulating effect of embryo extract.

Baker and Carrel (1926) obtained active fractions of the extract by precipitation with carbon dioxide and found that the activity was concentrated largely in the protein portion containing nucleoproteins and glycoproteins. It was further observed (Carrel and Baker, 1926) that proteoses and higher molecular weight protein degradation products also had very potent growth promoting properties. Growth promoting activity appeared to be associated particularly with fractions containing predominantly nucleoproteins of the ribonucleic acid type. Fractions relatively high in dooxyribonucleic acid appeared much less active. Active nucleoprotein fractions from adult chicken heart, brain, liver and spleen have been used but no indications of organ specificity were observed. The activity of the fraction also did not depend on their total nucleic acid content or on the age of the indivifuals from which they were prepared.

Preparation of Embryo Extract

Chick embryo extract is made from 10 to 11 days old embryos (before the calcifying mechanisms have become too active). The embryos are removed from the egg, then homogenized in a motordriven homogenizer. Six to eight embryos and a measured quantity of balanced salt solutions (*e.g.*, 2.0 ml per embryo) may be processed at one time. After homogenization, it is centrifuged and further diluted 10 to 20 times. Embryo extract may be stored indefinitely after it has been dried from the frozen state.

Complex Natural Media

Some of the complex natural media are as follows:

Supplemented Hanks-Simms medium

Weller and co-workers (1952) in their earlier work with polioviruses made excellent use of a combination of 3 parts Hanks's balanced salt and 1 part Simm's ox serum ultrafiltrate. For rollertube cultures of various human and animal tissues (embryonic, infant and adult), the complete medium consisted of Hanks-Simms solution (85%), beef embryo extract (10%), horse serum inactivated at 56 °C for 30 minutes (5 to 20%), penicillin (50 µg/ml) and streptomycin (50 µg/ml).

Supplemented bovine amniotic fluid medium

Milovanic and co-workers (1957, 1958) used the following medium:

Bovine amniotic fluid (37.5%), horse serum inactivated at 56 °C for 30 minutes (20%), bovine embryo extract (5%), Hanks balanced salt solution (37.5%), streptomycin (100µ /ml), penicillin (100µ/ml) and mycostatin (100µ/ml).

Serum-supplemented yeast extract medium

Various human cell lines and strains from other species have been successfully grown in this medium. The medium consists of:

Yeast extract medium (76 parts) [composition: 10 parts of 1% solution of Difco's yeastolate, 2.5 parts of 10% glucose solution and 87.5 parts of Hanks balanced salt solution], human serum (20 parts), and 1.4 per cent sodium biacrobonate solution (4 parts).

Serum-supplemented lactalbumin hydrolysate and yeast extract medium

This medium consisted of: Earle's saline containing lactalbumin hydrolysate (0.5%), yeast extract (0.1%), and human or ox serum (10-20%).

Chemically Defined Media

Earlier, the nutritive media for the cultivation of animal cells *in vitro* were derived from the organisms and consisted of blood plasma, blood serum, tissue extracts, etc. The complexity and variability of these naturally occurring materials made it difficult to use them in experiments designed to determine the nutritive substances required by the cells and the effect of particular substance upon them.

The first attempts to devise chemically defined media were made by Lewis and Lewis, Baker and Carrel, Vogelaar and Erlichman. Carrel's discovery (1912) that extracts of embryonic tissues contained an abundance of growth promoting substances made it possible for the first time to propagate animal cells indefinitely and stimulated the search for the particular substances responsible.

Fischer's supplementary medium, V-614 consisted of dialyzed plasma, dialyzed embryo extact, Tyrode's solution, glucose, fructose diphosphate, glutamine, cystine, glutathione, tryptophan, phenylalanine, threonine, isoleucine, leucine, valine, arginine, gistidine, and lysine. Fischer further suggested that different cell types may have different amino acid requirements. Thus, osteoblasts were more sensitive than myoblasts to lysine deficiency. He also stated that animal tissue cultivated outside the body might require certain nutrients not required by the intact animal.

White (1946) for the first time made serious attempt to cultivate animal tissues in a complete solution of known composition. He reported a feeding solution of 20 ingredents of known composition that supported relatively large masses of chick embryo heart tissue in a state of functional survival for several weeks.

Morgan et al. (1950) published the composition of a more adequate medium No. 199. The medium included almost complete complement of amino acids and vitamins as well as several nucleic acid constituents and certain intermediary metabolites and accessory growth factors. Glutamine was included because of the importance placed upon it by Fischer's group and Tween-80 was used as a water soluble source of fatty acid and as means of dissolving the fat soluble vitamins and cholesterol in a minimal concentration of ethyl alcohol. The medium also contained the salts of Erle's balanced salt solution, glucose, ferric nitrate and phenol red.

CHEMICALLY DEFINED MEDIA

Earlier, the nutritive media for the cultivation of animal cells *in vitro* were derived from the organisms and consisted of blood plasma, blood serum, tissue extracts, etc. The complexity and variability of these naturally occurring materials made it difficult to use them in experiments designed to determine the nutritive substances required by the cells and the effect of particular substance upon them.

The first attempts to devise chemically defined media were made by Lewis and Lewis, Baker and Carrel, Vogelaar and Erlichman. Carrel's discovery (1912) that extracts of embryonic tissues contained an abundance of growth promoting substances made it possible for the first time to propagate animal cells indefinitely and stimulated the search for the particular substances responsible.

Correl and Baker (1926) reported that Witt's peptone, proteoses and other degradation products when used with serum or plasma provided essential nutrients for fibroblasts, epithelial cells and blood monocytes. Vogelaar and Erlichman (1933) prepared a feeding solution consisting of irradiated beef plasma, Witte's peptone, hemin, cystine, insulin, thyroxine, glucose and the salts of tyrode's solution. They kept a strain of fibroblasts from the human thyroid in a state of active proliferation for 3 months. Baker later on added vitamin A and D, ascorbic acid, glutathione and

10% serum for the cultivation of epithelial cells. For blood monocytes certain B-vitamins were also added.

Fischer's supplementary medium, V-614 consisted of dialyzed plasma, dialyzed embryo extact, Tyrode's solution, glucose, fructose diphosphate, glutamine, cystine, glutathione, tryptophan, phenylalanine, threonine, isoleucine, leucine, valine, arginine, histidine, and lysine. Fischer further suggested that different cell types may have different amino acid requirements. Thus, osteoblasts were more sensitive than myoblasts to lysine deficiency. He also stated that animal tissue cultivated outside the body may require certain nutrients not required by the intact animal.

White (1946) for the first time made serious attempt to cultivate animal tissues in a complete solution of known composition. He reported a feeding solution of 20 ingredients of known composition that supported relatively large masses of chick embryo heart tissue in a state of functional survival for several weeks.

Morgan et al. (1950) published the composition of a more adequate medium No. 199. The medium included almost complete complement of amino acids and vitamins as well as several nucleic acid constituents and certain intermediary metabolites and accessory growth factors. Glutamine was included because of the importance placed upon it by Fischer's group and Tween-80 was used as a water soluble source of fatty acid and as means of dissolving the fat soluble vitamins and cholesterol in a minimal concentration of ethyl alcohol. The medium also contained the salts of Erle's balanced salt solution, glucose, ferric nitrate and phenol red.

TABLE 18.2: Different commonly used media (with serum), for animal cell and tissue culture, and their constituents (all quantities in mg/l)

Component	Eagle's MEM	Dulbecco's modi-fication	Ham's F12	CMRL 1066	RPMI 1640	199	L15	Fischer's	Way-mouth MB 752
Amino acids									
L-alanine	-	-	8.90	25.0	-	25.0	225	-	-
L-arginine (free base)	-	-	-	-	200	-	550	-	-
L-arginine-HCl	126	84.0	211	70.0	-	70.0	-	15.0	75.0
L-asparagine	-	-	-	-	50.0	-	-	-	-
L-asparagine-H_2O	-	-15.0	-	-	-	260	11.4	-	
L-aspartic acid	-	-13.3	30.0	20.0	30.0	-	-	60.0	
L-cysteine (free base)	-	-	-	-	-	-	120	-	61.0
L-cystine	24	48.0	-	20.0	50.0	-	-	-	15.0
L-cystine. 2Na	-	-	-	-	-	23.7	-	23.7	-
L-cysteine. HCL.H_2O	-	-	35.1	260	-	0.098 7	-	-	-
L-glutamic acid	-	-14.7	75.0	20.0	66.8	-	-	150	
L-glutamine 292	584	146	100	300	100	300	200	350	
Glycine	-	30.0	7.50	50.0	10.0	50.0	200	-	50.0
L-histidine (free base)	-	-	-	-	15.0	-	250	-	128
L-histidine HCl.H_2O	42.0	42.0	21.0	20.0	-	21.9	-	81.1	-
L-hydroxyproline	-	-	-	10.0	20.0	10.0	-	-	-

Component	Eagle's MEM	Dulbecco's modification	Ham's F12	CMRL 1066	RPMI 1640	199	L15	Fischer's	Waymouth MB 752
L-isoleucine	52.0	105	3.94	20.0	50.0	20.0	125	75.0	25.0
L-leucine	52.0	105	13.1	60.0	50.0	60.0	125	30.0	50.0
L-lysine. HCl	73.1	146	36.5	70.0	40.0	70.0	93	50.0	240
L-methionine	15.0	30.0	4.48	15.0	15.0	15.0	75.0	100	50.0
L-phenylalanine	33.0	66.0	4.96	25.0	15.0	25.0	125	67.0	50.0
L-proline	-	-	34.5	40.0	20.0	40.0	-	-	50.0
L-serine	-	42.0	10.5	25.0	30.0	25.0	200	15.0	-
L-threonine	48.0	95.0	11.9	30.0	20.0	30.0	300	40.0	75.0
L-tryptophan	10.0	16.0	2.04	10.0	5.0	10.0	20.0	10.0	40.0
L-tyrosine	36.0	72.0	5.40	40.0	20.0	-	-	-	40.0
L-tyrosine. 2Na	-	-	-	-	-	49.7	373	74.6	-
L-valine	47.0	94.0	11.7	25.0	20.0	25.0	100	70.0	65.0
Vitamins									
L-ascorbic acid	-	-	-	50.0	-	0.050	-	-	17.5
Biotin	-	-	0.0073	0.010	0.200	0.010	-	0.010	0.02
D-Ca-pantothenate	1.00	4.00	0.480	0.010	0.250	0.010	1.00	0.500	1.00
Calciferol	-	-	-	-	-	0.100	-	-	-
Choline chloride	1.00	4.00	14.0	0.500	3.00	0.500	1.00	1.50	250
Folic acid	1.00	4.00	1.30	0.010	1.00	0.010	1.00	10.0	0.40
i-inositol	2.00	7.20	18.0	0.050	35.0	0.050	2.00	1.50	1.00
Nicotinamide	1.00	4.00	0.04	0.025	1.00	0.025	1.00	0.50	1.00
Pyridoxal. HCl	1.00	4.00	0.062	0.025	-	0.025	-	0.50	-
Riboflavin	0.10	0.40	0.038	0.010	0.20	0.010	-	0.50	1.00
Thiamin. HCl	1.00	4.00	0.34	0.010	1.00	0.010	-	1.00	10.0
Vitamin B_{12}	-	-	1.36	-	0.005	-	-	-	0.20
Pyridoxine HCl	-	-	0.062	0.025	1.00	0.025	-	-	1.00
Cholesterol	-	-	-	0.200	-	-	-	-	-
Para-amino benzoic acid	-	-	-	0.050	1.00	0.050	-	-	-
Nicotinic acid	-	-	-	-	-	0.025	-	-	-
Menaphthone sodium bisulphite $3H_2O$	-	-	-	-	-	0.019	-	-	-
Dl-Â tocopherol $PO_4.2Na$	-	-	-	-	-	0.01	-	-	-
Vitamin Λ acctate	-	-	-	-	-	0.115	-	-	-
Riboflavin	-	-	-	-	-	-	0.10	-	-
$PO_4.2Na$ Thiamin mono $PO_4,2H_2O$	-	-	-	-	-	-	1.00	-	-
Inorganic salts									
$CaCl_2$ (anhyd.)	200	200	-	200	-	-	-	-	-
$CaCl_2.2H_2O$	-	-	44.0	-	-	186	186	91.0	120
$Fe(NO_3)_3.9H_2O$	-	0.10	-	-	-	0.10	-	-	-
KCl	400	400	224	400	400	400	400	400	150
KH_2PO_4	-	-	-	-	-	60.0	60.0	-	80.0

Component	Eagle's MEM	Dulbecco's modification	Ham's F12	CMRL 1066	RPMI 1640	199	L15	Fischer's	Waymouth MB 752
$MgCl_2.6H_2O$	-	-	122	-	-	-	-	-	240
$MgSO_4.7H_2O$	200	200	-	200	100	200	400	121	200
NaCl	6,800	6,400	7,599	6,799	6,000	8,000	8,000	8,000	6,000
$NaHCO_3$	2,200	3,700	1,176	2,200	2,200	350	-	1,125	2,240
$Na_2H_2PO_4.H_2O$	140	125	-	140	-	-	-	78.0	-
Na_2HPO_4 (anhyd)	-	-	-	-	-	47.5	190	60.0	-
$Na_2HPO_4.7H_2O$	-	-	268	-	1,512	-	-	-	566
$CuSO_4.5H_2O$	-	-	0.00249	-	-	-	-	-	-
$FeSO_4.7H_2O$	-	-	0.834	-	-	-	-	-	-
$ZnSO_4.7H_2O$	-	-	0.863	-	-	-	-	-	-
$CaNO_3.4H_2O$	-	-	-	-	100	-	-	-	-
Other components									
D-glucose	1,000	4,500	1,802	1,000	2,000	1,000	-	1,000	5,000
D-galactose	-	-	-	-	-	-	9,000	-	-
Lipoic acid	-	-	0.21	-	-	-	-	-	-
Phenol red	10.0	15.0	12.0	20.0	5.00	17.0	10.0	5.00	10.0
Sodium pyruvate	-	110	110	-	-	-	550	-	-
Hypoxanthine	-	-	4.10	-	-	0.30	-	-	-
Linoleic acid	-	0.084	-	-	-	-	-	-	25.0
Putrescine 2HCl	-	-	0.161	-	-	-	-	-	-
Thymidine	-	-	0.73	10.0	-	-	-	-	-
Cocarboxylase	-	-	-	1.00	-	-	-	-	-
Coenzyme A	-	-	-	2.50	-	-	-	-	-
Deoxyadenosine	-	-	-	10.0	-	-	-	-	-
Deoxycytidine HCl	-	-	-	10.0	-	-	-	-	-
Deoxyguanosine	-	-	-	10.0	-	-	-	-	-
Diphosphopyridine nucleot									

TABLE 18.3: Examples of selective media (modified from Freshney, 1987)

Cells of cell line	Medium
Bronchial epithelium	LHC
Endothelium	MCDB 130
Fibroblasts	MCDB 202
Fibroblasts	MCDB 110
Keratinocytes	MCDB 153
Mammary epithelium	MCDB 170
Prostate epithelium (human)	WAJC 404
Prostate epithelium (rat)	WAJC 404
Small cell lung cancer	HITES

TABLE 18.4: Selecting a suiTABLE medium* (modified from Freshney, 1987)

Cells or cell line	Medium with serum		
	Medium	Serum	Serum-free medium
Chick embryo fibroblasts	Eagle's MEM	CS	MCDB 202
Chinese hamster ovary (CHO)	Eagle's MEM	CS	MCDB 301
Chondrocytes	F12	FB	Adolphe et. al., 1983
Continuous cell lines	Eagle's MEM	CS	199, Waymouth, 1984 MB752/1. MD7505/1 CMRL 1066
Endothelium	DME, 199, MEM	FB	MCDB 130
Fibroblasts	Eagle's MEM	CS	MCDB 110, 202, 402
Glial cells	MEM, SF12	FB	Michler et al., 1984
Glioma	MEM, SF12	FB	
HeLa cells	Eagle's MEM	CS	Blaker et al., 1971
Hemopoietic cells	RPMI 1640, Fischer's	FB	Iscover, 1984
Human diploid fibroblasts	Eagle's MEM	CS	MCDB 110, 202
Human leukemia	RPMI 1640	FB	Breitman et al., 1984; Iscover, 1984
Human tumours	SF12, L15, RPMI 1640, DME	FB	
L cell (L 929, LS)	Eagle's MEM	CS	Birch and Pirt, 1970, 1971; Higuchi, 1971
Lymphoblastoid cell lines (human)	RPMI 1640	FB	Iscover, 1984
MDCK dog kidney epithelium	DME, F10/DME	FB	Taub, 1984
Melanoma	MEM. SF12	FB	Barnes and Sato. 1980
Mouse embryo fibroblasts	Eagle's MEM	CS	MCDB 402
Mouse Icukemia	Fischer's RPMI 1640	FB. HoS	Murakami, 1984
Mouse myeloma	DME, RPMI 1640	FB	Murakami. 1984 HB101
Mouse neuroblastoma	DME, F12/DME	FB	MCDB411
Skeletal muscle	DME, F12	FB. HoS	F12
Syrian hamster fibroblasts BHK 21	MEM, GMEM, DME	CS	Pardee et al., 1984
3T3 cells	MEM.DME	CS	MCDB402

* Abbreviations: SF12 is Ham's F12 plus Eagle's essential amino acids and non-essential amino acids as in DME (available as 100 times stock from Flow Labs., Gibco, etc.). Further recommedations on the choice of media can be found in McKeehan, 1977, Barnes *et al.*, 1984, Maurer, 1986.

Other Tissue Culture Media

Medium No. 612: It was observed that medium 199 had a very high oxidation-reduction potential. Healy and co-workers attempted to bring it near the physiological range by increasing very considerably the levels of three reducing agents present in the medium namely cysteine, glutathione, and ascorbic acid. Cysteine and glutathione increase the rate of cell multiplication and improve the appearance of the cells; the ascorbic acid has no apparent effect. Healy increased the levels of cysteine and glutathione 2,600 and 200 times respectively. He designated this medium as medium No. 612.

Medium No. 635: This medium was devised by omitting from medium No. 612

all the purines, pyrimidines as well as adenosinetriphosphate, adenylic acid, ribose and dexyribose. This medium gives a better growth response than that of medium No. 612, but the cultures rarely survive more than 40 days.

Medium No. 858: This medium includes all the deoxyribonucleosides, coenzymes, and sodium glucoronate in addition to medium No. 635. This medium contains only L-form amino acids, and yields ten-fold increase in the population of culture cells in 7 days. Addition of 10 to 20 per cent of horse serum yields 20 to 30-fold increase in 7 days.

Medium No. 866: Medium No. 866 is similar to that of medium No. 858 supplemented with three fatty acids namely linoleic acid, linolenic acid and arachidonic acid. This medium does not improve the growth of culture cells.

Medium CMRL-1066: This medium is identical to medium No. 858 except that the fat soluble vitamins (A, D, E and K), ferric nitrate and sodium bicarbonate included in medium No. 858 have been omitted. Five B vitamins (thiamine, riboflavin, niacin, niacinamide and sodium pantothenate) were added. It also contains 0.02 mg percent n-butyl parahydroxybenzoate, which offers protection from certain moulds. Antibiotics are added according to the need.

Eagle found that 12 amino acids are essential for the growth of both L-strain and HeLa-strain cultures even in the presence of small quantities of whole or diazlyzed serum. These amino acids are arginine, cystine, histidine, isoleucine, leucine, lysine, methionine, phenylalanine, threonine, tryptophan, tyrosine, and valine. Recent attempts have been made to determine the vitamin requirements of cells cultivated in chemically defined media containing dialized serum.

Glucose is generally added to tissue culture media as an energy source, other carbohydrates have also been tested. Harris and Kutsky have shown that chick heart fibroblasts can utilize D-fructose or D-mannose as well as D-glucose.

Interesting studies have also been made of the inorganic requirements of cells *in vitro*. Harris found that carbon dioxide is beneficial for the outgrowth of cells from explanted chick embryo tissues. Eagle has shown that sodium, potassium, magnesium, calcium, chloride and H_2PO_4 ions are essential for the survival of L-and HeLa cells.

LABORATORY FACILITIES FOR ANIMAL TISSUE CULTURE

For animal tissue culture the following laboratory facilities/methods are needed. (also see chapter on Plant Tissue Culture of this book). The important are: Sterile handling, Incubation, Preparation of glassware, media and tissue, Wash-up, Sterilization, Storage etc.

The clean area for handling should be available at one end of the room and the wash up and sterilization at the other end, with preparation, incubation and storage in between.

Other Facilities

1. The **laminar flow cabinets** or **hoods** are required for cleaning bench. It facilitates the maintenance of aseptic and sterile conditions, so that no separate room for sterile handling is needed and a laminar flow cabinet can be kept in an unspecialized laboratory space. The aseptic rooms may be designed in such a way so that filtered air may be supplied from the ceiling. It helps to sterile the complete working area (room).
2. **Incubation** is generally done in incubators or thermostatically controlled hot

rooms. In hot rooms, racks are designed for the placement of cultures (tubes, Petri plates, flasks, etc.).

3. The readymade media are available in market and may be purchased or may be prepared in laboratory.
4. The **washing and sterilization** are being done outside the tissue culture laboratory. Thease procedures generate moisture (increased humidity) and heat.
5. Space for **storage** is also required for the following: (filters, large receiver flasks).

TABLE 18.5: Tissue culture facilities (modified from Freshney, 1987)*

Minimum requirements (essential)	Important features required (beneficial) Other useful additions required
Sterile area: clean and quiet, no thorough traffic, separate from animal house and microbiological labs	Filtered air (air conditioning) Piped CO_2 and compressed air
Preparation area	Hot room with temperature recorder Store room for bulk plastic
Storage areas	Microscope room Containment room for biohazard work.
liquids-ambient, 4 °-20 °C	Dark-room Liquid N_2 storage tank (500 1)
glassware (shelving)	Service bench adjacent to culture area
plastics (shelving)	Separate preparation room.
small items (drawers)	Separate sterilizing room
specialized equipment (slow turnover), cup borard(s)	Cylinder store
chemicals-ambient, 4 °-20 °C (share with liquids but keep chemicals in sealed container over desiccant)	

*(For details also refer to the book Culture of Animal Cells: A Manual of Basic Techniques, R. Ian Freshney, Alan R. Liss Inc., New York).

THE SUBSTRATE ON WHICH CELLS GROW IN LABORATORY

Most of the vertebrate cells cultured *in vitro* are grown as monolayers on an artificial substrate. Spontaneous growth in suspension is restricted to **hemopoietic cell lines, rodent ascites tumour** cell lines and a few other selected cell lines. With these exceptions, most cells need to spread out on a substrate in order to proliferate. Inadequate spreading will inhibit cell proliferation. Cells shown to require attachment for growth are said to be **anchorage dependent.**

However, cells, which have undergone **transformation,** frequently become anchorage independent and can grow in suspension. (Note: In microbiology and plant cell culture, transformation means uptake of new genetic material but in animal cell culture, particularly mammalian cell culture, transformation means phenotypic modification of cells in culture, without involving the uptake of new genetic material, which is described as **transfection** to distinguish it from transformation). Whenever, a substrate is needed, it may be **adhesive** (glass, plastic, palladium, etc. or a metallic surface; these surfaces may sometimes be variously modified) or **non-adhesive** (agar, agarose, methocel) and will be briefly discussed in this section.

Glass as a Substrate: Glass is the most commonly used substrate, in the form of slides, coverslips, flasks and test tubes, which may or may not be variously modified. It is cheap, easily washed without losing its growth supporting properties.

Disposable plastic as a substrate: Polystyrene is often used as the most common and cheapest substrate, to be discarded after single use. This plasticware is supplied sterile and is not autoclavable. However, it is hydrophobic and needs to be treated by gamma irradiation or some chemical or with electric are to produce a charged surface, which thus becomes wettable. Other plastics used for tissue culture include the following: polyvinylchloride (PVC), polycarbonate, polytetrafluoroethylene or teflon (PTFE), thermanox (TPX), etc.

Palladium and metallic surface as substrates: For 90% of animal cell and tissue cultures, glass or plastic is employed as a substrate. For instance, palladium deposited on agarose (using electron microscopy shadowing equipment) was used as a substrate for growth of fibroblasts. Stainless steel discs and other metallic surfaces were also used.

Treatment of Substrate Surfaces

The substrate surfaces should be treated to improve cell attachment. The treatments with culture medium meant for another culture, or with purified fibronectin (1ng/ml) added to the medium or with collagen are commonly used. Coating with collagen can be achieved, using rat tail collagen or other commercially available forms, and pouring the collagen solution over the surface of the dish, draining the excess, and permitting the residue to dry. After coating with collagen, the substrate may be sterilized under UV and used either immediately or may also be stored. Sometimes on the inert coating of collagen (or gelatin or poly-D-lysine), a monolayer of an appropriate cell type may be used to provide a matrix for the maintenance of some specialized cells.

Feeder Layers on Substrate

Sometimes, on the substrate surface a monolayer of special kind of cells is used, partly to supplement the culture medium for growth and partly for conditioning of the substrate by cell products. These monolayers are called feeder layers, since they also feed the growing cultures. The feeder layer may consist of mouse embryo fibroblasts, normal fetal intestine, glial cells, etc. and has been effectively used for selective growth of breast and coelomic epithelium, central and peripheral neurons, and also for growing cells used for the production of transgenic animals through transfection.

The Gas Phase for Tissue Culture

The animal cell and tissue cultures also require for their growth a gas phase consisting of O_2 and CO_2 even though cultures (cell culture *vs* organ culture) may vary in their oxygen requirement. These gases also influence the pH and the HCO_3^- ion concentration of the culture.

CULTURE PROCEDURES

The major steps involved for culture are preparation and sterilization of glassware, equipment, reagents and media. The apparatus and liquids meant for tissue culture should be reserved for that purpose alone. The washing of glassware should also be done separate.

Preparation and Sterilization of Glassware and Apparatus

The following procedure and precautions should be followed:

1. Do not allow soiled glassware to dry, and always collect soiled glassware in water with sodium hypochlorite. It will prevent microbial contamination.
2. A non-toxic and effective detergent meant for your area should be used.
3. After washing, glassware should be thoroughly rinsed in tap water and then in deionized or distilled water and then should be dry inverted. The dried glassware should be sterilized by dry heat (in oven at 160 °c for 1 hr).
4. Automatic washing machines are also used.

Preparation and Sterilization of Reagents and Media

Reagents and media should be produced in pure form and should be sterilized either by moist heat *i.e.* by autoclaving (if heat stable) or by membrane filtration (if heat labile). During autoclaving (mosit heating by steam), the container may be kept sealed (if borosilicate or polycarbonate) or the caps may be left slack (if soda glass) to avoid breakage. The liquid layer in container may go down due to evaporation and should be restored with sterile distilled water after autoclaving. You may also use ready made pre-sterilized culture media available in market.

TABLE 18.6: Sterilization of equipment and apparatus (modified from Freshney, 1987)

Item	Sterilization
Apparatus containing glass and silicone tubing	Autoclave*
Dispenser tubing for compupet	Autoclave
Disposable tips for micropipettes	Autoclave
Filter-Millipore, Sartorius	Autoclave-do not prevac. or postvac.
Glass bottle with screw caps	Autoclave
Glass coverslips	Dry heat
Glass slides	Dry heat
Glassware	Dry heat+
Instruments	Dry heat
Magnetic stirrer bars	Autoclave
Pasteur pipettes-glass	Dry heat
Pipettes-glass	Dry heat
Screw caps	Autoclave
Silicone tubing	Autoclave
Stoppers-rubber, silicone	Autoclave
Test tubes	Dry heat

* Autoclave = 100 kPa (15lb/in^2); 121 °C for min., + Dry heat = 160 °C/l hr.

TABLE 18.7: Sterilization of liquids (modified from Freshney, 1987)

Solution	Sterilization	Storage
Agar	Autoclave*	Room temperature
Amino acids	Filter +	4 °C
Antibodies	Filter	-20 °C
Bacto-peptone	Autoclave	Room temperature
Bovine serum albumin	Filter-use stacked filters (see text)	4 °C
Carboxylmethyl cellulose	Steam-30 min**	4 °C
Collagenase	Filter	-20 °C

Solution	Sterilization	Storage
DMSO	Self-sterilizing, aliquot into sterile tubes	Room temperature-keep dark; avoid contact with rubber or plastic.
EDTA	Autoclave	Room temperature
Glucose-20%	Autoclave	Room temperature
Glucose-1.2%	Filter	Room temperature
Glutaminc	Filter	-20 °C
Glycerol	Autoclave	Room temperature
HEPES	Autoclave	Room temperature
HCl IN	Filter	Room temperature
Lactalbumin hydrolysate	Autoclave	Room temperature
Methocel	Autoclave	4 °C
$NaHCO_3$	Filter	Room temperature
NaOH IN	Filter	Room temperature
Phenol red	Autoclave	Room temperature
Salt solutions (without glucose)	Autoclave	Room temperature
Serum	Filter-use stacked filters	-20 °C
Sodium pyruvate 100mM	Filter	-20 °C
Transferrin	Filter	-20 °C
Tryptose	Autoclave	Room temperature
Trypsin	Filter	-20 °C
Vitamins	Filter	-20 °C
Water	Autoclave	Room temperature

* Autoclave=100 kPa (15 lb/in^2) 121 °C for 20 min., + Filter =0.2 μm pore size, ** Steam = 100 °C for 30 min.

Preparation of Animal Material

It is essential that all sort of contamination should also be avoided during experimental manipulations by collecting tissue aseptically or sterilizing it after removal. Embryo or other contents of uterus are free from contamination while other adult tissues are contaminated with bacteria. Note that embryo should be removed carefully under aseptic conditions eliminating the possibility of contamination. The adult tissue may be washed with a solution having high concentration mixture of antibiotic. The mixture is a *balanced salt solution* containing 100 units of penicillin and 0.5 mg of streptomycin or neomycin per ml. Further handling of tissue should be carefully done under fully aseptic conditions, which can be created either through preparing an aseptic room or through the use of *laminar flow cabinet* or *hood*. The use of hoods has greatly facilitated the handling of material under aseptic conditions.

PRIMARY CULTURE, CELL LINES AND CLONING

Disaggregation of Tissue and Primary Culture

A Primary cell culture may be obtained by either by allowing cells to migrate out from the tissue or by disaggregating the tissue mechanically or enzymatically for the production of suspension of cells. The normal untransformed cells can survive and proliferate easily and they produce *primary culture* when attached to a substrate. These cells are to be obtained by **disaggregation**. It is achieved by following methods:

1. **Physical disruption:** It involves cutting the tissue into pieces.
2. **Enzymatic digestion:** Several enzymes are being used for disaggregation like, trypsin and pronase. Collagenase, elastase, mucase, pancreatin. pappain may also be used for this purpose. Enzymatic disaggregation is labour intensive and involves damage of cells.
3. **Treatment with Chelating Agents:** Chelating agents are used for production of cell suspensions from established cultures. Epithelium tissues which needs Ca^{++} and Mg^{++} ions for its integrity, can be treated with chelating agents, *e.g.*, citrate and ethylene-diamine-tetra-acetic acid (EDTA).

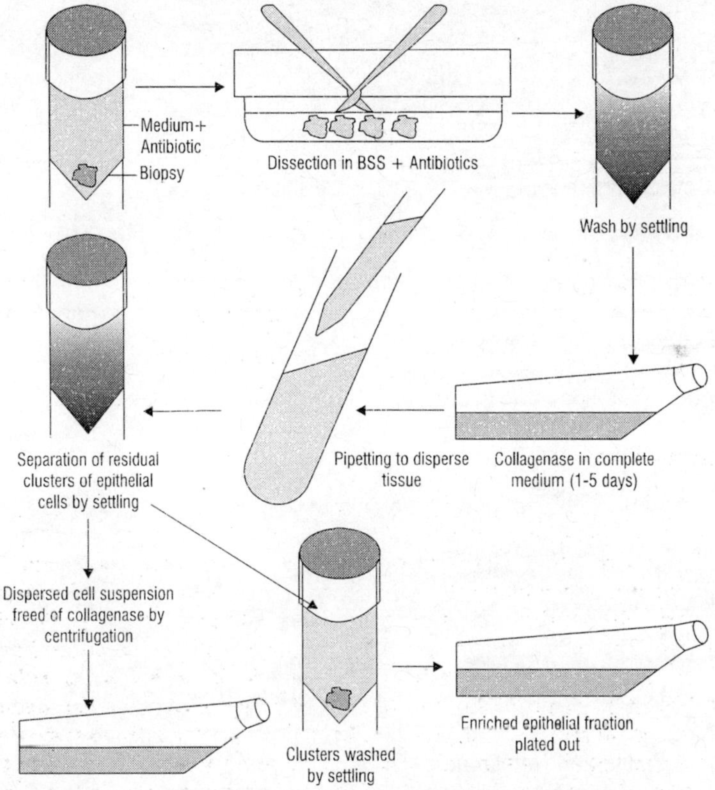

FIGURE 18.1: Stages in disaggregation of tissue for primary culture by collagenase.

Isolation of Tissue

For tissue isolation sterilize the site with 70% alcohol, remove the tissue aseptically. The isolated tissue may be stored in a refrigerator before transferring it to BSS or to a culture medium, because viable cells may be recovered from chilled tissue several days after explanation. Freshney (1987) described various protocols for isolation of tissues like mouse embryo, hen's egg, human biopsy material. For details refer to his book.

Enzymatic Disaggregation

The mechanical or enzymatic disaggregation gives a much higher yield of representative cells in a short duration. The embryonic tissue disperses more readily and gives higher yield than the newly born or adult. In several tomours, the tissue (being fragile) is mostly destroyed during enzyme treatment and viable cells are obtained with difficulty.

Disaggregation by Trypsin (for Embryonic Tissue) or Trypsinization

Trypsinization may be of two types: (1) warm trypsinization and (2) cold trypsinization. Crude trypsin is the most common enzyme used for disaggregation. It can be tolerated by a variety of cells and is effective for many tissues. Its residual activity is neutralized by serum of the medium or by a trypsin inhibitor (*e.g.* **soybean trypsin inhibitor**) in case of a serum free medium. The cells are exposed to the warm enzyme (36.5 °C) for a minimum period. The dissociated cells are collected every half an hour. The trypsin is removed by centrifugation after 3-4 hours. This time is required for complete disaggregation. Alternatively cold trypsinization may be used which involves soaking of tissue in trypsin at 40 °C (to allow penetration of enzyme), followed by incubation at 36.5 °C for a shorter period.

Disaggregation by Collagenase (for Embryonic, Normal and Malignant Tissues)

Sometimes the disaggregation by trypsin may be damaging for epithelial cells or it becomes ineffective for fibrous tissues. The intracellular matrix contains collagen, therefore, collagenase has proved effective for disaggregation of several normal and malignant tissues. These tissues may be sensitive to trypsin. Crude collagenase (with contamination of nonspecific proteases) is often used with a finely chopped tissue in complete medium. When tissue is disaggregated, collagenase is removed by centrifugation, and the cells may be seeded and cultured at a high concentration.

Mechanical Disaggregation

The cell suspension is more quickly obtained than in the enzymatic disaggregation. The mechanical disaggregation is **force-based technique** in which the tissue is carefully sliced and the cells, which spill out are collected. In this technique the cells are either pressed through the sieves of gradually reduced mesh or forced through a syringe and needle, or repeatedly pipetted. Sometime there may be a mechanical damage of the cells. The mechanical disaggregation provides good yield of cells in a shorter time.

Separation of Viable and Nonviable Cells

The dissociated cells obtained as above, usually described as primary cells. They grow well when seeded on culture plates at high density. These are known as **adherent primary cultures** in which the nonviable cells are removed at the first change of medium.

The primary cultures can also be maintained in suspension in which the the non-viable cells are gradually diluted out, when cell proliferation starts. The non-viable cells can be removed from primary disaggregate using centrifugation technique using a mixture of Ficoll and sodium metrizoate.

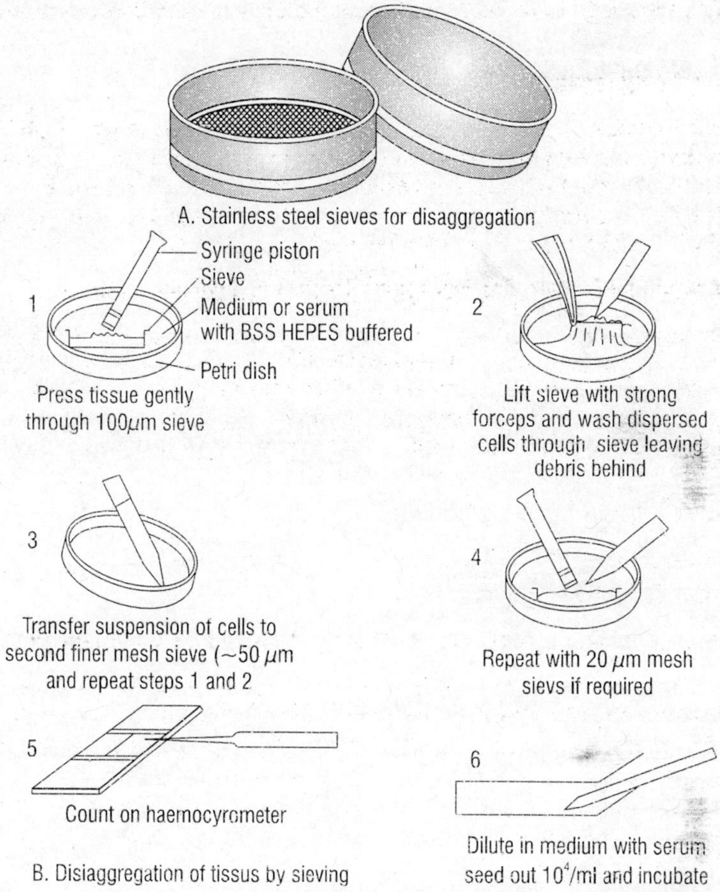

FIGURE 18.2: (a) Stainless steel sieves suitable for disaggeration of tissue, (b) Various steps in disaggeration of tissue by sieving.

SOMATIC CELL FUSION

Fusion of different types of cells has been successfully achieved in animals to produce hybrid cells. The technique is useful because it helps to study of the control of gene expression, differentiation, to know the problem of *malignancy*, viral replication, gene mapping, and production of hybridomas for antibody production.

The cell fusion in animals has been studied within the body *e.g.*, myoblasts fusing to form multinucleate muscle fibres. They can also be fused *in vitro* to produce binucleate heterokaryons (cells fuse, but two types of nuclei do not fuse) or uninucleate hybrid cells.

In 1960s, in France, hybrid cells were obtained from mixed cultures of two different cell lines derived from mouse. Later many successful attempts of cell fusion using widely different taxa were made. Sendai virus is often used to induce such a cell fusion. The cell fusion can be induced by polyethylene glycol (PEG). Removal of surface carbohydrates is also, sometimes, required for successful cell fusion.

TISSUE CULTURES

Primary Ex-plantation Techniques

Harrison (1907) and Carrel (1912) developed this technique for cultivation of pieces of fresh tissue derived from the organism. This technique can also used for embryo and organ culture, but are variously modified to become specialized techniques. The different explantation techniques are:

(i) Slide cultures, (ii) Carrel flask cultures and (iii) Roller test tube cultures.

Slide or Coverslip Cultures

This is the oldest method of tissue culture and is still quite widely used. The technique is being used for limited purposes, specially for morphological studies and for cinemicrographic investigations. The slides or cover slips are prepared by placing a fragment of tissue (*explantation*) onto a coverslip, which is subsequently inverted over the cavity of a depression slide. The advantages and disadvantages are as follows:

Advantages of Slide or Coverslip Cultures

1. It is simple and relatively inexpensive.
2. Cells in living state are spread out in a manner suitable for microscopy and photography.
3. Cells grow directly on coverslip and can be fixed and stained to make permanent slides.

Disadvantages of Slide or Coverslip Cultures

1. Supply of oxygen and nutrients is rapidly exhausted, so that the medium quickly becomes acidic and requires transfer of rapidly growing tissue.
2. Sterility cannot be maintained for a long period.
3. One can culture very small amount of tissues.

Single coverslip with plasma clot (Harrison, 1907)

This technique has following steps:

1. Prepare medium in two parts, one containing 50% plasma in BSS (balanced salt solution) and the other containing 50% embryo extract in serum;
2. Under sterile and aseptic conditions, using a capillary pipette, place one drop of plasma containing solution in the centre of each of one, or more cover slips (22mm);
3. Transfer a fragment (one or two pieces) of tissue (called explant) to this drop without crushing the tissue;
4. Add the embryo extract containing solution and mix thoroughly before clotting starts and then locate the explant;
5. Place two small spots of petroleum jelly (using a glass rod) near the concavity of a depression slide and invert this slide over the coverslip; apply gentle pressure, so that jelly sticks to coverslip;
6. Allow culture medium to clot; (vii) turn over the slide and seal the margins of coverslip with paraffin;
7. Label and incubate at 37 °C.

Double coverslip with plasma clot (by Maximov)

This technique resembles the single coverslip method and is completed in following steps. A large depression slide is used and the entire preparation is attached to it by petroleum jelly and wax in such a way that the small coverslip is not in contact with the slide at any point. The technique includes the following steps:

1. A small drop of BSS is placed on a large coverslip (40mm).
2. A square or round coverslip (22mm) is placed over BSS in the centre of large coverslip.
3. The above two steps are then followed by the steps listed above for single coverslip method.

Single coverslip with liquid medium (lying and hanging drop cultures)

Following steps are involved in this method:

1. Prepared explants are placed in culture medium in a watch glass.
2. The explants are then drawn into the tip of a capillary pipette
3. One explant is deposited in the centre of each coverslip.
4. The liquid medium can be spread out in a very thin circular film with the explant protruding above the surface.
5. A depression slide with petroleum jelly is applied immediately and prparation turned over with a quick flip to prevent the fluid from running into the crevice between the slide and the coverslip.
6. The coverslip is sealed and the slide incubated at 37 °C, upright or inverted; the tissue grows on the coverglass.

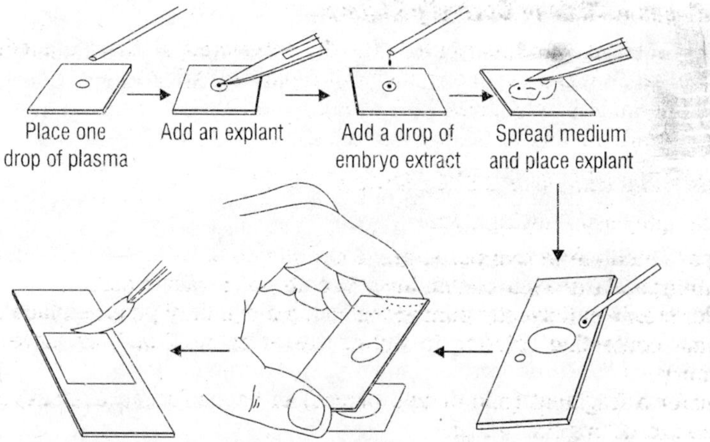

FIGURE 18.3: Preparation of single cover slip cultures.

Post -care of slide cultures: Single coverslip cultures are very useful for short-term studies but they are difficult to handle subsequently except by a process of transfer. Therefore, **double coverslip method** is recommended. It is desirable to leave the explant in its original location to obtain long term tissue cultures. This needs washing, feeding, patching and transfer of cultures.

Washing and feeding double coverslip cultures

Washing and feeding involves the following steps:

1. Remove seal using razor blade and remove large coverslip with small one still attached and flip it over, so that culture is uppermost in orientation.
2. Detach small coverslip from the large coverslip using needle and forceps
3. Transfer it to a Columbia staining dish (watch glass or Petri dish may also be used) containing balanced salt solution (BSS).
4. Remove small cover slip treated as above (one at a time) and place it on a large coverslip with culture up.
5. While removing small coverslip from dish with BSS, the amount of BSS brought with it may be controlled by the rate of removal.
6. Too much liquid will interfere in feeding operation and too little will allow air bubbles.
7. Feed the culture by adding a drop of feeding solution (*e.g.*, BSS: serum: 50% embryo extract = 1:1:1) to the small coverslip.
8. Attach a clean depression slide, using petroleum jelly, as done earlier.

Flask Cultures

The Carrel flask technique is meant for the establishment of a strain from fresh explants of tissue because it has excellent optical properties for microscopic examination. The polystyrene culture flasks can also be used for this purpose. There are two types of flask techniques:

1. **Thick clot cultures:** It allows rapid growth suitable for short term cultures.
2. **Thin clot cultures:** It can be maintained for a considerable period of time.

Advantages of Flask Culture: (1) The tissue can be maintained in the same flask for months or even years. (2) A large number of cultures can be easily prepared. (3) A large amount of tissue can be grown with large amount of medium.

Preparation of Flask Cultures: Place upto six D3.5 Carrel Flasks in a rack with their necks flamed and pointing to the right. (2) Place a drop of plasma on the floor or flask and spread this plasma out in a circle. (3) Use spatula and transfer the desired number of explants to the plasma and allow clotting to occur. (4) After clotting of plasma and fixing of explants in position, add extra medium. (5) For thick clots 1.2ml of dilute plasma and for thin clots 1.2ml of dilute serum is added instead of plasma; the whole thing is left for clotting. (6) The flasks are gassed with gas phase (5% CO_2 in air).

Renewal of Medium: It is essential to remove the medium periodically and is to be replaced in flask cultures in the following manner:

1. Old fluid is drawn off with the help of a pipette.
2. 1.2ml of fluid medium is added as replacement.
3. The flask is gassed as above.

Transfer of Culture: For transfer, the culture grown in a flask culture is to be removed and cut into pieces. These pieces are then used for replantation as usual.

Test Tube Cultures

The feeding, patching and transfer of culture is done as in other primary explantation techniques. It is the cheap technique and can be used for preparing a large number of cultures, which can be placed in stationary racks or roller drums. This technique provides poor optical property for microscopy. Difficulty also arises in quantitation due to the curvature and high risk of contamination. Cultures on plasma clots in test tube are prepared just like those in flasks, but tissues may be grown on the wall of test tube without a plasma clot. Test tubes may also be used for developing suspension cultures.

ANIMAL ORGAN CULTURE

Pieces of an organ or whole organ can be cultured *in vitro*. The main objective is to maintain the architecture of the tissue and direct it towards normal development. In this technique, it is essential that the tissue should never be disrupted or damaged. It requires careful handling. Media used for growing organ cultures are generally the same as those used for tissue culture. The techniques of organ culture can be divided into (i) those employing a **solid medium** and (ii) those employing **liquid medium.**

Culture of Embryonic Organs

Embryonic organs culture is easier than to normal organs from adult animals. Following are the three techniques used for embryo culture.

Organ Cultures on Plasma Clots

It involves following steps:

1. Prepare a plasma clot by mixing 15 drops of plasma with five drops of embryo extract in a watch glass.
2. Place the watch glass on a pad of cotton wool in a Petri dish; cotton wool is kept moist to prevent excessive evaporation from the dish.
3. Place a small, carefully dissected piece of tissue on top of the plasma clot in the watch glass.

The technique has now been modified, and a raft of lens paper or rayon net is used on which the tissue is placed. Transfer of the tissue can then be achieved by moving the raft easily. Excess fluid is removed and the net with the tissue placed again on fresh pool of medium.

Organ Cultures on Agar

Media solidified with agar are also used for organ culture and these media consist of 7 parts 1% agar in BSS, 3 parts chick embryo extract and 3 parts horse serum. Defined media with or without serum are also used with agar. The medium with agar provided the mechanical support for organ culture. It does not liquefy. Embryonic organs generally grow well on this medium, but from adults will not survive.

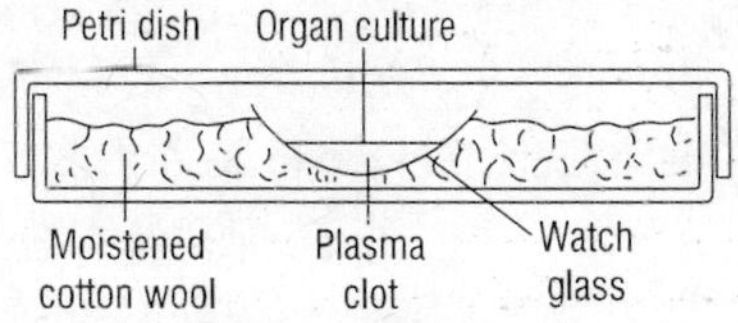

FIGURE 18.4: The classical organ culture technique.

The culture of adult organs or parts from adult animal is more difficult due to their greater requirement of O_2. A variety of adult organs (*e.g.* liver) have been cultured using special media (*e.g.* T8; sec Paul, 1975) with a special apparatus

(Towell's Type II culture chamber). Since serum was found to be toxic, serum free media were used, and the special apparatus permitted the use of 95% O_2.

WHOLE EMBRYO CULTURE

Culture of Chick Embryo (Spratt, 1956)

In this technique, 40-hours old embryos were used and the embryo development could be followed for another 24-48 hours *in vitro* before the embryo dies.

Steps of Chick Embryo Culture

1. Prepare a suitable defined medium and added to sterile watch glasses, placed on moist absorbent cotton wool pads in Petri dishes (as for organ culture).
2. Incubate hen's eggs at 38 °C for 40-42 hours to provide about a dozen embryos.
3. The shell is wiped with alcohol and broken into a sterile evaporating dish containing 50 ml chick saline or BSS.
4. A circular cut is made (using scissors) into the vitelline membrane around the blastoderm and the latter is transferred to a Petri dish containing BSS
5. The adherent vitelline membrane is removed with the aid of forceps and the embryo is examined under the microscope to determine the stage of development.
6. The blastoderm is transferred to the top of the medium in the watch glass prepared in (1) above.
7. The blastoderm is spread on agar gel (ventral side down) and the excess BSS is removed.
8. Culture is incubated at 37.5 °C.

ANIMAL TISSUE CULTURES IN BIOMEDICAL RESEARCH-GENETICS

Cell culture methods have come to be used extensively in both applied and theoretical genetic studies. The various genetic applications are as follows:

Karyological Studies

The karyotype of a population of cells or an organism is the catalogue of the chromosomes of a typical or an average cell. While karyotyping is a useful technique in experimental biology, for example for identifying the species of origin of cell-lines, its most important application in medicine is in the early diagnosis of some congenital abnormalities. Mostly these are abnormalities resulting from the inheritance of a unbalanced complement of chromosomes, such as Klinefelter's syndrome (XXY), Turner's syndrome (XO) or Down's syndrome (mongolism) is which chromosome number 21 is represented by 3 instead of 2. Some other anomalies such as translocations or deletions can also be recognized.

Identification and Study of Hereditary Metabolic Disorders

The precise nature of many of the genetic diseases can be determined only by demonstrating the metabolic abnormality, commonly the absence of an enzyme in tissue. Disorders such as absence of catalase in acatalasia, of alpha-D-galactose-1-phosphate, UDP glucose uridyltransferase in galactosaemia or the failure to decarboxylate branched chain keto-acid in maple syrup urine disease can be demonstrated in primary fibroblast cultures. In some instances, the heterozygous locus, a deficiency of the transferase enzyme per cell can be measured. Some human genetic disorders which can be studied in this way are: glycogen storage diseases, hemocystinuria, Hunter's syndrome, Hurler's syndrome, I-cell disease, Niemann-pick disease, orotic aciduria, Refsum's disease, xeroderma pigmentosa, etc.

Somatic Cell Genetics

Somatic cell genetic studies have three main aims: (i) study of the behaviour of heterokaryons following fusion of parent cells with different properties, (ii) study of the behaviour of hybrid cells derived from heterokaryons with the view to eliciting information about interaction between different genes, and (iii) studies with a view to mapping loci on different chromosomes. These studies can be made in tissue cultures.

Tissue Cultures in Biomedical Research-Virology and Host-parasite Relationships

The ability of tissue cultures to support the growth of viruses and to reveal their presence by lesions which are in some cases specific has been applied in virology for the following purposes:

1. The study of host-parasite relationships.
2. The detection and identification of viruses.
3. The production of viruses for vaccine manufacture.

The study of the relationships between viruses and cells has been greatly aided by the use of the tissue culture methods. These techniques are also useful for detection and identification of viruses from the suspected cases. In recent years development has been made in production of vaccines against poliomyelitis. Vaccines have been made from the viruses grown in tissue culture. In addition to viruses other intracellular parasites, which have been grown in tissue culture and studied are: Rickettsiae, mycobacteria (especially tubercle and leprosy bacilli), lepraemurium, parasitic protozoans, etc.

Tissue Cultures in Biomedical Research-Cancer

Tissue culture techniques have been very useful at understanding the problem of cancer. Since culture of canine lymphosarcoma by Beebe and Ewing (1906), and unbroken trail of pioneers such as Carrel, Warburg, Earle, Rous, Gey, Murray, and others worked on this problem. The breakthrough was the development of quantitative assay procedures for tumour viruses stimulated by the exploitation of cell culture methods by virologists. Since Rous demonstrated the infective nature of the fowl sarcoma, many other infective cancer-producing agents have been recognized.

CHAPTER 19

Immunology, Serology and Vaccines

IMMUNOLOGY

Immunology is the branch of microbiology deals with the study of immunity to infection. The study was first started in 1798 with Jenner's observations on vaccination against small pox. However, as early as 1000 AD Chinese physician Yo-Meishan successfully inoculated the emperor's grandson with dried crust of small pox to render him immune from a serious attack of the dreadful disease. Edward Jenner (1778) learnt from milk maid infected with cowpox that milk maids who developed cowpox, were immune to small pox. Pasture (1822-1895) developed attenuated vaccines for anthrax and rabies. The classical work of Russian scientist E. Metchinikoff (1845-1916) on the biological theory of immunity marked a new stage in the history of immunobiology. He discovered phagocytosis and intracellular digestion in mesodermal cells of some animals. The phagocytic theory of immunity was expounded in 1883 at VII Congress of Russian Naturalists and Physicians in Odessa.

Paul Ehrlich (1854-1915) gave a theory of **humoral immunity** according to which certain substances in the blood serum, secreted by special cells under the influence of microbes and their toxins play an important role in the defence reactions of the body. The ability of developing specific immunity to invading or infective agent is a unique property of vertebrates.

Von Pirquet (1906) stated that the individual after exposure to an antigen developed changed reactivity - in one case recognized as immunity in another as hypersensitivity. He coined the term **allergy** for this changed reactivity. Pirquet's concept was the fundamental one as it recognised behind all reactions to antigenic exposure no matter what their clinical outcome, a common biological process of specific sensitization. During the first four to five decades of this century investigations were mainly concerned with chemistry of antigen and antibodies. Modern immunological studies cover defence against infection, prevention of disease by immunization, blood banking, and hypersensitivity including autoimmunity. Immunological techniques are used to measure immune responses for diagnosis and progresses of certain diseases, hormones and drugs.

WHAT IS AN IMMUNE SYSTEM?

In body, the nonspecific immune mechanisms are usually inadequate to cope with foreign agents or substances, mainly when a particular virulent microorganism is involved and is able to evade phagocytic mechanisms. In vertebrate host, the **specific immune** system is endowed with three characteristics: **specificity, memory** and **recognition** of self-antigens.

- **Specificity**: The immune system has the property to recognize foreign substances *i.e.*, antigens or substances that can stimulate the formation of antibodies. After establishment of the contact, products of the immune system are elaborated and interact with antigen.

- **Memory:** During response to foreign substances some lymphocytes give rise to memory cells and are permitted to act with speed and vigour the next time the foreign agent is encountered. The capacity of this memory makes feasible the process of vaccination. The first time the foreign agent is encountered, there is short lag time before the immune system can generate enough immune products to overcome such an infectious agent.
- **Self-recognition:** There is an interaction of many foreign substances, with immune system. The immune system, however, can discriminate between the foreign substance and self substances. This is called self-recognition.

Many terms are often being used in immunological studies. The definitions of various terms are as follows:

- **Antigen (Ag):** A substance that initiates the immune system to form immune products specific for the substance. Chemically it may be protein, polysaccharides, or nucleic acids, that are either soluble or particulate. The antigens not only cause the formation of immune products but interact with them as well. They are also known as **immunogens** when the emphasis is on their ability to incite the formation of immune products (**immunogenicity**).
- **Antigenic determinant:** Small chemical groups on the surface of antigens with which immune products interact.
- **Partial antigen or Hapten:** It is the substance which can interact with specific antibody combining groups on an antibody molecule but which fails by itself to elicit the formation of a detectable amount of antibody (Hapten means *to grasp*).
- **Immunoglobulins (Ig):** These are proteins which have demonstrable antibody activity and/or share a common antigenic specificity with any known antibody and are produced by cells that form antibody. Thus proteins like myeloma proteins, Bence-Jones proteins and subunits of antibodies are also known as immunoglobulins. Functionally they are two types: **surface immunoglobulins:** they are present on the surface of the lymphocytes where they act as specific receptor (recognition molecules) for the antigen, and **secreted immunoglobulins** these are the products of B lymphocytes and appear in the body fluids (humors as antibodies).
- **Antibody (Ab):** An antibody is a immunoglobulin whose formation is induced by the introduction of an antigen in an animal body. It reacts with the corresponding antigen specifically in some observable way, that each antibody has binding sites for an identified antigen.
- **B lymphocytes (B Cell):** A major class of lymphocytes that produce immunoglobulins and are primarily involved in humoral immunity, that is the production of antibodies.
- **T lymphocytes (T Cell):** A major class of lymphocytes that are thymus dependent and form effector T lymphocytes on stimulation by antigens. They also produce **lymphokines**, which are non-antibody mediators associated with inflammatory events and also associated with immunoregulation.
- **Humoral immunity:** It is the immunity provided by antibodies, B cell immunity, antibody-mediated immunity.
- **Cell mediated immunity (CM):** It is the immunity provided by T cells: T-cell immunity.
- **Complement:** The term complement is applied to a group of co-factors

occurring in fresh normal blood, serum and some body fluids that are activated characteristically by antigen-antibody interactions and subsequently mediated certain biological events of immunological reactions.

- **Immunological tolerance:** Immunological tolerance is a central failure of responsiveness of immune system brought about by appropriate exposure to an antigen, in which immunologically competent cells fail to respond to that antigen.
- **Immune system:** It is the system of the body, which is responsible for all types of immune responses. Essentially it is constituted by the lymphoid organs and cells and is divisible into T cell division and B cell division.
- **Immunocyte:** A mature immunologically competent cell is known as immunocyte.
- **Mycelomas:** They are the cells of certain malignant tumours of bone marrow. They produce large quantities of abnormal immunoglobulines (antibodies) and can be grown *in vitro* indefinitely. Immunoglobulines produced by mycelomas (clones) *in vitro* have an identical structure. They are, in fact, monoclonal antibodies.

PRINCIPLES OF IMMUNOLOGY

Immunology is the study of immunity to infectious diseases in organisms. There are three types of protections against any infectious diseases. They are as follows:

1. **Nonsusceptibility:** This is species characteristic of the host and gives complete protection against a particular microorganism.
2. **Natural resistance:** This is the natural available capacity present in an organism and is due to physical and chemical characteristics of the host. The resistance of an individual varies according to time.
3. **Natural immunity:** This is basically dependent upon the natural antibodies (modified blood globulins), which can able to react with antigens.

IMMUNOGLOBULINS

These are protein molecules with demonstrable antibody activity. They are made of heterogenous group of proteins accounting for about 20% of total plasma proteins. They are mainly γ - globulins but a few are β-globulins.

Structure: They are glycoproteins and are composed of 82-96% polypeptide and 4-18% carbohydrate. The polypeptide part possesses the biological properties of antibodies.

Basic Unit: Each molecule of immunoglobulin has at least one basic unit or monomer, which contains four polypeptide chains in two pairs, and each one have similar chains. One of the pairs have two or more than 2 amino acids. The larger pair with more amino acid is called **heavy chain** while with smaller one is called **light chain**, they are also known as **H** and **L** chains respectively. Every chain possesses an amino terminal portion, which shows marked heterogeneity or variable region or **V** region and the carboxy terminal portion with a similar type of amino acid residue called constant region or **C** region. The `V' region of both the chains are of equal length. The antigen combining site is formed by the `V' region of `H' chain and `L' chain. Therefore, a monomeric immunoglobulin (Ig) molecule has two antigen combining sites.

When polypeptide chains are folded three dimensionally by disulphide linkage the structure is called **domains.** Such domain in `H' chains is known as VH, CH1, CH2 and CH3 and those in `L' chain VL and CL. Each such segment is made of about 110 amino acid molecules. The `H' and `L' chain are linked with a disulphide linkage, and the region is known as **hinge region** of the molecule. On the basis of inter-chain disulphide linkage, the Ig may be of four types: IgG1, IgG2, IgG3 and IgG4. In Ig, a glycopolypeptide chain (like the size of `L' chain) is also found (with mol. wt. 15,000) and called **joining chain** or `J' chain.

Carbohydrate moieties: This part of the Ig is found in secretary component, `J' chain and constant region of the `H' chain. It is not found in `L' chain and any of the `V' region. Its function is still not certain, however, it is suggested that it plays a role in secretion of Ig by plasma cells.

IMMUNOGLUBLIN CLASSES AND SUBCLASSES

Based on the antigenic character of heavy chains the immunoglobulins are classified into various types, the important are: Immunoglobulin G (IgG), Immunoglobulin M (IgM), Immunoglobulin D (IgD), Immunoglobulin A (IgA), Immunoglobulin E (IgE).

IgG is the major immunoglobulin in human serum, accounting for 70 to 75% of the immunoglobulin pool. IgG is presents in blood plasma and tissue fluids. The IgG class acts against bacteria and viruses by opsonizing the invaders and neutralizing toxins. It is also one of the two immunoglobulin classes that activate complement by the classical pathway. IgG is the only immunoglobulin molecule able to cross the placenta and provide naturally acquired immunity for the newborn.

There are four **IgG subclasses** (IgG1, IgG2, IgG3, and IgG4) that vary chemically in their chain composition and the number and arrangement of interchain disulfide bonds. About 65% of the total serum IgG is IgG1, and 23% is IgG2. Differences in biological function have been noted in these subclasses. For example, IgG2 antibodies are opsonic and develop in response to antitoxins. Anti-Rh antibodies are of the IgG1 or IgG3 subclass. IgG1 and IgG3 also bind best to monocytes and macrophages and activate complement most effectively. The IgG4 antibodies function as skinp sensitizing immunoglobulins.

IgM accounts for about 10% of the immunoglobulin pool. It is usually a polyer (pentamer) of five monomeric untis, each composed of two heavy chains and two light chains. The monomers are arranged in a pinwheel array with the Fc ends in the center, held together by a special **J** (joining) **chain**. IgM is the first immunoglobulin made during B-cell maturation and the first secreted into serum during primary antibody response. Since IgM is so large, it does not leave the bloodstream or cross the placenta. IgM agglutinates bacteria, activates complement by the classical pathway, and enhances the ingestion of pathogens by phagocytic cells. This class also contains special antibodies such as red blood cell agglutinins and heterophile antibodies.

Although, most IgM appears to be pentameric, around 5% or less of human serum IgM exists in a hexameric form. This molecule contains six monomeric units but seems to lack a J chain. Hexameric IgM activates complement up to twentyfold more effectively than does the normal pentameric form. It has been suggested that bacterial cell wall antigens such as gram-negative lipopolysaccharides may directly stimulate B cells to form hexameric IgM without a J chain. If this is the case, the immunoglobulins formed during primary immune responses are less homogenous than previously thought.

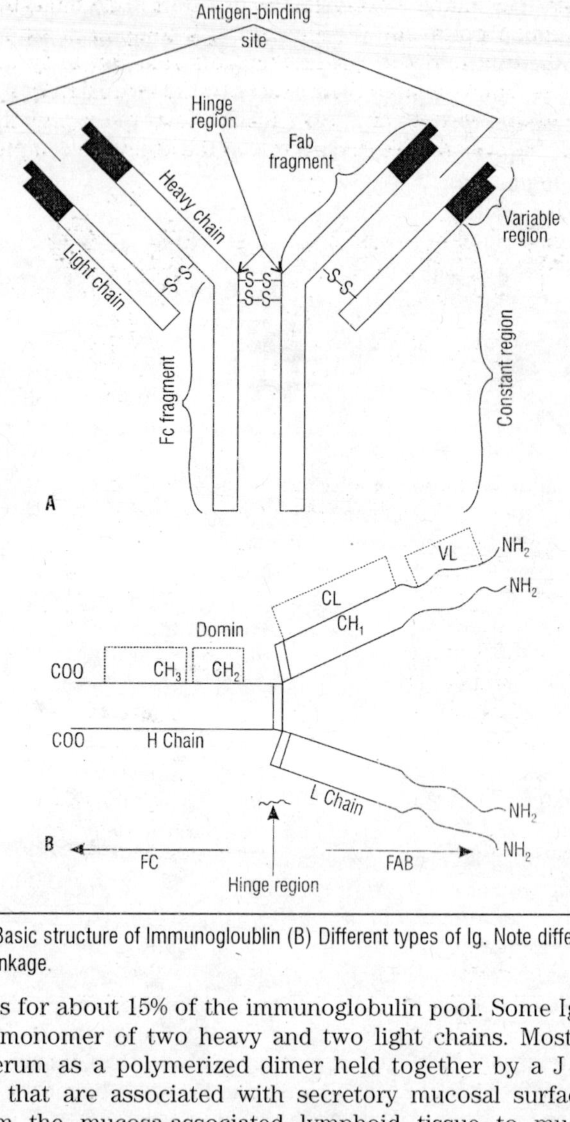

FIGURE 19.1: (A) Basic structure of Immunogloublin (B) Different types of Ig. Note different types of inter chain disulphides linkage.

IgA accounts for about 15% of the immunoglobulin pool. Some IgA is present in the serum as a monomer of two heavy and two light chains. Most IgA, however, occurs in the serum as a polymerized dimer held together by a J chain. IgA has special features that are associated with secretory mucosal surfaces. IgA, when transported from the mucosa-associated lymphoid tissue to mucosal surfaces, acquires a protein termed the secretory component.

Secretory **IgA (sLgA)**, as the modified molecule is now called, is the primary immunoglobulin of the secretory immune system. This system is found in the gastrointestinal tract, upper and lower respiratory tracts, and genitourinary system. Secretory IgA is also found in saliva, tears, and breast milk. In these fluids and related body areas, sLgA plays a major role in protecting surface tissues against infectious microorganisms by the formation of an immune barrier. For example, in breast milk sLgA helps protect nursing newborns. In the intestine, sLgA attaches to viruses, bacteria, and protozoan parasites such as *Entamoeba histolytica*. This prevents pathogen adherence to mucosal surfaces and invasion of host tissues, a phenomenon known as immune exclusion. In addition, sLgA binds to antigens within the muscosal lamina propria, and the antigen-sLgA complexes are excreted through the adjacent epithelium into the gut lumen. This rids the body of locally formed immune complexes and decreases their access to the ciruculatory system. Secretory IgA also may neutralize viruses and other intracellular pathogens that reside within epithelial cells. Secretory IgA also plays a role in the alternate complement pathway.

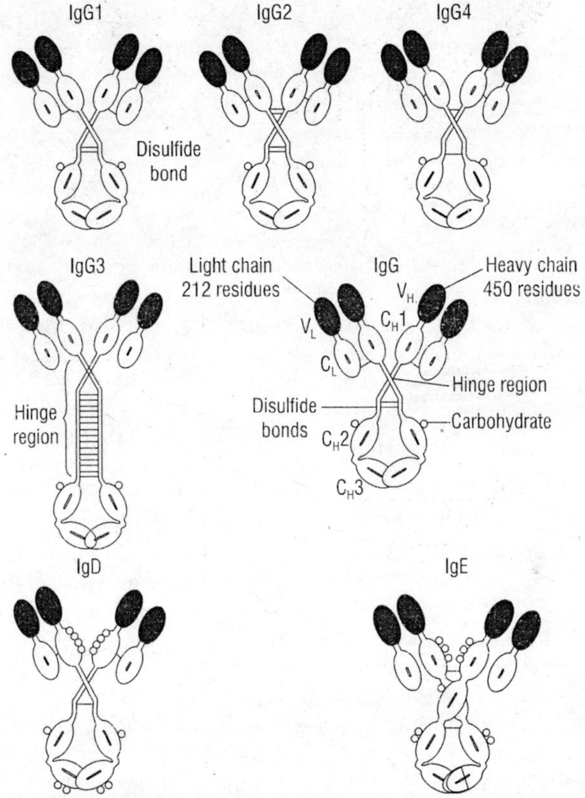

FIGURE 19.2: Different types of immunoglobulines.

IgD is an immunoglobulin found in trace amounts in the blood serum. It has a monomer structure similar to IgG. IgD antibodies do not fix complement and cannot cross the placenta, but they are abundant on the surface of B cells and bind antigens, thus signaling the B cell to start antibody production.

IgE makes up only 0.00005% of the total immunobulin pool. The classic skin-sensitizing and anaphylactic antibodies belong to this class. IgE molecules have four constant region domains ($C_\varepsilon 1$, $C_\varepsilon 2$, $C_\varepsilon 3$ and $C_\varepsilon 4$) and two light chains.

The Fc portion of the $C_\varepsilon 4$ chain can bind to special Fc_ receptors on mast cells and basophils. When two IgE molecules on the surface of these cells are corss-linked by binding to the same antigen, the cells degranulate. This degranulation releases histamine and other pharmacological mediators of anaphylaxis. It also stimulates eosinophilia and gut hypermotility (increased rate of movement of the intestinal contents) that aid in the elimination of helminthic parasites. Thus, through IgE is present is small amounts, this class of antibodies has very potent biological capabilities.

Immunoglobulin Function

All immunoglobulin molecules are bifunctional. The Fab region is concerned with binding to antigen, whereas the Fc region mediates binding to host tissue, various cells of the immune system, some phagocytic cells, or the first component of the complement system. The binding of an antibody with an antigen usually does not cause destruction of the antigen or of the microorganism, cell or agent to which it is attached. Rather the anitbody serves to mark and identify the target for immunologic attack and to activate nonspecific immune responses that can destroy the target for phagocytosis by neutrophils and marcophages. This ability of an antibody to stimulate phagocytosis is termed **opsonization**. Immune destruction also is promoted by antibody-induced activation of the complement system.

Source of Antibodies

An antibody is a immunoglobulin whose formation is induced by the introduction of an antigen in an animal body. It reacts with the corresponding antigen specifically in some observable way, that each antibody has binding sites for an identified antigen. The need for pure homogeneous antibodies has increased dramatically in recent years. Currently antibodies are produced either naturally by immunization or artificially through hybridoma formation.

Biosynthesis of Antibodies

Evidences are still lacking to explain the production of antibodies by cells following antigenic stimulation. Two theories have been introduced:

1. **Directive or Template Theory:** This theory explains that antigen in the antibody forming cells acts as a templet for biosynthesis of antibody having complementary configuration. The antibody formed than dissociates from the antigen molecule, which further acts as templet for next molecule of antibody. It has been suggested that antigen brings about genetic changes in the cell so that it and its daughter cells continue to produce specific antibodies.
2. **Selective Theory:** The theory was first proposed by Paul Ehrlich in 1880 and is also known as **Ehrlich side chain theory**. It explains that antibody forming cells have antibody molecules as side chains on their surface and the antigen selects its corresponding side chain, attaches to it and finally knocks it down. This acts as a trigger and then the cell starts synthesizing similar side chains repeatedly which are dislodged to free circulation and unite with the antigen.

DIVERSITY OF ANTIBODIES

One unique property of antibodies is their remarkable diversity. According to current estimates each human or mouse can synthesize more than 10 million different kinds of antibodies. How is this diversity generated? The answer is threefold:

1. Rearrangement of antibody gene segments,
2. Somatic mutations, and
3. Generation of different codons during antibody gene splicing.

Immunoglobulin genes are split or interrupted genes with many exons. Embryonic B cells contain a small number of exons, close together on the same chromosome, that determine the constant (C) region of the light chains. Separated from them, but on the same chromosome, is a larger cluster of exons that determines the variable (V) region of the light chains. During B-cell differentiation, one exon for the constant region is spliced exon for the variable region. This splicing produces a complete light-chain antibody gene. A similar splicing mechanism also occurs to join the constant and variable exons of the heavy chains.

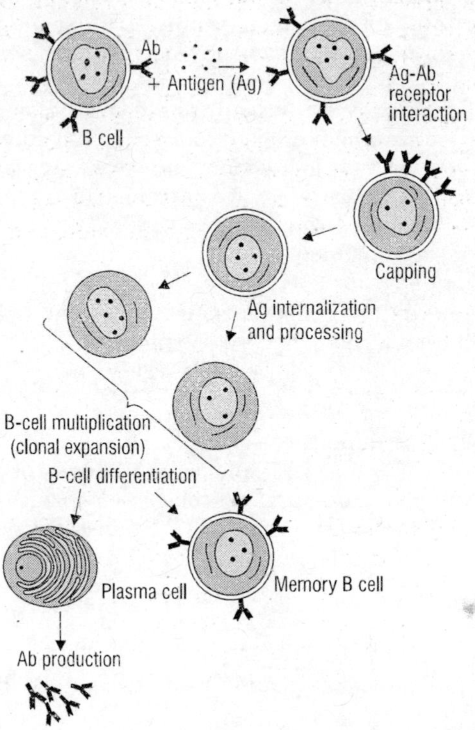

FIGURE 19.3: Clonal Selection. It is through clonal selection that the immune system can respond specifically to myriad of possible antigens, whether they are individual molecules or are attached to pathogens and abnormal cells such as cancer cells. B cells or B lymphocytes constantly roam the body, particularly the blood and lymphoid tissues. Each B cell synthesizes only one of the millions of possible antibodies and displays this antibody of the proper specificity (top left), it complexes with the antibody and capping occurs. (Capping is the regional aggregation of antibodies on the surface of the following Ag-Ab interaction.) The antigen is then internalized; the B cell swells and begins to divide rapidly, producing a B-cell clone. The activated B-cell clone differentiates into plasma cells and memory cells. Plasma cells form the specific antibody that immediately attack the antigen that provoked its formation. Memory B cells persist in the body and boost the immune system's readiness to eliminate the same antigen if it present itself in the future.

Because the light-chain genes actually consist of three parts, and the heavy-chain genes consist of four, the formation of a finished antibody molecule is slightly more complicated than previously outlined. The germ line DNA for the light-chain gene contains multiple coding sequences called V and J (joining) regions. During the differentiation of a B cell, a deletion (which is variable in length) occurs that joins one V exon with on J exon. This DNA joining process is termed combinatorial joining since it can create many combinations of the V and J regions. When the light-chain gene is transcribed, transcription continues through the DNA region that encodes for the constant portion of the gene. RNA splicing subsequently joints the VJ and C regions creating mRNA.

Combinatorial joining in the formation of a heavy-chain gene occurs by means of DNA splicing of the heavy-chain counteparts of V and J along with a third set of D (diversity) sequences. Initially, all heavy chains have the μ type of constant region. They corresponds to antibody class IgM. Another DNA splice joins the VDJ region with a different constant region that can subsequently change the class of antibody produced by the B cell.

In mouse the k light chains are formed from combinations of about 250-350 V_k and 4 J_k regions giving a maximum of approximately 1,400 different k chains. The Ó chains have their own $V_{\text{ó}}$ and $J_{\text{ó}}$ regions but smaller in number than their k counterparts (6 different Ó chains). The heavy chains have approximately 250-1,000 V_H, 10-30 D, and 4 J_H regions giving a maximum 120,000 different combinations. Because any light chain can combine with any heavy, there will be a maximum of 2×10^8 possible k chain antibody types.

The value of 2×10^8 different anitbodies is actually an undetrestimate because antibody diversity is further aungmented by two processes:

1. The V regions of germ line DNA are susceptible to high rate of somatic mutation during B-cell development in the bone marrow. These mutations allow B-cell clones to produce different polypeptide sequences.
2. The junction for either VJ or VDJ splicing in combinatorial joining can occur between different nucleotides and thus one VJ splicing event can joint the V sequence CCTCCC with the J sequence TGGTGG in two ways:

   CCTCCC + TGGTGG = CCGTGG,

   which codes for the amino acids proline and tryptophan,

   CCTCCC + TGGTGG = CCTCGG,

   which codes for proline and arginine. Thus the same VJ joining could produce polypeptides differing in a single amono acid.

Specificity of Antibodies

As noted previously, combinatorial joining, somatic mutations, and variations in the splicing process generate the great variety of anitbodies produced by B cells. From a large and diverse B-cell pool, specific cells are stimulated by antigens to reproduce and form a B-cell clone that contain the same genetic information. This is known as the **clonal selection theory**, a hypothesis to explain immunologic specificity and memory.

The existence of a small B-cell **clone** (a population of cells derived asexually from a single parent) that can respond to one or a few antigens by producing the correct antibody is the first tenet of this theory. The lymphoid system is thus considered to contain many B-cell clones, each clone able to recognize a specific antigen. The antigen selects the appropriate clone of B cells (hence the pharse *clonal selection*), and the cells from the other clones are unaffected.

According to Secon Tenet, each B-cell clone is genetically programmed to respond to its own distinctive antigen before the antigen is introduced. The particular antibody for which an individual B cell is genetically competent is ingrated into the plasma membrane of that B cell and acts as a specific surface receptor for the corresponding antigen molecule. The reaction of the antibody and antigen initiates the differentiation and multiplication of the B cell to form two different cell populations: plasma cells and **memory B cells**.

Plasma cells are literally protein factories that produce about 2,000 antibodies per second in their brief five- to seven-day life span. Memory B cells can initiate the antibody-mediated immune response upon detecting the particular antigen molecule for which they are genetically programmed (*i.e.*, they have specificity). These memory cells circulate more actively from blood to lymph and live much longer (years or even decades) than plasma cells. Memory cells are responsible for the immune system's rapid secondary antibody response to the same antigen.

Immunization

Specific antibodies can be produced naturally by the immunization of domestic animals or human volunteers. Whatever the source, purified antigen is injected into the host. The host's immune system recognizes and responds to the antigen, and its B cells proliferate and differentiate to produce specific antibodies. To promote the efficiency of antigen stimulation of antibody production, the antigen is mixed with an **adjuvant** (Latin *adjuvans*, aiding), which enhances the rate and quantity of antibody produced.

Following repeated antigen injections at regular intervals, blood is withdrawn from the post and allowed to clot. The fluid that remains after the blood clots is the **serum**. This serum has been obtained from an immunized host and contains the desired antibodies. It is called **antiserum**.

Antiserum is a major and convenient source of antibodies, however, its usefulness is limited in following ways:

1. Antibodies obtained by this method are polyclonal; they are produced by several B-cell clones and have different specificities. The decreases their sensitivity to particular antigens and results in some degree of cross-reaction with closed related antigen molecules.
2. Second or repeated injections of antiserum from one species to another can cause serious allergic or hypersensitivity reactions.
3. Antiserum contains a mixture of antibodies, not all of which are of interest in a give immunization.

The Primary Antibody Responses

During immunization procedures (and also in naturally acquired immunity) there is an initial lag phase of several days following a primary challenge with an antigen. During the *lag phase no antibody can be detected*. The antibody **titer**, which is the reciprocal of the highest dilution of an antiserum that gives a positive reaction in the test being used, rises logarithmically to a plateau during the second or log phase. In the plateau phase the antibody titer stablizes. This is followed by a decline phase, during which antibodies are naturally metabolized or bound to the antigen and cleared from the circulation. During the primary antibody response, IgM appears first, then IgG. The affinity of the antibodies for the antigen's determiants is low to moderate during this primary antibody response.

The Secondary Antibody Response

The primary antibody response primes the immune system so that it possesses specific immunologic memory through its clones of memory B cells. Upon secondary antigen challenge, the B cells mount a heightened or **anamnestic** (Greek *anamnesis*, remembrance) **response** to the same antigen. Compared to the primary antibody response, the secondary antibody response has a shorter lag phase, a more rapid log phase, persists for a longer plateau period, attains a higher IgG titer, and produces antibodies with a higher affinity for the antigen (affinity maturation).

Catalytic Antibodies

In the past several year immunologists have applied the principles of enzymology to create a new class of antibody molecules- **catalytic antibodies**. Catalytic antibodies accelerate specific chemical reactions by lowering the free energy of transition states. They accomplish this by binding reactants in a cleft or crevice on their surfaces and inducing structural changes in the substrate molecules. Because antibodies directed against a huge array of biopolymers, natural products, and synthetic molecules can be formed, catalytic antibodies offer a unique approach for generating tailor-made, enzyme-like catalysts.

Catalytic antibodies are made of coupling a transitionstate analogue to a carrier protein and injecting the combination into an experimental animal. Antibody-secreting spleen cells are taken from the animal and fused with myeloma cells. The hybrid antibody-secreting cells divide indefinitely and generate clone of cells, each hybrid clone secreting a monoclonal catalytic antibody with a unique antigen-binding pocket. A clone that makes catalytic antibody specific for the analogue is then selected.

Currently available catalytic antibodies transform relatively simple compounds. Much of the potential of catalytic antibodies for biotechnology and molecular biology depends on the development of catalytic antibodies able to act on proteins or nucleic acids. If this can be accomplished, catalytic antibodies could extend the immune system's innate capacity to defend the body. For example, one might stimulate the immune system of a patient with heart disease to produce antibodies that would break up the proteins in blood clots, forestalling heart attacks.

ANTIGENS

The name antigens (Gk. *anti* = against, *genos* = genus) is given to organic substances of a colloid structure (proteins and different proteins complexes in combination with lipids of polysaccharides). It upon injection into the body (subcutaneously, intracutaneously, cutaneously, into the mucous membranes, intramuscularly, intravenously and orally) are capable of causing the production of antibodies and reacting specifically with them.

Proportion of Antigens

An antigen may be soluble substance such as horse serum proteins or a bacterial toxin, or it may be present on particulate matter like red blood cells, a bacterial cell, or a virus. An antigen is always a foreign substance for the host. An antigen must be capable of inducing an antibody response. The molecular weight of any antigen should be more than 6000 daltons. The portion of antigen that specifically combines with antibody is called its determinant group. Antigenic properties are pertinent to toxins of a plant origin (ricin, robin, abrin, cortin, etc.), toxins of an animal origin (toxins of snakes, spiders, scorpions etc.), enzymes, native foreign proteins, various cellular component, bacteria and their toxins and viruses etc.

Antigens are of two types: (a) Complete antigens and (b) Partial antigens:

1. **Complete antigens:** They cause the production of antibodies in the body, and react with them *in vivo* as well as *in vitro*.
2. **Partial antigens:** They are also known as haptens and do not cause the production of antibodies, but can react with them. Haptens includes lipids, complex carbohydrate and other substances.

The immunological specificity of antigens is linked with a determinant group found on the surface of the antigen as one or more active areas.

Isoantigens: These substances have antigenic properties and are contained in some individuals of a given species. Isoantigens are found in erythrocytes of animals and man.

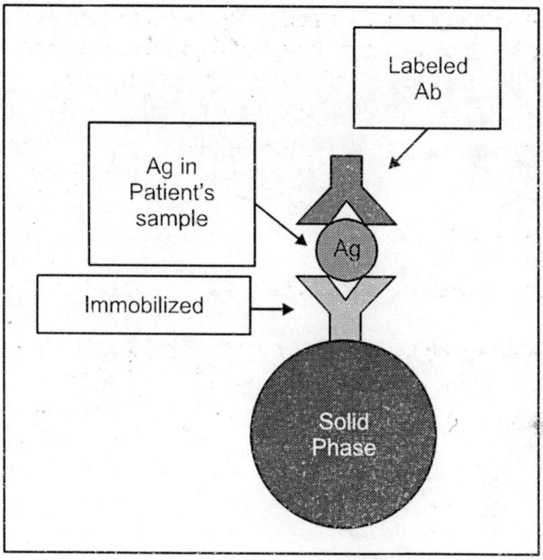

FIGURE 19.4: Antigen-antibody binding: an example of antigen binding represented in the model.

Antigen-antibody Binding

Every antigen monomer has two similar antigen combining sites and each site is formed by `V' region of `H' and `L' chains. This helps the antibody molecule to link 2 similar antigens together. When many antibody and antigen unit join together, it results in the formation of a *lattice*. A large antigen and the cell surface of the microorganisms have several antigenetically active sites. A large number of antibody molecules are usually linked with antigenic sites and form aggregates.

THE IMMUNE RESPONSE

In immune mechanism there is an involvement of special types of cells called **lymphocytes**. The immunological response in an individual is brought about by the introduction of antigens or immunogens. The immune response mechanism is of two types: **humoral immunity** - involving production of antibodies, and **cell-mediated immunity** in which the lymphocytes react directly with foreign material. An immunologic response to an immunogen consists of one or more of the following components:

1. **Antibody production:** It involves `B' cell division in immune system. Development and specific cell mediated immunity, which involves the `T' cell division of the immune system.
2. **Immunological memory:** Which involves one or both components of the immune system, is responsible for an accelerated immune response when the same antigen enters or is administered in the body after it has induced the first response (primary response).
3. **Immunological tolerance:** It is the specific immunological unresponsiveness brought about by certain antigens in certain circumstances.

LYMPHOCYTES

Origin of Lymphocytes

Lymphocytes are small, nonphagocytic, mononuclear leukocytes that are immunologically competent, or are precursors of such cells. They lack stainable cytoplasmic granules and are formed in lymphatic tissues. Lymphocytes are the pivotal cells of the specific immunologic response. Undifferentiated lymphocytes are derived from bone marrow stem cells. They are produced in the bone marrow at a very high rate (10^9 cells per day). Some lymphocytes migrate through the circulatory or lymphatic systems to the secondary lymphoid tissue (thymus, spleen, aggregated lymph nodules in the intestines, and lymph nodes) where they produce lymphocyte colonies.

T cells or T Lymphocytes: Thymus-dependent lymphocytes or T lymphocytes and migrate from thymus where they are influenced by the hormone-**thymosin** and become immunological competent. T lymphocytes are mainly involved in cellular type of immunological response that is with **cellular immunity**, such as rejection of foreign tissue.

TABLE 19.1: Classes of Lymphocytes

Lumphocyte	Role
T Cells	
T_H (helper) cells; also called CD4[1] cells	Provide assistance, or potenitiate expression of immune function by other lymphocytes
T_S (suppressor) cells; also called CD8 cells	Suppress or impair expression of immune function by other lymphocytes
T_C (cytotoxic) cells; also called CD8 cells	Bring about cytolysis and cell death of "targets"
T_D cells or T_{DTH} (delayed type hypresentivity) cells; also called CD4 cells	Recruit and regulate a variety of nonspecific blood cells and macrophages in expression of delayed (Type IV) hypresensitivity reactions
B Cells	
B lymphocytes	Proliferate and mature into antibody-producing cells
Plasma cells	Are mature, active antibody-producing cells
Null Cells	
Natural killer cells	Bring about cytolysis and death of target cells

Some T cells are transported away from the thymus and enter the bloodstream where they comprise 70 to 80% of the circulating lymphocytes. Other T cells tend to reside in various organs of the lymphatic system, such as the lymph nodes and spleen. This thymus-depended differentiation of T cells (or **theymoyctes**) occurs during early childhood, and by adolescence the secondary lymphoid organs of the body generally contain a full complement of T cells.

B Cells or B Lymphocytes

B-lymphocytes: The origin of these lymphocytes is from the *bursa of Fabricus* of birds (a mass of lymphoid tissue near the cloaca). The letter **B** was originally derived from the **b***usa of Fabricius*, a specialized appendage of the cloaca of chickens where these lymphocytes differentiate. B cells are distributed by the bloom and make up 20 various lymphoid organs along with the T cells. These lymphocytes are mainly involved in the production of antibodies- **humoral immunity**. B lymphocytes differentiate the fetal liver and adult bone marrow.

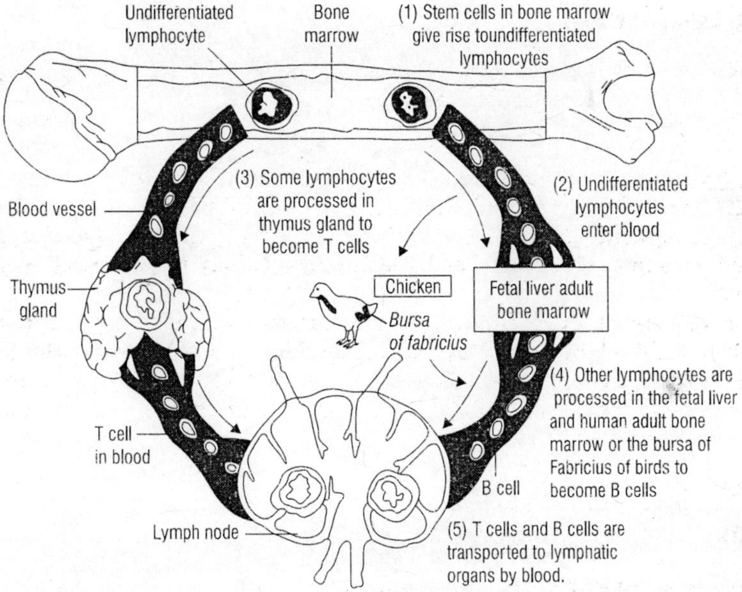

FIGURE 19.5: Schematic presentation of lymphocyte development. Bone marrow releases undifferentiated lymphocytes which after processing become T and B cells.

Plasma Blasts: These cells are produced by B lymphocytes following antigenic stimulation. In fact, the lymphocytes change themselves into plasma blasts, which multiply and differentiate into plasma cells. These are the large cells and contain relatively more basophilic cytoplasm, less developed endoplasmic reticulum, large nucleus with nucleoli and can multiply and differentiate themselves in plasma cells.

Plasma Cells: The plasma cells are uninucleated with amphophillic cytoplasm, rich in ribosomes, rough endoplasmic reticulum, with prominent Golgi bodies, acentric nucleus with cart wheel type chromatin.

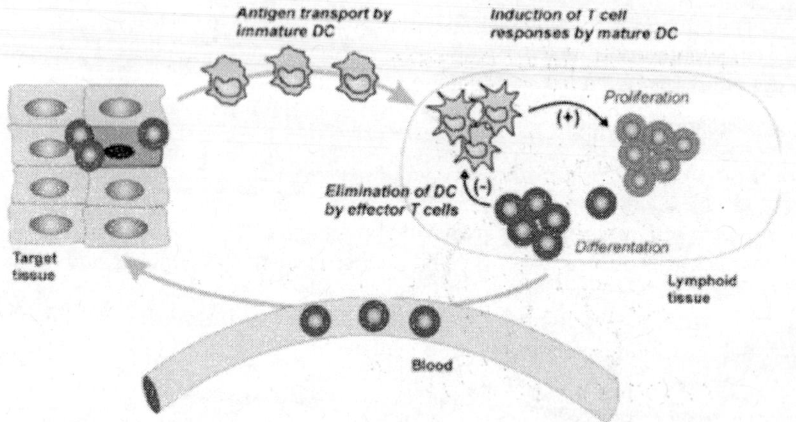

FIGURE 19.6: Interaction between T- and B-lymphocytes.

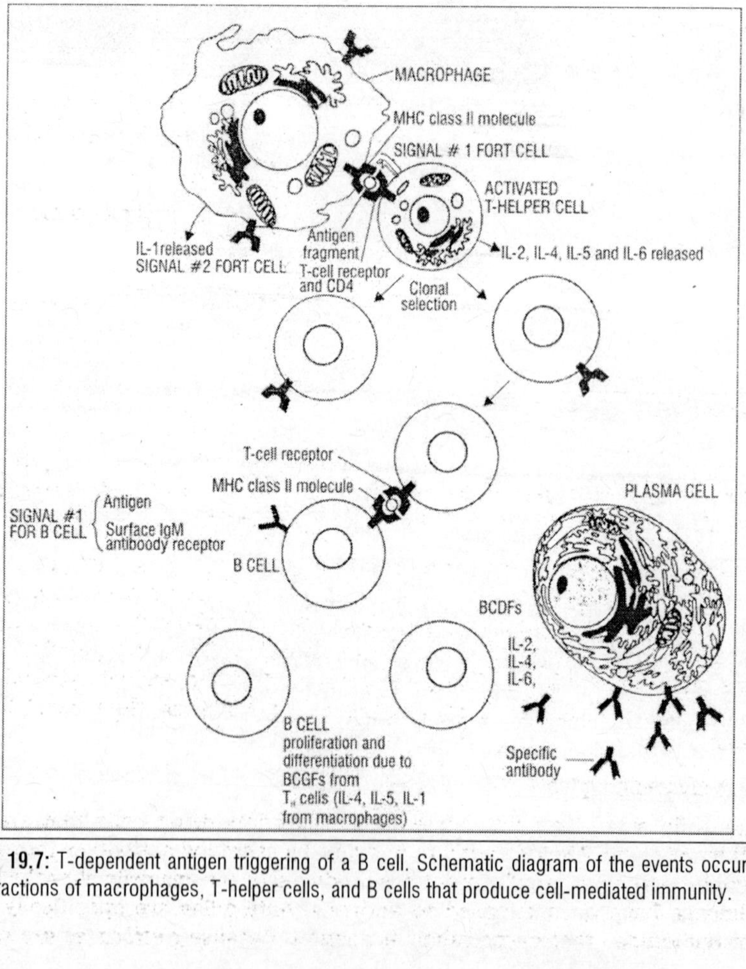

FIGURE 19.7: T-dependent antigen triggering of a B cell. Schematic diagram of the events occurring in the interactions of macrophages, T-helper cells, and B cells that produce cell-mediated immunity.

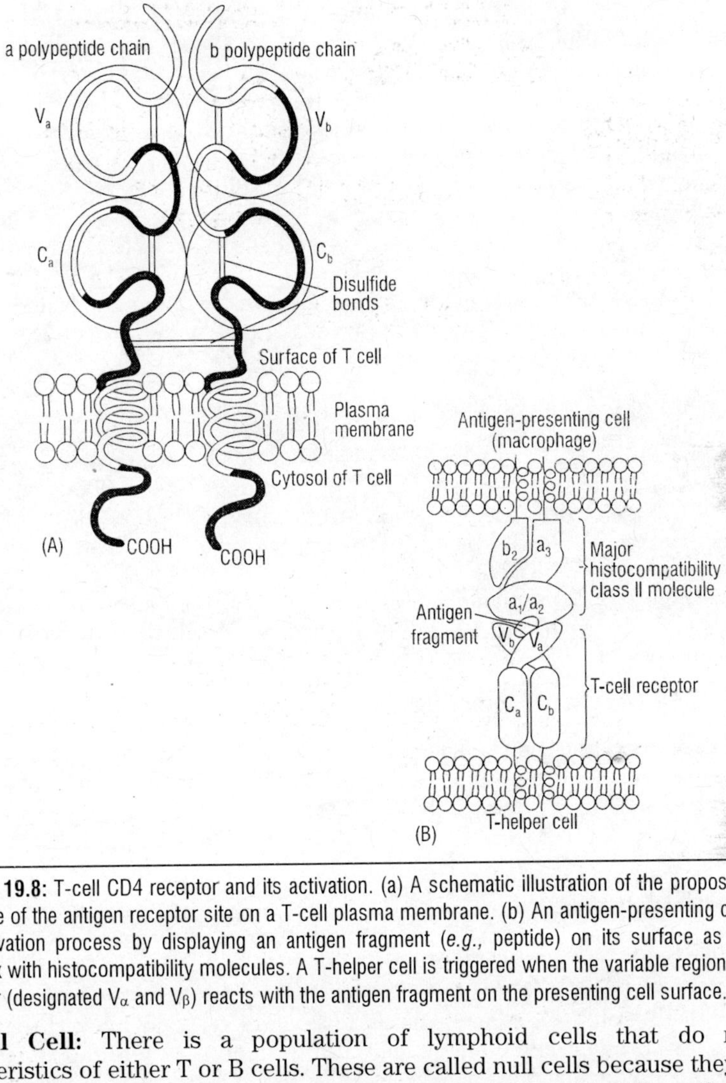

FIGURE 19.8: T-cell CD4 receptor and its activation. (a) A schematic illustration of the proposed overall structure of the antigen receptor site on a T-cell plasma membrane. (b) An antigen-presenting cell begins the activation process by displaying an antigen fragment (*e.g.*, peptide) on its surface as part of a complex with histocompatibility molecules. A T-helper cell is triggered when the variable region of itsCD4 receptor (designated V_α and V_β) reacts with the antigen fragment on the presenting cell surface.

Null Cell: There is a population of lymphoid cells that do not have characteristics of either T or B cells. These are called null cells because they lack the specific surface markers of B or T cells, and can be distinguished from them by the presence of cytoplasmic granules. It is currently believed that this population of cells contains most **natural killer (NK) cells** and antibody-dependent cytotoxic T cells. These cells are probably of bone marrow origin, however, their exact lineage in uncertain.

Function of Lymphocytes

Plasma cells are fully differentiated antibody-synthesizing cells that are derived from B lymphocyte. They respond to antigens by secreting antibodies into the blood and lymph. Antibodies are glycoproteins produced by plasma cells after the B cells in their lineage have been exposed to antigens. Antibodies are specifically directed against the antigen that caused their formation. Because *antibodies are soluble in* *blood and lymph fluids*, they provide **humoral** (Latin *humor*, a liquid) **immunity** or **antibody-mediated immunity**.

The humoral immune response defends mostly bacteria, bacterial toxins, and viruses that enter the body's various fluid systems. T cells do not secrete antibodies. Instead they attack (1) host cells that have been parasitized by viruses or microorganisms, (2) tissue cells that have been transplanted from one host to another, and (3) cancer cells. They also produce **cytokines**, chemical mediators that play specific augmenting and regulatory roles in the immune system. Since T cells must physically contact foreign cells or infected cells in order to destroy them, they are said to provide **cell-mediated immunity**.

Null cells (and particularly natural killer cells) destroy tumor cells and virus- and other parasite-infected cells. They also help regulate the immune response. Null cells often exhibit antibody-dependent cellular cytotoxicity.

Interaction of T and B Lymphocytes

Both the lymphocytes are quite distinct and independent in their function even they help each other in antibody production. The production of antibody increases in presence of T lymphocytes. How T lymphocyte increases the production of antibody in presence of B lymphocytes is poorly understood. However, T lymphocytes in this reference are known as helper cells. It has been suggested that T lymphocytes act by focussing antigen on `B' lymphocytes. Sometimes `T' cells also act as suppressor cells and may be involved in the maintenance of a state of immunological unresponsiveness.

Accessory Cells (A Cells): Macrophages

Macrophages are large uninuclear phagocytic cells and contain antigen. Those macrophages which do not take part directly in immune response are called **accessory cells** or A-cells of the immune system.

IMMUNE SYSTEM

Immunological Tolerance

Immunological tolerance is the failure to mount an immune response to an antigen. It can be:

- **Natural** or **"self" tolerance**. This is the failure (a good thing) to attack the body's own proteins and other antigens. If the immune system should respond to "self", an autoimmune disease may result.
- **Induced tolerance**. This is tolerance to external antigens that has been created by deliberately manipulating the immune system. Its importance:
  - to protect us from unpleasant, even dangerous, allergic reactions to such things as food (e.g. peanuts), insect stings, grass pollen (hay fever).
  - to enable transplanted organs (e.g., kidney, heart, liver) to survive in their new host; that is, to avoid **graft rejection**.
  - to reveal the mechanisms of autoimmunity in the hope of designing treatments for such diseases as systemic lupus erythematosus (SLE) and multiple sclerosis (MS).

Immunological tolerance is not simply a failure to recognize an antigen; it is an active response to a particular epitope and is just as **specific** as an immune response.

Both B cells and T cells can be made tolerant, but it is more important to tolerize T cells than B cells because B cells cannot make antibodies to most antigens without the help of T cells.

The important characteristics of immunological tolerance are: (i) it is induced by an antigen, (ii) it is specific, (iii) it is associated with immunological memory, and (iv) it is usually requires persistence of the antigen. Either both T and B cells or individual cells are involved in immunological tolerance.

Mechanisms of Immunological Tolerance Development

These are as follows:

1. **Clonal Abortion:** When an antigen comes in contact with immature immunologically competent cells (T or B cells), maturation of these cells is aborted, which results in lack of corresponding active T and B cells to react with antigen in the later life.
2. **Clonal Exhaustion:** When an individual is challenged with repeated doses of T cells independent antigen, all the corresponding B cells are stimulated to differentiate into short lived antibody forming cells (plasma cells). Thereafter no competent cell is left to react with the antigen.
3. **Functional Deletion:** This has been explained on the basis of two aspects (i) by T cell dependent antigens, and (ii) by T cell independent antigen.
4. **Antibody forming Cell Blockade:** T cell independent antigen can also produce tolerance by blocking the antibody forming cells. It, however, requires lesser amount of antigen.
5. **Generation of \`T' Suspensor Cells:** Sometimes antigen may stimulate generation of \`T' suspensor cells which directly suppresses corresponding \`T' and B' cells to induce tolerance.
6. **Factors Affecting Immunological Tolerance:** There are two main factors which affect tolerance: (i) Age of an individual organism or the maturation of immune system, and (ii) nature of antigen, its dose and clearance in the organism. The tolerant-capacity of an individual persists so long as threshold amount of antigen persists in immune system, thus tolerance with a replicated antigen (living cells) persists much longer than the foreign protein, which is eliminated rapidly by catabolism.

SEROLOGY

Serology deals with the study of antigen antibody reactions *in vitro*. It includes identification and quantitation of antigen or antibody using its known counterpart. The basis of these reactions and their application is the specificity of antigen antibody reactions.

Classification of Antigen - Antibody Reactions: The antigen-antibody reactions are termed on the basis of the observable effects of the reaction or the technique used. These include of:

1. Agglutination 2. Precipitation 3. Complement fixation 4. Opsonisation 5. Neutralisation 6. Immune cytolysis 7. Immune adherence 8. Immunofluorescence 9. Immunoelectrophoresis 10. Counter immuneelectro phoresis 11. Radio immunoassay 12. Enzyme linked immunosorbent assay and Immunoblotting.

Agglutination: When particulate form of antigen or antibody coated particles form clumps as a result of antigen-antibody interaction, the reaction is termed as agglutination reaction. Agglutination means clumping of the particles. In most agglutination reactions, the antigen is particulate and the antibody is in soluble form. However, if antibodies are coated on particles, agglutination of the latter can occur with soluble antigen. Agglutination occurs in two stages, the first stage- primary immunological reaction is the union between antigen and antibody and the second stage secondary reaction is the formation of visible clumps. The **first stage** is extremely rapid and is completed in few seconds. It is not affected by temperature variation (0° to 40° C) and it does not require electrolytes. Higher concentration of ions may inhibit reaction by covering the oppositly charged antigen and antibody molecules. The **second stage** of the reaction is influenced by temperature and requires electrolytes. The ions reduce negative charges on particles which help in aggregation. Most reactions are accelerated by raising the temperature from 0° - 30° C. Some however, occur at low temperature only *e.g.*, cold haemagglutination.

The agglutinate consists of a lattice of alternating antibody and antigen molecules. Immunoglobulin M is a potent agglutinating antibody. Because of its multiple valencies, one molecule of it can unite with 5 to 10 molecules of the antigen.

Precipitation: When soluble forms of antigen and antibody interact and form precipitate, the reaction is termed as precipitation reaction. Precipitation is an antigen antibody reaction in which the antigen is in soluble form. A precipitation reaction requires antibodies more than that for agglutination because with the decrease in size of particles, the total available surface of antigen increases. Though most precipitation reactions occur better at 37° C- 45° C, more complete precipitation is frequently obtained at 0°-4° C. So quantitative precipitation tests are practically always refrigerated for an interval of one or more days. It is done by three tests: 1. Simple mixture. 2. Interfacial ring test. 3. Gel diffusion test.

Complement Fixation: Following antigen-antibody interaction, complement, if present, is activated and fixed to the antigen-antibody complex. The fixation of complement is detected by an indicator system - the sensitized or antibody coated sheep R.B.C. The test by which antigen or antibody is detected by activation of complement is known as complement fixation test.

Complement fixation test is based on the principle of fixation of complement factors to antigen antibody complexes, which is detected by an indicator system consisting of sheep RBC and antibodies to sheep RBC. Unfixed complement causes haemolysis in indicator system. If complement is fixed to test antigen antibody complex, it is not available for the indicator system, hence haemolysis will not occur. If original test system is lacking in antigen or the corresponding antibody complement will remain free and haemolysis of sheep RBC occurs *i.e.* the test is negative (complement not fixed). Absence of haemolysis means complement is fixed to the test system *i.e.*, the test is positive. In complement fixation test guinea-pig serum is usually used as source of complement and a calculated amount of complement is used which is just enough to be completely utilised by the test antigen antibody system. Further, the antigen and the serum may have anti-complementry activity. Therefore, first the titre of complement in guinea-pig serum is determined in presence of the test amount of antigen and the serum separately, and also in presence of pooled normal serum, and compared with the titre of complement obtained in absence of antigen and serum. Extra complement is used in the test system if antigen or serum possesses anti-complementry activity. In test system 5/4 of the titre of complement of pooled guinea-pig serum obtained in presence of 1 vol. of antigen and 1/5 vol. normal serum, is used.

Complement fixation test is much more sensitive than agglutination and precipitation test but is more cumbersome to perform. At one time because of its sensitivity it was performed for detection of antigen or antibodies in diagnosis of a number of diseases and for the identification of the antigen. Complement fixation test has been used as Wassermann reaction in diagnosis of syphilis, and also for detection of specific antibodies to viruses, protozoa and rickettsia and a number of bacteria for diagnosis of the diseases caused by them *e.g.*, diagnosis of deep seated gonococcol infections and amoebiasis, kala-azar, trypnosomal infections. It has also been used for detection of viruses grown in tissue culture or chick embryo. As a number of newer more sensitive and simple tests have been introduced in recent past, complement fixation test is now rarely performed.

Anti-complementary activity in serum develops on being kept at room temperature for some time. Heating serum at 56° C for 30 minutes it can be eliminated.

Opsonisation: Attachment of antibodies to particular antigen makes the latter easily phagocytosed by phagocytic cells. This enhanced phagocytosis by antigen-antibody interaction is known as opsonisation.

Neutralization: When attachment of antibodies to antigen neutralises the toxic effects of the antigen, the reaction is known as neutralization *e.g.* Toxin-antitoxin interaction.

Immune Cytolysis: When antibodies and surface antigen of certain cells interact, it may cause cytolysis by complement activation.

Immune Adherence: Primate erythrocytes bear surface receptors for C 3. Therefore erythrocytes adhere to C3 attached to antigen antibody complexes. This is known as immune adherence. It is being utilised to detect antigen or antibodies as for complement fixation.

Immuno Fluorescence: When antigen or antibody detected by using fluorescent dye tagged antibody or antigen and fluorescent microscopy, the reaction/technique is known as immuno fluorescence. **Immunofluorescence technique** was introduced following the use of fluorochrome labelled protein by Coon's and Kaplan (1950). It involves labelling of antibody with fluorescent dye followed by its use in detection or identification of antigen. It combines the sensitivity and specificity of immunology with precision of microscopy. The technique is more sensitive than agglutination, precipitation and complement fixation techniques. It can detect protein of the order of less than 1 μg/ml. of the body fluid.

Fluorescent dyes absorb ultraviolet light (between wave length 290 and 295 nm.) and emit light of longer wavelength (525 nm) of visible spectrum. The fluorescent dyes in common use are Fluorescin isothiocyanate, which emits green or apple green light and Lisiamine rhodamine B (RB 200) which emits orange light.

Immuno Electrophoresis: When a mixture of antigens are separated by electrophoresis and detected by immuno diffusion, the technique is termed as immuno electrophoresis.

Counter Immuno electrophoresis: When oppositely charged antigen and antibody molecules are subjected to migrate in an agar gel under the influence of electric current, a quick precipitation occurs where they meet in optimal concentration. This quick precipitation under the influence of electric current is known as counter immune electrophoresis.

Radio Immuno Assay (RIA): When antigen antibody reaction is detected by utilisation of radioactive labelled antigen or antibody and the technique is used to assay the antigen or the antibody in a given sample, the technique is known as Radio immuno assay.

This technique is used for the detection of any substance that is antigenic and can be labelled with a radioactive isotope. In fact, this method is based on the competition between labelled (known) and unlabelled (unknown) antigen for the same antibody. The measurement of the amount of labelled antigen attached to antibody, it is essential to separate the antigen-antibody complexes from the mixture. Out of many available method, the most convenient method for such separation is solid phase radioimmunoassay where in the antibody is linked to an insoluble support *e.g.*, agarose beads. The insoluble complex is then mixed with known and unknown antigen. The separation of antibody-bound labelled antigen from free antigen is done by centrifugation and filtration. The radioactivity is then measured and percentage of labelled antigen bound to the antibody is calculated. Amount of unknown antigen is determined using reference standard curve.

Enzyme linked Immunosorbent Assay (ELISA): When the antigen antibody reaction is detected or one of the components is quantitated by enzyme labelled counter part and subsequent demonstration of fixed enzyme by its substrate, the reaction or the technique is known as enzyme linked immunosorbent assay.

ELISA, especially solid-phase ELISA is a improved diagnostic test since the technique readily lends itself to automation and is certainly feasible under field conditions. Although there are a number of different types of solid-phase EIA, the basic steps in each type are the same:

1. Attachment of the immunoreactant (generally antibody or antigen) to the solid phase to serve to capture the complementary reactant from the sample.
2. Incubation with the test sample so that the complementary reactants are always found in or compete for the second layer.
3. Amplification by, for example, enzyme-labelled antiglobulin.

The types of solid-phase EIA include: direct, indirect and bridge non-competitive Elas in which antigen is immobilized on the solid phase; non-competitive EIA with antibody immobilized on the solid phase; and, competitive EIA with either antibody or antigen immobilized on the solid phase. The solid phase can be composed of a wide variety of materials including plastic, nitrocellulose membrane, paper, glass and cloth.

Immunoblotting: When antigens are first separated by poly-acrylamide gel electrophoresis and transferred on to nitro-cellulose paper strips, which are than used for detection of antibodies in the unknown samples.

It was first described by E. M. Southern (1975). He devised a neat method for identification of DNA fragments from agarose-gels. The method involves the denaturation of DNA fragments to a nitrocellulose membrane, allowing the **probe** (radiolabelled RNA or complementary DNA) to hybridize with fragment of interest and finally detection of such fragment by autoradiography. This ingenious method is generally referred to as *Southern Blotting* after the name of its inventor. However, this method could not be applied directly to identify RNA fragments since RNA did not bind to nitrocellulose membrane. Alwine and his associates (1979) devised a method in which the nitrocellulose membrane was replaced by an RNA-binding paper (diazotized aminobenzyloxymethyl paper). This extension of Southern's method to RNA aquired the name *Northern Blotting*. Later, Thomas (1980) and others workers showed that RNA does, in fact, bind to nitrocellulose membrane under appropriate conditions. Towbin and his associates developed new method known as *Western Blot*.

Of the above reactions- agglutination, precipitation, complement fixation, neutralization, immunofluorescence, counter immunoelectrophoresis, radioimmunoassay and enzyme linked immunosorbent assay are commonly used in serology laboratories.

SEROLOGICAL TESTS

The serological diagnosis of an animal disease is a presumptive test, which is usually then confirmed by direct culture of the causative virus or bacterium from excised tissues. Nucleic acid probes afford the opportunity to detect the organism directly in the tissue. Epizootic Haemorrhagic Disease Virus (EHDV) of deer has much in common with BTV.

Microbiological is also applied to: the genetic engineering of new bacteria (*i.e. Salmonella* and *Brucella*) for antigen and vaccine production; fermentation technology for antigen production; and, micromanipulation of embryos and *in vitro* fertilization for embryo transfer procedures which provides greater ability to control disease than ever before.

Biotechnology and Diagnoses of Animal Diseases

Animal Health

Animal health care covers many aspects including among others:

1. The improvement of animal productivity through either genetic engineering, animal embryo technology or growth hormones.
2. The improvement of animal nutrition.
3. The prevention and treatment of animal diseases by vaccines, monoclonal antibodies or interferons. Another extremely important aspect of animal health care is the diagnosis of animal disease. The scope of animal disease diagnosis is vast.

Objectives

1. To measures and to safeguard the Indian livestock population from the introduction of foreign animal diseases - for example, the import inspection system allows Indian producers access to genetic material such as semen and animal embryos from around the world.
2. To control and eradicate serious infectious and contagious indigenous diseases which threaten the economic viability of the livestock.
3. To ensure meat and animal product safety.
4. Development of research programme, which promotes the effective achievement of these mandates.

Diagnostic Tests

A wide variety of diagnostic tests should be performed. It is essential to have the capability to rapidly diagnose diseases like African Swine Fever and Bluetongue to Trichinosis and Vesicular Stomatitis to prevent their introduction in country. Therefore, it is essential to perform several tests like: simple agglutination procedures to highly specialized techniques, agar gel immunodiffusion (AGID), buffered plate antigen test (BPAT), complement fixation (CF), culture, enzyme immunosorbent assay (EIA), fluorescent antibody (FA), histopathology, serum agglutination test (SAT), serum neutralization (SN) and tissue culture.

These classical diagnostic procedures reliable however, time consuming, labour-intensive and expensive. There is obviously a continuing need to improve the capability for diagnosing animal diseases through the development of rapid, inexpensive, rugged and yet, of utmost importance, sensitive and specific diagnostic tests. A field test which is simple and rugged would allow veterinarians to quickly identify outbreaks of infectious disease, evaluate their spread and institute containment measures without the time required to send samples to a central testing laboratory.

The following two relatively recent biotechnologies provide the potential for development of improved diagnostic tests are: Monoclonal Antibody Production and Nucleic Acid Probe Technology.

HYBRIDOMAS TECHNOLOGY AND PRODUCTION OF MONOCLONAL ANTIBODIES

Hybridoma - a biotechnological tool- is the new path for achieving the goal of complete immunization of human body from infections. In 1975, a new era in the immunology was launched with the discovery of the hybridoma technique, a method of creating pure and uniform antibodies (immunoglobulins) against a specific target (antigen).

Hybridomas are the hybrid cells of myceloma (cancer) cells with antibody producing cells (lymphocytes) from an immunized donor (animal). The hybrid cell or hybridoma resulting from this fusion has the ability to multiply rapidly and indefinitely *in vitro* and to produce an antibody of predetermined specificity, known as **monoclonal antibody**.

Somatic Cell Fusion

Barski et al. (1960) in laboratory of Virology and Tissue Culture of the Institute of Gaustave Roussy, at Villejuif (France); observed during their culture experiments of two stocks of tumour mouse cells that a new cell type was formed. This type had morphological characteristics and growth pattern that are different from those of parent cells. The nuclei of these new cells contained number of chromosomes equal to the sum total of chromosome numbers of the two parent cells. Unfortunately, the frequency of cell fusion was very low, between 10^{-4} to 10^{-6}.

Latter, the frequency of fusion of animal cells could increase by various workers using biotic and abiotic fusing agents. Okada (1962), succeeded in increasing the frequency of fusion between animal tumour cells by using the Japanese Haemagglutination Virus (JHV). He has also reported that JHV inactivated by ultraviolet radiation retained the ability to induce somatic cell fusion, so any complication resulting from using an infective virus could be avoided.

Harris and Watkins (1965), succeeded in somatic cell fusion between human HeLa cell and tumour mouse cells using inactivated Sendai virus as fusing agent. Weiss and Green (1967) noticed a peculiar feature in some somatic hybrid in which chromosomes of one of the parent cells gradually eliminated or lost. In somatic hybrid of human and mouse cells, human chromosomes generally lost after fusion while in somatic hybrid of monkey and mouse cells the chromosomes of monkey are eliminated. Davis (1981) used polyethylene glycol as fusing agent and could get somatic hybrids of animal and plant cells separately belonging to two different species and even hybrid of animal and plant cells.

Hybridoma Technology

The hybridoma technology for the production of standardized antibodies of a given class, specificity, and affinity has provided scientists with a tool that permits the analysis of virtually any antigenic molecule. Such reagents (antibodies) can be made in unlimited amounts whenever needed, thus, making them readily available to all investigators.

Kohler (1974) successfully produced a hybridoma by fusing a P3 myceloma cell (resistant to azaguanine) and a lymphocyte (from the spleen of a mouse) immunized against sheep-red blood cells. The experiment consisted of immunizing mice against red blood cells (the antibodies produced against this antigen are easily detected in the serum by means of an assay developed in 1963 by Jerne and Nordin), then mixing mouse myceloma P3 cells with spleen cells from immunized mice in the presence of polyethylene glycol. These chimeric cells, called hybridomas retained the property of immortality of the myceloma cells as well as that of secreting an antibody specific for a unknown antigen; resulting from the fusion of an antibody-secreting cell and of a tumour cell. They are capable of growing indefinitely in culture and of producing at the same time a particular species of antibody (a monoclonal antibody).

Production of Monoclonal Antibodies

The hybridoma technique seemed to be useful and applicable in producing monoclonal antibodies which is for affinity purification, tumor imaging, immunodiagnostics, and cancer treatment. They can also be useful in describing as well as predicting and optimizing secretion in antibody production system. The monoclonal antibody is defined as a chemical reagent of known structure that can be reproduced at will, whereas conventional antiserum is a variable mixture of reagents that can never be reproduced, once the original supply is exhausted. The monoclonal antibody was purified by passage through chromatography columns containing the known antigen and, within 6 to 12 months, unlimited quantities of a single antibody could be obtained with a degree of purity and homogeneity. The clones selected can be stored by freezing technique.

It is now possible to obtain consistently large number of hybrids and one can select the lines producing the antibody of choice. The critical component in the production of hybridomas is the preparation of cells for fusion. Where rodents are used as a source of cell for fusion, immunization protocols must be devised that optimize the proliferative response to antigen in the spleen. Plasmablasts appear to be more suitable as fusion partners than mature plasma cells.

The fusion and culture of hybridoma is quite straight forward. The scheme is equally useful when cultures of *in vitro* immunized cells are used as a source of plasmablasts. The production technique of monoclonal antibodies can be divided into three steps:

Step I: Fusion and Culture of Hybridomas

1. Boost mice with an intravenous injection of antigen 72 hours before use. On the day of fusion, collect the spleen and make a free cell suspension by injecting and flushing the spleen with sterile serum-free medium. Centrifuge the cells and resuspend in lysing solution. When sterile water is used, suspend the cell in 1 ml of water and immediately dilute in 20 ml of medium. Any delay will result in the loss of plasmablasts and a consequent reduction in antibody-producing hybrids.

2. Maintain plasma cells in cell culture and feed into fresh flasks and medium for 16-24 hours before fusion to ensure that they are in early phase of growth at the time of fusion. At the time of use, collect the cells, centrifuge, and resuspend in serum-free medium.
3. Count both myceloma and spleen cells and then mix in the appropriate ratio. Depending on the properties of the tumour cells, the ratio of spleen to tumour cells may vary from 5:1 to 2:1.
4. Following mixing, the cells are centrifuged into a loose pellet by spinning at 1000 rpm for 10 to 15 minutes. Remove the supernatant and overlay the pellet with 1 ml of PEG. For 3 minutes, mix the PEG into the pellet. In doing so breakup the pellet into uniform small clumps.
5. Following fusion, dilute the cells in 30 ml of serum-free medium with the first 10ml medium being added and mixed at 1 ml per minute. Slow dilution reduces the risk of osmotic disruption of the fused cells. Centrifuge the cells and resuspend in complete medium containing HAT and then dispense into 96-well tissue culture plates, 10 plates for each 108 splenocytes used in the fusion. Added 106 thymocytes to each well to serve as feeder-cells. The latter step has proven critical for optimizing that outgrowth of newly formed hybrids. Feeder-cells and 2-ME in the medium exert a synergistic effect.
6. In carbon dioxide incubator with high humidity, incubate the cultures for 3-4 days with rapidly growing cultures between changes of culture medium, replace half the medium with fresh HAT medium every 4th day.
7. Identify and mark the wells containing hybrid colonies (hybridomas) on day 9 or 10 and then allow the colonies to grow to 500 or more cells. In rapidly growing cultures, supernatants can be collected and assayed for antibody activity by day 12-14. Where appropriate, collect and test the supernatants from the largest colonies first; test the remainder 2-4 days later.
8. After each test for antibody, transfer positive cell lines to 24 well plates. Add 3-5 $\times 10^6$ feeder cells to each well to promote rapid cell growth. Maintain cells in static culture for a minimum of 2 weeks by removing 50-75% of the hybrid cells after 2-3 days interval. The maneuver select for stable, rapidly growing, antibody-producing hybrids. Slow growing hybrids and hybrids that cease to synthesize antibody are eliminated.
9. After 2 weeks, make duplicate cultures and allow the cells to overgrow and die. Collect the supernatants and assay for the presence of antibody. Take cultures producing antibodies of the desired specificity from the master plate and expand into 6-well plates (2-3 wells for each cells lines). Harvest the cells twice for preservation in liquid nitrogen. Replenish the cultures with fresh medium and allow the cells to overgrow and die. Collect final supernatant for further analysis. The 6-well plates are essential for minimizing labour and time during this phase of hybridoma production.

Step II: Cloning and Preservation of Hybridomas

1. Following preliminary selection of hybrids, screen the final supernatants in detail to identify antibodies of immediate interest. Take the parent cell lines from the freezer and clone by limiting dilution. When viability is good, clone the cell lines immediately. Take the remainder of the excess cells and culture them in a T75 flask for 1-2 days. As soon as enough cells are present, harvest the cells and freeze one ampule to replace the ampule used for cloning. The culture should not

be allowed to proliferate more than necessary to avoid change in composition of the cell line at this early stage of processing. As in the initial step, use feeder cells to promote growth.

2. At 6-8 days mark wells containing a single colony. At 12-14 days assay supernatants from the marked wells. Transfer 24-48 positive cultures to 24 well plates and maintain in static culture as described previously.
3. After noting which cloned lines are stable, expand 4-6 clones of each cell line into 6-well plates for cell preservation and production of antibody. Record which lines are stable and which are unstable.
4. Preserve 4-6 clones from each cell line in liquid nitrogen.

Step III: Production of Antibody

To produce antibody, culture the cloned cell lines *in vitro* or grow in ascites from the mice. After these steps, proper method is selected for assaying monoclonal antibodies in supernatants of hybridomas. Following methods are in use for assaying monoclonal antibodies:

(a) Enzyme-linked Immunosorbent assay (ELISA) (b) Radioimmunoassay (RIA). (c) Immunofluorescence (d) Cytotoxicity (e) Flow Cytometry, etc.

Application of Monoclonal Antibodies

Hybridomas can be stored by freezing technique. Hybridoma banks have been established in some institutes and laboratories in order to meet research needs. Many pharmaceutical firms are interested to the highest degree in the large-scale production of monoclonal antibodies from these hybridomas. Keeping in view their applications in various fields of medical science:

1. Dose determination of a medicine can be carried out by using the monoclonal antibodies of an animal, immunized against this particular medicine.
2. They are used to detect allergies, to carry out hormone tests, to diagnose viral diseases, to detect certain types of cancers, to monitor the presence or appearance of malignant cells after surgical or radio-therapeutic treatments.
3. The purification of complex mixtures or substances, the biological role, which is important (proteins, hormones, toxins, etc.) could also be carried out with monoclonal antibodies.
4. The use of these antibodies was also envisaged for the labelling and precise identification of specialized cells such as neurones in order to gain better knowledge of the way in which these cells associate and operate.
5. Monoclonal antibody technique is also of great value in the area of the structure of cell membrane as membrane proteins are hard to purify.
6. In the field of direct therapy, serotherapy can be made more effective with the administration of a monoclonal antibody.
7. Monoclonal antibodies could also be used in the preparation of very specific vaccines, particularly against certain viral strains and against other parasites.
8. Monoclonal antibodies could also neutralize the action of lymphocytes responsible for the rejection of grafts and destroy the auto-antibodies produced in auto-immune diseases.
9. In association with medicinal substances, they could considerably increase the effectiveness of the latter on the target cells, while avoiding the serious side effects of cancer therapies.

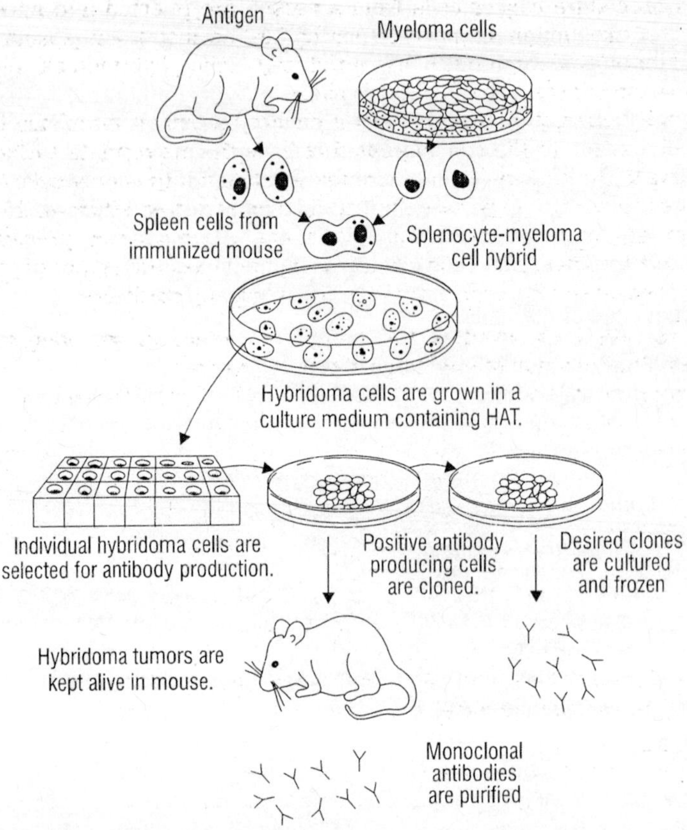

FIGURE 19.9: Technique for the Production Monoclonal Antibodies. Antigen-stimulated spleen cells are fused with special mutant myeloma cells, yielding hybridomas. Each of them secretes a single, *Monoclonal* antibody. Once the hybridoma secreting the desired antigen is identified, it is cloned to generate many antibody-secreting cells that yield the huge quantity of a single antibody needed in medicine or science. Some hybridoma cells may be stored frozen and later cloned for antibody production or kept alive in laboratory animals.

Many European and North American firms are interested in the applications of monoclonal antibodies. In California, for-instance, certain companies are preparing diagnostic kits designed for the screening of certain lethal diseases. It is anticipated that the future support of some aspects of this hybridomas based monoclonal antibody technology will be tailored to the needs of each developing country in the world.

IMMUNOTOXINS

One result of hybridoma research is the production of **immunotoxins**. Immunotoxins are monoclonal antibodies that have been attached to a specific toxin or toxic agent (*antibody* + *toxin* = immunotoxin). Immunotoxins kill target cells and no others, because the antibody binds specifically to plasma membrane surface antigens found only on the target cells. This approach is being used to treat certain types of cancer.

In this procedure cancer cells from a person are injected into mice or rats to stimulate the production of specific antibodies against their plasma membrane antigens. Monoclonal antibodies are produced using hybridomas, purified, and attached to an agent toxic to the cancer cells.

When the immunotoxin is given to a cancer patient, it circulates through the body and binds only to the cancer cells that have the appropriate surface antigens. After binding to the surface, the immunotoxin is taken into cancer cells by receptor-mediated endocytosis, and released inside. The immunotoxin then interfers with the metabolism of the target cells and kills them. Although this procedure is still experimental, it holds great promise in the treatment of certain types of cancer.

Monoclonal antibodies currently have following applications:

1. They are routinely used is the typing of tissue, in the identification and epidemiological study of infectious microorganisms.
2. They are used in the identification of tumor and other surface antigens
3. They are used in the classification of leukemias.
4. They are used in the identification of functional populations of different types T cells.

Anticipated future Monoclonal antibodies

1. Passive immunizations against infectious agents and toxic drugs.
2. Tissue and organ graft protection.
3. Stimulation of tumor rejection and elimination.
4. Manipulation of the immune response.
5. Preparation of more specific and sensitive diagnostic procedures.
6. Delivery of antitumor agents (immunotoxins) to tumor cells.

NUCLEIC ACID PROBE TECHNOLOGY

The use of nucleic acid probes for diagnostic purposes is based on an entirely different set of principles, that is, the hybridization of complementary sequences of DNA or of DNA and RNA. The assumption is made that if specific DNA is present in a test sample then the organism must also be present. Whereas monoclonal antibodies (Mabs) can be used for both antigen and antibody detection (*i.e.* for scrodiagnosis), nucleic acid probes can only be used to detect *antigen* for want of a better word. Basically the steps of the procedure are as follows. The nucleic acid of the disease organism in question is extracted and bound to a membrane. DNA or RNA of a nucleotide sequence known to be unique to a region of the DNA or RNA of the disease organism is labelled (the *nucleic acid probe*). Conditions are created for the maximum binding of the probe to the DNA or RNA bound to the membrane. Unbound probe is washed off the membrane. Bound probe is then detected. The advantages afforded by nucleic acid probes over Mabs include; ease of test sample preparation (samples can actually be rather crude and include feces, tissue, blood, pus and other exudates); and, the ability to detect pathogenic determinants which would not be revealed immunologically.

Disadvantages

One of the main disadvantages to the use of nucleic acid probes is that the achievement of maximum sensitivity of detection still requires the use of radioactive labelling. A number of non radioactive detection systems such as biotin-avidin labelling, enzyme immunoassay, enzymic labelling, and fluorescence are being developed but there are still difficulties with high background in cruder sample preparations with these detection systems. In addition the entire probe procedure is relatively time-consuming.

ENZYME-LINKED IMMUNOSORBENT ASSAYS (ELISA)

Microbial Research: Some Examples: The solid-phase ELSA can diagnose for a number of animal diseases including brucellosis, pseudorabies, bluetongue, paratuberculosis, infectious bovine, rhinotracheitis, trichinosis, epizootic haemorrhagic disease of deer, maedi-visna and rinderpest.

Brucellosis

Brucella abortus, the causative bacterium of brucellosis, causes uterine infections in cows which frequently result in abortions, and genital infections in bulls. It can also cause a persistent, latent infection in some animals. Brucellae are also highly infectious to humans causing a debilitating **undulant fever**. Intensive surveillance must be continued for a period to confirm that eradication is total and complete and to prevent reintroduction of the disease into the livestock. A highly standardized, automated, indirect solid-phase EIA technique should be used for detection of bovine antibody to *B. abortus* 2.

Pseudorabies

Pseudorabies is a serious infectious **viral disease** of swine, cattle, sheep, dogs, cats and rats but is only naturally transmissible through swine. Pseudorabies virus (PRV) causes death of neonatal and weanling pigs. An indirect solid-phase EIA for the detection and quantitation of porcine antibody to PRV is in common use. It is faster and far more convenient than the standard serum neutralization (SN) test. A modified solid-phase EIA (dot-ELISA) in a dip-stick type of configuration has been developed which could have application as a rapid and economical field test for PRV diagnosis.

Bluetongue

Bluetongue is a **viral disease** of sheep and occasionally cattle. It is transmitted by insect vectors and is characterized by catarrhal stomatitis, rhinitis and enteritis and also by lameness. Both an indirect and competitive solid-phase EIA using a group-specific Mab can be used for detection of antibodies.

ANIMAL VACCINE DEVELOPMENT AND PRODUCTION

Vaccine is an antigenic preparation administered with the object of stimulating the recipient's specific defence mechanisms in respect of given pathogen(s) or toxic agent(s). Some vaccines (*e.g.*, the Sabin vaccine) are given orally while other (*e.g.*, the Salk vaccine) are administered parentally. Vaccines are of following four main categories:

1. Inactivated vaccines *e.g.*, vaccines against typhoid and cholera.
2. Those comprising suspensions of life (attenuated) pathogens, *e.g.*, vaccines against yellow fever and tuberculosis.
3. Toxoids.
4. Those comprising a solution or suspension of the antigenic extracts of specific pathogens, *e.g.*, the vaccine containing polysaccharide capsular material of

Streptococcus pneumoniae.

Uses of Vaccines

The use of vaccines is extremely important for preventing various serious diseases. The development and production of these vaccines constitute an important function of the pharmaceutical industry. Vaccines are produced either by mutant strains of pathogens or by attenuating or inactivating virulent pathogens without removing the antigens necessary for eliciting the immune response.

Production of Vaccines

For the production of vaccines against viral diseases, strains of the virus are often grown by using embryonated eggs. Individuals who are allergic to eggs cannot be given such vaccine preparations. Viral vaccines are produced through tissue culture. For example, the older rabies vaccine, which was produced in embryonated duck eggs and had painful side effects, has been replaced with a vaccine produced in human fibroblast tissue cultures, which has far fewer side effects. The production of vaccines by bacteria, fungi, and protozoa generally involves growing the microbial strain on an artificial medium, which minimizes problems with allergic response. Vaccines should be tested and standardized before use.

The majority of licensed vaccines for humans and animals presently in use are produced by conventional methods by manipulating the genes of bacteria causing diseases, and using the restructured genes for making antibodies. Another approach is to clone the genes for coat protein (antigens) of viruses in bacteria and preparing vaccines from bacteria. This is less hazardous than growing the whole virus in the laboratory. Some viruses like the smallpox and marburg virus are so dangerous that one does not actually want to propagate them in the laboratory. These include killed vaccines and live attenuated or inactivated vaccines. At present, a large number of viral vaccines are of the killed variety.

Advantages with Killed Vaccines

One of the major advantages of such vaccines is that they are relatively stable under environmental conditions, therefore, it is not as crucial to maintain a cold chain to ensure efficacy of the vaccines.

In specific disease situations such as rabies virus, clinicians are often reluctant to use live viral vaccines, because of the fear that they may inject themselves with the vaccine and there may be some adverse side effects. Although this possibility is extremely remote, the psychological trauma of injection with a virus such as rabies is sufficiently great to discourage some clinicians from using live virus vaccines.

Disadvantages with Killed Vaccines

They do not replicate within the host and, therefore, large amounts of antigen are required for injection before induction of immunity. Since these vaccines are often produced in foreign tissue there is also the possibility of reactions developing against foreign proteins.

1. Since the vaccines are killed, they generally are injected intramuscularly.
2. A killed vaccine is more effective against **systemic viruses** than against viruses which replicate in **local mucosal sites**. This latter disadvantage has lead to the development of a large number of attenuated vaccines.

Advantages with Attenuated Vaccines

1. The main advantage of attenuated vaccines results primarily from their ability to replicate in the host.
2. Since their mode of action is similar to natural infections, immunity is generally of a broader spectrum than it is with killed virus vaccines. Thus they can induce a range of immune responses both locally, as well as systemically.
3. Attenuated vaccines develop immunity for longer duration than that of killed virus vaccines.
4. Since the virus replicates in the host and produces large quantities of proteins to which the host responds to the possibility of injecting foreign proteins is dramatically reduced with attenuated virus vaccines.

Disadvantages with Attenuated Vaccines

1. Since the vaccines are produced by passage in culture, to induce random mutation(s) or mutated with a specific agent and thereby reduce virulence, it is possible that passage in the natural host may result in reversion back to virulence, *e.g.*, attenuated polio virus. In the case of polio, reversion can occur within a few days of oral immunization.
2. Interference is also a potential problem. When viruses are grown in culture, there is a possibility to have other contaminating viruses present in it. For example the presence of BVD virus (a ubiquitous virus) in viral vaccines grown for immunizing cattle is very common. This virus is present in many of the cell lines and fatal bovine sera than are used for growing bovine viruses. Such interference may result in reduced replication of the attenuated virus vaccine and thus, reduced immunity.
3. Live attenuated virus vaccines are also extremely susceptible to environmental factors which may reduce their efficacy upon storage.
4. The attenuated virus vaccines induce latent infections and abortions if not administered properly or if administered at the wrong time in the animal's life.

Our Limitations

Killed and attenuated virus vaccines have not eliminated viral diseases (with the exception of small pox) completely. We still need to produce better vaccines that may be more efficacious and safer for use in human and animal medicine. There are a number of viruses for which we do not have vaccines due to the inability to grow virus in culture or in other economically acceptable culturing media. Some viruses may be of suppressive nature or impossible to attenuate by passage. In order to develop vaccines against exotic viruses, one requires excessive laboratory containment or restricts the use and application of such vaccines. Some of the newer technologies available would greatly eliminate some of these restrictions.

NEW TECHNOLOGIES

Newer technologies are available and used to produce new virus vaccines. These technologies are based on classical approaches (reassortants, temperature sensitive or cold adapted, heterologous vaccines). These are based on the ability to manipulate the genetic material of the viruses in such a way as to either reduce the virulence of a specific virus in a specific way or identify the specific protective proteins and express them in a foreign host.

Steps of Sub-unit Vaccines Production

1. Identify protective proteins or epitopes on the proteins. Once this is done an individual can either produce a sub-unit vaccine by recombinant DNA technology or by synthetic peptide technology.
2. Identify gene coding for the protein.
3. Clone the gene coding for the specific protein and express it in a suitable expression system.
4. Purify the protective protein to homogeneity using bovine herpesvirus-1. BHV-1 has four major glycoproteins: GVP I, GVP II, GVP III and GVP IV.
5. Monoclonal antibodies immunosorbent columns are prepared and used for purification of large quantities of the BHV-1 glycoproteins. These glycoproteins are then mixed with the adjuvant avridine and used to immunize animals against BHV-1 virus.

TABLE 19.2: Technologies for producing new vaccines

Methodology		Example
1.	Recombinant DNA - Expression of genes in foreign hosts	Influenza, AIDS, VSV
	viruses (baculovirus, herpesvirus, adenovirus, vaccinia)	
	bacteria (*Salmonella*)	Rotavirus
	Yeast	Hepatitis B
	mammalian cells	Herpes
2.	Reassortants	Influenza
3.	Heterologous viruses	Rota
4.	Genetic deletions	Herpes
5.	Mutations	Polio
6.	Antiidiotypes	Rabies

Monoclonal Antibodies and Their Uses in Lymphatic filariasis

Human lymphatic filariasis is most important vactor borne parasitic disease and is caused by two species of nematodes namely, *Wuchereria bancrofti* and *Brugia malayi*. This disease is endemic in India. A well known clinical symptom is swelling of legs, popularly known as elephantoid leg (elephant like). The methods developed to diagnosis the disease so far are not specific enough due to extensive sharing of antigen between helminths. Application of hybridoma-derived monoclonal antibodies to the diagnosis of lymphatic filariasis infection has offered a means for overcoming some of these limitations.

Vaccine Expression Systems

Once the specific protective proteins are identified, it is important to develop expression systems to produce large quantities of the specific protein in an economical fashion. At present, there are four different expression systems: (1) prokaryotic, (2) viruses, (3) eukaryotic and (4) mammalian.

1. **Prokaryotic expression** systems do not appear to be very useful for production of vaccines.
2. **Bacterial expression** systems is the viral protein produced in bacteria are often not folded properly for induction of the desired immune response. A considerable amount of activity is being directed towards using other viruses such as vaccinia, herpesviruses or adenoviruses to express specific viral proteins

in mammalian systems.

Virus expression or Vaccinia Expression

Another very popular expression system in the application of an insect virus, baculovirus, to produce high quantities of animal virus proteins in insect cells. Vaccinia virus will be used as an example where in a number of different viral proteins have been introduced into the vaccinia virus and are being used by a variety of different delivery systems to induce both local as well as systemic immunity. The advantages of vaccinia expression are that both a humoral, as well as a cellular immune response is ellicited. Even more attractive is that the vaccinia genome is very large and it is possible to delete large quantities of its genome and still maintain a viable virus. The non-essential vaccinia genes can be replaced with a number of genes coding for other proteins from other viruses. Expression of a number of genes in one virus would be much more economical to do than to culture each individual vaccine independently.

Vaccinia Virus Expression Systems is the thermo stable

Finally, vaccinia can replicate in a wide variety of hosts, making it attractive for controlling infectious diseases in veterinary medicine and in human medicine. Furthermore, the thermal stability and its ability to replicate in a wide variety of hosts provides the opportunity to immunize wildlife against infectious diseases that can be transmitted to domestic livestock.

Vaccinia Virus Expression Systems for Wild Animals

Recently this system has been used is the case of wildlife rabies, where vaccinia virus containing the rabies virus glycoproteins is incorporated in bait and seeded in rural areas by dropping the bait from planes. Foxes and raccoons (a North-American nocturnal carnivore), which can be carriers of rabies virus, would eat the bait and be immunized against rabies virus. Using this approach, the number of animals that can be immunized, thereby reducing the epideminological spread of virus in the environment.

Peptide vaccines

The introduction of the specific protein into various expression systems, help us to identify the specific epitopes involved in inducing protective immunity and synthesis of the peptide. Using monoclonal antibodies against different proteins of bovine rotavirus, one can identify a immunodominant neutralizing epitope on the outer coat glycoprotein of bovine rotavirus. This epitope is identified by the ability of monoclonal antibody directed against it to neutralize virus *in vitro* as well as to prevent diarrhea in animals *in vivo*. The advantage of peptide vaccines is that it is possible to identify crucial epitopes on all viruses. Synthetic peptides generally are not very immunogenic unless they are linked to specific carriers and incorporated in strong adjuvants. In addition to incorporate adjuvants into peptide vaccines, the peptides can be engineered in such a way that they are linked to specific carriers which can act as ideal delivery systems for presenting the important epitopes on the peptide. Experience with virus carriers for synthetic peptides clearly indicates that the immunogenicity of these peptides linked to virus carriers approaches that of whole virus.

Expression of Viral Genes in Eukaryotic Cells System

It is the most natural method of producing non-infectious viral vaccines. The reason for the attractiveness of eukaryotic cells is that the proper level and degree of glycosylation and folding is more natural than in prokaryotic systems. At present a number of viral genes have been successfully expressed in yeast, mammalian cells, and more recently in green algae and filamentous water fungi. Green algae and filamentous water fungi provide large quantities of cheap proteins with the correct post-translational modification required for proper recognition of the host's immune system.

Use of Yeast as an Expression System

Yeast (*S. cerevisiae*) is used as an expression system because of our extensive experience with this organism and animals already have antibodies to yeast. Further, yeast do not have any oncogenes. This makes vaccines expressed in yeast potentially safer than vaccines produced in mammalian cells. Unfortunately, in some cases yeast may over-glycosylate proteins, which may influence immune response to that specific protein. Thus, the degree of glycosylation of highly glycosylated proteins may preclude its use in vaccine development.

Use of mammalian cells

The ultimate eukaryotic expression system is the use of mammalian cells for the continuous production and secretion of viral proteins and glycoproteins. However, the level of expression is relatively low and the high cost of cell culture is serious disadvantages in the use of mammalian cells for production of vaccines for veterinary use.

Microcarriers

For mammalian, cells should be economically viable vehicle. The development of **microcarriers** to produce large quantities of mammalian cells in a very concentrated environment, as well as strong promotors is in need of development. Extensive progress is being made in developing microcarriers to culture mammalian cells in a continuous fashion. In parallel, with the development of microcarrier systems are the requirement for new media and profusion of the bioreactors so that cells can grow continuously with minimal manipulations.

Control of Hepatitis-B Virus through Vaccines

Hepatitis-B is a major public health problem. An estimated 210 million Hepatitis-B virus carriers are in the world. India is known to be the second largest reservoir of this virus. The disease caused by this virus is characterised by higher morbidity, mortality and an amazing speed of spread of infection. About 80% liver cancer is attributed to Hepatitis-B infection. Till date no chemotherapeutic agents are available for its treatment. Prophylaxis against this has come in practice in 1981 with the introduction of a plasma- derived vaccine. The scientists introduced this vaccine because of the possible danger of spread of other infections including AIDS. In 1986, a genetically engineered yeast-derived vaccine has been introduced that is of non-plasma in its origin and has widely been accepted by the public.

Hepatitis-B: Plasma Derived Vaccine

The discovery of a unique HB antigen called Australia antigen (HBs Ag) in 1965 in the blood of infected persons. This has lead to the development of two effective vaccines against this dreaded diseases: a plasma derived vaccine, in 1981, and a more acceptable recombinant DNA (r-DNA) technology based yeast derived vaccine, in

1986. Dr. Baruch Blumberg received Nobel prize in 1976 for his pioneering contributions to HB.

The HBs Ag is present in the serum of infected people as small particles of 22 nm size. These nucleic acid-free particles have no infectious properties. When blood serum taken from an acute case of HB, contained enough HBs Ag to accord at least this partial protection. In 1981, through this concept, HB vaccine was made available by Merck & Co., USA and Institute Pasture Production, Paris as Hepatavax-B.

Hepatitis-B: Genetically Engineered Vaccine

A second generation of HB-vaccine has been developed by employing the techniques of genetic engineering. The fragments of DNA are joint to the DNA of a suitable vector. The vactor may be plasmid, phage or a cosmid. This is done by the use of restriction endonucleases. Artificial *linkers* containing restriction sites can be attached to the foreign DNA fragments to allow insertion into the vector. Once joined, the composite DNA is introduced into the bacterial or eukaryotic cell system by either transformation or transfection. After successful integration of the composite genome into that of the host cell, it affects the metabolism of the host cell. This further, directs and to translate the additional genetic information packed in vactor DNA; and consequently leads to the synthesis os foreign proteins by the host cells. In this way host cell acts as mini-factory for the production of specific protein which is foreign to it.

MICROENCAPSULATION IN MEDICINE: A NEW APPROACH

Living mammalian cells can be microencapsulated within a semipermeable membrane for the purpose of an artificial endocrine pancreas or for the large-scale growth of mammalian cells. This system has been used for pancreatic islets to enable transplantation of islets into diabetic rats and for hybridomas, lymphoblastoid cells, and fibroblasts for the production of human monoclonal antibodies and interferon.

Polymeric Devices

They are used for replacement of many types of diseased tissues and organs in humans, *e.g.*, artificial joints, breast construction, large diameter vascular grafts, and controlled release of drugs. For these applications, insert surfaces, those do not interact with proteins or cells have been used to minimise long term tissue reactions. At the opposite extreme is the use of medical polymers as substrates for cell transplantation. In this case the ultimate replacement of the organ or tissue function depends primarily on the transplanted cells; the polymer plays an ancillary role as a substrate for adhesion of the cells and to give structure to the nascent tissue or organ.

PRODUCTION OF HUMAN INSULIN

Theoretically, there are two ways in which one could go about producing the insulin molecule. Insulin consists of two different protein chains, the so-called **A chain** and the **B chain**. One could produce the normal precursor of insulin, pro-insulin that is found in the pancreas. *Proinsulin* is a molecule that contains insulin but also contains an extra connecting peptide linking the two chains together. In the pancreas gland, this so-called connecting peptide is clipped out, leading to the production of insulin that is then released into the blood circulation system. One can mimic this process today in the laboratory and actually even in production, but up to the present it is not being used to produce human insulin on a large scale.

Presently the A chain and the B chain are made individually, and then are coupled in the plant to produce the bioactive insulin.

In separate plasmids, the genes have been introduced individually for the A chain and B chain of insulin, and then these plasmids have been transformed into bacterial cells. The *Escherichia coli* are then grown in large fermentation facilities. The product that is initially made is a large chimeric **protein consisting of the A chain or B chain** attached to the end of a naturally occurring *E. coli* protein. This protein is subjected to a cleavage reaction in which the A chain and the B chain are chemically cleaved away from the rest of the chimeric molecule. Then, following several further purification steps, these two chains are combined, and the biosynthetic human insulin is recovered and purified.

Large amounts of the gene product of this plasmid accumulate in the *E. coli*. A thin-section electron micrograph of *E. coli* producing human insulin polypeptide shows dense areas, which are deposits of that protein within the cell. The protein is produced in very substantial amounts and can occupy a major portion of the cell.

This is one of the advantages of biotechnology today-by using appropriate control systems and regulatory systems on the plasmid being dealt with, one can make the protein of interest a major portion of the total protein of the microorganism. It can become a very efficient process. It is a **crystalline protein**, and it has all of the characteristics of the insulin that is circulating in all of our bodies.

There are at least two advantages to being able to produce human insulin as opposed to continuing to use the pork and beef insulin that is currently used in many diabetic patients.

- **First**, the chemical structure of pork and beef insulin differs slightly from that of human insulin.
- The **second** advantage relates to the fact that currently produced pork and beef insulins are really by-products of the meat industry.

Some of the plasma proteins are albumin, globulins-α, β, γ, lipoproteins-α, β, plasminogen, fibrinogen, prothrombin and transferrin. **Albumin** is a protein and now manufactured using recombinant-DNA technology and many of the genes for other proteins in the plasma protein series have also been cloned.

GENETIC MAPPING FOR HUMAN HEALTH

Linkage Analysis is the Basis of Genetic Mapping

Now that we have assembled a set of markers with which to construct a genetic map we can move on to look at the mapping techniques themselves. These techniques are all based on *genetic linkage*.

It was first discovered by Bateson, Saunders and Punnett (1905), but not fully understood earlier. Thereafter, Thomas Hunt Morgan (1910-11) began his groundbreaking work with fruit flies in 1910-11.

The early geneticists of the 20th century recognized that genes are located in chromosomes and that each individual chromosome is inherited as an intact unit. In other words, if a *pair of genes* is located in the same chromosome then they are physically linked together and therefore should be inherited together.

This appeared to be a secure hypothesis, but when the early geneticists carried out genetic crosses similar to those published 40 years earlier by Mendel, they discovered the following:

1. That very few pairs of genes displayed complete linkage.
2. Pairs of genes were either inherited independently, as expected for genes in different chromosomes, or if they showed linkage then it was only partial linkage: (a) sometimes they were inherited together and (b) sometimes they were not.
3. The behavior of chromosomes during meiosis explains why genes display partial and not complete linkage.

Tomas Hunt Morgan made the conceptual leap between *partial linkage* and the behavior of chromosomes when the nucleus of a cell divides.

There are two types of nuclear division: mitosis and meiosis. Mitosis is more common, being the process by which the diploid nucleus of a somatic cell divides to produce two daughter nuclei, both of which are still diploid. Approximately 1017 mitoses are needed to produce all the cell required during a human lifetime. Before mitosis, begins, each chromosome in the nucleic is replicated, but the replicants do not immediately break away from one another. To begin with they remain attached at their centromeres, and they do not separate until later in mitosis when the chromosomes are distributed between the two new nuclei. It is obviously important that each daughter nucleus receives a complete set of chromosomes, and most of the intricacies of mitosis appear to be devoted to achieving this end.

Mitosis illustrates the basic events occurring during nuclear division but it is not directly relevant to genetic mapping. Instead, it is the distinctive features of meiosis that interest us. Meiosis occurs only in reproductive cells, and results in a diploid cell giving rise to four haploid gamete, each of which can subsequently fuse with a gamete of the opposite sex during sexual reproduction. The fact that meiosis results in four haploid cells whereas mitosis gives two diploid cells is easy to explain. meiosis involves two nuclear divisions - one after the other, critical difference between mitosis and meiosis is more subtle. Recall that in a diploid cell there are two separate copies of each chromosome. One can refer to these as pairs of homologous chromosomes. During mitosis, homologous chromosomes remain separate from one another, each member of the pair replicating and being passed to a daughter nucleus independently of its homolog. In meiosis, however, the pairs of homologous chromosomes are by no means independent. During meiosis I, each chromosome lines up with its homolog to form a bivalent. this occurs after each chromosome has replicated but before the replicated structure split, so the bivalent in fact contains to find its way into one of the four gametes that will be produced at the end of the meiosis. Within the bivalent, the chromosome arms (the chromatids) can undergo physical breakage and exchange of segments of DNA. This is called crossing-over or recombination and was discovered by the Belgian cytologist Janssens in 1909, just 2 years before Morgan started to think about partial linkage.

Partial linkage was discovered in the early 20th century. The parental cross gives the typical dihybrid result with all the F1 plants displaying the same phenotype, indicating that the dominant alleles are purple flowers and long pollen grains. The F1 cross gives unexpected results as the progeny show neither a 9: 3: 3: 1 ratio (expected for genes on different chromosomes) nor a 3:1 ratio (expected if the genes are completely linked). An unusual ratio is typical of partial linkage.

CHAPTER 20

Animal Health Biotechnology

Biotechnology is used to develop new medicines and treatments for farm and companion animals. Spending on animal health research and development totaled more than $400 million in 1999, more than 80 per cent of which, was in the development of pharmaceutical and biotechnology products. The Center for Veterinary Biologics at the U.S. Department of Agriculture has licensed 93 veterinary biotech products. In 1999, more than $4 billion was spent on animal health products in the United States, about two-thirds for livestock and farm animal care and the remainder on pets. The world's top 20 animal health companies recorded approximately $550 million in international sales of animal health biologicals in 1999. The following are the important aspects of animal health biotechnology:

1. Different strains of rabies vaccines are available today that protect companion animals as well as wildlife from contracting and spreading this deadly disease.
2. Genetic mapping and the development of DNA makers are being used to identify genes in chickens that have developed a resistance to Marek's disease, a virus-induced disease similar to cancer.
3. Recombinant protein vaccines are under development to control coccidiosis in chickens, which seriously impairs their growth.
4. DNA cloning technology is being used to research treatments for cryptosporidiosis, a parasitic disease found mostly in claves, but also in children and immuno-suppressed individuals, such as those inflicted with AIDS.
5. Sodium hyaluronate products, used in the treatment of joint disease in horses and other animals, decrease the effect of inflammatory enzymes in cartilage. In addition, a patented biofermentation process is now available that allows these therapies to be given intravenously.
6. A biological antitoxin prepared from the blood of healthy horses helps prevent and treat tetanus in domestic animals.
7. Many animal feed products are enhanced with proteins to boost nutrition and control disease.
8. Injectable products are being used to protect cattle from 36 stages of internal and external parasites, including ostertagia ostertagi, nematodes and trematodes.
9. A vaccine for brucellosis, or Bang's disease, is available for use in female cattle. This contagious cattle disease causes abortion and infertility in cattle and undulant fever in humans.
10. Monoclonal antibody technology is being used to develop treatments for canine lymphoma.
11. Other antibody technology is being used to develop diagnostics for bluetongue, avian leucosis, feline infectious peritonitis and feline immunodeficiency virus.
12. Using gene therapy, scientists have restored the vision of dogs with a version of Leber congenital amaurosis, an untreatable condition that causes almost complete blindness.
13. Drugs already on the market treat anemia and diabetes in companion animals.

14. A vaccine is available for feline leukemia, a deadly and debilitating disease.
15. Gene-based drugs and vaccines are being developed to treat arthritis, infectious disease and cancer in companion animals.
16. Diagnostics are available that better detect disease in livestock and pets.

WILDLIFE POPULATIONS AND HEALTH

DNA typing has become an important tool in wildlife population management. Scientists use the technique to determine how closely species are related to one another and whether endangered populations are being threatened by excessive inbreeding. Determine whether the animals being tested constitute a distinct species or a geographic variation of another species. This is important in identifying endangered species. Scientists performed DNA tests on fish caught in Alabama to determine if they were Mississippi River shovelnose sturgeon or Alabama sturgeon, which are believed to be extinct.

DNA testing has also been used to track the sale of caviar from endangered sturgeon on the world market. Some countries, including the United States, are using DNA testing to prevent the introduction of such caviar into their markets.

IMMUNITY

Immunity is the resistance to possible attack of an infectious agent *i.e.*, resistance to invasion and multiplication of a disease-producing organism. Acquired immunity is naturally acquired by natural infection (sub-clinical or overt) or by natural transfer of antibodies from mother to foetus or it is artificially acquired by vaccinations of specific antibodies. It is considered as actively acquired when the immune system is actively engaged in the process *e.g.*, by vaccination and natural infections; and passively acquired when immune system is not actively involved *e.g.*, administration of or placental transfer of antibodies. Immunity may be of two types: (i) **Innate immunity** and (ii) **Acquired immunity**. The acquired immunity is further classified as (a) **Active** (Natural and Artificial) and (b) **Passive** (Natural and Artificial). It is important to note that the terms **immunity** and **immunology** are *not synonymous. Immunity denotes only resistance to infection and involves non-specific factors* while *immunology is concerned with specific immune response to any foreign substance*; the response can even be harmful to the individual.

Innate Immunity

Resistance to certain infections is a natural gift and is seen in all forms of life. This natural non-susceptibility to infection is called innate immunity. The mechanism of its development is not known. Innate immunity may be species specific, race specific or individual specific.

Species specific immunity

Certain infections occurs only in particular species *e.g.*, syphilis, gonorrhoea, leprosy, measles, diphtheria, cholera, and many other diseases occur in man only but not in lower animals. Birds are immune to tetanus, a disease affecting man and certain lower animals. Conversely some disease occurring in animals are not found in man *e.g.*, rinder pest, chicken cholera etc. It seems that the tissues of one or some other species are unsuitable to serve as host to certain parasites but those of others provide congenial home for them.

Race specific immunity

All races of same species are not found to exhibit the same degree of susceptibility or resistance to infection *e.g.*, Algerian race of sheep is immune to anthrax, which is a common disease of other races of sheep. So far, no definite evidence of racial immunity in human beings have been reported.

Individual specific immunity

Some differences in susceptibility to certain infection do occur in individuals of same species, *e.g.*, individual of haterozygous traits of sickle cell anemia, thalassaemia, haemoglobin `C' disease, and deficiency of glucose-6-phosphate dehydrogenase are resistant to some types of malaria. Individuals of blood group `O' and `B' are more resistant to smallpox than those of blood group A.

Non Specific Defence Mechanisms

A number of defense mechanisms are operative non-specifically against a large number of microorganisms. They are: 1. Mechanical barriers. 2. Antagonism of indigenous flora. 3. Microbicidal substances of body fluids and those liberated by damaged cells. 4. Phagocytosis by microphages and macrophages. 5. N.K. cells and soluble factors. 6. Acquired nonspecific defence mechanisms.

Mechanical barriers

Skin and mucous membranes prevent access of many organisms to deeper tissues. Ciliary movements in epithelial cells of respiratory mucosa and peristaltic movements of intestine push the organisms away before they could invade. These are mechanical barriers.

Antagonism by indigenous flora

The normal microbial flora of mucous membranes prevent proliferation of pathogenic organisms on account of substrates competition, or by producing inhibitory substance *e.g.*, hydrogenperoxide, antibiotics or by altering the pH to make it unsuitable for the growth of other.

Bactericidal substances

The substances present in blood and body fluids have microbicidal activity. They are:

1. Long chain fatty acids present in skin secretions are lethal to many bacteria.
2. Lactenin of milk is bactericidal for *Strept. pyogenes.*
3. Hydrochloric acid of gastric juice is lethal to many bacteria.

Lysozyme which is a mucolytic enzyme (muramidase) present in many secretions, it is highly bactericidal for gram positive bacilli which splits their cell wall leading to leakage of their cell contents.

Basic polypeptides *e.g.*, spermine, spermidine, protamine derived from damaged blood and tissue cells are bactericidal. Other metabolites like lactic acid, carbondioxide which accumulate in an inflammed area and the depletion of oxygen by the inflammatory cell provide unfavourable conditions for growth of pathogenic organisms.

Properdin is lytic specially to gram negative bacilli. With complement and Mg^{++} it forms properdin system which provide non-specific immunity through the alternate pathway of complement activation.

A number of **plasma components** like C-reactive protein, α-1 antitrypsin, α-2 macroglobulin, fibrinogen, ceruloplasmin, C_9, factor B, collectively termed acute phase proteins show a marked increase in response to infection or tissue injury.

Antiviral substances: Nasal secretion and serum of normal human beings have the ability to neutralise certain viruses *e.g.*, influenza A and B, vaccinia, mumps and Newcastle viruses. This is due to the presence of certain enzymes like alkaline and acid phosphatases, and properdin in serum and secretions. They have the viricidal activities. **Interferon** is a non-specific antiviral agent. It is synthesized by cells in response to viral infections. It inhibits intracellular replication of viruses.

PHAGOCYTOSIS

The phagocytic cells, microphages and some macrophages migrate under the influence of chemotaxins to the site of infection and phagocytose the infective agents. Within the phagocytes the organisms are killed and finally disintegrated. The fixed marcophages *i.e.*, reticuloendothelial cells remove the organisms circulating in the blood and lymph. Phagocytosis is enhanced by opsonins. There are non-Non specific mechanism of killing of invaded bacteria specific opsonins, which increase phagocytic activity of phagocytes and specific ones produced following infection by a particular organism, which make the latter more susceptible to phagocytosis. When the organism is larger than phagocytes, then a number of phagocytes (macrophages) join or fuse together to form giant cell to engulf the organism.

The phagocytosed particle comes to lie in a vacuole called phagosome within the phagocytic cell. A lysosome granule then fuses with the vacuole to form phagolysosome in which the ingested microbe is killed/digested by a number of ways.

1. Phagocytosis is associated with marked increase in activity of hexose monophosphate shunt providing NADPH and the contact of microbe results in activation of NADPH oxidase of plasma membrane. This results in formation of superoxide ions *e.g.*, hydrogen peroxide, singlet oxygen hydroxyl radicals all of which are powerful microbicidal agent. The combination of peroxide, myeloperoxide and halide ions constitute potent helogenating system, which is bactericidal and viricidal.
2. Beside these low pH, lysosome, lactoferrin and cationic protein, which are not oxygen dependent function as bacteriostatic or bactericidal. The proteolytic and hydrolytic enzymes digest the killed organisms.

There is also an extracellular release of lysosomes during phagocytosis. They may play an amplifying role.

Natural killer (NK) cells and soluble factors

Natural killer cells are leucocytes. They are capable of recognizing cell surface changes on virus-infected cells. They bind to the target cells and can kill them. These are activated by interferons, which are themselves components of innate immune system. Interferon are produced by virus infected cell and some times also by lymphocytes. Apart from the activation of NK cells interferon induces a state of viral resistance in uninfected tissue cells.

Acquired Non-specific Defence Mechanisms

Injection of endotoxin obtained from Gram negative bacilli or B.C.G. vaccine or killed mycobacteria increases resistance of the host to infection with a wide range of antigenically unrelated microorganisms. This is because of increased phagocytic activity of phagocytes.

Acquired Specific Immunity

This immunity is due to specific antibodies or sensitized lymphocytes derived from immune system following antigenic challenge or transfused from an immune individual, accordingly, it is considered as actively or passively acquired immunity respectively. Both of these could be naturally or artificially acquired.

Naturally Acquired Passive Immunity

This occurs on account of transplacental transfer of antibodies (IgG) from mother to foetus and it lasts for nearly six months after birth. Secretory antibodies (IgA) present in the milk also provide local immunity in gastrointestinal tract of the breast fed infants.

Artificially Acquired Passive Immunity

This is achieved by administering specific antibodies or sensitized lymphocytes from an individual who possesses specific immunity to a particular infective agent. Usually antibodies against an organism or its toxin are raised in suitable animals by repeated administration of suitable antigen. The serum of such animals is used as a therapeutic measure in treatment of the disease caused by the infective agent or as a prophylactic measure to prevent infection in individuals who are likely to suffer by the disease in near future. For example **anti-tetanus serum** (A.T.S.) or antidiphtheric serum and are obtained from horses, immunised with corresponding toxoids. Since in such therapy foreign proteins are injected, the patient is always at risk of developing hypersensitivity reaction to the foreign serum-proteins *i.e.*, serum sickness and immune complex glomerulonephritis. Homologous gammaglobulins from convalescent patients are also in use for this purpose, these will have relatively less chances of development of serum sickness. Sensitized lymphocyte preparations are being used to provide specific cellular immunity in individual deficient of this immunity.

Naturally Acquired Active Immunity

Naturally active immunity is acquired by natural infections by the organisms, in large majority of cases this occurs by sub-clinical infections, which pass unnoticed, and in some it follows overt infections. This immunity is due to the formation of antibody as well as sensitized lymphocyte population following antigenic challenge of the infecting microbes.

Artificially Acquired Active Immunity

Artificial active immunisation is usually obtained by vaccinations or in case of organisms which produce potent exotoxins, by administration of toxoids.

ANIMAL VACCINE: DEVELOPMENT AND PRODUCTION

Vaccine is an antigenic preparation administered with the object of stimulating the recipient's specific defence mechanisms in respect of given pathogen(s) or toxic agent(s). Some vaccines (*e.g.*, the Sabin vaccine) are given orally while other (*e.g.*, the Salk vaccine) are administered parentally. Vaccines are of following four main categories:

1. Inactivated vaccines *e.g.*, vaccines against typhoid and cholera.
2. Those comprising suspensions of life (attenuated) pathogens, *e.g.*, vaccines against yellow fever and tuberculosis.
3. Toxoids.

4. They are comprising of solutions or suspensions of the antigenic extracts of specific pathogens, *e.g.*, the vaccine containing polysaccharide capsular material of *Streptococcus pneumoniae*.

Uses of Vaccines: The use of vaccines is extremely important for preventing various serious diseases. The development and production of these vaccines constitute an important function of the pharmaceutical industry. Vaccines are produced either by mutant strains of pathogens or by attenuating or inactivating virulent pathogens without removing the antigens necessary for eliciting the immune response.

Production of Vaccines: Using various strains of viruses production of vaccines against viral diseases is done. They are grown by using embryonated eggs. Individuals who are allergic to eggs cannot be given such vaccine preparations. Viral vaccines are produced by using tissue culture techniques. For example, the older rabies vaccine, which was produced in embryonated duck eggs and had painful side effects, has been replaced with a vaccine produced in human fibroblast tissue cultures, which has far fewer side effects. The production of vaccines by bacteria, fungi, and protozoa generally involves growing the microbial strain on an artificial medium, which minimizes problems with allergic response. Vaccines should be tested and standardized before use.

The majority of licensed vaccines for humans and animals presently in use are produced by conventional methods by manipulating the genes of bacteria causing diseases, and using the restructured genes for making antibodies. Another approach is to clone the genes for coat protein (antigens) of viruses in bacteria and preparing vaccines from bacteria. This is less hazardous than growing the whole virus in the laboratory. Some viruses like the smallpox and marburg virus are so dangerous that one does not actually want to propagate them in the laboratory. These include killed vaccines and live attenuated or inactivated vaccines. At present, a large number of viral vaccines are of the killed variety.

Advantages with Killed Vaccines

One of the major advantages of such vaccines is that they are relatively stable under environmental conditions therefore, it is not as crucial to maintain a cold chain to ensure efficacy of the vaccines.

In specific disease situations such as rabies virus, clinicians are often reluctant to use live viral vaccines, because of the fear that they may inject themselves with the vaccine and there may be some adverse side effects. Although this possibility is extremely remote, the psychological trauma of injection with a virus such as rabies is sufficiently great to discourage some clinicians from using live virus vaccines.

Disadvantages with Killed Vaccines

1. They do not replicate within the host and, therefore, large amounts of antigen are required for injection before induction of immunity. Since these vaccines are often produced in foreign tissue there is also the possibility of reactions developing against foreign proteins.
2. Since the vaccines are killed, they generally are injected intramuscularly.
3. A killed vaccine is more effective against **systemic viruses** than against viruses which replicate in **local mucosal sites**. This latter disadvantage has lead to the development of a large number of attenuated vaccines.

Advantages with Attenuated Vaccines

1. The main advantage of attenuated vaccines results primarily from their ability to replicate in the host.
2. Since their mode of action is similar to natural infections, immunity is generally of a broader spectrum than it is with killed virus vaccines. Thus they can induce a range of immune responses both locally, as well as systemically.
3. Attenuated vaccines develop immunity for longer duration than that of killed virus vaccines.
4. Since the virus replicates in the host and produces large quantities of proteins to which the host responds to the possibility of injecting foreign proteins is dramatically reduced with attenuated virus vaccines.

Disadvantages with Attenuated Vaccines

1. Since the vaccines are produced by passage in culture, to induce random mutation(s) or mutated with a specific agent and thereby reduce virulence, it is possible that passage in the natural host may result in reversion back to virulence, *e.g.*, attenuated polio virus. In the case of polio, reversion can occur within a few days of oral immunization.
2. Interference is also a potential problem. When viruses are grown in culture, there is a possibility to have other contaminating viruses present in it. For example the presence of BVD virus (a ubiquitous virus) in viral vaccines grown for immunizing cattle is very common. This virus is present in many of the cell lines and fatal bovine sera than are used for growing bovine viruses. Such interference may result in reduced replication of the attenuated virus vaccine and thus, reduced immunity.
3. Live attenuated virus vaccines are also extremely susceptible to environmental factors which may reduce their efficacy upon storage.
4. The attenuated virus vaccines induce latent infections and abortions if not administered properly or if administered at the wrong time in the animal's life.

Our Limitations

Killed and attenuated virus vaccines have not eliminated viral diseases (with the exception of small pox) completely. We still need to produce better vaccines that may be more efficacious and safer for use in human and animal medicine. There are a number of viruses for which we do not have vaccines due to the inability to grow virus in culture or in other economically acceptable culturing media. Some viruses may be of suppressive nature or impossible to attenuate by passage. In order to develop vaccines against exotic viruses, one requires excessive laboratory containment or restricts the use and application of such vaccines. Some of the newer technologies available would greatly eliminate some of these restrictions.

New Technologies

Newer technologies are available and used to produce new virus vaccines. These technologies are based on classical approaches (reassortants, temperature sensitive or cold adapted, heterologous vaccines). These are based on the ability to manipulate the genetic material of the viruses in such a way as to either reduce the virulence of a specific virus in a specific way or identify the specific protective proteins and express them in a foreign host.

Steps of Sub-unit Vaccines Production

1. Identify protective proteins or epitopes on the proteins. Once this is done an individual can either produce a sub-unit vaccine by recombinant DNA technology or by synthetic peptide technology.
2. Identify gene coding for the protein.
3. Clone the gene coding for the specific protein and express it in a suitable expression system.
4. Purify the protective protein to homogeneity using bovine herpesvirus-1. BHV-1 has four major glycoproteins: GVP I, GVP II, GVP III and GVP IV.
5. Monoclonal antibodies immunosorbent columns are prepared and used for purification of large quantities of the BHV-1 glycoproteins. These glycoproteins are then mixed with the adjuvant avridine and used to immunize animals against BHV-1 virus.

Monoclonal Antibodies and their uses in Lymphatic filariasis

Human lymphatic filariasis is most important vactor borne parasitic disease and is caused by two species of nematodes namely, *Wuchereria bancrofti* and *Brugia malayi*. This disease is endemic in India. A well known clinical symptom is swelling of legs, popularly known as elephantoid leg (elephant like). The methods developed to diagnosis the disease so far are not specific enough due to extensive sharing of antigen between helminths. Application of hybridoma-derived monoclonal antibodies to the diagnosis of lymphatic filariasis infection has offered a means for overcoming some of these limitations.

Vaccine Expression Systems

Once the specific protective proteins are identified, it is important to develop expression systems to produce large quantities of the specific protein in an economical fashion. At present, there are four different expression systems: (1) prokaryotic, (2) viruses, (3) eukaryotic and (4) mammalian.

1. **Prokaryotic expression** systems do not appear to be very useful for production of vaccines.
2. **Bacterial expression** systems is the viral protein produced in bacteria are often not folded properly for induction of the desired immune response. A considerable amount of activity is being directed towards using other viruses such as vaccinia, herpesviruses or adenoviruses to express specific viral proteins in mammalian systems.

Virus Expression or Vaccinia Expression

Another very popular expression system in the application of an insect virus (baculovirus) to produce high quantities of animal virus proteins in insect cells. Vaccinia virus will be used as an example where in a number of different viral proteins have been introduced into the vaccinia virus and are being used by a variety of different delivery systems to induce both local as well as systemic immunity. The advantages of vaccinia expression are that both a humoral, as well as a cellular immune response is ellicited. Even more attractive is that the vaccinia genome is very large and it is possible to delete large quantities of its genome and still maintain a viable virus. The non-essential vaccinia genes can be replaced with a number of genes coding for other proteins from other viruses. Expression of a number of genes in one virus would be much more economical to do than to culture each individual vaccine independently.

Vaccinia Virus Expression Systems is the Thermo Stable

Finally, vaccinia can replicate in a wide variety of hosts, making it attractive for controlling infectious diseases in veterinary medicine and in human medicine. Furthermore, the thermal stability and its ability to replicate in a wide variety of hosts provide the opportunity to immunize wildlife against infectious diseases that can be transmitted to domestic livestock.

Vaccinia Virus Expression Systems for Wild Animals

Recently this system has been used is the case of wildlife rabies, where vaccinia virus containing the rabies virus glycoproteins is incorporated in bait and seeded in rural areas by dropping the bait from planes. Foxes and raccoons (a North-American nocturnal carnivore), which can be carriers of rabies virus, would eat the bait and be immunized against rabies virus. Using this approach, the number of animals that can be immunized, thereby reducing the epideminological spread of virus in the environment.

Peptide Vaccines: The introduction of the specific protein into various expression systems, help us to identify the specific epitopes involved in inducing protective immunity and synthesis of the peptide. Using monoclonal antibodies against different proteins of bovine rotavirus, one can identify a immunodominant neutralizing epitope on the outer coat glycoprotein of bovine rotavirus. This epitope is identified by the ability of monoclonal antibody directed against it to neutralize virus *in vitro* as well as to prevent diarrhea in animals *in vivo*. The advantage of peptide vaccines is that it is possible to identify crucial epitopes on all viruses. Synthetic peptides generally are not very immunogenic unless they are linked to specific carriers and incorporated in strong adjuvants. In addition to incorporate adjuvant into peptide vaccines, the peptides can be engineered in such a way that they are linked to specific carriers, which can act as ideal delivery systems for presenting the important epitopes on the peptide. Experience with virus carriers for synthetic peptides clearly indicates that the immunogenicity of these peptides linked to virus carriers approaches that of whole virus.

Expression of Viral Genes in Eukaryotic Cells System

It is the most natural method of producing non-infectious viral vaccines. The reason for the attractiveness of eukaryotic cells is that the proper level and degree of glycosylation and folding is more natural than in prokaryotic systems. At present a number of viral genes have been successfully expressed in yeast, mammalian cells, and more recently in green algae and filamentous water fungi. Green algae and filamentous water fungi provide large quantities of cheap protcins with the correct post-translational modification required for proper recognition of the host's immune system.

Use of Yeast as an Expression System

Yeast (*S. cerevisiae*) is used as an expression system because of our extensive experience with this organism and animals already have antibodies to yeast. Further, yeast do not have any oncogenes. This makes vaccines expressed in yeast potentially safer than vaccines produced in mammalian cells. Unfortunately, in some cases yeast may over-glycosylate proteins, which may influence immune response to that specific protein. Thus, the degree of glycosylation of highly glycosylated proteins may preclude its use in vaccine development.

Use of Mammalian Cells

The ultimate eukaryotic expression system is the use of mammalian cells for the continuous production and secretion of viral proteins and glycoproteins. However, the level of expression is relatively low and the high cost of cell culture is serious disadvantages in the use of mammalian cells for production of vaccines for veterinary use.

Microcarriers: These are economically viable vehicle for mammalian cells. The development of **microcarriers** to produce large quantities of mammalian cells in a very concentrated environment, as well as strong promotors is in need of development. Extensive progress is being made in developing microcarriers to culture mammalian cells in a continuous fashion. In parallel, with the development of microcarrier systems are the requirement for new media and profusion of the bioreactors so that cells can grow continuously with minimal manipulations.

Control of Hepatitis-B Virus through Vaccines

Hepatitis-B is a major public health problem. An estimated 210 million Hepatitis-B virus carriers are in the world. India is known to be the second largest reservoir of this virus. The disease caused by this virus is characterised by higher morbidity, mortality and an amazing speed of spread of infection. About 80% liver cancer is attributed to Hepatitis-B infection. Till date no chemotherapeutic agents are available for its treatment. Prophylaxis against this has come in practice in 1981 with the introduction of a plasma derived vaccine. The scientists were fearing to introduce this vaccine because of the possible danger of spread of other infections including AIDS. In 1986, a genetically engineered yeast-derived vaccine has been introduced that is of non-plasma in its origin and has widely been accepted by the public.

Hepatitis-B: Plasma Derived Vaccine

The discovery of a unique HB antigen called Australia antigen (HBs Ag) in 1965 in the blood of infected persons. This has lead to the development of two effective vaccines against this dreaded diseases: a plasma derived vaccine, in 1981, and a more acceptable recombinant DNA (r-DNA) technology based yeast derived vaccine, in 1986. Dr. Baruch Blumberg received Nobel prize in 1976 for his pioneering contributions to HB.

The HBs Ag is present in the serum of infected people as small particles of 22 nm size. These nucleic acid-free particles have no infectious properties. When blood serum taken from an acute case of HB, contained enough HBs Ag to accord at least this partial protection. In 1981, through this concept, HB vaccine was made available by Merck & Co., USA and Institute Pasture Production, Paris as Hepatavax-B.

Hepatitis-B: Genetically Engineered Vaccine

A second generation of HB-vaccine has been developed by employing the techniques of genetic engineering. The fragments of DNA are joint to the DNA of a suitable vector. The vactor may be plasmid, phage or a cosmid. This is done by the use of restriction endonucleases. Artificial *linkers* containing restriction sites can be attached to the foreign DNA fragments to allow insertion into the vector. Once joined, the composite DNA is introduced into the bacterial or eukaryotic cell system by either transformation or transfection. After successful integration of the composite genome into that of the host cell, it affects the metabolism of the host cell. This further, directs and to translate the additional genetic information packed in vactor DNA; and consequently leads to the synthesis os foreign proteins by the host cells. In this way host cell acts as mini-factory for the production of specific protein which is foreign to it.

Microencapsulation in Medicine: A New Approach

Living mammalian cells can be microencapsulated within a semipermeable membrane for the purpose of an artificial endocrine pancreas or for the large-scale growth of mammalian cells. This system has been used for pancreatic islets to enable transplantation of islets into diabetic rats and for hybridomas, lymphoblastoid cells, and fibroblasts for the production of human monoclonal antibodies and interferon.

Polymeric Devices

They are used for replacement of many types of diseased tissues and organs in humans, *e.g.*, artificial joints, breast construction, large diameter vascular grafts, and controlled release of drugs. For these applications, insert surfaces, those do not interact with proteins or cells have been used to minimise long-term tissue reactions. At the opposite extreme is the use of medical polymers as substrates for cell transplantation. In this case the ultimate replacement of the organ or tissue function depends primarily on the transplanted cells; the polymer plays an ancillary role as a substrate for adhesion of the cells and to give structure to the nascent tissue or organ.

Production of Human Insulin

Theoretically, there are two ways in which one could go about producing the insulin molecule. Insulin consists of two different protein chains, the so-called **A chain** and the **B chain**. One could produce the normal precursor of insulin, proinsulin that is found in the pancreas. *Proinsulin* is a molecule that contains insulin but also contains an extra connecting peptide linking the two chains together. In the pancreas gland, this so-called connecting peptide is clipped out, leading to the production of insulin that is then released into the blood circulation system. One can mimic this process today in the laboratory and actually even in production, but up to the present it is not being used to produce human insulin on a large scale.

Presently the A chain and the B chain are made individually, and then are coupled in the plant to produce the bioactive insulin.

In separate plasmids, the genes have been introduced individually for the A chain and B chain of insulin, and then these plasmids have been transformed into bacterial cells. The *Escherichia coli* are then grown in large fermentation facilities. The product that is initially made is a large chimeric **protein consisting of the A chain or B chain** attached to the end of a naturally occurring *E. coli* protein. This protein is subjected to a cleavage reaction in which the A chain and the B chain are chemically cleaved away from the rest of the chimeric molecule. Then, following several further purification steps, these two chains are combined, and the biosynthetic human insulin is recovered and purified.

Large amounts of the gene product of this plasmid accumulate in the *E. coli*. A thin-section electron micrograph of *E. coli* producing human insulin polypeptide shows dense areas, which are deposits of that protein within the cell. The protein is produced in very substantial amounts and can occupy a major portion of the cell.

This is one of the advantages of biotechnology today-by using appropriate control systems and regulatory systems on the plasmid being dealt with, one can make the protein of interest a major portion of the total protein of the microorganism. It can become a very efficient process. It is a **crystalline protein**, and it has all of the characteristics of the insulin that is circulating in all of our bodies.

There are at least two advantages to being able to produce human insulin as opposed to continuing to use the pork and beef insulin that is currently used in many diabetic patients.

- **First**, the chemical structure of pork and beef insulin differs slightly from that of human insulin.
- The **second** advantage relates to the fact that currently produced pork and beef insulins are really by-products of the meat industry.

Some of the plasma proteins are albumin, globulins-α, β, γ, lipoproteins-α, β, plasminogen, fibrinogen, prothrombin and transferrin. **Albumin** is a protein and now manufactured using recombinant-DNA technology and many of the genes for other proteins in the plasma protein series have also been cloned.

Types of Vaccines

Killed or attenuated microorganisms used for artificial active immunisation are called vaccines. The objective of vaccination is to provide effective immunity by establishing adequate level of antibodies and a primed population of cells, which can rapidly expand on renewed contact with antigen. There are two types of vaccines: Killed vaccines and live vaccines.

Killed Vaccines

Suspensions of organisms in their virulent phase are killed by heat or antiseptic, care being taken not to denature important antigens by excessive heat or strong detergents. Two or more injections of these are given preferably at 4 weeks or longer intervals. Examples of killed vaccine are TAB vaccine for enteric fever, whooping cough vaccine, salk vaccine of poliomyelitis, antirabies vaccine etc.

1. **TAB Vaccine:** This is prepared from smooth culture of *S. typhi*, *S. paratyphi* A and *S. paratyphi* B. It is the suspension of these organisms containing 1000 million bacilli of *S. typhi*, 750 million bacilli each of *S. paratyphi* A and *S. paratyphi* B per millilitre sterilized by heating at 60°C for thirty minutes and preserved with 0.5% phenol. It is used for vaccination against enteric fever. The vaccine provides immunity lasting for about 2 years. Booster dose of 0.5 ml is given after every two years to provide a lasting immunity.
2. **Whooping Cough Vaccine:** This should be given to every child to prevent whooping cough. Formalin or formalin merthiolatie killed *Bordetella pertusis* organisms in a suspension of 200,000 million organism/ml are given in three doses of 1ml each intramuscularly at interval of 4 weeks. Vaccination of infants has been found to reduce the infection rate from 90% to 100% in endemic area.
3. **Salk Vaccine of Poliomyelitis:** This is a formalin-inactivated vaccine containing all the three polio viruses, type 1, type 2 and type 3. Two doses of 1 ml of it are given intramuscularly at an interval of 3 weeks. Thereafter, two booster doses are required.
4. **Antirabies Vaccine (Sample Vaccine):** It is prepared from sheep brain infected with fixed rabies virus. A 4% suspension of brain in which the virus is

inactivated by 0.5% phenol at 37° C is used. A new rabies vaccine has been introduced from virus grown in human diploid cells (HDC). This vaccine is near to perfect as regards potency, safety, tolerability but very expensive to produce.

5. **Purified Chick Embryo Cell (PCEC) vaccine:** It is similar in potency to HDC vaccine. This virus was adopted to chick embryo cells by 25 passages, inactivated by 0.025% β-propiolactone and purified by continuous zonal centrifugation. A complete course of vaccinations for adults and children consists of a total of 6 injections given intramuscularly one on each of the days 0, 3, 7, 14, 30 and 90.
6. **Meningococcal Polysaccharide Vaccine:** It is composed of purified group A and group C meningococcal polysaccharide 50 micrograms each lyophilized to be reconstituted in physiological buffer 0.5 ml. It is given subcutaneously.

Live Vaccine

Attenuation results in loss of pathogenecity without loss of antigenecity of the microorganisms, which is usually achieved by growing the microorganisms repeatedly on artificial media, sometimes in adverse conditions or in unnatural hosts. Such organisms multiply within the body, like the pathogens, without producing the diseases yet **inducing immune responses** like their pathogenic counterparts. The immune response occurs largely at the site of natural infection. Some of the commonly used live vaccines are as follows:

1. **Sabin Poliomyelitis Vaccine:** Attenuation of poliovirus is obtained by repeatedly growing a relatively avirulent strains on monkey kidney cell lines. All the three types 1, 2 and 3 strains are used. It is given orally in 3 doses each of 0.15 ml (3 drops) spaced an interval of 4-8 weeks.
2. **B.C.G. vaccine:** *Bacile Calmette et Guerin* (BCG) is a bovine strain of *Myco. tuberculosis* that had been cultured for many years on a bile potato medium by two French scientists - Calmette and Guerin. It is given intracutaneously in dose of 0.1 ml containing 0.05-0.1 mg. of moist weight of bacilli (1-2 million viable bcilli).
3. **Live Attenuated Measles Vaccine (Schsarz strains):** It is prepared from chick embryo tissue culture. Each dose of the reconstituted vaccine contains not less than 1000 TCID of measles virus. Reconstituted 0.5 ml of vaccine is injected subcutaneously. It confers long lasting immunity in most subjects.
4. **Small Pox vaccine:** It is prepared from vaccinia virus obtained from vasicles of artificially infected calves for this purpose. The crude pulp obtained by curettage is homogenised and treated with 2 parts of 1% phenol and then diluted 4 times with glycerol saline or phosphate buffer and stored at 10° C or freeze dried. The latter is recommended for fieldwork, it can be reconstituted immediately before use without loss of potency. Vaccine can also be prepared from cultures on chick embryo.

TOXOIDS

Toxoids are preparations of toxins inactivated by formalin. They retain the antigenic potency and thus like toxins, can induce antitoxin formation, therefore, they are used for artificial immunisation to protect against toxic effects of infection by exotoxin producing organisms.

Diphtheria Toxoid

Formal toxoid of diphtheria toxin is given in 3 intramuscular doses each of 1 ml at 4 weekly intervals. Toxoid antitoxin floccules (TAF) have been used to avoid risk of toxic effects of any unaltered remnant of toxin molecule. Purified diphtheria toxoid *per se* is a poor antigen, alum precipitated toxoid (APT) or purified toxoid absorbed on hydrated aluminium phosphate (PTAP) has been introduced. These are given in two divided doses of 0.5 ml at an interval of four weeks.

Tetanus Toxoid

Formal toxoid of tetanus toxin is given in three doses of 0.5 ml each intramuscularly at an interval of 6-12 weeks between first two doses and 6-12 months between second and third dose. A reinforcing dose should be given after 5-10 years for two or more occasions to maintain immunity. Purified tetanus toxoid absorbed on aluminium phosphate (Tetanus Vaccine-absorbed) is given in two doses each of 0.5 ml injected deep intramuscularly at an interval of 4-6 weeks between the doses. A booster dose of 0.5 ml is recommended 6-8 months later and whenever there is a tetanus prone injury.

Diptheria, Tetanus and Pertusis Vaccine (Absorbed) or D.P.T. Vaccine

This is composed of purified absorbed diphtheria toxoid 50 Lf, purified absorbed tetanus toxoid 10 Lf, killed pertusis organisms 40,000 million and aluminium phosphate gel 3.0 mg per ml. of vaccine. It is given in 3 doses of 0.5 ml intramuscularly at intervals of 4-6 weeks in children of 4 months age. A booster dose of 0.5 ml is recommended at 6 to 8 months later. If primary inoculation is done after one year of age, booster dose should be given at the age of 3 to 5 years (school entry).

INTERFERON OR ANTIVIRAL SUBSTANCES

Interferon provides **first line of defense** against virus infection; in animals treated with antiserum to interferon, virus infections progress much more rapidly and cause much more severe disease than in untreated animals. Interferons are cellular protein. Healthy cell do not contain detectable amounts of interferon; the formation of interferons must be included. These cellular proteins are host cell species-specific. Sometimes this specificity is very narrow.

Nature of Interferon

Human interferons are proteins that are about 145 amino acids long (molecular weight about 17,000). Three types of interferon are known: IFN-α, IFN-β (produced predominantly by leukocytes and fibroblasta respectively) and IFN-γ or earlier known as *immune* or type-2 interferon, which is produced by unsynthesized lymphoid cells in response to mitogens and by sensitized lymphocytes when stimulated with specific antigen.

Assay of Interferon

The antiviral activity of interferon is usually assayed by exposing cells to serially diluted interferon preparations for about 12 hours and then infecting them with standard amount of virus known to produce a certain number of plaque. The titer of an interferon preparation is the reciprocal of that dilution that reduces this number by 50 per cent.

Nature of Interferon Genes

There are 14 different human IFN-α-genes, one IFN-β- gene and one IFN-γ-genes. All these genes encode proteins that are exactly the same length, namely 166 amino acids long.

Biological Activity of Interferon

Interferons are powerful cellular regulators that interact with cell through specific glycoprotein receptors. There are separate receptors from IFN-α, IFN-β-and IFN-γ-. The binding of interferon to their receptors activates second messengers that induce formation of a series of proteins. Some of these proteins induce an antiviral state; others are surface glycoproteins that cause the cells to be recognized by the cells of the immune system, other have functions that have yet to be identified. Interferons interfere with virus multiplication; this is the property for which they are named. They interfere with the ability of parental or early viral messenger RNA molecules to be translated which results in the synthesis of specific type of proteins, no progeny viral genomes are formed, and infection is aborted.

Interferon affect variety of cell functions, which are mediated by the proteins, the formation of which is induced by exposure to interferon. Most remarkable of these effects are those mediated by IFN-γ-. This interferon is a lymphokine secreted by activated T lymphocytes. It activates macrophages, stimulates B cells, increases fibroblast and endothelial cell resistance to many non-viral parasites, and modulates cell surface proteins central immune regulation.

INTERFERENCE

An animal virologist, Schlesinger (1949) defined interference, when one virus modifies cells of a host so that the second virus or a closely related strain of the first virus cannot multiply normally or cannot produce characteristic injury. Henle (1950) restricted the term interference to the inhibitory effect of one virus or a component of it, upon propagation of another. Bennett (1951) used the term in sense of Schlesinger, but recognised that there might be a basic difference between interference of two closely related (species) strains of a plant virus and that between unrelated viruses.

The phenomenon was thought at one time to be restricted to strains of the same virus or at least to viruses having properties in common. Kassanis (1963), however, concluded that based on present knowledge, interference is more complete, but not necessarily of a different type between strains than between unrelated viruses and that more evidence is needed to decide whether the interference is also most frequent between strains. It refers to those instances when one virus interfere either with the multiplication of a second unrelated virus or with its disease producing capabilities (Price, 1964). For example, when PVY and Tobacco Etch Virus (TEV) are introduced separately or concurrently into potato or tobacco plants, multiplication of PVY is prevented or tobacco plants, multiplication of PVY may even be replaced by TEV. The mild strain of TEV reduces the concentration of PVY, does not prevent its multiplication completely. TEV and PVY are not closely related on the basis of properties and serological reactions.

Ross (1950) observed interference between unrelated viruses. He found that in the potato seedling USDA-41956, which is resistant to PVY, lesion formation by PVY was partially inhibited, if the inoculum contained PYX. Furthermore, the number of lesions produced by PVY was progressively reduced as the concentration of PVX in the inoculum was increased.

Interference within Inoculated Leaf

When a host leaf is inoculated with one virus reduces its susceptibility for another unrelated virus. When *Physalis floridana* plants inoculated simultaneously with PVY and a non-lesion forming strain of PVX, develop lession at a slower rate than when PVX is not present. The interference was caused by certain inhibitory substance. Ross (1959) suggested that, in the case of marked stimulation of a virus in a mixed infection, it is because the second virus either supplies specific substrates or prevents the action of by-products that are formed during the synthesis of the first virus and normally act to limit its multiplication.

Interference effects can also be studied by means of local lesions. According to McKinney (1940, 1941) the number of local lesions produced on the leaves of *Nicotiana tobaccum* and *N. sylvestris* were reduced or delayed if the plants were already infected with CMV (cucumber mosaic virus). Sadasivan (1940) found that fewer necrotic local lesion were produced by necrosis forming strains of TMV or PVX when they were inoculated along with a mottle forming strain of the same virus than when they were inoculated alone. As the concentration of the mottle forming strain in the mixed inoculum increased, so the number of lesions decreased until none were produced.

Thomson (1960) found a reduction in the number of local lesions when he used unrelated viruses in the same host plant, only one of which gave rise to local lesions. Thus, certain mixtures of viruses one being a local-lesion forming virus and the other not, when inoculated simultaneously produced fewer lesions than when inoculated singly.

As regard the reduction in the number of lesions some virologists presumed that some interferon like substances might be produced in response to some strains of virus, which reduces the number of local lesions. The converse is also true *i.e.*, certain pairs of viruses when inoculated together increase the number of lesions. Some of possible reasons attributed are: (1) concentration of virus, (2) species of the host, (3) Age of the host, (4) susceptibility of the host etc. As regards the increase in the number of lesions, when two viruses are simultaneously inoculated. Kassanis (1963) suggested that it might be due to infection by the assisting virus activates an enzyme system needed for the local lesion-forming virus to initiate infection or changes the general metabolism of the cell so that the local lesion forming virus can multiply.

SYNERGISM AND VIRUSES

When a host plant is invaded by two or more types/strains of viruses, the severity of the symptoms is enhanced as a result of interactions of viruses involved. Thus one type of virus enhances (increases) the synthesis of another strain. This interaction is known as *synergism*.

Relatively little quantitative work on synergism has been done. Perhaps the first recorded case of synergism was in the streak disease of tomato (Vanterpool, 1926) and similar early records on synergism are found in the potato crinkle diseases produced by the potato X and Y (Smith, 1931).

A good example of synergism by a mixed virus infection is that known as **double**

virus streak. The two viruses involved are tobacco (tomato) mosaic (TMV) and potato virus X (PVX). When occurring separately in tomato plants, the diseases caused by these two viruses are not severe, being mainly of the mottling type; when the two act together, much necrosis of stem and leaves develops and frequently causes the death of the host. The severity of the symptom does not vary or reduced, even if the virus strains involved are very mild strains.

Bennet (1949) showed that if tomato plants recovered from symptoms of the doffer latent mosaic virus were inoculated with TEV (tobacco etch virus) or TMV, severe symptoms recurred and there was a marked increase in the concentration of DLMV

Another example of synergism in viruses was observed by Garces-orejuela and Pound (1957). They found that in plants doubly infected with cucumber and tobacco mosaic viruses, the concentration of the latter was always higher in doubly than in singly infected plants. CMV was more concentrated 4 days after inoculation in singly than in doubly infected plants, but after two weeks, the effect was reversed, symptoms being more severe.

CHAPTER 21

Antimicrobial Drugs and Biotechnology

We are a vulnerable species, and even in these days of vaccines and antimicrobial drugs, infection continues to be a very serious threat to our future.

Professor Cedric Mims Edinburgh
International Science Festival (1997)

INTRODUCTION

The control of microorganisms is critical for the prevention and treatment of disease. Chapter 20 is concerned principally with the chemical and physical agents used to treat inanimate object in order to destroy microorganisms or inhibit their growth. In addition, the use of antiseptics is briefly reviewed. Microorganisms also grow on and within other organisms, and microbial colonization can lead to disease, disability, and death. Thus the control or destruction of microorganisms residing within the bodies of humans and other animals is of great importance.

When disinfecting or sterilizing an inanimate object, one naturally must use procedures that do not damage the object itself. The same is true for the treatment of living hosts. The most successful drugs interfere with processes that differ between the pathogen and host, and seriously damage the target microorganism while harming its host as little as possible.

CHEMOTHERAPEUTIC AGENTS

Chemotherapy, literally, the treatment of a condition by chemical means; however, it is usually used with reference specifically to the treatment of cancer by the use of specific drugs which slow down the rate of growth of tumour cells. Hence all these drugs were put together to be called **antimicrobial agents**. They may broadly be classified according to the types of organisms against which they act. They are: (1) Antibacterial drugs, (2) Antiviral drugs, (3) Antifungal agents, (4) Antiprotozoal agents, (5) Antihelmintic drugs.

Chemotherapy will exploit some property unique to malignant tumour cells that is not shared with normal cells. However, no such property has been discovered to date and the drugs used in chemotherapy are usually cytotoxic (cell-killing) for all dividing cells, both malignant and normal. This non-specific effect gives rise to some of the unpleasant side effects of some chemotherapies. In the future, cancer cells may be more specifically targeted by linking the chemotherapeutic agents to monoclonal antibodies.

Modern medicine is dependent on **chemotherapeutic agents**, chemical agents that are used to treat disease. *Chemotherapeutic agents destroy pathogenic microorganisms or inhibit their growth at concentrations low enough to avoid undesirable damage to the host.* Most of these agents are **antibiotics** (Greek *anti*, against, and *bios*, life), microbial products or their derivatives that can kill susceptible microorganisms or inhibit their growth. Drugs such as the sulfonamides are sometimes called antibiotics although they are synthetic chemotherapeutic agents, not microbially synthesized.

Many chemotherapeutic agents are now used and specific drug regimes exist for particular forms of cancer. The majority of the chemotherapeutic agents currently available interfere with one or more cellular processes involved in cell division (mitosis), including the movement of chromosomes during cell division. Because the process of cell division is common to both normal and malignant cells, chemotherapeutic drugs cannot in themselves be specific in their actions. Fortunately, normal cells from different tissues differ in their susceptibility to different drugs; the reasons for this are largely unknown.

There are several types of chemotherapeutic drugs now available for the treatment of malignancies. The first of these are the alkylating agents. These are synthetic compounds of considerable chemical diversity that have the common ability to add alkyl groups to a wide range of electronegative groups under mild aqueous conditions that prevail in the living cell, be it cancerous or normal.

Sulphonamides, also known as sulpha drugs, common name applied to a group of chemotherapeutic agents that are effective against a number of infectious diseases. In 1935 the German chemist, Gerhard Johannes Paul Domagk, discovered that an azo dye, Prontosil, cured streptococcal infections in mice. The active principle in Prontosil was found to be paraaminobenzenesulphonamide, commonly known as sulphanilamide. Clinical trials with sulphanilamide proved effective in arresting various bacterial diseases. Many derivatives of sulphanilamide have proved effective against such conditions as puerperal fever, scarlet fever, erysipelas, meningitis, pneumonia, and bacteraemia. All the sulphonamides are somewhat toxic, producing blood abnormalities and kidney damage when indiscriminately used. Since the discovery of penicillin, which is as effective as the sulphonamides although far less toxic, the use of sulphonamides has somewhat declined. Because bacteria often develop resistance to a particular kind of treatment, however, they are used when bacterial tolerance for penicillin has developed. Those still used include sulphabenzamide; sulpha methoxazole; sulphacetamide; sulphasalazine; and sulphathiazole.

Their action is believed to occur by the cross-linking of guanine molecules (parts of the building blocks of DNA on adjacent strands of DNA, thus mechanically inhibiting the uncoiling of DNA necessary for DNA replication and cell division. Examples of these agents are chlorambucil, melphalan, and mustine. In clinical practice they are used to treat Hodgkin's disease (a lymphoma-malignancy of lymphoid tissue) and other types of lymphoma; chronic lymphocytic leukaemia; multiple myeloma (tumour of plasma cells); and occasionally for the treatment of seminoma (tumour of the testis); ovarian carcinoma; breast carcinoma; neuroblastoma (a tumour of primitive nerve cells common in childhood); and some sarcomas (tumour of soft tissue, such as skeletal muscle, fat, and bone).

Chemotherapeutic agents, like disinfectants, can be either **cidal** or **static**. As mentioned earlier, static agents reversibly inhibit growth; if the agent is removed, the microorganisms will recover and grow again. The antibacterial drugs are often described as:

- **Bacteriostatic:** A substance that cuases a cessation of growth of the microorganism which is reversed when the chemical is removed. Such agents acting on bacteria are called bacteriostatic. The term bacteriostatic describes a drug the temporarily inhibits the growth of a microorganism. The effect is reversible. When the drug is removed, the organisms will resume growth and infection or the diseases may recur. Typical bacteriostatic drugs are the tetracyclines and sulfonamides.

- **Bactericidal:** A substance that kills the microorganisms. The term bactericide describes a drug that attaches to its receptor and causes the death of the microorganism. Typical bactericidal drugs are the betalactams (penicillins, cephalosporins) and the aminoglycosides. Many of the bacteriostatic drug in higher doses act as bactericidal agents. When the growth of bacteria is stopped by bacteriostatic drugs, the body defence mechanisms will kill the bacteria.

Antibiotics

They are chemical substances excreted by some microorganisms, which inhibit the growth and development of other microbes. Some of these drugs (chemicals) that were obtained naturally were put to chemical modifications (by removing some chemical groups and adding other) in attempts to enhance beneficial effects while minimizing the toxic effects. The resultant modified product is termed as **semisynthetic antibiotics**. Most antibiotics currently used are semisynthetic. The chemist has synthesized many drugs that have got the antibacterial property and less toxicity. These drugs are called **synthetic antibiotics** drugs. Naturally occurring antibiotics, their semisynthetic derivatives and synthetic antibiotics have got the same target *i.e.*, antimicrobial action.

Antibiotics have since transformed our capacity to combat these and many other conditions. In particular, the elimination of smallpox during the 1970s is rightly applauded as one of the most spectacular feats ever achieved by applied science. Thirty years ago, in light of widespread immunization, the *antibiotic revolution*, and other advances, it seemed that the conquest of dangerous viruses and bacteria was drawing to a close as a triumphant phase of human history.

Antiviral Drugs

Currently, no completely satisfactory treatments exist for viral infections, because most drugs that destroy viruses also damage the cell. The drug amantadine is used extensively in some countries for treatment of respiratory infections caused by influenza-A viruses, and the drug AZT is used in the treatment of HIV.

One promising antiviral agent, interferon, is produced by the cell itself. This non-toxic protein, which is produced by some animal cells infected with viruses, can protect other cells against such infection. The use of interferon for treating cancer is under intensive study. Until recently, study of the use of interferon has been restricted by its limited availability in pure form. However, new techniques of molecular cloning of genetic material now make it possible for scientists to obtain the protein in larger quantities. Its relative value as an antiviral agent has already been established.

The only effective way to prevent viral infection is by the use of vaccines. For example, vaccination for smallpox on a worldwide scale in the 1970s eradicated this disease. Many antiviral vaccines have been developed for humans and other animals. Those for humans include vaccines for rubeola (also known as measles), rubella, poliomyelitis, and influenza. Immunization with a virus vaccine stimulates the body's immune mechanism to produce a protein - called an antibody - that will protect against infection with the immunizing virus. The viruses are always altered before they are used for immunization so that they cannot themselves produce disease.

Viruses are so useful as model systems for studying events that control genetic information is that viruses are, in essence, small pieces of genetic information that is different from the genetic information of the cell. This allows scientists to study a smaller and simpler replicating system, but one that works on the same principle as that of the host cell. Much of the research on viruses is aimed at understanding their replicative mechanism in order to find ways to control their growth, so that viral diseases can be eliminated. Studies on viral diseases have also contributed greatly to understanding the body's immune response to infectious agents. Antibodies in blood serum, as well as secretions of the mucous membranes, all of which help the body eliminate foreign elements such as viruses, have been more thoroughly characterized by studying their responses to viral infection. Intense scientific interest is now concentrated on studies designed to isolate certain viral genes. These genes can be used in molecular-cloning.

Antigungal

The chemical agents, which act against fungal infection are called antifungal drug. Antifungals such as fluconazole or clotrimazole for thrush; and antiprotozoal drugs for trichomoniasis. The antifungal amphotericin, for example, disrupts the chemical structure of the cell membrane in fungi, thereby preventing vital nutrients from being absorbed and allowing toxins into the fungal cell.

GENERAL CHARACTERISTICS OF ANTIMICROBIAL DRUGS

A chemotherapeutic agent must have **selective toxicity:** it must kill or inhibit the microbial pathogen while damaging the host as little as possible. The degree of selective toxicity may be expressed in terms of (1) the therapeutic dose, the drug level required for clinical treatment of a particular infection, and (2) the toxic dose, the drug level at which the agent becomes too toxic for the host. The **therapeutic index** is the ratio of the toxic dose to the therapeutic dose. The larger the therapeutic index, the better the chemotherapeutic agent (all other things being equal).

A drug that disrupts a microbial function not found in eucaryotic animals cells often has a greater selective toxicity and a higher therapeutic index. For example, penicillin inhibits bacterial cell wall peptidoglycan synthesis but has little effect on host cells because they lack cell walls; therefore penicillin's therapeutic index is high. A drug may have a low therapeutic index because it inhibits the same process in host cells or damages the host in other ways. These undesirable effects on the host, called **side effects**, are of many kinds and may involve almost any organ system. Because side effects can be severe, chemotherpeutic agents should be administered with great care.

Drugs vary considerably in their range of effectiveness. Many are **narrow-spectrum drugs**- that is, they are effective only against a limited variety of pathogens. Others are **broad-spectrum drugs** and attack many different kinds of pathogens. Drugs may also be classified based on the general microbial group they act against: **antibacterial**, **antifungal**, **antiprotozoan**, and **antiviral**. Some agents can be used against more than one group; for example, sulfonamides are active against bacterial and some protozoa.

TABLE 21.1: Properties of Some Common Antibacterial Drugs

Drug	Primary Effect	Spectrum	Side Effects[a]	
Ampicillin	Cidal		Broad (gram +, some -)	Allergic responses (diarhea, anemia)
Bacitracin	Cidal	Narrow (gram +)	Renal injury if injected	
Carbenicillin	Cidal	Broad (gram +, many -)	Allergic responses (nausea, anemia)	
Cephalosporins	Cidal	Broad (gram +, some -)	(Allergic responses, thrombophelbitis, renal injury)	
Chloramphenicol	Static	Broad (gram +, -; rickettsia and chlamydia)	Depressed bone marrow function, allergic reactions	
Cipprofloxacin	Cidal	Broad (gram +, -)	Gastrointestinal upset, allergic responses	
Cindamycin	Static	Narrow (gram +, anaerobes)	Diarrhea	
Dapsone		Static	Narrow (mycobacteria)	(Anemia, allergic responses)
Erythromycin	Static	Narrow (gram +, mycoplasma)	(Gastrointestinal upset, injury)	
Gentamicin	Cidal	Narrow (gram -)	(Allergic responses, nausea, loss of hearing, renal damage)	
Isoniazid	Static or cidal	Narrow (mycobacteria)	(Allergic reactions, gastrointestinal upset, hepatic injury)	
Methicillin	Cidal	Narrow (gram +)	Allergic responses (renal toxicity, anemia)	
Penicillin	Cidal	Narrow (gram +)	Allergic responses (nausea, anemia)	
Polymyxin B	Cidal	Narrow (gram -)	(Renal damage, neurotoxic reactions)	
Rifampin	Static	Broad (gram +, mycobacteria)	(Hepatic injury, nausea, allergic responses)	
Streptomycin	Cidal	Broad (gram +, -; mycobacteria)	(Allergic responses, nausea, loss of hearing, renal damage)	
Sulfonamides	Static	Broad (gram +, -)	Allergic responses (renal and hepatic injury, anemia)	
Tetracylines	Static	Broad (gram +, -; rickettsia and chlamydia)	Gastrointestinal upset, teetch discoloration (renal and hepatic injury)	
Trimethoprim	Cidal	Broad (gram +, -)	(Allergic responses, rash, nausea, leukopenia)	
Vanocomycin	Cidal	Narrow (gram +)	Hypotension, neutropenia, kidney damage, allergic reactions	

[1]Occasional side effects are in parentheses. Other side effect not listed may also arise.

Chemotherapeutic agents can be synthesized by microorganisms or manufactured by chemical procedures independent of microbial activity. A number of the most commonly employed antibiotics are natural- that is, totally synthesized by one of a few bacteria or fungi. In contrast, several important chemotherapeutic agents are completely synthetic. The synthetic antibacterial drugs in Table 21.1 are the sulfonamides, trimethoprim, chloramphenicol, ciprofloxacin, isoniazid, and dapsone. Many antiviral and antiprotozoan drugs are synthetic. Semisynthetic antibiotics are natural antibiotics that have been chemically modified by the addition of extra chemical groups to make them less susceptible to inactivation by pathogens. Ampicilline, carbenicillin, and methicillin are good examples.

DETERMINATION THE LEVEL OF ANTIMICROBIAL ACTIVITY

Minimum Inhibition Concentration (MIC)

It is that concentration of a drug, which under the experimental conditions is the lowest concentration which will inhibit growth (as measured by observed turbidity). If the MIC of the drug is found to be doubled, this means that the concentration of the organism has doubled. It is done in the laboratory by the double dilution method, starting with the lowest drug concentration and then the doubling

Minimum Bactericidal Concentration (MBC)

This is the minimum concentration of the drug that kills the organisms completely. It is done in the laboratory after the MIC take a loop from all the tubes that show no turbidity in the MIC test and plate it. The first drug concentration in the tube showing no growth is the MBC

How to Make a Concentration

To get any concentration of a compound from any higher concentration given as a stock, measure out the required concentration value in ml and then make up the solution to the volume in ml of the stock solution concentration

Determination of antimicrobial effectiveness against specific pathogens is essential to proper therapy. Testing can show which agents are most effective against a pathogen and give an estimate of the proper therapeutic dose. It may be determined by two methods:

1. Dilution Susceptibility Tests, 2. Disk Diffusion Tests.

Currently the disk diffusion test more often used is the **Kirby-Bauer method**, which was developed in the early 1960s at the University of Washington Medical School by William Kirby, A.W. Bauer, and their colleagues.

MECHANISMS OF ACTION OF ANTIMICROBIAL AGENTS

It is necessary to know something about the mechanisms of drug action because such knowledge helps explain the nature and degree of selective toxicity of individual drugs and sometimes aids in the design of new chemotherapeutic agents.

Antimicrobial drugs can damage pathogens in several ways. The most selective antibiotics are those that interfere with the synthesis of bacterial cell walls (*e.g.*, penicillins, cephalosporins, vancomycin, and bacteriacin). These drugs have a high therapeutic index because bacterial cell walls possess a unique structure, not found in eucaryotic cells.

TABLE 21.2: Mechanisms of Antibacterial Drug Action

Drug	***Mechanism of Action***
Cell Wall Synthesis Inhibition	
Penicillin	Inhibit transpeptidation enzymes involved in the cross-linking of the polysaccharide chains of the bacterial cell wall peptidoglycan. Active cell wall lytic enzymes.
Ampicillin	
Carbenicillin	
Methicillin	
Cephalosporins	
Vancomycin	Binds directly to the D-Ala-D terminus and inhibits transpeptidation.
Bacitracin	Inhibits cell wall synthesis by interfering with action of the lipid carrier that transports wall precursors across the plasma membrane.
Protein Synthesis Inhibition	
Streptomycin	Binds with the 30S subunti of the bacterial ribosome to inhibit protein synthesis and causes misreading of mRNA.
Gentamicin	
Chloramphenical	Binds to the 50S ribosomal subunit and blocks peptide bond formation through inhibition of peptidyl transferase.
Tetracylines	Binds to the 30S ribosomal subunit and interfere with aminoacyl-tRNA binding.
Erythromycin and clindamycin	Binds to the 50S ribosomal subunit and inhibit peptide chain elongation.
Fusidic acid	Binds to EF-G and blocks translocation.
Nucleic Acid Synthesis Inhibition	
Ciprofloxacin and other quinolones	Inhibit bacterial DNA gyrase and thus interfere with DNA replication, transcription, and other activities involving DNA.
Rifampin	Blocks RNA synthesis by binding and inhibiting the DNA-dependent RNA polymerase.
Cell Membrane Disruption	
Polymyxin B	Binds to the plasma membrane and disrupts its structure and permeability properties.
Metabolic Antagonism	
Sulfonamides	Inhibit folic acid synthesis by competition with p-aminobenzoid acid.
Trimethoprim	Blocks tetrahydrofolate synthesis through inhibition of the enzyme dihydrofolate reductase.
Dapsone	Interfers with folic acid synthesis.
Isoniazid	May disrupt pyridoxal or NAD metabolism and functioning. Inhibits the synthesis of the mycolic acid *cord factor*.

Streptomycin, gentamicin, spectiomycin, clindamycin, chloramphenicol, tetracyclines, erythromycin, and many other antibiotics inhibit protein synthesis by binding with the procaryotic ribosome. Because these drugs discriminate between procaryotic and eucaryobic ribosomes, their therapeutic index is fairly high, but not as favorable as that of cell wall synthesis inhibitors. Some drugs bind to the 30S (small) subunit, while others attach to the 50S (large) ribosomal subunit. Several different steps in the protein synthesis mechanism can be affected: aminoacyl-tRNA binding, peptide bond formation, mRNA reading, and translocation. For example, fusidic acids to EF-G and blocks translocation, whereas mucopirocin inhibits isoleucyl-tRNA synthetase.

The antibacterial drugs that inhibit nucleic acid synthesis or damage cell membranes often are not as selectively toxic as other antibiotics. This is because procaryotes and ecuaryotes do not differ as greatly with respect to nucleic acid synthetic mechanisms or cell membrane structure. Good examples of drugs that effect nucleic acid synthesis or membrane structure are quinolones and polymyxins. quinolones inhibit the DNA gyrase and thus interfere with DNA replication, repair, and transcription. Polymyxins act as detergents of surfactants and disrupt the bacterial plasma membrane.

ANTIMETABOLITIE DRUGS

They block the functioning of metabolic pathways by competitively inhibiting the use of metabolites by key enzymes. Sulfonamides and several other drugs inhibit folic acid metabolism. Sulfonamides and several other drugs inhibit folic acid metabolism. Sulfonamides (*e.g.*, sulfanilamide, sulfamethoxazole, and sulfacetamide) have a high therapeutic index becuase human cannot synthesize folic acid and must obtain it in their diet. Most bacterial pathogens synthesize their own folic acid and are therefore susceptible to inhibitors of folate metabolism. Antimetabolite drugs also can inhibit other pathways. For example, isoniazid interfers with either pyridoxal or NAD metabolism.

Factors Influencing the Effectiveness of Antimicrobial Drugs

It is crucial to recognize that drug therapy is not a simple matter. Drugs may be administered in several different ways, and they do not always spread rapidly throughout the body or immediately kill all invading pathogens. A complex array of factors influence the effectiveness of drugs.

First, the drug must actually be able to reach the site of infection. The mode of administration plays an important role.

1. A drug such as penicillin G is not suitable for oral administration because it is relatively unstable in stomach acid.
2. Some antibiotics- for example, gentamicin and other aminoglyocosides- are not well absorbed from the intestinal tract and must be injected intramuscularly or given intravenously.
3. Other antibiotics (neomycin, bactracin) are applied topically to skin lesions. Nonoral routes of administration often are called **parenteral routes**. Even when an agent is administered properly, it may be excluded from the site of infection. For example, blood clots or necrotic tissue can protect bacteria from a drug, either because body fluids containing the agent may not easily reach the pathogens or because the agent is absorbed by materials surrounding it.

Second, the pathogen must be susceptible to the drug. Bacteria in abscesses may be dormant and therefore resistant to chemotherapy, because penicillins and many other agents affect pathogens only if they are actively growing and dividing. A pathogen, even through growing, may simple not be susceptible to a particular agent. For example, penicillins and cephalosporins, which inhibit cell wall synthesis, do not harm mycoplasmas, which lack cell walls.

Third, the chemotherapeutic agent must exceed the pathogen's MIC value if it is going to be effective.

Finally, chemotherapy has been rendered a less effective and much more complex matter the spread of drug resistance plasmids.

OTHER ANTIBACTERIAL DRUGS

Sulfonamides or Sulfa Drugs

A good way to inhibit or kill pathogens is by use of compounds that are **structural analogues**, molecules structurally similar to metabolic intermediates. These analogues compete with metabolites in metabolic processes because of their similarity, but are just different enough so that they cannot function normally in cellular metabolism. The first antimetabolites to be used successfully as chemotherapeutic agents were the sulfonamides, discovered by G. Domagk, **Sulfonamides** or sulfa drugs are structurally related to sulfanilamide, an analogue of paminobenzoic acid. The latter substance is used in the synthesis of the cofactor folic acid.

When sulfanilamide or another sulfonamide enters a bacterial cell, it competes with p-aminobenzoic acid for the active site of an enzyme involved in folic acid synthesis, and the folate concentration decreases. The decline in folic acid is detrimental to bacterium because folic acid is essential to the synthesis of purines and pyrimidines, the bases used in the construction of DNA, RNA, and other important cell constituents. The resulting inhibition of purine and pyrimidine synthesis leads to cessation of bacterial growth or death of the pathogen. Sulfonamides are selectively toxic for many pathogens because these bacteria manufacture their own folate and cannot effectively take up the cofactor. In contrast, humans cannot synthesize folate and must obtain it in the diet; therefore sulfonamides will not affect the most.

TABLE 21.3: Chemotherapy of Some Representative Bacterial Pathogens

Pathogen	Representative Diseases	Drugs of Choicea
Gram-Positive Bacteria		
Corynebacterium diphtheriae	Diphtheria	Erythromycin, penicillin G
Staphyolcoccus, pencillinase-positive	Boils, pneumonia, wound infections	A cephalosporin, cloxacillin, dicloxacillin.
Staphylococcus, pencillinase-negative	Boils, pneumonia, wound infections	Pencillin G or V, a cephalosporin, vancomycin
Streptococcus, hemolytic	Strep throat, skin infections, sepsis, rheumatic fever Pneumonia	Penicillin[b] G or V, erythromycin, or a cephalosporin
Streptococcus pneumoniae	Penumonia	Penicillin Penicillin[b] G or V, erythromycin, or a cephalosporin
Gram-Negative Bacteria		
Bordetella pertussis	Whoping cough or pertussis	Erythromycin, ampicillin
Escherichia coli	Urinary tract infections	Sulfonamide, cephalosporin, ampicillin
Haemophilus influenzae type b	Menigitis, pneumonia	Cefotaxine, ceftriaxone, ampicillin
Klebsiella pneumoniae	Pneumonia, urinary tract infections	Newer cephalosporins[c], gentamicin
Logionella pneumophila	Pheumonia	Erythromycin
Neisseria gonorrhoeae	Gonorrhea	Amoxicillin, ceftriaxone, spectinomycin
Pseudomonas aeruginosa	Urinary tract and burn infections, pneumonia	Carbenicillin or ticarcillin
Salmonella typhi	Typhoil fever, septicemia, gastroenteritis	Ceftriaxone, chloramophenicol, ampicillin

Pathogen	Representative Diseases	Drugs of Choicea
Shigella dysenteriae	Dysentery	Trimethoprim-sulfamethoxazole, quinolones, ciprofloxacin
Vibrio cholerae	Cholera	Tetracycline, trimethoprim-sulfamethoxazole
Acid-Fast Bacteria		
Mycobacterium-avium complex	Pneumonia	Rifampin plus ethambutol
Mycobacterium tuberculosis	Tuberculosis	Isoniazid plus rifampin ± pyrazinamide
Other Bacteria		
Chlamydia trachomatic	Nongonococcol urethritis, trachoma	Doxycycline, azithromycin, erythromycin
Mycoplasma pneumoniae	Pneumonia	Tetracycline, erythromycin
Rickettsia spp.	Rocky Mountain spotted fever, typhus fever	Tetracycline, chloramphenicol
Treponema pallidum subsp. pallidum	Syphilis	Penicillin G. tetracycline, ceftriaxone

The effectiveness of sulfonamides is limited by the increasing sulfonamide resistance of many bacteria. Furthermore, as many as 5% of the patients receiving sulfa drugs experience adverse side effects, chiefly in the form of allergic responses (fever, hives, and rashes).

Quinolones

A second group of synthetic antimicrobial agents are increasingly used to treat a wide variety of infections. The **quinolones** are synthetic drugs that contain the 4-quinolone ring. The first quinolone, nalidixic acid, was synthesized in 1962. More recently a family of fluoroquinolones has been produced. Three of these-ciprofloxacin, norfloxacin, and ofloxacin- are currently used in the United States, and more fluoroquinolones are being synthesized and tested. Quinolones are effective when administered orally. The sometimes cause adverse side effects, particularly gastrointestinal upset.

Quinolones act by inhibiting the bacterial DNA gyrase or topoisomerase II, probably by binding to the DNA gyrase complex. This enzyme introduces negative twists in DNA and helps separate its strand. DNA gyrase inhibition disrupts DNA replication and repair, transcription, bacterial chromosome separation during division, and other cell processes involving DNA. It is not surprising that quinolones are bacterial.

ANTIBIOTICS

Classification of Antibiotics

Antibiotics can be classified in following groups:

1. Penicillin, 2. Streptomycin and Dehydrostreptomycin, 3. Chloramphenicol, 4. Tetracycline, 5. Microlides, 6. Antifungal and 7. Miscellaneous

Further classification of antibiotics, their discovery, source, mode of action and administration of above-mentioned antibiotics have been presented in Table 21.2.

Requirements of Antibiotics

1. Antibiotics should not be toxic.
2. They should not precipitate serum proteins.
3. They should not cause haemolysis.
4. They should not affect the vague sites adversely.
5. They should not be pyrogenic.
6. They should not cause histamine like responses.
7. They should preferably, be soluble in water
8. They should reasonably stable.
9. They should be effective against pathogens.
10. They should be well tolerated in the doses required.
11. They should have few undesirable side-effects.

Not all antibiotics fulfil these requirements; but the most likely one to cover most these requirements is penicillin. Some antibiotics are toxic clinically but useful in research work, *e.g.* antibiotics that are lethal to nucleic acids. Some antibiotics are useful topically but toxic internally, *e.g.* bacitracin.

Mode of Action of Antibiotics

Antibiotics interfere with growth and metabolism of microorganisms, which supress the growth and other metabolic activities of cells. Waksman described various modes of action of antibiotics substitutes are as follows:

1. Acting as a substituent for essential nutrient.
2. Interfering substance during vitamin utilization.
3. Modifying the metabolism of bacterial cell.
4. Competing for enzyme required by bacteria.
5. Interfering with respiratory mechanism, specially hydrogenase system.
6. Favouring certain lytic mechanism of cell.

How Antibiotics Act?

There are five sites of action of antibiotic agents.

- **The cell wall:** The Peptidoglycan component of the cell wall in bacteria is very important for its integrity (It is not present in man). Penicillin and Cephalosporius interfere with the formation of peptidoglycan layer so that the bacterial cell absorbs water and brusts.
- **The cytoplasmic membrane:** Inside the cell wall is the site of most of the cell's biochemical activity. Colistin act at this level, it disorientates the molecule so that the membrane becomes permeable and vital metabolites escapes.
- **Inhibition of protein synthesis:** Tetracyclin, Chloramphenicol, Erythromycin and amoinglycosides interfere with the build up of peptide chain on the ribosomes.
- **Nucleic acid metabolism:** Rifampicin actionomycin and Nalidixic acid interfere with RNA and DNA metabolism.
- **Intermediary metabolism:** Sulfonamide, Trimethoprim, PAS and Isoniazed interfere with bacterial metabolism.

Use of Antimicrobial Drugs

1. Choice of drug can be made on clinical diagnosis; *e.g.* segmental pneumonia in a

young person usually caused by streptococcus pneumonia and can be treated by Penicillin, leprosy by leprae bacilli treated by Dapsone and Rifampicin.

2. Choice of drug on bacteriological identification and sensitivity test is done when: (i) infecting organisms not identified on clinical examination eg. meningitis or U.T.I. (ii) when though the infecting organisms can be identified by the clinical diagnosis but their sensitivity is not known *e.g.*, carbuncle, gonorrhoea etc.

Action on the Cell Wall

The mode of action of an antibiotic on bacteria such as staining properties, depend on their chemical composition. Gram-negative bacteria have a high lipid content and on hydrolysis they produce a complete range of amino acids, found in protein whereas a Gram-positive bacteria give lipids in small amount and 4 to 5 types of amino acids. Those antibiotics which act on the cell wall are penicillin, N-cephalosporine, novobiocin vancomycin etc. The selective action of streptomycin on the tubercle bacillus is due to the fact that the permeability of cell membranes in the bacilli and in the tissue cells of animals and man differs due to the dissimilar chemical structure of the cytoplasm of these organisms.

On protoplast membrane

The membrane of the living cell acts as osmotic barrier keeping the concentration of metabolites and nutrients in the cell and site for biosynthesis of other cell component is the site of action of following antibiotics: streptomycin, polymyxin, novobiocine, etc. Penicillin affects the formation of L-forms in the shape of pleomorphic protoplasmic structures.

On Nucleic Acid and Enzyme Biosynthesis

Antibiotics like streptomycin, actinomycin-D, chloramphenicol, tetracyclines, etc., act directly on DNA dependant polymerase synthesis. Chloramphenicol is a specific inhibitor of the biosynthesis of bacterial protein. It comes into action with the peptidyl transferase areas of 50S ribosome. Competing with the aminoacyl end of the aminoacyl tRNA, chloramphenicol blocks the formation of the peptide bond. Other antibiotics like tetracyclines, lincomycin, erythromycin, kanamycin, neomycin, spectinomycin sparsomycin, fucidine and others belong to the group of antibiotics which inhibits protein biosynthesis in bacteria at the ribosome level. The antibiotic rifampin supresses protein biosynthesis by inhibiting the activity of RNA polymerasse.

Streptomycin inhibits the incorporation of some amino acids in protein synthesis and attacks the bacterial enzyme with the participation of which the introduction of pyruvic acid into the tricarboxylic acid cycle by its union with oxalacetic acid takes place. Streptomycin also inhibits the activity of biotin-containing enzymes catalysing the union of carbon dioxide with carbonic acids. This disturbs reading of the genetic code and synthesize leucine instead of alanine.

The antifungal antibiotics impair the intactness of the cytoplasmic membrane in fungi. Antineoplastic antibiotics supress the synthesis of nucleic acid in bacterial and animal cells and bind with DNA which serves as the matrix for RNA synthesis. Bruneomycin leads to sharp inhibition of the synthesis of DNA or to its destruction.

Several theories and hypothesis have been given to understand the mechanism and action of antibiotics but still we lack the exact and precise mechanism which can solve the question completely.

Absorption, Metabolism and Extraction of Antibiotics

Absorption of antibiotics depends on the route of administration and the diffusion capacity of the drug from the site. Drugs administered parentally are more quickly adsorbed than orally or locally routed. The onset of drug action depends upon the route of administration and its adsorption. Delay in administration and its adsorption depends on the fact that the drug must be converted to an active component or to the products which are secondly responsible for the action. The drug (antibiotic) is metabolised by one of the following ways:

1. Kidneys are the most important channel for the elimination of drugs.
2. They are also excreted through faeces sweat and through the respiration, specially the volatile drugs.

Route of Administration

Local application: They are applied mainly to skin, mucous membranes of alimentary canal, respiratory, genitourinary tract and to the cornea. Even the tissue and organs sealed deeply can also be treated with the local injection of antibiotics.

Oral: They can be taken orally.

Parentral: Antibiotics are injected intera-muscularly, interavenously, intrathecally (in spinal cord) and in the bonemarrow etc. This route of administration is referred to as parentral. Interavenously route is less painful, less irritant and fast results, larger quantities of drugs can be given (bolus dose) while intera-muscularly route is cheaper and less complicated.

Inhalation: Antibiotics are also used in the form of aerosole that is they are dispersed into the small molecules and are sprayed in respiratory passages.

Combinations of Antibiotics

When do you want to use the combination of two or more antimicrobial agents? The indications for combination of antimicrobial agents are:

1. to obtain potentiation eg. Contrimoxazole, Penicillin and Gentamicin.
2. to delay development of drug resistance; e. g., in treatment of tuberculosis.
3. to broaden the spectrum of activity; when mixed infection is there.
4. to reduce severity or incidence of adverse reactions. In combination, lower therapeutic dose of each drug reduces adverse reactions.

Bactericidal drugs act on rapidly dividing organisms. Thus a bacteristatic drug, by reducing multiplication, may protect the organisms from bactericidal drugs.

When a combination of antibiotic is required, it is better to use two bacteristatics or two bactericidal drugs.

Doses of Antibiotics

A dose of an antibiotic or a drug depends on the termination of drug action which depends on the elimination from the body according to the proportion of the plasma concentration. The value of concentration approaches zero as the item increases. For example an antibiotic attains maximum concentration after 2 hours and disappears from that place after 8 hours; therefore, the drug should be repeated after 6 hours or 8 hours.

Demerits of Antibiotic Therapy

1. Antibiotics develop drug-resistant strain in body.
2. They develop narrow spectrum property of antibacterial activity in body.
3. Body failure to respond in certain infection caused by Gram-negative bacili and other microorganisms.
4. They develop nutritional deficiency in body.

Side Effects of Antibiotics

It is well known that large doses of penicillin and streptomycin have a neurotoxic action. Tetracyclines affect the liver. Chloromycetin has a toxic effect on the haemotopoietic organs, and chlortetracycline and oxytetracycline upon intravenous injection may lead to collapse with a lethal outcome. After injection of penicillin and streptomycin a rash, contact dermatitis, angioneurotic odema, anaphylactic reactions or allergic asthma may occur. On local application of antibiotics, allergic reaction may arise. Staphylococcal colitis proceeds very severally, and is characterized by profuse diarrhoea, dehydration of the body, toxic phenomena, shock and collapse. Penicillin treatment may cause a rapid drop in blood pressure, cyanosis, superficial breathing, loss of consciousness, and convulsions are observed, and in some cases death may occur.

Sometimes antibiotics may cause **skin allergy reaction**. This is caused by action of streptomycin. Quite often allergic manifestations are observed in the mucous membranes such as hyperaemia and oedema of the pharynx and tongue.

Antibacterial agents may induce **genetic disorder** in microorganism's cells and cause chromosomal aberration; some of them possess a teratogenic effect leading to the development of foetal monstrosities if they are taken in the first days of pregnancy.

General Principles for use of Antibiotics

1. Make correct diagnosis, find the site of infection and organisms responsible then use antibiotic agent after finding the sensitivity.
2. Remove barrier eg. lack of free drainage of abscesses (so drain the abscess before starting antibiotic)
3. Decide whether antibiotic agent is really necessary.
4. Select the best drug *i.e.* Activity of the drug should match with the infecting organisms. The drug should be capable of reaching the site of infection.
5. Antibiotics should be given in optimum dose with proper frequency and through most appropriate route.
6. Therapy should be continued till apparent cure is achieved and three days more to avoid relapse.
7. In Typhoid, tuberculosis and endocarditis the drugs should be continued for a longer time after apparent clinical cure.
8. Microbiological examination to be done; to prove the complete cure after withdrawal of antibiotic agent.
9. Prophylactic chemotherapy for surgical and dental procedure should start at the time of surgery and continue for 48 hours to reduce the risks of development of resistance.

Production of Antiobiotics

Antibiotics are obtained by special methods employed in the medical industry for the production of antibiotics strains of fungi, actinomycetes and bacteria are used, which are seeded in a nutrient substrate. Antibiotics are secreted by some outside of the cells and into the surrounding environment, others are largely retained within the cells and must be separated by extraction. After a definite growth period the antibiotic is extracted, purified and concentrated, checked for potency action. Common antibiotics are Penicillin, Streptomycin, Gramicidin, Aureomycin, Chloramphenicol and Terramycin.

Mode of Administration

Antibiotic drugs can be administered by mouth and also by intramuscular and intravenous injections. They are used not only in the treatment of infections but also in the prevention of certain infections. The number of antibiotics is being constantly increased. Some are useful clinically others are not satisfactory for clinical application but are more useful for other purposes. Antibiotics are used as growth stimulants in poultry and livestock feeds. Powerful antibiotics such as penicillin has proved to be of such tremendous importance for the destruction of organisms especially those capable of producing disease.

Side Effects of Antibiotics

Of the many hundreds of antibiotics discovered, only few are of wide application in medicine. They are Penicillin, Streptomycin, Chloramphenicol and Tetracycline. Prolonged use may weaken the body's natural defences against invading germs and may have undesirable side effects. Certain antibiotics, used without medical supervision, cause the patient to develop rashes, swellings and other symptoms of severe allergic reactions. Excessive doses damage the kidneys, in the case of streptomycin. They sometimes cause complete and permanent deafness. In every case, the appropriateness, choice, and dosage of antibiotics must be decided by the physician. Large doses of penicillin and streptomycin have a neurotoxic action, tetracyclines affect the liver, chloromycetin has a toxic effect on the haematopoietic (blood cell forming) organs, and chlorotetracycline and oxytetracycline upon intravenous injection may lead to collapse with lethal outcome. Allergic reactions arise during local application of antibiotics. A severe complication is anaphylactic shock from the use of penicillin in which a rapid drop in blood pressure, cyanosis, superficial breathing, loss of consciousness and convulsions are observed. Contact dermatitis is caused by the action of streptomycin using over long periods.

Antibiotics should be used only on physician's prescription, not in selfmedication. The popularity of antibiotics is due to their ability to destroy many kinds of pathogens and to their relatively nontoxic properties when given systematically.

Rational use of Antibiotics

There are many factors responsible for the development of resistance of microorganisms to antimicrobial agents. Inappropriate selection of an antimicrobial agent in the absence of bacteriological culture sensitivity results plays an important role in the development of resistance. Under such circumstances it becomes very essential for the physician to have a working knowledge of the common pathogenic microorganisms which would be involved in a particular disease and the specific antibiotic/antibiotics with could be used in order to obtain desired response. Following are some of the common diseases which encounter in routine practice, common pathogens involved and possible antibiotics which are prescribed in common diseases.

Antibiotics and Plant Diseases

For example, **Bacterial canker of cherry** caused by *Pseudomonas morsprunorum* has made it impossible to grow cherry on a large scale in the U.K. Borderaux mixture may control the disease, but the mixture kills the soft tissues of plants and has a deleterious effect on the spraying machinery. A small beginning was made to use antibiotics on an experimental scale. Presently antibiotics, can check as many as forty diseases.

Of these, **Fire Blight of Apple** in U. S. A., caused by *Erwinia amylovora* and **Stone-fruit Blast** in New Ireland, of which the causal agent is *Pseudomonas syringal*, are some of the diseases which have been controlled by antibiotic like streptomycin. It is sprayed for 2 to 3 times at different stages of fruit development.

Antibiotics and Animal Diseases

Cows usually suffer from a disease called **mastitis**, which is caused by streptcocci and staphylococci. The characteristic symptoms are the inflammation of the udder and decrease in the yield of milk. This disease is cured by giving local injections of penicillin. Antibiotics are used as antiprotozoal agents in many animal diseases. However, it may be mentioned that this aspect of antibiotic therapy is still needs research.

Antibiotics and Animal Feed

In Western countries, pigs are reared in large numbers. It is generally desired that the young ones should be fed on some food, other than the sow's milk (preferably cow's milk) so that the sow could bear another litter in the shortest possible time. This is done by maintaining the young ones on cow's milk to which is added some antibiotic like terramycin, aureomycin, streptomycin, or penicillin.

In America, antibiotics are also added to poultry feed which result in higher rate of growth. Antibiotics suppress the growth or completely eliminate the undesirable microbial agents in the gut of the poultry which would otherwise inhibit the optimal growth of birds. Antibiotics also help in the vitamin economy of birds, though the actual mechanism involved is not yet clearly understood. Perhaps it is due to the altered microflora of the gut. Laying of eggs increases in hens after administration of antibiotics. It is not certain whether this is due to the suppression of undesirable microbial flora or the vitamin sparing effect of antibiotics.

Antibiotics and Growth of Animals

Antibiotics aid in the growth of other animals too. For example ruminants like lambs, calves etc. are weaned at a very early age of a few weeks. Such administration of antibiotics stimulates their growth. At the time of weaning the ruminant has only one functional compartment for its stomach but the administration of antibiotics is found to hasten the typical reminant stage with the fully developed reticulorumen.

Antibiotics and Food Preservation

Antibiotics preserve foods too. Meat is among the most expensive and perhaps the most relished item of food. Even if it is slightly contaminated with bacteria during slaughtering and distribution, putrefaction and decay set in very rapidly, causing a great deal of economic loss. Therefore, in order to prevent such spoilage antibiotics such as streptomycin and penicillin are used. They are injected into the blood vessels of the animal either before or after slaughter. They can also be sprayed on the surface of the raw meat.

Greater care is required in the preservation of fish in comparison to meat. From the time of catching till it is sold at the counter, it takes considerably long time. This is particularly true of cod and haddock which are caught in deep water seas and take quite some time to be brought ashore. Even when kept in ice, they cannot normally be preserved for more than seven days. This causes heavy loss to the fish industry. By the time it reaches the counter another food bit of it will have decayed. Since a number of bacteria thrive even at temperatures as low as 0° to 5° C fish is still open to spoilage in spite of the relatively expensive preservation in ice. Hence people turned their attention to antibiotics. Aureomycin and terramycin have been successfully used for this purpose. This fish when still on board the ship is dipped in the antibiotic solution. It is then packed in ice containing the antibiotic and stored away in chilled (-1 to 1° C) seawater. U.S.A. has built fishing ships, which are specially fitted with antibiotic containing tanks and refrigerated stores.

Since the yeasty, old or stale, smell of antibiotics disappears during cooking the objection to food preservation using antibiotics disappears. Though primarily of chemotherapeutic uses, the antibiotics have already given sufficient proof of their value to humanity in other fields as well.

Antibiotic Secretion from Cyanobacteria

Some blue-green algae, such as *Nostoc*, secrete antibiotics called **bacteriocins** that kill related strains of the alga. A **bacteriocin** is a proteinaceous antibiotic that is active against procaryotic strains closely related to the organism that produces the antibiotic. Others blue-green algae secrete antibiotics that are active against a wide range of blue-green and eucaryotic algae. *Scytonema hofmanni* produces such an antibiotic. This antibiotic, called **cyanobacterin**, is a chlorine-containing gamma-lactone. All of these antibiotics probably play an active role in the survival of the producing organism by inhibiting growth of competing organisms.

Some blue-green algae respond to low concentrations of iron in the environment by excreting compounds called **solubilizing chelators** or **siderophores**, which solubilize iron in the environment. These siderophores are secondary hydroxamates and renere insoluble iron into an available form that can be taken up into the cell.

ANTIVIRAL DRUGS

HIV Drugs

The development of antiviral drugs to attack HIV has targeted specific stages in the viral replication cycle. One such target is the requirement for HIV to undergo reverse transcription (the conversion of viral genomic RNA into DNA) at an early stage of infecting a host cell; this is a process unique to retroviruses and performed by the viral enzyme, reverse transcriptase (RT).

Many of the licensed anti-HIV agents are RT inhibitors. There are two different classes of RT inhibitors. The nucleoside analogues work as *DNA chain terminators*. That is, because each appears to be a normal nucleotide base (the building blocks of DNA), the RT enzyme mistakenly inserts the drug into the growing viral DNA chain. However, unlike normal nucleotide bases, the drugs cannot be further elongated (no additional DNA bases can be added once the drug is inserted) and therefore viral DNA synthesis is terminated. The non-nucleoside reverse transcriptase inhibitors (NNRTIs) have a different mode of action; they are thought to inhibit RT by binding to the enzyme.

In the United States and Europe alike, five nucleoside analogues have been licensed: zidovudine (also known as ZDV or AZT and made by Glaxo Wellcome with the brand name Retrovir), didanosine (ddI or Videx, from Bristol-Myers Squibb), zalcitabine (ddC or Hivid, from Roche), stavudine (d4T or Zerit, from Bristol-Myers Squibb), and lamivudine (3TC or Epivir, from Glaxo Wellcome). A potent second-generation nucleoside analogue called abacavir (1592U89, from Glaxo Wellcome) is in advanced stages of development.

In the United States, one NNRTI has also been licensed: nevirapine (Viramune, from Boehringer-Ingelheim). Other NNRTIs in advanced development are delavirdine (Rescriptor, from Pharmacia & Upjohn) and loviride (from Janssen).

Protease Inhibitors

Protease inhibitors are the second major class of anti-HIV drugs is the protease inhibitors. These are drugs that specifically interfere with the action of the HIV protease enzyme.

Protease is employed at a later stage of the viral replication cycle, when new virus particles are being produced within an HIV-infected cell. The protein from which the core and envelope of the new particles will be formed is initially synthesized in a long strip, which has to be cut up by protease into smaller functional proteins. When the protease enzyme is inhibited, an HIV-infected cell can only produce immature, non-infectious viral progeny. In the United States and Europe, three protease inhibitors are licensed: saquinavir (Invirase, from Roche), indinavir (Crixivan, from Merck Sharp & Dohme), and ritonavir (Norvir, from Abbott). Additional protease inhibitors are under development.

Other Anti-HIV Drugs

Other anti-HIV drugs currently in development include agents that inhibit HIV's integrase enzyme, used to insert the viral DNA into the host cell's DNA after reverse transcription has been completed, and agents that may bind either to gp120 or to the cellular receptors to which gp120 attaches itself, thus interfering with the process of viral fusion and infection of susceptible human cells.

Some therapeutic consideration has also been given to targeting cellular processes that are strictly required for viral replication. Inhibiting these processes should not incur a risk of viral resistance because the selective pressure will not be directed at the virus itself, although toxicity is a concern. Several drugs have shown preliminary promise, most notably hydroxyurea.

Gene Therapy

Gene therapy is also being studied as a potential treatment for HIV-infected people. One approach uses small molecules called anti-sense oligonucleotides, which bind to the viral RNA strand, preventing it from acting as a template for viral proteins. Another antiviral strategy uses molecules called ribozymes that can detect specific parts of HIV's RNA within infected cells and splice it, rendering it inactive.

Other researchers are using gene therapy to insert a gene into immune cells taken from infected people, either to boost the cellular immune response against HIV or to protect the CD4 cells from infection. This is called adoptive cell therapy. The main problems with all these gene therapy approaches are delivering the new genes into cells, and ensuring that the altered cells are not identified as foreign and attacked by the host immune system.

Immune System Responses

Considerable research is continuing into the basic biology of HIV and its interactions with the immune system. Many scientists believe that better medicines could be developed if there was a fuller understanding of pathogenesis (the mechanisms by which HIV causes disease). Researchers are also intensively studying individuals who have been infected with HIV for many years without suffering immune damage, and those who have been exposed to HIV on multiple occasions yet have so far remained uninfected. The results to date appear to confirm the theory that inherited genetic factors are highly significant. For example, the genetic instructions for producing the CKR5 protein, which HIV uses as a co-receptor to enable it to infect cells, are contained in a specific gene. Everyone has two copies of this CKR5 gene, but in some individuals one or both copies of the gene contain a mutation that interferes in the production of the protein. People with one mutation in this gene have less CKR5 on the outside of their cells, reducing the cells' susceptibility to infection with HIV. Studies have shown that this is associated with a slower rate of disease progression among people infected with HIV through sexual intercourse. People who have inherited two mutant CKR5 genes may be protected against infection with HIV. These lines of research may eventually also lead to new approaches to treatment.

Prophylactic Treatments

Many of the improvements in the quality and quantity of life among people with HIV have resulted from better drugs to prevent or treat the AIDS-associated opportunistic infections. The use of prophylactic (preventative) antibiotics has dramatically reduced the incidence of PCP and toxoplasmosis, and clinicians have grown increasingly skilled at preventing and treating fungal infections. Consequently, many HIV-infected people do not now develop an AIDS-defining illness until they reach an advanced stage of immune suppression, when they become vulnerable to infections that are still challenging to treat or to prevent, such as cytomegalovirus (CMV) and *Mycobacterium avium* intracellulare complex. Intravenous drugs such as foscarnet, ganciclovir, and cidofovir are available to treat CMV disease, and an oral formulation of ganciclovir has been introduced for maintenance therapy and, potentially, for prophylaxis.

Zidovudine

Zidovudine appears to have a significant protective effect against HIV-related brain disease and dementia. This is due to the ease with which the drug crosses the blood-brain barrier, a quality not shared by other anti-HIV drugs that have come into use subsequently.

It was formerly known as AZT from its synthetic chemical name, azidothymidine, the drug most commonly used in the treatment of HIV (human immunodeficiency virus) infection. Zidovudine is the international non-proprietory name of the drug; Retrovir is its brand name. A laboratory at the United States National Institutes of Health discovered in 1985 that zidovudine inhibited the replication of HIV by interfering with the process of reverse transcription, which is necessary for the production of new virus particles. Zidovudine was shown by clinical trials in 1986 to be effective at improving survival in patients with AIDS and has since then been licensed as the first-choice treatment for HIV infection in North America, Europe, and Australia.

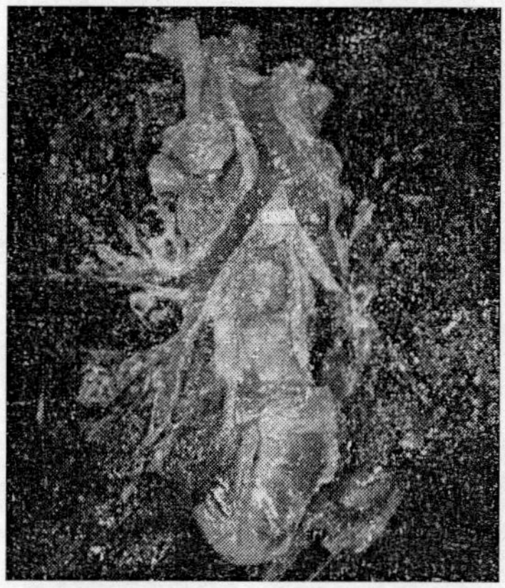

FIGURE 21.1: This section of human lung tissue shows light- cancerous tissue in the centre of the photograph. At bottom centre lies the heart. While normal lung tissue is light pink, the tissue surrounding the cancer is black and starved of oxygen, the result of a tar-like residue left by cigarette smoke. Most lung cancer begins in the cells lining the main air passages, or bronchi. In their cancerous state, these cells lack the cilia that normally catch and eliminate foreign particles inhaled into the lung. Mucus ordinarily cleared by bronchial cilia becomes trapped, blocking air passages. Cigarette smoking is directly responsible for 90 per cent of cases of lung cancer.

ANTICANCEROUS DRUGS

New methods of giving chemotherapy are being devised to find out whether side effects can be lessened and survival of sufferers improved. The symptoms of small cell lung cancer lung cancer (SCLC) are a persistent hacking cough, blood in the sputum, wheezy breathing, pain in the shoulder or chest, neck or facial swelling, and recurring pneumonia or bronchitis.

For instance, one recent trial gave SCLC patients the drug etoposide by continuous infusion (via a drip into a main vein over several days). Initial results were encouraging with patients reporting that they found the treatment more tolerable than the normal tablet method. Also, administering etoposide in this way eliminates the need for other anti-cancer drugs that can have debilitating side effects.

There are several new agents under clinical trial at present, including the anti-cancer drugs taxol, taxotere, topotecan, and vinorelbine, and biological therapies including interleukin-2, interferon, and granulocyte colony stimulating factor. Cytokines (proteins vital to the workings of the body's immune system) are also being used in cancer treatment to enhance the effects of anti-cancer drugs. Trials so far have shown a high response when giving the antiviral protein interferon and cisplatin together. Interferon, which occurs naturally in white blood cells, can be synthesized by genetic engineering. Alphainterferon is also being used in combination with cisplatin for treating non-SCLC.

There are a number of gene therapies under trial, mainly in the United States. One approach is to reactivate the p53 gene, which suppresses tumours. Mutated p53 genes are involved in a large number of cancers, including lung cancer.

CHAPTER 22

Transgenic Animal Technology

According to Gordon and Ruddle (1983) animals carrying new genes called *transgenic*. The term is now used to describe particular variants of species into which a new gene(s) has been inserted. In recent years a wealth of knowledge has accumulated as a result of the ability of researchers to introduce genetic material into intact mammalian organism. The production of transgenic mice by pronuclear microinjection (Gordon *et al.*, 1980) has provided an especially powerful new tool for the study of the regulation of gene expression in mammalian development. Transgenic technology has allowed the rapid elucidation of many fundamental principles of the tissue-specific expression of certain genes and has also been particularly useful in immunology, oncology, and studies of the genetic basis of disease. In addition to its importance for studies of genes expression, the introduction of DNA into the host genome has the potential for disruption of the integrity of host genes. The identification of insertional mutations and the cloning of the affected host genes, made possible by the insertion of defined sequences of DNA into the affected loci, is another important application of **transgenic technology**.

The success of the experiments with mice led to similar research aimed at enhancing growth performance in species of domestic animals raised for food. Using gene constructs that caused accelerated growth in mice, these investigators were unable to detect enhanced growth of a similar magnitude in the transgenic domestic animals that were produced. Efforts continue toward development of a greater understanding of the cascade of events involved in animal growth and the effective regulation of animal development through genetic engineering.

The production of transgenic mice was the culmination of previous advances in the areas of recombinant DNA and the micromanipulation of mammalian cells. Although the production of allophenic mice could be considered to be the first step toward the introduction of genetic material into intact mammalian organisms, this approach only allowed the introduction of whole genomes into chimeric mice by aggregation of genetically different embryos at the cleavage stage. Another approach to the transfer of genes into the germline resulted in the insertion of discrete sequences of DNA.

This technique is based on the introduction of teratocarcinoma cells into blastocyst cavities. These cells can be subjected to DNA-mediated transfer of genes *in vitro* and can also become phenotypically normalized and contribute to tissues of chimeric mice. The major drawback of this approach was the fact that the transformed cells rarely contributed to the germline of chimeric mice. A more efficient method is based on the use of **embryonal stem** (ES) cells. These cells can be transformed or selected for a particular phenotype and they also contribute frequently to the germ cell population of chimeric animals. This new and powerful approach is discussed in detail elsewhere in this volume.

Retroviruses have been successfully used to transform embryos by infection. Evidence for expression of Retroviruses introduced in this manner stems from the fact that Moloney murine leukemia virus (MoMuLV) is frequently activated later in development and causes leukemia.

However, this technology is extremely valuable for tracing cell lineages and the evaluation of insertional mutants.

Because the ES cell system is relatively new and more demanding to manage, and because the retroviral system has not yielded consistently high levels of expression of genes, microinjection has thus far been the most widely exploited method for the transfer of genes to the germ line.

THE CONCEPT OF TRANSGENE AND TRANSGENICS

Organisms into which heterologous DNA (transgene) has been artificially introduced and integrated in their genomes are called *transgenics*. Since the early 1980s, fruit flies, sea urchins, frogs, laboratory mice, and farm animals, such as cows, pigs, and sheep (Pursel, *et al.*, 1989), have been successfully produced. The transgenes are introduced into the prounclei of fertilized eggs by injection, and the injected embryos are incubated *in vitro* or implanted into the uterus of a pseudopregnant female for subsequent development. In these studies, multiple copies of transgenes are integrated at random locations in the genome of the transgenic individuals. If the transgenes are linked with functional promoters, expression of transgenes as well as display of change in phenotype is expected in some of the transgenic individuals. Furthermore, the transgenes in many transgenic individuals are also transmitted through the germline to subsequent generations.

TABLE 22.1: The transgenic animals play important roles in basic research as well as applied biotechnology

Type of biotechnology researches	Uses
Basic biotechnology research	Transgenic animals provide excellent models for studying molecular genetic of early vertebrate development, actions of oncogenes, and the biological functions of hormones at different stages of development.
Applied biotechnology research	Transgenic animals provide unique opportunities for producing animal models for biomedical research, improving the genetic background of broodstock for animal husbandry or aquaculture, and designing bioreactors for producing valuable proteins for pharmaceutical or industrial purposes.

Since 1985, a wide of transgenic fish species have been produced by microinjecting or electroporating homologous or heterologous transgenes into newly fertilized or unfertilized eggs.

INTEGRATION OF MICROINJECTED SEQUENCES INTO THE EMBRYO: A CASE STUDY OF MICE

The immature female mice were made to superovulate by sequential administration of FSH/LH and HCG and mated to fertile males. One-celled embryos are flushed from the oviducts and placed in a drop of medium and viewed by phase-contrast or interference microscopy.

While, the embryo at the pronuclear stage is held in place by suction, a microneedle loaded with a suspension of plasmid DNA. It is introduced through the zone pellucida and plasma membrane into the most accessible pronucleus (usually the male) and several hundred molecules of the recombinant DNA are injected in a volume of approximately 1 picoliter (pl). Embryos surviving the injection are transferred to foster mothers and allowed to develop to term. After birth, the presence of foreign material is studied by DNA hybridization with appropriate probes.

Since integration of Microinjected DNA is an event unique to each embryo. Most of the attention of researchers in laboratories that produce transgenic mice is focused on the expression of transferred genes. A very little is known about the mechanisms that operate in the fertilized oocyte and allow it to integrate the Microinjected DNA. However, several features have been recognized as characteristic of the integration process: the Microinjected molecules tend to form long, head-to-tail concatamers and, thereafter, to integrate at one or, rarely, two sites within the host genome; integration may or may not be delayed for several cleavage divisions after microinjection; and insertion of microinjected DNA is associated with rearrangements both of the donor material and the recipient genome.

The rate-limiting step for the integration of microinjected sequences is the disruption of the host genome, which is necessary to provide a target site for insertion, after which additional copies integrate by homologous recombination. Integration of microinjected DNA can ultimately result in deletions and duplications within host DNA as well as interspersion of *islands* of genomic DNA within the donor material. At the chromosomal level, breakage and translocations at the insertion site have also been documented.

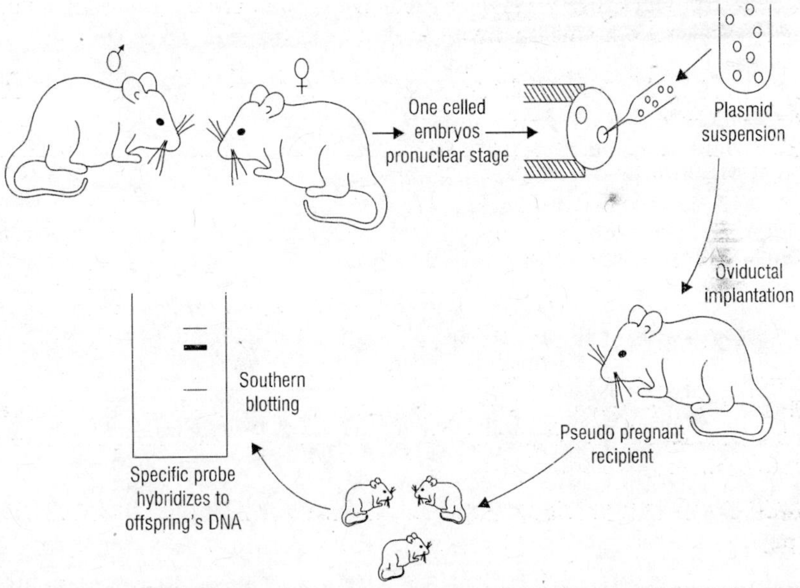

FIGURE 22.2: Production of transgenic mice by pronuclear microinjection (Gordon et al. 1980). One-celled fertilized eggs are recovered and the most accessible pronucleus, usually the male, is Microinjected. Embryos are then transferred to the oviducts of pseudopregnant females and evaluated after birth by Southern blot hybridization, or a related technique, for retention of foreign DNA.

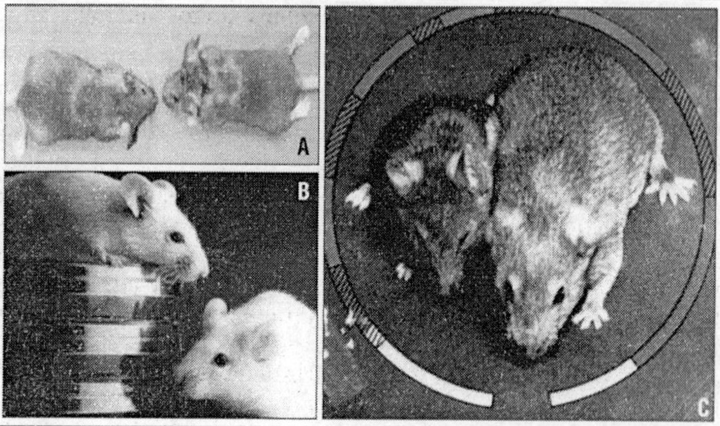

FIGURE 22.3: (A) High Contribution Embryonic Stem Cell- Mouse Chimeras. (B) Transgenic mouse. (C) Size of organism doubled as a result of the addition of genetic material by the new biotechnology.

Even after insertion, transgene sequences may be subjected to structural changes, which can cause loss of copies of the tandem array, perhaps by *looping out* of identical subunits that recombine with each other. Other reported alterations include transient amplification of transgenes, dispersion of donor material throughout the genome and maintenance of foreign material in the absence of integration.

In April, 2002, University of Michigan Transgenic Core successfully produced transgenic rats designed from two transgenes in Sprague-Dawley rats (Crl:CD (SD) IGS BR). The transgenes were designed to express either the green flourescent protein (eGFP) or the beta-galactosidase reporter gene (lacZ).

Genotyping Transgenic Mice by PCR

This is the test method of mice for the presence of the transgene by PCR. The method is designed for those people/ investigators who are unfamiliar with mouse genotyping and who need to establish a genotyping method.

1. Quantitate DNA
2. Prepare 20 µl aliquots of tail DNA diluted to 200 ng/microliter in autoclaved water.
3. Heat DNA for 1 minute in a dry bath set for 95 degrees C. Spin down tubes and place on ice.
4. Prepare PCR cocktail

Reagent	for 1 reaction	for 20 reactions
autoclaved water	14.0 microliters	280.0 microliters
10X PCR Buffer	2.5 microliters	50.0 microliters
Nucleotides (10 millimolar)	4.0 microliters	80.0 microliters
Primer A (10pmol/microliter)	1.25 microliters	25.0 microliters
Primer B (10pmol/microliter)	1.25 microliters	25.0 microliters
Taq Polymerase (0.3125 U/microliter)	1.0 microliters	20.0 microliters
Total Volume	24. microliters	480.0 microliters

5. Aliquot 24.0 microliter of cocktail into PCR tubes.
6. Add 1.0 microliter of heat treated DNA to PCR tube. (if tail DNA is less than 200

ng/microliter then add 200 ng of DNA in a volume up to 3 microliters)
7. Final volume of PCR reaction is 25.0 microliters.
8. Overlay with mineral oil and place into thermal cycler.
9. Amplify 30 to 35 cycles.
10. Analyze on appropriate ethidium bromide containing agarose gel. Analyze up to 60 samples on a 20 × 20 cm 1.5% agarose gel in TBE

Notes: (1) Prepare a cocktail with an extra 10% to account for pipetting errors. (2) Remember to include a negative control of water only and a positive control of known transgenic mouse DNA or linearized plasmid DNA diluted in mouse tail DNA to the one copy level. (3) Remember to include an internal positive control to ensure that the DNA sample is *amplifiable*. For this purpose use primers for mouse β-globin. Primers that amplify any single copy mouse gene may also be used. For example, amplification of β-globin indicates that the DNA is clean and *amplifiable*. This will prevent false negative results and positive animals will not be accidentally discarded. (4) Internal positive control primers may be combined with transgene specific primers if the two primer sets do not interfere with each other.

Transgenic Outline

This is a brief outline of the steps necessary to obtain a transgenic mice. Simply put, the investigator constructs a transgene with a promoter and a structural gene (for example a reporter gene such as lacZ or a transcription factor). DNA is prepared and microinjected into fertilized mouse eggs. Potentially transgenic mice are born. Transgenic founders are identified and bred to produce offspring for analysis. Core personnel are available for consultation on all aspects of transgenic research.

Plan the Experiment

The experiments are plant with the following aspects:

1. What is the purpose of your experiment?
2. Do you want to analyze tissue specific regulatory sequences?
3. Do you want to overexpress a protein in a specific cell lineage?

For thise purposes, you will need to obtain or clone the desired promoter and structural gene. Certain genes will be deleterious or incompatible with proper growth and development of the embryo, special arrangements should be made if you expect embryonic lethality from transgene expression. The expression of a transgene requires that the appropriate transcriptional control element be included in the DNA construct. Preliminary studies in cell cultures are recommended to verify the integrity of the construct and the function of the promoter. However, it is not always possible to predict in advance whether the transgene will have the capability of being expressed *in vivo*. The Core has a nuclear localized lacZ reporter vector (pnlacf) for investigators who wish to characterize regulatory elements in transgenic mice. A completed materials transfer agreement is required before this plasmid can be distributed to investigators. Commerically available vectors that may be useful in transgenic research include:

1. the CMV-IE promoter for widespread gene expression,
2. tetracyline regulated gene expression systems for inducible gene expression, and
3. luciferase and green fluorescent protein reporter genes.

Clone and the Verify the Transgene

In transgene design several things should be considered during cloning. For example, prokaryotic vector sequences interfere with the expression of some transgenes, thus unique restriction sites at the 5' and 3' ends of the construct should be available for vector removal. The transgene should contain unique markers so that its presence can be easily detected in DNA samples and so that its expression can be assayed and distinguished from endogenous gene expression. Sequencing of junction fragments should be carried out in order to confirm that the transgene has a functional promoter, initiation codon, and polyadenylation signal. Under the best circumstances, the transgene is tested for expression in a tissue culture system before transgenic mice are made.

Establish a Screening Method

First establish a PCR assay to rapidly identify transgenic mice. Before you submit your DNA for microinjection into fertilized mouse eggs, the Core requries that you provide evidence that you have a PCR or Sourthern blot assay that detects your transgene when it is spiked into mouse tail DNA at a one copy concentration. A second assay that will detect an endogenous mouse gene, such as beta-globin, is required in order to demonstrate that the DNA preparations are amenable to PCR. Mice are tested with both assays so that no transgenic mice are accidently discarded because the tail DNA is not suitable for PCR. You also need to have a Southern blot assay so that you can determine the copy number, integration site number, and transgene integrity in the transgenic founder mice prior to breeding.

Establish an Expression Assay

This can comprise the addition of a beta galactosidase substrate that will result in tissues stained blue, an antibody assay to an overexpressed protein (Western blot, radio-immuno precipitation, immunohistochemistry, etc.), an RT-PCR assay to detect transgene transcripts, or an RNAse protection assay.

DNA Purification and Microinjection

Purify the DNA. Simply perform a restriction enzyme digest on your cloning vector to liberate 10 ug of the transgene insert from the cloning vector. Run out a few hundred nanograms of DNA on a minigel to determine that the digest went to completion and that the bands are the correct size. Bring the remainder of the digest (in a final volume of 100 to 200 microliters) to the Core lab and we will purify the DNA for microinjection from the digest. Use the Nucleospin Extract Kit for purification of microinjection DNA. Note, if you want use large DNA fragments such as bacterial artificial chromosomes, that there is a specific protocol for the preparation of the BAC DNA for microinjection. Transgene constructs are then quantitated and microinjected into (C57BL/6 X SJL) F2 mouse eggs and surgically transferred to recipients. This is a fee for service provided by the Transgenic Core. The Transgenic Core prioritizes all requests for service on a "first-come, first-serve" basis. Your DNA will be added to the microinjection queue in the order that it is received.

Screen Potential Founders

Tail biopsies from potentially transgenic mice will be obtained 5 weeks after injecting eggs (3 weeks gestation time and 2 weeks of post-natal growth). The investigator then extracts DNA from the tail tips and tests for the transgene by PCR. Ideally, the investigator will identify which pups are transgenic before they are weaned at three weeks of age so that only transgenic pups will be delivered.

Southern Analysis

Between the time that the transgenic pups are identified and they are 6 weeks old Southern blot analysis should be done to determine how many copies of the transgene integrated, how many chromosomal sites the transgene inserted into, to verify transgenic status and to determine if the transgene is intact. With this information, transgenic founders with a good chance of transmission (at least 5-10 copies) of an intact transgene in a single insertion site can be selected for intensive breeding.

Breeding and Analysis of Transgenic Mice

The final stage in the process is to study animals carrying the transgene. Typcially, the transgenic founder animals are bred to mice of defined genetic background such as C57BL/6. Analysis of transgene expression and the consequences of expression is conducted in the offspring.

Advanced Cell Technology has performed research on cloning endangered species through a technology called *Inter-species Nuclear Transfer*". This technology differs from normal cloning in that the egg cell is provided by a related (usually domestic) species, and the pregnancy is carried in an animal other than the endangered animal. This technology could be used to preserve endangered species without the need to breed the animals in captivity. Advanced Cell Technology demonstrated the feasibility of this approach in January of 2001, with the birth of Noah, the first endangered animal born by inter-species nuclear transfer. (*Referencecs*: 1. Cloning of an Endangered Species (*Bos gaurus*) Using Interspecies Nuclear Transfer, *Cloning*, 2(2):79-90, 2000. 2. Cloning Noah's Ark - Biotechnology might offer the best way to keep some endangered species from disappearing from the planet, *Scientific American*, 283 (5):84-89, 2000

Rodent Cloning and Transgenesis

Rodent genome modification methods are being developed at Advanced Cell Technology by their inventors, Drs. Teruhiko Wakayama and Tony Perry. The mouse on the left is 'Source', ACT's first mouse cloned from a somatic cell nucleus. The mice on the right contain the gene for a green fluorescent protein, put there by a novel method called metaphase II transgenesis. This means that they glow green under 'black light' (long-wavelength UV) light. But producing green mice is just the first step using an easily identified marker gene; more importantly, the method can be used to introduce genes to study disease and produce more effective medicines. The cloning and transgenesis methods pioneered by Drs. Wakayama and Perry.

Expression of Foreign Genes in Transgenic Mice

Three major factors influence the expression of genes in developing eukaryotes: *cis*-acting elements in or around genes; *trans*-acting factors, which interact with genes in open chromosomal domains and stimulate transcription; and the location of a gene within the host genome. Because these same factors must operate to determine the regulation of expression of transferred genes, analysis of expression of foreign genes in transgenic mice produced by microinjection has provided important and basic information about the relative importance of these factors in the determination of the timing with respect to development, the efficiency, and the tissue distribution of gene expression.

Specific Applications of Transgenic Mice

Gene Expression

Transgenic Mice in Immunology: The ability of the immune system to distinguish and mount a response to myriad foreign antigens while recognizing *self* as nonantigenic has always been one of the most fascinating areas of biology. Information about the molecular genetics of the genes for immunoglobulins (Ig) and the major histocompatibility complex (MHC) has increased dramatically, and a major contribution to such information has come from studies with transgenic mice. Introduction of rearranged Ig genes into transgenic mice has helped enormously to clarify mechanisms of rearrangements of Ig genes and the importance of this phenomenon to the regulation of their expression.

The expression of rearranged heavy-chain genes in T cells indicates that the inability of the T cell to express heavy-chain genes is related to the absence of gene rearrangement in these lineages. This result is all the more intriguing since T cells are able to rearrange the T-cell receptor gene, which shares several features with the Ig gene.

One of the classical concepts in immunology, namely, that rearrangement of *k* genes inhibits rearrangement of genes (isotypic exclusion) was challenged by the finding that the presence of transgenic rearranged *k* genes did not, in all cases, result in isotypic exclusion. This observation led to the hypothesis that two separate B cell lineages exist, one that is capable of rearranging both *K* and * genes and one that can only rearrange *k* genes.

Transgenic Mice in Oncology

The study of transferred oncogenes has always been hampered by the fact that cell lines in culture have already been transformed to an abnormal phenotype. Thus, the transforming potential of an oncogenic sequence of nucleotides in a cell can be enhanced or obscured by preexisting proliferative abnormality. Our ability to insert oncogenes and proto-oncogenes into embryos and to study their effects in the normally differentiating cells of an intact organism has circumvented this problem, and results of such studies have made an enormous contribution to our understanding of **neoplastic disease** and its relationship to aberrant gene expression.

Transgenic Mice as Animal Models of Human Diseases

Animal models for human illnesses are useful for studying the pathogenesis of diseases as well as for developing and testing new therapies. However, many human diseases either do not exist in animals or are only developed by higher mammals, making models scarce and expensive to researchers. Human diseases can be induced in transgenic mice by expression of transferred genes, or by insertional disruption of endogenous sequences. Some examples of models created by transgene expression are listed below.

1. **Hepatitis B** is a human disease that lacks a readily workable animal model. Introduction of the HBsAg gene into mice results in transgenic mice that mimic the carrier state with production of HBsAg in the liver but with an absence of disease.
2. **Progressive multifocal leukencephalopathy** can be recreated in mice by injection of the JC viral genome. Another disease of the nervous system, neurofibromatosis, can be induced in mice by introduction of the gene for

tyrosine aminotransferase (TAT) of HTLV-1.

3. **Osteogenesis** imperfect is a dominant disorder that results from a mutation of the gene for Â1 (I) collagen. The simple, resultant amino-acid substitution results in a change in the helical structure of mature collegen. This condition has been induced in mice by microinjection of a mutant gene for collegen Â1 (I), created in the laboratory by site-directed mutagenesis.

Transgenic Mice as Models for Gene Therapy

Genes can be inserted into transgenic animals and function to alleviate disease states. Such model systems can be of great importance in improving our understanding of the potential for gene transfer as an approach to treatment of disease.

Mice with growth-hormone deficiency are markedly reduced in size and males suffer from infertility. Introduction of the growth-hormone gene into these animals leads to growth which exceeds that of normal animals and restores male fertility. However, the pattern of release of growth hormone that results from transgene function is apparently inconsistent with female fertility.

Mice lacking enes at the MHC region are unable to respond to the synthetic antigen poly (Glu-Lys-Phe). When the gene for Ia is inserted into transgenic animals, transgene function restores immunoreponsiveness to antigens. Insertion of either the mouse or human ß-globin gene can reduce the severity of ß-thalassemia in mice. In these experiments, the product of the human globin gene was able to associate effectively with the mouse Â chains, and it actually functioned better than the transferred mouse gene ß-globin in palliating the thalassemic state.

Mice with a deficiency in gonadotropin-releasing hormone (GnRH) are infertile and exhibit profound pertubations of their reproductive endocrine functions. Cloning of the GnRH gene and its transfer into mice has resulted in restoration of normal endocrine function and in fertility.

Transgenic Mice as Models for Genetic Engineering

Genetic engineering of resistance to chemotherapy is one technique that can assist in increasing the therapeutic margin of a drug. In cancer therapy the toxic doses of most antineoplatic drugs overlap with their therapeutic does, so that the intensity and duration of drug regimens are, of necessity, limited. Production of transgenic animals that are systematically resistant to the effects of a drug provides a test system with which to answer questions about whether intensive chemotherapy can improve the overall survival of tumor-bearing hosts or whether treatment would just select for highly resistant tumors.

Introduction of the gene for the receptor for **low-density lipoprotein** (LDL), under control of the MT-1 promoter, has resulted in inducible expression of the gene with a resultant decrease in levels of free LDLs within the circulation of the transgenic animals (Hoffman et al. 1988). This experiment suggests a potential strategy for a genetic approach to the control of high levels of LDL, which could eventually reduce the risk of atherosclerosis.

The successful production of transgenic rabbits, pigs, and sheep by microinjection suggests that, in the future, genetically engineered farm animals may play an important role in agriculture and medicine. The isolation of tissue plasminogen activator (TPA) from the milk of transgenic mice after linkage of the TPA gene to the promoter for whey acidic protein strongly suggests that transgenic animals might be exploited as *factories* for production of valuable products which, because of post-translational modification and other reasons, cannot readily be produced in bacteria.

Antisense Genes in Transgenic Mice

Another method for negating gene function involves the use of antisense transcripts. When genes are cloned in reverse orientation with respect to the promoter, RNA may be produced from the noncoding strand. This RNA, presumably by forming a heteroduplex with the sense RNA, can block translation of cytoplasmic mRNA. Thus, antisense genes can be used to obliterate production of proteins from specific genes in transgenic animals. The feasibility of this approach has recently been demonstrated by the transfer of an antisense construct of the gene for myelin basic protein (MBP) into mice. Interference with the production of MBP resulted in dysmyelination. Although this is still infancy, it has great potential for future experiments.

In addition to the specific used outlined above, studies with transgenic mice have had a significant impact in the understanding of development and its genetic basis.

USE OF TRANSGENICS IN ANIMAL AGRICULTURE AND RESEARCH MODELS

Transgenic Swine

In 1980 and 1981, six laboratories reported the successful transfer of foreign DNA into fertilized mouse ova. The potential of these studies was dramatically illustrated by the transfer of genes that caused accelerated growth in mice. In general, the mice that integrated and expressed a **growth hormone** (GH) **gene construct**, which was composed of either the gene for **rat growth hormone** (rGH) or **human growth hormone** (hGH) regulated by a metallothionein (MT) promoter sequence, grew to almost twice the size, by 7 to 12 weeks of age, of the sex-matched littermate controls.

The potential of transgenic livestock with enhanced growth performance was suggested by pioneering experiments in 1982. Working with growth hormone (GH) genes, Palmiter and coworkers (1982 and 1983) published their initial results on the significantly enhanced growth of transgenic mice. The first construct that they described included an rGH gene fused to a mouse MT-1 regulatory sequence (enhancer/promoter). Later, similar results were obtained with the MT regulatory sequence fused to a human or a bovine GH structural gene. It is noteworthy that the genomic rGH and hGH genes, under the control of their own (endogenoue) regulatory sequences, did not enhance growth of mice in early experiments. This negative result suggested that foreign genes for GH with endogenous promoters were subject to the normal regulatory mechanisms that influence a normal pattern of growth. The MT regulatory sequence was necessary to drive accelerated transcription of the gene, which resulted in elevated levels of GH peptide in the blood and enhanced growth in the mice. In addition, other regulatory sequences, namely, those associated with genes for albumin, murine leukemia virus, and phosphoenolpyruvate carboxykinase (PEPCK), were successfully used to drive expression of a GH gene with resultant enhancement of the growth of transgenic animals.

While the increased body size of mice transgenic for GH genes is important, perhaps of greatest interest to livestock producers are the various morphological characteristic associated with the MT-GH transgenic mice. These characteristics include increased feed efficiency and growth rate, increased lean-muscle mass, and reduced fat. It has been estimated that a modest 10% increase in feed efficiency and growth rate could equate to an annual saving of on billion dollars to swine producers in the United States.

The studies of exogenous administration of GH to livestock further demonstrate the potential impact of GH-transgenic livestock on the agriculture industry. The exogenous administration of GH to pigs can increase deposition of protein and muscle mass while simultaneously causing a decrease in fat deposition both in the muscle and subcutaneous regions. Exogenous administration of GH to dairy cattle has also been shown to increase milk production dramatically. GH is secreted from acidophiles in the anterior pituitary gland in response to the hypothalamic hormone; GH releasing factor (GRF). Exogenous administration of GRF to pigs, cattle, sheep, and rats stimulated release of GH from the pituitary with all the subsequent growth-performance characteristics discussed above.

As in the case of exogenous administration of GH, it has been established that GH-transgenic pigs do exhibit significantly greater feed efficiency and less back fat. The process of growth and development is a well-or-chestrated and intricate cascade of events. Therefore, one cannot become discouraged by the problems associated with the present state of transgenic pig production. The great potential for benefit to both the consumer and producer of pork in the United States warrants continued research into the development of a suitable GH-transgenic pig.

Prospects

In the future, three benefits from production of transgenic pigs are envisioned:

1. Enhancement of production characteristics;
2. Molecular farming; and
3. Use of such pigs as models of human disease.

Enhancement of production characteristics will necessitate tighter control of gene regulation in the production of transgenic swine. More precise control of transgenes, by a regulator such as that of PEPCK, may allow regulation *in vivo* of structural genes that have been unavailable to date.

Beyond the area of enhanced growth performance, the possibility of decreasing an animal's susceptibility to disease offers another potential mechanism for improving production efficiency. In addition to enhancement of production characteristics and molecular farming, further projects with transgenic pigs may include production of models for human diseases. The pig has been used extensively as an alternative to human subjects because of the many physiological similarities between pigs and humans. Models for cardiac and metabolic disorders or cancer may be best addressed in a transgenic pig.

In order to enhance growth performance in swine using the transgenic model, a number of approaches may be utilized in the future. These approaches may involve new genes of choice as well as improved methodology; for example, the targeting of genes with greater specificity and improvement of techniques for gene transfer hold great promise.

PRODUCTION OF SHEEP TRANSGENIC FOR GROWTH HORMONE GENES

Injection of lambs with growth hormone (GH) increases feed efficiency and decreases the fat content of the carcass. Introduction of transgenes to increase plasma levels of GH holds promise as a method for improving growth characteristics of sheep. Hammer et al. (1985) reported the introduction of a human GH fusion gene into the genome of a ewe lamb by microinjection of DNA into the pronuclei of fertilized ova. Subsequently, several investigators have reported the introduction of genes that increase circulating levels of GH in sheep.

Insertion of Genes

Microinjection of Genes

One limitation to the transfer of genetic material by pronuclear microinjection in farm animals is that yolk obstructs the view of pronuclei. In spite of the yolk, using differential interferencecentrast microscopy, reported that pronuclei were visible in about 80% of fertilized, one-cell, sheep eggs. Even so, pronuclei were not as clearly visible as those in mouse ova.

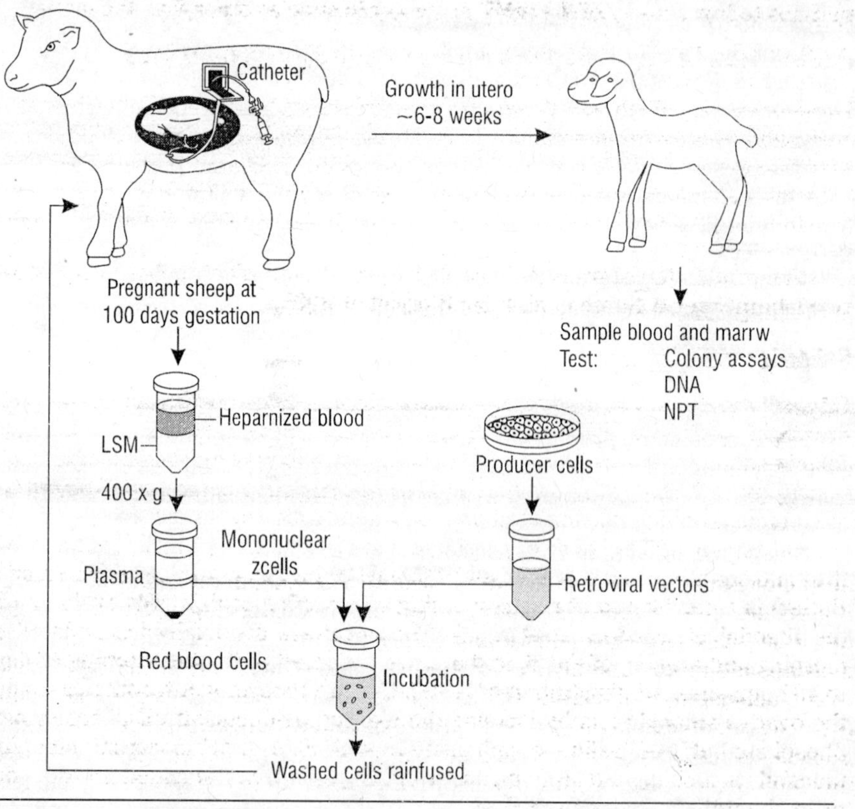

FIGURE 22.4: Schematic diagram of the protocol used for transducing circulating hematopoieric cells from fetal sheep.

Poor visibility of sheep pronuclei may account in part for the low rate of production of transgenic lambs, particularly when this rate is compared to the rate of production of transgenic mice. The first attempt to produce transgenic sheep resulted in only 0.1% of the microinjected eggs yielding transgenic lambs. Presently, 4.45% of eggs injected by the same group of researchers yielded transgenic lambs. The efficiency of production of transgenic sheep may improve with increased experience at microinjection. Other factors may have contributed to this improved efficiency, including the nature of the DNA that was microinjected.

Survival of Microinjected Embryos: Microinjection reduces the ability of fertilized one-and two-cell ova to develop to blastocysts in both pigs and sheep. The reduction was greater in sheep than in pigs.

Expression of Transgenes

Proportion of Expressing Transgenics

Expression of transgenes in domestic animals has been reported in only a few cases. Expression of transgenes varied from about 50% for transgenic sheep that expressed MThGH or MTbGH to about 14% for transgenic sheep that expressed MThGRF. Poor expression of the MThGRF transgene may be related to its high content of cDNA or perhaps to low activity of the mMT promoter in species other than the mouse.

PRODUCTION OF TRANSGENIC CATTLE BY PRONUCLEAR INJECTION

Pronuclear injection of one-cell embryos has been used extensively to produce transgenic mice and, to a lesser extent, rabbits, pigs, and sheep. One-cell bovine embryos were injected with a pRSVCAT construct and fetal tissues were collected for analysis of integration and expression. Integration was found to have occurred in seven fetal samples and expression of the transgene was observed in placental tissue of one sample.

The production of transgenic cattle by pronuclear injection has been reported by two laboratories (Church et al. 1986; Biery et al. 1988).

Collection of Embryos

One-cell bovine embryos were collected from excised oviducts of Holstein and crossbred, beef-type donors after induction of superovulation by injections of follicle-stimulating hormone (FSH). The superovulation regimen consists of eight injections of FSH (FSH-P, Schering) at 12-hour intervals over a **five-day period** (treatment with FSH are initiated on the evening following of day:

On 1st day a 25-mg dose of prostaglandin F2f (Lutalyse, Upjohn) is given with the fifth and sixth injections of FSH and 4,000 IU of human chronic gonadotropin (HCG, Butler) is administered at noon or during the evening of day 5 (44 or 48 hours after the first injection of prostaglandin). The cows are artificially inseminated on the morning and evening of day 6, and ova are collected furing the morning of day 7 (36 to 40 hours after administration of HCG). Ova are recovered after surgical removal of the ovaries and oviducts by flushing the excised oviducts with Dulbecco's modified phosphate-buffered saline supplemented with 0.4% bovine serum albumin, 100 units/ml penicillin and 100 µg/ml streptomycin. Ova remained in this medium throughout the injection procedure.

Pronuclear Injection

One-cell embryos are centrifuged at 15,000 g to aid in the visualization of pronuclei. Injections are performed under an inverted microscope (Zeiss or Nikon) equipped with Nomarski optics at 400 magnification. Embryos are placed in a drop of 3-5 µl of medium on a glass depression slide. A 2-µl drop of diluted DNA is then placed next to this drop and both drops were covered with paraffin oil. Manipulations are carried out with the aid of Leitz or Narishige micromanipulates. Embryos are held by a fine, polished, holding pipette (outer diameter approximately 150 µm) and the plasma and nuclear membranes are penetrated with an injection pipette (tip diameter approximately 1-2 µm). DNA is injected with the aid of an oil-filled microsyringe (Stoliting) until expansion of the pronucleus was visible (25% expansion or less). In the majority of embryos, the most visible pronucleus was injected. If both pronuclei are equally visible, the large pronucleus is injected.

Preparation of DNA

The plasmid pRSVCAT, containing the bacterial gene for chloramphenicol acetyltransferase (CAT) under the control of the **Rous sarcoma virus** long terminal repeat, is linearized by digestion with restriction endonuclease Ndel (New England Bio Labs). The DNA fragment is then purified by extraction with phenol : chloroform:isoamyl alcohol (25:24:1) and precipitated with ethanol. The purified fragment is re-suspended in 10mM Tris (pH 7.5), 0.25 mM EDTA. The concentration of the DNA is then determined spectrophotometrically, and the appropriate concentrations of DNA are made. The DNA is diluted for injection in 10 mM Tris (pH 7.5), 0.25 mM EDTA. The majority of the embryos are injected with DNA at a concentration of 2 ng/µl. In three separate experiments the concentration of injected DNA is varied to determine the effect of concentration of DNA on the viability of embryos and the rates of incorporation.

In the first experiment, concentrations of DNA of 1,2, and 4 ng/µl are injected. In the second experiment, 2, 25 and 50 ng/µl are injected, and in the third experiment, 2, 50, and 100 ng/µl of DNA are injected. Within each experiment different embryo donors and different injection technicians are equally represented in all treatments. The three experiments are conducted at different times, and, therefore, embryo donors and injection technicians varied between the experiments.

Culture and Transfer of Embryos

After pronuclear injection all embryos are cultured to the morula or blastocyst stage. Culture from the one-cell to the morula or blastocyst stage is conducted either in the ligated sheep oviduct or *in vitro*. Those embryos cultured in the sheep oviduct are transferred (either with or without embedding in double-layer cylinders of agar) into ewes whose oviducts had been ligated at the uterotubal junction according to procedures described by Willaden (1979). Embryos remained in the sheep oviduct for six days, at which time they are flushed from the oviducts and evaluated for development to the morula or blastocyst stage. Those embryos cultured *in vitro* are placed in 20-µl drops that consisted of a 1:1 mixture of Brinster's Mouse Ovum Culture Medium (BMOC) III medium and bovine oviductal fluid. Two to three microliters of bovine oviductal epithelial cells are added to each drop and drops are covered with silicon oil (Dow Corning).

Embryos are cultured at 38 °C in an atmosphere of 5% CO_2 and 95% air for seven days evaluated for development to the morula or blastocyst stage. In experiments where the effect of various concentrations of DNA is investigated, the method of culture is the same for all treatments.

All embryos that developed to the morula or blastocyst stage are transferred by a nonsurgical technique to synchronous recipients (the age of embryos is assumed to be seven days in all cases). In most cases only one embryo is transferred to each recipient but in a few cases two or three embryos are transferred to a single recipient in the same uterine horn.

Collection and Analysis of Tissue

Established pregnancies are carried to 60 to 65 days of gestation, at which time fetuses are surgically removed, with a sample of placental tissue.

Fetal and placental tissues are separated and both are sanp-frozen in liquid nitrogen. Tissue remained frozen until analysis for incorporation and expression of the transgene.

Fetal and placental tissue is homogenized in STE (0.15 M NaCl, 20 mM Tris, pH 7.8), 10 mM EDTA that contained 1% sodium dodecylsulfate and 0.2 mg/ml proteins K (Boehringer Mannheim Biochemicals)]. The homogenate is incubated at 37 °C overnight. DNA is then purified by extraction of the homogenate with an equal volume of phenol: chloroform: isoamyl alcohol (25:24:1), followed by precipitation with ethanol. The DNA is resuspended in STE and subjected to a second precipitation. The DNA is finally resuspended in 10 mM Tris (pH 7.8), 1 mM EDTA.

In order to check for the presence of pRSVCAT in the bovine DNA, the isolated DNA is subjected to Southern blot analysis. Ten micrograms of bovine DNA is digested with restriction endonuclease EcoRI (Boehringer Mannheim Biochemicals) and separated by agarose gel electrophoresis. The DNA is then transferred to nitrocellulose paper and probed with 32P-labeled pRSVCAT. The pRSVCAT is labeled using a nick translation kit (Betheseda Research Laboratories). Bovine DNA isolated from uterine tissue served as the negative control. pRSVCAT is added to bovine DNA at one and 10 copies per haploid genome to serve as positive controls.

Using above procedure transgenic cattle can be obtained.

METHODS FOR THE INTRODUCTION OF RECOMBINANT DNA INTO CHICKEN EMBRYOS

Introduction of recombinant DNA into the pronucleus of fertilized mouse eggs by microinjection or into early mouse embryos by use of murine retroviral vectors is a routine procedure in many laboratories. This technology, employing recombinant DNA, may be of significant value in agricultural animal husbandry. The introduction of recombinant DNA into the germline of chickens involves a technology different from that used for insertion of genes into mammalian embryos. Avian ova are telolecithal and are normally fertilized approximately 30 minutes after ovulation. Cell division occurs in the oviduct for approximately 20 hours before oviposition. At this time, the embryo is comprised of approximately 60,000 pluripotent cells, which are collectively called the **blastoderm.** The presence of a large yolk and multiple pronuclei makes direct microinjection of DNA impractical.

Kopchick and his associates (1991) attempted to insert DNA into the chicken genome using three different approaches.

1. The **first protocol** involved insertion of recombinant DNA into unfertilized follicles of female chickens.
2. The **second protocol** for the production of transgenic chickens involved insertion of *transfection* or recombinant DNA (pBGH-4) into day-1 fertilized embryos.
3. The **third protocol** for their attempts at generating germline transgenic animals and was developed using exogenous retroviruses.

PROBLEMS AFTER DEVELOPING TRANSGENIC ANIMALS

The Nature of Patents

Opponents of animal biotechnology are using the patent issue as a way to focus public attention on matters unrelated to the Patent Office's mandate. They are, in effect, demanding that patent law be revised to address concerns about product regulation, welfare, and morality. Many of the critics fail to understand what a patent, is and what it is not.

Yet critics persist in offering a number of philosophical arguments against patenting animals. For example, Jeemy Rifkin originated the claim that transgenic animals violate *species integrity*. This he defines as the *right* of an animal *to exist as a separate identifiable creature*. The concept has been echoed by the National Council of Churches, which objected to violating *creation's inherent structures and boundaries*"

However, the concept of species integrity, like *creation science*, runs counter to what is known about biology. As stated by the congressional Office of Technology Assessment, which has studied animal bioengineering: *There is no consistent or absolute rule that species are discretely bounded in any generally applicable manner*.

Animals as Tennis Balls?

Critics also argue that animal patents devalue animal life. The patenting of life reflects a dominionistic and materialistic attitude toward living beings that precludes a proper regard for their inherent nature, says John Hoyt, president of the Human Society of the United States. And according to Rifkin, patenting animals reduces the entire animal kingdom of this planet to the lowly status of commercial commodity, a technological product indistinguishable from electric toasters, automobiles, tennis balls, or any other patented product.

Animals are bought and sold daily, valued in the marketplace on the basis of their rarity and utility. We eat them, wear them, perform biomedical research on them, put them on leashes. As bioethicist LeRoy Walters of Georgetown University's Kennedy Institute for Bioethics has suggested, patenting them *seems relatively benign*. The Humane society argues, too, that transgenic animal research will result in what it calls a *dramatic increase in the suffering of animals*. Certainly, it is possible for genetic engineering to produce an animal with characteristics that interfere with its normal functioning. But it is equally possible to create dysfunctional animals through traditional crossbreeding activities. For example, modern turkeys have been bred with breasts so large that it is impossible for them to mate, and numerous breeds of dogs now possess inbred health problems ranging from arthritis to kidney failure.

Biotechnology is also likely to provide some welcome alternatives to the ways that animals are used in laboratory testing. Because animals can be engineered to be extremely sensitive to various materials, just as the Harvard mouse was made sensitive to carcinogens, scientists will be able to obtain meaningful data using fewer animals. And lower-order animals such as mice might be substituted in some research for higher-order animals such as primates. For example, the National Institutes of Health recently developed a transgenic strain of mice whose genes contain a portion of the human immunodeficiency virus (HIV) implicated in AIDS. The virus sits quietly in the animals' cells, just, as HIV can remain latent for years before flaring up and taking control of cellular operations. For certain kinds of AIDS research, these mice are the only substitutes for chimpanzees. And as Anthony Fauci, director of federal AIDS research, points out, the limited supply of laboratory animals is serious impediment to progress in this important field.

Down on the Farm

The patentability of animals is being challenged on economic as well as moral grounds. Some agricultural activists claim that the new policy will boost costs, citing in particular the possibility that farmers and ranchers will have to pay royalties for progeny produced by patented animals. But a wise farmer is not going to buy a patented animal, or any other item, unless it will increase profits. That is just what transgenic breeds are being engineered to do. The new animals will provide meat and milk at a lower cost of production. They will be healthier. And they will yield premium products, such as meat that is low in calories and cholesterol, which will fetch higher prices.

Time to Decide

Although the United States is the first country to patent a transgenic animal, it is not the only nation that recognizes the patentability of transgenic animals. A 1987 survey by the World Intellectual Property Organization shows that 53 countries have not expressly excluded animals from patent protection, and patents are already permitted in 10 of these countries: Japan Canada, Australia, Argentina, New Zealand, Turkey, Brazil, Greece, Hungary, and the Netherlands. It is, therefore, essential to mention that the *time will decide* the fait and impact of transgenic animals on society and nature.

PROBLEMS AFTER DEVELOPING TRANSGENIC ANIMALS

The Nature of Patents

Opponents of animal biotechnology are using the patent issue as a way to focus public attention on matters unrelated to the Patent Office's mandate. They are, in effect, demanding that patent law be revised to address concerns about product regulation, welfare, and morality. Many of the critics fail to understand what a patent, is and what it is not.

Yet critics persist in offering a number of philosophical arguments against patenting animals. For example, Jeemy Rifkin originated the claim that transgenic animals violate *species integrity*. This he defines as the *right* of an animal *to exist as a separate identifiable creature*. The concept has been echoed by the National Council of Churches, which objected to violating *creation's inherent structures and boundaries*"

However, the concept of species integrity, like *creation science*, runs counter to what is known about biology. As stated by the congressional Office of Technology Assessment, which has studied animal bioengineering: *There is no consistent or absolute rule that species are discretely bounded in any generally applicable manner*.

CHAPTER 23

Biotechnology and Transgenic Plants

Opportunities for producing transgenic varieties are endless. Organisms into which heterologous DNA (transgene) has been artificially introduced and integrated in their genomes are called transgenics.

In past, farmers have been plant breeders for ten thousand years, altering the genetic integrity of most crops without any knowledge of heredity. These farmers were the first genetic engineers (Jones, 1994), although genetics as such did not come into existence until the work of Mendel was rediscovered by De Vries (1900) and others. Using knowledge of the inheritance of traits, plant breeding assumed scientific status and during the past one hundred years has developed to allow very direct control over crop evolution for man's benefit. Until the advent of genetic engineering (GE) plant breeding was confined to making crosses within and between crop species which could occur naturally, albeit that some crosses were forced. Developing transgenic crops has become routine only within the last few years and has changed the nature of plant breeding substantially, raising a whole host of ethical considerations as a consequence.

Words and terms are frequently the root of problems associated with GE. *Transgenic* sounds very much like *eugenic* and could, therefore, be condemned by association, and *engineered* sounds more sinister than *domesticated* (Jones, 1994) though they are virtual synonyms.

Transgenic plants refer to plants in which functional foreign genes have been inserted. They help in understanding the mechanisms of gene expression. This could be possible only by using tissue culture and recombinant DNA techniques (efficient gene cloning methods, improved vector systems, organ specific promoters, marker genes, cloned DNA etc.). The techniques for transferring foreign genes into plant cells regenerating the transformed cells in fertile transgenic plants were established by Bevan et al, (1983) and Fraley et al, (1983). Thus, the year 1983 was a watershed for plant biotechnology. The technical break through fueled not only activities in basic research on the mechanism of plant gene regulation, but also intensive exploitation of its biotechnological application for crop improvement.

During the last 17 years, dramatic progress has been made in the application of transgenic technology for crop improvement. Because the transfer of one or two genes can be done reproducibly and routinely with this technology it is not surprising that the first generation experiments in plant biotechnology entailed the transfer and modification of single gene traits. These experiments were directed towards two commercial target areas: plant protection and quality enhancement (Chua, 1996). The subject has been reviewed and overviews (Goodman *et al.*, 1987; Uchimiya et al. 1989; Paszkowski et al. 1989; Raffa, 1989; Cornelissen and Melchers, 1993; Chua 1994, 1996; Kaul and Nirmala, 1995; Goy and Duesing, 1995; Beachy, 1999, Tyagi, et al. 1999).

ADVANTAGES OF TRANSGENIC PLANTS

1. Agronomic traits can be improved by producing plants with increased resistance

to pest, disease, stress along with increased vigor, yield.
2. Enhanced efficiency of physiological process like photosynthesis and improved nutritional qualities.
3. Transgenic plants are also used as an analytical tool to explore aspects of gene regulation.
4. Major advantage of molecular breeding is that when a particular gene has been isolated and reconstructed it can be first in model plants and later it can be used in a variety of cultivars of different crops.

Other Uses

- **Environment:** Transgenic plants may be used as a means of bioremediation *i.e.* decontamination of polluted land. Transgenic *Liriodendrom tulipifera* (yellow poplar) expressed bacterial mercuric reductase gene (Rugh *et al.*, 1988). These plants survive in high Hg levels and release elemental Hg.
- **Biomass/fuel:** Biomass producing crops include rapidly growing tress used for fuel or products (ethanol). Transgenic plants for this aim either over-expressed cellulose synthase gene (Arioli *et al.*, 1998) or cellulases that convert cellulose to ethanol.
- **Lignin/paper:** Cellulose is raw material for paper. Lignin is separated from cellulose fibers during pulping. Transgenic plants with modified lignin show ease of lignin solubilization and fragmentation. The only difference is the red brown coloured wood.
- **Plastics:** High value polymeric compounds like carbonyl include non calorific sweetness like fructan produced in transgenic sugar beet. Biodegradable plastics include polyesters of 3-hydroxy acids *i.e.* polyhydroxy alkanoates (PHA).
- **Terpenoids:** Aromatic qualities of essential oils is a feature of monoterpenes and sesquiterpenes belonging to biongoing to bio prenoid group of compounds. Construct of c-DNA library from oil gland secretory cells of peppermint has allowed menthol. Another way increasing essential oil synthesis is by increasing density of mint glandular trichomes.

Household- (Clothes and Ornamentals)

Transgenic approach on cotton include introduction of pigment compounds and synthesis of plastics like PHB in same cells. Coloured fibres avoid dying process whereas plasticity lowers thermal conductance. Genetic manipulation of ornamentals can produce coloured flowers that do not occur naturally. Vase life is increased by generating the antisense down regulation of an ethylene biosynthesis gene.

Food and Drink

- **Protein, sugars, starch, oil and vitamins:** Proteins can be modified either by changing the amino acids in a protein or by adding entirely new protein. Another application is expression of human milk proteins in edible plants. For example, gene for beta casein protein can be introduced in potato under the control of an amino auxin inducible promoter. Similarly, lactoferrin (Salmon *et al.*, 1998) proteins have been expressed in transgenic tobacco. It has antibacterial, anti fungal and antiviral properties.

  Degree of branching in carbohydrates can be altered (Heyer *et al.*, 1999) and degree of saturation and chain length of oils can be altered (Murphy, 1999) to produce transgenic plants useful for human and industry.

To overcome vitamin A deficiency psy gene encoding enzyme phytoene synthase can be introduced in plants deficient in vitamin A, production of carotenoid (vit A) is enhanced. Similarly, content of micronutrients can be increased. Endosperm of transgenic rice had high levels of Fe when gene encoding soyabean ferritin (an iron storage protein) was introduced and expressed under control of rice seed storage protein promoter (Goto *et al.*, 1999).

- **Allergens/Toxins:** Allergens can be successfully reduced in transgenic plants. Example, level of allergenic proteins (eg. AraHl) in peanut can be reduced. Similarly, caffiene level can be reduced by antisense down regulation.
- **Beer:** Transgenic barely is generated involving the modification of the glucanase enzyme as means of improving the efficiency of brewing process. Introduction of leuco anthocyanidin reductase gene improves malt quality.

Medical and veterinary applications

Vaccines/Antigenes/Antibiotics

This area include production of plant based vaccines and other medically related compounds. Transgenic potato has been successful in expressing human insulin (auto antigen) either alone or as a protein in which insulin was linked to c-terminus of cholera toxin B sub-unit (CTB).

Enzymes

Production of active enzymes is another area of interest. "World's most expensive drug" is the human lysosomal enzyme glucocerebrosidase, the only treatment for patients suffering from Gaucher's disease. It is purified from human placentae. Thus, it's production in plants is an attractive option.

Transgenic are not terminator crops

The most debated topic in agriculture and biotechnology is genetically modified (GM) crops, that is, transgenics. Genetic engineering (GE) techniques allow the transfer of a gene of interest from one species to another. It is nothing but the extension of conventional plant breeding. This technology helps the breeders and molecular biologists to introduce the only gene of interest with more selective modification and represents a significant advance.

Terminator technology is a technique of genetic engineering by which the plant is altered or modified in such a way that it produces sterile seeds, which will not germinate in the next generation. Normally, seeds have the ability to germinate generation after generation. In terminator seed, a toxic gene becomes active and is forced to die after one generation of survival. In terminator technology, three gene constructs are introduced through GE techniques to express the desired character, sterility.

The three gene constructs or stretches of DNA are referred as gene X (lethal gene), Y and Z. This entire system is under the control of an external inducer, that is, tetracycline. If only the lethal gene is inserted, then the first generation itself will not germinate. Initially, the lethal gene is prevented from being expressed for seed multiplication and thereafter, gene Y helps to excise out the 'blocking sequence' to make the gene X (ledder the control of a different gene, Z. The lethal gene becomes functional only at a later stage of seed development and allows the gene to produce toxin that kills the embryo. Ultimately, the seed harvested by the farmer lacks germination ability but according to patent claim, the seed or fruit can be used as food.

Terminator technology is developed to serve following two main purposes:

1. To force the farmers to buy seed each year for raising the next crop.
2. To prevent the piracy of the introduce special genes (that is biotic and abiotic resistance or nutritional characteristics) by researchers and multinational companies.

Green Revolution

The Green Revolution was possible due to the genetic manipulation of the plants by plant breeding. After the Green Revolution, most crops are suffering from yield plateauing and further boost may be possible from molecular breeding. To meet the challenges ahead, funds must be diverted towards new technologies to improve agricultural productivity Biotechnology may be able to solve some of the problems associated with lower productivity, and could play a major role in agricultural production.

A misconception still prevails among farmers about transgenic and terminator technology. They confuse one for the other and think that any transgenic crop will lead to sterility in the next generation crop. In both cases, the product is developed by using the same techniques of genetic engineering but the products are developed for different purposes.

A survey conducted among Indian farmers shows they are highly innovative and interested in adopting any new technology. However, it should be made available to them. A misconception still prevails among farmers about transgenic and terminator technology. They confuse one for the other and think that any transgenic crop will lead to sterility in the next generation crop. In both cases, the product has been developed by using the same techniques of genetic engineering, but the products are developed for different purposes.

The governments of developing countries have identified biotechnology as a promising and key research area with widespread application in diverse field. The developed nations benefit from biotech products because, of both private and public sector collaboration. Though there are long term risks and hazards associated with it, this new technology should be used to complement, not replace, traditional plant breeding methods to enhance productivity and quality.

Genomics and Transgenic Plants

The term genomics was coined by Thomas Roderick (1986) to describe the scientific discipline of mapping, sequencing, and analyzing genomes and to provide a name for a new journal – *Genomics*. Genomics is now undergoing, however, a transition or expansion from mapping and sequencing of genomes to an emphasis on genome function. The coded genetic information of organisms goes by the new buzzword genomics. Useful organisms are now being uncovered, *en masse*, in genome organization, expression, and interaction, rather than in terms of individual genes. The recent advances in genetic manipulation were possible as it is now possible to define the gene with respect to its function. Today, any gene of interest from any species may be identified, isolated and incorporated across species barriers. The gene has great impact on all aspects of our lives – from food production to health care, from society to politics. Recently, genes and genomics became the most discussed terms in several areas of Government and law, as they became important items of intellectual property due to the application of IPR on biological organisms.

The major revolution in the field of genomics in eukaryotes is possible due to the availability of recombinant DNA and PCR technology from the 1970s and 1980s, respectively. Though genomics is still in its infancy, it will increase the understanding of basic plant biology as well as the exploitation of genomic information for crop improvement.

Today's advances in genetics, miniaturization, computer-aided techniques and sophisticated data management have increased the possibility of solving the inherent problems within plant and animal systems. The management of the vast pool of genetic information generated by genomics research into easily accessible form has grown into a new branch of science-bio-informatics.

Bioinformatics helps in converting this data into an understanding at the gene function, which determines the scope for the successful application of genetics in humankind. The sequencing of an entire genome is time-consuming, and that is why genome technology is used to develop a cost-effective and rapid way to describe the entire genome of an organism approach (that is, *expressed sequence tags* or ESTs). The development of ESTs for individual genomes is also arduous, and has led to the development of a new tool – DNA chip technology. This technology helps parallel data acquisition for millions of DNA sequences through automation at a very fast rate using computer devices.

GM crops: global area coverage

The total global area coverage of genetically modified crops has increased from 1.7 million hectare in 1996 to 44.2 million hectare in the year 2000 indicating a 25-fold increase in a span of five years, according to Global Review of Commercialized Transgenic Crops: 2000 complied by the International Service for Acquisition of Agri-Biotech Applications (ISAAA). The number of countries cultivating GMC has gone up from six in 1996 to 13 in the year 2000. Eight of them are from industrialized nations and five from developing countries. The demand for GMC from farmers in developing countries is surging because of more convenient and flexible crop management, higher productivity and safer environment through decreased use of conventional pesticides. The study stated that earlier up to 85 per cent of GMC were grown in the industrialized countries. But with developing countries fast opting for these crops, their share of cultivation rose from 14 per cent in 1997 to 16 per cent in 1998 to 18 per cent in 1999 and 24 per cent in 2000. Now developing countries account for a quarter of the total global area coverage under GM crops of 44.2 million hectare. In fact, of the 4.3 million hectare increase in global coverage in 2000, 3.6 million hectare (equivalent to 84 per cent) was in developing countries as compared with 16 per cent (0.7 million hectare) in the industrialized countries.

To help address many of these concerns, a number of countries have developed regulations and restrictions specifying the requirements of confined field testing that are needed before commercial release (OECD, 2000). These requirements, which are necessary to reduce biological and economic risks, will undoubtedly continue to evolve. In addition to national laws and regulations, there are also broader international agreements on biosafety, *e.g.* the Cartagena Protocol on Biosafety (Convention on Biological Diversity, 2000). (adopted from Unasylva, FAO, Vol. 52: 2001/1).

GENETIC ENGINEERING AND TRANSGENIC PLANTS

Genetic engineering has unlimited scope for application, which include technologies that cater to human health and prosperity. The goal of plant, animal and microbial genetic engineer is to improve the quality and yield of products. In this chapter, various applications have been fragmented into three major subdivisions *viz.* transgenic plants, transgenic animals and miscellaneous applications.

Up till 1980s, production of transgenic plants was restricted mainly to tobacco, petunia or tomato of the family solanaceae. However, now in more than 40 dicot species transgenic plants have been successfully produced. The production of transgenic plants has now been extended to several monocotyledons like wheat, maize, rice and oats.

USES OF TRANSGENIC PLANTS

Engineered Resistance against Herbicide: The development of crop plants that are tolerant to herbicide is an important approach to control weeds. Tolerance to herbicides has been one of the offcited goals of the plant genetic engineer for several reasons. First, there are several economic advantages for farmers to have crop engineered to tolerate herbicides. Second, the biochemical pathways inhibited by herbicides have been well characterized and strategies to achieve resistance are relatively simple to devise. Third, resistance to herbicides can often be achieved by the transfer and expression of a single gene in a new host plant. Finally, resistance to certain herbicides may allow the farmer to adopt the use of some of the newer herbicides, which are considered as being environmentally safe. Most of the modern herbicides interfere with amino acid biosynthesis in plants. Once the mode of action of a herbicide is established, the transfer of resistance to the herbicide can be done by two different approaches:

1. The first approach is modification of the target side.
2. Detoxification of herbicide

Transgenic plants carrying the genes for herbicide tolerance has been produced in tobacco, petunia, tomato, potato, Populus etc.

Modification of the target: This approach has been made for developing resistance against at least three herbicides *viz.* glyphosate, sulphonyl urea and imidazolinones.

Resistance against glyphosate: Glyphosate, an active component of round up herbicides, is used as non-selective post-emergence herbicides. It is suggested that glyphosate inhibits aromatic amino acid biosynthesis by competitive inhibitor of enzyme 5-enol-pyruvyl shikimate-3 phosphate synthase [EPSPS]. EPSPS catalyzes the synthesis of phenylalanine, tyrosine and tryptophan. The aro A gene which codes EPSPS has been isolated and sequenced from *Escherichia coli*, *Salmonella typhimurium* and *Arabidopsis thaliana*.

There are two possible methods for producing glyphosate resistant plants by genetic engineering:

transfer of a glyphosate sensitive EPSPS under the control of a powerful promoter causing over expression of the protein and/or

transfer of gene which codes a mutated, glyphosate resistant EPSPS. cDNA of the EPSPS gene with 35 S cauliflower mosaic virus promoter was constructed and the transformed petunia cell lines with this construct exhibited 40-fold increase in EPSPS activity.

An alternative method is insertion and expression of mutated bacterial aro A gene coding for glyophosate resistant EPSPS. The source of the aro A gene was a mutagenized strain of *S. typhimurium* or *E. coli* and was transferred to tomato and/or tobacco. Transgenic tobacco plants, showing tolerance to commercial levels of glyphosate are field tested in USA.

Resistance against sulfonylurea and imidazolinone herbicides: The herbicidal action of sulfonylureas and imidazolinones is based on their ability to inhibit non-competitively an enzyme of branched-chain amino acid biosynthesis, acetolactate synthase (ALS). ALS is the first enzyme in the biosynthetic chain resulting in the synthesis of the branched chain amino acids valine, leucine and isoleucine.

Mutated strains resistant to sulfonylureas have been obtained from bacteria, fungi and plant cell cultures. The resistance of all these mutants can be attributed to possession of mutated forms of the ALS. Transgenic tobacco plants expressing a mutant ALS gene from tobacco or *Arabidopsis*, were produced that were tolerant to sulfonylurea herbicides.

Resistance against Phosphinothricin: L-Phosphinothricin (PPT) is a naturally occurring amino acid with herbicidal activity and is active ingredient of herbicide 'Basta'. PPT is a potent inhibitor of glutamine synthase and thus causes rapid increase in ammonia concentration in plants. This leads to death of plant cell. 'Bar' gene from *Streptomyces hygroscopicus* encodes phosphinothricin acetyl transferase enzyme that acetylates the free-NH2 groups of phophinothricin and inactivates the herbicide Basta. This 'bar' gene with CaMV 35S promoter has been transferred to tobacco, tomato and potato plants using *Agrobacterium* Ti plasmid vector system. The transgenic plants have been tested for 'Basta' resistance.

Resistance against Atrazine: Atrazine is another herbicide, which inhibits photosynthesis. A 32kDa protein, QB is responsible for herbicide binding and is encoded by psb A gene. The DNA sequences of psb A are highly conserved in different plants. More than 20 weed species have developed resistance to atrazine herbicides, for example, *Amaranthus hybridus*.

Detoxification or degradation of herbicide: This approach is based on selective use of herbicide, which will kill the weeds and not the crop. A number of detoxifying enzymes have been identified in plants as well as microbes. Few examples are given here: *(i) glutathione-S transferase* or GST (in maize and other plants): It detoxifies the herbicide atrazine; *(ii) nitrilase*: It is coded by gene bxn in *Klebsiella penumoniae*, and it detoxfies the herbicide bromoxynil, and *(iii) phosphinothricin acetyl transferase* or PAT (coded by *bar* gene in *Streptomyces* and transgenic plants using the *bxn* gene from *Streptomyces* spp).: It detoxifies the herbicide PPT (L-phosphinothricin). Transgenic tomato plants using the *bxn* gene from *Klebsiella ozaenae* and *bar gene* from *Streptomyces*, as well as, transgenic potato, oilseed rape (*Brassica napus*) and sugarbeet using *bar* gene from *Streptomyces* have been obtained and were found to be herbicide resistant. Other crops for engineered herbicide tolerance include soybean, cotton and corn.

Engineered Resistance against Pest: Pests and insects cause severe damage to our crops and thus use of insectides and pesticides is a common measure. With genetic engineering, crops can now be protected with insects without applying any synthetic chemical. More than 30 crop species have been successfully transformed including corn, cotton, soybean, and rice with insecticidal properties.

For transgenic plant production with pest resistance properties, two major approaches have been developed: (a) the introduction of protein delta endotoxins from Bt and, (b) introduction of protease inhibitors in plants.

***Bacillus thuringiensis* endotoxins:** The entomocidal bacterium *Bacillus thuringiensis*, upon sporulation normally produces a parasporal crystalline toxin. When ingested by a susceptible insect, a combination of the high pH and proteinases of the insects midgut solubilizes the crystal and yields active toxin. The effects of the toxin occur within minutes of indigestion, leading to disruption of insect's midgut cells. Bt toxin activity has been found against many species of insects within the orders of Lepidoptera, Diptera and Coleoptera. These delta endotoxins are very specific in their action and are safe insecticides, but their use is limited due to high production cost and due to instability of crystal proteins when exposed in the field.

The above toxin gene (*ht2*) from *B. thuringiensis* has been isolated and used for *Agrobacterium* plasmid mediated transformation of tobacco, cotton potato and tomato plants. These transgenic plants were resistant to the feeding damage of *Manducta sexta* larvae (tobacco horn worm), a pest of tobacco. Experiments of feeding the larvae of *M. sexta* on leaves of these transgenic plants showed 75%-100% mortality of the larvae, while the control plants carrying no transgenes were severely damaged.

Protease inhibitors: Protease inhibitors are proteins with antimetabolic activity against wide range of insects. Such inhibitors are widely distributed within the plant kingdom and can accumulate to high levels in seeds and storage organs. Other major advantages of protease inhibitors is their inactivation with cooking. In cowpea (*Vigna unguiculata*), trypsin inhibitor (CpTi) level was shown to be responsible for its resistance to attack by the major storage pest of its seeds (*i.e.* bruchid beetle = *Callosobruchus maculatus*) A variety of insects have shown to be toxic to CpTi. This CpTi gene was joined with a CaMV 35S promoter, and one marker gene with the transgene and was used to infect tobacco leaf discs. *Agrobacterium* was used for transformation and the transgenic tobacco plants express a high level of CpTi. The CpTi gene in transgenic plants is stably inherited and there is no serious 'yield penatly'. Thus like Bt toxin, CpTi can also be used as a protectant against insect attack in transgenic plants. However, extensive field trials are necessary before releasing these transgenic plants to the farmers.

TABLE 23.1: Insecticidal efficacy of CpTi in artificial diets and in transgenic plants

Insects killed by CpTi in artificial diets	**Insects, against whom resistance noticed in transgenic tobacco plants (with CpTi)**
Lepidoptera	
Heliothis virescens	*Helothis virescens*
Heliothis zea	*H. zea*
Spodoptera littoralis	*Spodoptera littoralis*
Chilo partellus	*Manducta Sexta, Autographa gamma*
Coleoptera: *Callosobrichus maculates, Anthonomus grandis, Diabrotica undecimpunctata, Tribolium confusum, Costelytra zealandica*	these insects do not attack control tobacco plants
Orthoptera: *Locusta migratoria*	

Gene for other insecticidal secondary metabolites: The production of secondary metabolites by plants can also implicate the resistance to insect attack. However, biosynthesis of each of these metabolites involves many steps, each controlled by a separate gene. Furthermore, these genes are tissue specific in expression. These features make the production of transgenic plants difficult in this case. Utilizing these facilities, transgenic plants with insect resistance due to secondary metabolites will be available in the near future.

Engineered Resistance against Viral Infection: Over seven hundred plant viruses are recognised causing various diseases and significant crop losses. Due to the lack of 'viricides', the practical control depends on methods that prevent or restrict virus infection. Following are the possible means:

Cross Protection: If susceptible strain of a crop is inoculated with a mild strain of a virus, the susceptible strain, as a result, develops resistance against more virulent strains. The phenomenon is known as **cross protection.** This method has been used to reduce yield losses in crops like tomatoes against **tomato moisac virus** (TMV), in potato against **potato spindle tuber viroid** and in citrus against **citrus tristeza virus**. In most cases of cross protection, the symptoms of infection are delayed, and even the replication of virus is suppressed, although eventually the severe strain may be able to overcome the protection.

The disadvantages of practicising cross protection includes:

1. Possibility of mutation in inducing mild virus strain.
2. Possibility of synergism between inducing virus and another unrelated virus.
3. Possibility of unnecessary spread of mild virus causing threat for future yield losses.
4. Possibility of some yield losses due to mild strain. Transgenic plants have been produced in tobacco, tomato, and potato with single gene using a broad spectrum of plant viruses.

Coat protein mediated protection: Coat protein - mediated resistance to viruses has been one of the successes of plant genetic engineering. Coat protein gene from tobacco mosaic virus (TMV), a positive strand RNA virus, has been transferred to genome of tobacco plants. In the transgenic plant, expression of coat protein (CP), as well as, low and delayed infection was observed when inoculated with TMV. However, in such transgenic plants, coat protein gene should be constitutively expressed and may thus have effects on the nutritional value of plants. Subsequently Cp genes isolated from different plus strand RNA plant viruses have been cloned into plant expression vectors and transferred to various crop plants like tobacco, tomato and potato, using *Agrobacterium* mediated plant transformation system. Potatoes have been produced which have coat protein genes and are tolerant in field tests to both potato virus X (PVX) and potato virus Y (PVY). A target DNA coding for a component of TMV replicase enzyme, was also transferred to tobacco plants, conferring resistance to TMV.

Antisense RNA mediated protection: Antisense constructs also generate protection against RNA and DNA viruses. Transgenic tobacco plants expressing antisense transcript (antisense - coat protein gene) were protected from CMV infection. Transgenic tobacco plants with Nucleocapsid (N) gene, CaMV 35S promoter and a leader sequence (to enhance expression) showed expression of N-gene. Such transgenic plants were resistant to tomato spotted wilt virus. (TSWV). TSWV is a negative strand RNA virus with RNA joined firmly to the nucleocapside protein.

Satellite RNA mediated protection: Satellite RNAs are associated with specific strains of some plant RNA viruses, though they are unrelated to viral genome. These extragenomic RNA species depend on a helper virus for replication. Some satellite RNAs are known to attenuate the symptoms of their helper virus. Thus satellite RNA might be used to protect crop plants against the effect of CMV infection. The nature of protection in transgenic plants by satellite RNA is different from coat-protein protection.

Defective Interfering mediated protection: Defective interfering (DI) particles are deletion mutants of genomic viral sequences, which depend on their parent virus for replication. Like satellite RNAs, DI particles can attenuate the disease symptoms of their helper virus by interfering with its replication. Artificial DI molecules of TMVY, TMV and BMV have been constructed and inserted in plant protoplast *e.g.*, deletion mutants of BMV RNA 2 exhibited reduced replication of MBV RNA1 and RNA2 in barley protoplasts.

Replicase mediated protection: It has been discovered that transgenic tobacco expressing part of replicase gene of TMV strain was highly resistant to this and closely related strains.

Currently, atleast three approaches are available to broad spectrum resistance. The first is based on the replication and cell to cell movement of virus. Second approach relies on the transgenic expression of antivirus protein of non-plant origin including antibodies. The third approach is based on genetic manipulation of natural viral defences in plants.

Engineered Resistance against fungal pathogen: Genetic engineering has opened vistas with isolation of resistance genes and gene transformation methods to develop transgenic plants. Resistance to fungal palthogen is achieved by isolating and transferring fungal resistance genes to the desired susceptible crop. Compounds toxic to fungus can also be used to produce transgenic plants as done in case of tobacco. Antifungal proteins like **endochitinase** and **ß-1,3-endoglucanases** are thought to inhibit fungal growth. Transgenic tobacco plants with endochitinase CH5B gene with Ca MV 35S promoter exhibits reduced seedling mortality when grown in presence of *Rhizoctonia solani*.

Another method is using ribosome inactivating proteins (RIPs). These RIPs do not interfere with the functioning of self-ribosomes but exert inhibitory activity towards fungal ribosomes. When RIPs are mixed with endochitinase or ß-1,3-glucanases, the antifungal activity exhibits synergistic increase in *in vitro* assay. Transgenic tobacco with barley type1 RIP gene and potato Wun1 promoter showed an increased resistance to *R. solani*. Table 23.2 gives a brief account of transgenic crops showing resistance against bacterial and fungal pathogens.

TABLE 23.2: Some pathogens for which resistance has been transferred in some crop plants

Pathogen	Disease	Resistance gene	Source of gene	Transgenic crop
Pseudomonas syringae	Wild fire	Acetyl transferase gene	-	Tobacco
Alternaria longipes	Brownspot	Chitinase gene	*Serratia marcescens* (soil bacterium)	Tobacco
Rhizoctonia solani		Chitinase gene	Bean	Tobacco
Phytophthora infestans	Late blight	Osmotin gene	Potato	Potato

Genetic Engineering and Plant Lipids

Plant lipids are major components of the human diet and are present in plants as storage oil. Engineered vegetable oils have been tested as field trials. A high stereate phenotype has been engineered in rapeseed by antisense approach. Stearoyl-acyl carrier protein (Stearoyl - ACP) desaturase is a chloroplast enzyme which catalyzes the first desaturation step in seed oil biosynthesis, converting stearoyl-ACP to oleayl-ACP. This coding region of the gene for rapeseed desaturase was fused in an inverted position to the napin storage protein promoter and to the promoter of seed-specific acyl carrier protein gene, and then introduced into rapeseed. This reduced the activity of desaturase enzyme in engineered plant resulting in increased levels of stearate in seeds (upto 40% of the total fatty acids), with corresponding decrease in oleate. Due to tissue specific expression of antisense RNA, integrity of membrane lipids in leaf remained unaffected.

Length of fatty acids can be manipulated with thioesterase enzyme, which is responsible for the accumulation of short chain fatty acids in triglycerides. The gene has been cloned and expressed in developing seed of *Arabidopsis*, where it caused the accumulation of C12 storage lipids. It is useful for application in confectionery production. The field of storage lipid modification via the engineering of the fatty acid biosynthesis enzymes promises to be a very fertile one that will contribute to production of healthier food and of chemical feed stocks.

TABLE 23.3: Modifications of lipid metabolism in transgenic plants

Modification achieved	Enzyme engineered	Source of gene
Lauric acid production	Acyl-ACP thioesterase	*California bay*
Increased Stearic Acid	Antisense of stearoyl ACP desaturase	*Brassica napus*
	Stearyl-CoA desaturase	Rat
Reduced saturated fatty acids	Stearyl-CoA desaturase 3-Ketoacyl-ACP synthase II Acyl-ACP thioesterase	Yeast Castor Soybean
Reduced saturated fatty acids in phosphatidyl glycerol	Acyl-ACP glycerol-3-phosphate acyltransferase	Squash, *Arabidopsis*
Increased saturated fatty acid in phosphatidyl glycerol	Acyl-ACP glycerol-3-phosphate acyltransferase	*Escherichia coli*
Petroselinic acid production	Acyl-ACP desaturase	Coriander
Increased-linolenic acid	$\omega 3$ desaturase	Arabidopsis
Cylopropane fatty acid production	Cylopropane synthase	*Escherichia coli*
γ-Linolenic acid production	Linolenic $\Delta 6$ desaturase	Synechocytis
Increased oleic acid	ACP: protein a fusion	Spinach

Genetic Engineering and Storage proteins: Human nutrition requires a balanced source of amino acids and the amino acid balance of many plant products is unsatisfactory. Genetic engineering may be carried out in crops making following three approaches: (a) expressing a desirable and heterologous storage protein, (b) increasing the level of a desirable, but little expressed, endogenons protein and, (c) suppressing the expression of antinutritional proteins. A heterologous species of sulphur-rich storage protein in Brazil nut containing 18% methionine and 8% cysteine has been expressed in tobacco and rapeseed. In transgenic tobacco, **phaseolin** gene has been expressed, leading to accumulation of methionine rich phaseolin. Another approach for increasing amino acid synthesis is by engineering of a rate-limiting enzyme. For example, in a tobacco mutant lysine overproduction was caused by a lysine-insensitive **dehydro-picolinate synthase**. Forty fold increase in free lysine has been obtained by expression of a bacterial dehydropicolinate synthase in plant chloroplasts. Genomic clones encoding two subunits of soybean **β-conglycin** (7S protein) genes were transferred into petunia plants. The temporally regulated expression of these two genes in transgenic plants mimic their temporal regulation during soybean embryo development. The gene encoding for 42 kDa potato storage protein, **patatin** was introduced into tobacco. Stable synthesis of patatin protein was confirmed in the heterologons environment.

Genetic Engineering for Nitrogen Fixation

- **Transfer of nif-genes from *Klebsiella pneumoniae* to *E. coli*:** *Klebsiella pneumoniae* is a non symbiotic nitrogen fixing bacterium. R.A. Dixon and J.R. Postgate (1972) transferred nif-genes of *K. pneumoniae* into *E. coli* cells by conjugation. The transgene in the new host produced functional nitrogenase system. The nif-genes of *K. pneumoniae* have been introduced into several other organisms, *e.g. K. aerogenes, Salmonella typhimurium, Erwinia herbicola, Serratia marcescens*. These organisms are genetically modified and are now able to fix atmospheric nitrogen.
- **Transfer of *nif*-genes of eukaryotic organisms:** *Nif*-genes from Rhizobium have been transferred to *Agrobacterium tumefaciens*. The expression of transferred gene has been successful in cereal crops like wheat, paddy etc. through the Ti-plasmids of *A. tumefaciens*.
- **Transfer of nod-genes to increase host range:** Cloned nod-genes of *Rhizobium leguminosarum* that nodulate pea have been transferred to *R. phaseoli* (this normally nodulates bean). The transformed *R. phaseoli* can now nodulate pea plants also.

Plants that Produce Plastic

Chris Somerville and coworkers have evolved a transgenic *Arabidopsis thaliana* to polyhydroxy butyrate (PHB). It is a natural and totally biodegradable plastic material. In future, plastic producing sugar beet and potatoes could also be produced. These scientists have isolated two genes from a bacterium *Alcligenes eutrophus* which produced PHB in nature and accumulates it as a coating. These two genes were inserted separately into two *A. thaliana* plants with the help of *Agrobacterium tumefaciens*.

Miscellaneous Applications

The knowledge of genetic engineering has been exploited in industries to deliver products and processes of economic and social value. Products of biotechnology include organisms and substances made by it that are consumed directly as such or serve as components for other industries. Processes of social value include technologies aimed at social hygiene and well-being, such as purification of drinking water, pollution control and waste disposal. The actinomycetes or soil microorganisms that produce the plethora of miracle drugs - the **antibiotics** have also been added to the list. The new techniques permit harnessing of single cells to produce non-native gene products from exogenously supplied genes. Industrial use of single cells and enzymes for the production of stated products may require special tailoring of the cells for adaptation to mass-scale production processes. The pharmaceutical and chemical industries were the first to exploit the gene engineering technology. A futuristic application is envisaged in the field named **bioelectronics** or **bionics**. The potential of biological material to serve as extra-sensitive conductors, sensors, and support matrices for semiconductor molecules is already being explored. The drugs and pharmaceuticals may be synthesized in heterologous cells or in animal cell lines that produce them. For instance, human chorionic gonadotropin (HCG), erythropoietin and calcitonin synthesizing cell lines have been reported. Of these, only HCG is successfully used for commercial production. The drugs and pharmaceuticals that are candidates for the genetic engineering are: (1) hormones, (2) growth factors, (3) blood-derived factors, (4) enzymes, (5) antibiotics, (6) immunoproteins, (7) immunodiagnostics ans (8) DNA probes for molecular diagnosis

TECHNIQUES OF PRODUCING TRANSGENIC PLANTS

Three gene-transfer techniques have been developed to such a stage of reproducibility and practical applicability that they can be recommended for future practical work. These are *Agrobacterium-mediated* gene transfer, *ballistic* gene transfer, and *direct* gene transfer to *protoplasts.*

Techniques that have yielded confirmed transgenic plants and that show some promise for future development are *microtargeting*, *microinjection*, *electroporation* into tissues, and *whiskers.*

TABLE 23.4: Transgenic crop plants obtained by *Agrobacterium*-Mediated Transformation

Latin name	English name	Method
Medicago sativa	Alfalfa	A
Malus pumila	Apple	A
Prunus armeniaca	Apricot	A
Asparagus officinalis	Asparagus	A
Populus tremula	Aspen	A
Hordeum vulgare	Barley	B
Phaseolus vulgaris	Bean	B
Lotus corniculatus	Birdsfot trefoil	A
Ribes nigrum	Black currant	A
Dianthus sp. caryophyllus	Carnation	A
Citrus	Carrizo Citrange	A
Daucus carota	Carrot	A
Brassica oleracea	Cualiflower	A
Apium graveoleus	Celery	A
Cicer arietinum	Chickpea	A
Cichorium endivia	Chicory	A
Chrysanthemum sp.	Chrysanthemum	A
Gossypium hisutum	Cotton	A, B
Zea mays	Corn	P, B
Vaccinium macrocarpon	Cranberry	B
Cucumis sativus	Cucumber	A
Festuca rubra	Fescue, red	P, B
F. arundinacea	Fescue, tall	P, B
Linum usitatissimum	Flax	A
Gerbera hybrida	Gerbera	A
Vitis spp.	Grapevine	A
Actinidia chinensis	Kiwi fruit	A
Lactuca sativa	Lettuce	A
Cucumis melo	Muskmelon	A
Brassica juncea	Mustard	A
Avena sativa	Oat	B

Latin name	English name	Method
Brassica napus	Oilseed rape (canola)	B, A
Dactylis glomerata	Orchardgrass	P
Dendrobium sp.	Orchid	B
Carica papaya	Papaya	A, B
Passiflora edulis	Passionfruit	A
Pisum sativum	Pea	A
Arachis Hypogaea	Peanut	A, B
Carya ovata	Pecan	A
Lolium perenne	Penennial ryegrass	
Solanum muricatum	Pepino	A
Petunia hybrida	Petunia	P
Prunus domestica	Plum	A
Populus sp.	Poplar	A, B
Solanum tuberosum	Potato	A, P
Boehmeria nivea	Ramie	A
Oryza sativa	Rice	A, P, B
Secale cereale	Rye	B
Sorghum bicolor	Sorghum	B
Glycine max	Soybean	A, B
Fragaria x Anannassa	Strawberry	A
Stylosanthes humilis	Stylo	A
Trifolium subterraneum	Subterranean clover	A
Beta vulgaris	Sugar beet	A
Saccharum officinarum	Sugarcane	B
Helianthus annuus	Sunflower	A, B
Liquidambar styraciflua	Sweetgum	A
Cyphomandra betacea	Tamarillo	A
Physalis ixocarpa	Tomatillo	A
Lycopersicon esculentum	Tomato	A
Poncirus trifoliata	Trifoliate orange	A
Hordeum x Triticum	Tritordeum	B
Nicotiana tobacum	Tobacco	A, P, B
Agrostis alba, Agrostis palustris	Turf grasses: creeping bentgrass; Redtop	P, B
Juglans regia	Walnut	A
Citrullus vulgaris	Watermelon	A
Triticum aestivum	Wheat	P, B
Trifolium repens	White clover	A
Sinapis alba	White mustard	A
Picea glauca	White spruce	B

(A) = *Agrobacterium* mediated transformation; (B) = Ballistic Methods; (P) = or Direct Gene Transfer to Protoplasts.

Agrobacterium Mediated Gene Transfer

For genetic transformation in plants *Agrobacterium tumefaciens* (a soil bacterium) is used. It transfers T-DNA into plant genome. Foreign genes are inserted in T-DNA through *Ti*-plasmid, co-transferred and integrated in the host genome. Only some sequences of T-DNA in *cis*-position are required for its transfer. By deleting T-DNA encoded genes and adding selectable markers a *disarmed plasmid vector* is prepared without disturbing endogenous balance. Disarmed strains with *Ti*-plasmid can be used to produce transgenic plants.

Plant-transformation Vectors

These vectors are designed on the basis of naturally occurring gene-transfer mechanisms. They are widely employed in plant molecular biology and in the genetic engineering of plants. Chilton (1993) described these vectors as *poor man's vector*. They are used for gene delivery to higher plants.

Advantages of Vector

1. They are convenient and efficient.
2. They allows the transfer of large segments of DNA with minimal rearrangements.
3. They are the integration of small numbers of copies of genes into plant chromosomes.
4. Foreign genes delivered by this method are usually transmitted to progeny plants in a Mendelian manners.
5. In the *Ti*-plasmid, the genes responsible for the transfer of T-DNA are clustered together in a region. The transfer process is active even when the virulence genes and the T-DNA are located on separate replicon in an *A. tumefaciens* cell.
6. In the widely used binary system, a *Ti*-plasmid services as helper; providing the virulence functions, and artificial T-DNA, which contains a selectable marker gene and other genes of interest, is placed on a second, small plasmid, which is often referred to as binary vector (An *et al.*, 1998).
7. In dicotyledonous plants the systems of *Agrobacterium* mediated transformation have been well established for many. However, monocotyledonous plants (cereal/grasses) were originally outside, the host range of *A. tumefaciens*.

Gene Cloning

Gene cloning is a technique, where an isolated single copy of a gene is cloned to obtain its indefinite identical copies. In gene cloning, we introduce a vector containing the desired gene into the host cell. Cloning can be done in bacterial host (*e.g. E. coli*) or in eukaryotes (*e.g.*, yeast). Basically, cloning involves four steps:

1. The vector DNA is cleaved with one or more restriction enzymes;
2. The DNA to be cloned, the target or insert is joined to the vector, generating a recombinant molecule;
3. The recombinant DNA molecules are introduced into the host bacterial cell. The host cell is said to be *transformed* by the introduction of such vector molecule;
4. Transformed colony is selected and amplified.

Another method of amplifying the desired gene is PCR, which offers this possibility in test tube. The two methods PCR and gene cloning are complementary techniques. Molecular cloning of a PCR product is now commonly used to isolate and manipulate genes. In this chapter, we will discuss gene cloning in *E. coli* and yeast, as well as PCR.

Creating Recombinant DNA

Recombinant DNA molecules are produced by inserting a foreign DNA segment into the DNA molecule of a vector. This involves joining of the broken ends of vector

DNA with the two ends of sequence to be cloned. These recombinant DNA molecules (also called as rDNA molecule) are subsequently cloned. There are three methods of joining fragments *in vitro*. The first uses ability of DNA ligase to join the cohesive ends produced by certain restriction enzymes. The second depends on the ability of T4 ligase to form phosphodiester bonds between blunt-ended fragments. The third utilizes the enzyme terminal deoxynucleotidyl transferase to synthesize homopolymeric tails at the ends of fragments. The three enzymes and their mechanism of joining DNA are separately dealt below.

DNA Ligase: The sticky ends created by restriction enzyme have the nick after a few base pairs in opposite strands. DNA ligase repairs these nicks and forms intact duplex. The optimum temperature for ligation of nicked DNA is 37 °C, but at this temperature the hydrogen-bonded joint between the sticky ends is unstable. Thus temperature is kept in range of 4 to 15 °C.

This technique has the advantage of regenerating two restriction sites in recombinant DNA. Thus, the foreign DNA segment can be retrieved from cloned DNA copies by cleaving again with the same enzyme. The disadvantages within this technique include:

1. The cohesive ends of foreign DNA may join end to end and self-circularize before getting inserted in vector.
2. The recognition site, particularly in sequence to be cloned, may not lie at a convenient position so that sometimes only a part of gene is inserted.

T4 DNA ligase: The *E. coli* DNA ligase can not catalyse ligation of blunt ends except under special reaction conditions of macromolecular crowding. Such blunt end ligation can be done with T4 DNA ligase. T4 DNA ligase can join the broken blunt ends of two DNA molecules irrespective of the sequences. The disadvantage of this technique is that any two broken ends may join including those belonging to same DNA molecule.

Linkers: They are self complementary synthetic oligonucleotides which contain restriction endonuclease recognition sites. They may be used to clone DNA fragment into plasmids or other vectors. These blunt ended linkers are first phosphorylated using polynucleotide kinase and labelled or unlabelled ATP molecules. These are then ligated to the blunt ended DNA fragment using T4 DNA ligase. The DNA fragment is finally treated with restriction enzyme to generate sticky ends and ligated into vector which has been cut by the same enzyme.

Stop Linker: They are 5'-phosphorylated double-stranded synthetic oligodeoxynucleotides which can be cloned into an expression vector to ensure transcription termination. Such linkers contain stop codons in each reading frame from both directions. Each stop linker contains an SspI restriction site, which can be used to screen clones for linker insertion.

Adaptors: They are linkers, which contain more than one restriction enzyme recognition sites. They are used to insert new restriction sites into cloning vectors or to join restriction fragments to vectors with incompatible cohesive ends.

Double-linkers: In some plasmid vectors like pUC8, duplex cDNA molecules can be cloned. This is done by double-linker approach, in which different linker molecules are added to the opposite ends of the cDNA. This is an advantageous method as: (1) Orientation of inserted DNA is fixed. (2) Vector reclosure without insertion of foreign DNA can be done. (3) Efficient for cloning of cDNA obtained from rare mRNA molecules. (4) Better than homopolymers where expression from vector-borne promoter is desirable.

Terminal Transferase: Besides adding cohesive ends or linkers, blunt ended DNA fragment and vector can also be ligated. This technique makes use of producing and annealing complementary homopolymer sequences. An enzyme, terminal transferase (purified from calf-thymus), is used to synthesize homopolymeric extensions. Using precursor dGTP, poly dG is added at both the 3'cut ends of vectors while poly dC is added to 5'cut end of foreign DNA. The vector and clone can then be joined by annealing the poly dG with poly dC tails and then ligating them using DNA ligase enzyme. The cloned sequence can be retrieved by using Pst I restriction enzyme. The method works out the chances of reannealing between the two cut ends of same DNA molecule or of two similar DNA molecules, thus is advantageous.

Cloning in Bacteria and Eukaryotes

Cloning in Bacteria: After ligation of target into vector, the recombinant DNA is multiplied in a host. Various bacterial strains are available as host. Most common prokaryotic host is *E. coli*, which is also termed as **workhouse of genetic engineering**. In this technique, the recombinant DNA is subjected to *in vitro* packaging and used to transform bacteria for its amplification. The host bacteria are modified and selected on the basis of high transformation efficiency. The type of bacterial host is selected on the basis of plasmid vector. Various bacterial hosts commonly employed are:

1. Gram positive bacteria *e.g. E. coli*: host for plasmids only.
2. Gram negative bacteria *e.g. Bacillus subtilis:* host for plasmid, phages and cosmid vectors. Chimeric DNA is inserted into bacterial cells to create transformed bacterial cells. Colonies of transformed cells are selected and used for multiplication in suspension cultures. The recombinant DNA is retrieved and isolated from the host cell when required.

Cloning in Eukaryotes: *E. coli* is workhouse of genetic engineering but, the chromosome structure and gene expression in prokaryotes and eukaryotes differ radically. Therefore, *E. coli* offers limitation to its use in cloning eukaryotic genes. The split genes can not be correctly expressed in prokaryotic host as latter do not have introns and thus splicing of mRNA can not take place. Therefore, eukaryotic cells are used to clone and express eukaryotic genes. Among eukaryotes, DNA cloning has been done in yeast, mouse and some plant species. The simplest kind of yeast vector contains a selectable marker such as TRP1, joined to plasmid vector. TRP1 encodes an enzyme in the tryptophan biosynthetic pathway and when introduced into TRP^- cell by DNA transformation, it renders the cell capable of growth in absence of added tryptophan. Vector used is a hybrid or shuttle type. When transformed into yeast, such a vector integrates into the yeast genome by recombination and makes the transformed yeast selectable on the basis of growth in absence of added tryptophan.

The PCR procedure makes use of synthetic oligonuclotides complementary to the known sequences spanning the region of interest to fetch *enzymatic amplification of this segment of DNA in the test tube*. PCR may eventually replace gene cloning technique. This technology is much easier and requires much smaller quantity of DNA (in ng) whereas for cloning, DNA is needed in microgram (μg) quantities.

Procedure: The PCR procedure involves three steps, each repeated many times to produce cycles of amplification.

1. **Step 1:** The genomic DNA containing the sequence to be amplified is denatured by heating.
2. **Step 2:** The denatured DNA is annealed to an excess of the synthetic oligonucleotide primers.
3. **Step 3:** DNA polymerase is used to replicate the DNA segment between the sites complementary to the oligonucleotide primers.

The primer provides the free 3'-OH required for covalent extension; the denatured genomic DNA provides the required template function. These three steps (denaturation, primer binding and DNA synthesis) represent a single PCR cycle. The products of the first cycle are replicated for further amplification. This reaction can be performed many times to supply unlimited copies of amplified DNA. Repetition is made possible by regular denaturation of freshly synthesized double stranded DNA molecules by heating it to 90-98 °C. At this temperature, the two strands separate. Once the double stranded DNA is made single stranded, it is mixed with two primers and is cooled to 40-60 °C. This allows the primers (which are in excess) to bind to their complementary strands through renaturation followed by replication with DNA polymerase. The cycle is repeated many times until the desired level of amplification is achieved.

Gene Transfer Technology

Gene transfer is of basic as well as applied interest. It enables to study the structure and function of isolated genes via modification, reintroduction and subsequent analysis of their function in transgenic plants, cell lines or even cell populations. Besides these, transfer of specifically designed hybrid genes to plant genomes creates novel varieties with designed characters. Gene transfer in plants can be accomplished by sexual and asexual methods.

Asexual methods include: (1) Non-specific gene transfer by protoplast techniques. (2) Specific gene transfer methods.

Sexual Method

1. **Gene transfer using pollen or pollen tube:** Pollen grains are treated with heavy dose of X-ray which pulverizes chromosomes. The pollen, if able to pollinate, assures incorporation of changed chromosomes into daughter progeny. It is assumed that DNA can be taken up by the nuclei or reach the zygote through the pollen tube pathway. Both these approaches have been tried, though several problems exist in this method like presence of cell wall, nucleases, callose plugs in pollen tube etc.
2. **Incubation of dry seeds, embryos, tissues or cells in DNA:** This method has been tried in many cases and expression of defined genes has been witnessed. In all the cases, plant cell walls work as efficient barriers, thus DNA uptake can be enhanced by PEG or electroporation or by any other device.

Agrobacterium tumefaciens: An Important Vector for Genetic Engineering

Agrobacterium tumefaciens is the most important tool in the genetic engineering of plants (the Ti plasmid of the soil bacterium *A. tumefaciens*). This bacterium is the causative agent of crown gall disease of dicotyledonous plants only (unable to develop gall in monocotyledonous species). The name refers to the galls or tumours that often form at the crown (junction between the root and the stem) of infected plants. Since the crown of the plant is usually located at the soil surface, this is where a plant is most likely to be wounded (*e.g.*, due to a soil abrasion from the plant blowing in a strong wind) and infected by a soil blowing in a strong wind) and infected by a soil bacterium such as *A. tumefaciens*. However, *A. tumefaciens* can infect a plant and induce a tumour at any wound site. In the normal disease process the bacterium enters the plant at the site of a wound. The infection often occurs at the crown, but it may involve an upper part of the stem, the petiole, or the leaf. The bacterium attaches to the wall of a cell and transforms the cell. Infected cells proliferate at the site of infection, forming a tumor or gall. The tumor can be fatal to young plants if it grows big enough to crush the vascular system, although often the tumor is merely debilitating and unsightly. Transformed cells also have the ability to grow in culture on a medium that lacks the hormones auxin and cytokinin. Finally, transformed cells produce opines, such as octopine and nopaline. These are chemicals that are formed from two amino acids. Argenine and alanine form octopine, and argenine and glutamine produce nopaline. Octopine and nopaline are not found in normal plant cells.

Infection of Agrobacterium tumefaciens

During the infection of a wound site by *A. tumefaciens*, following two key events occur:

1. The plant cells begin to proliferate and form tumours.
2. They begin to synthesize an arginine derivative called an opine.

The synthesized opine is usually either nopaline or octopine depending on the *A. tumefaciens* strain involved. These opines are catabolized and used as energy sources by the infecting bacteria. Interestingly, *A. tumefaciens* strains that induce the synthesis of nopaline can grow on nopaline, but not on octopine, and vice versa. Clearly, an interesting interrelationship has evolved between *A. tumefaciens* strains and their plant hosts. *Agrobacterium tumefaciens* is able to divert the metabolic resources of the host plant to the synthesis of opines, which are of no apparent benefit to the plant, but which provide sustenance to the bacterium.

Genetic Information Needed for Crown Gall Development (Ti Plasmid): The ability of *A. tumefaciens* to induce crown gall disease in plants is controlled by genetic information carried on a large (about 200,000 nucleotide-pairs) plasmid called the Ti plasmid for its tumor-inducing capacity.

Tumour-inducing Principle: The virulent bacteria all contain a large circular DNA plasmid. When strains of bacteria lose the plasmid, they lose the ability to infect plants. When bacteria regain a plasmid, they regain virulence. Further experiments by Rob Schilperoort's group in Leiden, Holland, demonstrated that many of the genes that control tumour characteristics (morphology, opine synthesis) lie on the plasmid. Finally, Mary-Dell Chilton et al. at the University of Washington in Seattle showed that a segment of the plasmid, the T (transferred) DNA, integrates into the genome of transformed cells. The plasmid (Ti plasmid) is thus identified as the tumour-inducing principle.

Two components, the T-DNA and the vir region, of the Ti plasmid are essential for the transformation of plant cells.

T-DNA (Transferred DNA)

During the transformation process, the T-DNA (for Transferred DNA) is excised from the Ti plasmid, transferred to a plant cell, and integrated (covalently inserted) into the DNA of the plant cell. The available data indicate that integration of the T-DNA occurs at random chromosomal sites; moreover, in some cases, multiple T-DNA integration events occur in the same cell. In nopaline-type Ti plasmids, the T-DNA is a 23,000-nucleotide-pair segment that carries 13 known genes. In octopine-type Ti plasmids, there are two separate T-DNA segments. Some of the genes on the T-DNA segment of the Ti plasmid encode enzymes that catalyze the synthesis of phytohormones (the auxin-IAA and the cytokinin isopentenyl adenosine). These phytohormones are responsible for the tumorous growth of cells in crown galls. The T-DNA region is bordered by 25-nucleotide pair imperfect repeats, which are required in cis for T-DNA excision and transfer. The deletion of either border sequence completely blocks the transfer of T-DNA to plant cells.

Vir Region (for Virulence)

The *vir* (for virulence) region of the Ti plasmid contains the genes required for the T-DNA transfer process. These genes encode the DNA processing enzymes required for excision, transfer, and integration of the T-DNA segment. *vir* genes can supply the functions needed for T-DNA transfer when located either *cis* or *trans* to the T-DNA. The *vir* genes are normally expressed at very low levels in *A. tumefaciens* cells growing in soil. However, exposure of the bacteria to plant cells or exudates from plant cells induces increased levels of expression of the operons containng the vir genes. Surprisingly, this induction process is very slow for bacteria, taking 10 to 15 hours to reach maximum levels of expression. The phenolic compounds like acetosyringone have been purified from plant exudates and shown to act as inducers of the *vir* operons. Thus, the induction process can now be studied *in vitro* by using these purified inducer molecules.

Disarmed Ti Vectors

When the T-DNA region of the Ti plasmid of *Agrobacterium tumefaciens* is transferred to plant cells and becomes integrated in plant chromosomes, the potential use of *A. tumefaciens* in plant genetic engineering seems to be obvious. The foreign genes can be introduced into the T-DNA region and, hopefully, these genes can be transferred to the plant with the rest of the T-DNA segment. In fact, this works very well. All the available data indicate that any DNA inserted any where between the T-DNA border sequences is transferred to plant cells and integrates in plant chromosomes with the rest of the T-DNA. The problem is that the transformed plant cells that have received the T-DNA from a wild-type Ti plasmid lose their normal control of cell division and form tumours. This oncogenicity of T-DNA renders wildtype Ti plasmids incompatible with the goals of most gene-transfer experiments.

Vectors

A shuttle vector is commonly used, which can replicate in *E. coli* (where recombinant manipulations can be easily handled), and then transferred into *A. tumefaciens* in preparation for transfer into plants. There are two basic modes of maintenance of the shuttle vectors in *Agrobacterium*: (1) either by integration into Ti plasmid by recombination at a region of DNA homology, (2) or, by autonomous replication in trans to the Ti plasmid. The former type of vector is referred to as cis or integrating vector while the latter is called a trans or binary vector. A selectable markers is required to recognize the transformed cells and on other hand, suppress the growth of wild type cells. This helps in identification of transformed cells, which are in small proportion.

Limitations: *A. tumefaciens* based gene transfer is hampered by host range limitations, which are especially disturbing when aiming at gene transfer into cereals or other graminaceous monocots.

Artificial Delivery Systems

Escape from host range limitations can be made by transferring the genes *directly* without using any biological vectors, into plant cells. Cell wall constitutes an effective barrier for DNA molecules to pass; naked plant cells, the 'protoplasts', have been found ideal experimental system to study vectorless gene transfer. Various artificial delivery systems are: (1) Gene Transfer Using Particle Bombardment Technique, (2) Gene Transfer by Microinjection Technique, (3) Poly-Cation Mediated DNA Uptake, (4) Ca-DNA Co-Precipitation Method, (5) Silicon Whiskers, (6) Ultrasonication, (7) U.V. Laser Microbeam.

EXPRESSION OF INDUCED GENES IN TRANSGENIC PLANTS

Genetic Engineering in plants includes formation of recombinant DNA, its introduction into cells or protoplasts and more importantly expression of the foreign genes. After introduction of foreign gene, complete plants are regenerated from transformed cells or tissues. Regenerated plants are then examined for expression of gene constructs. It is a lengthy process, involving selection and bulking of tissues for analysis of integrated genes. This duration can be avoided by studying the 'transient expression' of the constructs introduced directly into protoplasts. In this approach, foreign DNA is added to protoplasts by gene transfer method and these protoplasts are cultured for 1-2 days. The protoplasts are then harvested and assayed for products encoded by the introduced (but not necessarily integrated) genes. This confirms the incorporation of required gene into the protoplast.

Reporter Gene for Transient Expression

A reporter gene is added to gene of interest before its entry into the target cell. With the help of reporter genes, information on aspects of gene constructs such as the relative-level and tissue specificity of expression can be obtained. Reporter genes are frequently introduced into genetically modified plants for identifying and tracking genetic modification as they tag the transformed cells. They find more use where the genetically modified plants can not be regenerated from single cell and direct selection is not feasible or effective. The important features needed in reporter gene include its low background activity in plants and absence of any detrimental effect on metabolism. The gene product should have moderate stability *in vivo*, so that down regulation of gene expression as well as gene activation can be detected.

Problems involved in gene transfer

Following are the major problems in gene transfer: (1) expression system, (2) cellular localization, (3) proteolysis, protein folding and prosthetic group acquistion, (4) precursor availability (5) inhibitory environments (6) side reaction of new compounds

SCOPES AND ACHIEVEMENTS

Transgenic plants are widely grown all over the world. Most of these *first generation* products have specific agronomic traits designed to improve the efficiency of production. New varieties under test contain product quality or other higher value trails intended to provide specific benefits to end user. Examples of such *second generation* traits and attempts to predict range of household, medical, industrial products that might become available in coming years.

Our Need

Crop improvement by engineering for specific traits can also be achieved through production of enzymes and metabolites encoded by foreign genes. Thus, the amino acid composition of seed proteins has been altered and, for example, transgenic canola, expressing a Brazil nut albumin, contains up to 33% more methionine in its seed protein. The alkaloid composition of some medicinal plants has been improved. The production of scopolamine, a medicinally important anticholinergic drug is highly increased in transgenic *Atropa belladonna* plants expressing hyoscyamine 6β-hydroxylase from *Hyoscyamus niger*, which catalyzes the conversion of the precursor hyoscyamine to scopolamine. The shelf life of fruits and vegetables can be extended. Tomato expressing a bacterial ACC deaminase gene reduces ethylene synthesis, and the mature fruits remain firm for at least 6 weeks longer than the nontransgenic controls. Flavor can also be enhanced, transgenic lettuce and tomato have been obtained that express monellin, a sweet protein isolated from some African berries that elicits a flavor approximately 100,000 times sweeter than sugar on a molar basis. The freezing properties of harvested produce can be improved and, in tomato plants expressing an antifreeze protein from the polar fish, winter flounder, ice recrystallization is inhibited, making accumulation of the protein cold-specific. The toxicity of some vegetables can be reduced. More than 70% of human cadmium intake is contributed by vegetable products. Shoots or transgenic tobacco expressing the mouse metallothionine I gene contain about 24% lower cadmium concentration than nontransgenic plants, because the pollutant metal is sequestered in the roots as cadmium-metallothioneine complexes.

We need transgenic plants for (1) fungal resistance, (2) long lived fruits and vegetables, (3) race-specific resistance genes, (4) transposon tagging, (5) two-component systems for non-specific resistance, (6) anti-fungal protein, (7) ribosome-inactivating proteins (rips), (8) engineered resistance against virus diseases, (9) coat protein-mediated protection (cpmp), (10) defective interfering rna/ dna protection, (11) satellite rna-mediated disease attenuation, (12) anti-sense rna/ ribozyme-mediated protection, (13) replicase and protease-mediated protection, (14) movement protein-mediated protection, (15) resistance through transgenic expression of antiviral proteins, (16) herbicide tolerance genes, (17) herbicide target modification, (18) over production of target enzyme, (19) detoxifying enzymes, (20) coat protein genes for virus protection, (21) light regulated genes, (22) antisense rna (23) seed storage proteins, (24) bioactive peptides (25) antibacterial peptides, (26) human proteins: **human serum albumin** (hsa), (27) production of enzymes, (28) production of antibodies, (29) production of vaccines, (30) to develop metal resistance in plants, (31) production of transgenic plants with higher stress tolerance: water stress, temperature stress, salt stress (properties/characters required for improved stress tolerance, production of osmoprotective compounds, improved membrane flexibility, stress induced proteins, scavenging reactive intermediates).

ALARMING ISSUES RELATED TO TRANSGENIC PLANTS

Transgenic crops are now being cultivated in as many as 13 countries, including five developing nations with a total area of 44.2 million hectares. During the first wave of the transgenic revolution, emphasis was laid on the so-called **input traits** that confer agronomic advantages like resistance to pests and diseases and tolerance against herbicides. About 30 per cent of the total yield is lost every year due to weeds, diseases and pests. More food would be available for human consumption if the extent of this damage could be minimized. In fact, the development of pest resistant cultivars has been a major thrust area in our classical breeding programmes.

Adoption of transgenic seeds: Profit or Loss

Genetically modified (GM) seeds and derived foods have been the subject of a fierce debate currently raging in India, with issues such as health and ecological safety. The seeds, based upon their promise of improved productivity, have the potential to eliminate world hunger. The biotechnologists and ecologists have to examine the performance of these first generation seeds, modified for improved tolerance to herbicides, resistance to pests and viruses, with particular reference to farmers.

USA is the largest grower of transgenic seeds, close to 29 million hectares under cultivation (Financial Express, 06-12-2000). These are surprising results. A study by the US Department of Agriculture's Economic Research Service has showed that yields were not significantly different in engineered versus non-engineered crops in 12 out of 18 crop/region combinations, HT cotton showed no significant yield increase in either region where it was surveyed. Another study, which examined more than 8,000 field trials, found that a particular HT soybean brand produced fewer bushels than similar conventionally bred varieties. HT soybeans have resulted savings in herbicides use, as the use of other herbicides has declined significantly of offset the increased use of specific herbicides such as glyphosate and glufosinate. However for Bt corn, cost related to insecticide use have actually increased due to the tendency of Bt crops of lose their pest-resistance traits in the medium-long term. Here again, their performance is mixed. So, farmers, in actually, have not achieved either higher yields or the promised costs savings which they expected, and which drove them to adopt seeds in spite of them being more expensive.

LEGAL RIGHTS IN THE NEW BIOTECHNOLOGY

New biotechnology has developed many issues concerning the legal rights of newly introduced biotechnologically created new products for farmers, plant and animal breeders, and consumers. Various forms of legal protection are available, of varying degrees of importance and applicability, depending on the specific process and nature of the protection sought. Copyright, Plant Breeders' Rights and Patents are the main areas of the law that are relevant.

Transgenic Trees

In future, trees will be the next targets on the agenda for genetic engineers Ortiz (1998). If it happens then a new ethical and environmental concerns will emerge because of the following reasons James (1997):

1. Long-lived and little domesticated nature.
2. The problems that will ensue through possible pest adaptation.
3. Production of environmental toxins.
4. Enhanced invasiveness and transfer of transgenes.

According to James (1997): *man has an ethical obligation to the ecosystem and must be considered when balancing the risks and benefits of GE of trees for insect resistance versus application of toxic pesticides.*

James (1997) indicated the similarity between biocontrol and GE. Biocontrol is being concerned with the introduction of entire novel genomes, while GE with the introduction of novel genes.

Hokkanen and Lynch (1995) dealt with benefits and risks of biological control, including use of GMO. Many of the ethical issues are the same as those associated with GE, but it is interesting that biological control appears to have attracted a lot less attention from the media and the public than transgenic technology and has consequently had a much more positive press.

Transgenic crops may cause genetic diversity and its possible erosion. Hardon (1997) pointed out that plant breeding relies on genetically diverse germplasm for progress to be made and maintained, which in traditional agriculture is regarded as a common resource of great value and is freely available. Hardon (1997) considers it unethical to treat such traditional forms of agriculture as markets to be conquered by private interests (**biopiracy**).

The development of transgenic crops will enhance biodiversity by creating an increased need for exotic genes. Genetic diversity will be diminished through deployment of a narrow range of germplasm. Biodiversity, both on and off farm, is already in decline phase. It is due to current farming practices in both the developed and developing world. Whether transgenic crops will accelerate or dampen?. This remains a debatable issue. The dilemma is that the greatest biodiversity exists in the delicate ecosystems of the as yet uncultivated areas and the cropping systems of some of the world's poorest countries.

The effects of transgenics on the environment are controversial because of the difficulty in gauging the associated risks. Although all actions are potentially hazardous, there have been no problems involving transgenics to compare with those that have been encountered previously as a result of classical plant breeding.

TRANSGENICS AND HUMAN HEALTH

Plants are the major sources of the human food. A major worry of the public, aside from fundamental concerns, is that transgenic crops contain ethically sensitive genes, including, for example, antibiotic marker genes and promoter sequences derived from viruses. These genes have aroused concern to human health and may be adversely affected by consumption of transgenic crops and products derived from them. This aspect has developed to the extent that restaurants have removed GM foods from their menus and schools have outlawed GM products. There has been increasing demand in supermarkets for organic food. *Is this the start of a biotechnology backlash*?

The World Health Organisation (WHO) has judged antibiotic marker genes to be safe, but the outcome of their use might be hazardous if they represent a major source of resistance to a wide class of antibiotics. The fear is that these genes could spread from the plants into which they were inserted to wild plant populations and to bacterial populations that would then be advantaged in their natural environment.

Transgenic foods may be toxic or allergenic. Franck-Oberaspach and Keller (1997) reviewed the consequences of classical and biotechnological resistance breeding for food toxicology and allergenicity. They reported on many classes of actual and putative toxins and allergens, concluding that several naturally occurring defence substances found in plants are highly toxic to mammals, but also indicating that food safety can be severely influenced by natural pathogens and their products.

It is difficult to maintain good health on a purely vegetarian diet, but what if plants were made healthier through GE, would this be ethically sound from society's and the consumers' points of view? Strict vegetarians might object to gene sequences from animals being introduced into plants. Following questions lie at the heart of the debate on transgenic crops:

1. What of the benefits that have accrued for humans from GE to produce insulin and human growth hormone; are direct medical applications of GE regarded as being different from those which alter plant characteristics for an indirect benefit such as nutritional improvement?
2. Does GE of humans, animals, plants and microorganisms require different ethical considerations.

Human health already suffers as a consequence of agricultural practices. Commercial banana production, for example, requires application of large amounts of pesticides which pollute the environment, and whose residues accumulate in plantation workers. It is ethically not justifiable to produce a transgenic banana variety that allows for a reduction in pesticide application and a subsequent improvement in human health.

CHAPTER 24

Biotechnology and Forestry

Forest is the plant community, predominantly of trees or other woody vegetation, occupying an extensive area of land. In its natural state, a forest remains in a relatively fixed, self-regulated condition over a long period of time. Climate, soil, and the topography of the region determine the characteristic trees of a forest. In local environments, dominant species of trees are characteristically associated with certain shrubs and herbs. The type of vegetation on the forest floor is influenced by the larger and taller plants, but because low vegetation affects the organic composition of the soil, the influence is reciprocal. Disturbances such as a forest fire or tree-cutting by the timber industry may result in a shift to another forest type. Left undisturbed, ecological succession will eventually result in a climax forest community. Human intervention, in the form of forest conservation and management, is practised to maintain some desirable forest types.

The huge Indian population and its fast growth rate demand food, power, fuel wood, timber, etc. every day. Its land area is shrinking due to fast increasing population growth. India has about 130 M ha of wastelands. Wastelands are lands that are degraded and are lying unutilised due to constraints such as salinity, alkalinity, water logging, wind and soil erosion, etc. and are unsuitable for agriculture. The need of the hour is a quantum jump in existing afforestation targets, reclamation of wastelands and protection of forest cover, which will boost our forest products. Forests are the backbone of agriculture, animal husbandry, industrial development, etc. Large scale plantations requires huge amount of planting materials like seeds or seedlings. In order to achieve higher forest yields, it is necessary that the planting materials should be of perfect quality. Therefore, we have to develop high yielding novel varieties, which can resist various pathogens, pests, herbicide and stress, etc. Such plants can be obtained by conventional methods of tree breeding and non-conventional methods of genetic engineering and somatic hybridization.

Unlike annual crops, the breeding behavior of trees is complex and their life cycle is long. Therefore, one has to wait for many years to produce tree varieties with desirable traits. The modern non-conventional methods of genetic engineering, tissue culture and somatic hybridization have developed new hopes to enhance forest productivity with quick results.

The non-conventional methods of plant production is very expensive, therefore, it is necessary to combine conventional methods with new biotechnological methods for high productivity, both qualitatively and quantitatively.

The development time, from the laboratory to the field, for all new types of tissue culture or GM trees will be substantial, usually in the order of a decade or more. While this may provide forest scientists and managers with time to evaluate many of the issues being faced in agriculture, the economic realities of relatively long generations will continue to be a major challenge to inverstors in biotechnology in forest trees. It appears that genetic modification will therefore become a reality only for particularly novel and valuable traits in short-rotation species in intensively managed plantations. Herbicide resistance is likely to be the first trait for which genetic modification will become economically viable, but even this may be several years away from large-scale use.

SELECTION OF TREES FOR INDIAN FORESTRY

Forest cover provides healthy environment while deforestation causes environmental hazards, degradation, soil erosion, recurrent floods, drought and desertification. With less than 2 per cent of the world's forest area, we are called upon to meet the requirements of nearly 15 per cent of the world's population. The annual target of foresting 5 million hectares of land set by the Government of India. To achieve this target efforts have to be made by the different agencies associated with the task like forest department, voluntary agencies, individuals, societies and industrial houses, etc. We to raise productive forests by identified species. Selection of suitable species for different problem-soils and agro-climatic conditions is absolutely essential for effective reclamation of wastelands. A list of trees and shrubs for various agro-climatic conditions of India is given below:

Name of Plants	Uses
Arid Tropical Regions	
Acacia catechu, Acacia nilotica, Acacia tortilis, Albizia lebbeck, Anogeissus latifolia, A. pendula, Cassia siamea, Casuarina equisetifolia, Dalbergia sissoo, Diospyros melanoxylon, Eucalyptus sp., Gmelina robusta, Madhuca longifolia, Prosopis sp., Terminalia indiac	Fuel wood
Acacia nilotica, Acacia tortilis, Ailanthus excelsa, Albizia lebbeck, Albizia procera, Areca catechu, Dalbergia sissoo, Prosopis sp., Terminalia sp.	Forage
Albizia lebbeck, Albizia procera, Dalbergia sissoo, Gmelina arborea, Gmelina robusta, Holoptclea sp., Pongarnia pinnata, Shorea robusta, Stercularia sp., Tectona grandis	Timber
Bombax cciba, Diospyros melanoxylon, Eucalyptus sp.	Pulp wood
Humid Tropical Regions	
Acacia catechu, Albizia lebbeck, Cassia siamea, Casuarina equisetifolia, Dalbergia sissoo, Hibiscus integrifolia, Melia azadirachta	Fuelwood
Acaaadia catechu, Dalbergia sissoo, Gmelina sp., Terminalia sp. Adina cordifolia	Forage
Albizia sp., Artocarpus chaplasha, Chukrasia velutina, Dalbergia latifolia, Daibergia sisso, Gmelina sp., Kydia calycina, Michelia champaca, Phoebe attennata, Shorea robusta, Tectona grandis,	Timber
Eucalyptus sp., Populus sp.,	Pulp wood
Tropical Regions	
Acacia mearnsii, Acer campbellii, A. caesium, Alnus sp. Celtis australis, Quercus sp., Terminalia ciliata, Tsuga dumosa	Fuelwood
Acacia mearnsii, Grewia optiwa	Forage
Abies pindrow, Alnus sp., Cedrus deodara, Cryptomeria japonica, Juglans regia, Picea smithiana, Pinus sp., Salix alba	Timber
Eucalyptus globulus, Pinus patula	Pulp wood

FOREST RESOURCES

Tissue culture technology, together with mycorrhizae, nitrogen fixing microorganisms and institutional support, etc. have been used to enhance the productivity of forest trees in the United States, Brazil, India, Japan and some West European countries. Success has also been obtained in the case of orchids, ornamentals and a number of vegetable and fruit species. Species of strawberry and apple are now produced commercially by tissue culture. In India, the technique of raising plants through tissue culture has been perfected for a few tree species, *e.g.*, *Bamboo, Dalbergia, Eucalyptus, Leucaena, Prosopis, Santalum, Sesbania* and *Tectona* etc. In order to achieve the quantum jump in the production of biomass for fuel, forage, timber and pulp (soft) wood using the new tools of biotechnology, the following species have been identified for mass propagation through tissue culture techniques (micropropagation); *Acacia nilotica, Alnus nepalensis, Harrrdwickia binata, Madhuca latifolia, Prosopis cineraria, Tamarindus indica, Dendrocalamus strictus, Bambusa arundinacea, Bambusa vulgaris, Tectona grandis, Shorea robusta, Dalbergia latifolia, Santalum album, Populus deltoides.*

Mass propagation of elite plants through tissue culture, scaling up the production of artificial seeds, cytopreservation of the gene pools of elite trees, exploiting somaclonal variants for tree improvement, microspore and anther culture for fixation of heterosis, development, in some important tree species of a genetic transformation system using *Agrobacterium tumefaciens* and regeneration of transformed plantlets by tissue culture, genetic munipulation of trees through protoplast fusion or somatic hybridisation, large-scale field evaluation of tissue culture raised plants are some of the important ways to increase the forest production technology in present day.

The impact of biotechnology can be observed in the following manners:

1. Enhancing the planting and survival of trees on sites that are unproductive environmentally.
2. Increasing the yields of both traditional and new forest product.
3. Use of disease-free stock.
4. Improving the yield of wood-based products by efficient conversion processes including the use of microorganisms.
5. Facilitating the identification and conservation of genetic resources.

Techniques used to achieve these goals are rejuvenation through clonal propagation including cuttings, micrografting and tissue culture, haploid generation, somatic embryogenesis, protoplast fusion, gene transfer, cryopreservation breakdown of wood components; and forest soil microbiological improvement and risk detection. The use of these technologies varies from species to species and their out put also depends upon plant species.

SPECIFIC RECENT TECHNOLOGIES RELEVANT TO FORESTRY

Clonal Propagation Including Tissue Culture

Considerable progress has been achieved in developing new clones of many industrial crops like tea, coffee, cocoa etc. using modern biotechnological methods but still we need substantial work in this direction in India. However, in recent years in Australia, Brazil, Canada, Europe, Japan and the USA *inter alia* with a wide range of species including some 44 angiosperms and 19 gymnosperms; rejuvenation of tropical pines and temperate oaks and valuable ornamental woody plants is in progress through micropropagation. In Britain, clonal propagules of Sitka spruce may exceed a million in 1987. Propagation of 100-year-old trees of redwood and teak has been achieved but generally, juvenile material has been used. Micrografting is a technique that inserts that apical dome of a select tree on to the tip of a rootstock and it encourages rejuvenation; it has been successful with apple, cherry and citrus species, rubber and eucalyptus.

Clonal propagation through tissue culture offers the possibility of juvenile screening for growth rate and disease susceptibility. The recent work in this direction includes the development of model *in vitro* systems to examine the disease defense and resistance mechanisms of tree species. These will then be extended to evaluate all selected genotypes before bulking and distribution into national breeding populations. Tissue cultures and micropropagules, will also permit the evaluation of trees for tolerance of difficult soils (acid, alkaline, saline or affected by heavy metals), adverse climatic factors (extremes of temperature and rainfall) or aerial pollutants. The latter is of prime concern to temperate, industrialized countries.

However, the evaluation of trees for difficult environmental conditions is a major imperative for tropical countries where billions of hectares are below optimum potential productivity because of soil reaction or nutrient status; in tissue culture screening identifies disease resistance, it is a means of propagating virus-free planting stock. Meristem culture is well established for agricultural and horticultural species and have applications in tree species such as poplar, that are commonly affected by virus diseases.

Cryopreservation and in *Vitro* Storage

With this technique small tissue samples are maintained at very cold temperatures in order to maintain their current physiological condition. In many conifer species, physiologically juvenile plant material is typically cryopreserved. Trees developed from older tissue can show reduced growth potential later on, but this characteristic varies greatly among species and genotypes. Therefore, the evaluation of genotypes for efficient production of plant material later on is usually one of the main goals of cryopreservation. It is also important that the storage process itself does not induce chromosomal instability which can result in variable and undersirable plant forms. While the technology is useful and necessary for many applications in clonal forestry, it may have a special role in programmes for species with recalcitrant seed, for which basic seed storage is a major problem.

In vitro Selection

This technique involves selecting for a particular trait (*e.g.* heavy metal or salt tolerance) at an early stage in the micropropagation phase. The trait must also show stable expression for the life of the derived plant. Although *in vitro* selection has been used to some degree in crop plants, attempts in forest trees have been limited to selection of GM trees. *In vitro* selection techniques are a basic requirement in the process of screening for successfully GM-transformed clonal lines. Other traits can therefore be combined with basic *in vitro* selection criteria required for GM screening (*e.g.* mercury tolerance in yellow poplar.

RAPID PROPAGATION OF SOME FOREST TREES

Rapid Propagation of *Eucalyptus tereticornis* Sm.

Eucalyptus offers an ideal industrial feed stock for pulp and paper due to its short rotation cycle, by virtue of which it provides a competitive advantage against the increasing prices of superior quality, long duration timbers, such as *Tectona grandis*, *Dalbergia sissoo*, *Shorea robusta* etc. *Eucalyptus* timber is also suitable for various types of construction (for example door and window frames). To meet the increasing demand for timber in the future, fast growing *Eucalyptus* plantations are expected to make a great contribution.

For the production of uniform plant material *Eucalyptus*, being cross-pollinated, needs to be multiplied vegetatively. This is necessary in view of the heterogeneity observed in plantations raised from seed. In recent years, tissue culture technology has been successfully used in some *Eucalyptus* species *viz.*, *E. citriodora*, *E. resinifera* and *E. maculata*, *E. sideroxylon*, *Eucalyptus* species and hybrids, *E. camaldulensis* and *E. grandis* for the production of clonally uniform plantlets from the desirable germplasm. However, the success of exploiting this technique commercially has not been achieved in all the *Eucalyptus* species of commercial value. Dr. R. I. S. Gill and his associates of Forestry Department, Punjab Agricultural University, Ludhiana worked on the tissue culture aspects of *Eucalyptus* spp. The data presented here are based on their studies.

Methods for Tissue Culture: The mature trees of *Eucalyptus tereticornis* (6-8 years) are to be cut in February The coppice shoots developed within two months. The twigs (10-15 cm) comprising 5-8 nodes are then excised from the stump. The leaves are pinched off and the twigs having nodal buds are first washed thoroughly in distilled water to remove the dust particles and then cleaned with a swab of cotton dipped in alcohol (absolute). The twigs are then cut into stem segments (1.5 cm). The segments consisting of leaf petiole and nodal bud are surface sterilized (0.1% Mercuric chloride, 8 minutes) and washed thrice with sterile water. The material left in water at the final washing. The nodal segments are cultured on different media modifications based on Murashige and Skoog (1962) medium and the cultures are incubated at 25 ± 2 °C under 16 h light and 8 h dark conditions.

TABLE 24.1: *In vitro* shoot bud regeneration (%) from nodal segment explant of *Eucalyptus* cultured on different media compositions*

Kind of growth regulator (mg/l) in MS media	Weeks after culturing		Mean
	3WAC	6WAC	
Basal (MS)	31.66 (19/60) 34.13	35.0 (21/60) 36.22	33.33 (20/60) 35.17
BAP (1.0)	36.66 (22/60) 37.24	40.0 (24/60) 39.19	38.33 (23/60) 38.21
BAP (0.5)	16.66 (10/60) 24.03	23.33 (14/60) 28.76	20.0 (12/60) 26.40
BAP (1.0) + IBA (0.5)	43.33 (26/60) 41.14	46.66 (28/60) 43.05	45.0 (27/60) 42.10
BAP (1.0) + IBA (0.2)	25.0 (15/60) 29.91	28.33 (17/60) 32.12	26.66 (16/60) 31.02

L.S.D (P = 0.05) Media = 3.61, Weeks after culturing = 2.28, Interaction (Media x WAC) = NS

Figures in parenthesis indicate the number of responsive cultures (numerator)/ total number of cultures (denominator)., Figures given in italics are Arc Sine transformed values.

*(Based on R. I. S. Gill, S. S. Gill and S. S. Gosal, 2001, In: Trends in Plant Tissue Culture and Biotechnology, Agrobios (India) Jodhpur

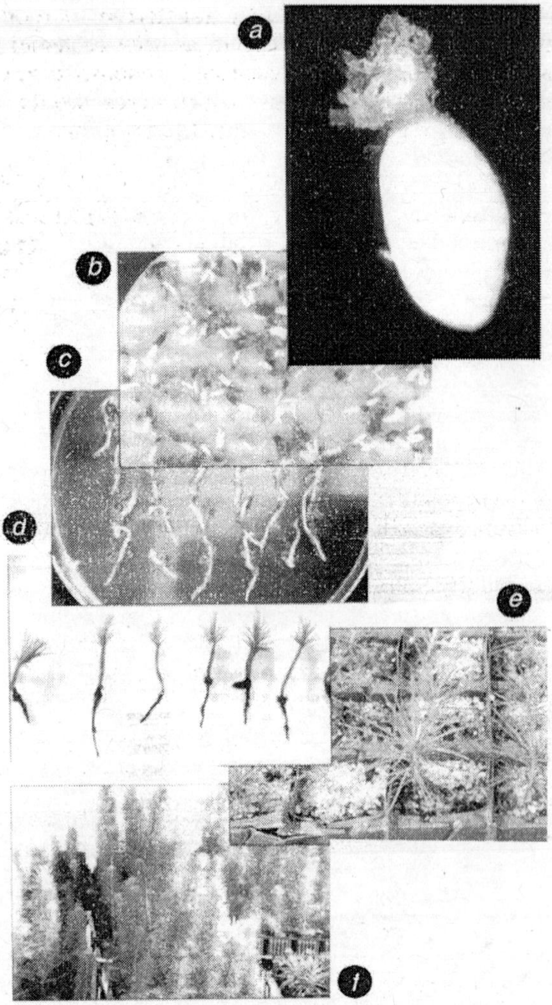

FIGURE 24.1: Trees developed through somatic embryogenesis: (a) initiation of somatic embryogenesis from immature megagametophyte in *Pinus strobus*; (b) mature somatic embryos of *P. strobus* after 12 weeks of culture on abscisic acid (ABA) and gellan gum medium; (c) *P. strobus* somatic embryos after 11 days on germination medium; (d) *P. strobus* somatic seedlings after 12 weeks on germination medium, prior to transfer to greenhouse; (e) *P. strobus* somatic seedlings in the greenhouse after two months of growth; f) white spruce (*Pecea glauca*) somatic seedlings after four months of growth in the greenhouse.

Tissue culture of *Eucalyptus* undergoes 4 main stages: (1) initiation (2) multiplication (3) rooting and (4) establishment. The shoot bud initiation takes 3-4 months for establishment of cultures. The multiplication of shoot buds can be carried out in high cytokinin medium. In this medium multiplication rate is increased upto 3 to 4 times, when the cultures are transferred to low cytokinin medium during subcultured period of 4 weeks. For shoot elongation, the subdivided shoot but clumps are transferred on half-strength MS medium having activated charcoal (0.2%).

The elongated shoots (3-4 cm) are then transferred to rooting medium. Rooting occurs within 10 to 15 days on both solid as well as liquid medium. The rooted plantlets thus, obtained may be hardened and established in open conditions. This method of shoot proliferation from mature trees would allow selection and multiplication of superior genotypes under field conditions.

TABLE 24.2: *In vitro* rooting (%) of tissue culture derived shoots of *Eucalyptus* in liquid media

Kind of auxin (mg/l) in 1/2 MS media	Days after culturing		Mean
	10 DAC	20 DAC	
IBA (0.5)	61.66 (37/60) 51.73	85.0 (51/60) 67.38	73.33 (44/60) 59.55
IBA (1.0)	43.33 (26/60) 41.15	63.33 (38/60) 52.77	53.33 (32/60) 46.96
IBA (1.0) + NAA (0.2)	20.0 (12/60) 26.25	20.0 (12/60) 26.25	20.0 (12/60) 26.25
IBA (0.5) + NAA (0.2)	23.33 (14/60) 28.77	26.66 (16/60) 30.93	25.0 (15/60) 29.85

L.S.D. (P = 0.05), Media = 5.68, Days after culturing = 4.01, Interaction (Media x DAC) = 8.03
Figures in parenthesis indicate the number of responding cultures (numerator)/ total number of explants cultured (denominator). Figures given in italics are Arc Sine transformed values.

The data given in Table (24.1 and 24.2) are means of three replicate batches of 20 cultures each. All the results were analysed statistically using ANOVA and means were tested for significance using least significance difference (LSD).

Direct Somatic Embryogenesis from Immature Seeds of Rosewood (*Dalbergia latifolia* Roxb.)

Biotechnological approaches of tree tissue culture lag behind those of herbaceous crop species mainly because tree tissues or at least those from mature individuals, cannot be similarly manipulated in culture to yield high frequency of regeneration of plantlets from any desired starting cell, cellular aggregates or organ (Haissig *et al.*, 1987).

Rosewood (*Dalbergia latifolia*) belonging to the family Leguminosae commonly known as East Indian Rosewood or Black wood is an important timber-yielding tree, which is of great commercial value. Bulk of this commodity in the world is met by India and is a good source of foreign exchange to the country.

In view of the continuous felling and lack of cultivated plantations, Rosewood has become a dearer commodity and production has substantially gone down. The gap between supply and demand had widened resulting in a near crisis situation in the world market. Due to the constraints involved in the conventional propagation methods like poor seed viability, there is shortage of planting stocks. This could be overcome by *in vitro* mass production. Dr. G. Laxmi Sita and M. Muralidhara Rao, Indian Institute of Science, Bangalore have undertaken a programme on tissue culture of Rosewood with a view to develop viable tissue culture methods for mass propagation. They earlier reported mass propagation from callus culture by organogenesis and enhanced axillary shoot multiplication. It is well recognised that the ultimate goal for mass propagation is by inducing somatic embryogenesis from suspension cultures. They found that the age of the explant plays an important role in the induction of somatic embryogenesis.

Maximum number of somatic embryos (32) was observed from 90 day old cotyledons where somatic embryos started emerging within 7-10 days whereas from 120 days old explants the induction was 20-25 days after transfer. Fully mature cotyledons, excised from the dry seeds, did not show any embryogenesis but callused profusely regardless of the media composition. Sixty days old immature seeds did not respond and only turned brown. For further development of these embryos into complete plantlets, embryos with well developed cotyledons were transferred to growth regulator free medium with full, half strength MS major salts. Approximately 30% of the embryos of normal shape germinated within 20-30 days after transfer.

Dr. G. Laxmi Sita and M. Muralidhara Rao are of opinion that cotyledons from immature zygotic embryos provide the best source for somatic embryogenesis in Rosewood. Cotyledons from 90 day old pods give the highest frequency of direct somatic embryogenesis. Direct regeneration from cotyledonary explants offers an ideal system for co-cultivation using *Agrobacterium* mediated genetic transformation. Work on these lines using marker genes is in progress.

Micropropagation of *Butea monosperma* (Lam) Taub.

Butea monosperma Lam (*Butea frondosa* Koen) is a deciduous tree belonging to the family Leguminosae (Papilionaceae). In summer the gorgeous canopy of scarlet flowers look like flames giving the tree its characteristics name the flame of the forest. *Butea* is a frost hardy, drought resistant tree. Due to heavy deforestation, the trees are facing extinction especially along the west coast of India. *Butea* would be very useful for afforestation of eroded, degraded lands and has a great potential as an ornamental and shade tree in parks and gardens. Leguminous trees besides being able to meet the demands for fodder, fuel and timber hold some promise as a means of maintaining soil nitrogen without the use of fertilizers. International bodies like FAO, NAS, ICRAF are actively promoting the planting of woody legumes.

Kavitha R. Kulkarni, Smitha Hegde and L. D' Souza (1997) reported that multiple shoots can be initiated from axillary buds of mature trees of *Butea* on WP medium with BAP. These were limited in number, only few shoots can be obtained from an axillary bud. The shoot tips turned brown and became necrotic. A large number of multiple buds can be obtained from cotyledonary nodes on half strength WP medium supplemented with BAP.

Cotyledon segments gives rise to white friable callus on MS medium with 5 mg/l kinetin. The callus gives rise to shoots some of which produced roots. Green nodular callus are formed from the cotyledon segments on MS medium with 5 mg/l BAP. The nodular callus gives rise to embryoids which germinated when subcultured on the same medium giving rise to plantlets with weak roots.

In nature root tubers are produced in *Butea* which give rise to new plants. Experiments were conducted by Kavitha R. Kulkarni and his associates to induce such tubers *in vitro*. According to them the hypocotyl of ten day old seedlings was cut off just below the cotyledon and the seedlings were cultured on MS medium with kinetin and phloroglucinol. The cut surface of the hypocotyl produced a mass of cells which developed into globular tuber like structures. These tubers when subcultured on WP medium supplemented with BAP, phloroglucinol, gave rise to shoots.

Secondary tubers were formed from the primary tubers. Shoots from axillary buds as well from tubers do not root easily. Roots could be induced in a few shoots by planting them in moist sand supplemented with $MnSO_4$ and IBA. Rooted plants have been transferred to pots in the green house and also to the field.

MOLECULAR GENETIC MARKERS

Genetic markers serve as *random locators* on nuclear or organelle DNA. The challenge to the geneticist is to look for relationships between these markers and characteristics of trees from pedigrees or specific populations. When they are interpreted correctly, genetic markers are invaluable for examining genetic variation among and within populations, assessing levels of outcrossing and in breeding, and genetic identification or *fingerprinting* of varieties or pedigrees.

Genetic marker data can also be used for assisting with early selection of better genotypes, rather than waiting for the tree to express the trait much later. There have been many developments in both agriculture and forestry in associating marker data with physical traits. However, marker-assisted selection (MAS) is not yet routinely applied in tree breeding programmes, largely because of time and cost constraints. It will also be necessary to show a clear economic advantage over conventional selection approaches. Thus it is likely that MAS will only be applied to a few species and situations, *e.g.* some of the major commercially used pine (Frewen *et al.*, 2000) and *Eucalyptus* species.

Most of the markers in use today are based on systems in which DNA is cut by enzymes, after which the DNA sections are multiplied (amplified) in reactors and then separated by electrophoretic techniques – *i.e.* DNA bands are separated out by their molecular weight and charge, in the presence of an electrical current on a gel medium (Photo 2). Rapid advances in DNA markers, mapping and sequencing technologies are increasing the basic understanding of the role of genes and their products in cellular processes. Investigations in this field, known as *genomics*, are well under way in humans as well as in animals, plants and a few tree species (Merkle and Dean, 2000).

Molecular markers are primarily information tool. They do not contribute directly to plant products, but they provide information that is critical to locating and working with the DNA that can be of interest for genetic transformation, or information on population structure, mating systems and pedigree confirmation.

GENETICALLY MODIFIED TREES AND GENETIC TRANSFORMATION

The term biotechnology is often associated entirely with genetic transformation, the most controversial of all these technologies as it involves the introduction of selected foreign genes into the plant genome. Well-characterized genes from other species are used, which typically allows for the expression of a novel trait in a new genetic background. Biolistics (*i.e.* the introduction of DNA into the cell nucleus on small metal particles using high-speed projection techniques) or microorganism vectors that carry the specific gene(s) of interest are typically used to introduce the gene(s). Of course, long-term or adequate expression of the gene in the GM plant is also critical; this is sometimes referred to as stability.

Genetic transformation techniques are fundamentally different from conventional plant breeding. At least in the initial generations, conventional breeding and selection bring about an increase in the frequency of desirable genes affecting some trait already present in the species. It is presumed that this occurs across many gene loci and that each gene has a small effect, although a few genes of large effect will also be important to the response in early generations. Later, new favourable mutations-most mutations are unfavourable and will probably be selected against – will accumulate as their frequency is increased through breeding (sexual recombination), testing and reselection.

Most forest tree species are still quite close to their wild relatives and have high levels of genetic variation for most traits of interest. Therefore, to be of value, GM trees must offer unique features that cannot be economically delivered through conventional breeding programmes and that are capable of offsetting the costs and time expended in developing the technology.

The traits that have so far been considered for potential genetic modification of forest trees are herbicide resistance, reduced flowering or sterility, insect resistance and wood chemistry. While conventional tree breeding programmes have paid attention to insect resistance and wood quality (but not many of the specifics of wood chemistry), they are likely to have little ability to incorporate traits such as herbicide resistance or reduced flowering.

OTHER TECHNIQUES

Two techniques commonly used to create new sources of genetic variation in crops, horticulture and fruit trees, which are not easily classified as either tissue culture or genetic modification, are protoplast fusion (*i.e.* the hybridization of species by fusion of protoplasts and genomes from related species but with reproductive barriers) and haploidization (*i.e.* the creation of completely homozygous clonal lines made by doubling haploid cells, such cells, such as pollen). Neither technique is well developed in forest tree species, but protoplast fusion research is under way in a few woody plants (Guo and Deng, 1999). Another techniques routinely used in crops and fruit trees is mutagenesis: a directed or quasi-random mutation of an existing gene, typically done with mutagenic chemicals. While these techniques are not effectively in use or even considered important in forestry today, they too point to the fact that large and potentially useful genetic modifications can be made with techniques other than GM technology.

An additional techniques now commonly used in both crops and forestry, *e.g.* in hybrid poplars (Zuffa, Lin and Payne, 1999), is embryo rescuing. This involves the removal of an embryo from a seed that would otherwise not survive on its own would otherwise not survive on its own and that embryo's cultivation until it becomes a successful "germinant" or seedling. This procedure is typically required when there are differences in basic seed biology between species or parental lines, such as incompatibilities in ovule or embryo development. Although the technique is a rather simple biotechnology, it is important to point out that the plants it produces would not exist without such a resuce effort.

MICROBIAL BREAKDOWN OF CELL WALL COMPONENTS

Paper industries and farmers face the problems of disposal of lignin in wood and straw, respectively. Lignin inhibits straw breakdown in soil and must be removed during pulp manufacture to facilitate fibre separation and subsequent bonding in the paper. Various wood-rot fungi have been shown to produce lignase enzymes, which can destroy lignin upto 3 to 4 per cent. The US Forest Products Laboratory has examined the mutants and genetically engineered variants of *Phanerochaete chrysosporium*.

Fermentation of xylose from hemicellulose in wood by *Candida tropicalis* is an important aspect of wood technology; this leaves the cellulose intact and the fermentation products including ethanol, acetone, glycerol and butanediol (precursors of synthetic rubber). This technology is useful to develop clean environment and requires less energy than that of the traditional wood processing methods.

Anaerobic digestion of plant biomass and sewage sludge in simple biogas generators is cheap and provides low purity methane for energy while leaving mineral nutrients and organic structure for soil improvement. On the large scale, higher purities of methane (90 per cent) may be obtained with thermophilic digesters packed with immobilized organisms, thus eliminating the need for purification of the gas.

APPLICATIONS OF BIOTECHNOLOGIES TO FOREST SOIL MICROBIOLOGY

The genetic manipulations of nitrogen fixing and relationships between plants, rhizobia and actinomycetes were reported by Postgate (1987). The principles clearly apply to the many leguminous trees now is used, particularly in the tropics and to the non-leguminous, nitrogen fixing species such as alder, *Casuarina* and some elms. Enhancement of the amount of nitrogen fixed has obvious benefits to rural populations in the Third World who cannot afford or are unable to import fertilizers. This is one of the major aims of agro forestry systems for adverse conditions such as high temperature, low rainfall, and extreme soil pH; for any condition there is potential for selection of fungal strain and for synthesis of tree-fungal association genotypes. This may be achieved *in vitro* and mass production of fungal spores for nursery inoculation in culture. One of the common problems in establishing tree plantations is the existence in the soil infected with fungal mycelia. It is hard to determine the risk of infection by normal sampling and microscopic examination because of the difficulty of species identification. The studies on the feasibility of using monoclonal antibody techniques to overcome this problem are in progress.

Many of the techniques applicable to forestry are similar to the ones used in agriculture, although, as shown in this article, the issues in forestry can be somewhat different and will require special attention.

Research and the application of biotechnology may take in the future, and at the degree to which governments can or should assist the development of biotechnology and regulate its use.

ISSUES SURROUNDING THE USE OF FOREST TREES FROM BIOTECHNOLOGY

Most of the biotechnologies used in applied forestry today fall into the categories of tissue culture and molecular marker applications. Advantages in these two areas of biotechnology have all been been logical progressions and refinements of techniques that have been used in plant and tree improvement for decades, if not centuries, to produce clonal lines or varieties.

Most of the popular concern about GM plants, or about the use of any of the other techniques discussed in this article, derives from concern about products grown as food for human consumption. This will rarely be a direct issue in forestry, although careful evalution will be necessary in the case of multi-use tree species that provide non-wood forest products (NWFPs).

The argument that the genetic changes made in GMOs are *unnatural* has been raised as a concern. It is, however, difficult to say that any particular technique in itself can pose increased biological risk. It is the gene products that may pose a lower or higher risk, irrespective of the technology used to obtain them. To evaluate possible risks fully, in-depth knowledge of the particular genetic transformation is necessary, *e.g.* the product produced, where the transformation occurred, what *promoter* genes were used and the reliability of the expression over time (Gutierrez, MacIntosh and Green, 1999). This may be particularly true when more than one or two transgenes are incorporated. In such cases there may be requirements for longer field-testing, environmental assessments and more caution in deployment (Burdon, 1999). In addition, mutation caused by gene transfer and tissue culture (somaclonal variation) can alter the function of non-target genes in ways that might take some time to detect. These, however, are not genetic issues, but a matter of having appropriate genetic testing and evaluation programmes in place prior to the release and use of GM (or even conventionally bred) trees in managed landscapes.

ISSUES ASSOCIATED WITH SPECIFIC TYPES OF TRAITS FOR TREES

Herbicide Resistance

Herbicide resistance in poplars is probably the best-developed GM technology in forest trees. The first concern with herbicide-resistant GM plants is evidence of the development of resistance in weed populations. The risk may be substantially less in forestry than in agriculture, as herbicides are only used for a short time and with fewer applications during the early period of plantation esbablishment. Furthermore, total weed control is not necessary in forest tree plantations, so there is less selection pressure for resistance to weeds.

The other concern is cross breeding with wild populations. While this is possible, it is likely that wild populations that do hybridize with GM trees would have little selective advantage unless adjacent wild populations are treated with herbicide, which is rare in forestry. The main question is then the effect on the genetic structure of local wild populations if cross-breeding does occur (*e.g.* in *in situ* conservation areas) and the acceptability of this risk to local resource managers. If this is a concern, reduced flowering or sterility transgenes may be required, along with herbicide resistance in GM trees.

The introduction of herbicide resistance through GM technology is likely to be the most feasible and the most frequently applied genetic modification in trees. Nevertheless, it is only likely for a few well-developed species in certain situations, such as in intensive poplar fibre farms where herbicides are sometimes an approved management tool.

Reduced Flowering or Sterility

Reduced flowering in forest trees may be disirable in order to steer the products of photosynthesis into wood production, rather than reproductive tissues. However, since such reallocation of resources has not yet been well quantified, the main justification for reduced flowering or sterility development is when it substantially reduces the gene flow to wild adjacent populations of the same species. This may help promote greater acceptance of intensive GM tree plantation forestry adjacent to natural forests. Although research on flowering mechanisms is under way (*e.g.* Skinner *et al.*, 1999), the stability of sterility-gene expression over time will have to be confirmed in field trials that reflect expected rotation.

Insect Resistance

The development of GM crops that are insect resistant is now common, but these crops also create some of the most complex ecological situations that need to be addressed. The first issue of concern is the possible toxicity of the compounds produced in GM insect-resistant plants when they are grown specifically for human consumption or for animal feed as part of associated food chains. Second, there are ecological concerns of cross breeding with wild relatives and the evolution of resistance in the pest populations, as with herbicide resistance. An additional and serious problem in forestry is that the long generation time of trees allows for many generations of insect populations to challenge a resistance mechanism.

The most developed GM approach for insect resistance in forestry, as in agriculture, has been the use of genes from a natural insect pathogen, *Bacillus thuringiensis (Bt.)*. Poplars are again among the tree species in which the technology is most advanced (TGERC, 1999). Research and development of other compounds is under way to reduce reliance on the relatively narrow group natural *Bt* toxins (ffrench-Constant and Bowen, 1999). Because of the complex ecological remifications and public concerns surrounding GM insect-resistance and plants, high levels of scientifically sound laboratory and field testing will be required.

Wood Property Chemistry

It is now technically possible to alter genetically the chemistry of lignin in trees for easier and more environmentally friendly pulping. Genes that are important to the pathway of lignin development in wood have been modified to produce unique wood composition in very young trees (Lapierre *et al.*, 1999). However, genes of relatively large effect on wood chemistry have also been found naturally (*e.g.* a major recessive gene in loblolly pine (Ralph *et al.*, 1997), so wood properties can also be modified through conventional selection and breeding. Therefore, many of the same ecological and economic considerations need to be taken into account with or without genetic transformation technology. Two important questions that remain in developing lignin-modified varieties or clones are how economically valuable plantations using such trees would be and whether altered wood may show susceptibilities to environmental stresses. If the answer to the latter is affirmative, it is again likely that reduced flowering or sterility genes would have to be incorporated into material used on a large scale when it is important that there be minimal gene flow to adjacent wild populations (*e.g.* in *in situ* conservation areas).

CAN GENETICALLY MODIFIED TREES BE SAFELY DEPLOYED IN THE ENVIRONMENT?

The main ecological concerns with GM plants is the issue of gene exchange with wild populations – an issue already being considered in forestry with regard to seed orchard seed from conventional breeding programmes. In most of the situations for which GM trees will be considered, the plantation species will be an exotic one, so gene exchange would not be a factor; but in cases where it could occur, reduced flowering or sterility is likely to be a basic requirement. Much has been and will continue to be learned from agricultural research on transgene flow from GM crops to their wild relatives. Investigations into these specific questions are under way in forestry (DiFazio *et al.*, 1999).

Although exotic plantation species may have limited risk of cross –breeding *per se*, the release into the environment of a GMO in most cases poses less of an ecological risk than the introduction of an exotic species. The introduction of an exotic species is a release into the environment of an entirely different genetic constitution, rather than the introduction of a single gene into a native species. The current regulations of the Forest Stewardship Council (FSC, 1999) prohibit the use of GM trees, but suggest that *the use of exotic species shall be carefully controlled and actively monitored to avoid adverse ecological impacts*. This recommendation largely runs contrary to the argument made here that the biological risks and economic realities of all forest management options need to be evaluated objectively. On the other hand, a large genetic change made to the overall fitness of a native species and released without adequate consideration of local environmental risks is not appropriate either.

Clearly, potential risks must be balanced with benefits in all types of improved forest trees, considering the deployment schemes that will be used in different locations and at different times. For example, clonal varieties of fruit trees have been used in large continuous orchards for hundreds of years, and this deployment and management approach is considered by most people to be ecologically and economically acceptable, as it presents no unmanageable biotic or abiotic challenges. In plantation forestry for wood production, clonal blocks may be appropriate in some situations, such as poplar plantations, while pure or family-mix plantaing patterns are likely to be apropriate for most other forestry situations.

In any event, deployment strategies must be besigned to minimize the risks of economic losses of the stand as well as future biological losses, such as the development of resistance in pest and disease popuolations (Roberds and Bishir, 1997). At a minimum, therefore, a few dozen well-tested GM clones will be necessary to meet the typical production and diversity requirements necessary even in intensive forestry programmes.

To help address many of these concerns, a number of countries have developed regulations and restrictions specifying the requirements of confined field testing that are needed before commercial release (OECD, 2000). These requirements, which are necessary to reduce biological and economic risks, will undoubtedly continue to evolve. In addition to national laws and regulations, there are also broader international agreements on biosafety, *e.g.* the Cartagena Protocol on Biosafety (Convention on Biological Diversity, 2000). (Adopted from Unasylva, FAO, Vol. 52: 2001/1).

EQUITY OF ACCESS TO GENETIC MODIFICATION BIOTECHNOLOGIES

Private investors have taken the lead for most investment in modern biotechnology, and in so doing have also had to manage the associated economic risks. In many situations such investiment risks are protected by patents. An obvious concern is, therefore, that access to GM crops and trees will be controlled almost entirely by private corporations. Agreements for the use of techniques or material could be prohibitively expensive, preventing the use of the technology where it would be of value.

In the past, governments were the main investors in breeding and molecular biology research. Their role may have to expand once again in this regard, in order to provide a flow of material and information that can be developed and shared by both private and public institutions (Santos and Lewontin, 1997), as opposed to being controlled largely by private companies. Nevertheless, financial constraints, rather than available technical knowledge, are probably the largest challenge ahead for applying modern biotechnology in less developed countries, although it has been shown, *e.g.* by the Agricultural Biotechnology Support Project (www.iia.msu.edu/absp/), that arrangements through donations are possible.

Even if financial considerations can be addressed in the research phase of biotechnology, moving the technology from the developmen stage to operational reality provides a new set of technical challenges with additional expenses (Polonenko, 1999). It is likely that only a few economically important species will warrant such additional investments, and it is on these economic situations and realities that the debate should focus. (Adopted from Unasylva, FAO, Vol. 52: 2001/1).

PUBLIC ACCEPTANCE OF GENETICALLY MODIFIED PLANTS

As has been alluded to previously, in terms of biotechnology research, one of the most important economic considerations separating forestry from agriculture is that trees require substantially more time for proper eveluation under both laboratory and field conditions. Rapid generation turnover in crop species has allowed genetic modification technology to develop quickly. Although this has been desirable from an economic point of view, the ecological ramifications have been far more difficult to study, as complex experiments must be carried out over several years. Public and government acceptance of GM plants is now probably as dependent on biological risk assessment and risk issue management (Leiss, 1999) as it is on technical development or economics alone.

For GM trees, there is cleraly a need to provide scientifically sound, neutral and intelligible information to the public, so that when and if GM trees become commercially available, informed decisions can be made about their release into the environment. Foresters are generally very aware of the need for public involvement in many other areas of forest management (*e.g.* chemical applications in forests, game management, felling patterns and plants, allowable annual harvesting levels), so decisions concening GM trees may simply be an additional issue to be managed in the process. (Adopted from Unasylva, FAO, Vol. 52: 2001/1).

FUTURE CHALLENGES*

- Government participation in the development of biotechnology appears necessary to keep some flow of material and knowledge in the public domain. Without this, the costs of using privately owned genes could seriously limit further interest and development of genetic modification technology in trees. Concerns about monopolies arise with any new products, but governments can step in to deal with substantial ineqities or corporate actions that are not in the interest of society as a whole.
- Even if GM trees are not used on a wide scale in the future, research and development in GM technology will provide a great deal of information about gene action and regulation, which could be of long-term value to conventional breeding programmes.
- Other forest management decisions with potentially more serious ecological consequences, including large-scale speices introduction or inappropriate use of provenances or improved trees from even conventional breeding, need to be evaluated by foresters, managers and regulatory agencies in the same way as the products of modern biotechnology are.
- Geneticists have always attempted to create genetic options for the future. If we look carefully at where these current and future biotechnology are heading in

forestry, it is obvious that the research and development will largely be used in support of advancing clonal forestry. Therefore, it is in the context of appropriate clonal forestry that most of the issues need to be examined and evaluated.

From a genetic perpective, concerns that biotechnology is *unnatural* ignore that dynamic changes in the genetic code that occur within and across species genomes through modification of transposable genes or elements by virus vectors and through mutation. This article has attempted to point out that humans have already had a huge effect on the genetic structure of many plants and animals, using many different technologies which will continue to develop and change overtime. However, while those in the forefront of any technology will promote its potential benefits, in the end it will be the economic and regulatory systems of governing bodies at the national and global levels that must evaluate the technology's relevance and appropriateness.

*(adopted from Unasylva, FAO, Vol. 52: 2001/1).

CHAPTER 25

Biotechnology of Biofertilizers Production

Biofertilizers are inputs containing microorganisms, which are capable of mobilizing nutritive elements from non-usable form to usable form through biological processes. They are less expensive, eco-friendly and sustainable. The beneficial microbes in the soil, which are the greater significance to horticultural crops are biological nitrogen fixers, phosphate solubilizers and mycorrhizal fungi which are the phosphate scavengers.

Nitrogen is one of the chief and important constituents of protein and nucleic acid molecules that play the basic role in cell metabolism, growth, reproduction and transmission of heritable characters. Therefore, without a constant supply of this unavoidable element, life can not go on.

Biological nitrogen fixation (BNF) is the reduction of atmospheric nitrogen to ammonia by microorganisms in the soil. It involves highly specialised and intricately evolved interactions between soil microorganisms and higher plants for harnessing the atmospheric nitrogen. It is a fascinating biological phenomenon studied extensively to provide low-cost nitrogen and improve crop productivity. The nitrogen fixing organisms associated with horticultural crops are the Rhizobium species, living in symbiotic relationship with the leguminous plants and free living fixers belonging to the *Azotobacter* family and the *Azospirilla* living in association with the root system of crop plants.

BIOFERTILISERS/MICROBIAL INOCULANT

Some soil microorganisms play an important role in improving soil fertility and crop productivity due to their capability to fix atmospheric nitrogen, solubilise insoluble phosphate and decompose farm wastes resulting in the release of plant nutrient. The extent of benefit from these microorganisms depends upon their number and efficiency which however, is governed by a large number of soil and environmental factors. When the number and activity of specific microorganism called microbial inoculant or biofertilizer is used to hasten biological activity to improve availability of plant nutrient. A number of products are now available that are generally referred to as soil and plant additives, of non-traditional nature. These products include:

1. Microbial fertilizers and soil inoculants contain unique and beneficial strains of soil microorganisms.
2. Microbial activators that supposedly contain special chemical formulations for increasing the numbers and activity of beneficial microorganisms in soil.
3. Soil conditions that claim to create favourable soil physical and chemical conditions which result in increased growth and yield of crops, and (iv) vermin-compost which helps in improving soil health and fertility.

Nitrogen fixing organisms can be provided to the farmers in the name of microbial inoculants otherwise termed as biofertilizers. The biofertilizers containing biological nitrogen fixing organisms are of utmost important in agriculture in view of the following advantage:

1. They help in the establishment and growth of crop plants and trees.
2. They enhance biomass production and grain yields by 10-20%.
3. They are useful in sustainable agriculture.
4. They are suitable in organic farming.
5. They play an important role in agroforestry / silvipastoral systems.

After the advent of the acetylene test for assessing nitrogen fixing potential, rapid progress has been made in identifying nitrogen fixing organisms. Out of a large number of microorganisms possessing the property of nitrogen fixation, only a few such as *Rhizobium*, *Azotobacter*, *Azospirillum*, BGA, *Azolla*, etc. have been commercially exploited. The reaction in biological nitrogen fixation is essential the same as in production of chemical fertilizers (Haber-Bosch process) *i.e.* the catalytic reduction of dinitrogen (N_2) to ammonia (NH_3).

TYPES OF BIOFERTILIZERS

Rhizobiuim Inoculant

Agrobacterium (*A. radiobacter*, *A. tumefacions*) has also been included in the species: *Rhizobium radiobacter*, but this splitting of *Rhizobium* at the generic level into *Agrobacterium* is not accepted by most of the microbiologists.

The presence of *Rhizobium* bacteria in the root nodule can be seen under high power microscope by crushing a washed nodule between two glass slider. This kind of bacteria, preferentially, infect legumes as compared to non-legumes. Structurally, *Rhizobium* are rod shaped but great variation can be observed during their life cycle. These are coccoid, very small, highly motile and ellipsoidal forms. The bacteroids are usually irregular with X, Y, star and club-shaped forms. They are 0.5 to 0.9 micron by 1.2 to 3.0 micron in size. All the species are non-sporing and non-acid fast. These symbiotic bacteria (*Rhizobium*) are difficult to cultivate in ordinary culture media but they grow on manitol agar. *Rhizobia* are susceptible to antibiotics (produced by other microorganisms of soil) and also to the action of bacteriophages. Fungicides, herbicides and other plant protectants are also toxic to *Rhizobia*.

The most widely used biofertilizer is *Rhizobium*, which colonizes the roots of specific legumes to form tumour like growths called root nodules. It is these nodules that act as factories of ammonia production. Rhizobia have the ability to fix atmospheric nitrogen in symbiotic association with legumes and certain non-legumes like *Parasponia*. A mature nodule consists of a central 'bacterial zone' surrounded by several layers of cortical cells. The process of N-fixation is wholly dependent on the activity of the enzyme nitrogenase, which is located within the bacteriods. The volume and number of bacteroids have a direct positive relationship with the amount of nitrogen fixed.

There are specific types of *Rhizobium* for every legume and inoculation with efficient strains of *Rhizobia* is essential for the nitrogen gains and better crop yields. Inoculation of pulse crop with appropriate cultures can give yield increases of the order of 15-30 per cent. Thus *Rhizobium*-legume symbiosis can generally meet 80 per cent of the N requirement of the legume crop. A starter does of N as chemical fertilizer is required (equivalent to about 20 per cent requirement of legume crop) for good crop yields.

The *Rhizobium*-legume association can fix up to 100-300 kg N/ha in one crop season and in certain situations can leave behind substantial nitrogen for the following crop. The range of nitrogen fixed per hectare per year by different legumes is 100-150 kg for clover, 80-85 kg for cowpea, 100-300 kg for alfalfa, 240-320 kg for faba bean, 90-100 kg for lentil, 150-200 kg for lupins, 50-60 kg for groundnut, 60-80 kg for soybean, 50-55 kg for mungbean and 100-400 kg for pasture legumes.

Rhizobium Culture

Rhizobium culture has been used for leguminous vegetable crops, is in paractice among farmers. *Rhizobium* forms symbiotic association with roots of leguminous crops forming nitrogen fixing nodules on the root system. Rhizobia enter the roots of legumes either through root hairs or directly at the emergence of lateral roots. They form infection threads through which the bacteria enter the root system. The entry of *Rhizobium* into the roots of plans is a perfect symbiosis. Initial stages is symbiosis is the reciprocal molecular conversation, transmission of a gene inducer from legume host to bacterium and the bacteria in response synthesizing a morphogen that is transmitted to the plant, switching the developmental fate of the legume root, the bacteria and formation of bacterioids in the nodules. It is enzyme nitrogenase that reduces atmospheric nitrogen to ammonia. This enzyme has been studied in a very great detail (Das, 1991).

There are 2 types of Rhizobia:

1. Slow growing *Bradyrhizobium* sp.
2. Fast-growing *Rhizobium* sp.

Soil contains native species of *Rhizobium* but all are not capable of forming nodules. Some of the strains are highly specific to certain species. These are called cross inoculation groups. For example, *Rhizobium leguminosarum* can nodulate peas only, while *R. leguminosarum bv. phasioli* can nodulate French bean and other beans and *Rhizobium* sps. Nodulate cowpea. Artificial inoculations help increase the native population of a particular species in the soil when that crop is grown.

The efficacy of *Rhizobium* inoculation has been established in India beyond doubt by the results of the coordinated trials conducted by the Indian Council of Agricultural Research, New Delhi, in farmers' field (AICRP 1983). Vegetable legumes – French bean, pea and cowpea – have been extensively studied. Effective nodulating strains have been isolated and developed after field testing. French been strains have been isolated and developed after field testing. French been strains has been modified from time to time to suit salinity, alkalinity and acidity of soil (Bhardwaj, 1975; Suryanarayana and Pramod Kumar, 1985; Tomar *et al* 1985; Yadav and Sanoria, 1994; Wange *et al* 1996). In iron mine waste soil also rhizobium inoculation could improve nodulation in cowpea. (Ravtray *et al*, 1996). Mutant strains of *Rhizobium leguminosarum* bv phaseoli superior to wild strains in nodulation have been induced in French bean through UV induction, antibiotic resistance, acid and azide resistance at the CCS Haryana Agricultural University, Hissar. For cowpea effective strains of *Rhizobium* sps. have been identified at University of Agricultural Sciences, Bangalore, Tamil Nadu Agricultural University, Coimbatore and CCS Haryana Agricultural University, Hissar.

TABLE 25.1: List of some plants in which *Rhizobium* is found

Name of the plants	*Rhizobium spp.*
Clover	*R. trifolii*

Bean	*R. phaseoli*
Lupinus	*R. lupini*
Ornithopus	*R. lupini*
Soybean	*R. japonicum*
Melilotus, Trigonella	*R. meliloti*
Pea	*R. leguminosarum*

Mundra and Bhati (1994) studied the role of ion, manganese and *Rhizobium* inoculation on growth, nodulation and iron manganese ratio and protein content in cowpea. They found that 20 kg/ha of *Rhizobium* inoculum increased the number of nodules 38%. The *Rhizobium* sp. also increased nodulation, nitrogen fixation and biomass yield by slow and fast growing cowpea rhizobia in gaur under different environmental conditions (Mand *et al*, 1992). Wange and Patil (1995) studied the response of pea cultivars of *Rhizobium leguminosarum* inoculation. An increased pod yield of 25-66.7% could be obtained in Bonevillae variety. Singh *et al* (1992) in a field trial in sandy loam soil in U.P. found that *Rhizobium* inoculation and phosphate application (46 kg/ha) gave maximum yield in pea Rachna. Singh and Singh (1992) also found that *Rhizobium* inoculation and sulphur application (0-30 ppm) improved seed yield in pea cv T163.

It is estimated that about one third off the electrons made available for reduction of nitrogen in legume nodules are used instead to reduce hydrogen and this gas just escapes into the soil atmosphere carrying away wasted energy. Certain species of *Rhizobium* contain uptake hydrogenase enzyme (Hup+ strains) that oxidizes much of the hydrogen to water before it escapes. During this oxidation ATP is produced from ADP and Pi. This process, therefore conserves energy and are more efficient N fixers. The *Rhizobium* strains possessing this enzyme yield more than the strains that do not possess them. The Hup+ strains have been identified by Dadarwal (1986) to be more competitive than Hup- strains.

Genetic Modifications in Rhizobium strains

Efforts have been made to develop genetically modified strains incorporating traits for better competitiveness; Khanuja and Suman (1993) obtained heat shock tolerant mutants in the process of improving rhizobial strains. Sharma *et al* (1997) introduced gene markers (Gus) in Rhizobium strains to monitor the release of genetically engineered strains in the environment. However genetically modified strains have not made any impact on legume production under field conditions.

Rhizobium in Root Nodule

The presence of these bacteria in the root nodule can be seen under high power microscope by crushing a washed nodule between two glass slider. Frank (1877) and Beijernick (1888) discovered *Rhizobium* a free living or symbiotic bacteria of leguminous as well as non-leguminous plants. This kind of bacteria preferentially, infect legumes as compared to non-legumes. Structurally, *Rhizobium* is rod shaped but great variation can be observed during their life cycle. These are coccoid, very small, highly motile and ellipsoidal forms. The bacteroids are usually irregular with X, Y, star and club-shaped forms. They are 0.5 to 0.9 micron by 1.2 to 3.0 micron in size. All the species are non-sporing and non-acid fast. These symbiotic bacteria (*Rhizobium*) are difficult to cultivate in ordinary culture media but they grow on manitol agar.

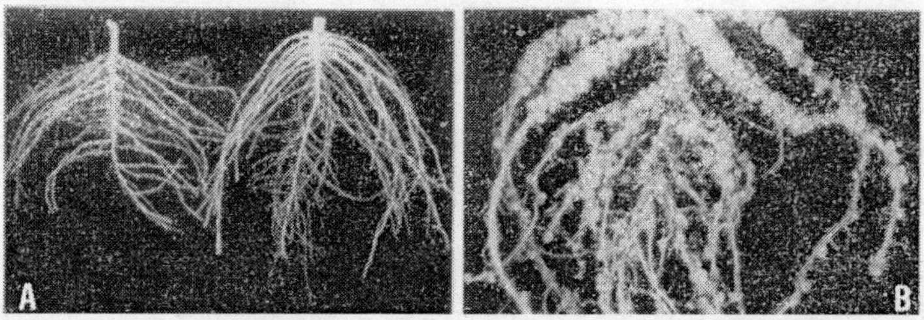

FIGURE 25.1: Bare uninoculated roots of soybean plant (A) and nodulated roots of soybean (B) inoculated with *Rhizobium.*

Rhizobia are susceptible to antibiotics (produced by other microorganisms of soil) and also to the action of bacteriophages. Fungicides, herbicides and other plant protectants are also toxic to *Rhizobia.* Occurrence of different species of *Rhizobium* in leguminous plants can be enumerated as follows:

***Agrobacterium (A. radiobacter, A. tumefacions)*:** It has also been included in the species: *Rhizobium radiobacter*, but this splitting of *Rhizobium* at the generic level into *Agrobacterium* is not accepted by most of the microbiologists.

One more kind of slow growing asymbiotic bacteria of lupin, soybean, cowpea have been identified and placed under a separate genus *Phytomyxa* (*P. japonicum*). In short, the root nodule genera can be delimited into two genera: *Rhizobium* and *Phytomyxa*: the former comprises of three species: *R. leguminosarum*, *R. meliloti* and *R. radiobacter*, while the latter bears only one species *P. japonicum.*

According to Elken (1969) *Rhizobium* can also be classified on the basis of DNA composition, for example guanine and cytosine composition of *R. leguminosarum* and *R. meliloti* is 56.6 to 63.1 per cent while G+C composition of *P. japonicum* is 62.8 to 65.5 per cent (Delay and Rassel, 1965).

Structure and Function of Nodule

The outermost layer of the nodule constitutes the bacteroid zone, which is enclosed by several layers of cortical cells. The rate of nitrogen fixation of nodule is directly proportional to the volume of the effective nodule. Sometimes ineffective strains produce ineffective nodules. These nodules are relatively small and contain poorly developed tissue associated with morphological abnormalities.

Formation of Nodule in Leguminous Plants

Biological nitrogen fixation is the reduction of atmospheric nitrogen to ammonia by microorganisms in the soil. It involves a highly specialised and intricately evolved interactions between soil microorganisms and higher plants for harnessing the atmospheric nitrogen. It is a fascinating biological phenomenon studied extensively to provide low-cost nitrogen and improve crop productivity. The nitrogen fixing organisms associated with horticultural crops are the Rhizobium species, living in symbiotic relationship with the leguminous plants and free living fixers belonging to the *Azotobacter* family and the *Azospirilla* living in association with the root system of crop plants. Roots of most of the leguminous plants possess circular out-growth or swelling called nodules or tubercules, which are formed after infection of certain types of nitrogen fixing bacteria particularly the different species of *Rhizobium.*

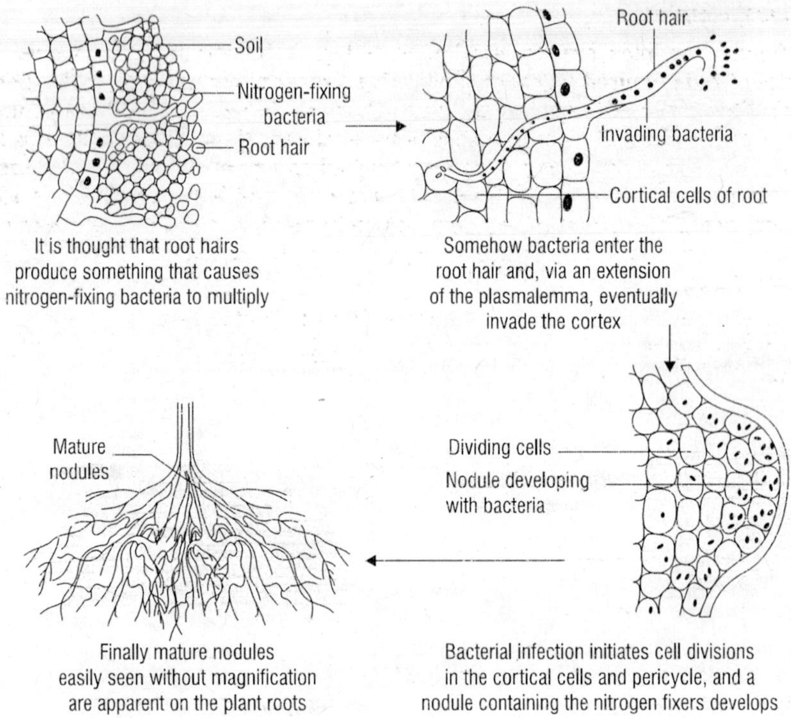

FIGURE 25.2: Nodule formation by *Rhizobium* on legume plants. The root hairs are the site of infection. Note the change in the root hair. A characteristic deformation is the curling of the root hair tip to produce a Shepherd's crook. The nodule can be seen on the root.

These bacteria have the capacity to fix free atmospheric nitrogen of soil in nodule. They infect or get their entrance in root through the soft-hair or other epidermal cells by damaging them. In the first stage of the infection, bacteria grow very profusely at the tip of the root hair and form a long filament in the root hair-called *infection thread.* This thread reaches the endodermis and pericycle area through cortex tissue. Cells of this area (cortex) go on dividing and form a young nodule. The newly formed young nodule pushes the overlying parenchyma and the epidermal tissue towards outside and produces a small swelling on the surface of the root. Anatomically, a nodule is made of thin walled parenchymatous cells which is filled up with the nitrogen fixing organisms. The size and shape of the root nodule varies according to plants in which occur. It is not necessary that all the bacteria, which infect the root, produce nodule.

According to Wipf and Cooper (1939) the root nodule always contains double number of chromosomes as against of normal somatic tissue. If the root lacks such cells (cells with double chromosome number), there will be no formation of root nodule, even after the formation of infection thread. Those plants which do not bear root-nodules will never be able to fix atmospheric nitrogen in the plants. It has been observed by Allen and Allen (1947) that out of 429 genera of family Leguminosae about 179 genera containing 949 species form nodules.

Leghaemoglobin

The effective nodules are usually larger and pink in colour. This is due to the presence of red coloured leghaemoglobin (leg indicating its presence in legume root nodule). This pigment is similar to haemoglobin of blood and is found in nodules between bacteroids and membrane envelops, enclosing them. Chemically, it is haem-protein and it contains a haem meoiety attached to a peptide chain and represents the globin part of the molecule. The molecular weight of leghaemoglobin is 16,000 - 17,000 daltons. The amount of leghaemoglobin in nodules has the direct relationship between amount of atmospheric nitrogen fixed by legumes. The functions of leghaemoglobin are as follows:

1. It represents an active site of nitrogen absorption and reduction.
2. It acts as a specific electron carrier in nitrogen fixation.
3. It regulates the oxygen-supply in the nodule.
4. It acts as an oxygen-carrier.

According to Scholander (1960), leghaemoglobin acts as a biological-valve in regulating the supply of oxygen to bacteroids in nodules.

Site of Nitrogen Fixation in Nodules

According to Bergersen (1969) the membrane envelops surrounding the groups of bacteroids are the site of nitrogen fixation, but in recent years it has been proved that bacteroids are the seat of nitrogen fixation.

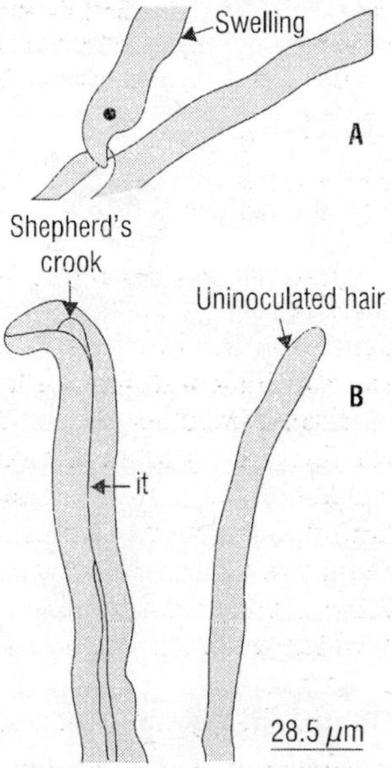

FIGURE 25.3: The early host responses to infection leading to the formation of N_2-fixing root nodules. (A) A root hair two hours after inoculation, showing curling and swelling. (B) A root hair (left) tow days after inoculation, showing a shepherd's crook and an infection thread (it). A thin uninoculated root hair is shown on the right.

Azotobacter Inoculant

Azotobacter is a free living (non-symbiotic) aerobic nitrogen fixing bacteria commonly found in a close relationship with vegetable crops. Azotobacter was first isolated by Beijerinck. Five species of *Azotobacter* are poplar. They are: *a. chroococcum*, *A. chroococcum*, *A. vinelandii*, *A. beijerink* and A. paspali. *Azotobacter chroococcum* appeared in acid soils and arable soils while *A. beijerinckii* in neutral and alkali soils. They form cysts to withstand adverse condition. Each cyst has a living cell with 2 coats. The cysts accumulate poly hydroxybutyric acid. With the onset of favourable conditions, the cysts give rise to vegetative cells. Pigment production is one of the important characteristics of *Azotobacter* sp. *Azotobacter chroococcum, A beijerinckii* species are deemed to be the most commonly occurring species in India. These strains also produce growth substances and anitifungal substances. The beneficial effects of *Azotobacter* biofertilizer on cereals, millets, vegetables, cotton and sugarcane under both irrigated and rainfed field conditions have been substantiated and documented. Application of Azotobacter and sorghum by 5-30% over control. Apart from nitrogen, this organism is also capable of producing antibacterial and antifungal compounds, hormones and siderophores.

Field experiments have been done extensively in India on *Azotobacter* inoculation of seed or seedling of onion, brinjal, tomato and cabbage under different agroclimatic conditions. At the IARI, New Delhi Agricultural Universities of Maharashtra, Punjab and Tamil Nadu (Sundara Rao *et al.*, 1963; Lehri and Mehrotra, 1968; Joi and Shinde, 1976). *Azotobacter* inoculation saves addition of nitrogenous fertilizers by 10 to 20%.

Azospirillum Inoculant

The ability to fix nitrogen by certain spirilla (Spirillum lipoferum) was first recorded by Beijerinck in 1925 and later on confirmed by several workers using not only conventional micro-Kjeldahl assay but also by the methods such as acetylene reduction technique and the isotopic enrichment method involving N. Tarrand and his associates (1978) renamed this organism as *Azospirillum* (N_2 fixing *Spirillum*).

Azospirilla are a group of bacteria found in loose association with the root system of many crop plants. It is a type of symbiosis where the bacterial cells are found colonizing the root cortical cells or the intercellular spaces in the cortex. These bacterial grow better under reduced oxygen levels. They fix nitrogen from 10 to 40 kg/ha. The *Azospirillum* inoculation helps the plans in better vegetative growth, saving nitrogenous fertilizers by 25-30%. *Azospirilla* are microarophilic in nature. They are found in association with vegetables crops either freely in soil or inside the root system. Four species of *Azospirillum* have been identified. They are *A. lipofreum, A. brasilense, A. amazonense, A. iraquense*. The *A. brasilense and A. lipoferum* are very popular in India soils. The *A. bangalorense* a new species is found in association with tomato Sukhada (1988). One of the characteristics of *Azospirillum* is its ability to reduce nitrate and denitrify. Hence it is necessary to select strains which do not possess these characters. Sukhada and Shaila (1996) detected the *nif HDK* genes on the chromosomal DNA rather than on the plasmids of *Azospirillum bangalorense* isolated from tomato.

The bacterium, *Azospirillum* colonises root mass and fixes N in loose association with plants. Their inoculation has shown positive interaction with applied N in several field crops with an average response equivalent to 25-30 kg ha^{-1}

of applied N. The crops which respond to *Azospirillum* inoculation are maize, barley, oats, sorghum, pearl millet and forage crops. *Azospirillum* applications increase grain yield of cereals by 5-20% of millets by 30% and of fodder by over 50%.

Inoculations with *Azospirilum* have registered increased yield in different vegetable crops. Subbiah (1994) reported increase in nutrient content and yield in chilli and Bellary onion when *Azospirillum* is applied @ 2 kg/ha. Similarly in okra, cabbage, brinjal, tomato, capsicum and chillie *Azospirillum* inoculations improve yield. Its application is common practice in vegetables in Tamil Nadu.

Blue-Green Algae Inoculant

As early as 1939, Dr. P. K. De suggested that fertility of tropical rice fields was largely due to activity of the N-fixing BGA. Blue-green algae are photosynthetic nitrogen fixers *i.e.* they use energy derived from photosynthesis to fix atmospheric nitrogen. They are also called cyanobacteria and are free living organisms. In general BGA show dominance over other classes of algae in India. The utilization of blue-green algae as a biofertilizer for rice is very promising. A judicious use of these algae could provide to the country's entire rice acreage as much nitrogen as obtained from 15-17 lakh tonnes of urea. Methods have been developed for mass production of algal biofertilizer and rice growers in many parts of the world have already started using these algae. Recent researches have shown that algae also help to reduce soil alkalinity and this opens up possibilities for bioreclamation of such inhospitable environments.

Blue green algae (BGA) when cultured in small pit and used as an inoculum in paddy fields at the rate of 12-15 kg ha^{-1} resulted in nitrogen economy to rice crop of the order of 20-25 kg N ha^{-1} with yield increase of 5-14 per cent.

Azolla-Anabaena Symbiosis

Azolla is an aquatic fern commonly found floating in ponds, pools, tanks, shallow ditches and channels. It is also found in rice fields. Nitrogen fixing Blue-green Algae (GBA) *Anabaena azollae* is found in the cavities on its dorsal leaves and fixes atmospheric nitrogen efficiently, which is available to *Azolla* plants. The recognition of *Azolla* contains 0.2-0.3% nitrogen on dry weight basis.

A small floating water fern, *Azolla* is commonly seen in low land fields and in shallow fresh water bodies. This fern harbours a blue-green algae, *Anabaena azollae*. The *Azolla-Anabaena* association is a live floating nitrogen factory using energy from photosynthesis to fix atmospheric nitrogen amounting to 100-150 kg N/ha/year from about 40-60 tonnes of biomass. The studies carried out under AICARP showed that incorporation of 5 t ha-1 *Azolla* gave rice yields equivalent to about 30 kg N ha-1 at several locations. Reports of its current use as a biofertilizer for rice China, Vietnam, India, Indonesia, Thailand and other East and South Asian countries are available. An integrated system of rice *Azolla* fish has been developed in China.

Phosphate Mobilising Biofertilizers

Phosphorus is a very important nutrient of plants required in large quantities. Inorganic forms of this nutrient are compounds of Ca, Fe, and Al, while organic forms are phytin, phospholipids and nucleic acids which are added to the soil by decaying vegetation. Rock phosphate is the raw material for production of phosphatic fertilizers. In India more than 75% of phosphattic fertilizers are imported.

Large amount of phosphorus applied to various soils get fixed and become unavailable to the plants. Several soil bacteria, particularly those belonging to the genera *Pseudomonas* and *Bacillus*na dfungi *Penicillium* and *Aspergillus* possess the ability to bring insoluble phosphates in soil into soluble forms by secreting organic acids such as acetic, formic, propionic, lactic, glycolic, fumaric and succinic acids. These acids lower the pH and bring about dissolution of bound form of phosphate. Some of the hydroxy acids may chelate with Ca and Fe resulting in effective solubilization and utilization of phosphates by crops.

Phosphate solubilizing bacteria belonging to the genera *Pseudomonas* and *Bacillus*, and fungi to the genera *Penicillium* and *Aspergillus* possess the ability to solubilize the bound phosphates in the soil by secreting organic acids acids like formic, acetic, propionic, lactic, glycolic, fumaric and succinic. Addition of these bacteria to soil increases the availability of phosphorus in the soil thereby bringing about a saving the input of phosphorus.

The efficiency of phosphatic fertilizers is very low (15-30%) due to its fixation in soil. Besides, native soil phosphorus is mostly unavailable to crops because of its low solubility. The introduction of efficient P solubilisers in the rhizosphere has been found to increase the availability of phosphorus from both applied and native soil P. The phosphorus which gets fixed in soil is made available to crops by the action of microorganisms which solubilise insoluble/fixed forms of phosphorus into forms which are readily taken up by the plants. The common phosphate solubilizing bacteria and fungi are *Pseudomonsa striata, Bacillus polymyxa, Aspergillus awamoori, Penicillium digitatum.* These microorganisms can grow on insoluble phosphate sources such as tricalcium phosphate, ferric, aluminium and magnesium phosphate, rock phosphate and bone meal and convert them into soluble forms. Inoculation of seeds or seedlings with microphos biofertilisers can provide 30 kg P_2O_5 ha^{-1} equivalent P applied from superphosphate by solubilizing the soil phosphorus. Another factor, which affects the effective utilization of P is its low mobility in soil. Fortunately some filamentous organisms like vesicular arbuscular mycorrhizae (VAM) which form symbiotic association with plant roots have the ability to mobilize phosphorus from soil and thereby helping in absorption of P by plant roots. Commercial exploitation of phosphatic biofertilizers can play an important role particularly in making the direct use of abundantly available low grade phosphate possible.

Azotobacter and phospho-bacteria also produce hormones *viz.*, indoleacetic acid and gibberellin. There hormones stimulate root growth and development. The use of growth stimulating seed inoculants help in greater uptake of plant nutrients from applied chemical fertilizers by increasing the root growth.

In India, Indian Agricultural Research institute, New Delhi conducting researches on phosphate solubilising bacteria and the bacterial inocula. From chilli Arka Jwala nitrogen-fixing and phosphate solubilising bacteria have been isolated and identified as *Bacillus* species. These bacteria improved the growth of chili plants on inoculation. Brinjal cultivars also harbour nitrogen fixing and phosphate solubilising bacterial association. These have also been isolated and identified as *Bacillus* species. These bacteria fix nitrogen and solublize phosphorus thereby increasing the availability of these elements in the soil. These bacteria fix nitrogen and solubilise phosphorus there by increasing the availability of these elements in the soil (Jennifer *et al*, 1997). Besides, these plans are also found to release plant growth hormones, which increase the growth and yield of plans on inoculation (Jennifer *et al*, under publication).

In India, inoculum of phosphate solubilising microorganisms (PSM) is in market in a large quantity as *Microphos*, *Phosphobacteria*, and *Sueprphos*. Inoculation is done to improve the population of microorganisms near the root zone of crop plants, so that more phosphorus is available to the crop plants. Even in orchards phosphobacteria is applied by many growers to save inorganic phosphorus.

LARGE SCALE INOCULUM PRODUCTION

The Division of Microbiology, IARI, New Delhi is responsible for collection of Rhizobium under the unit of the National Facility for Rhizobium Germplasm Collection centre. The scientists of the centre are responsible to collect the strains, select them for improvement and test them on crops. The *Rhizobium*, *Azotobacter*, *Azospirillum* and phosphate solubilising bacterial inocula are commercially produced in several Universities, Regional Biofertilizer Development corporations and by private entrepreneurs. Presently around 2 million tonnes of microbial inocula are produced in India, which is insufficient, because India needs around 35 million tonnes. (BCIL report, 1994). The major problem in inoculum production is inadequate quality control, scientific selection of strains for production using fermentors under controlled conditions, survival of the inoculum during storage in distribution centres, and lack of involvement of organized industry.

VA mycorhiza are obligate symbionts, they require a plant host for its production, therefore, they cannot be produced artificially like other microbial cultures. At IIHR, Bangalore an on-farm inoculum production technique has been standardized (Sukhada, 1997). From an area of 5m × 5m more than 3 tonnes of inoculum could be produced. Attempts to culture VAM fungi in artificial medium have met with little or no success. However attempts have been made to culture VAM fungi using Ri DNA transformed roots. Plant roots are transformed with *Agrobacterium rhizogenes* to develop *in vitro* hairy root cultures on which mycorrhiza is cultured. (Adholeya, 1997).

FUTURE THRUSTS

Developing strains of bacteria which can withstand high temperature and alkali, and are acid resistant and high pH tolerant; which produce antibiotics in the soil or any chemicals which impart the strain competitive edge over other strain is the need of the hour. Some of the genes responsible for production of plant hormones have been characterized and cloned. These genes could be introduced into *Rhizobium* strains. Strains that can fix nitrogen in the presence of added nitrogen and those that can increase nitrogen-fixing efficiency should be selected.

Efforts to mass multiply mycorrhizae in a large quantity using lighter carrier material should be intensified. The PCR techniques should be standardized to identify mycorrhizal colonization within plant roots using different species specific primers.

NITROGEN TRANSFER BETWEEN NITROGEN FIXING AND NON-NITROGEN FIXING MYCORRHIZAL PLANTS

Symbiosis

The term *symbiosis* was first used by Frank in 1877 to describe the regular coexistence of different organisms such as fungi and algae in lichens. It was used as a neutral term that did not imply parasitism. A decade later De Bary (1887) used symbiosis to include parasite as well. But the meaning of the terms *symbiosis* and *parasite* has been changed later on. Symbiosis was used more and more for mutually beneficial associations between dissimilar organisms, and parasite and parasitism came to be almost synonymous with pathogen and pathogenesis (Smith and Read, 1997).

In recent years and symbiosis is defined as *the living together of differently named organisms.* This definition includes all associations ranging from *mutualistic*, in which all organisms involved are believed to derive benefit; to *parasitic* in which one organism benefits to the disadvantage of other member of the association. A more precise definition of mutualism is that associations are *mutualistic* if the fitness (offspring produced) of the associating organisms is greater than they are living apart. In a symbiosis, the organism with the large size is the host and the smaller is the symbiont. The symbiont can either be external to the host (ectosymbiotic) or within it (endosymbiotic). The symbiosis is *obligate* for an organism which is unable to survive and reproduce in the absence of its living partner, and *facultative* if it is able to do so even if the partner does during the association.

In a dual association, symbiosis is wide-spread especially between higher plants and bacteria in N-fixing symbiosis; between higher plants and fungi in most mycorrhizae; between algae and fungi in lichens; between algae and coelenterate in corals and so on. However, it is not currently known whether symbiosis occurs between higher plants. In addition, the tripartite symbiosis of plants, N-fixing bacteria and mycorrhizae (either vesicular-arbuscular mycorrhiza or ectomycorrhiza) has also been found in some *Acacia*, *Albizia*, *Casuarina* and *Leucaena* species. Symbioses are often found in nutrient limiting conditions and nutritional interactions play a key role in most symbioses. There are two important types of symbioses: mycorrhizal symbiosis and N-fixing symbiosis.

Mycorrhizal Symbiosis

The word *mycorrhiza* is derived from the Greek *mykes* (fungus) and *rhiza* (root). Mycorrhizae are highly evolved, mutualistic symbioses or associations between soil fungi and plant roots. The partners in this association are members of the fungus kingdom (*Basidiomycetes*, *Ascomycetes* and *Zygomycetes*) and most vascular plants. Mycorrhizal plants have been found in every continent and in every major vegetation type. Depending on the plant and fungal species involved as well as distinct morphological patterns, at least seven different types of mycorrhizal associations have been recognised. They are: vesicular-arbuscular mycorrhiza (VAM); ectomycorrhiza (ECM); orchid mycorrhiza; ericoid mycorrhiza; ectendomycorrhiza; arbutoid mycorrhiza and monotropoid mycorrhiza. In addition, dual associations of both ECM and VAM have been found in some trees and shrubs such as *Acacia*, *Casuarina*, *Eucalyptus* etc.

Mycorrhizae is the symbiotic association of fungi with roots of vascular plants. The main advantage of mycorrhizae to the host plants lies in the extension of the penetration zone of the root fungus system in the soil, facilitating an increased phosphorus uptake. The interconnected net-work of external hyphae acts as an additional catchment and absorbing surface in the soil beyond the depletion zone that would otherwise be inaccessible to the plant roots. Endotrophic mycorrhizae have been shown to be present in a wide range of horticultural species including apple, walnut, almonds, citrus, avocado, strawberry and grape. In many cases the mycorrhizae have been shown to markedly improve the growth of plants.

Some soils are deficit in mineral salts and plants living in them have special means of obtaining nitrogen and other essential elements, for example, the roots of many moorland and woodland plants, particularly coniferous trees, which live in rich humus but deficient in mineral salts possesses a mycorrhizae. Mycorrhizae (**fungus-roots**) are symbiotic associations between fungi and the roots of vascular plants. Two main groups of mycorrhizae are recognized: the **ectomycorrhizae** and **endomycorrhizae,** although the rarer group with intermediate properties, the ectendotrophic mycorrhizae. In the ectomycorhizae, the fungal hyphae form a mantle both outside the root within the root in the intercellular spaces of the epidermis and cortex. No intracellular penetration into epidermal or cortical cells occurs, but an extensive network called the Harting net is formed between these cells. Ectomycorrhizae are common on trees, including members of the families pinaceae (pine, fir, spruce, larch, hemlock), Fagaceae (willow, poplar, chestnut), Betulaceae (birch alder), Salicaceae (willow, poplar, and few other. Shows scaning electron micrographs of two *Pinus contorta* roots, one uninfected and having root hairs and the other infected with an ectomycorrhizae fungus.

Endomycorrhizae consist of three subgroups, but by far the most common are the vesicular arbuscular mycorrhizae (VAM). The fungi present in VAM are members of the Endogonacae, and they produce an internal network of hyphae between cortical cells that extends out into the soil, where the hyphae absorb mineral salts and water. Although VAM fungi seem to penetrate directly into the cytosol of cortical cells (where they form structures called vesicles and arbuscules, giving them their name), the hyphae are surrounded by an invaginated plasma membrane of the cortex cell. The VAM are present on most species of herbaceous angiosperms, whether monocot or dicot, annual or perennial crops, or native or introduced species; they also occur in the gymnosperm genera *Cupressus*, *Thuja*, *Taxodium*, *Juniperus*, and *Sequoia* and in ferns, lycopods, and bryophytes.

The importance of mycorrhizae was first recognized in connection with efforts to grow orchids in greenhouse. Orchids have microscopic seeds that germinate to form a tiny pad of tissue called a **protocorn**. Cultivators of orchids found that the plants seldom developed beyond the protocorm stage unless they were infected with a particular kind of fungus. Subsequently it was found that if seedlings of many forest trees are grown in nutrient solutions and then transplanted to prairie or other grassland soils, they fail to grow. Eventually they may die from malnutrition even if a soil analysis shows that there are abundant nutrients in the soil. If a small amount (0.1 per cent by volume) of forest soil containing fungi is added to the soil around the roots of the seedlings, however they will grow promptly and normally. Mycorrihizae are now though to occur in more than 90 per cent of all families of plants.

In some mycorrihizal associations known as endomycorrhizae, the fungal hyphae penetrate the cells of the root, forming coils, swellings, or branches. The hyphae also extend out into the surrounding soil. Endomycorrhizae occur in about 80 per cent of all vascular plants and the fungal component is usually a zygomycete. In other associations known as ectomycorhizae, the hyphae form a sheath around the root but do not actually penetrate its cells. Ectomycorrhizae are characteristic of certain groups of trees and shrubs, including pines, beeches and willows the fungus is usually a basidiomycete but some associations involve ascomycetes including truffles. The exact relationship between roots and fungi is not known. Apparently the roots secrete sugars, amino acids, and possibly some other organic substances that are used by the fungi. Although the evidence is just now accumulating, it appears that the fungi convert minerals in the soil and decaying material into an available form and transport them into the root.

The majority of plants with mycorrhizal roots only obtain phosphorus and transfer phosphorus from the soil into roots, and perhaps nitrogen, compounds from the fungus. They can photosynthesize normally (*e.g.*, bird's nest orchid – a sickly looking inhabitant of dark woods) and can therefore, manufacture their own carbohydrate, some of which are absorbed by the fungus. There is evidence that water uptake is facilitated by the fungus.

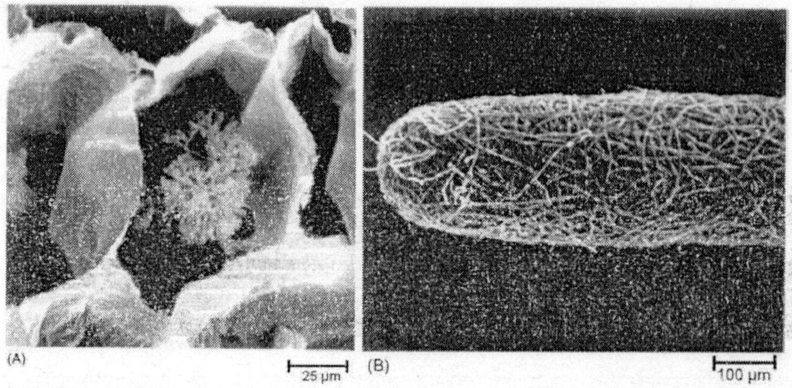

FIGURE 25.4: Scanning electron micrographs of mycorrhize. (A) A fully developed arbuscule of an endomycorrhiza in a plant cell. (The term arbuscule means little bush). As the arbuscule decomposes, it releases accumulated nutrients from plant. (B) The mycelial mantel of a typical ectomycorrhizal fungus surrounding a eucalyptus tree root.

A study of the fossils of early vascular plants has revealed that mycorrhizae occurred as frequently in them as they do in modern vascular plants. This has led to the interesting suggestion that the evolution of mycorrhizal associations may have been the critical step allowing plants to make the transition to the bare and relatively sterile soils of the then unoccupied land.

Recent studies have shown the possibility of domesticating *Mycorrhizae* in agricultural systems. Mycorrhizal fungi's assist in the uptake of phosphate and trace metals and possible influence water and nutrient via hormonal influences is not in doubt. Lack of a suitable inoculum production technology is the major limitation for commercial exploitation of this system.

Mycorrhizal fungi generally benefit their host plants by:

1. Increasing the physiologically absorbing surface area of the root system;
2. Increasing the ability of plants to capture water and nutrients such as nitrogen, phosphorus, or other essential elements from the soil;
3. Increasing the tolerance of plants to drought, high soil temperature, and extremes of soil acidity caused by high levels of metals such as sulfur, manganese, and aluminium;
4. Providing protection from certain plant pathogenic fungi and nematodes that attack roots; and
5. Modifying the transpiration rates and the composition of rhizosphere microflora by excretion of chelating compounds or ectoenzymes.

In return for these benefits, the fungus partner receives carbohydrates, vitamins and other nutrients supplied by the plant partner (for further details, refer to Smith and Read, Mycorrhizal Symbiosis, 2nd ed., Academic Press, 1997).

Ectomycorrhizae (ECM)

They are characterised by dense mycelial sheaths around the roots and a Hartig net between root cells, are limited to mostly temperate forest trees and *Basidiomycetes* and some other fungi. Mycorrhizae involve an intimate association of the host plant's root tissue and the fungus, but there is also fungal tissue that extends into the soil as individual hyphae and in some species as more complex strands. The external hyphae can take up mineral nutrients from the soil and transport them into the host root. Mycorrhizal associations can therefore be of great potential benefit to the host plant in nutrient limited systems.

Vesicular Arbuscular Mycorrhiza (VAM)

Zygomycete fungi form arbuscules and/or vesicles and external hyphal networks in the soil and grow extensively within the cells of the cortex, are formed by nearly all vascular plants. The endomycorrhizae, a fungus, (arbuscular mycorhizae) found in close association among angiosperms. The VA mycorrhizae are formed by the non-septate phycomycetes fungi belonging to the genera *Glomus*, *Gigaspora*, *Acaulospora* and *Sclerocystis* in the family Endogonaceae of the order Mucorales. They produce vesicles and arbuscules inside the root system. Arbuscules are highly branched fungal hyphae while vesicles are the bullous swellings of these hypae. These VAM fungi are beneficial to the plant which they colonise. They make more nutrients available to the plant, improve soil texture, disease resistance and help in better plant growth. Besides, mycorrhizae also help in the biological control of root pathogen.

An extensive research on VA mycorrhizal association in horticultural crops have been done at the Unviersity of Agricultural Sciences, Bangalore and Indian Institute of Horticultural Research (IIHR), Bangalore. Tomato, brinjal, okra, bell pepper, chilli and onions have been studied for their response to VAM inoculation (Sukhada, 1993). He also reported beneficial response of VAM fungi in cowpea has been reported (Sukhada, 1993).

In P-deficient sterile soil, dual inoculation with *Azospirillum* and *Glomus* spp. enhanced bulb growth of onion (Konde et. al., 1988). The *Glomus aggregatum* was the best in promoting nodulation, growth and yield of bean. Leela and Dwiedi (1987) found mixed inoculum of *Acalospora* and *Rhizobium leguminosarum* benefited pea to a greater extent than their treatment alone. Interaction of mycorrhizal fungi is synergestic with *Rhizobium*, *Azotobacter*, *Azospirillum* and phosphate solubilizing bacteria. Growth and yield of crops inculated with these strains has been always better than the strains used singly.

Mycorrhizal Fungi and Pathogen Interaction

Hegde and Rai (1984) reported that tomato plants inoculated with VAM fungi were highly resistant to *Phythium aphanidermatum* causing damping off. Control of nematodes was also reported due to VAM inoculations (Sukhada, 1993). Lakshmanan *et al* (1987) found accumulation of phytoalexin in cowpea root during the infection of *G. fasciculatum* and *G. aggregatum* which could be correlated with the degree of infection. Nematode infection had reduced significantly in mycorrhizal plants. Suresh *et al* (1985) reported that the root extract of mycorrhizal plants caused mortality of nematode larval compared to non-mycorrhizal root extracts. Singh *et al* (1990) established that tomato seedlings inoculated with VAM fungi were more resistant to *Meloidogynae javanica*. Rao *et al* (1995) found a similar control of nematode infestation in tomato and brinjal by inoculation with *G. mosseae* and neem cake.

TABLE 25.2: Types of crop and responses of inoculation

Crop	Inoculation and Response	Reference
Banana	Responds excellently to VAM inoculation. The *G. mosseae* and *G. fasciculatum* inoculationin combination with phosphate solubilizers and *Azospirillum* improved bunch weight in bale Elakki	Sukhada (1997)
Banana Dwarf Cavendish	Treated with *G. fasciculatum* 7 days prior to nematode treatment was able to offset the ill effects of the latter and had more vigorous root nematode population reduced.	Umesh *et al* (1988)
papaya, Citrus, Mango and Pomegranate	plans could be inoculated effectively with VAM fungi in the nursery and transplanted to the field The inoculation improves the plant establishment, improves of phosphorus in soil and their uptake (Sukhada, 1992). Due to the increased availability of phosphate in soil a saving in the addition of inorganic phosphate in the soil can be brought about.	(Sukhada, 1997). work conducted at IIHR, Bangalore
Litchi *(Litchi chinensis* Son)	Distribution of endomycorrhizal spores in the rhizosphere	Rana and Srivastava (1984)
Papaya (Coorg Honey Dew)	Studied the uptake of ^{32}P labeled super phosphate by endomycorrhizal and derived that mycorrhizal fungi besides acting as scavengers of phosphate also increased the availability of phosphates in the soil	Sukhada *et al* (1995)
	Standardized PCR amplification technique to identify different genera of VAM fungi	Sukhada *et al* (1997)

Nitrogen Transfer in Mycorrhizal Plants

The idea of nitrogen fixed by a legume component may be available to its associated non-legume plant originated from earlier studies in the late of. In several of their experiments they found that as much as 10 to 30% of the total N fixed in field pea was deposited in the growth media of sand, predominantly as amino acids, and a major part was taken up by an associated cereal. In general, the process of N-deposition and uptake in a neighbouring plant is often termed **N-transfer**. Since then substantial N-transfer have been observed in several legume/crop intercropping systems such as soybean or cowpea/maize or sorghum, cowpea/rice, gram clover/wheat, barley or oat/vetch or lupin etc., although some experiments showed little or no N-transfer between them

Compared to pure stand cultivation, possible benefits obtained by non-legumes or trees may partly be due to transfer of the symbiotically fixed N by legumes, either through directly release from nodulated roots or through decomposition of dead nodule and root tissue in the soil or through a common mycorrhizal network or even enhanced by mycorrhizal hyphae. However, the mechanism of N transfer and the role of mycorrhizal hyphae in the direct transfer of nitrogen are not well established. Therefore, studies in identifying the pathways of N transfer and whether mycorrhizal hyphae play a direct role in facilitating N transfer are needed.

Nitrogen Nutrition in Mycorrhizal Plants

Forms of Nitrogen used by Mycorrhizal Associations

The two most available forms of inorganic N for plants and both VA mycorrhizal and ectomycorrhizal fungi, are NO_3^- and NH_4^+. Originally, NH_4^+ is mainly derived from the reduction of atmospheric dinitrogen symbiotically fixed by nitrogen fixing plants, either by *Rhizobia* in legumes or by *Frankia* in actinorhizal plants. In general, NO_3^- is the dominant form of nitrogen available to plants and fungi in almost all agricultural soils due to the rapid nitrification of NH_4^+. In contrast, NH_4^+, which is released from soil humus and other organic N sources by ammonifying organisms, predominates and NO_3^- may be almost entirely absent in many undisturbed or very acidic soils. NO_3^- is highly mobile and is readily transported towards the plant roots by mass flow and diffusion. NH_4^+ is absorbed to negatively charged soil particles and transported towards the plant roots mainly by diffusion.

Mycorrhizal Effects on Nodulation and Nitrogen Fixation

The possibility of a direct involvement of ectomycorrhizal fungi in N acquisition by plants was first suggested by Frank in 1894. Then after 50 years of Frank's work, the probably first observation of growth, nodulation and mycorrhizal status of a large number of legumes was made by Asai in 1944. In most cases, improved nodulation and N fixation in mycorrhizal plants appears to be the result of relief from P stress and possibly uptake of some other essential micronutrients, which result in both a general improvement in growth and yield and indirect effects upon the N-fixing system. The differences between mycorrhizal and non-mycorrhizal plants usually disappear if the latter are supplied with a readily available P source.

It was known that cereals intercropped with grain legumes generally benefit from the association in terms of increased grain and nitrogen yields per unit area compared with monocropped cereals. This indicates that N-transfer from the nitrogen fixing plants (donor) to an associated non-nitrogen fixing plant (receiver) is most likely to happen in nature either via the interception and uptake of released fixed nitrogen from donor plant by the roots of receiver plant or through the root mycorrhizal between donor and receiver plants (Newman, 1988; Newman *et al.*, 1992), or even enhanced by mycorrhizal hyphae. Therefore, in agricultural and/or natural ecological communities, mycorrhizal associations may be important factors influencing the performance of both donor and receiver plants through the acquisition and translocation of nitrogen by the mycorrhizal fungus, particularly when the relatively immobile NH_4^+-N rather than the mobile NO_3^--N is the major source of plant available N.

It is therefore, concluded that Nitrogen fixing and non-nitrogen fixing plants can provide a good example for investigating the N-transfer between the plants where neighbouring plants may have differing nitrogen status. In general, with or without a split root system, combined with the fine nylon mesh to allow the direct mycorrhizal link but not root contact, together with ^{15}N-isotope labelling technique to enrich the N in the donor plant, some experiments have demonstrated a below-ground N-transfer whereas others found no evidence for transfer of nitrogen between donor and receiver plants via mycorrhizal hyphae. Furthermore, there is controversy about the extent to which direct N-transfer is actually being facilitated by mycorrhizal hyphae or by some other indirect means, and whether it is of agricultural or ecological significance if N-transfer do occur between these plants through mycorrhizal hypha.

The following questions still remain to be answered:

1. Does N transfer occurs between mycorrhizal plants at all? If so, how much N is transferred and how much N-transferred is enhanced by mycorrhizal hyphae?
2. How much net N transfer is from nitrogen fixing to non-nitrogen fixing mycorrhizal plants and *vice versa*?

Leguminous Plants / *Rhizobiaceae* Symbiosis

Symbiotic N_2 fixation in agriculture can be attributed mainly to legumes – the plants in the *Leguminosae*. It is estimated that *Leguminosae* contains more than 200 genera, and 20,000 species, which ranges from small plants such as the clover to the large trees such as *Acacia* species. Approximately 90% of them can fix nitrogen from the atmosphere with *Rhizobiaceae*, either with *Azorhizobium*, *Bradyrhizobium*, *Rhizobium* or with *Sinorhizobium* in root nodules. The important agricultural legumes can be divided into three groups: crops that grown for their commodities (*e.g.* grain legumes); forage legumes that may be grazed or harvested for animal fodder; and trees or shrubs in agroforestry systems. Worldwide approximately 1.5 million km^2 of land are cultivated with grain legume plants, mainly in *Glycine max*, *Phaseolus vulgaris*, *Pisum sativum*, *Arachis hypogaea*, *Cajanus cajan* etc. The annual harvest of grain legumes are about 200 million tonnes, which provides the plant protein source for human and animal consumption, or vegetable oil and other raw materials. The areas partially covered by the forage legumes mainly in *Trifolium*, *Lotus*, *Medicago*, *Stylosanthes*, *Macroptilium* and *Mimosa* etc., is even much larger, about 30 million km^2 of grassland in the five continents. The third group consists of the genera *Acacia*, *Albizia*, *Alnus*, *Leucaena*, *Robinia* etc., which are mostly used as timber, fuelwood or craftwood, and in the pharmaceutical industry as antibacterial and antifungal agents, or food additives and any other functions.

There are five genera of the *Rhizobiaceae*: *Azorhizobium*, *Bradyrhizobium*, *Rhizobium*, *Sinorhizobium* and *Photorhizobium*. All members of *Rhizobiaceae* are characterised by a gram-negative cell wall structure. Cells are generally rod-shaped, non spore-forming and motile with differently arranged flagella. All rhizobia are aerobic bacteria that persist saprophytically in the soil until they infect a root hair cell. The enzymes from the bacteria degrade part of the cell wall and allow bacteria entry into the root-hair cell itself, which lead the root hair to produce a threadlike structure called the infection thread. The bacteria multiply extensively inside the thread, which extends inwardly and penetrates through and between the cortex cells. In the inner cortex cells the bacteria are released into the cytoplasm and stimulate some cells (especially tetraploid cells) to divide. Each enlarged, non-motile bacterium is referred to as a bacteroid. These result in a proliferation of tissues, eventually forming a mature root nodule. A typical root nodule cell contains several thousand bacteroids. The nodule contains a protein called leghemoglobin, which gives legume nodules a pink color due to its prosthetic hem group. Leghemoglobin is thought to help transport O_2 into the bacteroids, which is essential for bacteroid respiration. Nitrogen fixation in root nodules occurs directly within the bacteroids. The host plant provides bacteroids with carbohydrates, which they oxidise and from which they obtain energy. These carbohydrates are first formed in leaves during photosynthesis and then are translocated through phloem to the root nodules. Sucrose is the most abundant carbohydrate translocated, at least in legumes. Some of electrons and ATP obtained during oxidation by the bacteroids are used to reduce N_2 to NH_4^+, which is catalysed by nitrogenase.

Non-leguminous Plants / *Frankiaceae* symbiosis

About 200 plant species from 25 genera, 8 families and 7 orders, all non-leguminous angiosperms, have been found to form nodule symbioses with N_2-fixing *actinomycetes* belonging to the genus of *Frankiae.* All of these species are perennial dicots and, with few exceptions, woody shrubs or trees. They are named actinorhizal plants from *actino* in *actinomycete,* and from *rhiza* in the Greek word for root. Actinorhizal plants can be found both on every continent except Antarctica and in most climatic zones. They typically grow on disturbed marginal soils and are pioneer species early in successional plant community development, such as *Dryas* species in arctic tundra; *Casuarina, Hippophae, Myrica* and *Elaeagnus* species in coastal dunes; *Alnus* and *Myrica* species in riparian; *Alnus* and *Dryas* species in glacial till; *Casuarina, Purshia, Ceanothus Cercocarpus, Comptonia* and *Cowania* species in chaparral and xeric; *Alnus* species in alpine; *Alnus, Casuarina, Coriaria* and *Shepherdia* species in forest. Globally, especially in wherever indigenous legumes are absent or rare, actinorhizal plants have potential applications in soil amelioration and reforestation, as fuelwood, timber and pulp, and as windbreak or even for addressing **pyrodenitrification**.

The symbiont *Frankia* is a gram-positive, filamentous bacterium belonging to the family *Frankiaceae* within the order *Actinomycetes.* Speciation in *Frankia* is not yet clear and within the genus different isolates are classified. Almost all of *Frankia* are characterised by three structural forms of hyphae, sporangia and vesicles. The hyphae are branched with a diameter of 0.5 to 1.5 μm and the mature vesicle is spherical with a diameter of 2 to 4 μm. Both the hyphae and the mature vesicles are septate. When actinorhizal plants, such as *Alnus* and *Casuarina* seedlings are excavated from soil containing *Frankia,* numerous small, multilobed, coralloid-type, amber or whitish nodules are found on their root systems. The oldest and biggest nodules are close to the stem base and the youngest are on the distal parts of the root system. Some *Casuarina* nodules may reach a size of around 5 – 10 mm in diameter and a weight of about 1 g in dry matter. It has been reported that *Frankia* produced sporangia and vesicles as soon as the microorganism escaped from the mother nodule. This indicates that the formation of *Frankia* structures inside the nodule might be under host control. In general, the nitrogen fixation rates of *Frankia*–actinorhizal plant symbioses are comparable to that of *Rhizobia*–legume symbioses.

Benefits from Nitrogen Fixing Plants To Non-Nitrogen Fixing Plants

The nitrogen fixation plant can directly fertilise the soil and indirectly neighbouring plants through above- and below ground litter, through root exudates and leakage from leaves and roots, and through the excreta of grazing animals. When nitrogen fixing plants are grown in mixed plantations with non-nitrogen fixing plants, an increase in both growth and yield of the non-nitrogen fixing plants have often been found. Moreover, the legume with the non-legume intercrops, on average, yield more efficiently per unit land with higher area- × -time equivalence ratios than either intercrops with two legume species or two non-legume species.

The nitrogen fixing plants (donor) and non-nitrogen fixing plants (receiver) could provide a good system for investigating nitrogen transfer, which was often termed the process of **nitrogen decomposition** and uptake in a neighbouring plant, where neighbouring plants might have differing nitrogen status.

Nitrogen transfer could lead to increase productivity of intercrops and forests without increasing the use of nitrogenous fertilisers if properly managed and quantified. However, the roles of mycorrhizal hyphae in direct N transfer were somewhat inconclusive, and it is not yet clear if the transfer can be large enough to contribute significantly to the N status of the receiver in agricultural or natural ecosystems.

NITROGEN FIXING TREES AND FOREST MANAGEMENT

To maintain the sustained productivity of forest ecosystems, nitrogen input to the soil from both biological and non-biological sources is essential. Natural forest ecosystems contain climax vegetation in which the soil has been developed for a long period by the interaction of microorganisms and higher plants. Nitrogen fixation is one of the main processes in which nitrogen is brought into the soil.

Future intensive forest cultivation, with consequent short rotations, will require replacement of nitrogen reserves at a greater rate than the present secondary succession leading to old-growth forests. With the increased use of trees genetically selected for increased yield, it will be necessary to maximize the potential for biological nitrogen fixation in future forest management, so as to maintain the long-term productivity of forest lands without significantly accelerating rates of nutrient depletion.

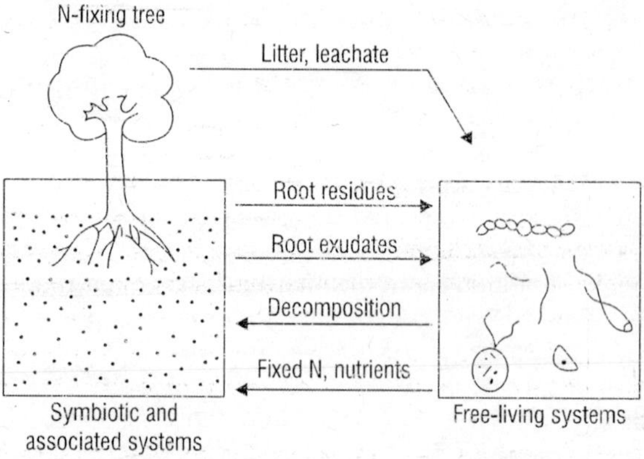

FIGURE 25.5: Interaction of Nitrogen-fixing tree with symbolic or non-symbiotic soil organisms.

Nitrogen fixing microorganisms which grow symbiotically with C-autotrophic higher plants, can indirectly utilize much more energy than free-living N-fixing microorganisms, and contribute the majority of the N_2 input in forest ecosystems.

Woody nitrogen-fixing plants have a much greater influence on the forest ecosystem than herbaceous ones. A total of 997 nitrogen fixing woody species were included in a masterlist from a database maintained by the University of Hawaii NiFTAL Project (Halliday and Nakao, 1982); even this masterlist is not complete. Brewbaker et al. (1983) recommended 44 species of 22 genera as economically important nitrogen fixing trees.

The following categories of nitrogen-fixing tree/soil/micro-organism associations have been studied: (a) root-nodule symbiosis with *Rhizobium*, (b) root-nodule symbiosis with actinomycetes, (c) mycorrhizal symbiosis, (d) rhizosphere systems, and (e) root-pathogen complexes.

MECHANISM OF NITROGEN FIXATION

Gaseous nitrogen is the most abundant element of atmosphere (78.08% v/v), and seems to have a highly complex nutrient cycle in the terrestrial and aquatic ecosystems. There is an interrelationship between different elements required for plant growth in environment. These all are affected by microbes. Atmospheric nitrogen is chemically inert. Therefore, it can be used, as such by most of the living organisms. The common source of nitrogen in the nature is the nitrate ions (NO_3). The nitrate ion is often absorbed by the plants as a mineral raw material from the environment. The absorbed nitrate ions are then converted into amino groups ($-NH_2$). The conversion of $-NO_3$ to NH_2 group is only possible by plants and not by animals. Minerals accumulation in soil, dissolution of rock by water, addition of fertilizers in soil are also the sources of NO_3 in the soil.

Apart from these sources, atmospheric nitrogen and oxygen combine together in presence of lightening which come down with the help of rain-water to the ground, and serve as NO_3 source on the earth. Absorbed nitrogen (in the form of NO_3) incorporates into organic structures of plants, which remain intact until death. Animals also obtain nitrogen by eating plants. Finally, both plants and animals die or decay. Through gradual decay of all nitrogen of dead plants and animals, it gets concentrated into ammonia (NH_3). The so forming NH_3 is then utilized as a source of nutrition for nitrifying bacteria. Usually, these bacteria are of two kinds:

1. Those bacteria which absorb ammonia and convert it into nitrite ions *i.e.*,

$$NH_3 \rightarrow NO_2.$$

2. Those bacteria which absorb nitrite ions and convert it into nitrate *i.e.*,

$$NO_2 \rightarrow NO_3.$$

Thus, the environment again gets NO_3 by the activities of these nitrifying bacteria. The available NO_3 in the environment acts upon denitrifying bacteria, which converts it into molecular, atmospheric nitrogen. The free molecular nitrogen is then, utilized by nitrogen fixing organisms in which few species of bacteria and blue green algae have been included. They are often present in soil and water. They absorb nitrogen and incorporate it into ammonia and protein. The process is called **Nitrogen fixation**.

Nitrogen is the mineral nutrient most needed by plants and it often limits plant growth. Some plant species have formed mutualistic symbioses with nitrogen fixing *prokaryotes* and some *eukaryotes*. Those organisms that can directly utilise atmospheric nitrogen as a nitrogen source, are called "*diazotrophs*", and belong to the kingdoms *eubacteria* and *archaebacteria*. They are able to live independently on soil N for growth. Inside the root nodules, the bacteria on the other hand are supplied with carbon from the host and are sheltered from competition with other organisms. The most important mutualistic symbioses are root nodule symbioses, mainly formed by members of the genera *Rhizobium*, *Bradyrhizobium* and *Azorhizobium* on legumes, and by the genus *Frankia* on some non-legumes. The reduction of atmospheric dinitrogen (N_2) to ammonium (NH_4^+), which occurs in nitrogen fixing organisms is catalysed by an enzyme complex called *nitrogenase*. A minimum 16 ATP and $8e^-$ are needed for a reduction of one molecule of N_2. It is estimated that nitrogen fixation could range from one to a few kg ha^{-1} $year^{-1}$ in lichens and freeliving bacteria, and up to a hundred or possibly a few hundred kg ha^{-1} $year^{-1}$ in legumes and actinorhizal plants.

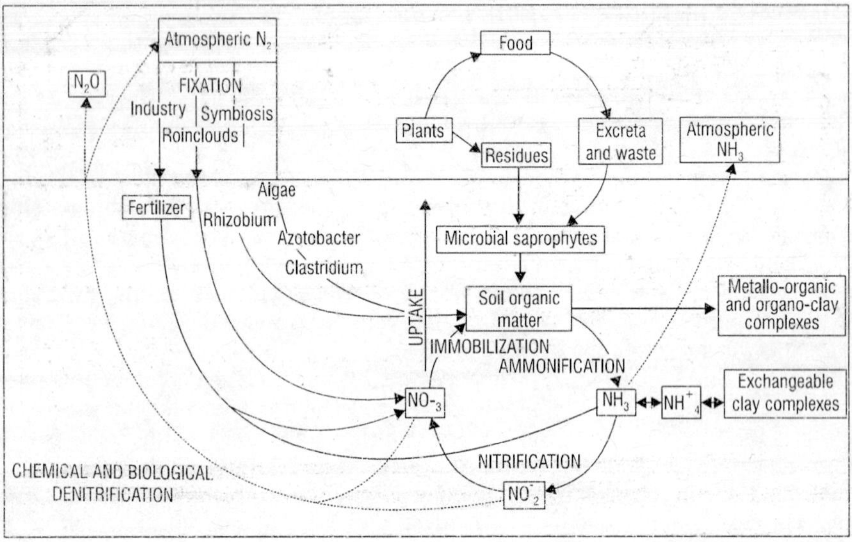

FIGURE 25.6: The chemical conversion in the nitrogen cycle. The main activities are indicated together with some of the organisms concerned.

Nitrogen fixation has always been a subject of great importance in biology, but since two decades the recent biotechnological development has lent its practical urgency. Nitrogenous fertilizers have become more and more expensive in terms of fossil energy, and hard cash; the population pressure has increased the need for high protein plant food. Biotechnologists are actively engaged in improving the efficiency of microorganisms to fix atmospheric nitrogen in fields. This will improve the functioning of the nitrogen cycle in biosphere, which will ultimatly increase plant productivity. The programme of improvement also includes the creation of nitrogen-fixing symbiotic association other than those existing between leguminous plants and bacteria of the genus *Rhizobium*. This will help to improve agricultural production.

Diazotrophic Microorganisms

The fixation of atmospheric nitrogen by prokaryotic organisms is known as diazotrophy. The phenomenon has also been observed in eukaryotic unicellular green alga, isolated from hot spring, by Yanada and Sakaguchi (1980).

BIOLOGICAL NITROGEN FIXATION

The process is brought about by nitrogen fixing microorganisms. These are soil inhibitants *e.g.*, bacteria, blue green algae, molds, etc. Those microorganisms, which utilize gaseous nitrogen directly and independently in the soil are known as asymbiotic or non-symbiotic nitrogen fixing organisms and the process by which they brought about is referred as non-symbiotic nitrogen fixation. Those microorganisms, which utilize gaseous nitrogen indirectly through the mediation of other living organisms in the soil are called symbiotic nitrogen fixing bacteria and the process brought about by them is referred as symbiotic nitrogen fixation.

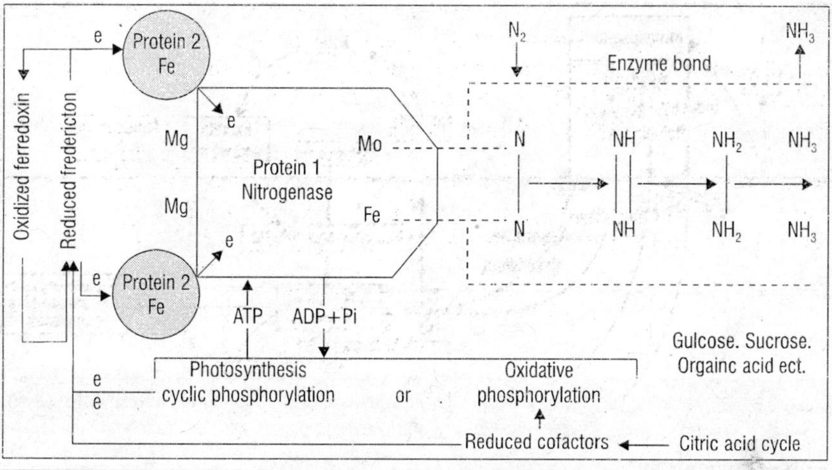

FIGURE 25.7: A generalised scheme for the action of nitrogenase (incorporating results from studies on various organisms).

ASYMBIOTIC NITROGEN FIXATION

Microorganisms

Bacteria: As described earlier, soil contains free-living bacteria that are capable of fixing molecular nitrogen into its compounds. This process was first recognized in bacterium *Clostridium pasturianum* which is a Gram-positive, spore forming rod-shaped bacterium. After seven years of the isolation of *C. pasturianum*, two more important free-living nitrogen-fixing bacteria were isolated by Beijernick (1901). These newly identified bacteria were *Azatobacter chrooccum* and *A. agile*.

Azatobacter chrooccum is usually found in field-soils. They are short, thick, rod-shaped with rounded ends. Some larger ovoid forms are almost yeast-like in appearance. The cells are arranged singly or in end to end pairs. They measure 2 to 3 nm by 6 nm in size. They appear-brown in old cultures. They are Gram-negative and non acid fast. They are motile and the motility is due to the presence of polar flagellum. Physiologically, they are aerobic and remain active in between 25°C. They fix atmospheric nitrogen only after utilizing carbohydrate (dextrose, maltose, lactate, etc.) and give carbon dioxide as a by product. *A. glile* also actively fixes atmospheric nitrogen and produces carbon dioxide.

Apart from *Azatobacter*, other non-symbiotic bacteria like *Rhodospirillum pneumoiniae*, *Rhodopseudomonas*, *Chlorobium*, *Diplococcus pneumoiniae*, *Azatobacter aerogenes*, *Micrococcus sulfurens* have also been known to fix atmospheric nitrogen asymbiotically.

pentose phosphate pathway. Polar nodule are not shown.

The ability to fix nitrogen by microorganisms was confirmed by means of the technique known as *acetylene reduction* to *ethylene* by diazotrophic microorganisms. The mechanism of this conversion is controlled by an enzymatic complex (or nitrogenous enzyme) which can reduce gaseous nitrogen to ammonia.

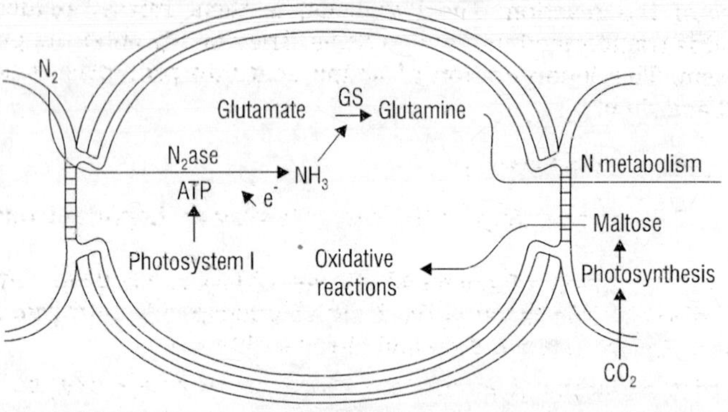

FIGURE 25.8: Nitrogen and carbon flow associated with nitrogen fixation in the heterocyst of blue green alga. N_2ase = the nitrogenase enzyme as GS = glutamine synthetase, oxidative reactions including the oxidative

The enzyme nitrogenase is sensitive towards oxygen. There are reports which reveal that several groups of microorganisms fix nitrogen in presence of minute quantities of oxygen. Such microorganisms are known as **microaerobic fixers.** They oxidize methane. The examples are bacteria, Spirilla (*Aquaspirillum and Azosprillium*), *Xanthobacter autorophicus* and *S. flavus*, *Thiobacillus ferrooxidans and* non-heterocystous microaerobic cyanobacteria (*Oscillatoria*, *Plectonema*). Certain coliform bacteria also fix nitrogen only in aerobic conditions (*e.g.*, *Citrobactor*, *Enterobacter*, *Erwinia*). It is established that oxygen not only inhibits the activity of nitrogenase enzyme but also regulates its biosynthesis, so that in conditions that are physiologically hardly favourable to nitrogen fixation, the enzyme is not synthesized.

Mechanism of Asymbiotic Nitrogen Fixation

The knowledge of asymbiotic nitrogen fixation is still insufficient. It was previously believed that *Azatobacter* fixes atmospheric nitrogen with the help of enzyme system called azatase and nitrogenase is only one of the compounds of this system. Beijerinck (1901) indicated that fixation of atmospheric nitrogen took place at the nitrous acid stage, but it was not proved. According to one more concept, nitrogen is fixed through the stage of hydrolysis to hydroxylamine or to ammonium nitrate which is produced from nitrogen and water as shown below:

$$N_2 + 2H_2O \rightarrow NH_4NO_2$$

But this concept has not been proved. The hydrolysis of nitrogen is very difficult under normal conditions.

It was further proposed that *Azatobacter* fixes nitrogen after its reduction by the active hydrogen. However, this hypothesis was also not proved.

At last the mechanism of nitrogen fixation was described on the physiological basis. It was proved that the protoplasm of *Azatobacter* produces special catalysts, which take part in fixing free nitrogen. The catalysts contain carboxyl and amino group as an important parts which do not take any active part in fixing atmospheric nitrogen. Phenyl hydrogen and hydroxylamine are also present in the composition of the catalysts. It was presumed that molecular nitrogen reacts with catalysts of nitrogen fixation through oxygen of carboxyl group and produces hydrazine as the first product of the reaction. The hydrazine, is then, further reduced by active hydrogen and is transformed into amino acids. They finally enter the proteins of the cell protoplasm. This incorporation of amino acid into protoplasms helps into the growth of a bacterium.

Requirements of Nitrogen Fixation

1. Oxygen and carboxyl group of the catalysts play an important role in nitrogen fixation.
2. A very small amount of chemical energy (ATP) is used up during nitrogen fixation. About 1 kilo calories fix 2 mg of atmospheric nitrogen. It shows the relationship between respiration and nitrogen fixation.

Some strict anaerobic bacteria are more sensitive to oxygen. *Clostridium pasteurianum* is an obligate anaerobe, therefore, the mechanism of nitrogen fixation of such organism is similar to that *Azatobacter*, because they produce large amount of hydrogen during their metabolic reaction. The various possible pathways of nitrogen fixation have been shown in different illustrations.

Symbiotic Nitrogen Fixation

Agriculturists have noted that a relatively large group of plants- the legumes, are capable of fixing atmospheric nitrogen through a symbiotic association with soil bacteria called *Rhizobium*. These bacteria or nodule bacteria, usually dwell in the roots of various beans, peas, lupines, cloves and other leguminous plants.

Hellriegal and Wilfarth (1888) first of all demonstrated that an increase in nitrogen content in soil is due to the presence of small tumor-like outgrowth on the roots of leguminous plants. It was found that in absence of root nodules, growth of succeding plant-crop was retarded. The results of various experiments reveal that root nodule forming plants can feed upon atmospheric nitrogen and this capacity of plants can be obserbed only in those plants, which are growing in non-sterilized or bacteria containing soils. These symbiotic bacteria *e.g.*, *Rhizobium* utilize the free atmospheric nitrogen and synthesize it into new nitrogenous compounds, which are utilized by plants for their growth; and bacteria get their food from these plants. Such a mutual beneficial association of bacteria and plants is referred to symbiosis.

Symbiosis was originally defined by Bary in 1879. Symbiosis is the living together of any two organisms. Mutulism is a relationship where both partners benefit, though it greads into those where the advantage or disadvantage to one of the partner may not always be obvious. Commensal relationships are usually rather loose association of the benefit of another without any effect on itself.

MECHANISM OF NITROGEN FIXATION IN LEGUMES

The mechanism of nitrogen fixation in legumes has not yet been understood. However, the basic prerequisite for nitrogen fixation in extracts of nodule-bacteriods are similar to those that have been described for asymbiotic bacteria such as *Azatobacter*. It has not been well established that how in both asymbiotic and symbiotic system ^{15}N is converted into NH_3 and then to amino acids, because the intermediate products between ^{15}N to NH_3 have not been determined.

A good number of theories have been proposed by various workers. Two of them are important, which are as follows:

Theory of Virtanen

Nitrogen fixation in root appears immediately after nodule formation. Virtanen (1948) proposed the following scheme of nitrogen fixation in root nodules:

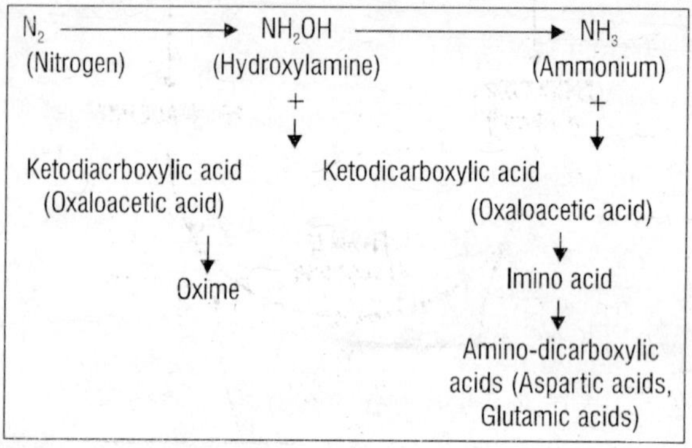

FIGURE 25.9: Mechanism of nitrogen fixation (Virtanen, 1948).

According to him young plants fix more amount of nitrogen than the old plants. A great part of nitrogen is converted into L-aspartic acid and L-glutamic acid. Apart from these, α-alanine is also present in the nodule which is produced from L-aspartic acid by decarboxylation. In addition to this, small amount of Oxime-N and Nitrite-N are also present.

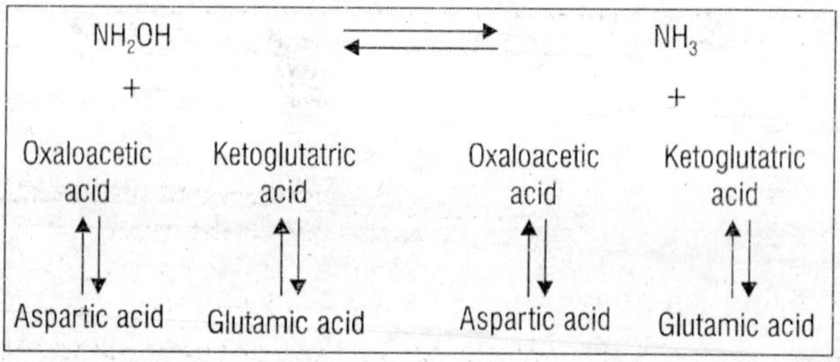

FIGURE 25.10: Theory of Burris and Wilson.

Theory of Burris and Wilson

According to this theory hydroxylamine is the central compound of nitrogen fixation, from which ammonia is formed through reduction or it can also directly react to the keto acid. The proposed scheme of Burris and Wilson (1945) is as follows:

Both these theories reveal the formation of amino dicarboxylicacid as the primary products in biological nitrogen fixation

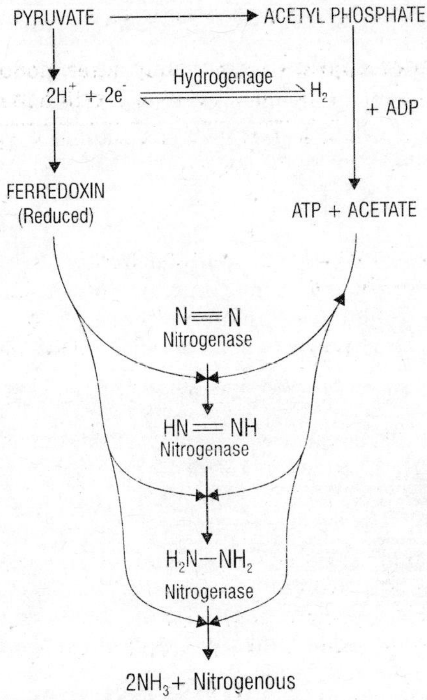

FIGURE 25.11: Scheme proposed for mechanism of nitrogen fixation.

NITROGEN CONVERTERS IN THE SOIL

The oxidation of ammonia to nitrate in the soil is one of the important phases in nitrogen cycle. This is brought about by two groups of bacteria- *Nitrosomonas* and *Nitrobacter*. The required energy for the growth of these bacteria is obtained through the oxidation of ammonia or nitrate. Winogradsky (1891) first isolated these autotrophic bacteria and described the conversion of ammonia to nitrite, and nitrite to nitrate. This is called **nitrification**. The conversion of nitrate to nitrous oxide and nitrogen gas by various kinds of soil organisms is called **denitrification**. The process releases nitrogen gas to the atmosphere and completes the complex nitrogen cycle in nature.

Cyanobacteria and Nitrogen fixation

Frank (1889) first reported the ability of nitrogen fixation by blue green algae. According to Drewes (1928) *Nostoc punctiforme* and *Anabaena variabilis* have the ability to fix nitrogen in the soil. The principal genera of this group known to fix nitrogen are *Nostoc* spp. *(N. cummune, N. punctiforme, N. muscorum); Anabaena* spp. *(A. ambigua, A. cylindrica, A. fertilissima. A. circularis,* etc.), *Cylindrospermum* spp. (*C. gorakhporense, C. licheniforme)*- all of them belong to the family Nostocaceae. A few of members of the family Microchaetaceae and Rivulariaceae like *Aulosira fertilissima* and *Calothrix brevissima* respectively are known to fix atmospheric nitrogen in rice fields. Significantly most of the free living nitrogen fixing members of this group produce **heterocyst** which is considered to be the site of nitrogen fixation (Kulasooriya, 1972).

The free living diazotrophic cyanobacteria are the largest contributors of the process of biological nitrogen fixation, the second most important biological process on this planet. Their nitrogen fixing ability was first related to the presence of specialized non-oxygen evolving cells called heterocysts in which nitrogenase; a highly oxygen-sensitive enzyme is produced from oxygen.

Nitrogen Fixing Fungi

The fungi also independently play an important role in fixing free nitrogen in soil. The fungi that are responsible for this function are of species of *Mactosporium commune*, *Cladosporium herbarum*, *Phoma*, *Alternaria tenuiis*, *Rhodotorula* spp. etc. The occurrence of these fungi has been noted in forest-land.

BIOCHEMICAL ASPECTS OF DIAZOTROPHY

An American company (DuPont) in 1960 started the fundamental research on the biochemistry of nitrogen fixation on nitrogenase activity in cell free extracts of *Clostridium pasteurianum*. The experiments were conducted in absence of air because of the very great oxygen sensitivity of nitrogenase. The techniques like chromatography, electrophoresis and fractionation under anaerobic conditions, helped the researchers to isolate nitrogenase from *Clostridium pasteurianum*. Thereafter, nitrogenase was easily isolated from other anaerobic nitrogen fixers while this extraction was more difficult with *Azotobacter vinelandii*. The so isolated enzyme has the property to accept electorn from sodium dithionite and was oxygen-tolerant and evolved hydrogen in the absence of nitrogen. In 1981, nitrogenase in the form of crude preparations was isolated from about 30 microbes and out of which about 6 of them were purified.

Biochemically, nitrogenase is a binary enzyme and consists of two brown metalloproteins, of which the joint activity is essential to reduce nitrogen to ammonia.

During nitrogen conversion, nitrogenase binds to molybdoferroprotein (MoFe-protein) which was named **disnitrogenase**. When nitrogen binds at the molybdenum level in a separable fragment of protein, called **FeMoco**. The two component proteins of the enzyme nitrogenase are quickly and irreversibly destroyed by exposure to oxygen.

$$\text{Mo-Fe protein} + \text{2Fe Protein} \rightleftharpoons \text{Nitrogenase}$$

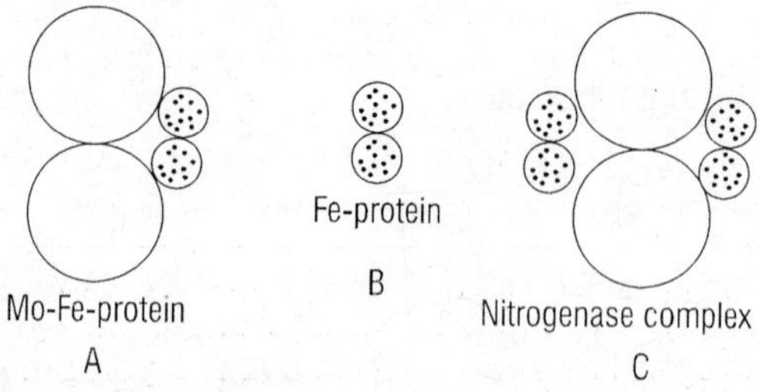

FIGURE 25.12: Nitrogenase enzyme.

Nitrogenase is also able to reduce other substrates in the place of nitrogen, including hydrogen ions and, in this case it evolves hydrogen.

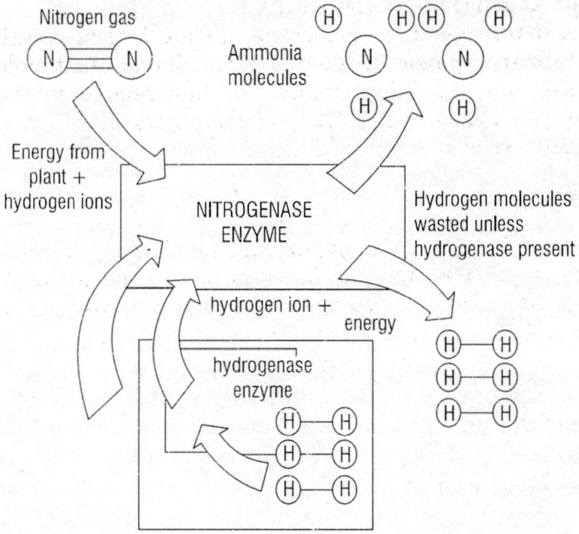

FIGURE 25.13: Representation of the mechanism of nitrogen fixation and the action of hydrogenase.

Nitrogenase Producing *E. coli* Cells

Because of the close relationship between *E. coli* and *Klebsiella pneumoniae*, *E. coli* is specially qualified for the investigation of the nitrogenase system. With *E. coli* C-M74 cells, high nitrogenase activity can be attained in culture medium, supplemented with 50mg/l ammonium sulfate, 1% aspartic acid, and 0.1% yeast extract.

During reduction of nitrogen to ammonia, electrons are required which are transferred to nitrogenase by specific transport proteins; the *Ferrodoxins* or the *Flavodoxins*. ATP serves as energy source. The consumption of ATP molecules is 12 to 15 per nitrogen molecule. The reason for this high consumption of ATP has not been entirely elucidated.

As evident from the reactions that hydrogen is produced during nitrogen fixation. Certain nitrogen-fixing aerobic bacteria possess hydrogenase enzyme, which has the ability to recycle hydrogen produced by nitrogenase *in vitro*. Therefore, the re-utilization of this hydrogen generates more ATP (by oxidative phosphorylation) and consequently improves the efficiency of nitrogen fixation.

Rhizobium is also associated with soybean plants which contain hydrogen uptake (or *hup*) genes, which have the ability to recycle hydrogen and back into the nitrogenase system and fix nitrogen. Through this mechanism the energy is harvested by plants, which is otherwise lost.

The nitrogenase enzyme of bacteria fix nitrogen by converting nitrogen gas into ammonia using hydrogen ions and energy by host plant. During the process there is a production of energy rich hydrogen gas. Some bacteria possess hydrogenase enzyme which can capture hydrogen gas and converts it into hydrogen ions and release energy which can feed back into nitrogenase enzyme.

GENETICS OF FREE-LIVING AND SYMBIOTIC DIAZOTROPHS

Organization of Nitrogen-fixation Genes

In molecular terms, very little is known of the means by which the prokaryote specifically recognizes and invades its respective host-plant. However, there has been a growing interest in approaching this problem by identifying and analysing the relevant symbiotic genes and their gene products. Because of the agricultural importance of the *Rhizobium*-legume interaction, the most detailed studies have been conducted on this system. Also, because of bacteria are simpler than plants. Our knowledge of the symbiotic genes of *Rhizobium* is better than that of the plant genes. There have been several recent advances in the analysis of the *Rhizobium* genes that are involved in nodulation, host-range specificity and nitrogen fixation. By dissecting the structure, organization and regulation of these genes, a better understanding of their functions may be forthcoming.

In the fast-growing *Rhizobium* species, which nodulate temperate legumes such as clover, alfalfa, peas and field beans, the genes for nodulation and nitrogen fixation are clustered on large symbiotic plasmids. One such plasmid, pRL1JI, was isolated from a strain of *R. leguminosarum* (which nodulates peas) and in this case the genes that determined the ability to nodulate peas were located between two groups of genes required for nitrogen fixation. The study of the nitrogen-fixation (*nif*) genes in *Rhizobium* has been greatly facilitated by the fact that at least some of them are very similar to the corresponding *nif* genes in the free-living nitrogen-fixing bacterium - *Klebsiella pneumoniae.*

In *Klebsiella*, 17 *nif* genes have been identified which are variously involved in *nif* gene regulation, the synthesis of the iron-molybdenum cofactor (FeMoCo). Using DNA sequence comparisons, *Rhizobium* species have been shown to contain the *nifHD* and *K* genes (nitrogenase proteins) *nifA* (regulation) and *nifB* (synthesis of FeMoCo). Further studies may well demonstrate similarities between other *Rhizobium* and *Klebsiella nif* genes.

The study of nitrogen fixation genes was first carried out in *Klebsiella pneumoniae* (strain M5al); and spectaular progress achieved in 1970s. Although the first report came from the mutants of nitrogen fixing bacteria which was isolated and biochemically characterized as early in 1959. The genetic research by Streicher et al. (1971) of U.S.A. and Dixon of Agric. Research Council, Unit of Nitrogen fixation (U.K.) added more knowledge in this field. Dixon and Postgate (1971) successfully transferred the nitrogen fixation genes, called *nif*, to *Klebsiella pneumoniae.* Later on they could able to transfer these genes to *Escherichia coli.* This work encouraged the researchers of this field specially for *Rhizobium* and the presence of *nif* genes in this microorganism. More than a dozen genes, termed the *nif* genes are involved in the assembly of nitrogen-fixation apparatus. The *nif* genes are not found in a free state but are clustered in one region (they are not scattered throughout the bacterial DNA). Therefore, it is much easier to stretch of DNA in a *Rhizobium* chromosome and insert the whole batch into another organism. This has also been done in *Agrobacterium tumefaciens* (Ti plasmids). In 1981, the number of *nif* genes was 17 and they were organized in eight transcription units (or operons), one of which was monocistronic. Brill (1980) also included two other genes: *nif*-R between L and F, and *nif*-W between F and M.

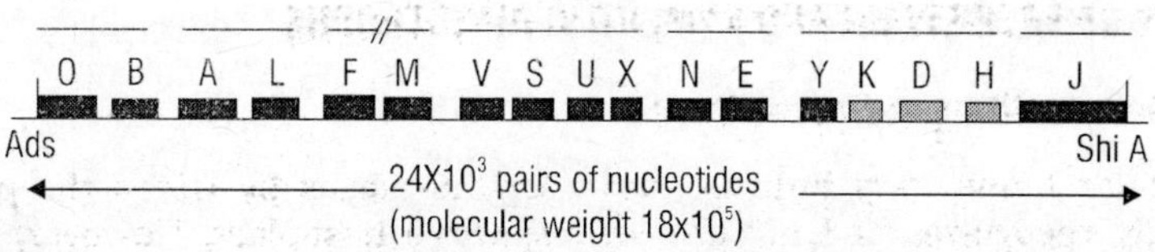

FIGURE 25.14: Map of the *nif* gene cluster of the *Klebsiella pneumoniae* chromosome. The capital letters denote the genes (cistrons), the *nif* cluster being located between the genes for biosynthesis of histidine (his) and those for shikimic acid uptake (shi A). The arrow indicate the separate operations and the direction of their transcription. In 1981 the status of F and M as one or two distinct operons was not clear. The size of most of the genes, however, were known.

nod-Genes for Nodulation

Concerning the genes (called *nod* genes) for nodulation and host-range specificity, an important observation is that, despite the morphological complexity of the infection process, only a few genes on the symbiotic plasmid are required for nodulation. In the *R. leguminosarum* symbiotic plasmid pRL1JI, less than 10kb appears to be required for nodulation and for the determination of host-range specificity for peas. The reason has been analysed by DNA sequencing (and thus identifying genes as long open reading frames), isolation and characterization of mutants and by studying the regulation of the *nod* genes.

The organiztion of *nif*-genes of other free-living diazotrophs from which *nif*-mutants were isolated (*Azatobacter vinelandii, Azospirillum lipoferum, Clostridium pasteurianum, Rhodopseudomonas capsulata* and a few cyanobacteria) was as like to that of *Klebsiella pneumoniae.*

REGULATION OF NITROGEN-FIXATION GENES

The regulation of *nif* genes is rather complex. Ammonia and nitrogenous compounds (like nitrates and amino acids) inhibit the expression of nitrogenase activity. Excess of aeration in the culture medium also inhibits the expression of *nif*-genes. For induction of *nif*-genes, the presence of nitrogen is not necessary, because these genes can express themselves in cells cultivated in an argon atmosphere. In fact, the *nif*-genes expression is the result of a de-repression rather than that of an induction

Eady et al. (1978), Roberts et al. (1978) reported that all the products of *nif*-genes are not present in the cultures carried out in the presence of ammonia. When ammonia is added to a completely derepressed cultures, a rapid repression of the *nif*-phenotype occurs and nitrogenase activity as well as the enzymic proteins disappear within 45 minutes.

The presence of ammonia in the medium plays very important role in the synthesis of various biomolecules, *e.g.*, in presence of ammonia, glutamine synthetase reacts with ATP and seems to lose the enzymic and regulatory functions of *nif*-genes.

The presence of oxygen in the culture medium represses the biosyntheis of nitrogenase enzyme in *Klebsiella pneumonia.* Similar results have also been observed in aerobic and anaerobic bacteria. However, the mechanism of oxygen repression seems to be independent from that of ammonia in such microorganisms.

Molybdate does not have any direct effect on the regulation of b-*nif*-genes, however, molybdoprotein is probably involved in the regulation of at least one of the *Klebsiella nif* operons (*nif* YKDH). The presence of molybdenum transport and storage proteins is known in *Clostridium pasteurianum* and other diazotrophs.

It is now established, after number of current reports that the regulation of the *nif*-genes of *Klebsiella pneumoniae* is carried out by both *nif* A and *nif* L genes as well as by genes that are remote from the *nif* cluster (*gln* genes). However, there are other genes which are involved in the expression of *nif*-genes, they are as follows:

- *nar D* = which is involved in molybdenum processing.
- *unc* and *a* gene in his operon = which influence ATP supply.
- *nim* gene = gene of the uncertain function near tip.

GENETICS OF SYMBIOTIC DIAZOTROPHS

Much works has been done on the fast growing nitrogen-fixing bacteria-*Rhizobium*. The genetic map of *Rhizobium* is now established. The studies reveal that *R. leguniosarum*, *R. phaseoli* and *R. trifolii* have very similar gene organization. The genes for the component protein subunits of nitrogenase (molybdoferroprotein and ferroprotein) are formed by a single operon in *Rhizobium leguminisarum*. Similar situation has been reported in *Azatobactor vinelandii* and in *Klebsiella pneumoniae*.

TRANSFER OF *NIF*-GENES TO MICROORGANISMS

As mentioned earlier that *nif*-genes are not found in a free state but are clustered in one region (they are scattered throughout the bacterial DNA). Therefore, it is much easy to cut out the relavent stretch of DNA in a *Rhizobium* chromosome and insert the whole batch into another organism. The construction of self-transmissible plasmids (Ti-plasmids) bearing *nif*-genes made it possible to shift the nitrogen-fixing capacity to non-fixing species or to non-fixing mutant of diazotrophic species like *E. coli (E. coli* C-M74), *Salmonella typhimurium*, *Serratia marcescens*, *Pseudomonas flurescence*, and *nif*-mutant of *Azatobacter vinelandii*. It is quite easy to transfer *nif*-genes from one species to another, or form one microbial genus to another under laboratory conditions. This may be done by three methods of gene-transfer: conjugation, transduction and transformation. Therefore, the transfer of *nif*-genes between the plasmid and bacterial chromosomes can take place under laboratory as well as under natural conditions

TRANSFER OF *NIF*-GENES AND DEVELOPMENT OF NEW NITROGEN-FIXING PLANTS

It is easy to transfer grouped genes and the *nif*-gene cluster. Plant viruses could be used as vectors for this purpose. The cauliflower mosaic virus is a deoxyribovirus to which it is possible to join certain *nif*-genes which could become integrated into the plant genome or which could be transcribed into the plant cell at the same time as those of the virus when the latter's replication takes place.

Agrobacterium tumefaciens is a pathogenic bacterium, which contains a large plasmid, Ti and is responsible for the induction of tumours in plant tissues on the site of the infection by the bacterium. These plasmids are of 150 to 230 kilobases and can able to develop tumours, therefore, they are called Ti or **tumour inducing plasmids**. Ti -plasmids are introduced by either transformation or by conjugation. The DNA of Ti-plasmids have two following regions:

1. The larger region contains information that makes it possible for the bacterium to catabolize derivatives of the basic amino acids, or opines, synthesized by the tumour cells.

2. It corresponds to the T-DNA and is incorporated into the genone of the plant cell. This T-DNA includes the ability of utilization of the latter as well the transformation of its metabolism in order to produce opines. The molecular weight of T-DNA is 15 x 10^6 daltons.

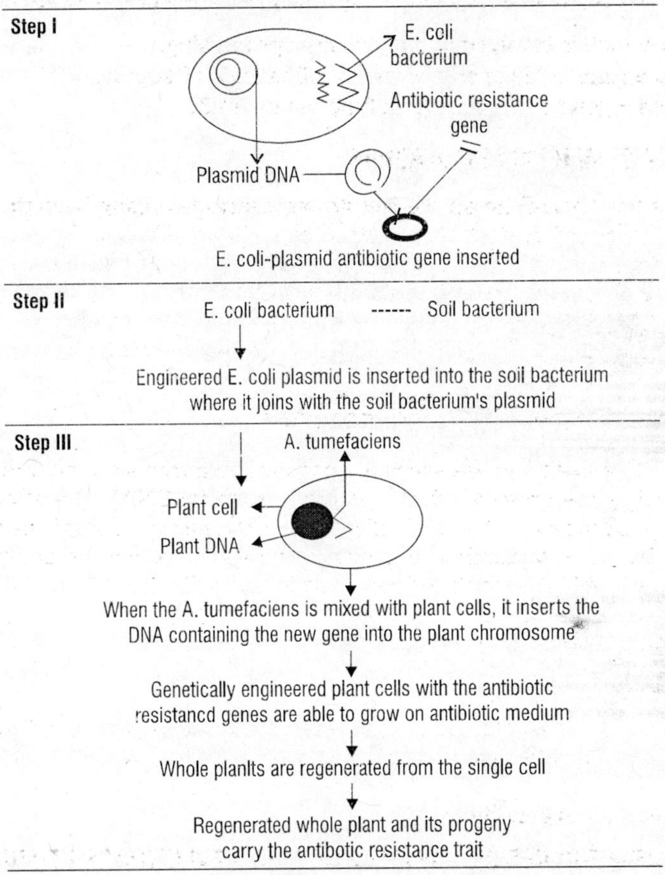

FIGURE 25.15: Schematic presentation of plant genetic engineering with Ti plasmids from *Agrobacterium tumefaciens.*

The development of tumours in plant tissue by Ti -plasmid of *Agrobacterium tumefaciens* is brougnt about by the transfer of a segment of bacterial DNA (from a prokaryotic) and its integration into the genome of eukaryotic cells. This introduction of Ti -plasmid was successfully made by Schell and his coworkers. Out of the seven genes of T-DNA of Ti -plasmid, they found that five of them are responsible for tumorization that is in blocking cell differentiation. It is of interest to mention that *Agrobacterium tumefaciens* infects only dicotyledonous plants, however, it is not easy to introduce Ti plasmids into the cells of monocotyledonous plants like cereals.

Kemp (1981) used nucleic acid recombination and cloning techniques to transfer genes to plant cells. He has transferred genes for the bean protein- **phaseolin** to sunflower plants. This transfer was followed by the synthesis of mRNA of the storage protein in the sunflower cells, made tumoral by the T-DNA of *Agrobacterium tumefaciens*, which was used as a vector for the gene.

The development of plants, which can able to fix atmospheric nitrogen independently of symbiotic microbes remains a difficult and complex task. However, in the present situation, it is possible to develop and gain better knowledge of the factors that induce nitrogen-fixing symbiosis, with a view of improving their efficiency.

NITROGEN FIXATION RESEARCH IN INDIA

The word on biochemistry of nitrogen fixation has mainly been done at Haryana Agriculture University, Indian Agriculture Research Institute, Punjab Agriculture University and BARC. At HAU, a pathway for ureide biogenesis in nodules of pigeonpea has been proposed. The further metabolism of ureides in aerial parts particularly leaves and developing pods has also been worked out. Detailed biochemical and physiological studies explaining nodule senescence have also been carried out at IARI. Attempts have been made to understand the regulation of uptake hydrogenase so as to reduce the energy cost of biological nitrogen fixation. In addition, studies are concentrated on increasing nitrogen fixing efficiency by insertion of uptake hydrogenase genes or by increasing nitrogenase activity in nodules. At BARC, early interactions in legume- *Rhizobium* symbiosis have been investigated, according to which, host-induced alterations of capsular polysaccharides and de novo synthesis of specific proteins by both the partners in response to each other, appear to be among the first steps in the series of signal response interactions. At PAU, the role of extracellular invertase of *Rhizobium* in free sugar metabolism in developing root nodules of legumes has been ascertained (Adopted from Dr. Randhir Singh, In: Souvenir, Int. Cong. Plant Physiology, Feb. 15-20, 1988, New Delhi).

The activity of nodule is also controlled by nitrogenase enzyme. This enzyme is about 75% efficient. This is because, when soil aeration is poor and nitrogen availability is limited, electrons instead of being used to reduce nitrogen, now combine with protons forming hydrogen. As a result, nodules evolve hydrogen instead of fixing nitrogen. This is a wasteful process. Sufficient progress is being made to identify strains of *Rhizobia* which evolve less hydrogen and fix more nitrogen.

The most ideal situation would be the one in which the higher plant is able to fix nitrogen without the help of the bacteria. Towards this end, attempts have been made to transfer nitrogen fixing genes (*nif* -genes) to higher plants from *Rhizobium*. However, it appears to be a long way before it is achieved.

In India, intensive forest cultivation of nitrogen fixing trees, with consequent short rotation is needed. This will require replacement of nitrogen reserves at a greater rate than the present secondary succession leading to old-growth forests. With the increased use of trees, genetically selected, it will be necessary to maximize the potential for biological nitrogen fixation in future forest management, so as to maintain the long term productivity of forest lands without significantly accelerating the rate of nutrient depletion. India is in urgent need of additional professional training and better transfer of technology in this context. Further, improved strains and new species of nitrogen-fixing microorganisms should be investigated/developed in order to reduce the use of chemical fertilizers in the fields.

CHAPTER 26

Enzymes and Biotechnology

Biotechnology in industry employs techniques of modern molecular biology to reduce the environmental impact of manufacturing. Industrial biotechnology also works to make manufacturing processes more efficient in industries such as grain, cleaning, textiles, paper and pulp, and specialty chemicals. Some observes predict biotechnology will transform the industrial sector in much the same way that it has changed the pharmaceutical sector. Industrial biotechnology will be a key to achieving industrial and environmental sustainability.

INDUSTRIAL SUSTAINABILITY

Industrial sustainability (clean and efficient) means employing technologies and know-how to use less material and energy, maximizing renewable resources as inputs, minimizing generation of pollutants or harmful waste during product manufacture and use, and producing recyclable or biodegradable products. It is the continuous innovation, improvement and use of clean technology to reduce pollution levels and consumption of resources and modern biotechnology provides avenues to achieve this goal. Any change in production processes, practices or products that makes production cleaner and more efficient per unit of production or consumption is a move toward sustainability.

In recent years, policy-makers, corporate executives, private citizens and environmentalists have become more concerned about sustainable development. In response to that concern, many leading industrial companies are doing more than meeting their legal minimums. Many are developing policies and implementation plans for sustainability that include guidelines for environmental health and safety and product stewardship.

By replacing conventional, environmentally harsh chemicals, advances in biotechnology have led the way in the pursuit of industrial sustainability. For example, protease enzymes can replace phosphates in detergents, and enzymes can be used for grain processing instead of acids. Other products created through biotechnology methods reduce waste emissions and help companies use raw materials more efficiently.

Applications of Industrial and Environmental Biotechnology

1. The chemical industry, as a source of biocatalysts to produce novel compounds, reduce waste byproducts and improve chemical purity.
2. The petrochemical industry, to lessen the impact of manufacturing plastics and improve the recycling process.
3. The paper industry, to improve manufacturing processes, including the use of enzymes to lower toxic byproducts from pulp processes.
4. The textiles industry, to lessen toxic byproducts of fabric dying and finishing processes. Fabric detergents are becoming more effective with the addition of enzymes to their active ingredients.
5. The food industry, for improved baking processes, fermentation-derived

preservatives and analysis techniques for food safety.

6. The livestock industry, adding enzymes to increase nutrient uptake and decrease phosphate byproducts.

Green Plastics

Biotechnology also offers us the prospect of replacing petroleum-derived polymers with biological polymers. Cotton genetically modified to contain a bacterial gene produces a polyester-like substance that is biodegradable and has the texture of cotton, but is warmer. Other biopolymers with the potential to replace synthetic fabrics and fibers are under development in Japan and the United States. Industrial scientists have genetically modified both plants and microbes to produce polyhydroxybutyrate, a feedstock for producing biodegradable plastics.

Finally, genetic engineering also provides us with the opportunity to produce abundant amounts of natural protein polymers, such as spider silk and adhesives from barnacles, through microbial fermentation. In summary, no matter what stage of industrial production you select – inputs, manufacturing process or final product – biotechnology provides industry with tools, techniques and know-how to move beyond regulatory compliance to proactive pollution prevention and resource conservation strategies that are the hallmarks of industrial sustainability.

BIOCATALYSTS

Industrial biotechnology companies develop biocatalysts, such as enzymes, to be used in chemical synthesis. Enzymes are proteins produced by all living organisms. In humans, enzymes help digest food, signal cells to turn on and off, and perform other complex functions. Other animals use enzymes to break cellulose into sugar or break up proteins.

Biotechnologists are trying to locate enzymes in the natural environment with special functional characteristics that have industrial value. Based on biotechnology, the desired enzyme can then be manufactured in commercial quantities. Most enzymes are manufactured in fermentation systems in the same way that human therapeutic proteins are. In some cases, genetically altered microbes are used in this process. Fermentation vessels represent contained use of these microbes. The process uses renewable resources as a raw material feedstock.

Enzymes are characterized according to the compounds they act upon. Some of the most common enzymes are proteases, which break down protein; cellulases, which break down cellulose; lipases, which act on fatty acids and oils; and oils; and amylases, which break starch down into simple sugars.

TABLE 26.1: Examples of Industrial Enzymes

Enzymes	Source or Type	Applications
Carbohydrases		Laundry detergents, dishwashing detergents, industrial pope/tank cleaners, textiles, pulp and paper, fermentation ethanol
Alpha-amylase	Bacterial α-amylase (*e.g., Bacillus subtilis*), Fundal α-amylase (*e.g., Aspergilius niger*), Alkaline a-amylase	Textiles, starch syrups, laundry and dishwashing detergents, paper desizing, fermentation ethanol, animal feed
β-amylase	From a strain of Bacillus	Brewing, maltose syrup

Enzymes	Source or Type	Applications
Cellulase		Laundry and dishwashing, animal feed, textiles
β-Glucanase	exo-β-1,4-glucanase, endo-β-1,4-glucanase	Brewing industry
Dextranse	Made by various microorganisms (*e.g., Leuconostoc mesenteriodes*)	Hydrolyzes the polysaccharides dextran
Dextrinase (almost identical to α-glucosidase)		
α-Galatosidase (melibiase)		Could increase yield of sucrose; potential use in the beet sugar industry
Glucoamylase	Aspergillus niger, Rhizopus, Endomyces	Manufacture of dextrose syrup and high-fructose syrup
Hemmicellulase/ Pentosanase/ Xylanase	*Thermomyces lanuginosus, Penicillium simplicissimum*	Baking, fruit juice manufacture, wood pulp processing
Invertase		Manufacture of invert syrup from cane or beet sugar (use is minor)
Lactase	Kluyveromyces lactis, Aspergillus oryzae, Bacillus	Eliminates lactose from dairy foods
Naringinase		Debitter citrus peel
Pectinase		Fruit processing
Pullulanase	Klebsiella aerogenes, Bacillus acidipullulyticus, Bacillus subtilis	Antistaling agent in baked goods
Proteases		Brewing, breaking goods, protein processing, distilled spiritis, laundry detergents, dishwashing detergents, lens cleaners, leather and fur, chemicals
Acid proteinase	Endothia parasitica, Rhizopus, Aspergillus niger, A. oryzae	
Alkaline protease	Bacillus subtilis, Bacillus licheniformis	Detergents, leather and fur
Bromelain	Pineapple stem	Food industry
Neutral protease	Aspergillus oryzae	
Pepsin	Porcine or bovine stomach	Cheese production
Peptidases		
aminopeptidase	*Lactococcus lactis*	Food and animal feed
endo-peptidase		
Subtilisin	Bacillus subtilis var. Carlsberg, Bacillus lichenformis	Chiral resolution
Lipases and Esterases	Phospholidases, pregastric esterases, phosphatases	Cleaners, leather and fur, dairy, chemicals
Amidases		Chemicals, dairy
Aminoacylase	Porcine kidney and Aspergillus melleus	
Glutaminase	Bacillus, Aspergillus	Conversion of glutamine to glutamate
Lysozyme	Chicken egg white, Saccharomyces cerevisiae, Pichia pastoris	Antibacterial (germicidal in dairy industry)
Penicillin acylase	Bacillus megaterium, Escherichia coli	Chemical synthesis

Enzymes	Source or Type	Applications
Isomerase		
Oxireductases		Chemicals, detergent bleaches, pulp bleaching
Alcohol dehydrogenase	Saccharomyces cerevisiae, Thermoanarobium brockii	Chiral synthesis
Amino acid oxidase	Porcine kidney, snake venom	Chiral resolution of racemic amino acid mixtures
Catalase	Aspergillus niger	desugaring of eggs
Chloroperoxidase	Algae, bacteria, fungi, mammalian tissues	Steroid synthesis
Hydroxysteroid dehydrogenase	*Pseudomonas testosteroni*	
Peroxidase	*Horseradish*	Laundry and wood pulp bleaches
Lyases		
Acetolactate decarboxylase		Brewing industry
Aspartic β-decarboxylase		Manufacture of L-alanine from L-aspartic acid
Histidase	Achromobacter liquidum	Cosmetics
Transferases		
Cyclodextrin glycosyltransferase		Manufacture of cyclodextrins from starch

The applications of enzymes (biological catalysts) that can change plants and animals in precise and often remarkably dramatic fashion. In the hands of knowledgeable biotechnologists, *enzymes become the tailor's scissors and the surgeon's scalpel.* There is a strong dependence of advances in enzymology on agriculture. Discovery of enzymes and elucidation of many of their properties were by agricultural chemists. The earliest enzymes studied were primarily from agriculturally important animals, plants and microorganisms. The fast developing wide field of biochemical engineering/biotechnology, and its tremendous promise for the future, have brought basic and applied scientists together in private sector companies, at universities, and in government and industrial laboratories. There are many reasons for the use of microbes in enzyme production. The important characteristics that have made microbes useful in enzyme industries are:

1. Their ability to grow on easily available and cheap raw materials.
2. Their ability to maintain a physiological constancy
3. Their ability to bring about biochemical transformations under simple culture conditions. Microbes have tremendous capacity of carrying out a variety of reactions (especially secondary metabolism resulting in an inexhaustible supply of secondary metabolites available for commercial exploitation).
4. High ratio of surface area to volume, which facilitates the rapid uptake of nutrients required to support high rates of metabolism and biosynthesis.

These properties of microorganisms are highly preferable over synthetic processes. Presently, industrial microbiology has established as a strong arm of applied microbiology and it is unlikely that, at least in some industries, the microbes could be replaced by synthetic techniques in the near future.

Nature provides rich resources for innovative solutions in many industries.

Companies involved in industrial biotechnology are constantly striving to discover and develop high-value enzymes and bioactive compounds that will enhance current industrial processes. Chemical processes, including paper manufacturing, textile processing, oil field chemicals and specialty chemical synthesis reactions, sometimes need to run at very high or very low temperatures or high or low pHs. The challenge is to find organisms that can survive and even thrive in these environments. The opportunity to identify unique bioactive molecules is vast. Fewer, than one per cent of the microorganisms in the world have been cultured and characterized.

Discovering or Creating Novel Biocatalysts

Since the dawn of life, microbes have adapted to every imaginable environment. No matter how harsh the environment, some microbe has found a way to make a living there. Life in unusual habitats makes for unique biocatalysts, and the great majority of that biochemical potential remains untapped. Through bioprospecting, scientists are discovering novel biocatalysts that will function optimally at the relatively extreme levels of acidity, salinity, temperature or pressures found in some industrial manufacturing processes – hence the name, *extremophiles*. Recently acquired information from genomic studies of microbes is helping researchers capitalize on the wealth of genetic diversity in microbial populations. They use DNA probes to fish, on a molecular level, for genes that express enzymes with specific biocatalytic capabilities. Once snared, such enzymes can be identified and characterized for their ability to function in industrial processes, with corresponding reduction of waste and pollution.

Properties of Enzymes

Enzymes are characterized by many bio-physical properties. Some common properties are given below:

Proteinaceous Nature

Enzymes are made up of protein. They may be either purely made up of protein or associate a non-protein part with protein part of enzyme.

Catalytic Properties

Enzymes act as catalysts and influence the speed of chemical reaction but themselves remain unchanged. A small quantity of enzyme can catalyse the transformation of a very large quantity of the substrate into end product *e.g.* the sucrase can hydrolyse 100,000 times of sucrose as compared with its own weight.

Specificity of Enzyme Action

The ability of an enzyme to catalyze one specific reaction and essentially no other is perhaps its most significant property. Close examination reveals that most enzymes can catalyze the same type of reaction.

Reversibility of Enzyme Action

Most of the reactions catalysed by enzymes are reversible and the enzyme can catalyze the reactions in both directions *e.g.* the lipase can catalyse not only the hydrolysis of fats into fatty acids and glycerol but also can synthesize fats from fatty acids and glycerol as shown below:

$$\text{Fats} \xrightarrow{\textit{Lipase}} \text{Fatty acids + glycerol}$$

Sensitivity of the Enzymes

The enzymes are sensitive to rise in temperature and are destroyed at higher temperature of 60-70° C.

TABLE 26.2: Basic enzyme nomenclature

Oxidoreductase	The enzyme catalyzes oxidation and reduction reactions by the transfer of hydrogen and/or electrons.
Transferases	The enzyme catalyses the transfer of certain groups from a donor molecule to a suitable acceptor molecule.
Hydrolases	It catalyzes hydrolytic reactions.
Lyases	It catalyzes cleavage reactions nonhydrolytically, leaving a double bond, or catalyzes the addition of group to double bonds.
Isomerases	It catalyzes reversible transformations of isomeric compounds.
Ligases (synthetases)	It catalyzes the covalent linkage of the molecules with the stimulations cleavage of an energy-rich bond (e.g., in ATP).

Improving Existing Biocatalysts

To improve the productivity-to-cost ratio, scientists are modifying genes to increase enzyme productivity in microorganisms commonly used in manufacturing. They also use genetic engineering to make other microbial enzymes that are too expensive or even impossible to cultivate. The biotechnology techniques of protein engineering and directed protein evolution have been used to modify the substrate specificity of enzymes, improve catalytic properties or broaden the reaction conditions under which enzymes can function so that they are more compatible with existing industrial processes.

ENZYME CLASSIFICATION

A system of rules by which enzymes are classified on the basis of the substrate they react with and the type of reaction catalyzed. This system provides both a systematic name and a four-part number code. The first number of the code places the enzyme into one of six groups indicating the type of reaction involved. The next two numbers indicate the groups involved in the reaction and the fourth number provides the absolute identification of the enzyme. The enzymes have been classified into following types:

1. Hydrolysing enzymes, 2. Oxidation-reduction enzymes, 3. Ligases, 4. Group transfer enzymes, 5. Desmolases, 6. Isomerizing enzymes, 7. Carboxylation enzymes.

Hydrolysing Enzymes

They catalyse the hydrolysis of complex big molecules into simple, smaller molecules. Depending upon the nature of food substance upon which the enzyme act, they can be further classified into following types.

1. **Carbohydrases:** They hydrolyse the complex polysaccharides into simpler monosaccharides *e.g.* sucrases, maltases, lactase, cellulase etc.
2. **Esterases:** They hydrolyse the substances containing ester linkage *e.g.* lipase, phosphatase.
3. **Proteolytic enzymes:** They hydrolyse the proteins into peptones, and amino acids *e.g.* pepsin, peptidases.

4. **Amidases:** They hydrolyse amides into ammonia and acids *e.g.* urease.
5. **Oxidation-Reduction Enzyme:** They catalyse oxidation and reduction reactions *e.g.* Oxidases, reductases, catalases, dehydrogenases.
6. **Ligases:** They bring linkage between two molecules with the simultaneous breakdown of ATP molecule which supplies energy *e.g.* synthetases which join amino acids to RNA.
7. **Group transfer enzymes:** They catalyse the transformation of a group from one kind of molecule to another or from one position of molecule to another position in the same molecule and are called as transferases.
8. **Desmolases:** They catalyse the reactions in which long carbon chain is broken or lengthened *e.g.* aldolase.
   a) **Isomerizing enzymes:** They catalyse reactions in which an organic molecule is transformed into its isomeric form and are known as isomerases.
   b) **Carboxylation enzymes:** They catalyse the reactions in which CO_2 is added or removed and are known as carboxylases or decarboxylases.

ENZYMES AS CHEMO-THERMO REGULATORS

The chemical reactions that take place within the living cell must be precisely controlled and coordinated. These reactions interlock somewhat as a multitude of assembly processes interlock on a modern day production line. For example glucose and other fuel molecules releases energy in a cells by burning. The cells could not tolerate and survive in such high temperatures nor effectively utilize energy that is released in short sudden bursts. Therefore, cells need a slow, steady release of energy that they must be able to regulate to meet metabolic energy requirements. In cellular respiration, fuel molecules are slowly oxidized and energy is extracted in small amounts, which includes sequences of 30 or more reactions (as many as 20 or 30 chemical transformations before it reaches some final state). Such chemical transformations require a system of flexible chemical control. The key elements of this control system are the remarkable enzymes.

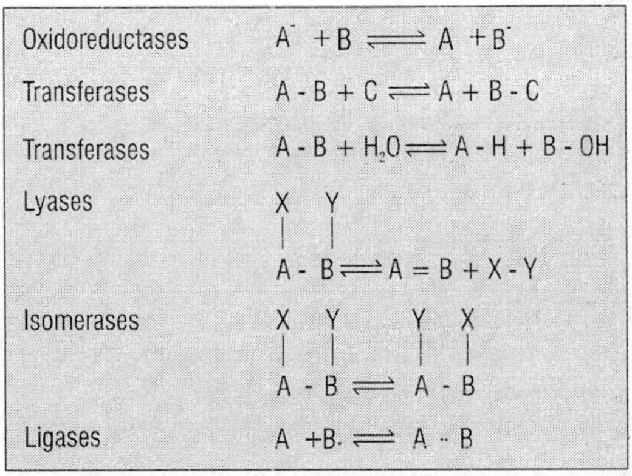

FIGURE 26.1: Main classes of enzymes with their reactions.

WHAT ENZYMES DO?

An enzyme increases the speed of a chemical reaction without being consumed itself. An enzyme affects the rate of a reaction by lowering the energy needed to activate the reactions. Even a strongly exergonic reaction that releases more than enough energy as it proceeds is prevented from beginning by an energy barrier. This is because before new chemical bonds can be formed, existing ones must be broken. The energy required to overcome this barrier and get the reaction going is called **activation energy.** An enzyme greatly reduces the activation energy necessary to initiate a chemical reaction. Enzyme promotes a chemical reaction. It does not influence the *direction of a chemical reaction* or the final concentrations of the molecules involved. They simply *speed up reactions*. For example carbonic anhydrase is an enzyme which promotes the interconversion of carbonic acid with carbon dioxide and water:

$$CO_2 \quad H_2O \quad \textit{Carbonic anhydrase} \quad \underset{\textit{Carbonic acid}}{H_2CO_3}$$

This reaction occurs in animal cells and tissues (kidneys and red blood cells). Carbonic acid ionizes, forming bicarbonate ions, the forms in which most of the carbon dioxide in the blood is transported. The reaction shown above could proceed without the enzyme but would be very slow. However, in presence of carbonic anhydrase, the reaction proceeds about 10 million times faster. This reveals that a single molecule of this enzyme can promote the conversion of an estimated 600,000 molecules of carbon dioxide into carbonic acid each second.

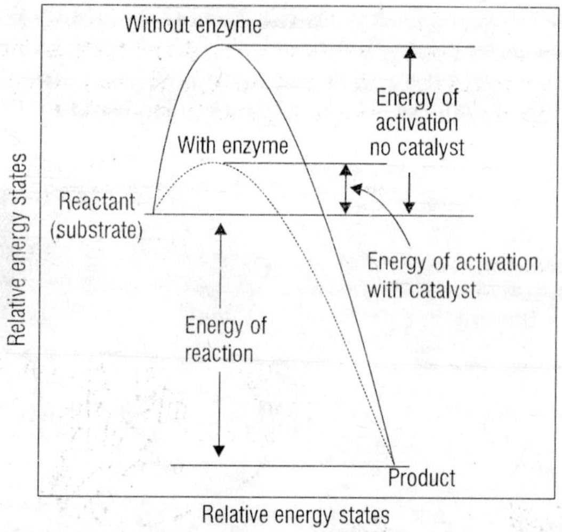

FIGURE 26.2: An enzyme accelerates the rate of reaction through lowering activation energy.

WHAT IS ENZYME KINETICS?

It is the study of enzymes in action. The extremely high rate of enzyme-catalyzed reactions greatly facilitates this study. Consider, for example, the hem-containing proteins, hemoglobin and catalase. Hemoglobin binds oxygen. It may bind and release many oxygen molecules in the course of a minute but they remain oxygen molecules, and at any instant, only one is associated with each hem centre. Catalase, being an enzyme, has a cumulative effect. Again no more than one H_2O_2 molecule will be bound per hem, but while it is bound it may react, and one therefore observes a rapid evolution of oxygen - about a million molecules per minute per enzyme molecule.

HOW ENZYMES WORK

The Chemicals upon which an enzyme operates are referred to as its **substrates**. Enzymes are very **specific**. An enzyme will catalyze only a few closely related chemical reactions, or in many cases only one particular reaction. Enzymes form temporary chemical compounds with their substrates. Theses complexes then break up, releasing the product and regenerating the original enzyme molecules for reuse.

Enzyme + Substrate 1 + Substrate 2 ⟶ Enzyme Substrate Complex ⟶ Enzyme + Product(s)

It is important to note that the enzyme itself is not permanently altered or consumed by the reaction.

Why does the enzyme-substrate complex break up into chemical products different from those that participated in its formation? As shown in Figure 26.3, each enzyme has one or more regions called **active sites,** which in the case of a few enzymes have been shown to be actual indentations in the enzyme molecule. These active sites are located close to one another on the enzyme's surface, so during the course of a reaction, substrate molecules occupying these sites are temporarily brought together and react with one another. It is thought that when the enzyme and substrate bind together, the shape of the enzyme molecule changes slightly. This produces strain in critical bonds in the substrate molecules so that these bonds break. The new chemical compound thus formed has little affinity for the enzyme and moves away from it. An enzyme can be thought of as a molecular lock into which only specifically shaped molecular keys- the substrates- can fit.

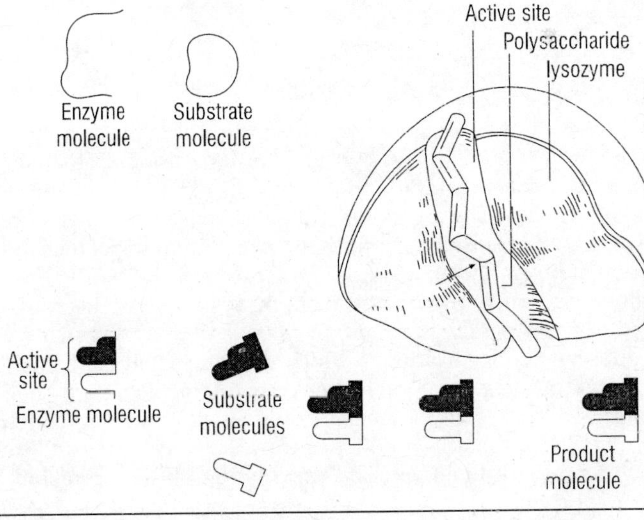

FIGURE 26.3: (a) Enzyme-substrate (ES) complex formation, (b) Enzyme in an active site of substrate, (c) Induced-fit hypothesis (Lock a-s key mechanism).

Similar to a lock and key, however, the enzyme and its substrate seem not to be exactly complementary shapes. A recent model of enzyme action, known as the **induced-fit model**, is based on data indicating that the active sites of an enzyme are not rigid. When the substrate binds to the enzyme, it may induce a change in shape in the enzyme molecule, resulting in an optimum fit for the substrate-enzyme interaction. The change in shape of the enzyme molecule can put strain on the substrate. This stress may help bonds to break, thus promoting the reaction.

An organic, nonpolypeptide compound that serves as a cofactor is called a **coenzyme.** Many coenzymes are synthesized from vitamins, particularly from the B vitamins. The coenzyme serves as an adaptor, permitting the enzyme to accept a substrate for which it would, by itself, have little affinity.

ENZYME ACTIVITY

Enzymes perform a wide range of chemical modifications and re-arrangements. For example,

Ethanol Alcohol Dehydrogenase Acetaldehyde

H_2O_2 *Catalase* $O_2 + H_2O$

Xanthine + $H_2O + O_2$ *Xanthine Oxidase* Urate + H_2O

Glucose + $O_2 + H_2O$ *Glucose Oxidase* H_2O_2 + Gluconic acid

Starch *amylase* glucose + maltose

Starch *amylase* maltose + dextrin

Sucrose *Rennin* paracasein

Lactose Lactase glucose + fructose

Casein Rennin paracasein

Enzymes speed up the reaction by lowering their activation energy. They catalyzed it. They are sensitive to environmental conditions. The rate of reaction depends on reactant concentration and the rate increases indefinitely as the concentration increases. The reaction- rate increases linearly with substrate concentration at low concentrations, but then levels off and becomes independent of the concentration at high concentrations.

At high substrate concentration the reaction velocity reaches at limiting value Vmax.

Km is the substrate concentration at which the rate is half maximal.

At high concentrations, most of the enzyme molecules have their active site occupied, and the observed rate depends only on the rate at which the bound reactants are converted into products. Further increases in the substrate concentrations then have little effect. The explanation of this behaviour is known as Michaeli-Menton mechanism.

Michaelis-Menten Constant (Km)

It supposes that an enzyme catalyzed reaction must pass through two or more steps: first enzyme (E) and substrate (S) bind together to form enzyme-substrate complex. The catalysis occurs on account of formation of transient enzyme-substrate (ES) complex. When substrate concentration is high, addition of enzyme can enhance the rate of reaction, till substrate concentration becomes limiting. Then conversion into product (P) occurs within this complex, and the product is released and the original free enzyme regenerated.

Similarly, there is usually a direct proportionality between rate and substrate concentration until the enzyme concentration become limiting. The substrate concentration required to cause half the maximal reaction rate, a value named as Michaelis-Menten constant (Km). Km values are mostly constant and do not depend upon amount of enzymes. Usually the Km values for most of the enzymes studied vary from 10^{-3} to 10^{-7} molar Km value can be implicated as indicator of substrate concentration, affinity of enzyme with its substrate and it partly indicates enzymes substrate concentration in the cellular compartment, where reaction occurs. It is the affinity part, for which Km values are used most. Km values are inversely proportional to the affinity of enzyme for its substrate. Therefore, higher Km values suffers lower stability of ES complex.

$$E + S \underset{k-1}{\overset{\text{fast } k1}{\rightleftharpoons}} ES \xrightarrow[k_2]{\text{slow}} E + P \quad \text{.......... (1)}$$

Equation 1 shows slow step in the reaction. It is assumed to be formation of E and P from ES, the velocity of the reaction should be

$$V = \frac{d[p]}{dt} k_2[ES] \quad \text{.......... (2)}$$

A maximum velocity (Vmax) is obtained when all of the enzyme is in the form of the Enzyme-Substrate complex. Since the total concentration of enzyme [Et] is equal to [E] + [ES],

$$Vmax = K_2[Et] = k_2([E] + [ES]) \quad \text{.......... (3)}$$

Dividing equation (2) by equation (3) gives:

$$\frac{V}{Vmax} = \frac{[ES]}{[E] + [ES]} \quad \text{.......... (4)}$$

By making use of dissociation constant of the ES complex in equation (1), Ks

$$Ks = \frac{[E][S]}{[ES]} \text{ and } [ES] = \frac{[E][S]}{[Ks]} \quad \text{.......... (5)}$$

Substituting this value of [ES] into equation (4) rearranging gives

$$V = \frac{Vmax[S]}{Ks + [S]} \quad \text{.......... (6)}$$

Equation (6) is the *Henri-Michaelis-Menton* equation. It relates the reaction velocity to the maximum velocity, the substrate concentration, and the dissociation constant for the enzyme-substrate complex.

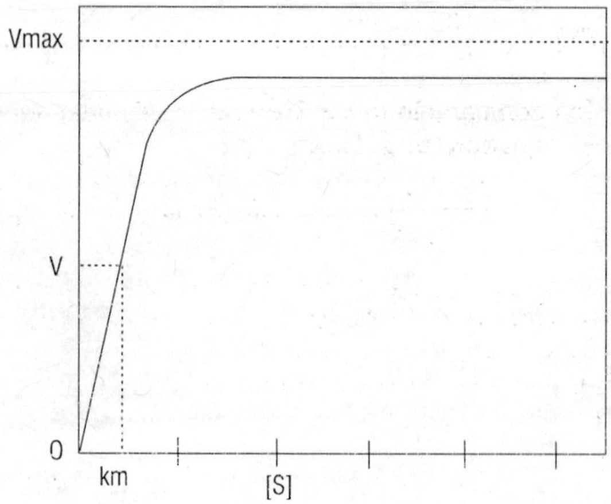

FIGURE 26.4: Presentation of reaction velocity V as a function of the substrate concentration [S] for an enzyme catalyzed reaction.

Shortly after the enzyme and substrate are mixed, [ES] becomes approximately constant and remains so for a period of time termed the steady state. Steady-state kinetic analysis assumes that the concentration of the Enzymes-Substrate complex remains nearly constant. The system following a brief period when the concentration of enzyme-substrate complex [ES] builds up. The ES concentration then remains almost constant for the duration of the steady state, while the concentrations of the substrate and product continue to change.

Therefore, the equation (1) can be presented as:

In this, the ES complex forms from E and S with rate constant k_1. ES can either dissociate again with rate constant k_1 or go on to P with k_2.

For measuring the initial rate of the reaction in the steady state, the rate of formation of ES, Vf, the equation can be expressed as:

$$Vf = k_1 [E] [S] \quad \text{.......... (8)}$$

Similarly, the rate of disappearance of ES, Vd, as:

$$Vd = k_{-1} [ES] + k_2 [ES] \quad \text{.......... (9)}$$

If the concentration of ES is virtually constant during the steady state, the rate of formation and disappearance of ES must be nearly equal, Vf = Vd: Therefore, equations, (8) and (9) that describes the situation in the steady state can be represented as

$$k_1 [E] [S] = (k_1 + k_2) [ES] \quad \text{.......... (10)}$$

or

$$\frac{[E]\,[S]}{[ES]} = \frac{k_1 + k_2}{k_1} = Km \quad \text{.......... (11)}$$

The constant Km is called the Michaelis constant. If the equation (11) is rearranged, it becomes

$$[ES] = \frac{[E][S]}{Km} \qquad (12)$$

An expression comparable to the Henri-Michaelis-Menten equation (6), with Km in place of Ks, the equation (6) or (13).

$$V = \frac{Vmax [S]}{[S] + Km} \qquad (13)$$

By rearranging equation (13) and taking reciprocals of both sides, the equation (13) can be expressed as follows:

$$\frac{1}{V} = \frac{1}{Vmax} + \frac{Km}{Vmax}\frac{1}{[S]} \qquad (14)$$

Km is the substrate concentration at which the rate is half maximal. Km and Vmax often can be obtained from a plot of 1/v versus 1/[S].

The expression shows that the plot of 1/v versus 1/[S] fits a straight line with the slope of Km/Vmax. The intercept of the line on the ordinate occurs at 1/V = 1/Vmax and the intercept of abscissa occurs at 1/[S] = -1/Km Vmax and Km thus can be determined readily from the graph.

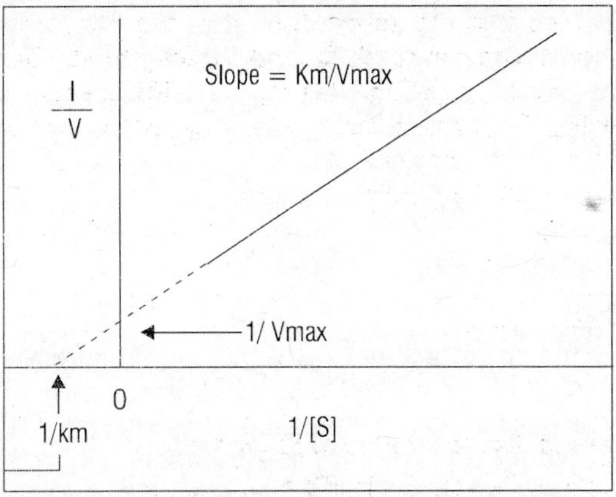

FIGURE 26.5: A plot of the reciprocal of the rate (1/v) as a function of the reciprocal of the substrate concentration (1/[S]).

If ES remains in equilibrium with free enzyme and substrate, Km remains equal to dissociation constant for the complex (Ks). Km depends on at least three rate constants and is larger than in Ks.

The turnover number Kcat is the maximum of molecules of substrate converted to product/ unit time/ active site. At high substrate concentrations the rate of reaction remains maximum. At this stage all the active sites are occupied with substrate.

The turnover number is a measure of how rapidly on enzyme can operate once the active site is filled, *i.e.*, at low substrate concentration. This can be expressed as follows:

$$Kcat = \frac{Vmax}{[Et]} \quad \text{.......... (15)}$$

The above equation is the best index to show the effectiveness of an enzyme.

Multi-substrate Enzymes

When enzymes catalyze reactions of two or more substrates, they work in a varied ways and can be differentiated by kinetic analysis. Certain enzymes bind their substrates in a fixed order; while some bind in random order. Sometimes bindings of one substrate gives a partial reaction before the second substrate binds.

The only true one-substrate enzymes are the isomerases, which catalyse reactions of the type A= B, and the lyases, which catalyse reactions of the type A - B + C, and are, therefore, one-substrate enzymes in one direction only. Hydrolases, catalysing reactions of the general type A-B + H_2O = A-OH + BH may be regarded as honorary one-substrate enzymes, since one substrate, water, is normally present at constant concentration.

The remaining groups are:

$$\text{Oxidant} \quad \text{Reductant} \xrightarrow{\text{Oxidoreductases}} \text{Reduced product} \quad \text{Oxidized product}$$

$$\text{A} \quad \text{BX} \xrightarrow{\text{Transferases}} \text{AX} \quad \text{B}$$

This large group includes methyl transferases, transaldolase, transketolase, acyl transferases, glycosyl transferases, transaminases, kinases etc.

$$X + Y + ATP \xrightarrow{\text{Legases}} XY + ADP + P_i \text{ or } AMP + PP_i$$

These three groups of enzymes by definition catalyse reactions involving more than one substrate.

ENZYME OPTIMA

Enzymes act better under certain narrowly defined conditions known as *optima*. These conditions are optimum at appropriate temperature, pH, and salt concentration, etc. Enzyme pepsin (protein-digesting enzyme of the stomach) works best at the strongly acid pH of 2 whereas amylase (starch-digesting enzyme in saliva and pancreatic juice) works better at pH 8.5 (slightly alkaline). Strong acids or bases irreversibly *inactivate* most enzymes. pH permanently changes the molecular conformation of enzymes.

The Michaelis constant Km is affected by ionizations of both free and bound species, and tends to behave in a more complicated way. Enzymes like other proteins, are stable over a limited range of pH. Outside this range, changes in the charges on ionizable amino acid residue results in modifications and eventually lead to denaturation. But within the range of its pH is a characteristic more of the enzyme than of the substrate.

Temperature dependence of the catalytic process can only be meaningful when studied within a range in which thermal denaturation is not significant. It has a narrow range from 5° to 40°C. At low temperatures, enzymatic reactions occur very slowly or not at all, but their activity resumes when the temperature is raised to normal. At lower temperature, the temperature dependence of Kcat can be related to the activation energy of the slowest step in the catalytic pathways. The rates of most enzyme-regulated reactions increase with increasing temperature, within limits. Temperatures greater than 50 °C or 60 °C rapidly inactivate most enzymes by altering their secondary and tertiary level structures. The enzyme is denatured at high temperature. This happens everyday while cooking an egg white; it changes in consistency as the protein is denatured.

ENZYME INHIBITORS, ACTIVATORS AND INACTIVATORS OF ENZYMES

The rate of an enzyme-catalyzed reaction may sometimes be altered in a specific manner by compounds other than the substrate(s). Activators increase the rate; inhibitors and inactivators decrease it. The study of such agents is of practical importance for several reasons:

1. Inhibition and activation of enzymes by key metabolites provides the normal means of metabolic *fine control* superimposed on the *coarse* control achieved by regulation of the synthesis and breakdown of active enzymes.
2. External interference with metabolism, whether by drugs, pesticides etc. or by undesirable toxic agents, often depends on the inhibition of enzymes.
3. Inhibitors, and especially inactivators, provide a powerful tool for studying the chemical mechanisms of enzyme action.

Enzyme inhibition may be reversible or irreversible. Reversible inhibitors can be competitive or noncompetitive. In **competitive inhibition** the inhibitor completes with the normal substrate for the active site of the enzyme. A competitive inhibitor usually is chemically similar to the normal substrate and so fits the active site and binds with the enzyme. However, it is not similar enough to the normal substrate to take its place effectively. The enzyme cannot act upon it to form reaction products. A competitive inhibitor occupies the active site only temporarily and does not damage the enzyme irreversibly.

In **noncompetitive inhibition** the inhibitor binds with the enzyme at a site other than the active site. Such an inhibitor renders the enzyme inactive by altering its shape. Many important noncompetitive inhibitors are metabolic substances that help regulate enzyme activity by combining reversibly with the enzyme.

Many poisons are **irreversible inhibitors** that permanently inactivate or even destroy the enzyme. Nerve gases are irreversible inhibitors that poison the enzyme cholinesterase, essential in the normal function of nerves and muscles. A number of insecticides and drugs are irreversible inhibitors. The antibiotic penicillin and its chemical relatives inhibit a bacterial enzyme necessary for bacterial cell wall construction. Unable to produce new cell walls, susceptible bacteria cannot multiply effectively. Since human body cells do not have cell walls (and so do not employ the susceptible enzyme), penicillin is harmless to humans, except for the occasional allergic patient.

Reversible and Irreversible Inhibition

Enzyme activity can be curtailed by various non-specific agents (acid or alkali, urea, detergents, proteases etc.), which disrupt protein structure. These agents interact with a protein at a small number of loci without markedly disrupting the three-dimensional structure. The two most important considerations in their classification are specificity and reversibility.

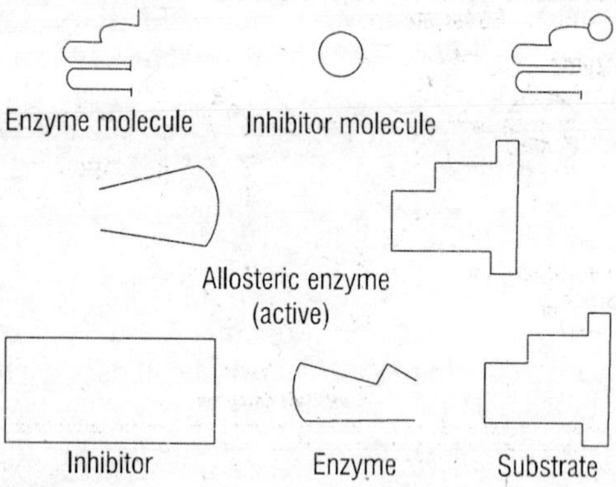

FIGURE 26.6: Enzyme inhibition (a) non competitive, (b) Allosteric.

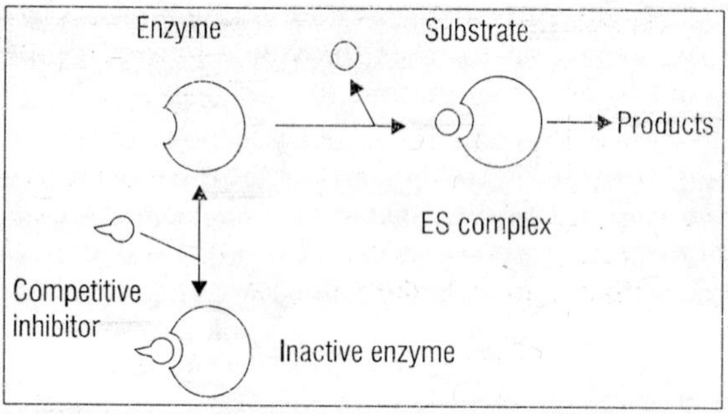

FIGURE 26.7: A competitive inhibitor completes with the substrate for binding at the same site on the enzyme.

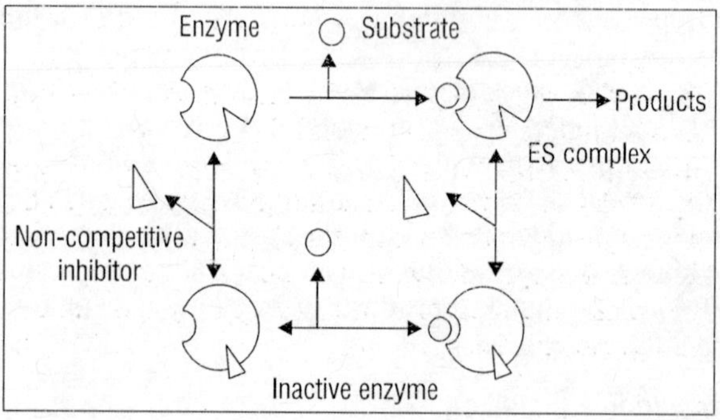

FIGURE 26.8: A noncompetitive inhibitor to a different site but block the conversion of the substrate to products.

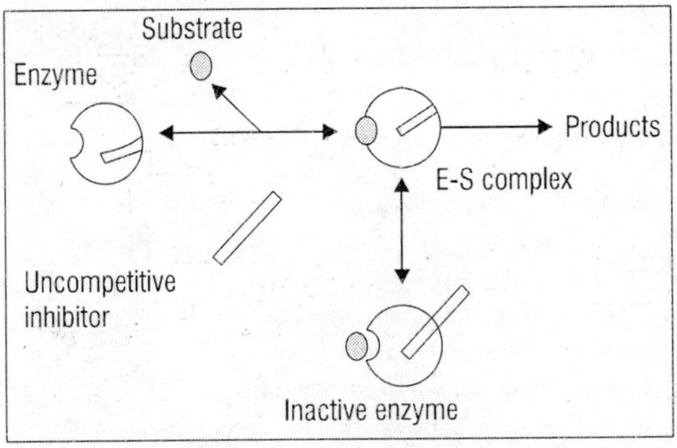

FIGURE: 26.9: An uncompetitive inhibitor binds only to the substrate-enzyme complex.

ENZYME SECRETION BY PLANT CELLS

Enzyme secretion is a common feature of most of the living cells. By this process, cells may act on their environment by modifying its chemical composition and ensure their defence againt external aggressions. In pluricellular organisms, groups of cells (glands) become specialized in the secretion of enzymes, which are utilized in a function useful for the whole organism. The control of such a release of enzyme is often mediated by chemical substances, which migrate from one tissue to another one composed of secreting target cells. This coupling between stimulus and secretion is widely distributed in animal organisms.

The Mechanism of Protein Secretion

The synthesis, intracellular transport, and release of secretary proteins are the basic cellular function common to most eukaryotic cells. In the pancreatic exocrine cell for example, the secretary proteins are the object of six steps or operations, which are: *synthesis, segregation, intracellular transport, concentration, intracellular storage* and *discharge*. Proteins for export are generally synthesized on polysomes, attached to the membrane of the rough endoplasmic reticulum. In etiolated radish seedlings submitted to far red light, which is known to induce the synthesis of β-fructosidase, the enzyme activity is found associated to endoplasmic reticulum in a first time, then in Golgi apparatus and in cell wall. There is no evidence for the existence of a single intracellular route leading to enzyme secretion. Although the migration of proteins synthesized in endoplasmic reticulum, through Golgi towards the exterior of cell after exocytosis is likely to occur in some cases, direct transport from reticulum to plasmalemma and transfer of cytoplasmic enzymes across plasmalemma cannot be excluded.

The Control of Secretion

The secretary process is a complex mechanism. It is known that calcium is essential for the control of the secretary process. Calcium plays a critical role in the exocytosis process, which is a **fusion-fission response** involving the interaction the of the plasma membrane and secretary vesicle membrane. A second requirement for the occurrence of secretion is metabolic energy. An adequate intracellular ionic equilibrium is also necessary. Ca^{2+} is considered as a second messenger in animal cells, able to trigger the discharge of secretary products by regulated cells. In addition, non-regulated cells often requires Ca^{2+} for their secretion. It would be, therefore, necessary to explore the knowledge concerning the regulation of Ca^{2+} in plant cells. It is known that Ca^{2+} is involved in the secretion of some plant enzymes, including peroxidase, α-amylase, and phosphatase. Recently, several articles have been published, which described modes of Ca^{2+} transport across pant membranes. An ATP-dependent Ca^{2+} uptake by isolated membranes vesicles was reported.

Some elements exist for substantiating the hypothesis that phytohormones regulate protein secretion through the mediation of second messenger such as c-AMP or Ca^{2+}/calmodulin. However, the existence of an exchange mechanism between H^+ and Ca^{2+} suggests that plant growth regulators especially auxin could modify secretary process by a modification of the distribution of protons which indirectly affect Ca^{2+} compartmentation.

SOURCES OF ENZYMES

Industrial enzymes can be obtained from plants, animals or microorganisms. Various factors such as specificity, pH, thermostability, activation or inhibition, availability and cost, determines the selection from any of the sources.

The important enzymes are:

1. **Glucose Oxidase:** This converts glucose to gluconic acid, which is an industrial chemical and is also used extensively in diagnostic test for measuring blood sugar.
2. **Rennin**, used in cheese production.
3. **Papain**, an enzyme derived from papaya plant and added to animal feeds as a meat tenderizer.
4. **Glucose isomerase** converts glucose to fructose
5. **Pepsin**, an animal protease used in the manufacturing industry.
6. **Urokinase** is used as an anti-thrombotic agent in treatment or pulmonary embolism.
7. **Asperaginase** used in cancer chemotherapy
8. **Tyrosine hydroxylase** which converts tyrosine into DOPA which is specific against Parkinson's disease.

TABLE 26.3: Sources of animal enzymes

Type of enzyme	Source
α-amylase	Pancreatic gland of bovine and porcine
catalase	Liver
chymotrypsin	Pancreatic gland
esterase	Pancreatic gland
glucose oxidase	Liver
lipase	Pancreatic gland
pepsin	Fundus portion of hog stomach
rennet	Calf stomach
trypsin	Pancreatic gland of bovine and porcine

Animal gland *e.g.*, the pancreas, is source for hydrolyzing enzymes used as digestive aids. The pancreas, a very rich source contain about 23% trypsinogen and 10-14% chymotrypsinogen. Pancreatin contains several enzymes such as amylase, lipase and protease.

TABLE 26.4: Sources of animal enzymes

Type of enzyme	Source
proteases (bromelain and papain)	pineapple and papaya
amylolytic	tissues of barley, wheat, rye, potatoes, sweet potatoes, beans and soybeans.
α-amylase and β-amylase	Seeds

The extraction from plants and animals sources is much simpler and less costly. The toxicity and contamination is not a problem.

MICROBIAL ENZYMES

The enzymes used in the industry are obtained from bacteria, fungi and yeasts. Efforts have been made to replace animal or plant enzymes with enzymes from microbes *e.g.*, amylases and endo-β-glucanases from *Bacillus* and *Aspergillus*, plant and animal proteases by *Aspergillus* and *Thermoactinomyces*, calf chymosin by *Mucor*. The application of genetic engineering gained enormous potential in the use of microbes to produce animal or plant enzyme. The strains constructed by gene cloning procedure will be able to produce abnormal amounts of foreign proteins *i.e.*, synthesis of calf prochymosin by *E. coli/Saccharomyces cerevisiae* and urokinase normally occurring in human urine by *E. coli* cells. The various enzymes and their microbial sources are given in following.

TABLE 26.5: Enzymes produced by bacteria

Type of enzyme	Bacteria
α-Amylase	*Bacillus spp.*
β-Amylase	*Bacillus cereus*
Dextran sucrose	*Leuconostoc mesenteroides*
-β-1,3-Gluconase	*Bacillus subtilis*
Glucose isomerase	*Arthrobactor globiformis Bacillus coagulans. Streptomycin spp.*
Penicillin acylase	*Bacillius megaterium*
Proteinase	*Escherichia coli, Bacillus subtilis*
Pullulanase	*Klebsiella aerogens*
Streptokinase	*Streptococcus spp.*
Urokinase	*Bacillus fastidions*

TABLE 26.6: Enzymes produced by fungi

Types of enzyme	Fungi
α-Amylase	*Aspergillus oryzae*
Amyloglucosidase	*Aspergillus niger*
Catalase	*Aspergillus niger*
Cellulase	*Trichoderma reesi, Penicillium funiculsosum*
Dextranse	*Penicillium* spp.
Glucoamylase	*Aspergillus niger, A. awamori and Rhizopus spp.*
Glucose oxidase	*Aspergillus niger*
Invertase	*Saccharomyces spp.*
Lactose	*Kluveromyces fragilis, Aspergillus niger*
Lipase	*Candida lipoytica, Rhizopus delemar*
Pectinase	*Aspergillus niger*

Types of enzyme	Fungi
Proteinase	*Aspergills oryzae*
Raffinase	*Mortierella vinacea*
Renin	*Mucor miehes*

Microorganisms have biochemical diversity. The enzyme concentration in these microorganisms is dependent on environmental and genetic manipulations. Microbial enzymes may have varied stability and different pH and temperature optima. Microbial cells require short fermentation times, inexpensive media and simple screening procedures. Microbes can be geneticically manipulated.

MECHANISM OF ENZYME BIOSYNTHESIS IN MICROBIAL CELLS

Metabolism is mainly regulated by change in the rate of enzyme reaction. The enzyme concentration can be varied by controlled protein synthesis and controlled protein degradation.

Enzymes synthesis by microbial cells may be influenced by various mechanisms. These include-

Induction

Biosynthesis requires the presence of substrates in the medium. The structural genes coding for the production of many catabolic enzymes are repressed in the absence of substrates of the enzymes. By the addition of substrate, enzyme synthesis is induced or derepressed. In the case of lac operon, the inducer (lactose) binds the repressor and inactivates it. Transcription thus begins and enzyme synthesis occurs. This can be seen in case of the synthesis of sugar or amino acid degrading enzymes.

Repression

The repressed enzymes can be of the constitutive or of the inducible types. Enzymes are often repressed by the presence of intermediates or end products of the enzyme reactions. This type of regulation is known as end product repression or feedback repression.

Catabolic repression

The biosynthesis of the most of extra-cellular depolymerases is influenced by the level of catabolites present in the growth medium. It occurs when cells grow rapidly on readily metabolizable carbon sources *i.e.*, repression of β-galactosidase in *E. coli* by glucose.

Transcription control during the growth cycle

The different behaviour of enzyme biosynthetic in relation to the growth is caused by different regulatory mechanisms. In case of *B. subtilis* transition of cells from vegetative growth to sporulation is accompanied by changes in the predominant forms of RNA polymerase. Four forms of RNA polymerase have been identified in vegetative and early stationary phase cells. Sporulation forms of RNA polymerase recognizes the specific promotor sequence that control expression of genes during growth cycle and sporulation. Genes coding for extracellular proteases indicates overlapping promoters, ensuring gene expression during both growth and stationary phase. Therefore, altered promoter specificity is one of the cellular tools to influence gene expression on the level of transcription during growth. Further, translation efficiency of a gene is influenced by several factors. Rate of translation efficiency of a gene is influenced by several factors. Rate of translation efficiency is affected by the ribosomal binding site, stability of mRNA, the codon usage by the translation machinery, occurrence of repression by attenuation, effectiveness of the secretion etc.

GENETICS OF ENZYME FORMATION

Modern biotechnology was born because scientists learned to manipulate (engineer) DNA. This capability was derived largely from the field of nucleic acid enzymology. Prior to 1970, there was simply no method available for cutting a duplex DNA molecule into discrete fragments. Discovery of DNA metabolizing enzymes allowed scientists to contemplate and initiate genetic engineering. With the advent of genetic engineering, barriers to the exchange of genetic material were crossed to improve the formation of desired enzyme in various organisms.

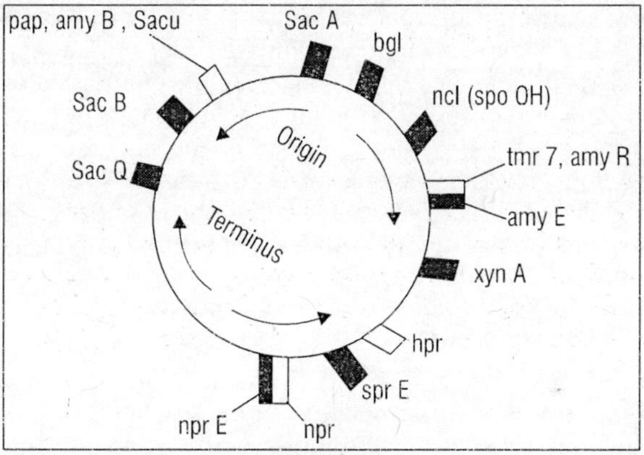

FIGURE 26.10: Presentation of location of genes coding for extra cellular enzymes on the linkage map of *B. subtilis*.

Genes coding for intra- or extra- cellular enzymes in Gram negative bacteria are organized in operons while in gram positive bacteria, however, the occurrence of genes for exoenzyme synthesis in clusters in uncertain. Linkage of regulating genes with related structural genes are known to be occurring *i.e.*, amylase (amy R, amy E), levansucrase (sac Q, sac B). Besides regulatory genes, there are genes enhancing the level of simultaneous secretion of different genes (pap, amy B, sac U, in *B. subtilis*.

Classical genetic methods have also been used for the improvement of enzyme formation, *e.g.*, mutation. Through mutations overproduction of enzymes can be obtained by altering mechanisms of regulation and by increasing copies of responsible genes for the production of enzymes. The method of site directed mutageneis of cloned gene is also being used for genetic alteration of enzyme. Chemical mutation is also helpful for the isolation of natural enzyme and modification to its structure.

In vitro methods is also being used to overcome the barriers to genetic exchange between unrelated organisms. Genes encoding enzymes with industrial importance have been cloned. The potential hosts expressing cloned genes are *E. coli*, *B. sublitis* and *S. cereviiae*. Cloning of the structural genes for α-amylase from *B.*

amyloliquefaciens in plasmid pUB 110, and transformation of this hybrid plasmid into *B. subtilis* has enhanced the productivity of α-amylase to about 2000 fold. Thus, it becomes possible to produce industrial enzymes of very high quality and purity. Enzymes can be modified by evaluation of their performance. The main objective is to enhance the activity, stability change in pH or temperature optima, change the specificity to catalyze the conversion of different substrate and to perform function in a changed environment.

ISOENZYMES

Isoenzymes were discovered about 30 years ago and were at first regarded as interesting but of rare occurrences. Since then a wealth of information on enzyme heterogeneity has accrued and it now seems likely that at least half of all enzymes exist as isoenzymes. This is important in many areas of biological and medical science. Thus isoenzyme studies have provided the main experimental substance for the neutral drift controversy in genetics and evolution. Isoenzymes have greatly extended our understanding of metabolic regulation not only in animals but also in bacteria and plants; their existence has made available a multitude of highly sensitive markers for the study of differentiation and development, as well as providing indices of aberrant gene expression in carcinogenesis and other pathological processes. Isoenzymes are also being used increasingly in diagnostic clinical biochemistry. Isoenzymology crosses the traditional boundaries of the biological disciplines and it seems that advances and new applications in this field, are likely to occur at a rapid pace.

The Cause of Enzyme Multiplicity

There are various causes of enzyme multiplicity and they may be divided into two categories. These are (a) **genetic** or **primary causes**, whereby the organism carries multiple genes each one encoding a different type of enzyme subunit; and (b) post-translational or secondary causes, whereby homogeneous enzyme subunits are modified differentially so as to produce a range of subunits from a single gene. There are, in turn, two types of genetic multiplicity; firstly, multiple alleles at a single genetic locus and secondly, multiple genetic loci.

Primary or Genetic Isoenzymes

Isoenzymes due to Multiple Alleles at a Single Genetic Locus

In the diploid genome, each genetic locus is represented twice. For each locus, the individual will either be homozygous, possessing two identical alleles, or heterozygous, possessing two different alleles. Where the genetic locus encodes an enzyme subunit, the homozygous individual can only produce one type of subunit. However, the heterozygous individual with two different allelic variants will produce two different types of enzyme subunits. Within the individual the degree of enzyme multiplicity produced by multiple alleles is limited, as two different alleles per diploid locus is the maximum possible genetic variation of this type. However, from one individual to another, there may be considerable variation in the range of enzyme subunit types produced since there may be a variety of different alleles for the locus in the gene pool of the species.

The enzyme subunit types produced as a result of multiple alleles are likely to differ from each other only in minor ways, such as by individual amino acid substitutions caused by point mutations in the DNA nucleotide sequences. Where a genetic locus is active, both alleles will usually be expressed. Thus in the same individual, although the total activity of the enzyme may vary considerably between different kinds of cell, the isoenzyme profile will be constant throughout, homozygous individuals displaying only one subunit type, and heterozygotes possessing two different subunit types.

Isoenzymes due to Multiple Genetic Loci

Many enzymes are encoded at more than one genetic locus and, where this the case, each locus will produce a different type of enzyme subunit. As the expression of each genetic locus can be controlled independently, the organism may synthesize one type of enzyme subunit in a particular cell, and another enzyme subunit elsewhere. Furthermore, the expression of genetic loci may alter during the course of development, and therefore the type of enzyme subunit produced in a tissue may change. Thus multiple genetic loci permit **differences in isoenzyme profile** both from one tissue to another, and from one developmental stage to another even within the same tissue. Such variation in isoenzyme profile are not possible where the enzyme multiplicity is due to multiple alleles operating at only a single locus. However, as all members of the same species will possess the same genetic loci, multiple enzyme-encoding loci in the absence of multiple alleles cannot account for isoenzyme differences between one member of the species and the next. The isoenzyme subunits produced by multiple loci are likely to differ extensively as a result of numerous amino acid substitutions, and also deletions and additions of residues may have occurred resulting in small size differences between the subunits.

Secondary or Post-translational Isoenzymes

Proteins may be modified in numerous ways following their synthesis. Such possible modifications include the addition of carbohydrate, limited proteolysis, and the covalent modification of amino acid side chains. Post-synthetic alterations affecting only part of the enzyme subunit population, so that modified and unmodified subunits are found in the same organism, will result in isoenzymes. Where the post-translational modification process is very active in some tissues but not in others, the result will be a tissue-specific distribution pattern of the secondary isoenzymes, mimicking the effect of multiple genetic loci. An example of this is one particular pyruvate kinase subunit type. There are three major types of pyruvate kinase subunit in mammals, each coded for by an independent genetic locus.

TABLE 26.7: Enzymes, coenzymes, and mineral activating substances

Enzyme	Coenzyme or co-factor	Activating mineral elements
	In processes of glycolysis	
Phosphatase	Phosphate	Mg^{2+},
Phosphoglutamase		Mg^{2+}
Aldolase		Fe^{2+}, Zn^{2+}, Co^{2+}
Enolase		Mg^{2+}, Mn^{2+}, Zn^{2+}
Pyruvate kinase	ADP In the tricarboxylic cycle	Mg^{2+}, K^+, NH_4^+
Decarboxylase and pyruvate dehydrase	Thiamine pyrophosphyte fatty acids, CoA	Mg^{2+}, Mn^{2+}
Isocitrate dehydrogenase	NADP	Mn^{2+}, Mg^{2+}

Enzyme	Coenzyme or co-factor	Activating mineral elements
Succinate dehydrogenase	FAD	Ca^{2+}, Cr^{3+}, Al^{3+}
Aconitase		Fe^{2+}, -SH
Dehydrogenase		Mn^{2+}, K^{+}, Rb^{+}, NH_4^{+}
Pyruvic oxidase		Mg^{2+}, Mn^{2+}

Among the three most important functions namely, the mechanical, osmotic and chemical, the later depends solely upon the bio acceleration of metabolic reactions caused by enzymes.

CHAPTER 27

Production of Enzymes and Fermentation technology

Microorganisms, plants and animals are the major sources of natural enzymes, but much focus has been diverted on microorganisms as a source of enzymes. Scientists and industrialists rely on enzymes of microbial source. Recombinant DNA technology has greatly influenced the possibilities for optimizing enzyme yield and type through strain selection, mutation, induction and selection of growth condition etc. As discussed in the chapter *Biology of enzymes*, enzymes differ greatly in their stability to temperature and to extremes of pH. For example, bacterial proteases are relatively heat stable and remain active under alkaline conditions and is being used as soap powder additives. On the other hand, fungal amylases have their greater sensitivity to heat and are being used in the baking industry. Microbial enzymes are used in fermentation processes at commercial level and therefore, substrate is required in large quantities. These substrates are starch hydrolysate, molasses, corn steep liquor, whey and cereals. For industrial production of enzymes suitable and low-prices substrates are required. Enzymes at industrial level are produced by solid substrate process using fungal sources for commercial extracellular enzymes production. Other technique is conventional batch submerged culture for bacterial source and is commonly used.

SOLID SUBSTRATE FERMENTATION

Solid substrate methods for production of fungal enzymes includes growth of filamentous fungus on a moist wheat or rice bran with added nutrient salts as substrates to produce amylases, proteases, pectinases and cellulases. During the process, the control of pH, temperature and humidity is very difficult.

Fermenters

The fermenters are rectangular or circular trays of a few centimeter depth, mounted on racks and air is blown over the surface and beneath the mesh bottom. Another type is of two stage rotary system in which partially fermented bran from an upper chamber is conveyed to a lower rotary tray where fermentation process is completed.

Substrates composed of longer beds can be used. These can also be of fixed bed types in which air is forced though a bed of inoculated substrate which is periodically agitated by some mechanical device, or they can be of conveyed type. The other type of fermenter has been developed in which the rotating drum used horizontally, disposed cylinders, mounted on rollers and provides both support. It acts as rotation device.

Medium

The media comprise of cereal, which provide nutritional requirements to the microorganisms. The cereals are cracked and grinded to make them in utilizable form. They are sterilized using steaming technique at low pH or by chemical methods, or a combination of both. The mass of the moistened bran is inoculated with a suspension of spores or vegetative inoculum of the selected strain. Incubation is done for 1-10 days at temperature 40° to 84 °C. Moisture content and temperature of the fermenting media should be controlled properly, though it is a difficult task. During the process, several metabolic reactions are under operation. Such reactions generate metabolic heat, which causes loss of water from cultures.

TABLE 27.1: Types of media employed for the commercial production of enzymes

Source	Enzyme type	Medium
Aspergillus niger	Lactase	Wheat bran 100 parts), Zn, Fe and Cu (traces in 60 parts) 0.2 N.HCl
Aspergillus niger	Amyloglucosidase	Cassava meal (10 parts), $(NH_4)_2$ SO_4 (0.97 parts), urea (0.24 parts), tap water (10 parts)
Aspergillus oryzae	Proteinase	Wheat bran (10 parts) and 0.2 N.HCl (5 parts)
Coniothyrium diplodiella	Pectinases	Defatted rice bran (10 parts) and tap water (6 parts).
Mucor pusillus	Rennin	Wheat bran (10 parts), water (7 parts).

- **Advantages:** The volume of fermenter is needed in less quantity as compared to submerged fermenter system. Inoculum stages are generally unnecessary. Spore seeding can be done directly. Recovery by extraction of the harvest with small volume of water yields relatively highly concentrated solutions of enzymes. The sterilization process is not expensive.
- **Disadvantages:** Solid substrate fermentation process has several disadvantages and limitations. The process is limited to fungal organisms. The important one to maintain and control the environmental conditions of the fermenter, this includes temperature, pH, moisture content and oxygen transfer. It is a difficult task. Pretreatment of moist media except in rice, is usually required. Control of the progress of the fermentation is difficult because of in-homogenous condition of the culture.

Submerged Fermentation

In submerged fermentation process bioreactor are used similar in design and function to those used in antibiotic production processes. It is constructed from stainless steel and has a capacity of 10-50 m^3 and includes systems for mixing by mechanical internal agitator, external pumps, bubble columns, and air lift loop. Cultivation involves the suspension growth in liquid medium. Sterilization and process control of submerged fermentation are easy.

The medium is prepared after adjusting optimum or required pH value. The medium is pumped to previously stem sterilized fermenter vessel through HTST sterilization units. Thermolabile additives are added separately to the sterile medium. Inoculum buildup should be before transfer to the production stage vessels. Sterile compressed air is introduced into the fermentation broth through a sparger system of a ring type or a single or multiple inlet type. Agitation is done using multiple, flat bladed disc turbines mounted on a vertical shaft. Often types include axial flow propellers or counter current stirrers. Temperature of the fermenters is maintained by using internal cooling coils or external heat exchange surface.

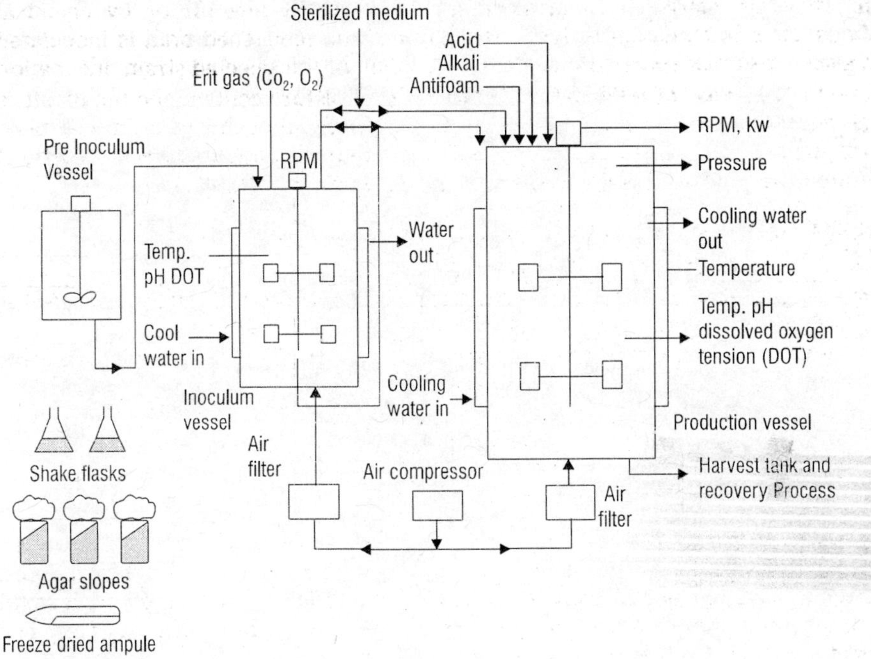

FIGURE 27.1: Schematic representation of a typical fermentation plant.

In situ probes and instruments are used to monitor and control varied physical conditions during development of the inoculum during production stages. pH value, dissolved oxygen, CO_2, redox potential, etc should be controlled properly.

Steps of Enzyme Production

Development of Inoculum: The stock cultures obtained from a freeze dried ampoules used for the development of inoculum. These cultures after rehydration are used to prepare master cultures on agar slants. Which is further used for preparation of subsequent liquid culture inoculum. Growth from the shake-flask stage for inoculum build up is carried in stirred, aerated fermenters. At first stage, harvesting of the cells or spores is done aseptically from solid medium to obtain suspension as inoculum. The inoculum is then transferred by pumping or air pressure to the next stage of inoculum build up or to the production fermenter stage.

Fermenter stage: The fermentation is done in either batch, fed batch or continuous cultivation.

Batch Culture	In this culture growth proceeds, nutrients are consumed cell mass increases, and the enzyme yield rises to a maximum level before conditions become deleterious. The deleterious conditions develop due to exhaustion of essential nutrients or toxic/inhibitory end product accumulation. At the termination stage of the fermentation may be judged by various parameters like changes in dissolved oxygen, pH. CO_2 output, etc. At final stage the broth the transferred from the fermenter for harvesting of the cells followed by extraction of intracellular enzymes from biomass or extracellular enzymes from culture filtrate.
Fed Batch Culture	This fermentation technology is used when the substrate causes catabolite repression. The process needs feeding of additional nutrients, to extend the production phase at particular

	times and in response to specific physiological state of culture.
Continuous Culture	It needs continuous feeding of fresh sterile medium to the culture, while at the same time removing the same volume of broth. It maintains constant volume of culture for indefinite time in a steady state. The fermentation is carried in a chemostat.

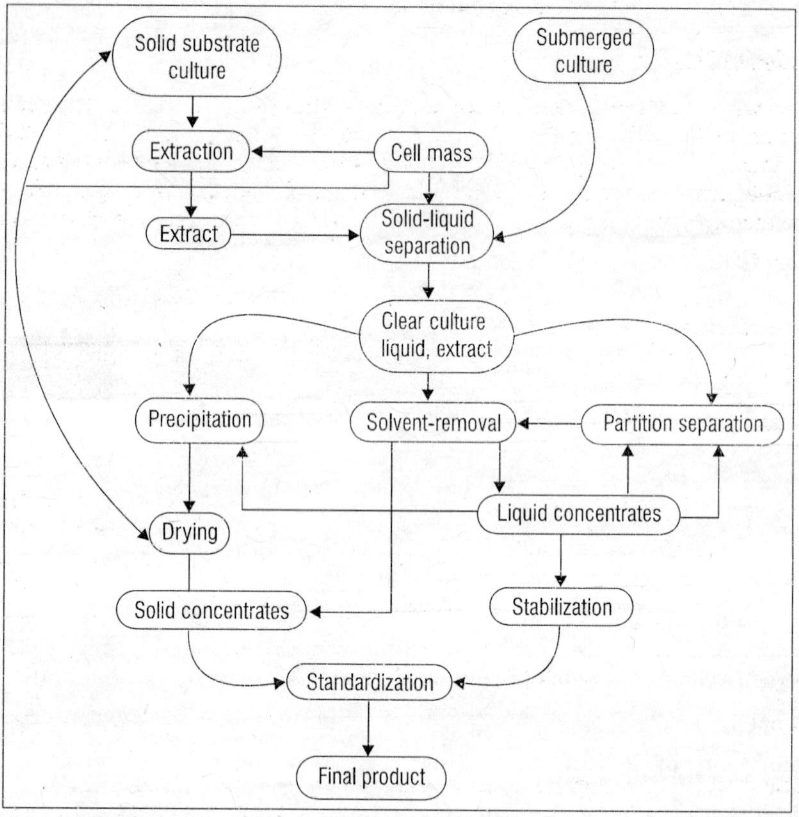

FIGURE 27.2: Presentation of outline of the extraction and purification of an enzyme.

Factors Affecting Submerged Culture

Temperature: Optimum temperature is required for the production of a particular enzyme and growth of the microorganism and it varies. The activity of an enzyme towards a used substrate is also influenced by temperature. Therefore temperature during fermentation should range in such a way that cell growth is properly encouraged and subsequently changes with enzyme accumulation.

pH: The pH optima is required for stability of an enzyme and it varies. For getting maximum growth rate of the organism it is essential to maintain pH optima. Therefore, pH profile during fermentation and enzyme production phase should be imposed in such a way that the maximum growth and enzyme production could be obtained.

Dissolved Oxygen Tension (DOT): Proper aeration rate, agitation ratio and gas phase pressure are required to maintain dissolved oxygen tension. The oxygen below its critical concentration affects the growth of organisms. Adequate aerobic condition in growth culture is an essential requirement. The level of oxygen in submerged microbial cultures can be achieved by either increasing the mass of oxygen supplied to the fermenter/unit time by increasing the overpressure in the fermenter head space or by increasing the rate of air supply to the fermenter. Oxygen enriched air may effect higher oxygen transfer rates.

Extraction of Enzyme

Various techniques are available for enzyme extraction. Therefore, the choice of extraction method depends on factors like nature of the source (extracellular or intracellular scale of operation) and stability of the enzyme. For enzyme extraction cell disintegration is required which releases major proportion of enzyme. Following are the methods for cellular disintegration which depends on characteristics of cells.

Physical Disruption Method

It is done by pressure homogenization or grinding in the pressure of an abrasive material, and chemical or enzymic lysis.

Grinding with Abrasives	It includes: Grinding with alumina using mortar and pestle for small scale production. Agitation of cells with Dynomill instrument is carried out with glass or metal heads in grinding mills for large scale.
Liquid Shear	This method is useful for disruption of bacterial, yeast and fungal cells. The process involves passage of suspensions of cells at high pressure through office into a chamber at atmospheric pressure. In case of filamentous organisms, it requires to macerate material prior to disruption.
Solid Shear	It is used on for small scale production and involves extrusion of cell material at high pressure through a narrow office at low outlet temperature (-20°C) resulting in ice crystal formation aiding disruption.

Chemical Treatment Method

The method involves treatment with alkali, detergents, osmotic shock, organic solvents, lysozyme and EDTA.

Treatment with Alkali	The cells are disrupted at a pH within range of 10.5 to 12.5. No live cells remain to be carried over into final product, for example for production of L-asparaginase from Erwinia at a pH 11.5 using NaOH. In this treatment the enzyme remains stable for 20-30 minutes.
Detergents	Detergents act on both on cell wall and cytoplasmic membrane under low stringent conditions. This makes the cell permeable to certain protein materials. The method is useful for the extraction of membrane bound enzymes like cholesterol oxidase from Nocardia sps. Detergents like cholates, sodium dodecylsulphate, ceytilmethyl ammonium bromide (CTAB). Tween and Triton (X-100 and X-450) are in common use.
Osmotic Shock	This technique is suitable for Gram negative organisms. The osmotic shocks release hydrolytic enzymes present in the perilasmic spaces. It is done by rapid change in the solute concentration of the suspension buffer.
Organic Solvents	Isopropyl alcohol, ethanol, and ethyl acetate are used for extraction of enzymes from yeast cells. Organic solvents are costly, toxic, cause protein denaturation and flammability, therefore, they are not used for large-scale enzyme extraction.
Lysozyme and EDTA	It is a delicate and specific method of cell disruption. It is suitable for small-scale production. Lysozyme is effective with gram positive bacteria.

Purification of Enzyme

Enzyme purification is a complex process and various steps are to be conducted in sequence for the purification of any enzyme. For enzyme purification such method should be used which can give high degree of purity; high overall recovery of activity; reproducibility. Therefore, the purification steps have to be selected and linked accordingly.

After the homogenization of the original raw material, the cell debris are separated using centrifugation or filtration method. This will give more or less clear extract. With microorganisms the extract may contain nucleic acids and polysaccharides besides proteins, therefore, nucleic acids, cell debris, preliminary purification and concentration steps should be followed first then final purification and is done. Finally concentrated and purified enzyme is obtained.

Removal of Nucleic Acids and Cell Debris

The release of nucleic acid makes the solution more viscous because it contains broken cell parts as major contaminant. The removal of nucleic acids and cell debris is done either by differential sedimentation or precipitation, and it can be affected by centrifugation or filtration. Protamine sulphate streptomycin, ceytyltrimethylammonium bromide are used as precipitants. Digestion with nuclease may reduce the viscosity of the solution and can be removed in later stages of purification. Thus, soluble proteins may be separated from organelle-sequestered proteins. At second step, the supernatant which contains the enzyme be further subjected to process for the removal of small organic and inorganic molecules, other proteins, unwanted contaminant and water.

Preliminary Purification

Success of purification depends on picking a number of procedures and combing them in an effective manner. Procedure is combined to purify the specific enzymes from crude whole cell extracts. Following are the methods:

Separation Based on Solubility: Solubility based separation is mainly based on precipitation. Once a crude extract of protein is made the mixtures of different fractions are separated, involving precipitation steps. The solvent should be selected in such a way that it should not after the solubility and the structure of protein. It is also necessary to control pH, temperature and the composition of solvent.

At isoelectric point proteins show a minimum solubility. The decrease in solubility at the isoelectric point shows that the individual protein molecules (which all have similar charges at pH values away from their isoelectric points) cease to repel each other. Contrarily, they coalesce into soluble aggregates.

Precipitation: The solubility of proteins depends on the concentration of salts in the medium. The solvent properties are changed by specific interaction between charged side chains and the solution ions, or particularly at high salt concentrations. Ammonium sulphate is commonly used salt. A salt is the weak acid. Salt together with the possibility of a slow loss of ammonia, effects the change in the pH. Sodium sulphate is an effective salt. It has low solubility-Phosphates and used as buffers in the biological pH range.

Precipitation of protein depends on salt concentrations. A salt is added to an aqueous buffered solution of a protein to a concentration just below that at which the required component get precipitated. The initial precipitate is removed by centrifugation. Further salt is then added to the clear supernatant to a level just high enough to precipitate the enzyme. This helps in removal of unwanted material in the first precipitate. Further unwanted materials are left in the solution and are removed in the second step. Organic solvents (polyethylene glycol or polyacrylic acid) are not used for this purpose due to price factor. Such solvents are only used for low scale production.

As the solubility of protein molecule is lowest at its isoelectric point, successive precipitation of different enzymes from a solution can be achieved by changing the pH. These precipitants get settled easily and can easily be separated by using centrifugation technique.

Adsorption: Crude extract processing is performed by batch adsorption and elution in initial stages of purification and concentration. Resins, substituted dextrans or agarose, and substituted cellulose are used as adsorbents on small scale. Hydroxyapatite is also used because of its low cost. Differential elution of many bound proteins can be performed with increasing concentration of phosphate. A common feature of all adsorption techniques is the principle of adsorption, followed by adsorption or elution. Separation is achieved by adsorption or elution of either enzymes or impurities.

Aqueous two phase separation: Removal of polysaccharides and separation of cell debris is done by using an aqueous liquid-liquid two phase extraction method. The process permits processing of large volumes, which decreases the starting volume in two parts. Aqueous two phase systems is prepared by mixing solutions of polyethylene glycol and dextran, or polyethylene glycol and specific salts (*i.e.* potassium phosphate or ammonium sulphate).

1. **First Step:** It is a two-phase separation process of enzyme in which enzyme remains in the upper PEG-rich phase.
2. **Second step:** In this stage the enzyme is found in the lower phosphate rich phase. The partitioning depends on the molecular weight and charge, the concentration and molecular weight of the polymers, the temperature, pH and ionic strength of the mixture, and the presence of polyvalent salts. This is an easier method to separate liquids of different density, than solids from liquids on large-scale. It is advantageous for large-scale enzyme purification.

Final Purification

Chromatography technique is the most widely used for the isolation of proteins. For large-scale isolation, all of the commonly used techniques may be employed. Low volume, adequate purity and high priced products of biotech pharmaceuticals are obtained by using this technique. The products should be isolated from a complex mixture of other protein.

Ultrafiltration method is also used for separation of abundant phosphate and PEG from enzyme. It lowers the ionic strength for the following batch wise adsorption to an ion-exchanger. Even after adsorption from ion-exchanger the enzyme solution have a relatively high ionic strength. For this purpose, hydrophobic chromatography is suitable.

After desorption by decreasing salt gradient the enzyme solution may be too diluted and must be concentrated before following get-filtration. Concentration may again be done by ultrafiltration or by precipitation with ammonium sulphate or an organic solvent, which permits further fractionation. Dye or affinity chromatography for may also be applied. For highest purity preparations electro focusing may followed as the final step.

PRODUCTION OF ENZYMES BY FERMENTATION

Fermentation-derived enzymes are produced mainly by variants of the solid substrate techniques which is suitable for filamentous fungi, and submerged fermentation in aerated stirred tanks for bacteria. The enzymes of microbial origin are the oxidoreductases and kinase. But majority of enzymes used on large-scale are simple hydrolases.

Oxidoreductases

Pyridine Nucleotide Dehydrogenases

It is mainly used for clinical diagnostics and other analytical applications. Conversion of oxidized and reduced forms of NAD and NADP could be detected by monitoring a change in the absorption at 340 nm. Redox enzymes with pyridine nucleotides as cofactors are used in chemical synthetic steps. The analytical applications used the enzymes from mammalian organs, although they may be supplemented by enzyme from microbial origin.

NAD/NADP Dehydrogenase

Most microbial enzymes are species for either NAD OR NADP. This class includes lactate dehydrogenases, malate dehydrogenases glutamate dehydrogenases and diaphoresis. The commercial lactate dehydrogenase is prepared from yeast and *Leuconostoc* species. The enzyme is used for determination of ADP, alanine aminotransferase, lactate, lecithin, creatine, pyruvate, pyruvate kinase and triglycerides. The commercial preparations for malate dehydrogenase is obtained from yeast, *Bacillus stearothermophilus*, and *Thermos thermophilus*. The enzyme is used for determination of asperate aminotransferase, and CO_2 in blood sample. The strain is cultivated on a glucose salt-yeast extract. Glutamate dehydrogenase enzyme is used in coupling reaction of urease with NAD/NADH system for determination of urea in blood samples.

Production of glycerol dehydrogenase: The enzyme is used for estimating triglycerides in blood samples. It is being produced from *Cellulomonas flavigena* and is cultivated on glycerol-polyptone-yeast extract-salts medium while *Candida valida* is cultured on glycerol and dihydroxyacetone as carbon source. Strains of *Geotrichum* and *Endomyces* utilize propane 1,2-diol, butan-1,2-diol, and acetone as carbon source. The carbon source is exhausted within 24 hrs.

Production of glucose dehydrogenase: This enzyme is used for determination of blood glucose. Fermentation is done by bacteria - *Bacillus megatherium*. Production of enzyme is during stationary phase in batch fermentation using glucose as substrate. The maximum rate of enzyme production occurs after initial utilization (5%) of glucose (*i.e.*, after 10 hrs) and persists for further 10 hrs.

Oxidases

Commercially, oxidases are used in analytical methods.

Production of Glucose Oxidase

Fungi like *Aspergillus niger* and *Penicillium* spp. are used for production of glucose oxidase through fermentation processes are developed to produce high levels of glucose oxidase and catalase. Concurrent production of catalase is advantageous to keep hydrogen peroxide concentration at low under conditions of use.

Small-scale Production: Presence of succinate, malate, asparate, glutamate or ammonium ions affects the rate of enzyme production. Ammonium ion inhibition can be reduced by production of asparate. The enzyme is extracted from mycelial cell by disruption. *Penicillium purpurogenum*, under optimum conditions secrete the enzyme in to the medium and gives maximum yield and requires a longer period of three days for production.

TABLE 27.2: Growth medium for small scale production of Glucose Oxidase

Sucrose (as carbon source) Beet molasses are also used	5%
Corn steep liquor	2%
Nitrogen source	Nitrates and urea
Temperature for inoculated media	28°C
Time	48 hours (Maximum production can be achieved within 16-20 hours)

Cholesterol Oxidase

The enzyme is used for determination of cholesterol in the blood sample. It is obtained from *Nocardia rhodochrous*. Cholesterol is required for the organism as an inducer for the synthesis of this enzyme. A poorer contact between cholesterol in the medium and the cell may result into a loss in the enzyme yield.

TABLE 27.3: Growth medium for small scale production (800 L fermenter) of cholesterol oxidase

Glycerol	6.g L^{-1}
Yeast extract	12 g.L^{-1}
Salts	
pH	6.7
Incubation temperature	29°C
Dissolved Oxygen Tension (DOT)	within the range of 35-50% saturation

The enzyme is harvested and can be released without cell disruption by washing with Triton X-100 (isoctylphenoxy-polythoxyethanol).

Hydrolases

Glycosidases

Bacterial α-amylases (α-1, 4-glucan glucanohydrolase): The enzyme is obtained from *Bacillus* species, *Pseudomonas saccharohiba* and *Clostridium* spp. using fermentation technique. It is carried out by the aerated submerged cultivation technique. *Bacillus licheniformis* and by *Bacillus stearothermophilus* produce highly thermostable enzymes. In stationary culture *B. subtilis* gives high yield. A careful balance of carbohydrate and nitrogen ingredients of the medium is vital. Concentration of nitrogen source (organic/inorganic) should be higher than necessarily required for growth of the organism. However, it should be combined with small amount of proteinaceous compounds.

Effect of Sugar (carbon source): Readily metabolizable sugar in the medium causes poor production during the growth phase and causes catabolite repression. Higher yields can be obtained by using glucose as carbon source than that of maltose. A high carbohydrate level in the medium stimulates protease production and decreases amylase production.

The pH of the medium should be maintained near neutrality. The incubation at 25-35°C has to be carried for 3-4 days.

Bacillus subtilis in stationary culture produces surface-pellicle growth and is associated with higher yield of amylase, therefore, sterile air should be circulated over the pellicle. At the time of harvest the culture can either be filtered or centrifuged and aqueous portion concentrated by evaporation, or amylase can be precipitated from aqueous solution by addition of acetone, ethanol, isopropanol or ammonium sulphate.

TABLE 27.4: Medium constituents, temperature, time duration, organisms and equipments used for bacterial α-amylases production

Media constituents	Temp.	Duration	Species	Type/Scale of equipment
Yeast extract Na_2HPO_4, NaCl, $CaCO_3$, and glycerol	55°C	20 hrs	*B. coagulans*	500 L. fermenter batch
Corn starch, peptone corn steep, liquor, salts	55-65°C	40-72 hr	*B. stearothermophilus*	Shake-flasks 50 ml culture
Barley, malt sprout, ammonium phosphate	30°C	40 hrs	*B. subtilis*	6-L. fermentation batch.
Potato starch, ground barley, soybean flour, Na_2SO_4, $CaCO_3$	30°C	144 hrs	*Bacillus licheniformis*	Shake-flask 100 hr culture

Fungal α-amylases: The enzyme produced from fungal source is low in thermal stability and the spectrum of sugars produced from the starch differs for fungal amylases. They yield maltose and some glucose.

It is mainly produced from *Aspergillus oryzae*, and *A. niger*. *A. oryzae* is universally used as the source for commercial fungal α-amylase. For commercial production of α-amylases from *A. oryzae* solid state fermentation is used while submerged fermentation technique is used for *A. niger*. This fungus grows on starchy-salt medium and produce other enzymes like amyloglucosidase. Wheat bran serves as basic component of the medium, and is spread in relatively thin layers in trays. It is moistened with water or dilute acid, sterilized, and inoculated with spores. After growth, the harvest can be dried at 50°C or less and then ground to liberate amylase. Amylase can also be extracted by water from wheat bran culture, precipitated by the addition of alcohol, and dried at 55°C or less.

β-amylase

The enzyme is produced from barley, malt or Soybean seeds. Bacteria like *Bacillus polymyxa* (starch-peptone-salt medium), *B. circulans*, *B. cereus* (in shake flasks), *B. cereus* var. *mycoides* (in 10 L fermenter) are used.

The gene responsible for β-amylase obtained from *B. cereus* has been cloned in *E. coli*. Recombinant DNA techniques have also been used to obtain the gene for enzyme on a plasmid suitable for cloning in *B. subtilis* using *E. coli* as intermediate host. A transformed *B. subtilis* strain can be grown in shake flasks at 30°C using a thinned starch, soya meal, sodium phosphate medium to produce 10-20 fold more.

Amyloglycosidase (Glucoamylase, α-1,4-glucan glucohydrolase): It is used for production of glucose and high fructose syrups from starch in conjunction with α-amylase and glucose isomerase. The enzyme occurs in various microorganisms like starch degrading molds (*Aspergillus*, *Mucor*, *Rhizopus*, *Endomyces* etc.) and in bacteria (*Aerobacter* and *Clostridium*). For commercial scale production of the enzyme utilizes fungi like *A. niger*, *A. awamori* and *A. foetidus*.

A. niger is used as the production strain in submerged cultivation. *Mucor* and *Rhizopus* are used in solid-substrate fermentation.

The submerged fermentation medium contains 12-20% organic matter. Maize, wheat, barley, rye or sorghum are used as starchy raw ingredients. The inorganic nitrogen source is ammonium salts. Removal of transglucosidases is important and can be achieved with range of techniques. Co-precipitation with maleic anhydride co-polymers and heteropoly acids are commercially employed for removal of transglucosidases.

Cellulase

Microorganisms like bacteria and fungi are cellulolytic in nature. Cellulase is commercially prepared from *Aspergillus niger*, *Trichoderma viridae*, *Neurospora* and some other organisms. *Trichoderma viridae* produces an enzyme which degrades insoluble cellulose.

Cellulase in fungi is an inducible enzyme and they produce cellulase when fungal cells are grown on cellulose, on glucan of mixed linkages including β-1,4 bond, and on few oligosaccharides. The inducing effect is due to cellobiose. It is the soluble hydrolysis product of cellulose. Other inducers are β-1,4 galactoside, saphorose, and β-1,2-glucoside. At low concentration (0.1%), cellobiose serves as an inducer of cellulose while at high concentration (0.5-1.0%) it represses cellulase formation, and it can also act as an inhibitor of cellulose action.

High yields of cellulase is obtained from *A. niger* using wheat bran tray method.

Trichoderma reesei produces cellulases when grown on a glucose carbon source, provided that appropriate trace elements and calcium are present. *Trichoderma reesei* in solid substrate cultures are able to produce more concentrated extracts than were submerged cultures, at 57% moisture. Continuous submerged cultures using *T. reesei* with a glucose medium in a 10 L fermenter, yields were higher at pH 3.0. Trace elements like iron, manganese, zinc and cobalt are needed for enzyme production but not for growth of *Trichoderma reesei*. The peptone, Tween, and cellulose concentrations are occasionally varied to a minor degree. Use of protein hydrolysate such as peptone enhances the production of cellulase. Tween 80 enhances the production of soluble cellulose.

During fermentation the pH value lower down from 5.7 to around 2.7. This occurs because ammonium ions uptake is followed by consumption of cellulose. For optimum growth and enzyme production pH regime should be at 3.5. For production inoculum needs 4-5 days. Concentration and purification of the enzyme is done using precipitation, adsorption or gel filtration techniques.

Proteolytic Enzymes

Proteinase enzymes are commercially important. The important proteinase enzymes are as follows:

Type	Source
Carboxyl proteinases (acid)	*Aspergillus* spp., *Mucor* spp., Calf stomach (rennin), Pig stomach (pepsin)
Metalloproteinases (Neutral)	*Bacillus thermoproteolyticus* (thermolysins), *Bacillus amloliquefaciens*, *Bacillus subtilis*, *Aspergillus* spp.
Serine proteinases (alkaline)	*Animal pancreas* (trypsin and chymotrypsin), *Bacillus licheniformis*, *Bacillus subtilis* and *Bacillus amyloliquefaciens*
Thiol proteinases	Papaya (papain), Pineapple (Bromelin)

Proteinases of Fungal Origin: The important protease producing fungi are *Aspergillus oryzae. A. sojae, A. niger. A wentii, Mucor pusillus, Mucor miehei, M. delemar* and *Amylomyces rouxii*. The fungus is grown on wheat bran under fermentation conditions similar to those for amylase production. At sporulation, proteolytic enzymes are present in the medium.

Microbial Rennin: Under laboratory condition and at low scale (2L-capacity fermenter) microbial rennin is obtained from *Endothia parasitica* strain. A 5% inoculum obtained from 96 hrs- shake flask stage is used for the production in a stirred, aerated (0.5 vvm) vessel for 48 hrs at 28°C.

TABLE 27.5: Composition of the medium for Inoculum development and for production of rennin by *E. parasitica*

Inoculum preparation	(per litre)
Casein hydrolysate	5.0 g
D. Mannitol	5.0 g
$FeSO_4.7H_2O$	15.0 g
Soluble starch	10.0 g
Soya protease digest	2.0 g
Trace elements	1.0 g
Yeast extract	2.0 g
Main fermentation	(per litre)
Glucose	10.0 g
KH_2PO_4	0.5 g
$MgSO_4.7H2O$	0.25 g
$NaNO_3$	3.0 g
Skin milk	10.0 g
Soybean meal	30.0 g

Solid substrate cultivation of *Aspergillus oryzae* and *A. sojae* are used for proteinases production which produce a mixture of enzymes containing acid aspartyl proteinase, neutral Metalloproteinases, and serine proteinase are produced. The optimum pH for activity should remain 4.0 to 5.0. In submerged culture, with nutrient broth, *A. oryzae* produce only serine proteinase. *A. niger* and closely related species with black spores often produce acid proteinase of the pepsin type. Proteases are recovered by procedures similar to those for mold amylases.

Proteases of Bacterial Origin: Bacterial strains like *Bacillus licheniformis*, *B. amyloliquefaciens* and *B. stearothermophilus* produce proteases enzyme. High yields could be obtained from *B. subtilis* if grown satisfactorily in culture. High carbohydrate level in the medium stimulate protease production and depresses amylase production. During fermentation, insoluble protein of the medium is first partially hydrolyzed by boiling in dilute acid/enzymatic treatment. pH of the medium should be kept neutral. Fermentation proceeds for 3-5 days at an incubation temperature of 37°C.

The biosynthesis of this enzyme is correlated with particular growth phases of the microbial culture. *Bacillus* spp. produces extracellular protease during post-experimental growth phase. The production of enzyme depends on exponential growth phase and medium composition. Catabolic repression by glucose declines proteinase production. Carbon source in the media is ground barley while source of nitrogen may be protein hydrolysates or sodium glutamate. The level of the starch level is limited.

For harvesting of enzyme, culture is filtered or centrifuged. The aqueous portion is concentrated using evaporation technique at reduced pressure and at temperature (not less than 40°C). Recovery can also be carried out by precipitation.

Penicillin Amidases (Penicillin Acylase)

The enzyme is used for preparation of 6-amino penicillanic acid (6APA) from naturally produced penicillin G or V. This compound is an important intermediate in the synthesis of semisynthetic penicillins.

TABLE 27.6: Types of penicillins produced by industrial fermentation

Source	Product	Fermenter	Grown on	Medium/L	Temperature
Bacteria (E. coli)	Penicillin G (phenyl acetyl 6-APA)	100 L aerated fermenter vessel	phenyl acetic acid and glutamate	KH_2PO_4, 3g; K_2HPO_4, 7g; $(NH_4)SO_4$, 1g; $MgSO_4.7H_2O$, 0.2 g; Phenyl acetic acid, 2 g and Sodium glutamate, 5 g.	30°C (8-10 hrs)
E. coli and Molds	penicillin V-amidases	25 L		Glucose, 30 g; KH_2PO_4, 1g; Yeast extract, 10 g; $MgCl_2.4H_2O$, 05 g; $Ca(NO_3)_2.4H_2O$, 0.5 g; and $FeSO_4$, 0.5 g.	27°C

Transferases

Glycosyl Transferases

Glycosyl transferases enzyme is used for manufacture of dextrans. It is used for medical and laboratory purpose.

Cyclodextrin Glycosyl Transferase

The sources of this enzyme are *Bacillus* spp., *Klebsiella pneumonia* and *Micrococcus varians*. The enzyme produces cyclic oligosaccharides from starch. A mixture of cyclodextrin containing hexamer, heptamer, octamer is produced. The preparations for these depends on the source of enzyme and the condition of the reaction.

TABLE 27.7: Medium for production of cyclodextrin glycosyl transferase

Compound	Concentration/L
$CaCO_3$	1.5 g.
Caseinhydrolysate	6 g
$FeSO_4.7H_2O$	0.25 g
KCl	0.5 g
KH_2P_4	1 g
$MgSO_4.7H_2O$	0.5 g
NH_4Cl	3g
Sodium citrate	0.5 g
Starch	16 g
Yeast extract	6 g

Strains in 200 ml culture were incubated for 12-24 hrs at 25°C. Static culture gave higher yields of activity than shaken cultures.

Glycerol Kinase

The enzyme is used for determination of triglycerides levels in blood samples. *E. coli*

K_{12}. *Candida mycoderma* are used for production of this enzyme at commercial level.

Medium: The medium for seed culture for production of glycerol kinase includes (in per L) Biotin (5 μg), $CaCl_2$ (0.1 g), $CuSO_4.5H_2O$ (1 mg), $FeSO_4.7H_2O$ (1 mg), Glycerol (90%) (9g), KCl (0.4g), $MgSO_4$ (0.1 g), $NH_4H_2PO_4$ (0.85 g), Vitamin B_{12} (0.1 mg), ZnSO4.7H_2O (1 mg), and pH (adjusted with ammonia solution 7.0. It should be held for 30-40 hrs at room temperature with aeration.

Glucose Isomerase

The enzyme is used to catalyses the isomerization of D-xylose to D-xylulose. Bacterial glucose isomerase reacts with D-glucose to product D(-)-fructose which is commercially used in the preparation of sweet syrups from starch hydrolysates. The enzyme is produced using strains of *Streptomyces flavogriseus*, *Streptomyces violaceus*, *S. olivochromogens*, *S. wedmorensis*, *Bacillus coagulans*, *B. stearothermophilus*, *B. licheniformis*, *Arthrobacter* spp. and *Actinoplanes missouriensis* etc. It is produced by submerged fermentation either in batch culture or in continuous culture. Most of the wild strains requires xylose as an inducer, as glucose cannot act as inducer.

Production of Glucose Isomerase using Bacillus coagulans

For laboratory scale production, continuous fermentation with different limiting nutrients are used with dual carbon-oxygen limitation. Catabolite repression regulates the production of glucose isomerase. Production in continuous culture is repressed in the presence of surplus carbon and inorganic growth limiting factors. In batch fermentation, growth on xylose, this strain produces enzyme during cell growth.

Medium: The medium for Glucose Isomerase production by *Bacillus coagulans* includes (in g/L) $(NH_4)_2SO_4$ (3.0), K_2HPO_4 (1.0), maize meal (80.0), $MgSO_4.H_2O$ (0.2), $MnSO_4.H_2O$ (0.05), xylose (4.0), and yeast extract (5.0). Initial pH should be maintained at 7.0. Culture in shake-flask (single stage) is incubated at 50°C for 40 hrs.

Production by Streptomyces wedmorensis

The enzyme is produced by *Streptomyces wedmorensis* when an inert suspended solid is added to the medium. Production-scale process with two 10% inoculum stages uses 5 m^3 of the medium in the main fermentation. Addition of 0.1% histidine to casein hydrolysate and yeast extract promotes enzyme production.

Medium: The medium for the production of glucose isomerase by *Streptomyces wedmorensis* (25 L fermenter for 2 stage inoculum) includes (in g/L) $COCl_2.6H_2O$ (0.24), corn steep liquor (40.0), wheat bran (40.0), time required (48 h), temperature (30 °C), and pH (7.0).

Purification: For purification of enzyme cell rapture (enzyme is intracellular) and solubilizing of preparations techniques are used. After removing the cellular material, the enzyme is then adsorbed on DEAE-cellulose, recovered and washed.

APPLICATIONS OF ENZYMES

Enzymes are proteins, biological or organic catalysts and are associated with metabolic reactions, respiration, the conversion and transfer of energy within living systems, and the formation of various macromolecules and cellular components. They exhibit specificity, therefore, used in pharmaceutical industries, in therapeutics and in clinical systems. At least 2,000 different enzymes are now known, each of them capable of catalyzing a specific reaction. Moreover, different cell types synthesize different types of enzymes – no cell contains all of the known enzymes. The specific enzymes produced by a cell are the major factors determining the biological activities and functions performed by that cell.

For thousands of years, processes such as brewing, bread making and production of cheeses have involved the use of enzymes. Enzymes of fungi and bacteria have a wide variety of industrial applications, including alcoholic beverages, food, detergents, and pharmaceuticals. In the production of alcoholic beverages, microbial amylase may be used instead of the enzyme from barley malt to prepare grains for fermentation. Protease can also chill proof beer by degrading the proteins that cause cloudiness in such beverages upon refrigeration. Enzymes are used in varied industrial sectors, consumer products, and scientific pursuits.

In past few years interest in various applications of enzymes have been developed because of greater understanding of the function and nature of enzymes and also advances involved in handling of these, particularly their immobilization. Most of the enzymes catalyze the reactions different from their inherent reactions as well as under special conditions, *i.e.*, hydrolases catalyze, transferase reactions and semi synthesis or transformation of antibiotics etc., carried out based on their non-physiological characteristics.

Applications of Enzymes in Pharmaceutical Industries

Enzymes possess multicatalytic functions. They are used for the synthesis of optically active amino acids. Enzymes demonstrate stereo specificity in catalysis.

Enzymes decarboxylases catalyze decarboxylation of L-amino acids and also stereo specific protonation of the formed amines. The synthetic route for preparation of cortisone is from stigmasterol, which chemically converts it into progesterone. Hydroxylation of progesterone is carried out by *Rhizopus nigaricus*. It yields II-α-hydroxy progesterone. Use of microbes in transformation of steroid is an important aspect of pharmaceutical industries. All the enzymatic reactions are based on fermentation technology.

Synthesis of Amino Acids

Enzymes are used for synthesis of optically active amino acids *e.g.*, D-amino acids, and their derivatives. A variety of procedures for the synthesis of amino acids and their derivatives with microbial enzymes have been developed. Mainly hydrolytic enzymes [*e.g.*, pyridoxal 5'-phosphate (pyridoxal-p)] are used. Pyridoxal-p dependent enzymes play the important role in amino acid metabolism because they catabolize transamination, decarboxylation, racemization, replacement, addition, elimination and a few other reactions of amino acids.

Synthesis of Nucleosides and Nucleotides

Enzymatic procedure for the production of inosine 5'-monosphate (IMP) and guanosine monophosphates (GMP) has been developed with 5'-phosphodiesterase nucleases. Similarly, a number of antibiotics, antiviral compounds, antineoplastic compound, immunosuppressors, coenzymes, and sugar containing nucleosides or nucleotides have also been synthesized. Currently, these nucleosides and nucleotides are produced by a salvage synthesis *i.e.*, microbial conversion of an intermediate synthesized chemically or enzymatically, by an enzymatic or chemical conversion of an intermediate produced by fermentation, or by direct fermentation.

Synthesis of other Compounds

Antibiotics: Penicillin acylase catalyzes the deacylation of benzyl penicillin to yield 6-aminopenicillanic acid phenyl acetic acid. The reaction is based on pH. At pH 7.5 the reaction proceeds while at pH 6.00 it becomes reverse. The industrial semi-synthesis or transformation of penicillins and cephalosporins is with an immobilized acylase. The enzyme is also used for the stereo specific acylation of intermediates in the chemical synthesis of β-lactam antibiotics.

Peptides and Proteins

1. **Peptides:** Different proteases and carboxypeptidases are employed for the peptide bonds *i.e.*, the conversion of porcine insulin to human insulin. Only carboxyl terminal amino acid is different in human and porcine insulin (*i.e.*, alanine for porcine and theonine for human insulins). The synthesis of human insulin from porcine insulin is carried out with a lysine specific protease enzyme of *Achromobacter lyticus*. Different proteases and carboxy peptidases are also used for the synthesis of pharmaceutically important peptides like trypsin (human insulin), *Achromobacter* protease I (human insulin), chymotrypsin (encephalin, caerulein) subtilisin (angiotensin), carboxypeptidases Y (human insulin, encephalin, caerulein), thermolysins (angiotensin, caerulein), and pepsin and fungal carboxypeptidases (eldocin, aerulein). Aspartame (L-aspartyl-L-phenylalanine methyl ester) is a dipeptide sweetener. The synthesis of the dipeptide with thermolysins immobilized on an ion exchange resin or by a microbial exopeptidase has also been developed.
2. **Proteins:** Peptidoglutaminases hydrolyze r-amide group of glutamine in glutaminyl-peptide converts it in to glutamate residue.
3. **Triglycerols (triglycerides):** Enzyme lipase produced by *Rhizopus delemar* converts olive oil to cacao butter-like oil.
4. **Cyclodextrin:** Cyclomaltodextrin glucanotransferase in starch medium synthesizes cyclodextrins in the presence of complex forming reagents such as acetone, sodium dodecyl sulphate, I-decanol.
5. **Dentifrice enzymes:** Dextranase hydrolyses dextran. This reaction is effective in reduction and protection of dental plaques and caries. They hydrolyze dextran to glucose and isomaltose at pH 5.5 with 55% hydrolytic efficiency.

Applications in Therapeutics

In some heritable human genetic disorders there remains deficiency or even a total absence of one or more enzymes in the diseased tissues, and under abnormal conditions there may be an excessive activity of a specific enzyme. These abnormalities are sometimes may be controlled by a drug designed to inhibit its catalytic activity. Some body enzymes are misses due to inborn errors of metabolism. Therefore, missed enzymes are replaced.

These enzymes are in solubilized form or immobilized on some substrate and may be given orally or injected or implicated in soft tissues as prosthesis.

For Treatment of Gaucher's, Tay-sach's, and Fabry's Diseases

Gaucher's, Tay-sach's, and Fabry's are hereditary diseases and are caused due to deficiency of enzymes and result into abnormal accumulation of materials that would otherwise broken down by missing enzymes.

Gaucher's disease (a lysosomal storage disease) occurs due to absence of enzyme glucocerebrosidase and leads to accumulation of glucocerebrosides in various tissues. If the enzyme is replaced in body, the symptoms may be relived in an individual.

Tay sach's disease is caused due to absence of enzyme hexose deaminase. The enzyme is usually present in the lysosomes of ganglion brain cells and removes the carbohydrate residues of the ganglioside lipids. If the ganglioside concentration in these cells accumulates, it affects the brain function and ultimately leads to the death of an individual.

Fauvism disease is caused due to lack of the enzyme *glucose-6-phosphate dehydrogenase* in the red blood cells. This affects the ability of cells to regenerate glutathione, which leads to membrane fragility and haemolytic anemia.

Not all the enzyme deficiency diseases require enzyme replacement. For treatment of such diseases offending substance should be removed from diet. For example, phenylketouria (PKU) is caused due to inability of body cell to metabolize phenylalanine, which results in the accumulation of toxic levels of phenylalanine and its abnormal metabolites. Other example are galactosemia (*galactose or galactose urydyltransferase*), Orotic aciduria (*orotidine-1-phosphate decarboxylases*) and arginosuccinuria (arginosuccine lyase) etc.

Uses of hydrolases or oxidase enzyme regenerating systems are also common for some enzyme replacement therapy. The inherited deficiency of *galactokinase* is cured by injecting coencapsulated galactokinase with ATP/ADP and pyruvate kinase. It initiates ATP generation system.

The treatment of malabsorption secondary to pancreatic insufficiency is caused by chronic pancreatitis, pancreatectomy and cystic fibrosis. The manifestation of pancreatic malabsorption is steatorrhea a voluminous malodorous stool laden with fat that is not being adsorbed. If the output of pancreatic lipase is less than 10% of normal, clinical steatorrhea will not occur, therefore, for the treatment of steatorrhea replacement of preparation lipase enzyme is essential.

For treatment of chronic pancreatitis and pancreatic fistulae, pancreatic enzymes (a mixture of *lipase*, *amylase* and *protease*) are used.

Treatment of acute lymphocytic leukemia, T-cell leukemias and lymphomas, is dependant totally or partially upon exogenous asparagines, which are enzymatic destructed enzyme asparaginase. It is injected into plasma. It arrests their growth and sometimes result in reduction of tumour mass.

Blood clots are dissolved in tissue by plasminogen activator (TPA). They convert plasminogen to plasmin. Plasmin enzyme breaks down protein fibrin which is the main component of blood clot.

Blood clots are dissolved by enzymes urokinase and streptokinase and both soluble fibrinogen and insoluble fibrin clots are destroyed. These enzymes activate plasmin.

Enzyme hyaluronidase hydrolyse hyaluronic acid and accelerates the subcutaneous spread of both particulate matter and solutions of depolymerising the hyaluronic acid. The enzyme is injected through drug.

Subtilins are proteolytic enzymes. They digest the denatured proteins present in necrotic tissues. These enzymes are used as adjunct for biochemical debridement of lesions of burns, decutibus ulcers, incisional traumatic and pyrogenic wounds, and ulcers secondary to peripheral vascular disease.

Burnt areas and dermal ulcers are cured with the help of enzyme collagenase. Papain is used in the debridement of necrotic tissues. Solution of crystallized trypsin is inhaled to liquefy viscous sputum.

Fibrin and liquefy pus are being cured with a mixture of fibrinolysin of bovine plasma and deoxy ribonuclease when used topically. It is obtained from bovine pancreas. The mixture is also used as debriding agent in surgical wound, ulcerative lesion and, second and third degree burns. It is also used intravaginally in severe cervicitis and vaginitis.

Clinical Analysis

Diseases are diagnosed by clinical analysis, which includes the measurement of activity of certain enzymes in the blood plasma, red blood cells, or tissues samples. Serum enzymes have their importance in clinical analysis. They are intracellular and elevated in hyperactivity diseases, malignancy or injury to cardiac, hepatic, pancreatic, muscle, bone and tissues. For identification of specific tissue involved in the disease is determined by the type of enzyme elevated. It is helpful for determinations and differentiation of various pathological conditions.

Transferases

Transfer of amino or phosphate group to another is catalyzed by enzymes transferases like aspartate aminotransferase and alanine aminotransferase. They are helpful in clinical diagnosis. Aspartate aminotransferase is found in liver, cardiac and skeletal muscles. It is elevated in myocardial infraction and Duchenne muscular dystrophy. Alanine aminotransferase is found in the liver tissues. The levels of both the enzymes increased during liver diseases, acute toxic or viral hepatitis, obstructive jaundice and hepatic cirrhosis. These enzymes catalyze the transfer of amino group from glutamic acid to keto acids (oxaloacetic or pyruvic) to form aspartic and α-ketoglutaric acid with Aspartate aminotransferase while alanine and α-ketoglutaric acid with alanine aminotransferase. These products are analyzed using colorimetric and spectrophotometric methods.

Ornithine Transcarbamylase

Ornithine transcarbamylase enzyme is involved in urea cycle in serum. It is used in the clinical investigation of the liver disease. The enzyme catalyses the conversion of ornithine to citruline. The normal serum value is 0 to 0.4 U/L.

Creatine Kinase

Creatine kinase (a transferase enzyme) present in the muscle and brain tissue. The enzyme catalyses the transfer of phosphate groups from creatine phosphate to adenosine diphosphate (ADP) and converted into adenosine triphosphate (ATP). Activated CK activity is observed by increase of ATP in the creatinine phosphate-ADP reaction in the presence of glutathione or cysteine thiol activators. Fluorimetric method is used for ATP determination. The enzyme is elevated in myocardial infraction and Duchenne muscular dystrophy. The level of enzyme remains normal in liver disease.

Oxidoreductases or Dehydrogenases

This group of enzyme catalyzes hydrogen transfer in cellular oxidation process. Lactic, α-hydroxybutyric, Malic, glutamic, isocitric, and sorbitol dehydrogenases are of diagnostic importance. Lactic dehydrogenases catalyzes the reversible conversion of pyruvic to lactic acid in the presence of NADH. The level of lactic dehydrogenases increases in hepatic disease, pernicious anemia and muscular dystrophy. Lactic dehydrogenases and Malic dehydrogenases phosphatases and leucine aminopeptidases are found in isoenzyme forms. Isoenzymes have similar substrate specificity but different biophysical properties. Malic and sorbitol dehydrogenases in the presence of NAD, catalyze the conversion of malate or sorbitol to oxaloacetate or fructose respectively. They are used for diagnostic importance in MI and acute liver injury.

Hydrolases

These enzymes catalyse the addition of elements water across the bond, which is cleaved. Hydrolases like amylases, lipases, phosphatases, 5-nucloetidase, γ-glutamyl transferase and leucine aminopeptidases are used for clinical purposes.

Salivary and pancreatic enzymes: These enzyme hydrolyze starch to maltose and dextrins. The activity of amylase is measured using method based on the loss in certain properties of starch or by the generation of reducing substances. Elevation in concentration is observed in acute pancreatic, acute abdominal conditions and salivary gland diseases.

Lipases: They catalyze the conversion of triglycerides to glycerol and fatty aids. Determination of serum lipase is used for the diagnosis of acute pancreatitis (10 fold increase), pancreatic injury or inflammation of organs contiguous to pancreas.

Phosphatases: They catalyze the hydrolysis of orthophosphoric esters, and are grouped into acid or alkalie phosphatases. Acid phosphatase is of first diagnostic value in metastatic carcinoma of prostate. Acid phosphatase activity (prostate enzyme) is investigated by using tartrate inhibitor.

5'-nucleotidase: It is an alkaline phosphomonoesterase. It hydrolyses nucleotides with a phosphate radical attached to 5'-position of the pentose (*i.e.* AMP). It is elevated in liver disorder.

Serum lysozyme (muramidase): The activity of this enzyme is increased in certain kinds of leukemia. Enzyme serum arginasea hydrolyses arginine to ornithine and urea, and serum guanase. They are sensitive indicators of hepatic necrosis.

Serum γ-glutamyl transferase: The activity and level of this enzyme is increased during diseases of liver, bile ducts and pancreas. Together with alkaline phosphatase, leucine aminopeptidases, and 5'-nucleopeptidase, serum γ-glutamyl transferase can be tested in the group of cholastasis-indicating enzymes. This method is based on the hydrolysis of γ-glutamyl-p-nitroanilide.

CHAPTER 28

Enzyme Immobilization

Microbes are, in many ways, packages of enzymes. The use of enzymes in industrial applications is limited because most of the enzymes are relatively unstable, of high cost isolation, purification, and recovery of active enzymes from the reaction mixtures after the completion of catalytic process. Due to these reasons, industries have been making limited use of free enzymes to manufacture many products such as high-fructose syrups or semisynthetic antibiotics such as ampicillin. To do this, the *enzyme must be immobilized on the surface of some solid support or otherwise manipulated so that it can convert a continuous flow of substrate to product without being lost.* These techniques have also been adapted to live whole cells, and sometimes even to dead cells. Whole cell systems are difficult to aerate, and they lack the single-enzyme specificity of immobilized enzymes. However, whole cells are advantageous if the process requires a series of steps that can be carried out by one microbe's enzymes. They also have the advantage of allowing continuously running processes with large cell populations operating at high reaction rates. Immobilized cells, which are usually anchored to microscopically small spheres or fibers, are presently used to make high-fructose syrups, aspartic acid, and numerous other products of biotechnology.

IMPORTANT FEATURES ENZYME IMMOBILIZATION

1. Enzyme immobilization involves confining soluble protein catalysts, or individual buoyancy of cells in a reactor system, which the charge is allowed to pass continuously.
2. Enzyme immobilization is used in development of biosensor, bioelectronics sensor in fermentation technology as well as enzyme therapeutics.
3. Enzyme immobilization is utilized in anchoring on the surface phase however, may be in the form of fine particulate, membranous or monolithic spheres.
4. Enzyme in turn may be bound to another enzyme via cross-linking. Thus, rendering the overall composite to be an insoluble, but polymeric enzyme system.
5. It implies for restrictive localization of enzymes.
6. The immobilization is obtained via covalent coupling employing adsorption or physical entrapment of enzymes within the enzymes phase (polymeric matrix).
7. The nature of immobilized enzyme is characteristically dependent upon the character of matrix and enzyme phase.

Disadvantages of Enzymes

1. The use of enzymes in industrial applications is limited.
2. The enzymes are relatively unstable and are rapidly inactivated by heat.
3. One has to pay high cost for isolation, purification, and recovery of active enzymes from the reaction mixtures after the completion of catalytic process.
4. For soluble enzymes in batch operations is uneconomical because active enzyme

is lost after each reaction.

Advantages of immobilized Enzymes

1. The above disadvantages could be overcome using immobilized enzymes.
2. Immobilized enzymes are physically confined during a continuous catalytic process.
3. Immobilized enzymes could be recovered from the reaction mixture and used over and over again, thus improving the economy of the process.
4. Immobilized enzymes have advantages over their soluble counterparts and can be reused.
5. They can be operated continuously and can be readily controlled.
6. The products can be easily separated and enzyme properties (activity and stability) can be altered favourably.

Properties of Immobilized Enzymes

Enzymes can be used in best form if we best understand the changes, which occur after immobilization, mainly in their physical and chemical properties. In such enzymes, changes occur in their stability and kinetic properties because of the microenvironment imposed upon them by the supporting matrix and by the products of their own action.

Stability

During insolubilization enzymes coupled to inorganic carriers were generally more stable than those attached to organic polymers when stored at 4 to 23 ° centigrade. The stability of the enzymes might be expected to either increase or decrease on insolubilization, depending on whether the carrier provides a microenvironment capable of denaturing the enzymic protein or of stabilizing it. Isolating the enzyme molecules from mutual attack by immobilizing them on a matrix reduces inactivation due to autodigestion of proteolytic enzymes. Stability to denaturing agents sometimes changes upon insolubilization.

Kinetic Properties

Kinetic properties generally decreased in specific activity of an enzyme upon insolubilization. It can be attributed to denaturation of the enzymic protein caused by the coupling process. After insolubilization of an enzyme it finds itself in a microenvironment, which may be drastically different from that existing in free solution. The new microenvironment may be a result of the physical and chemical character of the support matrix alone, or it may result from interactions of the matrix with substrates or products involved in the enzymatic reaction.

The Michaelis constant is decrease by more than one order of magnitude when substrate of opposite charge to the carrier matrix is used. This happens at low ionic strengths, and when neutral substrates are used.

The diffusion of substrate from the bulk solution to the microenvironment of an immobilized enzyme can limit the rate of the enzyme reaction. The rate at which substrate passes over the insoluble particle affects the thickness of the diffusion film, which in turn determines the concentration of substrate in the vicinity of the enzyme and hence the rate of reaction. Diffusion of large molecules is also limited by stearic interactions with the matrix. This reflects the relative activity of bound enzymes towards high molecular weight substrates. It is usually found to be lower than towards low molecular weight substrates. This, however, may be an advantage in some cases, since the immobilized enzymes may be protected from attack by large inhibitor molecules.

Types/Methods of Immobilization

The methods of immobilization fall into four main categories (1) Physical adsorption onto an inert carrier, (2) Inclusion in the lattices of a polymerized gel, (3) Cross-linking of the protein with a bifunctional reagent, and (4) Covalent binding to a reactive insoluble support.

These methods depend upon physical relationship of the catalyst to the matrix (carrier). The selected matrix must enhance the operational stability of the immobilized enzyme purification. The carriers used for this purpose may be porous or nonporous materials with organic (natural or synthetic) or inorganic nature. The catalyst may be covalently bonded to the polymer, physically adsorbed onto the polymer, cross-linked with itself and possibly another inert protein, entrapped inside a polymer matrix or encapsulated in a polymer bag.

Adsorption: Adsorption is the oldest of techniques used to immobilize enzymes, dating back to 1916 when Nelson and Griffin used both charcoal and aluminium hydroxide to adsorb invertase. Since that time wide range of organic and inorganic substances have been utilized as supporters for adsorbed enzyme. Both organic materials such as charcoal, various cellulose derivatives, and ion exchange resins and inorganic materials including silica, alumina, titania, glass and various naturally occurring minerals have been used.

Physical adsorption of an enzyme onto a solid is the simplest way of preparing immobilized enzymes. The method depends on non-specific physical interaction between the enzyme protein and the surface of the matrix, brought about by mixing a concentrated solution of enzyme with the solid. Various types of compounds are used for adsorption like calcium phosphate (α-amylase), charcoal (catalase), cellophane - followed cross-linking with glutaraldehyde, inorganic adsorbents-(glucose oxidase), charcoal and DEAE-sephadex (invertase), agarose gel, DEAE-sephadex (amyloglucosidase) and cellulose (subtilisin).

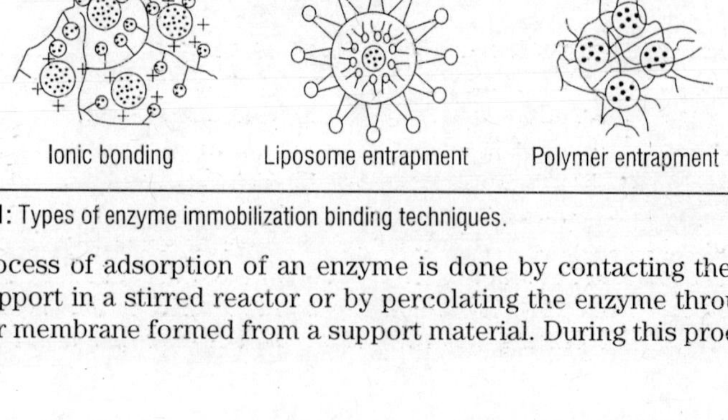

FIGURE 28.1: Types of enzyme immobilization binding techniques.

The process of adsorption of an enzyme is done by contacting the enzyme and polymer support in a stirred reactor or by percolating the enzyme through a packed bed, tube or membrane formed from a support material. During this process different specific and non-specific forces are applied *e.g.*, electrostatic, hydrophobic interactions or affinity bonding to specific legends attached to the matrix. The amount of enzyme, which is adsorbed is dependent on the concentration to the unit surface of the carrier and the activity increases with increasing concentration of enzyme which approaches to a saturation value, with decrease of the specific activity. The procedure includes the mixing of enzyme under suitable conditions like pH, nature of the solvent, ionic strength, concentration of the enzyme and adsorbent, and temperature.

Since no reactive forces are involved in the process therefore, there are no conformational changes in the enzymes on immobilization. Alumina, activated carbon (charcoal), clays, collagen, glass diatomaceous earth, Hydroxyapatite, cellulose metal oxides and various siliceous materials are commonly used adsorbents.

Physical adsorption of enzymes is the hydrophobic interactions. The adsorption is based on both ionic and hydrophobic attractive forces. Because of the weak bonds involved, desorption of the protein is dependent on changes in temperature, pH, ionic strength or even the mere presence of substrate.

Advantage of adsorption: For insolubilizing enzymes no reagents are required. Only minimum of activation steps are needed. Adsorption is cheap, easily carried out. It tends to be less disruptive to the enzymic protein than chemical means of attachment, the binding being mainly by hydrogen bonds, multiple salt linkages, and Van der Wall's forces.

Occlusion: Occlusion involves no disruption of the protein molecules. Confining enzymes within the lattices of polymerized gels method is used for enzyme immobilization. The free radicals generated on the course of the polymerization may affect the activity of entrapped enzymes. In this process, only low molecular weight substrates can diffuse rapidly to the enzyme. Therefore, this method is unsuitable for enzymes, which act on macromolecular substrates, such as ribonuclease, trypsin, Dextranase, etc. This is the disadvantage.

Occlusion allows the free diffusion of low molecular weight substrates and reaction products. The method is based on polymerization of hydrophilic matrix in an aqueous solution of the enzyme and break up the polymeric mass to the desired particle size. In this process, there is no bond formation between the enzyme and the polymer matrix.

Polyacrylamide gel has pores and the broad distribution in pore size of synthetic gels of the polyacrylamide type inevitably results in leakage of the entrapped enzyme, even after prolonged washing. This disadvantage may be overcome by cross-linking the entrapped protein with glutaraldehyde. Sometimes, ultrafiltration membranes of well-defined pore size may be used to occlude the enzyme is also used.

Cross-Linking: Intermolecular cross-linking of the protein is another method for enzyme immobilization. Since the enzyme is covalently linked to the support matrix, very little desorption is likely using this method. It is achieved by intermolecular cross-linking of the protein, either to other protein molecules or to functional groups on an insoluble support matrix. Cross-linking an enzyme is expensive and insufficient, because as some of the protein material inevitably acts mainly as a support which results in relatively low enzymic activity. The method of cross-linking is best used in conjunction with one of the other methods. This helps to prevent the leakage from polyacrylamide gels as mentioned earlier. It is used more widely as a means of stabilizing adsorbed enzymes. For example, it is reported that carbamyl phosphokinase cross-linked to alkyl amine glass with glutaraldehyde lost only 16% of its activity after continuous use in a column at room temperature for fourteen days.

Covalent Binding: It is the common method used for enzyme insolubilization. Enzymes are made of chains of amino acids and have number of reactive side chains, which can be utilized for forming chemical bonds with appropriately active support. The technique includes the formation of covalent bonds between the enzyme and the support matrix. For selection of type of reaction through which a given protein is insolubilized, the choice remains limited because the binding reaction is performed under conditions, which do not cause loss of activity of enzyme. In this method the active site of the enzyme should be unaffected by the reagents used.

Covalent bonding has an advantage of an attachment not reversed by pH, ionic strength or substrate. However, the active site of an enzyme may be blocked through the chemical reaction and the enzyme rendered inactive.

The various groups of enzyme that take part in the formation of chemical bonds are amino, imino, amide hydroxyl, carboxyl, thiol, methylthiol, guanidyl, imidazole and phenol ring. The functional groups of proteins are used for covalent binding under mild conditions. The important functional groups are: (i) the alpha amino groups of the chain and the epsilon amino groups of lysine and arginine, (ii) the alpha carboxyl group of the chain end and the beta and gamma carboxyl groups of aspartic and glutamic acids, (iii) the phenol ring of tyrosine, (iv) the thiol group of cysteine, (v) the hydroxyl groups of serine and theonine, (vi) the imidazole group of histidine, and (vii) the indole group of tryptophan.

The activated polymers used are hydro gels incorporated with diazo, carbodimide or azide groups.

TABLE 28.1: Covalent coupling. Binding agent or reagents, enzyme and carrier matrix used for enzymes immobilization

Binding agent/Reaction	Enzyme	Carrier Matrix
Direct coupling	α-Amylase	DEAE-cellulose
Cyanuric chloride	Amyloglycosidase	DEAE-cellulose
Isocyanate	Cellulose	Polyurethane
Isocyanate	Glucose isomerase	Polyurethane
Isothiocyanate	Glucose oxidase	Porous glass
Isocyanate	Pectinase	Polyurethane
Carbodiie activation	Pronase	CM-Sephadex

The above table shows that the process needs number of reactions to couple with functional groups on the protein other than the amino and phenolic residues. Coupling of amino ethyl cellulose to the carboxylic acid residues of enzymic protein in carried out in presence of carbodiimide and thiol residues of a protein. It is oxidatively coupled to the thiol groups of a cross-linked copolymer of acrylamide and N-acryloyl-cystein. Increased number of reactive residues of an enzyme may increase yield of insolubilized enzyme. The alternative reaction sites are essential for activity of an enzyme. The wide variety of binding reactions, and insoluble carriers with functional groups capable of covalent coupling, or being activated to give such groups, makes this a generally applicable method of insolubilization, even if very little is known about the protein structure or active site of the enzyme to be coupled.

Entrapment: The term entrapment has been used to cover a range of immobilization techniques. O'Driscoll (1976) has chosen to distinguish between those methods, where a gel or membrane is formed around enzyme by polymerization and those methods where the enzyme is retained in a preformed polymer by subsequent formation of a cross-linked network. Microencapsulation and fiber entrapment are clearly other examples of this immobilization technique. Hollow fiber and membrane devices have also been used to retain enzymes in given location without actually binding enzyme to a support material.

The technique is based on coupling enzymes to the lattice of a polymer matrix or enclosing them in semipermeable membranes. It prevents the release of proteins while allowing the diffusion of substrates and products. In this method the enzyme itself does not bind to the membrane or gel matrix, and there is a little inactivation of the biological activity as compared with the coupling method. The active sites of enzyme molecules are not blocked by chemical bonds and enzyme remains in its native state.

This method is easy to perform. The enzymes are dissolved in a solution of the polymers precursors. The polymers may be polyacrylamide gels or natural gels (cellulose triacetate, agar, gelatin or alginate). To prevent the leakage of the low molecular weight enzymes from the gel, the average pore size of the gel should be as high as possible. The excessive diffusion limitation variability of pore size has to be controlled.

Advantages: That allows high local concentration of enzymes. Enzymes can be contained without any chemical modification or bonding that may lead to activity loss. Multiple enzyme systems can be handled readily since entrapment is essentially the method living cells to retain their enzyme systems.

Disadvantages: (1) Polyacrylamide gel is used with sensitive enzymes of viable cells. (2) The free radicals generated during the course of polymerization are toxic. (3) Agar and carragenin can be depolymerized by mild heat. (4) For viable cells calcium alginate is the suitable gel for immobilization.

Penicillin acylase is fibre entrapped enzymes. It is immobilized by entrapment in the micro cavities of synthetic fibres. The physical entrapment is carried out by dissolving a fibre forming polymer (cellulose triacetate) in an organic solvent immiscible in water and emulsifying this solution with aqueous solution of enzyme. The emulsion is extruded through a spinneret into liquid coagulant (toluene or petroleum ether) that precipitate the polymer in a filamentous form, with a micro droplet of enzyme solution entrapped in the fibre. This method is helpful in reducing the diffusion limitation.

Encapsulation: Encapsulation provides large surface area to enzyme to contact with the substrate. This method is useful because several enzymes can be immobilized in a single step. Enzymes are immobilized within microcapsules. These are prepared from organic polymers. The membranes encloses the enzyme and remain semipermeable to the substrate and the products. This is an easy and economic technique. The stability of the biocatalyst in solution is an important aspect of this technique. This method is not applicable for high molecular weight substrates. Occasionally inactivation of enzyme occurs during immobilization procedure, and the enzyme may become incorporated into membrane wall. Leakage of enzyme takes place through microcapsule. Using this technique, capsules of suitable size can be obtained. The diffusion limitation is also controlled. Capsules are made from ethyl cellulose nitrocellulose, polystyrene, polyvinyl acetate, polyamine glycol, polyethylene etc. A variant of this technique is the entrapment of enzyme solution in the lumen of hollow, semipermeable fibres.

Choice of Immobilization Method

Immobilization is the method in which surface of the enzyme are attached with reactive groups outside the active catalytic and binding site. It is necessary to know the active sites of particular enzymes. It helps to select and avoid reaction with the essential groups therein. Alternatively, these active sites can be protected during attachment as long as the protective groups can be removed without loss of enzyme activity. Sometimes, this protective function can be fulfilled by a substrate of the enzyme or a competitive inhibitor; this also contributes towards retention of tertiary structure of the enzyme.

Type of method	Characteristics
Physical adsorption and ionic bonding	It is prepared easily under mild conditions. Any variations in the ionic strength or pH of the solution, due to weak binding forces between the enzyme and matrix, results into leakage of the enzyme from the matrix. Helpful to retain initial high activity and low operational stability.
Intermolecular cross-linkage and covalent binding	It is the chemical modification of the enzyme. It results into conformational changes of its structure and partial loss in activity. To minimize these problems, reactions should be carried out under suitable possible conditions. The operational stability of such immobilized enzymes high.
Entrapment method possess	Enzymes immobilized by this method have high retention of specific activity because there is no binding between enzyme and carrier. The technique is limited to the use of low molecular weight substrates and product molecules because strong mass transfer resistance is imposed by the entrapping polymer or membrane.

The surface on which the enzyme is immobilized plays several following vital roles:

1. Retaining of tertiary structure in the enzyme by hydrogen bonding or the formation of electron transition complexes.
2. Retention of tertiary structure may also be a vital factor in maximizing thermal stability in the immobilized state. Therefore, it is essential to have knowledge about new findings in the chemical nature of soluble thermostable enzymes.
3. The microenvironment of surface and the immobilized enzyme has an anionic or cationic nature of the surface, which causes displacement in the optimum pH of the enzyme up to 2 pH units. This may be accompanied by general broadening of the pH region in which the enzyme can work effectively.

Comparison and Evaluation of Immobilization Techniques

The choice of the methods depends on the characteristics of the enzymes and their substrates including. It should be of low cost and effective. Efficient immobilization of enzymes can be achieved by combination of methods *i.e.*, adsorption followed by cross-linkage. Each technique has specific limitations.

Effects of Immobilization on Kinetics and Properties of Enzyme

The immobilization process changes catalysts from homogenous (soluble enzyme) nature to heterogeneous one, in which enzyme is associated with a supporting or enveloping matrix. During immobilization, the activity of the enzyme is usually lost because of the reactions involved in the process or by occlusion of active sites in the enzyme support complex.

After immobilization of the enzyme there occurs many changes due to the physical and chemical nature of the carrier used, and the conformational changes in the enzyme structure. These changes result into conversion of catalysts to heterogenous nature with significant change in its properties. The reactivity of enzyme also changes because of actively stability, pH and temperature optimum, kinetic constants (resulting from a change in activation energy) and substrate specificity.

Michaelis Constant

Michaelis constant (Km) is increased or decreased after enzyme immobilization. The determination of Km value reflects the affinity between enzyme and substrate. A decrease in the Km value of an immobilized enzyme increases rate of reaction than its soluble native form. Conversely, an increased Km value implies the use of higher substrate concentration to accomplish the same rate of reaction obtained with the free enzymes. The apparent Km value lowers down when the charges on the support and substrate are opposite. The decrease can be attributed to partition effects due to an increase in the electrostatic attractive forces between the carrier and the substrate. It leads to an increase in the concentration of the substrate in the microenvironment of the immobilized enzyme. Km value also decreases when internal and external diffusional effects are present under the operational conditions applied.

TABLE 28.2: Types of diffusion effects

External diffusion	Limited due to an unstirred layer (the Nernst layer) around the particles of an enzyme.
Internal or pore diffusion	It is caused by substrate having to diffuse through the support matrix. It is significant when enzyme is immobilized by binding on porous supports and in entrapping techniques.

Km value increases when conformational changes of the enzymes protein molecule and the interaction of the substrate with the enzyme occur. It is affected by stearic hindrance. These effects are pronounced in the covalent binding techniques because enzyme molecules are chemically modified.

Maximum Reaction Velocity (Vmax)

The maximum reaction velocity of an immobilized and normal enzyme remains almost same. The Vmax value for an immobilized glucoamylase in the presence of maltose (as substrate) is 10 times more than the native enzyme. For gel-entrapped β-D-fructofuranocidase, the Vmax is 10 times lower than the free enzyme. The effectiveness depends on enzyme activity and diffusion limitation during immobilization.

pH Activity: Immobilization of enzyme causes changes in pH profile and depends on the charges of the enzyme molecule. In the support binding method, when the matrix is charged, the kinetic behaviour of the immobilized enzyme vary from that of the free enzyme. This difference occurs due to partition effects that cause different concentrations of charged species (*e.g.*, substrates, products hydrogen ion, hydroxyl ions etc.) in the microenvironment of the immobilized enzyme and in the bulk solution, due to electrostatic interactions with fixed charges on the support.

Presence of H^+ ions has pronounced effect on the enzyme activity. It depends on whether the initial pH is above or below the pH optimum. Substrate diffusion limitation also affects the response of an enzyme reaction rate and the response of an enzyme to change in pH.

Temperature: Enzyme has a temperature optimum. It is active only in narrow range of temperatures. Beyond this optimum enzyme is rapidly denatured and inactivated. The enzymes remain viable between 30°C and 80°C. Enzyme activity as a function of temperature may be expressed using Arrhenius equation.

$$k = A_e\ H/RT$$

Where, k = reaction rate, T = absolute temperature, A = arrhenius constant, H = activation energy and R = gas constant.

Diffusional effects in case of entrapment and binding on porous supports, protects enzyme against heats denaturation. Therefore, the optimum temperature of the enzyme becomes higher than that of the native enzymes. The diffusional effects, which protect the enzyme against heat denaturation lead to both lower activation and deactivation energies.

Stability: Stability is the retention of activity for a longer periods under suitable conditions of storage and depends on the nature of the carrier surface to which it is bound. The prevention of conformational inactivation or protection of active groups on enzymes from reactive groups in solutions enhances the stability of immobilized enzymes. During operating conditions, the activity of enzymes is lost due to enzyme denaturation and physical loss from the carrier. Loss from matrix may be either as a result of carrier erosion or from breaking of bonds between enzyme and carrier or from gel entrapment matrix. Covalent coupling leads to stable preparations, while with weakly bound, physical adsorbed, or ionic bound enzymes the activity is lost into solution depending on temperature, pH, ionic strength and physical operating conditions.

Stability is also dependent on the type of reactor used. Abrasion or attrition may cause loss of activity for enzymes immobilized on organic support. Microbial contamination also causes loss of enzyme activity under operating conditions. Loss of activity of immobilized enzymes is diffusion limited.

Stability of immobilized enzyme is also affected by pH. Partition effects enhance pH stability. Stability enhances on alkaline side, when immobilized on polyanionic supports and on acid side if it were on polycationic support.

Heat stability is enhanced by covalent-coupling and entrapment methods, while it is decline in physical adsorption or ionic linking methods. An increase in the storage stability for enzyme by covalent coupling is usually at low temperatures (40°C).

Immobilization Techniques for Cells

Cell immobilization methods are the extensions and modifications of techniques developed for immobilization of enzymes. These include cross-linking, copolymerization, covalent binding and particularly entrapment. Following are the methods of cell immobilization.

Cross-linking

Cells walls of microbes contain free amino or carboxyl groups, which can be cross-linked by a bi or multifunctional reagents. These are glutaraldehyde or toluene diisocyanate. Cells are also immobilized by ionic cross-linking through a flocculation mechanism by addition of poly-electrolyte. The method is also employed in combination with entrapment techniques as an additional cell fixing and gel stabilizing procedure.

Copolymerization

This method is the extension of cross-linking method. The method involves the use of an inert *spacer* (gelatin, albumin or polyethylenimine), which is added to the cell suspension before cross-linking with glutaraldehyde. This results in biocatalyst with cells entrapped in a covalent network.

Covalent Binding

Covalent binding is the linkage of biocatalyst to the carrier through reactive groups on the matrix. The coupling agents like glutaraldehyde, diisocyanate, aminosilane, carbodiimide are used to introduce a space group on the carrier surface. This subsequently can interact with reactive groups on cell surface.

Adsorption

A suitable adsorbents displaying high affinity towards biocatalyst causes minimal denaturation are used for this purpose. The adsorption is an electrostatic interaction between the charged support and charged cell and is dependent on the chemical nature cell wall. It provides the ionic sites for attachment to a charged support. Carrier, and biocatalyst remain together through van-der-walls bonding forces, inorganic bonds or H-bridges.

Entrapment

For physical entrapment techniques, plastic polymers are used. By pectin and carrageenan additional partial covalent bonds are formed between the cell and the support. Polyacrylamide involving a free radical polymerization results in damage to the cells. The technique is associated with a diffusion limitation. Rate of cellular enzyme system is declined. The permeability barriers imposed by cell membrane can be reduced by controlled autolysis, lyophilization, drying or freezing of cells, or by treatment of the cells with toluene or surfactants. Physical entrapment affects the cell viability, however, it conserves enzyme activity.

SELECTION OF SUITABLE STRAINS AND MUTANTS OF MICROORGANISMS

Bacillus and *Aspergillus* as Enzyme Sources

Microorganisms are very convenient enzyme sources, because the enzyme concentrations may be markedly increased by acting on environmental conditions and genetic manipulations. They also have rapid growth rate on inexpensive media. The selection of suitable microbial strain as a source of enzyme is dependent on the fact, that the organism must give high yields of enzyme in shortest possible fermentation time. Extracellular enzymes are usually preferred, because their isolation is relatively simple and expensive processes for disintegrating the cells and can be avoided. The enzyme producing strain should not produce any toxic substances and antibiotics on the medium. Most of the technical enzymes are obtained from two genera, namely *Bacillus* and *Aspergillus*. The α-amylase from these genera have substituted those of malted wheat and barley in brewing, backing, biscuits-making, and in textile industry.

The strains of *Bacillus* are selected from the mutants, not from the spores. In case of *Aspergillus*, cultures are frequently inoculated with conidia, and great value is placed on good spore formation. In enzyme production industry, improvement of the microbial strains is a permanent feature, because most of the microorganisms are not very well investigated genetically. However, genetic engineering is expected to play a major role in the future. During the strain improvement programme for enzyme production following aspects should be taken into following considerations:

1. Mutants that produce the enzyme constitutively, that is without an inductor.
2. The production of the desired enzyme in the mutants is not inhibited by the repressors.
3. The yield of the enzyme is considerably increased by multiplication of the gene copies.

Nutrient Media for Enzyme Production

The nutrient media for enzyme production may be composed of synthetic or natural raw materials. The synthetic media are cheaper and are more effective if demands for trace substances are not adequately known. Every medium should contain carbon, energy, nitrogen sources along with the necessary mineral substances and growth factors when auxotrophic microorganisms are used. For the production of inducible enzymes, the medium must contain the inductor. All care should be taken to avoid the substance that cause repression of enzyme production. The important inductor substances are, for example, starch for amylase, urea for urease, and xylose for xylose isomerase. Coenzymes may also have inductive effects. Thus, thiamine increases the production of pyruvate carboxylase.

APPLICATIONS OF MICROBIAL ENZYMES

Enzymes are used in agricultural industries like food industry, post harvest storage, storage after processing, determining and describing the genetic diversity of plant and animal genomes, in developing new plants, and in the control of pest and pathogens. The important applications of enzymes in agriculture are as follows:

TABLE 28.3: Areas of industrial use of microorganisms, and of application of major enzymes from microbes (main microbial species)

Industrial uses	Microorganisms
Alcoholic Fermentation	Bear (Saccharomyces cerevisiae, S. carlsbergensis, S. uvarum), cider (S. cidri), wine (S. cerevisiae), sake (Aspergillus oryzae, Lactobacillus and Leuconostoc spp., S. cerevisiae) and other fermentations of fruit juices, distilled sprits, etc.
Amino acids, mononucleotides	Corynebacterium glutamicum
Baker's yeast	Saccharomyces cerevisiae; Candida milleri
Caratenoids	β-carotene: Blakeslea trispora; astaxanthin: Phaffia rhodozyma
Dextrans	Leuconostoc mesenteroides, levans, mannans; xanthans (Xanthomonas campestris).
Ethanol	Kluyveromyces fragilis, S. cerevisiae, Zymomonas mobilis) n-butanol and acetone (Clostridium acetobutylicum, C. saccharoacetobutylicum); acetic acid (Acetobacterium woodii, Clostridium aceticum) citric acid (Aspergillus niger, Saccharomycopsis lipolytica).
Fodder yeast	Candida utilis, Saccharomycopsis lipolytica
Fumaric and lactic acids	Lactobacillus delbrueckii
Gibberellins	Gibberella fujikuroi and other plant growth hormones
Production of antibiotics	Penicillins (Penicillium chrysogenum), cephalosporins (Cephalosporium

Industrial uses	Microorganisms
	acremonium), streptomycin, kanamycins, neomycins, tetracyclines, etc. (Strptomyces spp.), gramicidin-S (Bacillus brevis), polymyxin-B (Bacillus polymyxa), bacitracin (Bacillus subtilis)
Production of Fermented Beverages and Foods	Dried bonito, soyasauce (Aspergillus oryzae, Pediococcus soyae, Saccharomyces rouxii, Torulopsis spp.), vinegar (Gluconobacter suboxidans), pickled vegetables, cheeses (Penicillium camembertii, P. roqueforti, Propionibacterium shermanii, Streptococcus spp.), yoghurt (Lactobacillus bulgaricus, Streptococcus thermophilus), lactic acid (sour) drinks.
Single-cell proteins	Spirulinas, Chlorellas, and other unicellular algae; (Methylophilus methylotrophus, Candida tropicalis, C. utilis, Saccharomycopsis lipolytica).
Steroids	Arthrobacter simplex, Mycobacterium sp., Rhizopus arrhizus, R. nigricans.
Vaccine and microbial bioinsecticides	Bacillus popilliae, B. thuringiensis
Vitamins	Rriboflavin: Eremothecium ashbyi; Vitamin B_{12}: Propionibacterium sp., Pseudomonas denitrificans).
Abatement of pollution	Treatment of industrial effluents, waste waters, disposal of wastes and garbage; recovery and reuse of biodegradable wastes. Microbial leaching of ores and recovery of mining and colliery wastes.

There are about 3000 enzymes known and only few are manufactured at large scale. These enzymes are mainly extracellular hydrolytic enzymes which have the property to degrade naturally occurring polymers for example starch, proteins, pectins, and cellulose. Enzyme glucose isomerase is, however, an exception in this regard.

Enzymes are the directing and controlling biocatalysts present in all living matter which determine a particular chemical reaction. They accelerate the course of chemical reactions by several orders through a substantial decrease in the activation energy. The catalytic activity of the enzyme secreted by the cells or isolated from them is maintained under suitable conditions and permits the use of these enzymes as catalysts outside the cells.

1. Mutants that produce the enzyme constitutively, that is without an inductor;
2. The production of the desired enzyme in the mutants is not inhibited by repressors; and
3. The yield of enzyme is considerably increased by multiplication of the gene copies, and/or changes in the single sequences proceeding the structural gene to bring about high expression.

CHAPTER 29

Industrial Fermentation Technology

According to need of the industry varying environment requirement, and types of product various kinds of industrial fermenters have been developed and designed. They provide optimum growth and metabolism of industrial processed strains for production of quantities of commercially desired product. Fermenter maintains: aerobic/anaerobic conditions, temperature at the desired level, culture in pure state throughout the process to support the growth for optimum product formation. While designing a fermenter, an operation/designing engineer considers various criteria in his mind. An ideal fermenter should have the provisions and control over various operations like temperature, pH adequate aeration and agitation (to meet the metabolic requirements of the microorganisms), less evaporation loss, low power consumption, proper sampling facilities, use of cheapest material, operated aseptically for a long period throughout the operation, vessel of similar geometry (smaller and larger vessels), vessel with smooth internal surfaces, vessel with minimal use of labour during operation, harvesting, cleaning, suitable for variety of reactions, etc.

Important types of industrial fermenters are stirred, baffled, and aerated tanks types. These are provided with systems of temperature, pH, and foam formation control. Most of the commercial fermenters have mechanical agitation system which is design to get proper mixing and oxygen transfer, while a few are design in such a way which depend on very high gas inputs without mechanical agitation. The design of a fermenter (bioreactor) also depends on the type of environment required for an organism, its structure and the product. Therefore, following are the major types of industrial fermenters: (1) mechanically agitated fermenter, (2) Non-mechanically agitated fermenter and (3) Non-agitated fermenter.

CONTINUOUS CULTURE

For continuous culture of organisms required for process should have a reservoir of sterile medium. Culture is kept in vessel with constant volume. It should also be provided with a collecting vessel in which culture leaving the fermenter accumulates.

The components of a fermentor

The main subdivisions of a bench-scale fermentor are as follows:

1. Base components including drive motor, heaters, pumps, gas control, etc.;
2. Vessel and accessories;
3. Peripheral equipment such as reagent bottles;
4. Instrumentation and sensors.

These components perform the following functions combinedly:

1. Provide operation free from contamination;
2. Maintain a specific temperature;
3. Provide adequate mixing and aeration;

4. Control the pH of the culture;
5. Allow monitoring and/or control of dissolved oxygen;
6. Allow feeding of nutrient solutions and reagents;
7. Provide access points for inoculation and sampling;
8. Use fittings and geometry relevant to scale-up;
9. Minimize liquid loss from the vessel;
10. Facilitate the growth of a wide range of organisms.

Parts of fermentors

Vessel

The vessel is a single-walled cylinder of borosilicate glass with a flat bottom or as a glass-jacketed system having a typically round bottom. The top plate is made from stainless steel and is compressed onto the vessel flange by an easily released clamping system. The vessel glass and the top plate is separated by a seal. Port fittings of various sizes are provided for insertion of probes, inlet pipes, exit gas cooler, cold fingers, sample pipes, etc. These work by compressing the sides of the probe/pipe against the seal. A special inoculation port will have a membrane seal held in place with a collar. Culture can be withdrawn into a sampling device or a reservoir bottle via a sample pipe situated in the bulk of the fermentor fluid. A gas sparger is also fixed into the top plate and this terminates in a special assembly, which ensures that incoming air is dispersed efficiently within the culture by the flat-bladed 'Rushton-type' impellors fixed to the drive shaft. A drive motor is attached for the purpose of stirring to the drive shaft and is usually fitted directly to the drive hub on the vessel top plate. An exit gas cooler is also provided to the vessel, which works like a simple Liebig condenser to remove as much moisture as possible from the gas leaving the fermentor to prevent excessive liquid losses during the fermentation. It also prevents the wetting of the exit air filter.

A narrow platinum resistance temperature sensor is also attached with the vessel, which control the temperature either by direct heating with a heater pad or by circulating warm water around the vessel jacket. A cold finger is also used to cool the vessel contents, if direct heating is used.

The sensors which fit into the vessel do so either by direct coupling with a thread on the body of the electrode, as is the case in the gel-filled type of pH electrode, or by a special fitting on the vessel top plate, as in the case of the dissolved oxygen electrode (polarographic type).

Peripheral parts and accessories

Reagent Pumps

Pumps are used for the essential parts of the instrumentation system for measuring pH and antifoam and control. Peristaltic pumps are basically used and the flow rate is normally fixed with a timed system of control. Flow rates will depend on the bore of the tubing used and it is a good idea to move the tubing every few days so that one piece does not become worn out by the pump rollers. A dip tube goes to the bottom of the bottle. A filter in the top of the reservoir bottle is kept open during autoclaving to prevent a build-up of pressure. For extremely high accuracy of addition, the reservoir bottles are placed on analytical balances, which can be used to determine how much reagent has been pumped in a given time.

Medium Feed Pumps and Reservoir Bottles

Medium feed pumps are often used with variable speeds so as to give the maximum possible range of feed rates. The reservoir bottles must be changed several times during a long continuous culture experiment, so it is usual to fit an aseptic coupling in the tubing. An effluent pump is often used to remove culture fluid from the fermentor vessel into a storage reservoir bottle.

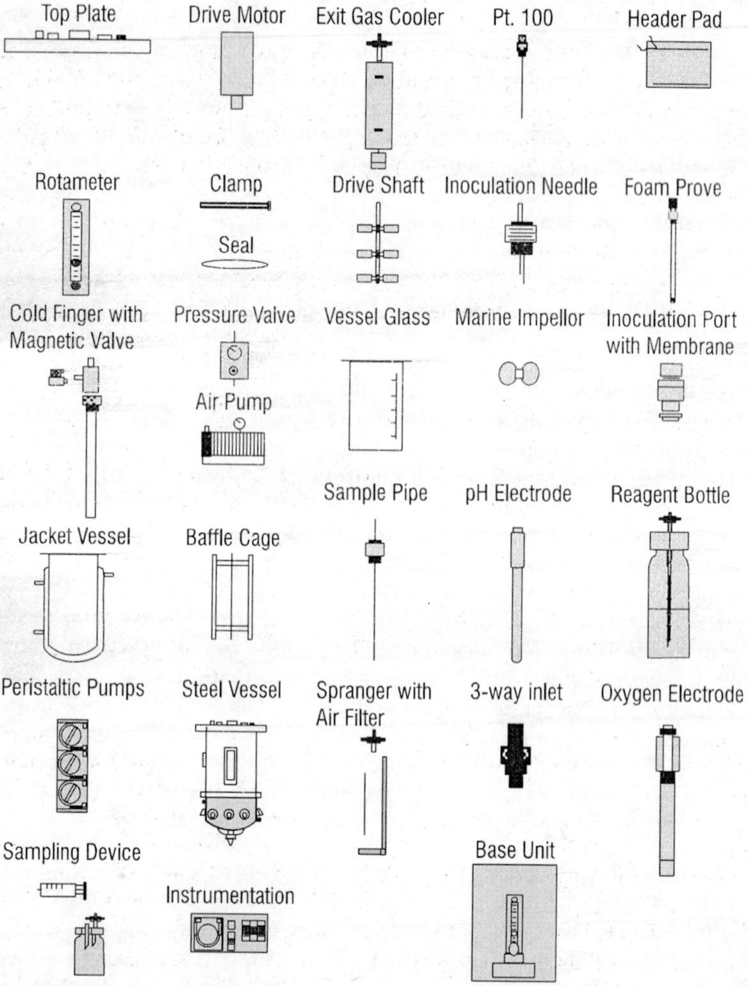

FIGURE 29.1: Illustration of major components of fermentor.

Rotameter/gas Supply

A laboratory air supply is provided from a separate pump, which must be oil free. A variable area flow meter or rotameter is used to control the airflow rate into the fermentor vessel. A pressure regulator valve is also attached before the rotameter, which ensures safer operation. A sterile filter (usually 0.22 µm) is used as a bridge between the tubing from the rotameter and that connected to the air sparger of the fermentor.

Sampling Device

This allows culture fluid to be removed aseptically during the fermentation at intervals decided by the user. The frequency of sampling and the size of each sample are determined empirically according to the needs of the experiment.

Alternative vessel designs

There are various types of alternative vessel designs commonly found for the fermentation processes. Usually, alternative vessel designs are tried when the standard vessel configuration does not allow adequate growth of the organism. Shear forces in fermentors with turbine impellors often disrupt for example animal cells. These are also used when the scale-up criteria require a different design of bioreactor. For example production of large quantities of single-cell protein is cheaper on a large scale if airlift fermentors are used to eliminate energy costs associated with a drive system. A number of these special designs are available at the bench/pilot scale of operation to allow small-scale research into the suitability of a particular method.

Air Lift

By the use of airlift the need for a stirrer system can be minimized or can be neglected. A tall, thin vessel with an aspect ratio of around 10: 1 (height to base diameter) is the best shape of the airlift. Sensors can be mounted in a steel base section, from a collar at the base of the conical section or from the vessel top plate. A common use of airlift fermentors is the growth of shear-sensitive cells such as plant and animal cultures. Also, the design has been used for the production of large amounts of biomass as single-cell protein.

During the fermentation process the culture fluid is mixed and aerated by a jet of air, which enters into the vessel from the base of the vessel. A hollow pipe or draft tube in the centre of the vessel, which rises the air, which is full of bubbles to move upwards to the top of the vessel.

A large headspace is provided above the top of the draft tube, which allows easy gas transfer from the liquid to the gas phase and causes the density/specific gravity of the liquid to increase. It then descends to the bottom of the vessel and the descending liquid returns to the base of the vessel, which is then regassed.

Fluidized Bed

Inm fermentation process the microbes/cells are trapped in a physical medium and then put into the vessel by a mesh. The medium is recirculated with a pump, which is easily adapted to give a continuous/semi-continuous flow to allow the trapped cells to effect chemical changes on constituents of the medium without being washed out along with spent medium.

Hollow Fibre

In this cells are embedded in fibres contained in a cartridge, which are bathed in circulating culture medium. This is often used for mammalian cell culture, where anchorage-dependent cell lines can be perfused with oxygenated medium. An extension of this method is to use cartridges containing two different bundles of fibres as a separation 'membrane' between a pair of fermentor vessels and allow dissolved gases and metabolites to be exchanged without cells crossing the barrier to allow, for example, It is used for the study of toxicity or interactive studies.

In situ Sterilizable Fermentors

For safety and insurance purposes, vessels above the recommended size are usually made of stainless steel and are sterilized *in situ* using house steam or an electrical steam generator, which may be built into the base unit. The heating for the vessel is normally done through a double jacket, which can either be the full length of the vessel or cover just the bottom. The bottom section contains large port fittings for electrodes and usually has some kind of steam-sterilizable sampling device/harvest valve. The mechanical seal and drive shaft usually enter from the bottom on this size of vessel. In some fermentors, the air inlet filter and connecting pipe to the air sparger are also provided.

Containment

If the organism to be cultured is pathogenic or genetically modified then an *in situ* sterilizable fermentor may have to be altered so that any microorganism cannot release in the environment. It is provided with special features such as a double mechanical seal, magnetic coupling, additional air filters, extra foam control systems and special sampling devices. There are several different categories of containment (1-3 for pathogens and 1-4 for genetically modified organisms). Requirements differ at each stage and relate to building and working protocols as much as the design of the fermentor.

Additional accessories and peripherals

Feed Pumps

For fed-batch or continuous applications a separate feed pump is used. The type of pump depends on the size of the vessel, the required flow rates, the nature of the additive (*e.g.* viscous, vorrosive, etc.) and the speed at which the addition should be made.

Peristaltic pump: The pumps used for medium feed are typically variable speed units, which can accept signals from an external source such as a computer or process controller to allow adjustment of feed rates based on, for example, respiratory quotient (RQ) or optical density (OD). This is the most common type of addition pump used in fermentor applications. The key advantages of peristaltic pumps are as follows:

1. The liquid being pumped is not contaminated by any part of the pump.
2. The liquid being pumped does not contaminate the pump.
3. A wide range of flow rates is possible using tubing of different bores.
4. The accuracy of delivery is good over a wide range of flow rates.
5. The pump can run safely even when the tubing is empty.

The disadvantages are:

1. The flow is pulsed and cannot 'push' against high backpressure.
2. The tubing wears over time and flattens, reducing accuracy and increasing the risk of bursting.
3. Silicone tubing is not suitable for all liquids and alternative tubing material may be too rigid to allow correct peristaltic action.

The problem with tubing wear can be partly overcome by leaving extra length in the tubing when connecting it to the fermentor vessel and moving a new length into the pump head every few days to stop wear in just one small section.

Syringe pump: This type of pump is typically used in medical applications for the precise delivery of drugs. Most now allow for computer control. In this case, a syringe of various sizes from 1μl to 100 ml, is filled with the liquid to be added and secured onto the syringe pump. The advantages of syringe pumps are:

1. Very precise and accurate delivery; non-pulsile flow.
2. Very low flow rates possible.
3. Can work against backpressure.
4. Can pump very viscous fluids, *e.g.* oils.
5. The disadvantages are:
6. Must be replaced or refilled regularly.
7. Range of flow rates not as wide as with peristaltic pumps.
8. Usually more expensive.

Diaphragm/positive displacement pump: It uses a flexible membrane and soft tubing to displace the liquid and control its flow but also employs a piston and pump heads of fixed volume. A stainless steel pump head is connected to soft tubing and autoclaved. It is then located onto the pump and held securely. Advantages of this type of pump include:

1. Accurate delivery.
2. More choice in type of tubing for corrosive liquids, for example.

39. DISADVANTAGES ARE:

1. Less flexibility on flow rate ranges for each pump head.
2. Stainless steel chamber and diaphragm may not be suitable for some liquids.
3. Pulsed flow even more pronounced than with a peristaltic pump.

Exit Gas Analysis

The exit gas may need to be conditioned (*e.g.* moisture removed) before going into the analyzer, depending on the type of instrument used.

Infra-red carbon dioxide analyzer: An infrared detector measures the amount of radiation reaching it after the gas absorbs some. This type of detector allows continuous measurement with good sensitivity, accuracy and selectivity.

Paramagnetic oxygen analyzer: A dumb-bell of gas-filled spheres is linked to a support mechanism suspended in a magnetic field created by permanent magnets. If oxygen is present in the test gas, its attraction to the magnetic field will cause the dumb-bell to be displaced. The movement is detected using a mirror in the centre of the balance system, which displaces a beam of light shone via the mirror onto a photocell. The signal form the photocell will be proportional to the amount of oxygen present in the sample. A low flow rate is needed for this system to work properly, so inlet gas is typically pumped into the detector cell with most being discarded through bypass pipe work.

Mass spectrometer: With the help of mass spectrometer the analysis is rapid, so it allows a multi-inlet system to be used, which 'shares' the analyzer between separate vessels within a bank of fermentors. This is metal plate, which generates a tiny electric current whenever a gas ion strikes it. This signal can be amplified and displayed. By re-tuning the magnetic field very quickly (milliseconds) different ions can be detected and measured in a sequential way, which is so fast that it appears to give an almost simultaneous measurement.

Types of Reactors

Mechanically agitated Stirred Tank Reactors

These are the most widely used bioreactors for industries. There are several problems in this kind of fermenter. The agitator shaft rotates and there is a micro clearance between the shaft and stuffing box. This is an important factor in its design. It cannot be neglected and overtime it increases due frictions. To ensure aseptic condition in the fermenter special arrangements are needed to avoid contamination and which needs additional expenses. It has high shearing and tearing effect of impeller blades. Mechanically agitated stirred tank reactor is not suitable for mycelial fungal strains or for tissue cultures. Since it is made of a very large capacity vessels, therefore, it is difficult to achieve uniform mixing. To overcome this problem, various other types of bioreactors have been developed. They are: (1) air-lift bioreactors, (2) air-lift fermenter with external loop, (3) continuous fermentation stirred tank, (4) cyclone type bioreactor, (5) deep jet fermenter, (6) fluidized bed bioreactor, (7) hollow fibre bioreactor, (8) ICI Air-lift fermenter with internal loop, (9) membrane recycle bioreactor, (10) modified air lift bioreactor, with both internal and external loop type (IIT Kharagpur), (11) packed bed bioreactor. The important one are discussed below:

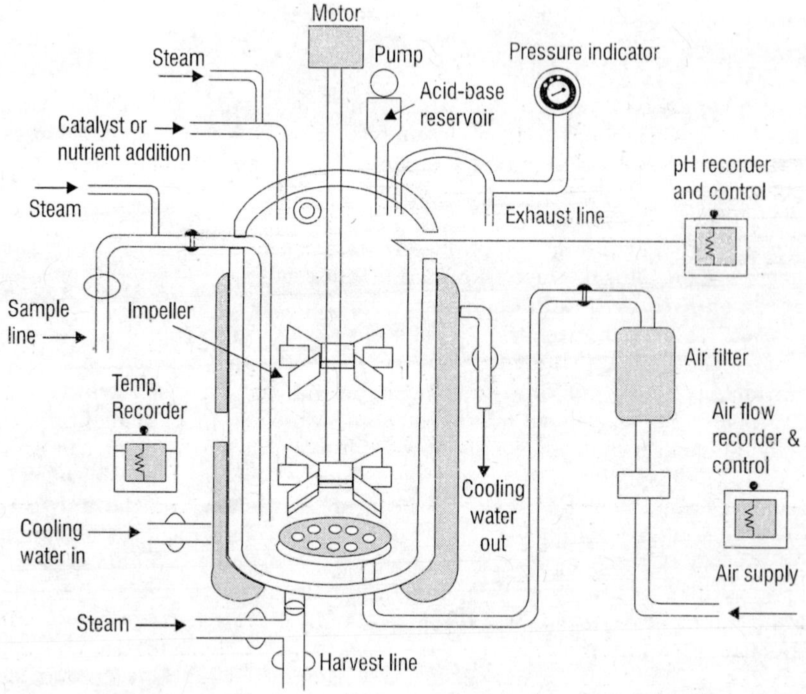

FIGURE 29.2: A typical bioreactor.

Air-lift Bioreactor and Modified Air Lift Bioreactors

This kind of fermenter works on principle of an air lift pump. It is of two kinds: (1) internal loop type (2) external loop type. The reactor's volume is determined by its capacity, kinetic data, and specific growth rate of the organism used. The rate of airflow of the reactor depends on the volumetric mass transfer coefficient in the reactor system. Most of the industries are using bioreactor developed by IIT-Kharagpur. It is a uniform cylindrical cross type and has an internal loop or external loop riser configuration, diverging converging. The external loop riser configuration is adjustable and the change in the configuration improves the O_2 transfer rate vis-à-vis mass transfer coefficient for a particular rate of airflow. This helps provide required particular dissolved O_2 concentration for specific microbial system. This reactor reduces the operating cost for pumping air through the bioreactor.

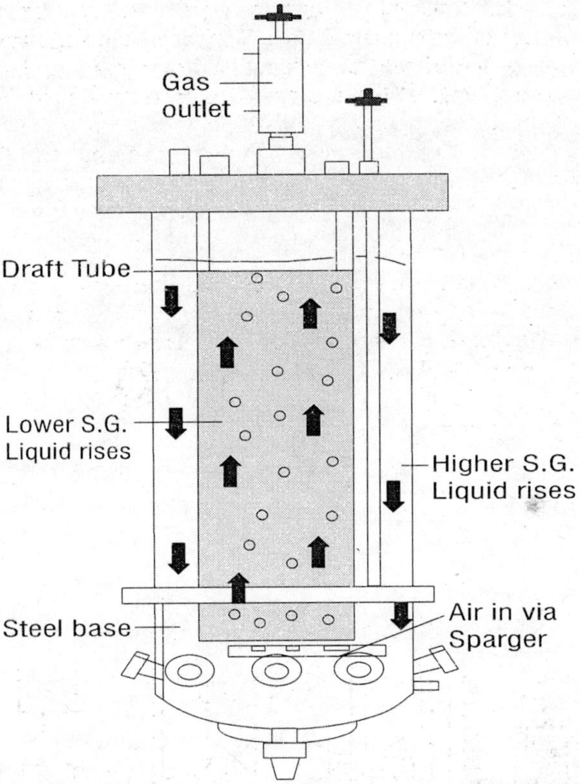

FIGURE 29.3: Air lift fermenter.

Novel Seesaw Bioreactor

Foam formation occurs while aeration and agitation in the bioreactor, which disturbs the physical system and blocking the flow passages and the cell mass attaches to the foam, thereby reduces the cell density in the broth. Cells in contact with bubbles may be destroyed. In such cases aeration is to be done from outside the reactor. This increases the cost of the system. Novel Seesaw bioreactor is design in such a way to consider certain inherent problems. In this bioreactor aeration of broth is done by surface diffusion which avoids bubbling and reduces the cause of foam formation. Shear effect is also negligible.

The reactor has minimum two bioreactor chambers and two gas chambers. Each bioreactor chamber is connected to gas chamber, which controls the gas pressure inside the chamber by means of valve and blower. The gas is alternately forced into each bioreactor chamber. Gas forces the liquid levels inside the bioreactor for alternate up and down ward movement. The system is a closed circuit. Inflow of gas is from outside, and supply is controlled. It has the provision to remove excess of gas. The bioreactor has additional solid surfaces for improving the aeration efficiency. The reactor has also controlling device to control pH, dissolved O_2, CO_2 level and temperature.

Different types of fermentor instrumentation

Various kinds of fermentor instrumentation are being used in fermentation technology. These can range from simple analogue control modules arranged as a 'stack', to powerful, embedded microprocessors which operate as on-board computers to directly operate the complete system.

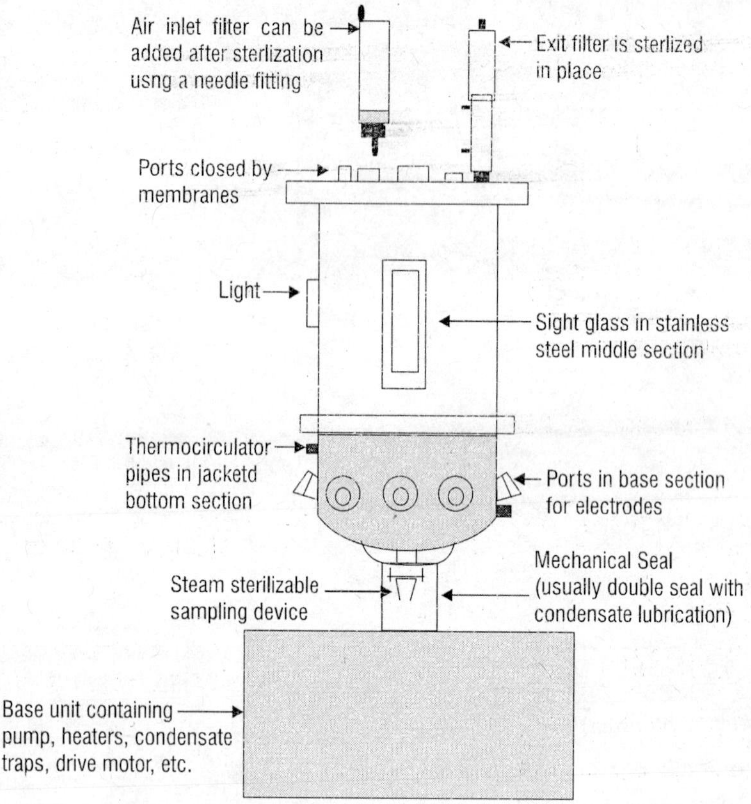

FIGURE 29.4: Illustratration of major parts of an in situ sterilizable fermentor vessel.

Analogue Controllers – Rack System

For compact, flexible instrumentation the individual modules for the measurement and control of each parameter are made to plug into a rack system. A bus system in the racking transmits signals from one module to another to allow measured values to be passed to controllers and for one controller to influence another, *e.g.* oxygen levels altering speed is one of the such examples.

Analogue Controllers – Separate Modules in Housings

The modules may be stacked one on top of another and can be supplied with 'pass through' power connections so that only one power socket is needed. In this each measurement/control module has a separate housing and is operated in isolation. This system allows gradual building up or swapping of instrument modules between several fermentors.

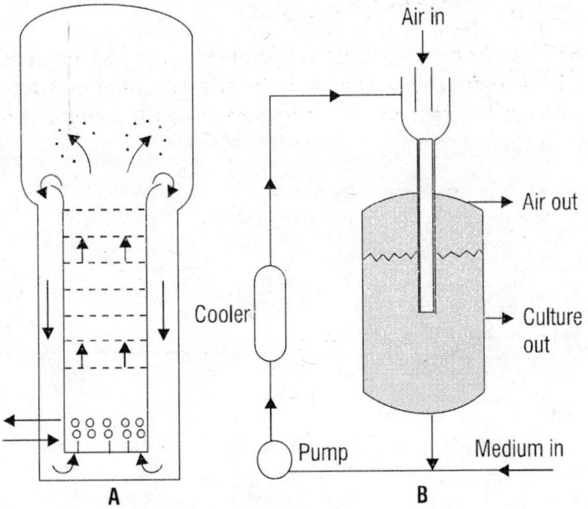

FIGURE 29.5: Different types of fermenter. (A) Air-lift fermenter with internal loop. (B) Deep jet fermenter.

Digital Controllers – Embedded Microprocessor

The measurement sensors link directly to the single control module and several parameters are displayed immediately on a single screen. Control is by direct action on heaters, valves, etc. (Direct Digital Control or DDC). The microprocessor is permanently embedded in the instrumentation and may even be a single chip. Operation is usually via a simple menu system.

Digital Controllers – Process Controllers

The controller is usually 'programmed' using simple commands to input set-point values, etc. Usually from a production control environment, a complete process controller is added to a housing containing all the signal processing and control actuators for the fermentors. It controls in the same way as an embedded controller but is essentially a 'plug-in' component.

Digital Controllers – Direct computer Control

The processing power and speed of modern PCs made the process more than capable of replacing separate PLCs or embedded controllers. A special Input/Output (I/O) card is needed for the computer which allows the input values to be accessed by the measurement and control software and sends signals out to operate relays, *e.g.* to turn a heater on or off. In this case, there is no external instrumentation or processor between the actuators and the computer. A printed circuit board with operational amplifiers for the probe input signals is the only electronic part which may be present in the fermentor base unit. The advantage with this system is that the computer display and control software is integrated totally with the fermentor.

Common measurement and control systems

Speed Control

Speed control basically relies on the feedback from a tachometer, which is located within the drive motor and determines the power delivered by the speed controller to maintain the speed set-point value, which is set by the user. A digital display shows the actual speed in rpm, as determined by the tachometer signal. Where speed is used to control the level of dissolved oxygen, an external signal from the oxygen controller can have an effect on stirrer speed. An absolute maximum and minimum value for speed can be set on the speed control module to limit the effects of the oxygen controller.

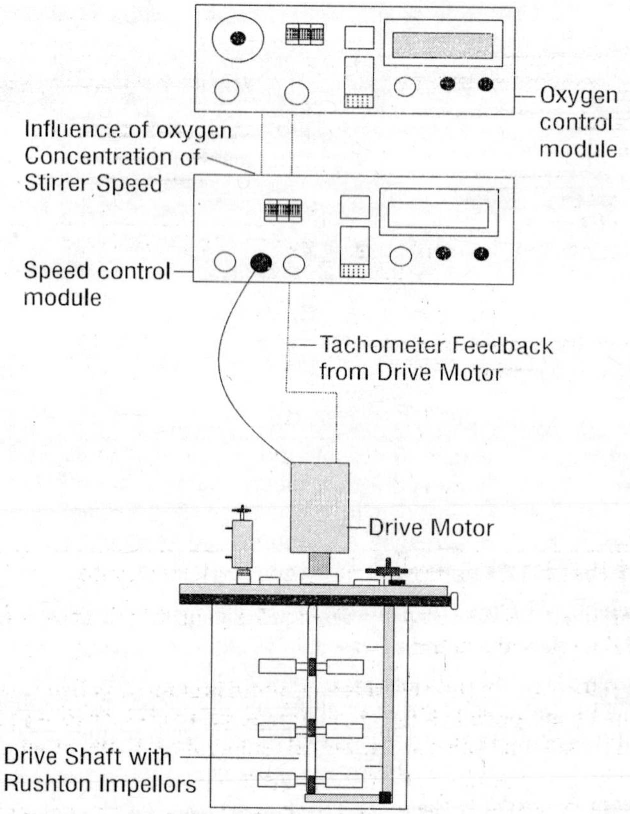

FIGURE 29.6: Illustration of speed control system.

Temperature Control

A thermocirculation system around a vessel jacket has been used for the temperature control because it is the most complex of all the methods. For simple direct systems such as a heater pad, it is simply a matter of fixing the heater, setting the desired temperature and switching on. Cooling is normally via a cold finger and flow of cooling water is controlled via the action of a solenoid valve.

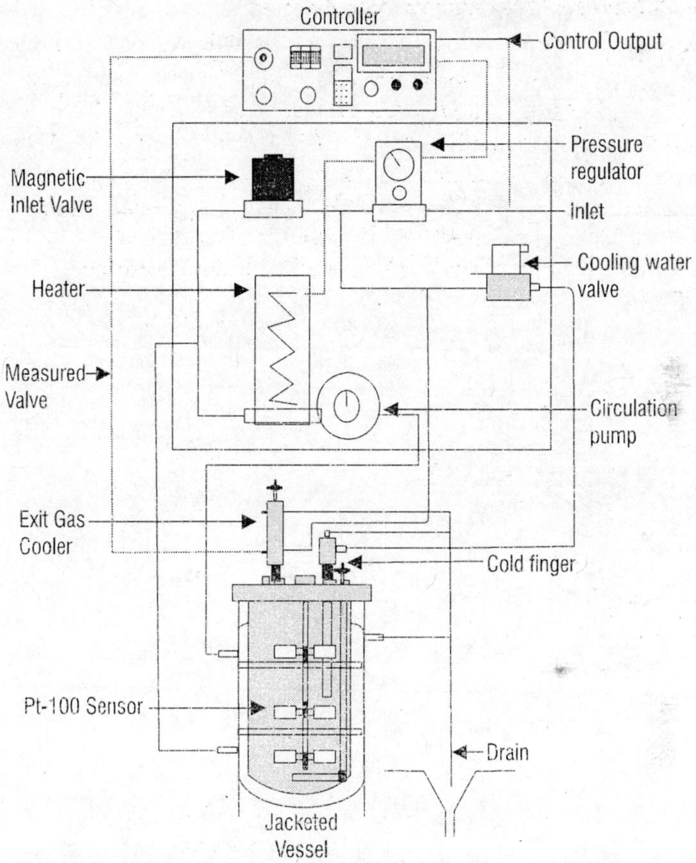

FIGURE 29.7: Illustration of temperature control system using water circulation.

The Pt-100 sensor provides the feedback signal, which causes the controller to take one of the following actions:

1. Heat at full power as the actual temperature is some way below set point;
2. Pulse the heater power as the actual temperature is close to set point;
3. Turn on the cooling valve as the actual temperature is above set point.

The heating and cooling are controlled in exactly the same way as a directly heated system. The jacket provides a large surface area in contact with the vessel wall for heat exchange. Good temperature control can be achieved from approximately 5-8°C above the ambient temperature or 5°C above the temperature of the cooling water. Counter-cooling with water ensures stable temperature control when operating near ambient temperatures.

Control of gas Supply

A pressure regulation valve ensures that air reaches the vessel at a maximum of 1.5

bar and rotameter is used to control the actual flow rate of air through the fermentor. A valve at the bottom of the rotameter is turned and the indicator 'ball' in the rotameter tube rises or falls in proportion to the valve position. The end of the sparger is typically a ring with small holes through which the air is forced. A 'head space' of around 20% is normally left between the culture level and the vessel top plate. For certain types of fermentation, *e.g.* mammalian cell culture, a gas mixing station can be used to pre-mix several gases before they are introduced into the fermentor.

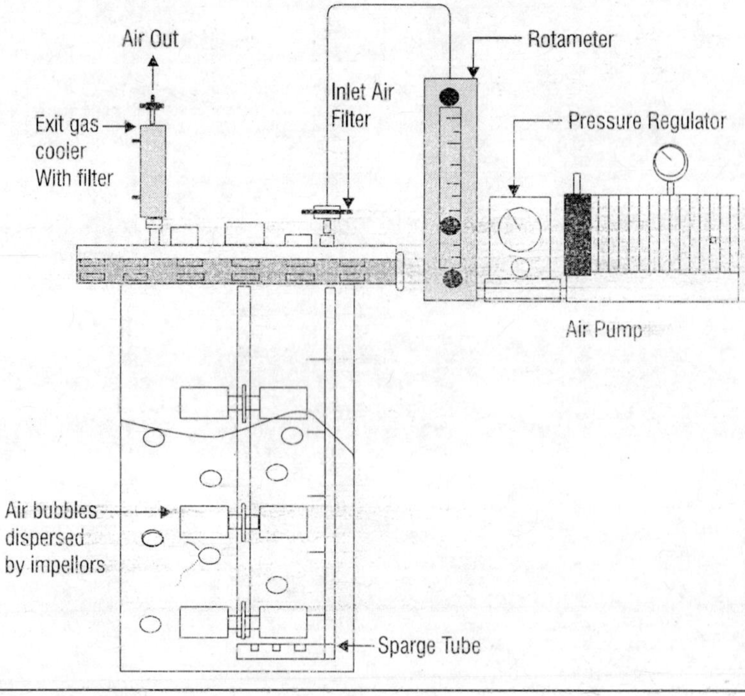

FIGURE 29.8: Illustration of gas supply system.

Control of pH

pH control is achieved by the addition of either acid or alkali to correct changes in the pH of the culture during growth. The controller uses a pH electrode (either glass or gel type) to sense these pH changes and provide a feedback signal. The reagent bottles are connected to the fermentor via transfer lines of silicone tubingNormally, solutions of between 0.2 to 0.5 M of acid and base are used as a starting point.

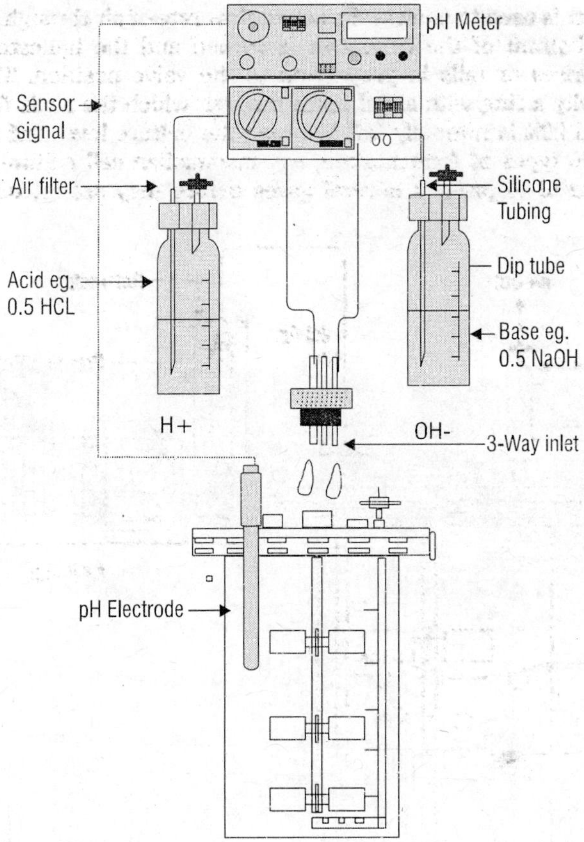

FIGURE 29.9: Illustration of pH measurement and control.

Control of Dissolved Oxygen

Control of dissolved oxygen is the most important and the most difficult parameters. The electrodes used to measure dissolved oxygen are of two distinct types. These are, Galvanic electrodes, which are generally simple, cheap, slow and have a limited life and Polarographic electrodes, which are generally more complex, accurate, rapid and robust but expensive.

The polarographic electrode is used more commonly as it requires a voltage to polarize the anode and cathode of the detecting cell. This electrode must be connected to its relevant module, which in turn must be switched on.

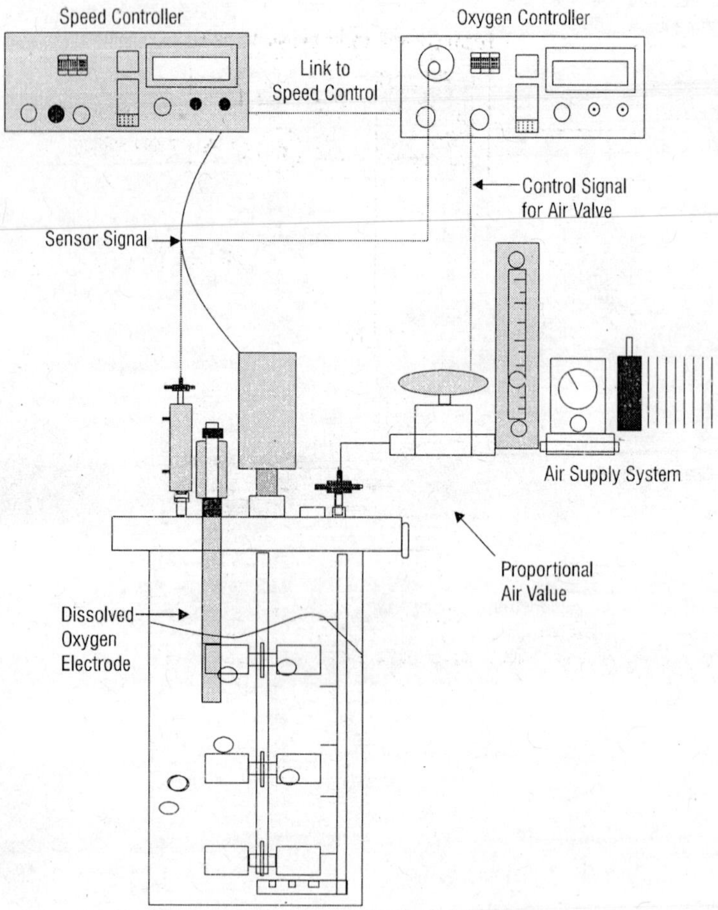

FIGURE 29.10: Illustration of dissolved oxygen measurement and control.

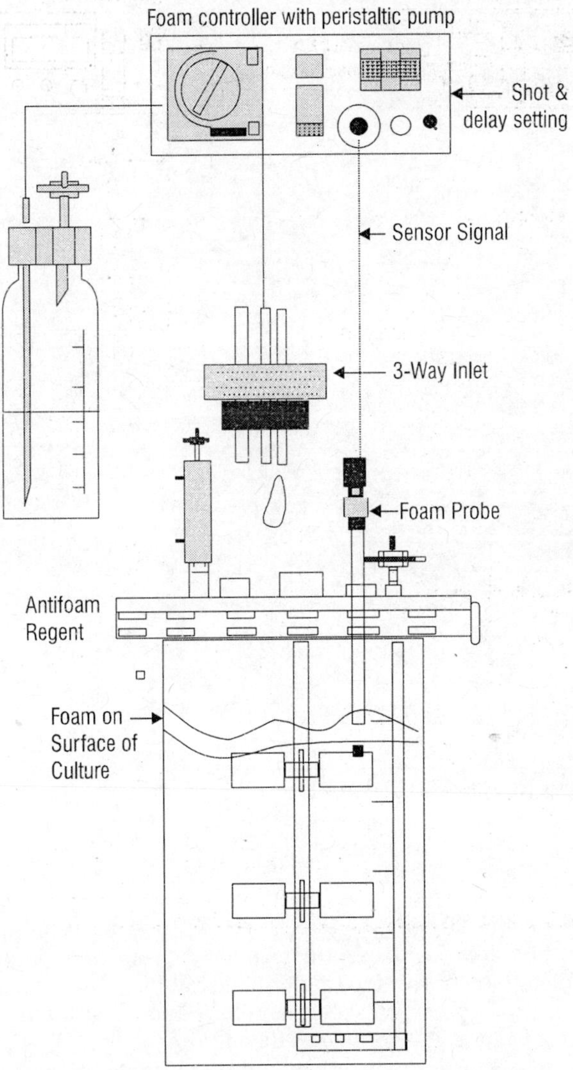

FIGURE 29.11: Illustration of foam control system.

Antifoam Control

If foam is allowed to build up unchecked it can eventually reach the exit gas filter so blocking it and providing a path for contamination, so antifoam reagents are used. Antifoam reagents like mineral oils, vegetable oils or certain alcohols are commonly used in the fermentation process. Commercial preparations are available for use with cultures, which ultimately provide materials for pharmaceutical manufacture. The key thing with using oils is that they can form a 'skin' on the surface of the culture and interfere with gas transfer at the liquid/for interface.

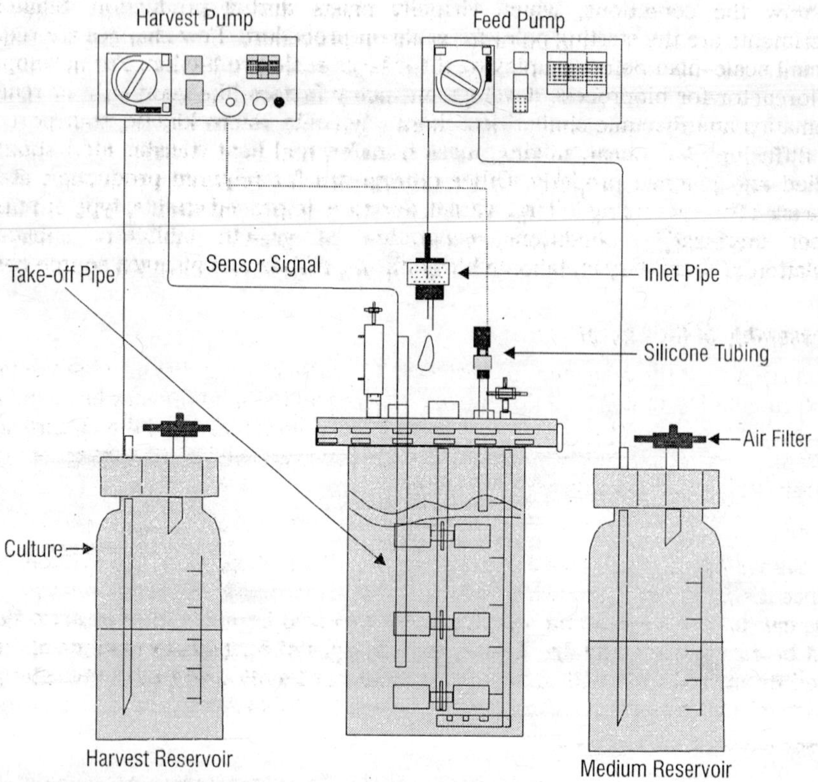

FIGURE 29.12: Illustration of simple continuous culture.

Simple continuous culture

There are a number of different ways of setting up a continuous culture. The method of choice has the virtue of being able to be added to any fermentor vessel without modification or the addition of extra controllers beyond the acquisition of a feed pump and a harvest pump. The feed pump is variable speed but the harvest pump can be fixed speed as long as its speed is greater than that of the feed pump. The harvest pipe, being sited at the surface of the culture, has the disadvantage of taking off only the top of the culture (which may not be representative of the bulk culture) but the advantage of helping to prevent build-up of foam. If foam is a problem then antifoam reagent can be added to the medium feed at a background level, *e.g.* 1 part in 20,000. Samples can be taken by putting a 'Y' piece in the take-off tubing and placing a sampling device in one arm of the 'Y'.

Fermentor preparation and use

Scaling-up of Fermentation

Before designing and planning any fermentation process, it is necessary to scale-up experimentation required for fermentation process. Small to big differences exist in design and efficiency of bioreactor. There is a vast difference between the laboratory fermentation process/conditions and pilot plant. Therefore, detailed study is required to know the conditions, which virtually exists during production. Small-scale experiments are the starting point for scale-up procedure. Few changes are required in small scale–plan before employing it for large-scale production. For development of bioreactor for bioprocess development many factors like geometric of reactors, kinematics and dynamic similarities, thermodynamic, micro kinetic, transport, flow and diffusion (*i.e.*, shear, mixing, mass transfer, and heat transfer etc.) should be studied and planned properly. Other criteria are for required production at large scale are efficient mixing in large vessel, aeration, improved strains, type of nutrient, proper sterilization conditions, separation of growth inhibitory substances, regulation of secondary metabolite biosynthesis, carbon and nitrogen source control, etc.

Disassembly of the Vessel

For carrying out the fermentation process, it is necessary to disassemble the vessel. The fermentation unit is shut down from the control unit and transfer lines and cable connections are removed. The vessel should be re-autoclaved and the culture should be disposed of as laid down by departmental safety procedures. The complete vessel including its each and every part is disassembled.

Cleaning

The vessel should be rinsed several times in distilled water to remove any loose culture residues. During cleaning, an examination of any chips or cracks in the vessel glass can be carried out and a replacement can also be made, if necessary. Vessels must be stored clean and dry. In use, any spillages of reagents or medium should be wiped up immediately with a damp cloth and not be allowed to dry out. The pump heads and covers must be thoroughly cleaned if a tube breaks and reagent leaks out.

Preparations for Autoclaving

Before proceeding for the autoclaving, the vessel seal should be removed and lightly greased with suitable silicone grease. On replacing the seal, it must be correctly located so that there is no chance of any part lifting or kinking. All fittings such as pipes etc. are fitted. Ports not in use have 'stoppers' fitted, and their O-ring seals should have a light coating of silicone grease applied. The pH and dissolved oxygen electrodes should be fitted, taking care not to damage them by careless insertion into the port. Both must be tightly capped to prevent moisture getting into the electrical contacts. Reagent bottles are prepared in a similar way to the fermentor vessel.

The exit gas cooler should be fitted to one of the wider ports. The air outlet line must be kept open during autoclaving. A short length of silicone tubing must be fitted to the air sparger inlet pipe with a 0.2 μm disposable filter mounted on top. The tubing between the sparger pipe and the filter must be clamped shut during autoclaving.

Autoclaving

On a steel tray or in an autoclave basket the vessel and reagent/sampling bottles already connected by silicone tubing are assembled together. It should check that all the outlets and inlets are properly closed. A quantity of liquid is certain to be lost during autoclaving (approximately 10%) so either the medium is over-diluted to compensate for this or sterile, distilled water is added afterwards to restore the volume. Some form of indicator such as autoclave tape should be included to provide a warning if the correct sterilization procedure has not been carried out. Autoclaving at 121°C for 30 min is normally considered adequate for vessel sterilization to minimize damage to the constituent chemicals of the medium. The autoclave used must have good pressure equalization during the cooling down phase of operation to prevent medium being boiled off. The vessel and any accessory bottles must be allowed to cool completely before handling.

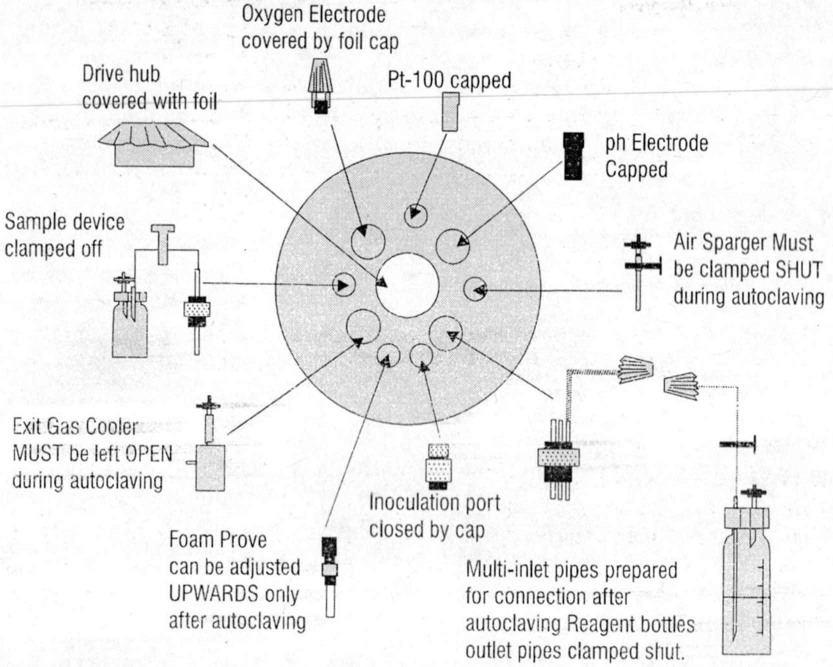

FIGURE 29.13: Illustration of vessels and accessories which are prepared for autoclaving process.

Set-up following Autoclaving

The air sparger is connected to the rotameter by a piece of silicone tubing from the top of the filter to the air outlet of the rotameter. The air sparger line is unclipped between the metal pipe and the air filter. The exit gas cooler is connected to the water supply, either directly or via the fermentor base unit. The tubing for water in, out and drain is connected to the vessel jacket for a water system, and the water turned on so that the vessel jacket is filled. Alternatively, any pads or heater cartridges are connected to the base unit or temperature control modules.

Aseptic connections must be made first if the reagent bottles were autoclaved separately from the vessel. The clamps are removed so liquid can flow freely. The Pt-100 temperature sensor is connected to the control module and the pH electrode by removing the shorting cap and screwing in the cable. The dissolved oxygen electrode is connected to the appropriate cable. Connections to the foam probe are made, usually one wire into the electrode and one on the vessel top plate to make a circuit. Setting the temperature control at this stage will ensure the fermentor is ready to inoculate. The maximum stirrer speed to be used and the maximum airflow required on the rotameter are set. The fermentor is now ready to inoculate.

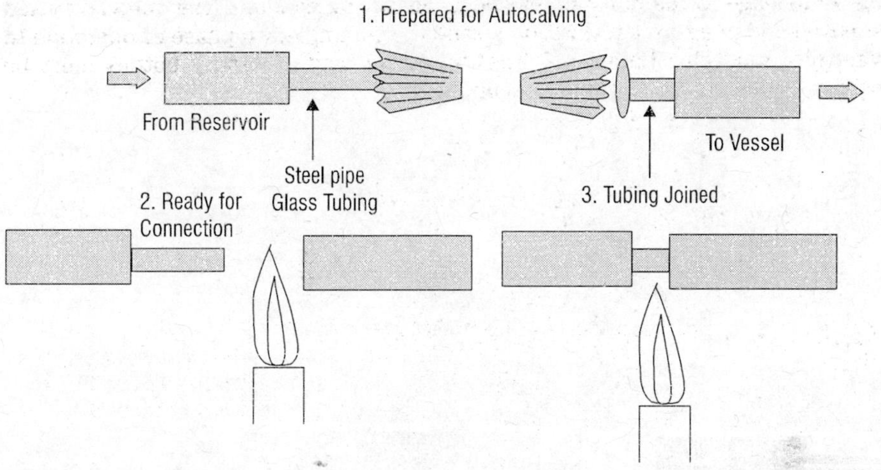

FIGURE 29.14: Illustration of how tubes are connected aseptically.

Sampling from a Fermentor Vessel

Aeration is stopped during this process to prevent 'surging' of culture into the syringe. This method can be prone to contamination and is not suitable for organisms with any risk to operators. This sampling device is a bottle, which has two metal needles/pipes permanently, fixed through both the metal and rubber seals of its cap. A syringe is fitted to the air filter after autoclaving. The sample device is usually attached to the vessel top plate so that the glass bottle hangs down vertically beneath the cap and a supply of bottles of the same size are autoclaved ready for use. When a sample is to be taken, the clamp on the sample pipe tubing is released, and the syringe pulled back to create a partial vacuum in the sample bottle. Culture will flow into the sample bottle. When the required volume of sample has been taken, the syringe is pushed in to clear the line and the sample tubing is clamped shut again. The sample bottle with the culture is quickly removed and capped with a sterile cap from a new glass bottle, which replaces it under the sampling device.

Inoculation of a Fermentor Vessel

The inoculum, which should normally be not more than 5-10% of the total culture volume, is aseptically transferred to a sterile, disposable syringe of a suitable size. The port fitting is removed and held vertically to prevent contamination of the bottom end. The syringe needle is quickly pushed through the membrane and the inoculum transferred into the vessel. The vessel may be actively aerated during this procedure to minimize the risk of a contaminant getting into the vessel. The syringe needle is quickly withdrawn and the silicone membrane reseals. The port fitting is now replaced. Aseptic connection can be made to an inlet pipe.

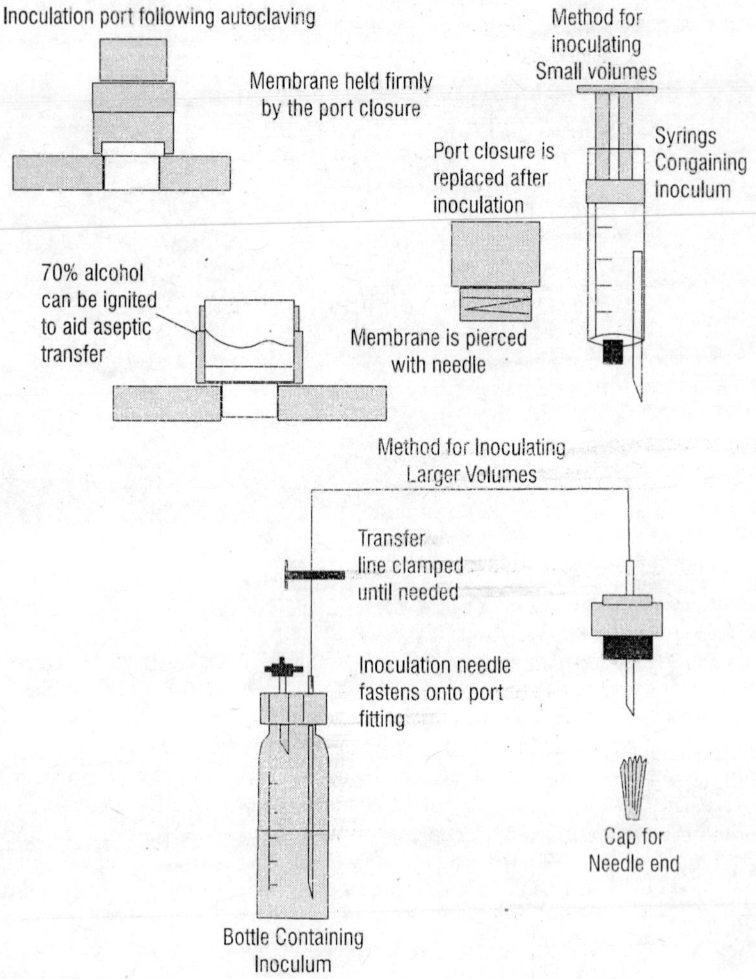

FIGURE 29.15: Illustration of inoculation process of a fermentor vessel.

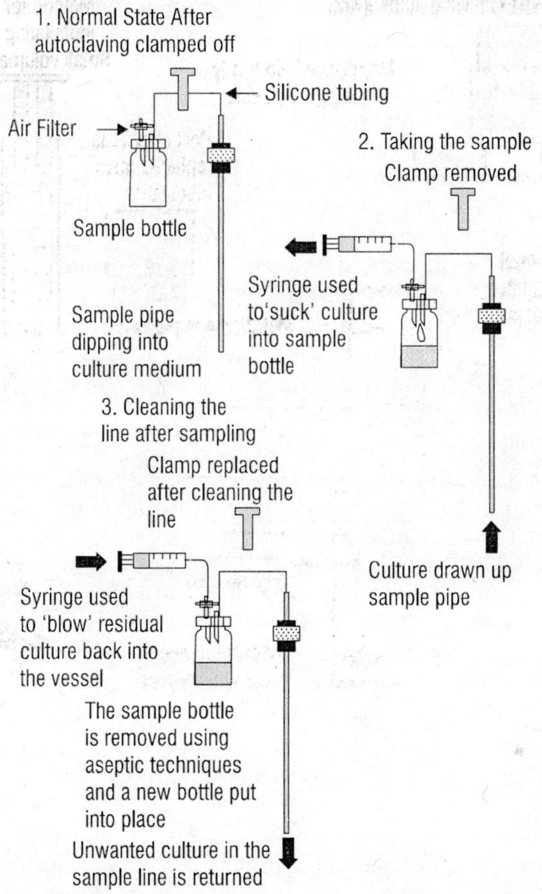

FIGURE 29.16: Illustration of sampling.

Maintenance of Aseptic Conditions

Bioreactor should remain contamination free. The contamination is caused by microorganisms and results in a variety of consequences *e.g.*, depletes nutrients, nature of the final product, reduction in yields, degradation of the desired metabolite, interference with downstream recovery etc. Therefore, the bioreactor should be designed in such a way so that there should be minimum or no contamination occurs. Integrated efforts should be made while designing bioreactor, use of materials and layout, effective operating procedure, scheduled checks and trained personnel. Contamination may be minimized by using sterile inoculum; adequately sterilized nutrient medium, the design, material and fabrication of the bioreactor (aeration and agitation systems, sampling and monitoring ports, and foaming) air liquid transfers. The operation of sterilization and aseptic additions of industrial plants involve complex procedures and perhaps, manipulations of hundreds of valves. The following are some of the important factors to be considered for an aseptic fermentation:

1. For proper aseptic condition in the bioreactor, regular preventive maintenance of vessels is essential.
2. The fermenter must be designed properly in such a way that the fermenter and its contents are steam sterilizable.
3. Entry and exit of steam should be proper.
4. The agitated drive shaft should have double mechanical aseptic seal. Seals should be of best quality to withstand with host water lubrication.
5. Filtered and sterilized air should be supplied to bioreactor.
6. The vessel should be operated at positive pressure.
7. Addition or transfer of liquid systems in a vessel should be designed in aseptic manner.

Transfer of Oxygen

Oxygen is required for microbial culture activity throughout fermentation because aerobic microbes need oxygen at higher rate. The oxygen present in the culture is even utilized by them within 15 seconds. Oxygen supply to microbial processes needs simultaneous aeration and mixing. Mixing is done by agitation. Yeasts and bacteria do not require mixing of the cultures by separate agitation. Well-placed air spargers are used for such processes. Actinomycetes and molds are filamentous microbes. They require mechanical mixing. Aeration and mixing in submerged cultures are very much related to optimum rate of air flow and optimum impeller frequency. Saturation of dissolved oxygen concentration is achieved by sparging air into the vessel throughout the course of fermentation process. The transfer of oxygen from the gaseous phase proceeds by molecular diffusion. The rate of oxygen transfer into a solution can be expressed as follows:

$$\frac{dC_L}{dt} = K_L a\,(c^*\text{-}C_L) \quad \text{.......... (1)}$$

Where C_L is the dissolved oxygen concentration (m mol dm^3) t is the time, (h), C* is the saturated dissolved oxygen concentration, KL is the mass transfer coefficient (cm h^{-1}), a is the gas/liquid interface area in mass transfer and dC_L/dt is the oxygen transfer rate (m mol^{-3}h^{-1}). The term K_L a represents volume coefficient of oxygen transfers characterizing the aeration capacity of the system. The oxygen requirement of a given biological system can be represented as:

$$\frac{dC_L}{dt} = K_L a\,(c^*\text{-}C_L) \quad \text{.......... (1)}$$

where 'r' is the rate of respiration of microorganisms and X is the concentration of cells. If the rate of oxygen consumption exceeds the rate of absorption, the whole system will become oxygen limited. Above two equations hold for an ideally mixed system *i.e.*, homogenous gaseous and liquid phases; in fermenters usually the oxygen concentration differs different places. If the oxygen concentration in the liquid is zero, equation (1) can be simply represented as:

$$\frac{dC_L}{dt} = K_L a.C^* \quad \text{.......... (3)}$$

which, gives the maximum rate of oxygen transfer under given conditions. $K_L a$ value depends on different factors like vessel design, degree of agitation in a stirred vessel, rate of airflow, viscosity of the culture broth and the available antifoam agent in the medium. The bioreactor should be designed in such a way that during operation microbes should get sufficient oxygen. The above equation (3) reveals that the rate of oxygen transfer is maximal if the concentration of dissolved oxygen is zero.

Critical concentration (C.crit): It is the lowest dissolved oxygen concentration at which the specific oxygen uptake is maximum. If dissolved oxygen concentration is increased, the specific oxygen uptake rate also increases up to a maximum rate. Therefore, low oxygen concentration below C.crit will bring about a decline in the rate of respiration. Hence, it is necessary to keep a fermenter and culture in a fully aerobic state. The available dissolved oxygen concentration should remain above the C.crit.

Cultures of filamentous organisms have non homogenous environment. In such environment local oxygen shortage arise, which ultimately increases critical concentration value (apparent critical concentration value, AC.crit). The value of AC.crit in a few microbial processes may be quite high. IT may be varied. Thus, the optimum aeration conditions for microbial product formation may be different from those giving biomass production. Hence, it may be necessary to operate a fermenter at a dissolved oxygen concentration either below critical concentration or at apparent critical concentration (*i.e.*, below or above C.crit).

The value of K_{La} in stirred vessel increases with rising superficial air until it reaches a certain critical value. The critical value corresponds to the point of impeller chocking *i.e.*, where the impeller rotates virtually only in the air.

The value of K_{La} does not depend on the bubble size. Increase in K_{La} occurs with very small bubbles. A relative increase or decrease in the bubble surface area can be attributed to surface active agents (*i.e.*, sodium lauryl sulphate, Tween 80, silicon oil etc.) that can alter the K_{La} value.

The viscosity of the medium depends on the nature of the microorganisms. Filamentous microbes increase medium viscosity. They also affect the degree of agitation. The oxygen transfer rate considerably reduces with increase in viscosity of the culture broth. The viscosity of the broth decreases with increasing agitation. Therefore, it is essential that, the agitation regime should govern good oxygen transfer in a region of high shear but also circulates the broth through the high shear zone. At higher viscosity the transfer rate does not rise even on increasing the impeller frequency.

Fermentation Medium

The fermentation medium includes nutrients essential to support the growth of microorganisms, and formation of desired end products. The choice of the nutrient should be based on nutritive source and economic aspects. The important sources are carbon, nitrogen, and phosphorus. Following table presents various nutrient sources used in industrial fermentation.

TABLE 29.1: Nutrient sources used for industrial fermentations

Nutrient	Raw material
Carbon source glucose	Corn sugar, molasses, starch.
Fats and hydrocarbons	Vegetable oils, petroleum fractions
Nitrogen source protein	Soybean meal, cornsteep liquor (from corn milling) distiller's solubles (from alcoholic beverage manufacture)
Ammonia	Pure ammonia or ammonium salts

Nutrient	Raw material
Nitrate	Nitrate salts
Nitrogen	Air (from nitrogen fixing organisms)
Phosphorus source	Phosphate salts

For fermentation, crude raw materials are usually employed in the medium. There are several factors which should be considered for better fermentation results like trace elements in the medium, quality of water, nature of pipes used for supply of solutions to fermentation reaction centres, aeration (optimum oxygen concentration), pH, required enzymes, optimum temperature, etc.

Regulatory Mechanisms and Industrial Fermentations

Several enzymes are involved in different metabolic pathways of a microorganism which act in an integrated manner. This is achieved by the regulatory mechanisms (*e.g.*, induction, feedback regulation, catabolite regulation and energy charge regulation) which help the microbe to compete efficiently with other forms of life and to survive in nature. An ideal cell does not produce excess of metabolites, regardless of its environment. However, at industrial level, it is expected that microbes should produce excessive amount of metabolites which can be isolated. Organisms are screened for their ability to over produce the desired product from culture collections or from nature.

CHAPTER 30

Enzyme-based Industrial Fermentation Technology

Enzymes are the important sources of industrial products because of the following reasons:

1. Their rapidity and efficiency of action at low concentrations and under mild conditions of pH and temperature.
2. Their lack of toxicity.
3. The easy termination of their action by mild treatments.

The microbes are the major source of biological enzymes because of the reasons: (i) the ease with which enzymes levels may be increased by environmental and genetic manipulations. (ii) Enzyme fermentations are economical on a large scale because of short fermentation cycles and inexpensive media. (iii) The screening procedures of microbes are very simple and a large number of culture samples can be examined in a short period. Once an active microbial strain is identified, fermentation parameters are optimized to maximize the growth.

INDUCTION OF FERMENTATION ENZYMES

There are several catabolic enzymes, which are of commercial importance and fall into the inducible category. The typical inducers are substrates *e.g.*, starch for amylase, sucrose for invertase, lactose for β-galactosidase, etc. Certain analogues of the substrates are also known which act as potent enzyme inducers. There are reports which indicate that the products also act as inducers of enzymes.

The use of mutation techniques help us to eliminate the dependence of enzyme formation on inducer addition. Such technique of mutation is known as **regulatory mutation**, since its locus is not a structural but a regulatory gene. Mutants which produce a normally inducible enzyme without inducer are termed as **constructive mutants.**

Feedback Repression

During the fermentation process, microbes grow actively which leads to the repression of enzyme production. This occurs when pathway end-products build up in concentration or are added to growth media. These end-product are of low molecular weight (co-repressor) and can combine with an intercellular protein (aporepressor), coded by the regulatory gene, to produce a repressor. The repressor then stop the coding of structural gene for the production of enzyme. Such enzymes are known as **repressible enzymes**. If internal accumulation of end-product (co-repressor) becomes limited, there is an increase in enzyme productions. This can be achieved by mixing an inhibitor of the pathway in the fermentation medium, and by limiting the growth factor supply fed to an auxotrophic mutant. This develops partial starvation for microbes, but the production of enzyme is increased.

TABLE 30.1: Depression of biosynthetic enzymes by limited feeding of requirement to auxotrophs

Auxotrophic requirement	Depressed enzymes	Increase
Leucine	Acetohydroxy acid synthetase	400-fold
Thiamine	4 enzymes of thiamine biosynthesis	upto 1,500-fold
Biotin	7-oxo-8-amino parlargenate and inotransferase	400-fold

Catabolic Repression

The catabolic inducible enzymes markedly repressed when cells are growing fast on a readily utilizable carbon source, many enzymes of industrial importance are subject to this type of regulation. If the use of repressing carbon sources is avoided in the fermentation medium the production of enzymes sensitive to catabolite repression is greatly stimulated. For example, use of mannose for growing *Pseudomonas fluorescens* var. *cellulose* results in cell producing over 1,500 times as much cellulose as cells growing on galactose. Mutation can be used to obtain mutants resistant to carbon catabolic repression.

Hyperproduction by Deregulated Mutants - Gene Dosage

Regulatory mutants have often been obtained which produce more enzymes than their parents. For example, a constitutive polygalacturonase-producing mutant of *Acrocylindrium* was found to produce more enzyme than its inducible parent even in the presence of inducer. Sometimes hyperproducing mutants, contain multiple copies of structural gene coding for the enzyme. Increased number of copies of a gene increases production of its specific enzyme. In microorganisms, an increase in gene copies by genetic manipulation has been achieved by transferring plasmids or by the use of transducing phase.

TABLE 30.2: Carbon catabolic repression of enzymes

Enzyme	Organism	Repressive carbon source
α-amylase	Bacillus stearothermophilus	Fructose
Cellulose	Trichoderma viride	Glucose, glycerol, starch, cellobiose
Protease	Bacillus megaterium	Glucose
Amyloglucosidase	Endomycopsis bispora	Starch, maltose, glucose, glycerol
Polygalacturonic	Aeromonas liquefaciens	Glucose, polygalacturonic acid, transeliminase acid
Invertase	Neurospora crassa	Mannose, glucose, fructose

PRODUCTION OF ALCOHOLIC BEVERAGES

The alcoholic beverages include beer, wine, whiskey, and other fermented beverages are economically important. The origins of bread and beverage marking are lost in antiquity, but it is known that the Sumerians produced a beer consisting of moistened, fermented bread prior to 7,000 B.C. The Egyptians also made this **bread beer**, and regarded it as a holy gift from Osiris, the God of the death. They were also the first to make leavened bread. Both bread making and brewing were later refined by the Greeks and Romans, and numerous changes in the manner of making beer have been made since these early times.

Wine

The fermentation of the juice of grapes, cherries, and berries to produce wine is an old and well-established procedure. The characteristic and distinctive flavours of wine are partially determined by the variety of fruit used, the environmental conditions under which the fruits were grown, the parts of the fruit used, and the ability of the yeast to form flavoured by-products (particularly esters). In this instance the sugar from these juices may be converted to alcohol via the Embden-Meyerhof pathway. Flavours and aromas occur in the wine as a result of the activities of chemical reactions other than sugars that proceed at the same time. The wind industry is basically the same the world over. Some of the differences that are found in wine originate in the type and quality of the grapes that are used. The physical environment of the grape plant, such as amounts of moisture and climatic temperature changes, as well as the general health of the plants, all reflect in the quality of the grape used in wine-making. Some have larger quantities of sugar, while others contain materials that are conducive in producing more desirable aroma, flavour, or other qualities in the wine.

The organisms used in the production of wine are also important. The type of organism used will influence the quality of the wine, and a variety of different species are used, some to produce especially dry or sweet wine. Traditionally, the yeasts used to ferment the juices were those occurring naturally on the surface of the fruit. Recently the trend has been utilize laboratory cultures of strains of *Saccharomyces cerevisiae* var. *ellipsoideus*. These strains are chosen for their ability to properly ferment the variety of grapes used and for their ability to impart flavours by formation of by-products which are characteristic for a particular wine.

The wine maker grow the yeasts in the winery by first inoculating about 1 to 5 lit of fruit pulp (must) from the laboratory culture slant and then serially transferring the inoculum to successively larger volumes of fresh must until a quantity suitable for bulk fermentation is obtained. The grape juice is treated with bisulfite to kill undesirable yeast and bacteria.

Fermentation is done in vats. They are usually of wood or stone, and vary in capacity from a small keg to one that holds 190,000 lit or more. The vat is covered to maintain anaerobic conditions that encourage fermentation and also discourage growth of acetic acid bacteria which could convert the vine into vinegar. The course of fermentation (particularly the nature of by-products) and the concentration of alcohol produced are influenced by the temperature, sugar concentration, acidity, and tannin content of the must and the amount of sulfite added.

Temperature is especially important as the yield of alcohol is higher at the lower temperatures and it also encourages the formation of pleasant flavours. At higher temperatures the alcohol resistance of the yeast is decreased. A favourable temperature for fermentation is in the vicinity of 10° C.

In the sugar content is over 30%, the fermentation is inefficient because alcohol accumulates and arrests the activity of the yeasts before all the sugar is converted to alcohol. A low acid content favours production of acetaldehyde, glycerol, and volatile and fixed acids, which have a detrimental effect on the flavour, colour, and stability of the wine. In addition, a low acid content gives a lower yield of aromatic principles, which give the wine its bouquet.

After the partial fermentation, the racking operation begins and continues throughout the remainder of the fermentation period. In racking, wine is siphoned off from the sediment, which consists of dead yeast cells and other materials which settle at the bottom of the vat and is transferred to a fresh vat. This procedure is repeated for several times until the desired clarity of the wine is obtained. Before the last racking, a final clarification is performed by adding some substance (like casein, or bentonite) that carries additional sediment to the bottom,. Fermentation continues until the alcohol content is about 12%; and above this point the alcohol kills the yeast cells so that no more fermentation takes place. The wine is then stored in completely filled and sealed tanks for aging. Additional blending, fortification with additional alcohol, heat treatments, refrigeration, or filtration may be required before the wine is bottled.

Beer

Beer is an alcoholic beverage prepared from fermented grains, usually barley. Several different starting materials may be used in the production of beer, but they all achieve the same end- the production of a carbonated alcoholic drink. The top fermenting yeast, *Saccharomyces cerevisiae*, is the most widely used among all the yeasts. Strains should be chosen that are low-temperature-tolerant varieties. In this manner the low temperature favours the growth of the yeast and not bacteria, which may enter as contaminants on the starting materials. Not all beer is made from *Saccharomyces cerevisiae*. For example, *Saccharomyces carlbergensis* and *Saccharomyces monacensis* are used, especially in Holland. These yeasts grow at the bottom and are known as bottom fermenters.

Step I

The initial steps of beer production, barley is **malted** through a controlled germination and grains are washed and soaked for 2 to 3 days to stimulate development of the embryo; the water is then drained off and the seeds germinated. The embryo is allowed to grow until the plumule attains a length equal to approximately three-fourths of the kernel length and is then dried to halt growth. During the short period of germination, the embryo produces a number of digestive enzymes which begin to hydrolyze food reserves in the seed. From the brewer's standpoint, the most important of these are the carbohydrates which attack starch and sugars, and of these the most important are especially the amylases, which convert the starch into dextrins, maltose, and a little glucose. The maltose is the principal substratum for yeast fermentation.

Step II

Second step in beer production is known as **mashing**. The dried malt is ground and mixed with hot water. Most of the enzymatic conversion of starch to maltose by amylases takes place during mashing, which takes about 2 hours. The aqueous extract is separated from insoluble materials and husks, and is then boiled with hops, the female inflorescence of the hop plant containing essential oils and resins which impart characteristic flavours to the beer.

Step III

In this step the aqueous extract is cooled to a temperature between 8°C and 16°C (the temperature is partially determined by the type of beer being produced) and placed in fermentation vats. A selected strain of yeast is added. Traditionally *Saccharomyces carlsbergensis* is used to produce larger beer while *S. cerevisiae* is used to produce ales (in the United States, *S. carlsbergensis* may be used for both). During a fermentation period of about 5 to 14 days, the sugar is converted to alcohol. The yeasts settle to the bottom of the vat in a flocculent material in the production of the larger type of beer. In contrast, bubbles of carbon dioxide rise to the top of the vat and carry with them the yeast cells and dark flocculent materials from the liquid in the production of the ales. The resultant foamy scum must be periodically removed. When the fermentation period is over, the newly formed beer is allowed to rest for a few days. This period allows the yeast cells to settle out and is then drawn off into weeks. The beer is clearified by addition of gelatinous materials in a manner similar to that in which wines are cleared and may also be filtered through diatomaceous earth. Antioxidants are added since beer changes flavour upon oxidation, and carbon dioxide is added either as the pure gas or by mixing in some freshly fermented beer. The beer is then bottled for sale.

Whiskey

They are made from fermented grains (corn, wheat, barley malt, or rye malt), which are mixed in varying proportions according to the type of whiskey being produced, and fermented by yeasts. The procedures are similar to those involved in beer production, the major exception is that the fermented grain broth is distilled in order to concentrate the alcohol.

Miso

This is an important commodity in Japan, made by fermentation of soybeans. It is sold as pale-brownish paste, from which is made a potage type of soup, serving as a regular morning dish. According to Sakaguchi (1961) the annual production of miso in Japan exceeds 50,000 tons. Cooked soybeans, *koji* made from rice, and 10 to 12 per cent of salt, are ground together along with a little miso from a previous batch. The mixture is packed into closed containers and allowed to ferment at 35 to 45° C, without aeration, for 3 to 5 months. It is then allowed to age from a month or more at room temperature before packaged for sale.

Organic Acid Fermentation

Citric Acid

Citric acid is the product of fermentation of numerous organisms. However, certain strains of the fungus *Aspergillus niger* produce commercially high yields of citric acid from a variety of 2-, 3-, 4-, 5-, 7-, or 12-carbon compounds. Four theories have been proposed for the mechanism of citric acid formation by *Aspergillus niger*. It would appear that metabolic shunt (induced by environment) is at work, since citric acid is usually not a metabolite that accumulates in the medium but is readily utilized as a carbon source. The culture conditions are minimal for nitrogen and carbon at low pH. Phosphate is usually deficient. *Aspergillus niger* appears to have more than one systems for the formation of citric acid since, it utilizes variety of different length carbon chains under special conditions.

Uses of Citric Acid: The important organic acid produced by fungi is citric acid which is used commercially as a flavouring ingredient in beverages and foods, especially in dry mixtures such as gelatins, and soft drink powders as tablets, and as the principal acid in the preparation of soft drinks, desserts, jams, jellies, candies, wines, and frozen fruits. About 90 % of the supply comes from *Aspergillus niger* fermentation. The acid is rapidly and almost completely metabolized in the human body and has wide pharmaceutical uses. Specially its incorporation is effervescent products and as citrates in blood transfusion. Citric acid is also used in astringent lotions to adjust the pH, in hair rinses and hair-setting preparations, in electroplating, in leather tanning, and in reactivating clogged with iron.

Citric acid was originally produced from calcium citrate obtained from cut lemons. Methods for producing citric acid from fungus metabolism were introduced in the United States in 1923.

Mechanism of Citric Acid Formation: Citric acid is one of the principal organic acids produced in the citric (CA) cycle. Recent evidences indicates that the probable origin of citric acid is directly from the CA cycle. When mycelium actively grows, citric acid is produced as an intermediate in the CA cycle and is further diverted to growth-promoting biosynthesis or energy release. For commercial production of citric acid, culture conditions which are inhibitory to growth of the fungus are maintained and the CA cycle itself is inhibited or stopped by enzymatic inhibition of the low pH or by specific enzyme inhibitors, *e.g.*, copper ions. During the production of citric acid, the activity of the condensing enzyme (operating in the condensation of acetyl CoA and oxaloacetic acid to citric) is increased, while the activities of the isocitric acid dehydrogenase and acotinase disappear. The enzyme acotinase is responsible to control the biosynthesis of isocitric acid from citric acid, and in turn isocitric dehydrogenase mediates in the hydrogen removal which yields oxalosuccinic acid from isocitric acid. Therefore, it has been suggested that inactivity of these latter enzymes is the reason for citric acid accumulation.

Commercial Production of Citric Acid: In commercial production of citric acid, *Aspergillus niger* may be cultured on the surface of the shallow pans or as submerged mycelium in aerated vats. Shallow-pan culture has been widely accepted and rapidly added by more efficient vat culture. The requirements and methodology for both the cultures are similar, although in actual plant operation many minute details are different. Beet molasses is the least expensive carbohydrate source, and has a high metallic ion content which may cause low yields of citric acid to be produced. Beet molasses has been widely used in the pan techniques, although pure sucrose or highly refined syrups give higher yields in submerged cultures in vats. Metallic cations are removed from the carbohydrate source by the use of cation-exchange processes and absorbents or (or in the case of beet molasses) by treatment with ferricyanide. The carbohydrate is diluted to a concentration of about 20% to 25%. This high sugar concentration inhibits formation of acids other than citric acid. The manufacture of citric acid needs a low pH, and hydrochloric acid is added to reduce the medium to the range of pH 2 to 5 when the fungal spores in the inoculum germinate. In the vat, the pH is kept below 3.5. Nitrogen is provided by adding ammonium salts. For vat cultures, copper or organic ions may be added as antagonists to iron and aid in the control of mycelial growth which increases citric acid production.

The prepared medium is added with spores from stock cultures. Highly aerobic conditions are needed, and submerged cultures are aerated with sterile air and agitated. Temperature must be maintained in the range of 25° to 30°C during incubation period (7 to 10 days). Therefore, the harvesting of the citric acid is started. Lime is added to the culture medium to precipitate any oxalic acid which formed, and the mycelium and calcium oxalate are filtered off. Additional filtration may be required to clarify the medium. A slurry of calcium citrate, which precipitates out. The calcium citrate is filtered out and then treated with sulfuric acid which precipitates the calcium. The dilute citric acid solution is purified by treatment with carbon and is demineralized by successive passage through cation- and anion-exchange resins. This purified citric acid solution is then evaporated, leaving behind citric acid crystals, which are further purified by recrystallizations from water.

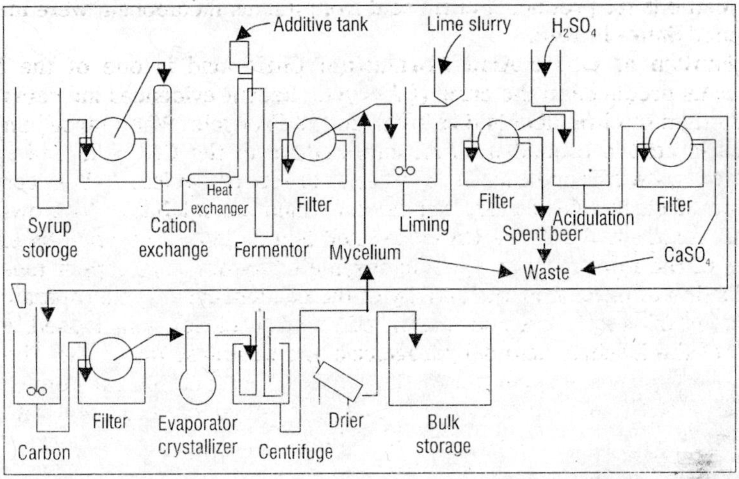

FIGURE 30.1: Commercial production of citric acid.

Gluconic Acid

It is formed from sugars by the action of a large number of species of moulds, chiefly species of *Aspergillus* and *Penicillium*. The first fungus to be used was *Penicillium purpurogenum* var. *rubri-sclerotium*, and the fermentation was carried out in shallow pans of pure aluminium. Later it was found that certain strains of *P. chrysogenum* gave better results, and still later selected strains of *Aspergillus niger* were used.

D-Lactic Acid

Most of the work on the production of this acid has been done by American investigators. The fungus used is *Rhizopus oryzae*. Following a preliminary study of the physiology of the mould, a rapid process was worked out, using a rotary fermenter with forced aeration. The time for the fermentation was reduced to 30-35 hours, and yields of 70-75 per cent were claimed.

Gallic Acid

It was obtained by Calmette in 1902 by fermenting a clear extract of tannin by means of an organism which he named *Aspergillus gallomyces* (a strain of *A. niger*), the fungus being grown in a wall-aerated and agitated liquid.

Fumaric Acid

It is produced, in yields of upwards of 65 per cent of the sugar consumed, when a strain of *Rhizopus arrhizus* is grown in shake-cultures in flasks. The sugar concentration was 10-16 per cent, and it was found to be essential to neutralize the acid continuously by means of calcium carbonate. The acid is required chiefly for the manufacture of plastics and varnishes.

Itaconic Acid

This substance was first obtained as a mould metabolic product of *Aspergillus itaconicus* (*A. glaucus* group). Of more interest in this connection was a paper by Calam, Oxford, and Raistrick (1939) describing the production of itaconic acid by a strain of *Aspergillus terreus*.

Glycerol

Glycerol is formed in small amounts during the normal alcoholic fermentation of sugar by yeasts, the maximum yield being about 3 per cent of the sugar consumed. It was found that the yield may be much improved by carrying out the fermentation in an alkaline medium, and still more so by adding sodium sulphite to the culture medium, which has the additional advantage that it inhibits the growth of bacteria without affecting the activity of the yeast. The yield of glycerol obtained was about 25 per cent of the sugar consumed.

Fermentation products have long been recognised as invaluable aids to the livestock producers of the world. As therapeutic antibiotics, such as penicillins and tetracyclines, they have been successfully used for individual animal treatment via injection, or for multiple animal treatments via drinking water or feed systems. These products were initially developed for animals as an extension to their use in human medicine. Over the past twenty years however, fermentation products have been introduced specifically for animals as prophylactic and most importantly as growth promoting agents. These products promote the efficient production of meat under intensive conditions.

It is possible for medicinal agents to be added via drinking water systems, but this is not a convenient route except for short term medication of therapeutic or prophylactic medicines. All other methods of administration, however sophisticated in terms of multiple dosing, are on a single animal basis.

PRODUCTION OF VITAMINS

Vitamins are organic substances that are essential in small amounts for the health, growth, reproduction, and maintenance of one or more animal species, which must be included in the diet since they either cannot be synthesized at all or found in sufficient quantities in the body. Each vitamin performs specific function, hence, one cannot replace or, act for, another. In general, the human body cannot synthesize them, at least in large enough amounts to meet its needs. However, vitamin D is exception; when a person is exposed to ultraviolet rays, the vitamin is synthesized from its precursor, which is found in the skin.

Vitamins: General Aspects

Nomenclature and Classification: There is no universal agreement on the nomenclature of the vitamins. But the modern tendency is to use the chemical name, particularly in describing members of the B complex. In this book, the most common designations are used. Today, vitamins are generally classed as (1) fat-soluble *vs* water-soluble vitamins, (2) vitamin B complex, and (3) vitamin like substances.

Fat-Soluble *vs* Water-Soluble Vitamins: Several phenomena of vitamin nutrition are related to solubility, vitamins are soluble in either fat or water. Consequently, it is important that both nutritionists and consumers be well informed about solubility differences in vitamins and make use of such differences in programs and practices. Based on solubility, vitamins may be grouped as follows:

TABLE 30.3: Various types of fat and water soluble vitamines

The Fat-Soluble Vitamins	The Water-Soluble Vitamins
Vitamin A	Biotin

Vitamin D	Choline
Vitamin E	Folacin (folic acid)
Vitamin K	Niacin (nicotinic acid; nicotinamide)
	Pantothenic acid (vitamin B-3)
	Riboflavin (B-2)
	Thiamin (vitamin B-1)
	Vitamin B-6 (pyridoxine; pyridoxal; pyridoxamine)
	Vitamin B-12 (cobalamins)
	Vitamin C (ascorbic acid; dehydroascorbic acid)

It is necessary that vitamin C is the only member of the water-soluble group that is not a member of the B family.

Chemical composition: The fat-soluble vitamins contain only carbon, hydrogen, and oxygen, whereas the water-soluble B vitamins contain these three elements plus nitrogen.

Occurrence: Vitamins originate primarily in plant tissues which includes vegetable products (cabbage, carrot, orange, lemon, corn or maize oil, and corn or maize bran etc.) and microorganisms (brewers yeast, bakers yeast etc.). Vitamins are also obtained from animal products like fish ox or calf liver oil, eggs etc. Vitamins C and D are present in animal tissues only. If an animal consumes foods containing them or harbors microorganisms that synthesize them. Fat-soluble vitamins can occur in plant tissue in the form of a pro-vitamin (or precursor of a vitamin), which can be converted into a vitamin in the animal body. But no pro-vitamins are known for any water-soluble vitamin. Also, the B vitamins are universally distributed in all living tissues, whereas the fat-soluble vitamins are completely absent from some.

Storage: The fat-soluble vitamins are stored in appreciable quantities in the body, whereas the water-soluble vitamins are not. Any of the fat-soluble vitamins can be stored wherever fat is deposited; and the greater the intake, the greater the storage.

Excretion: The fat-soluble vitamins are excreted exclusively in the faces via the bile. The water-soluble vitamins are excreted primarily in the urine, although limited amounts may be present in the faeces. This difference in pathway of excretion reflects the difference in solubility.

Vitamin B Complex

With the exception of vitamin C, all of the water-soluble vitamins can be grouped together under the vitamin B complex, of which there are the following nine: biotin, choline, folacin (folic acid), niacin (nicotinic acid; nicotinamide), pantothenic acid (vitamin B_3), riboflavin (vitamin B-2), thiamin (vitamin B-1), vitamin B_6 (pyridoxine; pyridoxal; pyridoxamine), vitamin B_{12} (cobalamins)

Vitamin B_{12} belongs to a group of compounds known as cobalamins. Chemically, vitamin B_{12} is composed of a central cobalt atom coordinated by a porphyrin-like group called corrin. The axial coordination sites are occupied by a base, dimethylbenzimidazole, and a cyano group. Other cobalamins are also known. The compounds containing bases different from dimethylbenzimidazole are known as B_{12} analogs.

Vitamin B_{12} (Cobamide) Production

Vitamin B_{12}, like so many other members of the B complex, is not a single substance; rather, it consists of several closely related compounds with similar activity. The term *cobalamins* is applied to this group of substances because all of them contain cobalt. Vitamin B-12, which is the most active member, is cyanocobalamin, named after the cyanide ion in the molecule. Other chemically related compounds known to have vitamin B_{12} activity include hydroxocobalamin, nitritocobalamin, and thiocyanate cobalamin.

Chemistry: Vitamin B_{12} is the largest and the most complex of vitamin molecules. The main part of the molecule consists of a porphyrin ring containing cobalt as the central element. A cyanide(CN) group may be attached to the cobalt, in which case the compound is called cyanocobalamin (or vitamin B_{12}); the commercially available form of the vitamin, little of which occurs naturally. The cyanide group attachment to the cobalt can be replaced by a hydroxy group (-OH), giving hydroxocobalamin, the common naturally occurring form of the vitamin; or it can be replaced by a nitrite group (-NO_2), giving nitritocobalamin, a form found in certain bacteria.

Vitamin B_{12} is the only vitamin produced by fermentation. For the commercial production of riboflavin, chemical or semisynthetic procedures are feasible.

Various types of microorganisms like of *Pseudomonas* (*i.e. P. denitrificans*) and *Propionibacterium* (*P. shermanii* and *P. freudenreichii*) are used for commercial production of vitamin B_{12}. These were preferred to Streptomyces and other species because of their rapid growth and high productivity of selected mutants.

Vitamin B_{12} production includes a laboratory-scale fermentation process from *Pseudomonas denitrificans* and pilot plant-scale fermentation process from *Propionibacterium shermanii*. The process based on carbohydrates of the culture media.

Vitamin B_{12} from Pseudomonas denitrificans

Mutant strains have been developed from the original wild-type of *P. denitrificans* for commercial production of vitamin B_{12}.

Medium: Medium for laboratory-scale fermentation process for vitamin B_{12} from *Pseudomonas denitrificans* includes (in g/L) beet molasses (60.0), brewers yeast (1.0), Nz amine (1.0), $(NH_4)_2HPO_4$ (2.0), $MgSO_4.7H_2O$ (1.0), $MnSO_4.7H_2O$ (0.2), $ZnSO_4.7H_2O$ (0.02), $Na_2MoO_4.2H_2O$ (510-3), agar (25.0), and pH (to 7.4). The inoculated medium is incubated at 28°C for 4 days.

Seed culture medium includes the same composition as mentioned above but it is devoid of agar. It is incubated for 3 days at 28°C on rotary shaker.

Production culture medium includes (in g/L) beet molasses (100.0), yeast (2.0), $(NH_4)_2HPO_4$ (5.0), $MgSO_4.7H_2O$ (3.0), $MnSO_4.H_2O$ (0.2), $CO(NO_3)_2.6H_2O$ (0.188), $ZnSO_4.7H_2O$ (0.02), $Na_2M_0O_4.2H_2O$ (5 × 10-3), 5,6-DBI (0.025), and pH (to 7.4). The media inoculated with the seed culture is incubated for 90 hrs at 29°C with agitation (420 rpm) and aeration (1v/v/m).

Carbohydrate source: Sugar beet molasses containing 5-10% betaine (trimethyl glycine). It stimulates the production of vitamin B_{12} by promoting synthesis of Ala-synthetsae. It helps in production of δ-aminotvulinic acid (the first intermediate of the pathway of cobalamin biosynthesis).

The cobalamin biosynthesis by *Pseudomonas denitrificans* require external supply of 5,6-dimethylbenzimidozole (5,6-DB1) and cobalt salt.

Fermentation: Aerated condition with agitation bioreactor is used for growth of *Pseudomonas* and biosynthesis of vitamin B_{12}.

Vitamin B_{12} from Propionibacterium shermanii

Medium: Maintenance medium for *P. shermanii* includes (in g/L) tryptone (10.0), yeast extract (10.0), filtered tomato juice (200.0), agar (10.0) and pH (to 7.2). The inoculated media is incubated for 4 days at 30°C.

Seed Culture Medium: This is different types and prepared according to stages.

First stage medium: It is similar to maintenance medium but is devoid of agar. It is incubated for 2 days at 30°C without agitation.

Second stage medium: It includes corn steep liquor, 20 g/L, glucose, 90 g/L and pH maintained at 6.5. Stainless steel bioreactor is used. The medium is incubated at 30°C for 24 hrs without aeration, pH is adjusted to 6.5.

Main culture medium: The production media includes (in g/L) corn steep liquor (40.0), glucose (100.0), $COCl_2.6H_2O$ (0.02), and pH (to 7.0). It is incubated at 30°C. The first 80 hrs is allowed to proceed without aeration, with slight nitrogen with agitation and slight aeration (0.1 v/v/m). pH is adjusted to 7.0.

Propionic organisms are grown on carbohydrate based media in an *unaerated* conditions. These organisms produce cobaltocorrinoids. Cobalt supplement is necessary for cobalamin production. It also depends on the internal formation or external supply of 5,6-dimethylbenzimidazole (5,6-DBI). The mutant strains of *P. shermanii* synthesis their own 5,6-DBI. It increases the yield up to 65 mg/L on pilot-scale.

Aeration promotes formation of 5,6-DBI, but it decreases vitamin B_{12} biosynthetic pathway at one of the stages. Therefore, at first stage (80 hrs), fermentation is conducted in absence of oxygen (anaerobic condition), but with little agitation until all the sugar in the media is utilized for the growth and the formation of cobinamide. This kind of operation will have no repressive effect. The subsequent stage (next 88 hrs) is followed with agitation and slight aeration. Aeration at this stage induces biosynthesis of 5,6-DBI and cobinamide is converted in to cobalamin.

Isolation and Purification

The extraction process depends on the release of unstable cobalamin from the cells lysed and subsequent treatment of this with cyanide to convert into more stable cyanocobalamin. Cells are separated from the culture broth. Cells are lysed by heat treatment at 80 to 120°C for 10-30 minutes at pH 6.5-8.5. The cells on lysis release various cobalamins. These are then solubilized with potassium-cyanide in the presence of sodium nitrite. The obtained cobalamins gets converted into cyanocobalamin.

The purification of the product is done using adsorption method for substances like amberlite IRC 50, Dowex 1x2, alumina, silanized silica gel, and Amberlite XAD2. It is then followed by elution with water-alcohol or water-phenol mixtures.

Vitamin B_2 (Riboflavin) Production

Riboflavin is present in virtually all living cells; and, like niacin, it has an essential role in the oxidative mechanism in the cells. Chemically, riboflavin is composed of an alloxine ring linked to an alcohol derived from the pentose sugar ribose. In living cells, riboflavin generally occurs combined either with phosphoric acid, or with phosphoric acid and adenylic acid, both of which may be combined with specific proteins (*i.e.*, protein bound FMN and FAD). It results from the combination of flavin, iso-allozine, and a polyol, D-ribitol, derived from D-ribose and are found in the form of two coenzymes *i.e.*, flavin-mononucleotide (FAM-riboflavin 5'-phosphate) and flavin adenine dinucleotide (FAD-riboflavin 5-adinosyldiphosphate).

Properties: In pure form, riboflavin exists as fine orange-yellow crystals, which are bitter testing and practically odorless. In water solutions, it imparts a greenish-yellow fluorescence. It is sparingly soluble in water. (It is much less soluble in water than thiamine). It is heat-stable in neutral or acid solutions, but it may be destroyed by heating in alkaline solutions. It is easily destroyed by light, especially ultraviolet light; for example, it may be destroyed by sunlight striking milk kept in glass bottles. (Milk in cartons is protected against such losses). Synthetic riboflavin should always be kept in dark bottles. Because of its heat stability and limited water solubility, very little riboflavin is lost in processing and cooking foods.

It is produced from bacteria: *Clostridium acetobutylicum* and *Candida flareri*. They produce 100 mg/L in 4 days and 600 mg/L in 7 days respectively. Two mutant strains of *Ascomycetes* spp. (*Eremothecium ashbyii* and *Ashbya gossypii*), and one recombinant bacterium *i.e.*, *Bacillus subtilis* can also produce vitamin B_2. These organisms are not affected by the presence of Fe^+ in the production medium. *Ashbya gossypii* is most preferable strain than *Eremothecium ashbyii*.

Production by Fermentation of Ashbya gossypii (NRRL Y 1056)

The hyphae of *Ashbya gossypii* can accumulate large amounts of riboflavin. Under optimal condition and in suitable culture medium *Ashbya gossypii* can produce riboflavin up to 10-15 g/L after 10 days. The crystals of the product sometimes appear outside the mycelium.

Medium: The production medium includes (g/L) corn steep liquor (45.0), peptone (35.0), soybean (45.0), and glycine (3).

Carbon source: Glucose, sucrose, and maltose.

Vegetable oil: Preferred for growth.

Nitrogen source: Peptones are produced by enzymatic hydrolysis of collagen like proteins (*e.g.*, gelatin, pancreatic hydrolysate) and corn steep, yeast extract, or distillers solubles. **Vitamins:** Biotin, inositol, thiamine.) are better source for nitrogen. Glycine (1-3 g/L) is also used as precursor of guanine. It increases the yield to 10-30%.

Fermentation: The fermentation is conducted in three phases:

Phase One: It is the initial rapid growth phase of the organism. During this phase glucose is utilized and pyruvic acid accumulates. The pH level decreases. Carbon source of the medium get exhausted. The growth ceases.

Phase Two: It is the production phase. During this sporulation occurs. The level of the pyruvate reduces. Ammonia in the medium accumulates due to deaminase activity. This results into rise in pH level.

Phase Three: The phase is characterized by the synthesis of cell bound riboflavin in the form of FAD and FMN.

Phase Four: It is the last phase and is characterized by autolysis of the cells. This causes release of free riboflavin into the medium.

The fermentation is carried out under aerobic condition. It is important to note that high-level aeration is not suitable for growth because it inhibits mycelial production and reduces the yield. The optimum temperature for production should be between 28-29°C for approximately 4-5 days. The pH of the medium should remain 6-7.5. An yield of 4-2 g/L can be obtained in 5 days.

Isolation: To obtain more impure form of riboflavin, simple concentration method of the broth at pH 4.5 and drying is used. The procedure includes heating of the broth at 60 °C for 3 hrs with bacterial alkaline protease. The insoluble fraction is obtained after cooling the mixture to 25°C. It is then followed by centrifugation at pH 7.

To obtain more pure form of riboflavin the concentration of the broth by heating to 121°C for 1 hr at pH 4.5 is used. The riboflavin is solubilized and the insoluble fraction is discarded. The solution is further treated with titanium chloride as reducing agent it will precipitate riboflavin. It is then reoxidized in the air and dissolved at 60°C in 10% HCl. After cooling, the solution is neutralized to yield purer forms of riboflavin crystals.

Vitamin C (Ascorbic Acid)

Vitamin C or ascorbic acid, dehydroascorbic acid, hexuronic acid, and the antiscorbutic vitamin – is the very important substance first found in citrus fruits, which prevent scurvy, one of the oldest scourges of mankind. All animal species appear to require vitamin C, but a dietary need is limited to humans, guinea pigs, monkeys, bats, certain fish, and perhaps certain reptiles. These species lack the enzyme L-gluconolactone oxidase, which is necessary for vitamin C synthesis from 6-carbon sugars.

Chemistry: Vitamin C is one of the simplest vitamins, the L(+)-isomer of which is biologically active. Ascorbic acid is a compound of relatively simple structure, closely related to the monosaccharides sugars. It is synthesized from glucose and other simple sugars by plants and by most animal species. Two forms of vitamin C occur in nature; ascorbic acid (the reduced form), and dehydroascorbic acid (the oxidized form). Although most of the vitamin C exists as ascorbic acid, both forms appear to be utilized similarly by the human. Also, the body efficiently utilizes either synthetic L-ascorbic acid or the vitamin in its natural form as in orange juice.

Ascorbic acid is easily oxidized to dehydroascorbic acid, which is just as easily reduced back to ascorbic acid. However, dehydroascorbic acid may be irreversibly oxidized, particularly in the presence of alkali, to diketogluconic acid, which has no antiscorbutic activity.

Certain derivatives of vitamin C (for example, erythrobic acid and ascorbyl palmitate) are used as antioxidants in food products to prevent rancidity, to prevent browning of fruit, and to cure meat. Erythrobic acid (D-araboascorbic acid) is poorly absorbed and has little antiscorbutic activity.

Properties: Ascorbic acid is a white, odorless crystalline power, which is quite stable when dry. Of all the vitamins, ascorbic acid is the most unstable when in solution. It is highly soluble in water, but not in fat. The oxidation (destruction of ascorbic acid is accelerated by air, heat, light, alkalies, oxidative enzymes, and traces of copper and iron. It is markedly destroyed by cooking, particularly where the pH is alkaline. Cooking losses also result because of its solubility. The destruction of ascorbic acid is slowed down by foods that are acidic, by refrigeration, and by protection from exposure to air.

Animals and plant tissues are the source of this vitamin. Plant sources include vegetables – cabbage, spinach, tomato, and fruits such as oranges and lemons. Microorganisms such as fungi, yeasts and algae also produce ascorbic acid but, in small quantities.

Commercially vitamin C is obtained with semi synthesis from D-glucose. All the processes are operated via 2-keto-L-gulonic acid. The lactonization and isomerization of this 2-keto-L-gulonic acid results into the production of L-ascorbic acid. The 2-

keto-L-gulonic acid is also obtained using different oxidative or reductive reactions. It is obtained by reduction of D-glucose involving the inversion of the carbon sequence or by oxidation of D-glucose without inversion of carbon sequence.

$$\text{D-glucose} \xrightarrow{\textit{catalytic reduction}} \text{D-sorbitol}$$

$$\text{D-sorbitol} \xrightarrow{\textit{bacterial (Acetobacter on sorbitol) oxidation}} \text{L-sorbose (Poor yield)}$$

$$\text{D-sorbitol} \xrightarrow{\textit{bacterial (Gluconobacter oxydans) oxidation}} \text{L-sorbose (Good yield)}$$

$$\text{diacetone-sorbose} \xrightarrow{\textit{chemical oxidation}} \text{diacetone 2-keto-L-gulonic acid}$$

$$\text{D-glucose} \xrightarrow{\text{by L-idonic acid pathway; or 2,5-diketo-D-gluconic acid pathway}} \text{2-keto-L-gulonic acid}$$

The 2-keto-L-gulonic acid is efficiently obtained in double fermentation by 2,5-diketo-D-gluconic acid pathway. It eliminates all the chemical stages, involving only two stages.

2,5-Diketo-D-gluconic Acid Pathway: It is the fermentation for Ca-2,5-diketo-D-gluconate. *Erwinia* sp. ATCC 31626 is used for this purpose. This first phase is followed second phase of fermentation of Ca-2,5-diketo-D-gluconate using *Corynebacterium* sp. ATCC 31090. It produces Ca-2-keto-L-gulonate. The sequence of conversion is presented in following stages:

D-Glucose

↓

D-Gluconic acid

↓

2-keto-D-gluconic acid

↓

2,5-Diketo-D-gluconic acid

↓

2-keto-L-gulonic acid

Phases of Fermentation using Erwinia sp.

Medium: The media used in shake-flask and seed tank is same. The production medium for Ca-2,5-diketo-D-gluconate includes (in g/L): glucose (58.0), CSL (11.3), $(NH_4)_2HPO_4$ (5.6), $CaCO_3$ (184.0), Antifoam agent (0.2).

First Phase of Fermentation Using *Erwinia* sp.: The starting culture of *Erwinia* sp is maintained in an agar test-tubes. The culture is being done on an agar medium containing glycerol, yeast extract peptone, KH_2PO_4 and $MgSO_4$. It is incubated at temperature of 28°C for 24 hrs. A shake-flask culture (20 hrs at 28°C) is inoculated into a seed tank and incubated at 28°C for 10 hrs with agitation and aeration.

Second Phase of Fermentation Using *Erwinia* sp.: The fermentation is carried at 28°C for 26 hrs with agitation (160 rpm) and aeration (1.5 v/v, pressure 1.5 Kg/cm^2). After 3 hrs the fermentation culture media should be supplied intermittently with 1152 Kg glucose in 120 L of sterile solution. The addition of glucose solution should be stopped after 15 hrs. The final volume should be 4200 L.

Fermentation Stage using Corynebacterium sp.

Production Medium: The medium includes (in g/L): glucose (20.0), CSL (30.0), $NaNO_3$ (3.45), KH_2PO_4 (0.67), $ZnSO_4$-$7H_2O$ (4.9 x 10^{-3}), $MnCl_2.7H_2O$ (0.8 x 10^{-3}), Thiamine. HCl (0.22 x 10^{-3}), Ca-D-patothenate (0.17 x 10^{-3}). The initial culture is maintained on agar test tubes at 28°C for 40 hrs. The media is inoculated with *Corynebacterium* sp. (ATCC 31090) at 28°C for 66 hrs. Fermentation has to be carried with agitation (160 rpm) and aeration (0.25 v/v/m). At 16 hours, the fermenter should be provided with $NaNO_3$ (1 g/L). The media is inoculated with 6L of the 1st stage seed.

The seed culture can be obtained by culturing *Corynebacterium* sp. in a seed tank (470 L in 1 m^3 stainless steel fermenter) at 28°C for 24 hrs with agitation (244 rpm) and aeration (1 v/v m). media is inoculated with 6L of the 1st stage seed.

The production media is employed in the main fermenter (4-23 m^3 in 10 m^3 stainless steel fermenter).

Harvesting and Isolation

The 2-keto-L-gulonic acids is isolated from the harvested broth at the end of second stage fermentation by treating with sodium carbonate. The subsequent concentration to crystallization yields 90% 2-keto-L-gulonate.

COMMERCIAL PRODUCTION OF ANTIBIOTICS

In the original sense; any microbial product which, in low concentrations (of the order of micrograms/millilitre), is capable of inhibiting or killing (susceptible) microorganisms. The term was first used by Waksman in the 1940s; it distinguished the (then newly-discovered drug penicillin from the synthetic) sulphonamides which had been developed in the 1930s. Difficulties in terminology become apparent when the penicillins (and other natural antimicrobial products) were subjected to chemical modification or synthesized de novo in the laboratory.

Currently, the term antibiotic is often extended to include drugs such as the Sulphonamides, Nalidixic Acid, and the semi-synthetic Penicillins. Many antibiotics are Chemotherapeutic agents but others are too highly toxic to be of any clinical value; certain antibiotics (*e.g.* colicins) are used for non-therapeutic purpose. Most of the antibiotics used as chemotherapeutic agents are active against bacterial pathogens; some (*e.g.*, griseofulvin) are antifungal, others (*e.g.*, Fumigillin, suramin) are antiprotozoal, while a few (*e.g.* the rifamycins) have limited antiviral activity.

The idea of using one microorganism to combat the evil effects of another is by no means a new one. Pasteur was probably the first to describe clearly the production of an antibiotic, and, during the intervening years, many claims have been made as to the therapeutic value of bacterial products.

Production of antibiotics (antibacterial or antifungal compounds) is one of the largest and most important microbiological industries. Interest in utilization of antibiotics for therapy began in 1929 when Alexander Fleming found that a mold has contaminated his cultures of a pathogenic bacterium, *Staphylococcus aureus*, and had killed bacteria in its immediate vicinity leaving a clear ring of lysed bacteria. The mold was a *Penicillium* (later found to be *P. notatum*). Fleming named the unidentified **lytic principle penicillin.**

TABLE 30.4: Some antibiotics produced by microorganisms

Antibiotics	*Microorganisms*
Amphotericin B	*Streptomyces nodosus*
Bacitracin	*Bacillus licheniformis*
Carbomycin	*Streptomyces halstedii*
Chlorotetracycline	*Streptomyces aureofaciens*
Chloramphenicol	*Streptomyces venezuelae*
Erythromycin	*Streptomyces erythreus*
Fumagillin	*Aspergillus fumigatus*
Griseofulvin	*Penicillium griseofulvin* *P. nigricans* *P. urticae*
Kanamycin	*Streptomyces kanamyceticus*
Neomycin	*S. fradiae*
Novobiocin	*S. niveus* *S. spheroides*
Nystatin	*S. noursei*
Oleandomycin	*S. antibiotics*
Oxytetracycline	*S. rimosus*
Penicillin	*Penicillium chrysogenum*
Polymyxin B	*Bacillus polymyxa*
Streptomycin	*S. griseus*
Tetracycline	Dechlorination and hydrogenation of chlorotetracycline; direct fermentation in dechlorinated medium
Vira A (Adenine arabinoside)	*S. antibiotics*

Screening of Antibiotic Producers

The search for antibiotics in the pharmaceutical industry presents a good example of how screening procedures are employed to select microorganisms for industrial applications. The discovery of new antibiotics results from laborious searches. Sample from many sources, including soil from around the world, are examined as potential sources of antibiotic-producing microorganisms; countless strains of microbial isolates are tested by pharmaceutical laboratories. One of the best penicillin-producing strains of *Penicillium* was isolated from an orange purchased at a road side fruit stand. Several antibiotic-actinomycetes were isolated from a manure-enriched pasture.

A useful antibiotic-producing strain must produce metabolites that inhibit the growth or reproduction of pathogens. This essential property can be assayed by using test strains and examining whether the isolate being screened produces substances that inhibit the growth of these test organisms. A positive result in such a primary screening procedure in no sense ensures the discovery of an industrially useful antibiotic-producing strain. It simply identifies those strains of microorganisms that have the potential for further development.

The search for new antibiotics still goes on, and new ones are frequently announced. Genetic engineering has opened up several new possibilities for employing microorganisms to produce economically important substances. The mutation and selection approach is hit or miss, whereas the use of recombinant DNA technology permits the purposeful manipulation of genetic information to engineer a microorganism, which can produce high yields of a variety of products. The use of biotechnology has great social consequences.

β-Lactam Antibiotics

The naturally occurring penicillins have been included in β-lactam family. Antimicrobially active β-lactam compounds are represented by penicillins and cephalosporins. The penicillins fused to a thiazolidine ring, whereas the cephalosporins have the β-lactam fused to dihydrothiazine ring. The discovery of the 7α-methoxy cephalosporins provided the first new, naturally occurring β-lactam nucleus following the isolation of Cephalosporin C.

Penicillins

Not only did penicillin developed interest in antibiotics and launch the antibiotic industry, but penicillin is still the most widely used antibiotic. Most penicillins are produced by species of *Penicillium* while others are semi synthetic. It is produced from *Penicillium notatum* (penicillin F) and *Penicillium chrysogenum.* Numerous species of Streptomyces also produce penicillin N together with cephalosporins, cephamycins, clavams, or cephapanems. It is the drug of choice, when infection is caused by organism susceptible to it. Penicillin is effective against Gram-positive bacteria and also against some of the larger viruses and rickettsia. Penicillin is a generic term applied to an entire group of antibiotics, which are closely related in structure.

Chemical Nature and Biosynthesis: Penicillins are N-acyl derivatives of 6-aminopenicillanic acid (6-APA). They are synthesized in two types of fermentation. Type-1 penicillins synthesized with non polar side chains as the only β-lactam, and type 2 penicillins N (2) is synthesized along with other β-lactams. The type I *i.e.* penicillins with non polar side chain is found in fungi. The nature of the side chain ring is determined by addition of a suitable side chain precursors to the fermentations *i.e.*, addition of phenyl acetic acid as precursor to the fermentation produces benzylpenicillins.

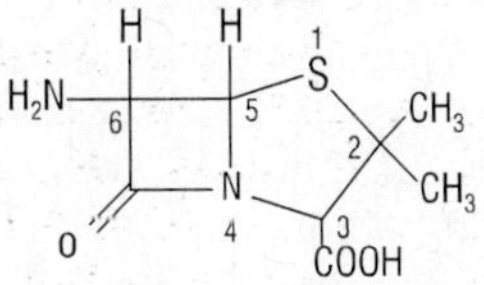

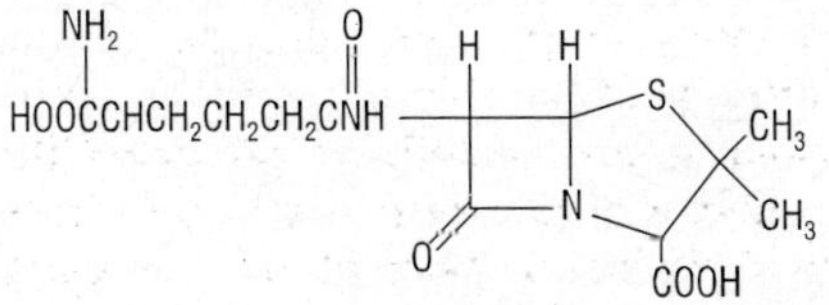

The naturally occurring penicillins have the following basic structure and differ in the R groups. The R group could be provided by precursor with the structure RCH_2COOH or its salt, amide or ester, although $RCH_2CH_2NH_2$ also could serve as precursors. The various R-group side chains may effect relative potencies, to a certain extent, the relative activities against sensitive microorganisms. Several species of penicillin molds produce penicillins with non-polar side chains.

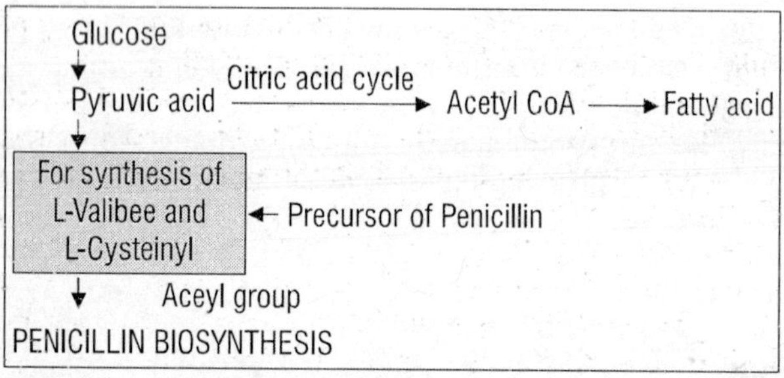

FIGURE 30.2: Biosynthesis of Penicillin.

Penicillin is produced along synthetic pathways not required for growth but superimposed upon those pathway required for maintenance. Key intermediates in the pathway are pyruvic acid, valine and cystine. Penicillin production is at its maximum level when the citric acid cycle is not actively taking place or if a great deal of pyruvic acid is not being converted to acetyl CoA and then to fatty acid. The accumulating pyruvic acid can then be available for synthesis of L-valine, to form a dipeptide precursor of penicillin, L-cysteinly-L-valine. This last intermediate is then combined with the acyl group from phenyl acetic acid in the case of penicillin G or acyl groups from other specific precursors in the synthesis of the other penicillins. Many of the details concerning penicillin biosynthesis are still unknown.

Commercial Production of Benzylpenicillins (Penicillin G): The original *P. notatum* Straub isolated by Fleming gave low yield of penicillin. Finally a strain of *P. chrysogenum* was isolated and was found to give superior yields of penicillin. Strains of *Penicillium* may produce more than 180 times as much penicillin as the original isolate with which the breeding program was initiated. Penicillin is produced in submerged vat cultures using a selected strain of *P. chrysogenum*. High yielding strains have been developed using mutation or genetic engineering techniques. Yield has been increased from less than 10 μg/ml to about 30 μg/ml. These strains have high titre, improved growth, tolerance to side chain precursors, ability to accumulate intracellular sulphate, acetyltransferase activity, and other properties as per the need.

The Inoculum: Master stock (spores) is the major source of inoculum. Spores above or below a critical level show differences in morphology and productivity. Spores of *P. chrysogenum* are developed from vegetative mycelium which is prepared in a series of inoculum development steps. The high yielding strains are genetically unstable. Spores from working stock cultures are suspended in water or non-toxic lauryl sulphonate. These are added to flasks containing wheat bran and nutrient solutions. A shake flask culture of 4 days old is inoculated into a seed tank for 3 days. It acts as inoculum. Heavy mycelial growth is obtained with agitation and aeration. Care should be taken to avoid all sort of contamination. The main purpose of inoculum development process is to increase the concentration of fungal mycelium.

The Medium: A typical production medium includes glucose, sodium phenyl acetate, corn step liquor (CSL), ammonium sulphate, and potassium hydrogen phosphate. Lipid nutrients are used by the fungus during fermentation. They also utilize oil as an antifoam agent. These nutrients contribute to both the quantities of mycelium and product yields, but high levels are deleterious in both the early and late stages of fermentation. The on set of production phase can be marked by the addition of phenyl acetic acid (PAA) by continuous feed.

Fermentable carbohydrate: The principal carbohydrate in precursor molecules (phenethylamine and phenyl amine). It is needed for penicillin production and are present in the corn steep liquor. It is the most favourable carbon source for penicillin production because it is assimilated slowly, giving the fungus a steady carbon source over a period of time and does not lead to the accumulation of organic acids. In general 65% of the consumed carbon is used for maintenance, 25% for mycelial growth, and only 10% for penicillin production (the final yield is in the range of 3.5% based on carbohydrate consumed). If glucose is available in less quantity from lactose it leads to starvation conditions required for the penicillin formation.

Aeration (Oxygen supply): Supply of oxygen in a bioreactor is the limiting factor penicillin biosynthesis. If oxygen availability falls below critical level, it will reduced the growth. Aeration conditions should be adjusted in such a way that fast growth can be achieved only until the cell production reaches maximum density.

Biomass Production: Production of penicillin depends upon biomass production therefore, it is desirable to have a high biomass concentration in the vessel. The medium contains carbon compounds and other nutrients and they allow organisms to grow initially near the maximum specific growth rate. This rapid growth rate causes a considerable increase in the initial oxygen uptake rate and carbon dioxide evolution rate. Penicillin production is increased by increasing and improving mycelial biomass. It is achieved by increasing the agitation rate and power.

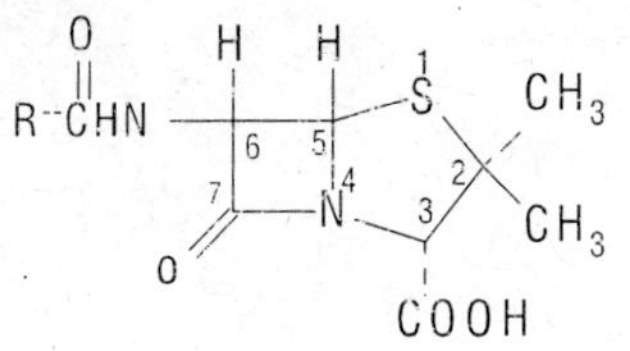

Penicillins	R
Benzylpenicillins/Penicillins G	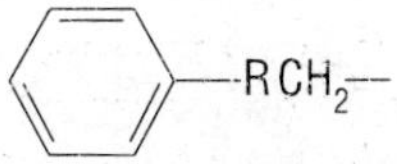
Phenoxymethylpenicillins/Penicillin V	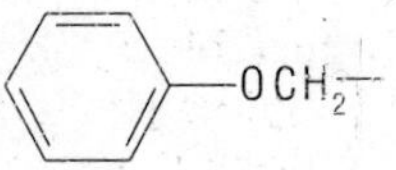
2-Pentenylpenicillin/Penicillin F	$CH_3CH_2CH{=}CHCH_2$—
n-Amylpenicillin/Dihydropenicillin F	$CH_3(CH_2)_4$—
n-Heptylpenicillin/Penicillin K	$CH_3(CH_2)_6$—
p-Hydroxylbenzylpenicillin/Penicillin X	

FIGURE 30.3: Different types of penicillins produced by fermentation of *Penicillium chrysogenum*.

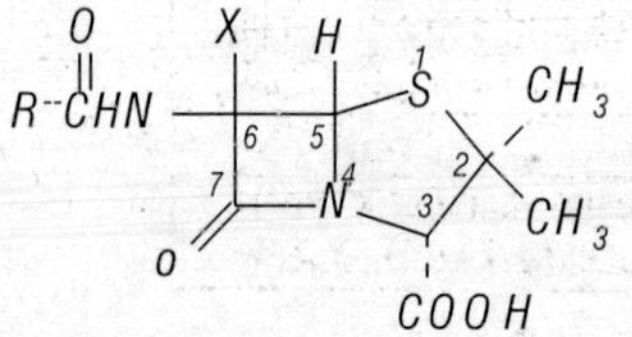

Penicillins	X	R
Benzylpenicillin	–H	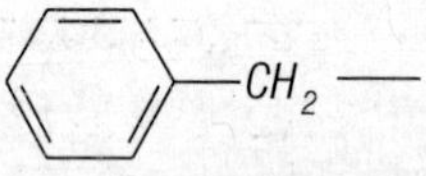
Methicillin	–H	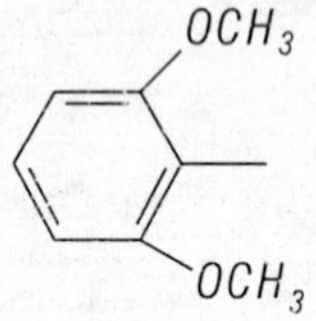
Ampicillin	–H	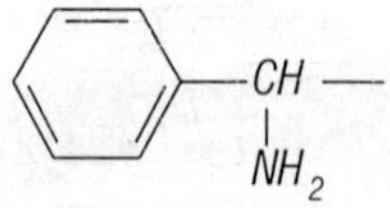
Ticarcillin	–H	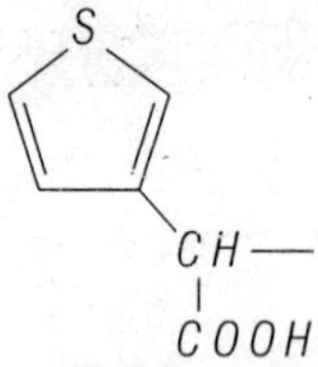
Piperaicillin	–H	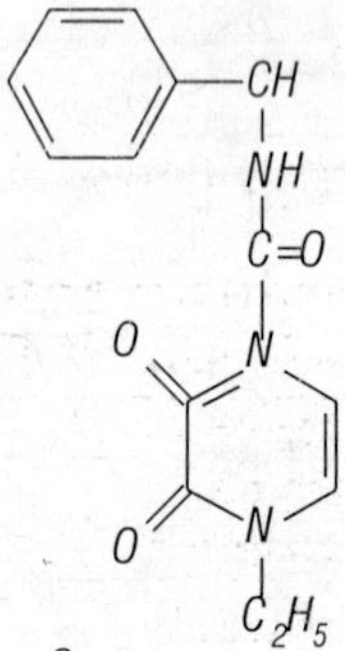
Temocillin	$-OCH_3$	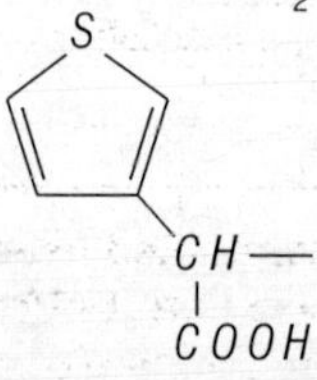

FIGURE 30.4: Various types of semi synthetic penicillin.

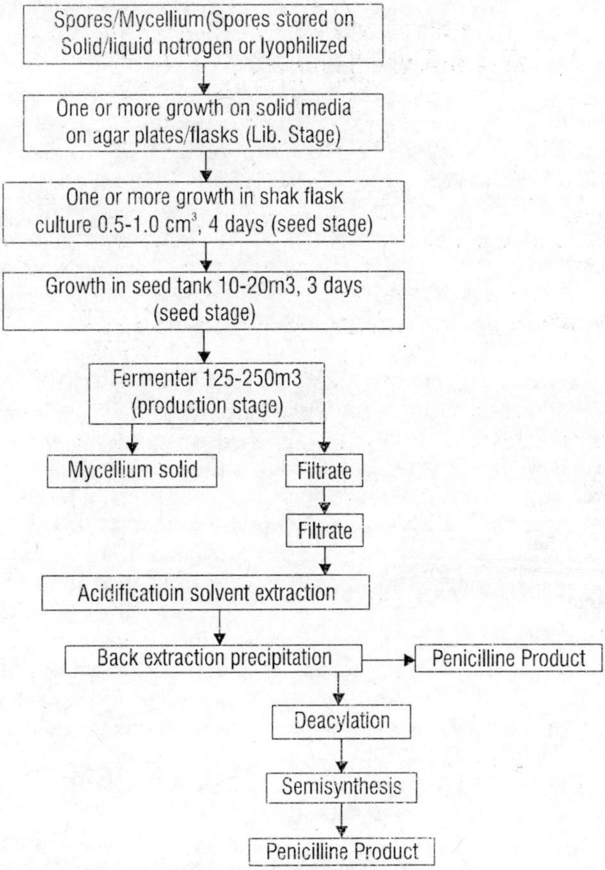

FIGURE 30.5: Presentation of flow chart of penicillin production.

TABLE 30.5: The major constituents of typical medium (Jackson) includes

Fermentable carbohydrate	**Corn steep (3.5%), Lactose (3.5%), glucose (1%)**
Potassium dihydrogen phosphate	0.4%
Organic nitrogen source	
Phenyl acetic acid precursor	
Edible oil	0.25%
Calcium carbonate (acts as buffer)	1%
Organic salts	
PH after sterilization	5.5 to 6.0

pH: It is maintained near neutrality by calcium and magnesium carbonate in the medium by phosphate buffer. It is also controlled by adding sodium hydroxide or sulphuric acid in the medium.

Procedure: About 30,000 liters of the medium are placed in a tank, sterilized and inoculated with an aqueous suspension of *P. chrysogenum* conidia. During the incubation period, the medium is aerated with sterile air and agitated. The tank is equipped with devices which allow the continuous addition of glucose syrups, sodium hydroxide, and sulphuric acid to maintain the pH between 6.8 and 7.4, cooling coils to maintain the temperature between 23°C and 25°C, devices for the introduction of antifoam agents, and pumps for the addition of the acyl or precursor. The most commonly used precursor is phenyl acetic acid. The other precursors in the form of a salt, amide, or ester of the corresponding acid or amine may be added to yield penicillins bearing the desired acyl group. At first, the mycelium grows actively and utilizes lactic acid and organic nitrogen compounds as sources of carbon. Ammonia is formed during the breakdown of these nitrogenous compounds. Ammonia is now actively assimilated and the pH is lowered. Active penicillin production is associated with this phase of lactose and ammonia utilization. Penicillin production ceases when the lactose is exhausted.

The duration of the incubation period is about 5 to 6 days. After incubation, the mycelium is filtered from the liquid medium. It contains the penicillin. The penicillin is mixed with a solvent (amyl or butyl acetate) and the resulting emulsion is centrifuged to extract the acetate solvent, which now contains the penicillin. A phosphate buffer is added to the acetate, and the penicillin is extracted with the phosphate buffer by centrifugation. This last step may be repeated, using successively smaller quantities of liquid. Butanol is added to the aqueous mixture, and the potassium salt of penicillin is crystallized from the solution. Potassium penicillin may be further purified and used in this form or it may be converted to procaine penicillin.

Recovery and Purification: Harvested culture broth includes penicillin G along with a variety of other metabolites. Vacuum filter is used for separation of mycelium from the broth on a rotary. The procedure is conducted under aseptic conditions. Penicillin (acid form) is extracted under controlled condition of temperature, pH, sterility of the penicillin containing filtrate. Care should be taken to minimize chemical and enzymatic degradation of the penicillin in the pumps, collecting vessel, and the extractor. Conversion of penicillin to the anionic form occurs at low pH (2.0 to 2.5). The pH is lowered done by adding phosphoric acid or sulphuric acid. The mixture is fed to Podbieliak counter current solvent extractor, with an organic solvent such as amyl acetate, methyl isobutyl ketone, or butyl acetate. For removal of pigments and other impurities from solvent containing penicillin, it is treated with active charcoal. The charcoal is separated from the extract on a precoated rotary vacuum filter and washed with solvent. The product is back extracted into water from solvent by adding potassium or sodium hydroxide to form its salt. So obtained aqueous solution is further subjected to repetition of the process to acid purification. The end product of penicillin is then crystallized into sodium or potassium penicillin.

Semisynthetic Penicillins: The semisynthetic penicillins contain 6-aminopenicillanic acid (6-APA) nucleus. 6-APA is obtained by fermentation in the absence of precursor. This procedure is not suitable because it reduces the yield and also contaminated with different lipid substances. 6-APA is prepared on large scale by removal of the phenyl acetate side chain from penicillin G. Semisynthetic β-lactam antibiotics now, have been synthesized from penicillin G, by converting into other β-lactam antibiotics. Enzyme acylases of microbial origin is used for this purpose.

Enzyme penicillin amidases (acylases): This enzyme catalyses the removal of the side chain from benzylpenicillins. It is a membrane bound enzyme found in *E. coli* and *Alcaligenes*. It has high specificity for penicillin G. Several types of enzymatic deacylation processes are used. Penicillin is treated with intact bacterial cell or with isolated enzyme. Immobilized cells or enzymes are also used. They are advantageous because they can be reused (batch process) or used continuously (column process).

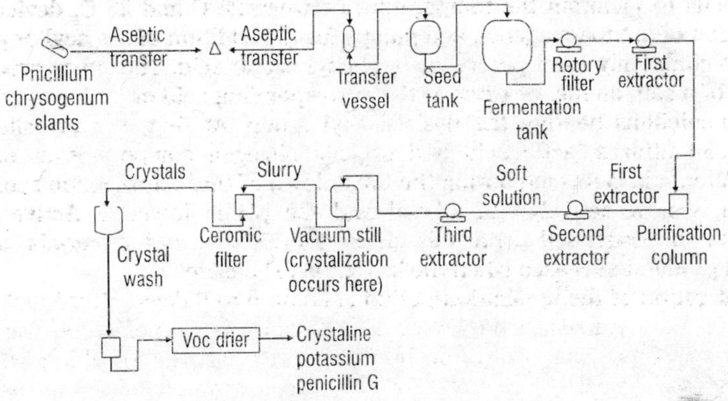

FIGURE 30.6: Commercial production of Penicillin.

6-APA is also used for production of new penicillins like Methicillin, nafcillin, and isoxazolyl penicillins, the broad spectrum penicillins, amoxicillin, epicillin, and cyclacillin; antipseudomonal penicillins such as carbenicillin and piperacillin, azocillin, and mezlocillin. These are obtained through chemical acylation with appropriate acid chlorides.

Commercial Production of 6-APA using Penicillin G. Acylase: The production is based on deacylation reaction, For this purpose different types of reactors are used. The conventional stirred tank reactors used for the original cell bound enzymation process with certain modification. The 6-APA is extracted from the cooled enzymation liquors. The pH of the liquor is adjusted to 2.5 by adding hydrochloric acid. Methyl isobutyl ketone (0.5 vol.) added to extract phenyl acetic acid and residual penicillin G. After separation, the pH of the aqueous phase is adjusted to pH 7.8 using sodium hydroxide. It is than evaporated under vacuum to obtain 6-APA concentration of 12-15%. 6-APA is precipitated by adjusting the pH to isoelectric point 4.3. Crystals washed successively with water and acetone, and dried under vacuum.

Cephalosporins

A Cephalosporin C is made as the fermentation product of *Cephalosporium acremonium*, but this form of the antibiotic is not potent enough for clinical use. The cephalosporin C molecule, however, can be transformed by removal of an α-aminoadipic acid side chain to form 7-α-amino-cephalosporanic acid, which can be further modified by adding side chains to form clinically useful products with relatively broad spectra of antibacterial action. We are at present into the so-called third-generation cephalosporins, such as moxalactam, which have been developed to combat bacteria that produce enzymes capable of degrading penicillins and cephalosporins.

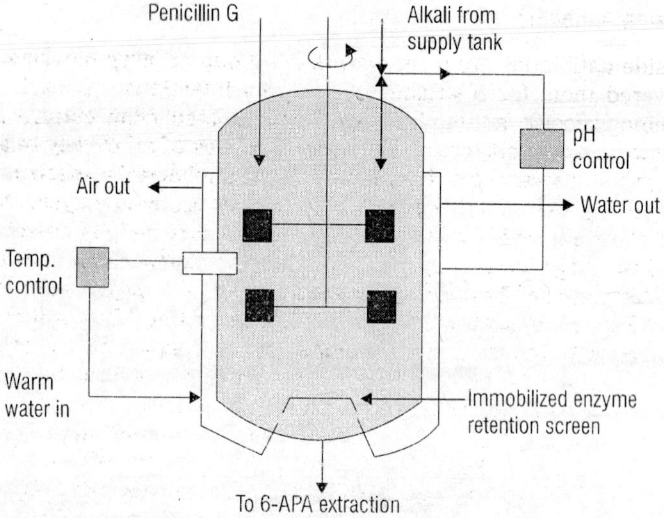

FIGURE 30.7: Modified batch process stirred tank-reactor.

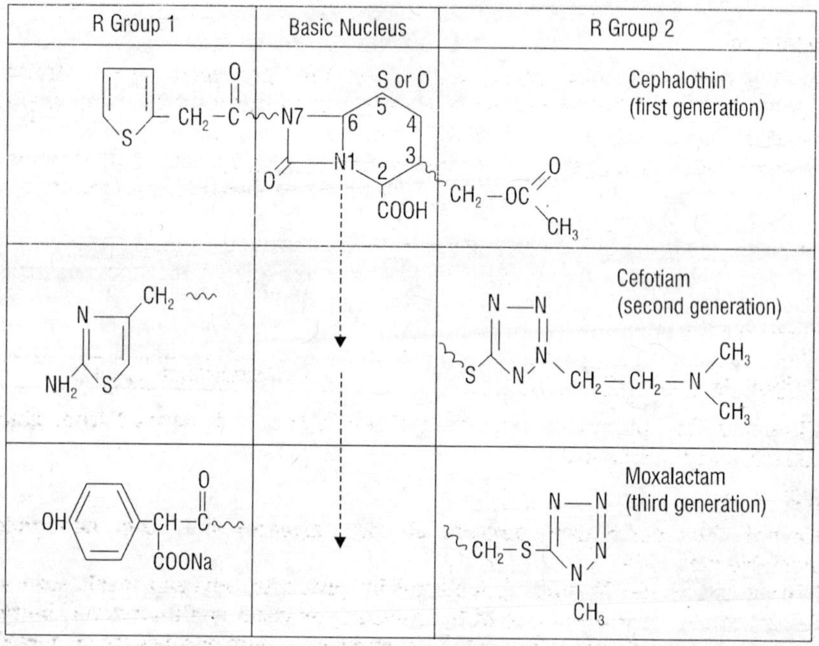

FIGURE 30.8: The structure of cephalosporins. Like penicillin, they have a beta-lactam ring (red), but a different main ring (yellow). However, unlike penicillins, they have two sites for placement of R groups (at positions 3 and 7). This makes possible several generations of molecules with greater versatility in function and complexity in structure.

0Aminoglycoside Antibiotic

Amino glycoside antibiotics are a representative group of streptomycins. Waksman (1944) discovered them for treatment of bacterial infections. About 152 naturally occurring aminoglycoside antibiotics have been isolated from culture filtrated of various bacteria and actinomycetes. These are mixtures of all closely related water-soluble basic pseudosaccharides. They have a broad antibacterial spectrum.

Streptomycin is used for treatment of tuberculosis. Kannamycin is a second generation of aminoglycosides and is used for treatment of serious infections caused by different Gram negative pathogenic bacteria. Gentamicin is another member of this group. It has expanded antibacterial spectrum of aminoglycoside antibiotics to the member of Pseudomonadaceae family and is hardly affected by other antibiotics.

Single bacterial strain may produce many analogous compounds of aminoglycoside antibiotics. For example kannamycin is produced by *Streptomyces kanamyceticus* and gentamicin by *Micromonospora purpurea* etc. Therefore, it is difficult to separate a single aminoglycoside antibiotic from the culture filtrate in the pure state. The techniques like column chromatographic separation with alumina, silica gel, cellulose, ion-exchange cellulose (*e.g.*, carboxymethyl-cellulose, phosphocellulose and sulphoethyl cellulose) or iron exchange gels (*e.g.*, C M Sephadex, SP Sephadex and CM Sepharose) HPLC, etc. have been used to separate and isolate these closely related compounds.

Streptomycin

Streptomycin and various other antibiotics are produced using strains of *Streptomyces griseus*. It is an important chemotherapeutic agent active against gram positive and gram negative including mycobacteria. As a modification of streptomycin, dihydrostreptomycin was prepared by hydrogenation of streptomycin with platinum as catalyst. Dihydrostreptomycin is commercially more successful because it is thought to be less toxic.

Type of Streptomycin	Produced by organism
Streptomycin (by fermentation)	Streptomyces griseus, S. humidus.
Mannosidostreptomycin (Streptomycin B), hydroxystreptomycin (reticulin)	S. reticuli
Mannosidohydroxystreptomycin	Streptomyces species.

Chemical Composition: It contains three sugars each derived from glucose, with C.H.O. and N elements.

Medium

1. **Carbon Source:** Starch, dextrin, glucose, glycerol and other economically available materials.
2. **Nitrogen source:** Natural agricultural by products, soybean meal, corn steep liquor, cotton seed flour, casein hydrolysate, or yeast and its extract. Inorganic nitrogen salts like ammonium sulphate, and ammonium nitrates are also used.

Apart from these mineral salts and vegetable or animal oil are often fed to the fermenter.

TABLE 30.6: The Hockenhul medium

Glucose	2.5%
Extracted soybean meal	4%

Distillers dried soluble	0.5%
Sodium chloride	0.25%
pH	7.3-7.5 (before sterilization)

Inoculum: High yielding mutated *Streptomyces griseus* spores are maintained as soil stocks or lyophilized in a carrier such as sterile skim milk. The spores from these stock culture are inoculated into a Sporulation medium. It provides enough sporulated growth to initiate liquid culture build up of mycelial inoculum in flasks or inoculum tanks.

Fermentation process: As in penicillin fermentation, spores of *S. griseus* are inoculated into a medium to establish a culture with a high mycelial biomass for introduction into an inoculum tank, with subsequent use for mycelial inoculum to initiate the fermentation process in a tank. The basic medium for the production of streptomycin contains soybean meal as the nitrogen source, glucose as the carbon source, and sodium chloride. Yield in production vessel, strongly responds to high aeration and agitation condition. Temperature range of 25-30°C (approximately 28°C) and pH range between 7 and 8 (peak production 7.6-8) are required. Fermentation lasts 5 to 7 days and the streptomycin fermentation passes through 3 phases.

The classic fermentation process for the production of streptomycin involves three phases.

1. **Phase I:** Rapid growth of *S. griseus*, with production of mycelial biomass. Proteolytic enzymatic activity of *S. griseus* releases ammonia to the medium from the soybean meal, causing a rise in pH. During this initial fermentation phase there is little production of streptomycin. This phase is characterized by the proteolytic activity from soybean meal resulting into release of ammonia into the medium (pH raises to 7.5). Carbon nutrients of the soybean meal are utilized for growth. Glucose of the medium is slowly utilized with slight production of streptomycin.
2. **Phase II:** A little additional production of mycelia. The glucose added in the medium and the ammonia released from the soybean meal is consumed during this phase. The pH remains fairly constant (7.6 to 8).
3. **Phase III:** It is the final phase of the fermentation, after depletion of carbohydrates from the medium, streptomycin production ceases and the bacterial cells begin to lyse. There is a rapid increase in pH because of the release of ammonia from the lysed cells.

Recovery and Purification: In the end of the fermentation, the mycelium is separated from the broth by filtration and the streptomycin is recovered. For recovery, the broth is acidified, filtered and neutralized. It is then subjected to column containing a cation exchange resin to adsorb the streptomycin from the broth and subsequently the column is washed with the water and streptomycin eluted with hydrochloric acid before concentration *in vacuo* almost to dryness. The streptomycin is dissolved in methanol and filtered. Acetone is added to the filtrate to precipitate the antibiotic. In the end the precipitate is washed with acetone and dried *in vacuo* before being dissolved in methanol for preparation as pure streptomycin chloride complex. The purification consists of adsorbing the streptomycin onto activated charcoal and eluting with acid alcohol.

Tetracyclines

Tetracyclines are significant chemotherapeutic agent. Tetracyclines include two types: chlortetracycline and oxytetracycline. It was first prepared by catalytic dehydrogenation of chlortetracycline. It was biosynthetically produced by *Streptomyces aureofaciens*. Demethyltetracyclines and decarboxyamide are also included in tetracycline group. These are tetracycline derivatives.

Production of Tetracycline

It is commercially produced using fermentation processes. Two strains of *Streptomyces aureofaciens*: ATCC 13908-13911 and Ncl B-9114 are used for industrial production. The stock cultures is maintained for long periods in the form of spores. Spores are either lyophilized or kept under liquid nitrogen. The bioreactor and other equipments are made of stainless steel. To obtain high production, bioreactor should be well aerated and should have sufficient agitation. Bioreactor requires special device for continuous monitoring. Automatic control of physiological parameters of the culture regulates the fermentation by sterile feeding of nutrients and pH adjustment. The content of nutrients, growth of the culture, production of the antibiotic, morphology of the culture and sterility are usually tested. Liquid nutrient media are usually sterilized for 40 minutes at 120 °C.

Medium: The tetracycline production is affected by the ratio C : N source in the medium. The medium contains glycerol, starch and sucrose as carbon sources, ammonium salts as nitrogen source, soybean meal in combination with mineral salts serve as nitrogen source. The medium also includes peanut meal, cotton seed meal, corn steep liquor, amino acids, casein, meat extract etc. For high production, it is essential that the content of chloride ions in the medium should remain low. Synthetic media is also used for tetracycline production used for the production. It is composed of deionised corn steep liquor/other raw materials freed from chloride ions. Optimal temperature (28 °C) and pH ranges 5.5-6.5 (5.8-6.0) vary.

Inoculum: Type of inoculum (quality of spores or vegetative inoculum *i.e.*, its age, genetic homogeneity, metabolic activity) used for production determines biosynthesis of tetracycline. In spite all favourable conditions required for fermentation type of inoculum plays important role in yield. Optimum yield is obtained from medium containing inoculum for 24 hrs. Optimum pH value of inoculum is 5.6-6.2. Amount of inoculum be in the range of 2-10%.

Aeration: Submerged cultures of *S. aureofaciens* require intensive aeration from the beginning of the cultivation. Interruption in aeration during the first hours result in a substantial decrease of production.

Production

Production of tetracycline is obtained in submerged culture. It includes three phases.

1. **Phase I:** It is a growth phase and is characterized by rapid consumption of nutrients. Cell mass increases in this phase. It is influenced by the phosphate concentration in the medium. During production phase of fermentation secondary mycelium (thin hyphae) regulates contents of phosphate ions in the medium. The production type of the mycelium is not formed in the presence of excessive phosphate ions.
2. **Phase II:** It is a production phase. The growth rate is decreased and sometimes ceases. Maximum amount of antibiotic is produced in this phase.
3. **Phase III:** In this phase the production becomes low. Mycelium is fragmented and lysis starts.

Isolation

Tetracycline is obtained from the filtrate of the acidic medium by adsorption on active material and subsequent elution. Tetracycline is precipitated in the form of salts with metals of alkaline earth. Extraction is carried from the broth in the presence of a carrier *i.e.*, quaternary ammonium compounds. Tetracycline forms complex salt with divalent Ca^{2+} and Mg^{2+} (at pH higher than 7). This salt is poorly soluble in water, however, readily soluble in organic solvents. After the separation of the organic phase, the tetracycline is transferred back to the aqueous phase. In the end it is salted out or crystallized.

Chloramphenicol

Chloramphenicol was isolated from *Streptomyces venezuelae* in 1947. It is one of the oldest known antibiotics and has marked inhibitory activity Gram positive and Gram negative cocci, bacilli, some mycobacteria, actinomycetes etc. It is also effective against anaerobic bacteria (*Lymphogranuloma psittacosis* group and *Vibrio cholerae*). It is especially active against *Haemophilus influenza*, *Salmonella typhi* and *Bacterioides fragilis*. Though it is quite effective antibiotic, however, it has severe side effects. It affects bone marrow, therefore, it is strongly restricted for human therapy.

Chloramphenicol Production

- **Medium:** For submerged aerobic fermentation complex media are used. Chloramphenicol is obtained by *Streptomyces venezuelae.* For 30 litre fermenter, about 18 liters of fermentation medium is required. Medium is sterilized at 120°C for 1 hr.
- **Carbon source:** Glycerol (1%) is used, because it gives higher titres and is superior to glucose, maltose, or lactose. Sometimes molasses and dried distillers grain slops (0.5%) are also used.
- **Nitrogen sources:** Proteinaceous materials like yeast fermentation solubles, hog stomach residue preparations etc. Tryptone is also a best source of nitrogen.
- **Mineral nutrient:** Sodium chloride (0.5%), zinc and iron in traces
- **pH:** It is adjusted to 7.5 with NaOH.
- **Production:** After inoculation in the fermenter the peak yield and the maximum cell mass is obtained within 3-4 days at 25°C. The highest obtained antibiotic level varies from was 200 to 300 mg/L. In defined media based on glycerol, DL serine, and lactate, *S. venezuelae* grows slowly, however, it gives relatively high yield after 10-15 days fermentation.
- **Isolation and Purification:** It is extracted from the clarified broths. It is filtered at a slightly acidic pH (about 4.0), at a neutral or slightly alkaline pH (8.5-9.0) with ethyl – or amyl acetate. The extracts are concentrated, diluted with kerosene, and then washed with diluted acids (acetic acid), alkalis (sodium bicarbonate) and water. Lipids with petroleum ether are removed from evaporated residue. The crude product is decolorized by passing the organic solution through a short column of charcoal or alumina. The purified product is dissolved in hot water, decolorized, clarified, and cooled to induce crystallization. The product is recrystallized from ethylene or an ether petroleum ether mixture.

Griseofulvin

It is a lass toxic, systemic, antifungal antibiotic and used orally for the treatment and control of fungal diseases of skin, hair, and nails caused by various dermatophytes. It is produced from genus *Penicillium*: *Asymmetrica fasciculate* and *Asymmetrica divaricata*. The strains are the mutants of *P. patulum*, *P. raistrickii*, or *P. urticae*. They are maintained on cracked corn in sand. Agar plates can also be used. The strains with conidia yields maximum product.

Inoculum

Both spore suspension and vegetative cells have been reported as suitable inocula for laboratory-scale fermentations.

Medium

There are three types of media, (1) sporulation inoculum, (2) germination medium for vegetative inoculum and (3) vegetative inoculum.

Sporulation medium: It provides inoculum suitable for direct inoculation of shake-flask culture. The medium contains (in g/L) whey powder lactose (30.0), whey powder nitrogen (50.0), KH_2PO_4 (4.0), KCl (0.5), CSL solids (3.8).

Germination Medium for Vegetative Inoculum: It contains (in g/L) protopeptone (20.0), malted cereal extract (10.0), glucose (40.0), soluble starch (20.0), $NaNO_3$ (3.0), KH_2PO_4 (1.0), $MgSO_4.7H_2O$ (0.5) and $FeSO_4.7H_2O$ (0.02).

The Seed Stage (Vegetative) Medium: It contains (in g/L) C.S.L. nitrogen (3.0), brown sugar (20.0), chalk (10.0), maize oil (10.0), Hodag M.F. (0.3).

Typical Production Medium: It contains (in %) corn steep liquor – N source (0.175), $CaCO_3$ (0.4), KH_2PO_4 (0.4) and KCl (0.15).

Production

For production of griseofulvin nutrient level in the fermenter is the limitation factor. For cell production it is necessary to maintain aerating potential (good aeration) of the fermenter and control of both pH and available nitrogen. Good yield could be obtained when carbohydrate level (glucose, lactose, sucrose, up to 12%) is sufficient. Phosphate (0.4-0.5%) and chlorine are also required during fermentation in sufficient amount for good yield otherwise the obtained product will be dechlorogriseofulvin (devoid of antifungal property). The carbohydrate glucose syrup (50%) is added stepwise after the first 16-20 hrs (10-12%). pH maintained in the range of 6.8-7.2 with continuous glucose addition. The fermentation is carried at 25°C with airflow of 1 vvm. The yield at the end will be 6-8 g/L after 10 days. Further improvements (12-15.5 g/L) can be had from the addition of various methyl donors (chlorine salts, methyl xanthate, and folic acid) to the medium.

Extraction and Purification

For extraction of griseofulvin from the cells they are treated with organic solvent and removed by filtration, then the wet mycelium is treated with butyl acetate followed by subsequent evaporation. The crude griseofulvin is then washed with chloroform. It is recrystallized from aqueous methanol. This procedure gives yield up to 58%.

If the extraction of mycelium is done with methylene chloride (after evaporation and crystallization) about 88% pure product can be obtained with 95% yield.

After recrystallization with acetone improved product with 99% purity of 99% is obtained.

Macrolide Antibiotics

Macrolides are group of lipophillic antibiotics with a macrocyclic lactone ring in their structure. Macrolides are active against β-lactam or aminoglycoside. Various types of macrolide antibiotics are available, the important are erythromycin, josamycin, leucomycin, midecamycin, oleandomycin, spiramycin and tylosin. These have been successfully produced at commercial scale.

Erythromycin

Erythromycin is produced from Streptomyces (*S. erythraeus*, *S. griseoplanus*), and Micromonospora. During fermentation process different types of erythromycin are produced like erythromycin-A (major product), B, C and D (as minor products).

- **Inoculum:** The stable inoculum is prepared from suspension of at least 10^8 viable cells/mL. The Sporulation of *S. erythraeus* is carried out on tryptone agar slants. The cells are harvested from agar plates and the suspensions is taken in sterile water. It is stored at 4°C.
- **Medium:** Production media for erythromycin production include ingredients (in%) sucrose (5), corn steep liquor (0.5), soybean oil meal (1.5), yeast (1.0), NaCl (0.5), $CaCO_3$ precipitate (0.3), pH (7.0-7.2). For obtaining high yield the fermentation medium should be of proper composition and concentration, with optimum pH and viscosity along with proper concentration of inorganic phosphate, nitrogen and metal ions, as well as organic nitrogen and carbon, and substrate precursor.
- **Fermentation:** Fermentation is carried out in a stirred tank fermenter. It should have proper aeration, agitation, pH, temperature, viscosity, and dissolved oxygen concentration. Production of erythromycin occurs when growth reaches the stationary phase and consumption capacity of inorganic phosphate, ammonium nitrogen and metal ions as well as nitrogen sources, and a high concentration of dissolved oxygen by *Streptomyces*. The addition of n-propanol as precursor increases erythromycin titre.

The quality of inoculum enhances erythromycin yield. It also depends on the aeration and agitation conditions in the fermenter. For agitation of 1000 litre media in a fermenter 1.85 kW power input is required, and the same volume is aerated at 0.4 vol/vol/min. from 0-12 hrs, and at 0.9 vol/vol/min from 12 hrs till harvest. Carbon dioxide is added at 0.1 vol/vol/min or 11% of the inlet air. The supplement of CO_2 do not affect pH and growth, but increases the erythromycin yield to 40% of the control.

Isolation and Extraction

- **Isolation:** It is extracellularly produced in the fermentation broth. Mycelium is separated from the broth by filter press, centrifuge, or drum filter with a filter aid. The acidic condition helps to separate mycelium from the broth.
- **Extraction:** The erythromycin is extracted from the filtrate using a water immiscible organic solvent (methyl-iso-butyl-ketone or ethyl acetate). It is than transferred to acidic water. pH is adjusted with HCl, H_3PO_4; acetic acid or citric acid. The purification and concentration is carried with ion exchange resin *i.e.*, amberlite 50. Further during purification steps antibiotic is absorbed on resin is eluted by a mixture of organic solvent and water at pH 3 to 8.

Rifamycins

This new group of antibiotic obtained from *Nocardia mediterranea, Streptomyces* sp. *Micromonospora locustis, M. halophytica* etc. The isolated product has five active substances *i.e.*, rifamycins A, B, C, D and E. Rifamycin B is most active. It spontaneously transforms to more active products like rifamycins O, S and SV. These are microbiologically active. *In vivo* rifamycin SV shows good activity, tolerability and solubility properties (treats infections from gram positive bacteria).

Inoculum

Stock cultures of *Nocardia mediterranea* is maintained in sealed ampoules in lyophilized state. Cultures of a frozen vegetative mycelium of selected high producing colonies in small vials at a low temperature are highly stale over a long period of storage.

Medium

The vegetative medium for rifamycin includes (in g/L) peanut meal (25), soybean meal (10), $(NH_4)SO_4$ (10), propylene glycol (5), glucose (110), glycerol (added when glucose level falls below 5%) (60). Fish meal (20-40 g/L) may also be used as nitrogen source. The composition of the vegetative media is an important factor influencing the final yield. It depends on types of strain used. The best yields can be obtained when 5% inoculum of a preculture grown for 24 hrs or with a 1.25% inoculum of 40 hrs old cultures is used in aerated fermenters at 28°C. It gives an yield of 6-7 g/L. During fermentation *N. mediterranea* has high oxygen requirement in a definite period of growth-production cycle. Therefore, an airflow ranging from 0.8-1.5 l/min is essential.

Fermentation

It is carried out in conventional bioreactors of 20-100 m^3 volume. It is equipped with turbine stirrers, baffles, air ring spargers, and heating-cooling systems. In a fermenter, consumption of glucose, growth of mycelium and production of antibiotic occur at the same time. At initial stages of growth, consumption of glucose and nitrogen is slow, however, it becomes very fast when mycelial growth starts. The demand of oxygen is also very high at this stage. Metabolic activity of mycelium changes the initial pH 6.2-6.4 to 6.6-6.7, later it decreases to 5.5-5.7. pH again rises slowly until the end of fermentation (optimal pH 6.2-6.4). The fermentation lasts for 300 hrs.

Recovery and Purification

Purification of broth after harvest is done at pH 7.5-8.0. The filtrate is acidified (pH 2.0). Extraction of the product be carried with chloroform. Re-extraction from chloroform be done in phosphate buffer of pH 8 followed by acidification of the aqueous solution and extraction with ethyl acetate from which it crystallizes.

ANIMAL FEED PRODUCTION AND MEDICATION TYPES

Animal feed medication can be separated into the above three types and, although these appear to be distinctly different, there is appreciable overlap.

Veterinary therapeutics

these are high potency antibiotics which are used in a manner similar to human pharmaceuticals.

Prophylactics

These vary from high potency wide spectrum to relatively weak narrow spectrum antibiotics, they are given not only to prevent the development of diseases and growth of parasites, but also to avoid detrimental effects on animal growth. In the major group, the anticoccidial agents, the antimicrobial effect is incidental to the antiparasitic effect, but can provide some growth promotional effect.

TABLE 30.7: Typical feed additives and their uses

Active Ingredient	Species	Use
Apramycin*	Pigs	Antibacterial vs. enteritis
Avoparcin	Pigs, Broilers, Cattle	Growth Promotion
Bambermycin	Poultry, Pigs, Cattle	Growth Promotion
Chlortetracycline*	Calves, Pigs, Poultry	Antibacterial, wide spectrum
Levamisole	Cattle, Sheep	Anthelmintic
Lincomycin*	Pigs	Antibacterial, vs. dysentery
Olaquindox	Pigs	Growth Promotion
Monensin	Broilers Cattle	Anticoccidial Growth Promotion
Narasin	Broilers	Anticoccidial
Salinomycin	Broilers	Anticoccidial
Sulphamethazine*	Cattle, Sheep, Pigs,	Antibacterial vs. atropic rhinitis
Tylosin	Pigs Pigs	Growth Promotion Antibacterial, prevention and control of dysentery
Virginiamycin	Pigs, Broilers, Turkeys	Growth Promotion
Zinc Bacitracin	All	Growth Promotion

*Items which require veterinary prescription.

Growth promoters

The antimicrobial effects of these compounds alter the composition of the flora and fauna of the gut and hence promote better feed utilisation. In some cases this means faster growth but the main benefit is feed saving. These two parameters are normally measured by the rate of weight gain and feed conversion ratio of F.C.R. All of the current FSFA products are not used in human medicine and most have narrow ranges of activity.

The bulk of feed additives are used as growth promoters or prophylactic agents with over a thousand tones sold per annum in the U.K. alone. In terms of sales, the fermentation products outweigh synthetic chemicals by a ratio of over ten to one.

The following list gives some of the large number of additives in the market-place, covering the varying disease challenges, housing and feeding conditions - especially for growth promotion in pigs.

Animal Feed Types

There are three broad types of feedstuff manufactured in the industry; mineral, vitamin supplements, protein concentrates and finished feeds; however, there is considerable variation within each type, especially in concentrates for cattle. The animal vitamin supplement contains most of the essential minerals and vitamins. It is an integral part of the other two types of feed, and constitutes a 0.2 to 3 per cent of the final ration. Medicinal additives especially growth promoters and prophylactics tend to be added at this stage. The **protein concentrate** is a concentrated high protein ration, which would form twenty to forty per cent of the complete feeding-stuff. Finished feed is a complete ration, which can be fed throughout life. It contains all the essential minerals, vitamins, proteins and other nutrients. A typical composition is given by the following example of a pig starter feed. Finished feeds and concentrates are often pelleted. This prevents ingredient segregation problems and gives a higher density diet. Considerable feed wastage by some animals is also avoided. Virtually all feeds for chickens are pelleted, ensuring that their strict nutrient requirements are met. About fifty per cent of pig rations are pelleted with about ten per cent for cattle. The pelleting process involves treatment of the feed with steam and then the resulting hot wet mash is forced through a circular die by one or more rollers. The pellets are then cooled/dried in a counter current of air. Medicinal additives can be added to all the types of feed and they will undergo the various mixing, transportation, and other processes to which the feed is subjected.

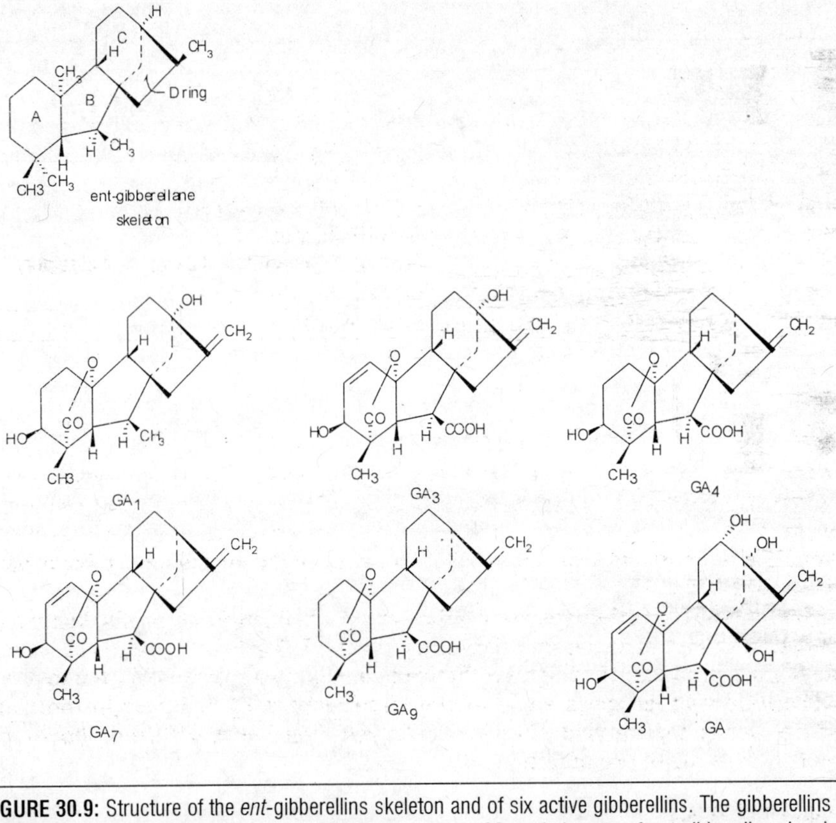

FIGURE 30.9: Structure of the *ent*-gibberellins skeleton and of six active gibberellins. The gibberellins are numbered as for *ent*-gibberellane, except that of the carbon 20 methyl group of *ent*-gibberellane has been oxidized and then released as CO_2 to form the 19-carbon gibberellins shown here. Furthermore, in these gibberellins (and some others), the carbon 19 methyl group of *ent*-gibberellane has been oxidized to a carboxyl and then used to form a lactone ring.

GIBBERELLIC ACID

The story of discovery of gibberellins is recent and very fascinating. The Japanese plant pathologist Kurosawa (1926) while working in the paddy field in Formosa noted the behaviour of some seedlings to be different from the rest; they were usually tall and pale in colour. These are the usually symptoms of the *bakanae disease* or *foolish seedling disease* known in Japan for over a century. The disease is due to the attack of an ascomycetes fungus whose sexual form is known as *Gibberella fujikuroi* and the asexual stage as *Fusarium moniliforme*.

Kurosawa, in 1926, showed that symptoms of the disease could be reproduced in healthy maize and rice seedlings by the filtered fungal extract which contained a heat-stable substance. Later, in collaboration with T. Yabuta he investigated the nature of the active material present in the fungal culture. But untimely death of Kurosawa gave setback to the isolation of this substance. Yabuta and Sumiki (1938) after repeated trials isolated a crystalline active material, which they named as gibberellin after the name of the fungus from which it was isolated. The active substance, a metabolic product of the fungus, increased the shoot growth remarkably by internodal elongation and leaf expansion, and inhibited the root growth.

The study of the Japanese workers on the biological and chemical properties of the active substances aroused little interest amongst the European and American scientists up to the middle of this century. The monographs on the plant-growth substances written during this period by several well-known authors did not mention of this fungal product. This presumably is due to the fact that most of the research workers studying growth substances were swayed by the impact of the indoleacetic acid and other synthetic growth substances on horticultural operations and possibilities of using them in agriculture as weed killers. Interest on gibberellins in the U.S.A. and Great Britain was first shown in 1950 (Mitchell and Angel, 1950, 1951), followed by many other countries. Some workers notably Barlow *et al.* (1955), at the Imperial Chemical Laboratories, England, produced a pure homogenous product from the mixture of gibberellins, which they named as gibberellic acid.

At about the same period Stodola (1958), in the U. S. A., demonstrated two other gibberellins, one gibberellic acid and the other known as gibberellin A, the latter being previously isolated by Japanese workers. During this period several remarkable effects of gibberellins on plants were recorded by them and others. Thereafter for the next ten years research on gibberellins gained a new momentum because of the possibilities of using the chemicals for practical purposes as well as for understanding the basic principles of plant growth and reproduction. Several important research centres in the U.S.A. and Europe are now actively conducting investigations on gibberellins.

In Japan an association known as *Gibberellin Association* has been formed with the object of disseminating knowledge on gibberellins to those interested in the problem. The outcome of the investigations carried out by the workers in the U.S.A. and England led to demonstrate that the gibberellin isolated originally by Yabuta and Sumiki is a mixture of several closely related compounds known as gibberellins. Amongst these gibberellic acid, or gibberellin A_3, has been largely used by British workers to show several growth-promoting properties. Workers in the U.S.A. mostly use a mixture of gibberellin A_1 and gibberellic acid. Despite the structural peculiarities of different gibberellins they all have more or less similar physiological actions. The investigations on gibberellins have been extended to several important phenomena in plant life, of which particular mention may be made of the following: (i) genetics of tallness; (ii) effect on vegetative growth; (iii) low temperature and day length requirements for flowering; (iv) seed dormancy; (v) fertility; (vi) tree growth and root growth ; (vii) cell division; (viii) relation with natural indoleacetic acid and dependence on auxin action; (ix) relation to plant metabolism; and (x) wide distribution in higher plants.

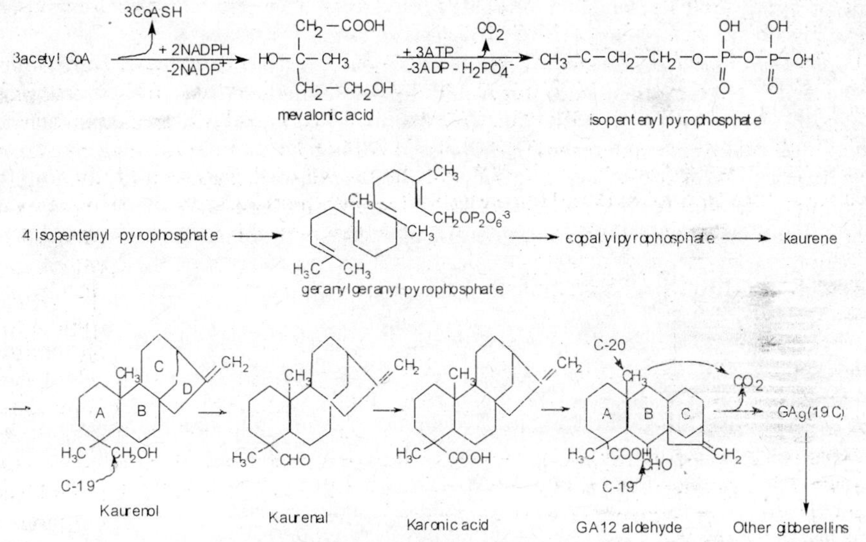

FIGURE 30.10: Some reaction of gibberellin biosynthesis. Many steps indicated as single arrows actually involve more than one enzyme-catalyzed reaction, especially those before kaurene.

As of 1990, 84 gibberellins have been discovered in various fungi and plants (Takahashi *et al.*, 1990). Of these 73 occur in higher plants, 25 in the *Gibberella* fungus, and 14 in both (Salisbury and Ross, 1992). Seeds of the cucurbit *Sechium edule* has at least 20 gibberellins and seeds of *Phaseoles vulgaris* contain as many as 16, but most other species have very few gibberellins. All gibberellins have derivation from the *ent*-gibberellane skeleton. They are acidic and are named GA with a different subscript to distinguish them. Thus, we have GA$_3$ _-_, GA$_7$, GA$_{53}$ _-_ etc. Gibberellins have 19 or 20 carbon atoms grouped in either four or five ring systems. One carboxyl group is always attached to carbon 7 and in some additional carboxyl group is attached to carbon 7 or to carbon 4. However, GA$_3$ is the first highly active and long time commercially available gibberellin and is referred to as gibberellic acid. The number of hydroxyl groups on rings A, C and D ranges from none to four with carbon 3 or carbon 13 or both commonly hydroxylated. One may add that gibberellins constitute an extremely complex array of structures for a phytohormone class, and certainly a specific physiologic function can be assigned to GA$_1$ and GA$_3$.

Gibberellins are synthesized from mevalonic acid in young tissues of the shoot. Its synthesis in the roots is still uncertain.

GAs are transported in the phloem and xylem tissues.

Gibberellins have several effects in plants and some of these include: hyper-elongation of stems by stimulating cell division and cell elongation; bolting in long day plants; induction of seed germination especially in seeds which require stratification or light; stimulate production of several enzymes notably hydrolases in germinating cereal seeds; fruit setting and growth; and induction of maleness in dioecious flowers.

Gibberellins differ from indoleacetic acid in structure and properties.

All GAs produced by fungi mentioned above are already known from culture filtrates of *G. fujikuroi*. Therefore, it can be assumed that they are formed along the same biosynthetic route as elucidated in *G. fujikuroi*. This pathway might exist in all fungal organisms, which are able to pro-produce GAs.

The commercial production of gibberellins can be used to enhance agricultural productivity. Gibberellins acid is formed by the fungus *Gibberella fujikuroi* (= *Fusarium moniliforme*) and can be produced commercially, using aerated submerged culture. A glucose-mineral salts medium, an incubation temperature of approximately 25°C, and slightly acidic pH conditions are employed for the production of gibberellic acid. Production normally takes 2 to 3 days, with accumulation of gibberellic acid lagging behind the growth of the fungus.

ENZYMES IN FOOD INDUSTRY

Applied enzymology has moved significantly beyond the early broad extra cellular hydrolytic enzyme preparation such as the bacterial α-amylase, papain, pectinase, and pancreatin where the commercial concentrate might contain as much as one per cent of the active labelled principle. Hydrolytic enzymes that modify starch, pectin, protein and fats to their component parts, and a few others like glucose isomerase and glucose oxidase, newly produced enzymes have become or are becoming commercially important in specific chemical transformation in food industry. The enzymes are commonly used in modification in flavour (cheese and butter flavour), in low, high, normal sweetness sweeteners, in corn wet milling, in feed, soy bean milk, baking, in modifying food gums, etc.

Bitterness in Orange and Grape Fruit Juices

The bitterness of orange and grapefruit juices at commercial level is a serious problem which develops due to the presence of limonin and naringin. Naringin is about 0.01 as bitter as limonin but is often produced in higher amount.

Bitterness caused by limonin (it is a triterpenoid) can be eliminated as follows:

1. By preventing its biosynthesis (probably synthesized via the mevalonate pathway). This can be done by preharvest treatment with 1-naphthalene acetic acid.
2. By removing the rag and pulp from freshly expressed juice as soon as possible to prevent the precursor. The precursor of limonin is limonic acid, A-ring (mono) lactone.
3. By use of immobilized microbial cells which contain NADP-dependent limonin dehydrogenase. The enzyme on hydrolysis converts limonin to non-bitter products.

Bitterness caused by naringin can be eliminated as follows:

1. The bitterness caused by naringin can be eliminated by an enzyme, **naringinase**.
2. It can also be eliminated by using recombinant DNA techniques in the limonin biosynthetic pathway.

CHAPTER 31

Applications of Enzymes in Industries

Enzymes are proteins, biological or organic catalysts and are associated with metabolic reactions, respiration, the conversion and transfer of energy within living systems, and the formation of various macromolecules and cellular components. They exhibit specificity, therefore, used in pharmaceutical industries, in therapeutics and in clinical systems. At least 2,000 different enzymes are now known, each of them capable of catalyzing a specific reaction. Moreover, different cell types synthesize different types of enzymes – no cell contains all of the known enzymes. The specific enzymes produced by a cell are the major factors determining the biological activities and functions performed by that cell.

For thousands of years, processes such as brewing, bread making and production of cheeses have involved the use of enzymes. Enzymes of fungi and bacteria have a wide variety of industrial applications, including alcoholic beverages, food, detergents, and pharmaceuticals. In the production of alcoholic beverages, microbial amylase may be used instead of the enzyme from barley malt to prepare grains for fermentation. Protease can also chill proof beer by degrading the proteins that cause cloudiness in such beverages upon refrigeration. Enzymes are used in varied industrial sectors, consumer products, and scientific pursuits.

In past few years interest in various applications of enzymes have been developed because of greater understanding of the function and nature of enzymes and also advances involved in handling of these, particularly their immobilization. Most of the enzymes catalyze the reactions different from their inherent reactions as well as under special conditions, *i.e.*, hydrolases catalyze, transferase reactions and semi synthesis or transformation of antibiotics etc., carried out based on their non-physiological characteristics.

APPLICATIONS IN PHARMACEUTICAL INDUSTRIES

Enzymes possess multicatalytic functions. They are used for the synthesis of optically active amino acids. Enzymes demonstrate stereo specificity in catalysis. Enzymes decarboxylases catalyze decarboxylation of L-amino acids and also stereo specific protonation of the formed amines. The synthetic route for preparation of cortisone is from stigmasterol, which chemically converts it into progesterone. Hydroxylation of progesterone is carried out by *Rhizopus nigaricus*. It yields II-α hydroxy progesterone. Use of microbes in transformation of steroid is an important aspect of pharmaceutical industries. All the enzymatic reactions are based on fermentation technology.

Synthesis of Amino Acids

Enzymes are used for synthesis of optically active amino acids *e.g.*, D-amino acids, and their derivatives. A variety of procedures for the synthesis of amino acids and their derivatives with microbial enzymes have been developed. Mainly hydrolytic enzymes [*e.g.*, pyridoxal 5'-phosphate (pyridoxal-p)] are used. Pyridoxal-p dependent enzymes play the important role in amino acid metabolism because they catabolize transamination, decarboxylation, racemization, replacement, addition, elimination and a few other reactions of amino acids.

Synthesis of Nucleosides and Nucleotides

Enzymatic procedure for the production of inosine 5'-monosphate (IMP) and guanosine monophosphates (GMP) has been developed with 5'-phosphodiesterase nucleases. Similarly, a number of antibiotics, antiviral compounds, antineoplastic compound, immunosuppressors, coenzymes, and sugar containing nucleosides or nucleotides have also been synthesized. Currently, these nucleosides and nucleotides are produced by a salvage synthesis *i.e.*, microbial conversion of an intermediate synthesized chemically or enzymatically, by an enzymatic or chemical conversion of an intermediate produced by fermentation, or by direct fermentation.

Synthesis of Other Compounds

Antibiotics

Penicillin acylase catalyzes the deacylation of benzyl penicillin to yield 6-aminopenicillanic acid phenyl acetic acid. The reaction is based on pH. At pH 7.5 the reaction proceeds while at pH 6.00 it becomes reverse. The industrial semi-synthesis or transformation of penicillins and cephalosporins is with an immobilized acylase. The enzyme is also used for the stereo specific acylation of intermediates in the chemical synthesis of β-lactam antibiotics.

Peptides and Proteins

Peptides: Different proteases and carboxypeptidases are employed for the peptide bonds *i.e.*, the conversion of porcine insulin to human insulin. Only carboxyl terminal amino acid is different in human and porcine insulin (*i.e.*, alanine for porcine and theonine for human insulins). The synthesis of human insulin from porcine insulin is carried out with a lysine specific protease enzyme of *Achromobacter lyticus*. Different proteases and carboxy peptidases are also used for the synthesis of pharmaceutically important peptides like trypsin (human insulin), *Achromobacter* protease I (human insulin), chymotrypsin (encephalin, caerulein) subtilisin (angiotensin), carboxypeptidases Y (human insulin, encephalin, caerulein), thermolysins (angiotensin, caerulein), and pepsin and fungal carboxypeptidases (eldocin, aerulein). Aspartame (L-aspartyl-L-phenylalanine methyl ester) is a dipeptide sweetener. The synthesis of the dipeptide with thermolysins immobilized on an ion exchange resin or by a microbial exopeptidase has also been developed.

Proteins: Peptidoglutaminases hydrolyze r-amide group of glutamine in glutaminyl-peptide converts it in to glutamate residue.

Triglycerols (triglycerides): Enzyme lipase produced by *Rhizopus delemar* converts olive oil to cacao butter-like oil.

Cyclodextrin: Cyclomaltodextrin glucanotransferase in starch medium synthesizes cyclodextrins in the presence of complex forming reagents such as acetone, sodium dodecyl sulphate, I-decanol.

Dentifrice enzymes: Dextranase hydrolyses dextran. This reaction is effective in reduction and protection of dental plaques and caries. They hydrolyze dextran to glucose and isomaltose at pH 5.5 with 55% hydrolytic efficiency.

APPLICATIONS IN THERAPEUTICS

In some heritable human genetic disorders there remains deficiency or even a total absence of one or more enzymes in the diseased tissues, and under abnormal conditions there may be an excessive activity of a specific enzyme. These abnormalities are sometimes may be controlled by a drug designed to inhibit its catalytic activity. Some body enzymes are misses due to inborn errors of metabolism. Therefore, missed enzymes are replaced.

These enzymes are in solubilized form or immobilized on some substrate and may be given orally or injected or implicated in soft tissues as prosthesis.

For Treatment of Gaucher's, Tay-sach's, and Fabry's Diseases

Gaucher's, Tay-sach's, and Fabry's are hereditary diseases and are caused due to deficiency of enzymes and result into abnormal accumulation of materials that would otherwise broken down by missing enzymes.

Gaucher's disease (a lysosomal storage disease) occurs due to absence of enzyme glucocerebrosidase and leads to accumulation of glucocerebrosides in various tissues. If the enzyme is replaced in body, the symptoms may be relived in an individual.

Tay sach's disease is caused due to absence of enzyme hexose deaminase. The enzyme is usually present in the lysosomes of ganglion brain cells and removes the carbohydrate residues of the ganglioside lipids. If the ganglioside concentration in these cells accumulates, it affects the brain function and ultimately leads to the death of an individual.

Fauvism disease is caused due to lack of the enzyme *glucose-6-phosphate dehydrogenase* in the red blood cells. This affects the ability of cells to regenerate glutathione, which leads to membrane fragility and haemolytic anemia.

Not all the enzyme deficiency diseases require enzyme replacement. For treatment of such diseases offending substance should be removed from diet. For example, phenylketouria (PKU) is caused due to inability of body cell to metabolize phenylalanine, which results in the accumulation of toxic levels of phenylalanine and its abnormal metabolites. Other example are galactosemia (*galactose or galactose urydyltransferase*), Orotic aciduria (*orotidine-1-phosphate decarboxylases*) and arginosuccinuria (arginosuccine lyase) etc.

Uses of hydrolases or oxidase enzyme regenerating systems are also common for some enzyme replacement therapy. The inherited deficiency of *galactokinase* is cured by injecting coencapsulated galactokinase with ATP/ADP and pyruvate kinase. It initiates ATP generation system.

The treatment of malabsorption secondary to pancreatic insufficiency is caused by chronic pancreatitis, pancreatectomy and cystic fibrosis. The manifestation of pancreatic malabsorption is steatorrhea a voluminous malodorous stool laden with fat that is not being adsorbed. If the output of pancreatic lipase is less than 10% of normal, clinical steatorrhea will not occur, therefore, for the treatment of steatorrhea replacement of preparation lipase enzyme is essential.

For treatment of chronic pancreatitis and pancreatic fistulae, pancreatic enzymes (a mixture of *lipase*, *amylase* and *protease*) are used.

Treatment of acute lymphocytic leukemia, T-cell leukemias and lymphomas, is dependant totally or partially upon exogenous asparagines, which are enzymatic destructed enzyme asparaginase. It is injected into plasma. It arrests their growth and sometimes result in reduction of tumour mass.

Blood clots are dissolved in tissue by plasminogen activator (TPA). They convert plasminogen to plasmin. Plasmin enzyme breaks down protein fibrin which is the main component of blood clot.

Blood clots are dissolved by enzymes urokinase and streptokinase and both soluble fibrinogen and insoluble fibrin clots are destroyed. These enzymes activate plasmin.

Enzyme hyaluronidase hydrolyse hyaluronic acid and accelerates the subcutaneous spread of both particulate matter and solutions of depolymerising the hyaluronic acid. The enzyme is injected through drug.

Subtilins are proteolytic enzymes. They digest the denatured proteins present in necrotic tissues. These enzymes are used as adjunct for biochemical debridement of lesions of burns, decutibus ulcers, incisional traumatic and pyrogenic wounds, and ulcers secondary to peripheral vascular disease.

Burnt areas and dermal ulcers are cured with the help of enzyme collagenase. Papain is used in the debridement of necrotic tissues. Solution of crystallized trypsin is inhaled to liquefy viscous sputum.

Fibrin and liquefy pus are being cured with a mixture of fibrinolysin of bovine plasma and deoxy ribonuclease when used topically. It is obtained from bovine pancreas. The mixture is also used as debriding agent in surgical wound, ulcerative lesion and, second and third degree burns. It is also used intravaginally in severe cervicitis and vaginitis.

CLINICAL ANALYSIS

Diseases are diagnosed by clinical analysis, which includes the measurement of activity of certain enzymes in the blood plasma, red blood cells, or tissues samples. Serum enzymes have their importance in clinical analysis. They are intracellular and elevated in hyperactivity diseases, malignancy or injury to cardiac, hepatic, pancreatic, muscle, bone and tissues. For identification of specific tissue involved in the disease is determined by the type of enzyme elevated. It is helpful for determinations and differentiation of various pathological conditions.

Transferases

Transfer of amino or phosphate group to another is catalyzed by enzymes transferases like aspartate aminotransferase and alanine aminotransferase. They are helpful in clinical diagnosis. Aspartate aminotransferase is found in liver, cardiac and skeletal muscles. It is elevated in myocardial infraction and Duchenne muscular dystrophy. Alanine aminotransferase is found in the liver tissues. The levels of both the enzymes increased during liver diseases, acute toxic or viral hepatitis, obstructive jaundice and hepatic cirrhosis. These enzymes catalyze the transfer of amino group from glutamic acid to keto acids (oxaloacetic or pyruvic) to form aspartic and α-ketoglutaric acid with Aspartate aminotransferase while alanine and α-ketoglutaric acid with alanine aminotransferase. These products are analyzed using colorimetric and spectrophotometric methods.

Ornithine transcarbamylase

Ornithine transcarbamylase enzyme is involved in urea cycle in serum. It is used in the clinical investigation of the liver disease. The enzyme catalyses the conversion of ornithine to citruline. The normal serum value is 0 to 0.4 U/L.

Creatine kinase

Creatine kinase (a transferase enzyme) present in the muscle and brain tissue. The enzyme catalyses the transfer of phosphate groups from creatine phosphate to adenosine diphosphate (ADP) and converted into adenosine triphosphate (ATP). Activated CK activity is observed by increase of ATP in the creatinine phosphate-ADP reaction in the presence of glutathione or cysteine thiol activators. Fluorimetric method is used for ATP determination. The enzyme is elevated in myocardial infraction and Duchenne muscular dystrophy. The level of enzyme remains normal in liver disease.

Oxidoreductases or Dehydrogenases

This group of enzyme catalyzes hydrogen transfer in cellular oxidation process. Lactic, α-hydroxybutyric, Malic, glutamic, isocitric, and sorbitol dehydrogenases are of diagnostic importance. Lactic dehydrogenases catalyzes the reversible conversion of pyruvic to lactic acid in the presence of NADH. The level of lactic dehydrogenases increases in hepatic disease, pernicious anemia and muscular dystrophy. Lactic dehydrogenases and Malic dehydrogenases phosphatases and leucine aminopeptidases are found in isoenzyme forms. Isoenzymes have similar substrate specificity but different biophysical properties. Malic and sorbitol dehydrogenases in the presence of NAD, catalyze the conversion of malate or sorbitol to oxaloacetate or fructose respectively. They are used for diagnostic importance in MI and acute liver injury.

Hydrolases

These enzymes catalyse the addition of elements water across the bond, which is cleaved. Hydrolases like amylases, lipases, phosphatases, 5-nucloetidase, γ-glutamyl transferase and leucine aminopeptidases are used for clinical purposes.

Salivary and Pancreatic Enzymes

These enzyme hydrolyze starch to maltose and dextrins. The activity of amylase is measured using method based on the loss in certain properties of starch or by the generation of reducing substances. Elevation in concentration is observed in acute pancreatic, acute abdominal conditions and salivary gland diseases.

Lipases

They catalyze the conversion of triglycerides to glycerol and fatty aids. Determination of serum lipase is used for the diagnosis of acute pancreatitis (10 fold increase), pancreatic injury or inflammation of organs contiguous to pancreas.

Phosphatases

They catalyze the hydrolysis of orthophosphoric esters, and are grouped into acid or alkalie phosphatases. Acid phosphatase is of first diagnostic value in metastatic carcinoma of prostate. Acid phosphatase activity (prostate enzyme) is investigated by using tartrate inhibitor.

5'-Nucleotidase

It is an alkaline phosphomonoesterase. It hydrolyses nucleotides with a phosphate radical attached to 5'-position of the pentose (*i.e.* AMP). It is elevated in liver disorder.

Serum Lysozyme (Muramidase)

The activity of this enzyme is increased in certain kinds of leukemia. Enzyme serum arginasea hydrolyses arginine to ornithine and urea, and serum guanase. They are sensitive indicators of hepatic necrosis.

Serum γ-glutamyl Transferase

The activity and level of this enzyme is increased during diseases of liver, bile ducts and pancreas. Together with alkaline phosphatase, leucine aminopeptidases, and 5'-nucleopeptidase, serum γ-glutamyl transferase can be tested in the group of cholastasis-indicating enzymes. This method is based on the hydrolysis of γ-glutamyl-p-nitroanilide.

CHAPTER 32

Biotechnology Biomass Energy

O'Energy! Thou are the container of the entire Cosmos since Eternity. Thou art bestower of sacrifice, Knowledge and technology. O'Respectable One'! Thou art the source of light, seasons and all that is beautiful. Thou art the Creator and preserver of all the precious-stones elements. I bow to thee.

Rig Veda

In India the concept of energy as *Shakti* has been almost at the focus of philosophic, scientific and metaphysical thought from immemorial. The term **energy** means *capacity to do work*. It was coined by Thomas Young (1773-1829), eighty years after Newton and applied it to what is now called kinetic energy. The two laws of thermodynamics describe the behaviour of energy: first law states that energy may be transformed from one form to the other, but can not be created or destroyed: second law states that because some energy is always dispersed into unavailable heat energy, no spontaneous transformation of energy from one to other form (light to protoplasm, for example) is 100 per cent efficient.

The earth's planet cover is equivalent to, over 1,800 billion tones of dry matter, that is an energy equivalent of 30.10^{10} Joules, corresponding to the known reserves of **fossil energy**. Forests make up about 68 per cent of terrestrial biomass, grass ecosystems about 16 per cent, and cultivated lands only 8 per cent. For the earth as a whole, the 173 billion tones of dry matter produced every year by photosynthesis over 20 times the fossil energy consumed in the world, or again 200 times the energy contained in the food of the planet's 4 billion inhabitants.

The conventional energy sources of the world are dwindling fast. We have to come to realise that the world plenty of non-renewable natural sources does indeed have a bottom self. Bioenergy can play an important and vital role to meet energy crisis of the world. It has special relevance to India as its 80 per cent population resides in villages needing energy for cooking, lighting, and operating pumps for irrigation and drinking water, etc. India having largest population of cattle in the world and sizable forest potentialities, bioenergy can safely be developed as an alternative source of energy on dependable lines.

Renewable Energy

Some business leaders and government officials are beginning to discuss ways to move toward a biobased economy in which agricultural operations will be the energy and natural resource fields of tomorrow.

Recent activities include encouragement of industrial use of plant matter "with specific attention to rural economic interests, energy security and environmental sustainability. There is a need for development of enzyme biomass conversion technologies and the construction of green bio-refineries. The goal of such activities is to triple the nation's use of bio-based products and bioenergy by 2010.

Thrust Areas for Biomass Energy

1. Development of bio-based Research.
2. Promotion and use of bio-based industrial products.
3. Research and development on enzyme and biomass technologies.
4. Increase in the use of bio-based fuels.
5. Future panning to development and expansion of bio-energy up to the year 2020.
6. Need to increase the amount of agricultural and forest products used to make energy and other products.
7. Development of The Bio-Based Economy of the 21st Century.
8. Agricultural expansion into health, energy, chemicals and materials.

Bioenergy includes those processes where biological forms of matter such as plants, vegetables, bacteria, enzyme, etc. provide the basis for energy or its conversion from one form to another. The widest use of bioenergy is the traditional way where wood plants and agricultural matter are directly burnt to provide heat.

Vegetable biomass is a new name for plant organic material wherein solar energy is trapped and stored through the process of photosynthesis in which carbon dioxide and water are transformed and form energy rich compounds. **Biomass** includes both terrestrial as well as aquatic matter and can be conveniently grouped into new plant growth, plant residues and wastes. The *new plant growth* includes wood, short-rotation trees, herbaceous plants, conventional crops, algae (fresh water and marine), aquatic plants. The *residues* cover not only crop materials, such as straws, husks, bagasse, corn cobs, etc. but also secondary level products such as cowdung, animal droppings, forest based residues like bark, saw dust, wood shaving etc. The term *wastes* has been loosely used. It is matter of vegetable origin in wrong place. It is of disposable nature like garbage, night soil, sewage solids and industrial refuse.

TABLE 32.1: World energy consumption since 1971 to 1987 (million tonnes of oil equivalent)

Year	Coal	Petroleum	Natural Gas	Hydroelectric	Nuclear	Total
1971	1632	2413	997	318	28	5388
1973	1668	2798	1066	332	49	5913
1975	1709	2725	1709	358	87	5959
1977	1830	2986	1162	376	132	6486
1978	1863	3082	1206	403	150	6704
1979	1976	3124	1273	413	153	6940
1980	2007	3001	1297	421	169	6895
1981	2003	2902	1321	430	198	6854
1982	2047	2825	1316	451	218	6858
1983	2101	2801	1326	475	240	6943
1984	2180	2845	1410	485	282	7202
1985	2273	2809	1494	511	348	7435
1986	2318	2899	1487	517	377	7598
1987	2387	2941	1556	524	404	7811

Source: BP Statistics, World Science News, 29 (5): 19, 1992.

TABLE 32.2: Crops residue

Crop	Area million ha	Production million tonnes	Cal. Value kcal/kg.	Moisture % wet basis
Rice husk	4.07	1.79	3440	19.5
Bagasse	0.32	6.12	3800	15.0
Cotton stalk	0.79	2.39	3300	12.0
Paddy straw	4.07	22.40	3000	10.6

The Planning Commission (India) has estimated production of crop residue in 1979 as 203 million tones as against the food production of 200 million tones. By 2000 A. D., the availability of crop residue would arise to the tune of 336 million tones.

The urban garbage @ 0.4 kg per head amounts to 19.98 million tones per year, which can be burnt as a calorific value of 1100 kcal/kg on 50% moisture.

There are several methods to use the biomass for energy production. Some of the sophisticated methods of thermochemical conversion include pyrolysis, gassification, producer gas, bariquetting, hydrolysis and liquification.

COMPOSITION OF BIOMASS

Plants are the major source of biomass because their cell wall is constituted by 6 components: (i) cellulose, (ii) hemicellulose, (iii) lignin, (iv) water soluble sugars, amino acids and aliphatic acids, (v) ether and alcohol-soluble constituents (*e.g.* fats, oils, waxes, resin and many pigments), and (vi) proteins. These components build up plant biomass. Proportion of these constituents vary in different groups of plants and even in the same group. If the concentration of sugar is high, the biomass will be sugary *e.g.* sugarcane, and sugar beet. Similarly, high amount of starch present in biomass yields the starchy biomass *e.g.*, potato and tapioca.

Cellulose

Cell wall is mainly constituted of cellulose and its fundamental unit is glucose. Formation of cellulose is a complex process. From each glucose unit, one molecule of water is removed to yield an anhydrous glucose. The anhydrous glucose units are linked end to end with ß-1,4-linkage to form the long chain polymer of cellulose $(C_6H_{10}O_5)n$. Here n represents the degree of polymerization, the number of which varies from 5000 to 10,000. Enzymatic hydrolysis of cellulose and production of glucose are given under.

Hemicellulose

It is made of sugars (xylans), which comprises of 20-25% plant biomass on dry weight basis. It also contains glucose and several other hexoses (galactose and mannose) and pentoses (xylose and arabinose). The proportion of these constituents varies plant to plant. Degree of polymerization to yield hemicellulose does not exceed beyond 50. The polymers has branched chains. It occurs as amorphous mass around the cellulose strands. Hemicellulose is insoluble in water but easily solubilised in alkali.

Lignin

It is a complex and high molecular weight polymer and is formed by de-hydrogenation of (II), and sinapyl (III) alcohols. Presence of these alcohols differs in different alcohols, angiosperm lignin is formed from coniferyl alcohols, angiosperm lignin is formed from the mixture of coniferyl and sinapyl alcohols, and grass lignin from mixtures of coniferyl, sinapyl and coumaryl alcohols. Lignin is phenolic in nature; it is very stable and difficult to isolate and occurs between the cells and cell walls. It is deposited during lignification of the plant tissue and gets intimately associated within the cell walls with cellulose and hemicellulose and imparts the plant an excellent strength and rigidity. As a result of photosynthesis, an enormous amount of plant biomass is accumulated in terrestrial and aquatic systems, which are then utilized into different ways as the source of energy.

TYPES OF BIOMASS

Terrestrial Biomass

Terrestrial biomass is used to fulfill the need of food, feed, vegetables, fibre, furniture and cooking purpose as well. Traditionally the need of fire/fuel was fulfilled by trees, remains of time, we totally became dependent on conventional energy sources of fossil fuel and electricity. But gradually increasing world wide human population and diminishing stock of fossil fuel have challenged us to seek out the alternative sources of energy.

Aquatic Biomass

It is obvious that the first life originated in water. Therefore, water bodies support a vast community of plant and animal. Many aquatic plants become troublesome for aquatic animals and human as well such as the aquatic weeds like water hyacinth, *Salvinia*, *Hydrilla*, *Lemna*, *Pistia*, *Wolffia*, etc. In addition to higher plants, the lower plants (especially blue-green algae and green algae) have much future prospects, as far as production of biomass conversion of aquatic biomass into biogas/hydrocarbon and abatement of pollution (in sewage oxidation) are concerned.

Salvinia

Salvinia, a member of Pteridophyta, is commonly known as water fern. It grows luxuriantly in stagnant water, for example ponds, pools and lakes. *S. molesta* is the world's worst weed known so far. In India, it predominates in Kerala, Kashmir and North-East states. Biogas production from *Salvinia* has recently been suggested.

Water Hyacinth (Eicchornia crassipes)

It is the most noxious weed of the world and grows abundantly in tropical regions in nonsaline water in ponds, pools, lakes reserviors, rivers and even in paddy field. it is believed that water hyacinth occupies about 2,00,000 acres land in Bihar and 30,000 acres in West Bengal. It grows luxuriantly at temperature 28-30 °C. It rapidly multiplies on domestic sewage. Generally the huge amount of biomass is of no use. Now a days, cultivation of water hyacinth on sewage for minimizing pollution and use of water hyacinth in biogas production has been suggested.

WASTES AS RENEWABLE SOURCE OF ENERGY

Waste is the spoilage, loss or destruction of either matter or energy, which is unusable to man. Gradually increasing civilization through industrialization and urbanization, has led to increase in generation of wastes into environment from various sources. Waste generation is, therefore, a necessary outcome of consumption, and also because of insufficient process, general ignorance, wasteful habits and social attitudes.

Types of Wastes

Wastes are classified into (i) energy wastes and (ii) material wastes. The main source of energy in various parts of world is petroleum oil, followed by coal. In India, about 50% oil is imported each year. Coalmines are concentrated only in a few regions. Coal is used in generation of electricity, steam engines and fire. Most potential energy of coal is wasted during electric generation in thermal power plants. Thermal loss in India is about 20-30% because of lack of suitable technologies.

Classification Based on Chemical Nature

1. **Inorganic wastes:** Those generated by metallurgical and chemical industries, coal mines, etc.
2. **Organic wastes:** Agricultural products, dairy and milk products, slaughter houses, sewage, forestry, etc.
3. **Mixed wastes:** Those discharged from industries dealing with textiles, dyes, cake and gas, plastic, wool, leather, petroleum, etc.

The inorganic wastes may be recovered by chemical/mechanical treatment, whereas organic and mixed wastes require biological as well chemical treatments.

Classification Based on Physical State

The wastes occur in three states, the solid, liquid and gaseous ones.

1. The **solid wastes** can be burnt, thermally decomposed, anaerobically digested to get methane and other combustible gases or biologically converted to a variety of products.
2. **Liquid wastes** are most troublesome, because of the presence of non-retractable chemicals, and their further return such as NO_3, NO_2, NH_3, CO_2, SO_2, etc.
3. When concentration of these **gases** increases in the atmosphere they cause gaseous pollution, which has its bad impact on plant and animal lives.
4. The organic wastes and residues are the major sources of renewable energy.

Composition of Wastes

Waste is a general term. It embraces all types of wastes irrespective of constituents and phases. Therefore, composition of waste differs with differing nature, phases and sources. It may be inorganic, organic or mixed types. Organic wastes play a major role in being is renewed and becoming a source of energy. Composition of organic materials is given under `composition of biomass.

SOURCES OF WASTES

Industries: Following industries generate various types of wastes/by products which contain sufficient amount of energy.

Chemical Industries: The chemical wastes are maleic anhydride and phthalic anhydride.

Cotton Mills: Cotton mills produce the cotton seeds and fibers as wastes.

Dairy: Dairy industry is one of the important industries, which requires special attention, as far as treatment and disposal of waste are concerned. Dairy wastes contain milk whey, butter milk, unused skim milk, plant washings and traces of detergents. The waste is a dilute solution or suspension containing lactose, protein, fat and minerals. Therefore, dairy wastes serve a food substrate for production of single cell protein, lactic acid, vitamins, ethylalcohol and alcoholic beverages.

Food Industry: Waste materials of food industries are the collagen meat packaging waste and lactoserum (a by-product of cheese making food industry).

Oil Refineries: They produces wastes as gas, oil, paraffins (n-alkanes.) olefins (n-alkenes) and other hydrocarbons.

Paper Mill: The wastes are bisulphite liquor and long cellulosic pulp.

Sugar Mills and Distilleries: Sugar cane (*Sacchrum officinarum*): Sugar cane belongs to family Gramineae. It is a tall, perennial grass, the stems of which are the source of cane syrup.

Sugar beet (Beta vulgaris): Sugar beet is a member of Chenopodiaceae. It is biennial herb with fleshy leaves and swollen roots. For sugar production good crops of sugar beet can be had in Rajasthan, Punjab, Haryana and U.P. Importance of using bagasse as an alternative source of energy for sugar manufacturers has been realised in recent years. The Engineering Staff and College, Hyderabad organised a workshop in October, 1990 on *Strategies for the development of co-generation of electric power in sugar factory.* The Indian Renewable Energy Development Agency (IREDA) sanctioned around 97 projects in this field. Utter Pradesh Government launched a programme for producing alternative energy from sugar cane waste in sugar mills. The first project of its kind in the country is being installed with the Sheh Road Sugar Mill in Bijnor. It will produce 6 MV electricity from the sugarcane waste. In this way fuel consumption would be reduced from 40 to 58%.

Agriculture: In agriculture, a huge amount of residues/wastes are produced which, however, are thrown into field because of non-availability of technologies for utilization at village level.

Paddy (*Oryza sativa*): Paddy plant produces paddy and straw; the products of paddy are rice, husk and bran. Husk is the outer most hard coat of paddy. Bran is the thin papery layer present between husk and rice. Out of total (about 80 million tonnes) production of paddy, about 16-18 million tonnes of husk (*i.e.* 20-25% of paddy) are produced per annum. Due to lack of utilization technology bran is thrown as waste, and probably in some part it is used as cattle feed. Recently, bran has become a source of rice bran oil, whether edible or non-edible. Paddy husk is used as fel in rice mills and villages as well. Recent analysis of paddy husk of different species has shown the presence of high caloric value *i.e.* 3200-3500 KCal/Kg, which can replace about 10 million tonnes of coal per annum It has been found that 1 tonne of husk can replace 450 litres of furnace oil.

TABLE 32.3: Some renewable sources of biomaterials

Plants	Residues/wastes	Products
Cashewnut	Shell, testa	Gum, tannin
Coconut	Coir, shells and pith	coirboard, coir fiber, xylose
Cotton	Fibre	fuel
Maize	Cobs	Single cell protein (SCP), Fuel
Paddy	Husk, bran, straw	Bran oil, vitamin, SCP,
Sugar beet	Pulp	Ethanol fuel
Sugar cane	Bagasse, molasses	SCP, fuel/fire, alcohol
Sunflower	Husks	SCP, Fuel (alcohol)
Tapioca (cassava)	Tubers	Ethanol
Tea		Tea waste, Caffeine

Plants	Residues/wastes	Products
Trees	Seeds and leaves	Many products
Wheat	Straw	SCP, fuel

India has given special attention to develop technologies for utilization of paddy husk. Recently, the Central Fuel Research Institute (C.F.R.I.), Dhanbad had developed a process to produce oxalic acid from cellulosic matter and silica from, mineral matter. India had started a thermal power plant from paddy straw, which is first kind in the world which can generate 62 million unit of energy peranum. A rice straw-fired Thermal Power Plant was set up at a village Jalkheri (Punjab). Paddy Processing Research Centre (Tiruvarur) has also developed methods for parboiling and milling operation in rice mill to extract about 92% potential energy of husk.

Tapioca (Manihot esculenta)

Tapioca or is a member of Euphorbiaceae. It is cultivated in Kerala, Tamil Nadu, and Karnataka. Kerala alone contributes 80% tapioca in the country. It grows in alkaline soil in marginal and infertile lands. It is a small shrub producing tubers inside the soil. Tubers are rich in starch, therefore, cassava has been exploited commercially for starch, sago and flour and recently, as a source of alcohol. Tapioca can yield alcohol about 180 litres/tonne in contrast with sugarcane which produces about 70 litres/tonne. Central Tuber Crop Research Institute (CTCRI), Trivandrum has carried out work on alcohol production from tapioca. Starch is extracted from the tubers which is then fermented into alcohol.

Forestry

Forests contribute a considerable amount of biomass, which could be variously used as a source of energy. Lignocellulosic content varies from 60-75% of dry weight. Soft wood has higher lignin to cellulose ratio than hard wood. Residues/wastes generated from forestry are wood chips, saw dust, dried tree branches, tree twigs, tree-bark, leaf litter, etc.

Types of various fuel wood species

- **Fuel wood species for Arid and Semi arid Regions:** Acacia brachystaschya, A. cambagei, A. cyclops, A. nilotica, A. saligna, A. senegal. A. seyal, A. tortilis, Adhatoda vasica, Albizia lebbek, Anogeissus latifolia, Azadirachta indica, Cājanus cajan, Cassia siamea, Colophospermum mopane, Emblica officinalis, Eucalyptus camaldulensis, E. citriodora, E. gomphocphala, E. microtheca, E. occidentalis, Haloxylon aphyllum, H. persicum, Parkinsonia aculeata, Pinus helepensis, Pithecellobium dulce, Prosopis alba, P. chilensis, P. cineraria, P. juliflora, P. pallida, P. tamarugo, Tamarix aphylla, Zizyphus mauritiana, Z. spina-christi.
- **Fuel wood Species for Humid Tropics:** Acacia aurriculiformis, Calliandra calothyrsus, Casuarina equisetifolia, Derris indica, Gliricidia sepium, Gmelina arborea, Guazuma ulmifolia, Leucaena leucocephala, Mangroves spp., Mimosa scabrella, Muntingia calabura, Sesbania bispinosa, S. grandiflora, Syzyjium cumini, Terminalia catappa, Terma spp.
- **Fuel wood Species for Tropical Highlands:** Acacia mearnsii, Ailanthus altissima, Alnus acuminata, A. nepalensis, A. rubra, Eucalyptus globulus, E. grandis, Grevillea robusta, Inga vera.

Fire Wood as a Traditional and Future Source of Energy

More than one-third of the world's population depends on wood for cooking and heating. Around 86% of all the wood consumed annually in the developing countries is used for fuel, and of this total atleast half is used for cooking. The situation is growing so desperate that wood is poached from forest reserves. In the face of global concern over the dwindling supply of fuel wood, the rate of forest decimation to provide basic human necessities in developing countries is alarming. No less than one and a half billion people in developing countries derived at least 90% of their energy requirements from wood and charcoal. Indeed, it has been estimated that at least half the timber cut in the world still serves its original role for mankind: as fuel for cooking and heating.

The firewood fuel is seriously threatened particularly in the developing countries. By the turn of the century, at least 300 million people will be without wood fuel for their minimum cooking and heating needs and will be forced to burn dried animal dung and agricultural crop residues, thereby further decreasing food crop yield. Because of the severity of the firewood crisis we need those firewood crops, which are aggressive and quick growing. We can also look forward for those firewood crop plants, which may be slow growing and possess low propagation property, can be improved with the help of biotechnological devices. While planning the biotechnological project on firewood crop development the first priority should be given to local land races. Following are the selected firewood plant species, which have been identified as economical species.

Firewood crops that deserve increased recognition and research through genetic engineering and tissue culture methods to solve energy crisis of near future.

Municipal Sources

High amount of municipal wastes are generated from cities, as a result of anthropogenic activity which are thrown near cities in open lands or in rivers. These wastes again become a serious hygienic problem as it contain high amount of organic matter and pathogenic microorganisms. Municipal and domestic wastes include sewage and sludge, garbage, horse dung, cattle dung and wastes from animal slaughter houses.

1. **Sewage and Sludge:** Sewage is a product of water, which are thrown away after its use. Treatment of sewage results in generation of another waste, which is called as sludge. Sludge is a solid matter in the settling tanks of sewers, and other treatment operations in a sewage treatment plant. There are 142 class I cities in India which produced around 9,000 million litres of sewage per day. However, there is no sewage treatment facilities in about 70 class I cities such as Srinagar, Ranchi, Dhanbad, Bhopal, Jabalpur. Although methods for single cell protein production from sewage oxidation pond and irrigation of agriculture crops by treated water have been developed, yet this facility is available only at limited places. Moreover, if 900 million litres of sewage is converted into sullage gas per day from the major cities, 20% of their energy demand could be met.
2. ***Urban (City) Garbage:*** Garbage potential of Indian cities is quite high. It is estimated that production of city garbage in India is about 41,000 tonnes per day, the annual production is about 15 million tones. Nonetheless, city garbage produced in Bombay, Madras and Calcutta is comparable to that of developed countries. In India garbage is thrown near the city. In some cities like Madras, Calcutta, Delhi, Baroda, Jodhpur, etc. Municipal solid waste composting plants

are in operation. Central Mechanical Engineering and Research Institute, Durgapur has established a first pilot plant to produce electricity by using city garbage, The plant has a capacity to use about 500 kg garbage/ha, as a result of which about 5Km h electricity of garbage, anaerobically, into biogas and in turn into electricity.

METHODS FOR ENERGY PRODUCTION

Pyrolysis of Wood

It was first performed by Robert-Mudoch in 1792. The pyrolysis of wood results in production of gas, liquid and char which can be used as fuels. The gas can be synthesized into methanol or liquid hydrocarbons.

Pyrolysis is defined as the destructive distillation or decomposition of organic matter, for example, solid residues, wastes (saw dust, wood chips, wood pieces) in an oxygen-deficient atmosphere or in absence of oxygen at high temperature (200-500 °C or rarely 900 °C). Products of pyrolysis are gases, organic liquids and chars, depending on the pyrolysis process and temperature of reaction. The condensable liquids separate into aqueous (pyroligneous acid), oil and tar fraction (if the substrate is wood). The composition of gas is carbon monoxide (28-33%), methane (3-5-18%), higher hydrocarbons (1-3%) and hydrogen (1-3%). During pyrolysis, hydrogen content of gas increases with increasing the temperature.

After pyrolysis, the amount of different products varies with the nature of wood, type of equipment and systems employed. For example, low temperature favours liquids and char; low heating rates favour gas and char and short gas residence time favours liquids. In contrast high heating rate, favours liquids and the long gas-residence time favours gas. Thus, the liquid is obtained before the solid is completely burnt to yield gases. The liquid is very useful for high energy fuel.

Wilson *et al.*, (1978) have described a mobile system for the pyrolysis. The unit can move from one place to another and process the transportation cost of wastes/residues. Energy transported as coal and oil would be about 2.8 times greater than transporting the wet wood waste.

Pyrolysis has been employed to produce charcoal for the last few decades. Charcoal is a smokeless and low sulphur fuel used mostly for cooking purpose. Besides wood, other residues used in pyrolysis are cotton, bagasse, ground nut shell, etc.

Gassification of Wood

When biomass reacts with steam and oxygen it produces BTU gas which consists mainly of carbon monoxide and hydrogen. This gas can be burnt as a fuel or can be used as an intermediate for the synthesis of fuels or energy intensive chemicals, including methanol, substitute gasoline, hydrogen and ammonia.

It is a process of thermal degradation of carbonaceous material under controlled amount of air or pure oxygen, and high temperature upto around 1,000 °C. As a result of gassification, high amount of gases is produced, Gassificaation of biomass is done in a gasifier designed in various ways, Success for gassification process is based on its desinging. Therefore the design of a gassfication process is based on its designing. Therefore, the design of a gasifier is an important factor in controlling gas quality. GAs is used in a controlled manner for irrigation, pumping and electricity generation.

Following are the advantages of gassification of wood over coal:

1. much low oxygen requirements
2. practically no steam requirements
3. low cost for changing H_2/CO_2 ratios which are high in wood gas, and
4. no or very little desulfurization cost (Goldstein,1980).

When gassification of farm wastes (manure) takes place, the phenomenon is known as hydro-gassification, because gassification of organic wastes occurs in the presence of hydrogen at 500-600 °C.

Three to five kilograms of biomass per hour is needed for generating power for an hour. In a year it has to run for at least 15,000 hours for which 6 tonnes of biomass is required. Therefore, it is very essential to make sure that the biomass is continuously available.

Bariquetting

The process consists of drying cellulosic wastes using solar energy and then partially carboniging the material to give virtually ash-free carbon.

Liquefaction

Liquefaction involves the production of oils for energy from wood or agriculture and carbon residues by reacting them with carbon monoxide and water/steam at high pressure (4,000 lb/in^2) and temperature (350-400 °C) in the presence of catalysts. By this method about 40-50% oil can be obtained from wood. This oil serves a good source of fuel.

The Biological Process (Bioconversion)

Bioconversion involves the conversion of organic materials into energy, fertilizer, food and chemicals through biological agency. The term biological agents means the microorganisms *i.e.* bacteria, actinomycetes, fungi and algae. In broad sense bioconversion involves two following steps:

1. Photosynthetic production of biomass
2. Its subsequent conversion into more useful energy forms (gaseous, liquid or solid fuel; heat and electricity).

Enzymatic Digestion

This process involves the conversion of cellulosic and lignocellulosic materials into alcohols, acids and animal feeds by using microbial enzyme *e.g.* cellulase, hemicellulase, amylase, pectinase, etc.

Degradation of Cellulose

It is clear that cellulose is a polymer of ß-1,4 linked anhydrous glucose units, comprising of 40-60% of cell wall materials of plants. Microorganisms, which produce cellulase and other enzymes in high amount like *Cellulomonas*, *Trichoderma reesei*, *T viride* and others are used for the production of cellulases in high amount.

There are 3 enzyme components of cellulase:

1. β-1,4-endoglucanase
2. β-1,4-exoglucanose
3. β-1,4-glucosidase

ß-1,4-endoglucanase randomly attacks along cellulose chain; ß-1,4-exoglucanase splits from non-reducing end of cellulose and ß-1,4-glucosidase *i.e.* cellobiase cleaves 2 molecules of glucose from cellobiose. Following is the sequence of cellulose degradation.

Cellulose chain $\xrightarrow{\beta\ 1,4\ endoglucanase}$ Smaller polymers and soluble oligomers

β 1,4 endogluconase, $\xrightarrow[\beta\ 1,4\ exogluconase]{}$ Cellobiose $\xrightarrow[and\ Glucose]{\beta\ 1,4\ glucosidase\ cellobiase}$ Glucose 2molecules

Degradation of Hemicellulose

Sugars constituting hemicellulose. An analogous system of enzymes is involved in the degradation of hemicellulose. This enzyme-system consists of 3 enzymes:

1. Exoxylanase
2. Endoxylanase
3. ß-xylosidase (which split xylose and other short chain xylobioses)

Anaerobic Digestion

An aerobic digestion is a partial conversion by microorganisms of organic substrates into gases in the absence of air. The gases produced are collectively known as **biogas**. Anaerobic digestion is accomplished in 3 stages:

1. **Solubilization** of complex substrates by enzymes into simple forms *i.e.* fatty acid, sugars, amino acids).
2. **Fermentation** of hydrolysed organic substrates into simplest forms *e.g.* organic acids.
3. **Methanogenic** production of methane from simple substrates by methanogenic bacteria under anaerobic conditions.

Anaerobic digestion is carried out in a digester, which is a brick-lined or concrete-lined chamber covered completely to prevent the entry of air.

Aerobic Digestion

Aerobic digestion involves the conversion of organic substrates by micro-organisms into utillizable forms in the presence of air, for example composting (biological decomposition of organic wastes/residues under controlled conditions to result in release of C, N, P, K, etc.) and oxidation systems (of sewage in oxidation ponds by bacteria and algae) to produce gases, single cell protein, fertilizers, etc.

Hydrolysis of Wood Ethanol

It is the process in which biological matter is converted into liquid fuel via hydrolysis of woody material from sugars, followed by fermentation to alcohol. It can be done in the form of hydrolysis by:

1. dilute acid, high temperature 180-200° C
2. concentrated acid, and
3. enzymatic process.

The last process (**enzymatic process**) is mainly concerned with microorganism. The biological conversion processes involve enzymatic or bacterial break down by microorganisms at relatively low temperature. This technique is useful for production of methane to biogas from a wide variety of plant, animal, human and industrial wastes during the process of anaerobic digestion. The process is known as fermentation. Microorganisms have, therefore, an essential role in the production of biological energy. They could also be used directly in certain energy conversion reactions as in case of *Botryococcus braunii*, to mass culture, with a view to produce hydrocarbons.

Ethanol Production for Energy

Brazilian government is the pioneer in the field of fuel alcohol production from yeast and sugarcane plants whose work is being followed as ambitious programmes in America, Canada, Australia, New Zealand, Indonesia, Kenya, and Europe. In Brazil, the Brazilian National Alcohol Programme (also known as **Gas alcohol programme**) was started in the first decade of the programme, the sugar cane production was raised to 30 per cent using conventional plant breeding techniques. Then the fermenter was also designed which reduced the time of fermentation from 24 hours to 6 hours. At present 2500,000,000 gallons of alcohol is produced every year. All Brazilian cars now run either on pure alcohol (95%) or on an alcohol-petrol mixture.

Due to high rise of oil prices, led the Brazilian government to assign a first priority to sugar cane production programme and, from 1980 to 1985, the production reached to its level of satisfaction. In United States, ethanol production has now reached to 719,000 tones (not counting alcohol beverages). The mixture of 6 to 9 parts of petrol for one part of ethanol (*gasohol*) is now commercially used in United States at about 900 service stations.

Gasohol is a blend of nine parts unleaded gasoline and one part alcohol (ethanol or methanol), used extensively in some countries to reduce the cost of gasoline as automobile fuel. Raw materials for methanol production are coal and organic wastes, especially waste-wood products, while ethanol may be distilled from grain, sugar crops, or almost any starchy plant. Although in most of the world in the early 1980s it remained more expensive than gasoline, gasohol is derived from renewable sources. Alcohol was used interchangeably with gasoline in the first internal-combustion engines in the 1870s, and gasoline-alcohol blends have been used periodically in Europe when petroleum was in short supply. Two gasoline-alcohol blends, alcoline and agrol, were sold in the U.S. in the 1930s but were unable to compete successfully with low-cost gasoline. The oil shortages of the 1970s prompted a revival of interest in alcohol blends, an interest further increased in 1985 by the proposed banning of leaded gasolines by the end of the 1980s. Gasohol can be used without modifying the carburetor, ignition timing, or fuel lines of an automobile and provides a slightly higher octane than unleaded regular gasoline.

It has been estimated that replacing all the petrol consumed in USA by gasohol would require a production of at least 50.6 billion liters of ethanol per year. Surplus cereals could be used for such production. The utilization of cereals in ethanol production is common in Middle West, for example, Archers Daniels Midland, located at Des Monines, Iowa (USA) has annual production capacity of 0.8 million tones alcohol. For 1995, about 50 million tones of such production has been estimated.

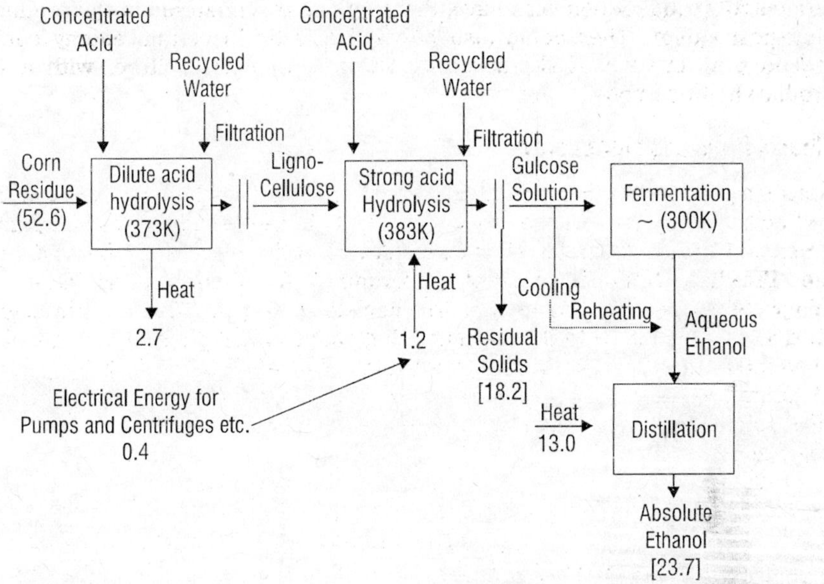

FIGURE 32.1: Energy account for the production of 1 dm^3 of ethanol for the acid hydrolysis of corn residues. The unbracketed numbers are energy inputs, while the bracketed numbers are energy contents, both in MJ.

In France, in the Bouches-du-Rhone department much research work is going on for production of alcohol from sugar beet, Jerusalem artichoke or sugarcane. However, in 1980 the price of ethanol was 3 to 5 times higher than petrol. The Jerusalem artichoke appeared to be superior to other energy crops, due to the genetic improvement of the variety and produces large quantities of haulms, which could meet the heating requirements of distillation. In France, active research is in action at Institut Francais du Petrol where extraction of inulin is carried out, as well as on the hydrolysis of this carbohydrate, and on acetonebutanol fermentation.

In 1980, India produced 6 million hectoliters of ethanol from the fermentation of molasses, of which 80,000 hectoliters were used by the chemical industry.

Before starting industrial production of above cited crops in India, the farmers will have to be trained for this new energy source and government have to liberalise its policy of alcohol production out of these crops.

In Japan, production of fuel alcohol from sugarcane is of prime importance. Long term objective has been started to meet one-third of the petrol needs for the country. Government of Japan has envisaged co-operation with South-East Asia to build plants for production of fuel alcohol products. According to one report, an annual production of 100 million kiloliter of fuel alcohols will be produced by such co-operation.

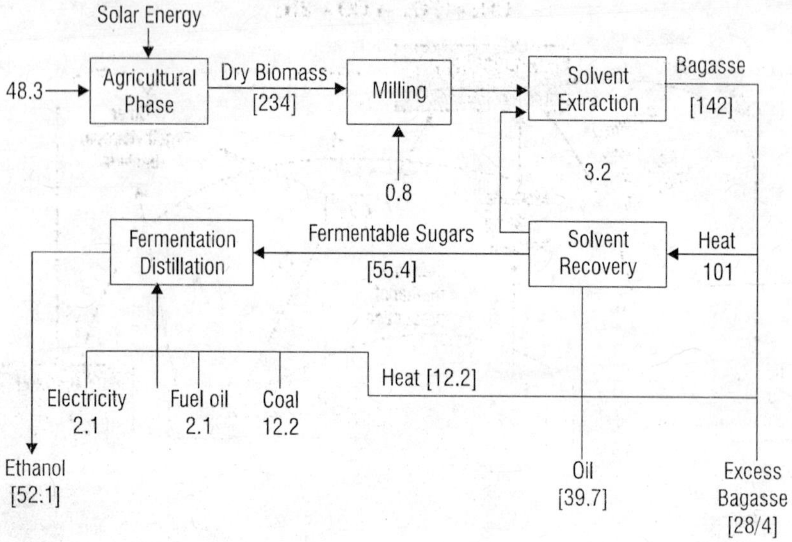

FIGURE 32.2: Illustration of energy account for the production of oil and ethanol from *Euphorbia lathyris*.

TABLE 32.4: Alcohol production from some important crops

Crop	Alcohol yield lit/ha.	Crop yield lit/tone	Alcohol production tone/ha.
Sweet Sorghum	60	1.32	80
Sugarcane	70	56.04	3923
Sugarbeet	110	30.21	3323
Sweet potatoes	125	8.36	1045
Cassava	180	8.70	1575
Molasses	245	-	-
Corn (Maize)	30	3.27	1175

In the Philippines, ten plants have been established for large scale production of alcohol. In Australia, alcohol is being produced from beet sugar or canesugar.

CONVERSION OF METHANE INTO THE SYNTHETIC GAS

There are two main routes through which methane can be converted into gases containing carbon monoxide and hydrogen, partial combustion and steam reforming. Partial combustion of methane, using a limited supply of oxygen, can be effected with or without the presence of a solid catalyst and the main part of the process is represented by the equation

$$CH_4 + \frac{1}{2}O_2 \rightarrow CO + 2H_2$$

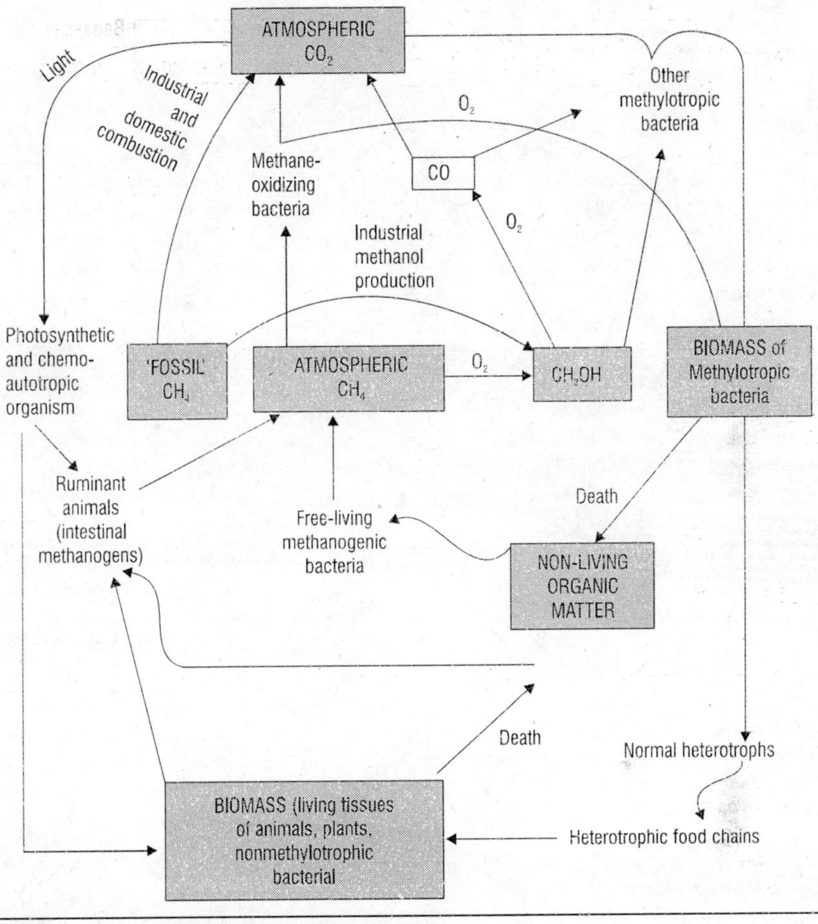

FIGURE 32.3: Diagrammatic presentation of methane cycle in nature.

The typical composition of the gas resulting from this process, expressed in the percentage by volume of each gas in the dried product, is 61% (hydrogen), 34.5% (carbon monoxide), 3% (carbon dioxide) and 0.5% unreacted methane. The energy content of the product gas is approximately 65% of that of the original methane.

Steam reformation of methane takes place at elevated temperatures in the presence of a solid catalyst, typically based on nickel. The central process is represented by the equation:

$$CH_4 + H_2O \rightarrow CO + 3H_2 \quad \text{reaction I}$$

Which has an endothermicity of 206.1 kj mol[6]. Also involved is the water-gas shift reaction represented by equation:

$$CO + H_2O \rightarrow CO_2 + H_2 \quad \text{reaction II}$$

The final composition of the product gas is governed by the chemical equilibria corresponding to equations (I) and (II). Under the typical operating conditions of a pressure of 1.2 MPa and temperature of 1088 K, the gas composition by volume is 14% (carbon monoxide), 14% (carbon dioxide), 71% (hydrogen) and 1.6 % (methane).

Factors Affecting Methane Formation

Addition of Algae: Ramamoorthy and Sulochana (1989) have found an enhancement in biogas production from cow dung on addition of the green algae, *Zygogonium* sp. The amount of biogas produced from the algae was twice (344 ml/g dry algae) of that obtained from cow dung (179/g dry cow dung) alone. Also, the duration of gas evolution increased with increasing the proportion of slurry. Addition of algae holds promise to get biogas in sufficient amount even in winter season also.

Carbon-nitrogen (C:N) Ratio: Maximum digestion occurs when C: N ratio is 30:1. Amendment of nitrogen or carbon substrates should be done exogenously according to chemical nature of substrates used in fermentation.

Creation of Anaerobic Conditions: It is obvious that methane production takes place in strictly anaerobic conditions therefore, the digesters should be totally air tight. In Indian conditions, digesters are burried in soil.

Nitrogen Concentration: Excess amount of nitrogen inhibits growth of bacteria, and thereby lowers methane production. Therefore, use of such materials should be discouraged.

pH: For the production of sufficient amount of methane, optimum pH of digester should be maintained between 6-8 as the medium lowers methane formation.

Seeding: In the beginning seeding of slurry with small amount of sludge of another digester activates methane evolution. Sludge contains acetogenic and methanogenic bacteria.

Slurry: Proper solubilization of organic materials (the ratio between solid and water) should be 1:1 when it is house hold things.

Temperature: Fluctuation in temperature reduces methane formation, because of inhibition in growth of methanogens. In case of mesophilic digestion, temperature should be between 30 °C, and 40 °C, but in case of thermophilic ones, it should be between 50 °C and 60 °C.

BIOGAS TECHNOLOGY

Biogas technology is anaerobic digestion of organic material producing clean fuel for cooking, lighting and running machinery and the bio-digest slurry besides providing plant nutrients both macro and micro to the crops, benefits the soil by bringing about physical, chemical and biological enrichment. This valuable organic manure not only releases plant nutrients slowly but also improves many of the soil properties like structure, water holding capacity, cation exchange capacity, resistance to soil erosion, and also provides energy for the activity of soil microflora, which enrich the soil and in turn increase productivity. The manurial value of the biogas slurry is superior to traditional FYM or compost in increasing crop productivity, and it enriches the soil with ammonical nitrogen and available phosphorus. While chemical fertilizers do increase crop yield over a short period, they do not maintain sustained productivity due to various reasons like deterioration of soil structure, deficiency of micronutrients and disintegration of soil microflora including N fixing and P solubilizing organisms.

The slurry can be applied as liquid under wet, air dried and sundried conditions for enhancing the yield of agricultural and horticultural crops and is also found to be suitable as a seed coating media, fortified with *Rhizobium*, *Azospirillum*, Phosphobacteria and micro nutrients, which enhances seed germination, seedling establishment and induces vigour to crops. Biogas slurry enriched with inorgainc fertilizers and biofertilizers such as a *Rhizobium* revealed higher crop productivity and sustained soil fertility.

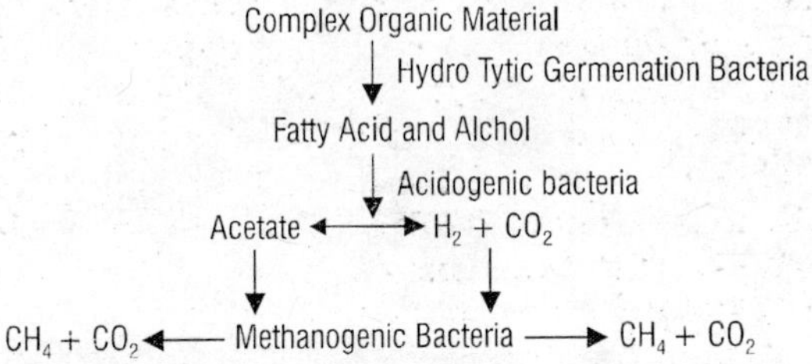

FIGURE 32.4: Steps of biogas production.

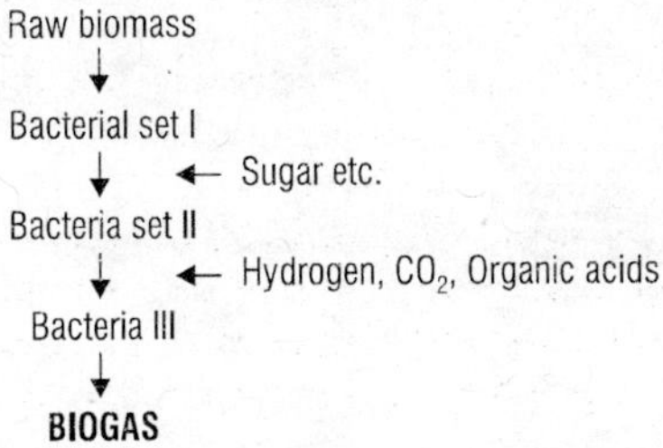

FIGURE 32.5: Schematic representation of the stages of methanogenesis.

The Gobar Gas Scheme, a development and popularization agency, provided producers of biogas with technical assistance and is responsible for the allocation of funds for construction of digesters, provide 3-5 head of cattle, with the view to meet energy needs of villages.

According to the New China News Agency, 7.15 million biogas installations have been made at the end of 1978, and current reports reveal that up to 1985 China have installed about 70 million of biogas plants. Government of India is also supporting in establishing regional and local offices which are responsible to establish biogas plants in every village. We are hopeful to meet out the demand of energy in near future through *gobar* gas.

Generation of Bio gas from Cotton Dust

Cotton dust is dust present in the air when handling or processing cotton. This dust may contain a mixture of many substances including ground-up plant matter, fiber, bacteria, fungi, soil, pesticides, non-cotton matter, and other contaminants which may have accumulated with the cotton during the growing, harvesting, and subsequent processing or storage periods.

The technological options for the utilization of cotton dust at the Indian spinning mills are (1) to generate biogas as an additional source of energy and manure and (2) converting to biomanure by incorporating certain natural recycling larva/grubs. One kilogram of microdust could generate about 200 liters of biogas in 50 days. It is advantageous for the mills to use their non-saleable waste like cotton dust, which is in perennial supply for biogas generation at their premises itself. This article describes the work carried out on generation of biogas from cotton dust and this work could be utilized for disposing of the polluting cotton dust by adopting this biological methods. However, handling of solid waste like microdust for bio gas generation unlike cow dung used for the production of gobar gas necessetities for modifications in the type and design of the digester arises.

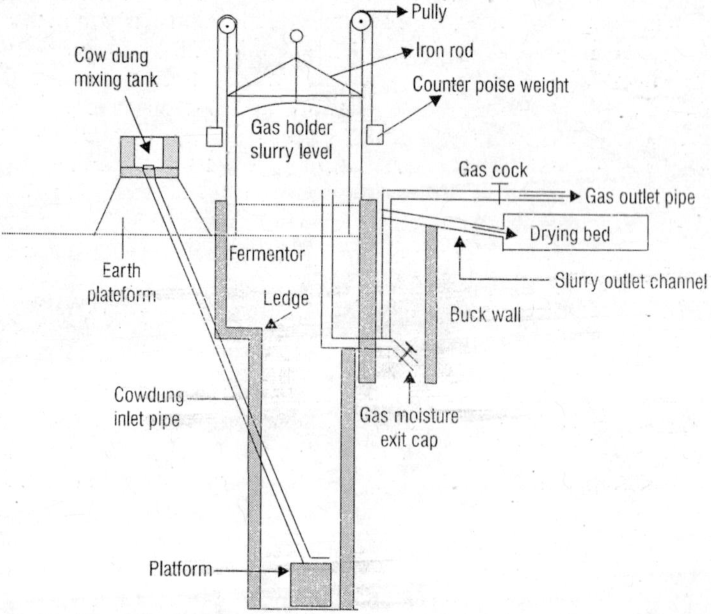

FIGURE 32.6: Outline of *gobar* gas plant.

The Process: The biogas being a clean fuel, burns with a smokeless blue flame without emission of polluting vapors. Methane will absorb heat and is good for green house gas. A typical biogas may contain, methane - 60%, carbon dioxide - 30% and hydrogen-10%. In a mill it can be used in canteen, heating boiler feed water, lighting, etc. (*References:* Joseph Zacharia and P. P. Krishnan, (2001), *Bio Energy News*, vol. 5 no. 2, June 2001; A. V. Jamode, et. al., (2003) Generation of Bio gas from Cotton Dust: A need of Waste Minimisation, *Agrobios News Letter*, Vol. 1: No. 9 February, 2003).

Composition of Biogas Slurry

Cattle dung has been used practice in India since long in the form of dung cake as a domestic fuel and as compost manure. With the advancement of science, a technique of anaerobic digestion came into existence in late thirties, through which an efficient gaseous fuel *i.e.* biogas and digested slurry with higher manurial value can be obtained from the digestion of cattle dung. Besides, being rich in major plant nutrients *i.e.* N (1.5 per cent-2 per cent), P_2O_5(1 per cent), K_2O (1 per cent) biogas slurry is also a good source of micro nutrients like Zn, Fe, Mn and Cu. One tonne of biogas slurry on dry weight basis will provide approximately the following nutrients and the equivalent cost of chemical fertilizer as given in the table below:

Nutrient	One tonne biogas slurry	Equivalent	Cost Rs.

	(dry weight basis)	chemical fertilizer	
N	18 kg	40 kg urea	109.40
P_2O_5	10 kg	63 kg SSP	189.00
K_2O	8 kg	14 kg MOP	66.90
			365.30

In tropics, addition of organic manures to soils is very important from fertility and productivity point of view. Since organic manure is of biological origin, it contains nutrients and improves physical, chemical and biological properties of soil. There is, however, wide variation of nutrient availability in these manures due to differences in animal species, feed consumed and size and health of the animal.

In the biogas plant, nutrient recovery represents an economic return to the farmer using this technology. The liquid effluent from the anaerobic digestor is a relatively stable product in comparison to the influent. There is now a broader realization that recycled organic nutrients offer an alternative to reliance on chemical fertilizers. In view of increaing prices of chemical fertilizers and withdrawal of subsidies on them, farmers should be provided with technology for enhancing them efficiency specially that of urea or some alternate source. Biogas slurry is one of the alternatives. The manure obtained from biogas plants has more nitrogen compared to conventional composting. It is reported that fermentation increases the ammonia content by 120 per cent and available phosphorus by 150 per cent. The output of sludge per year per plant (10 cm capacity) is roughly 10 cubic meter. The output of effluent is about 14 cubic meter per year.

Aerobic decomposition of organic materials for manure production resuls in a loss of 55 per cent of organic matter and 30 to 50 per cent of nitrogen. Whereas under anaerobic fermentation in the biogas plant, the loss of organic matter is 25 to 30 per cent and almost complete conservation of nitrogen: NH_4 - N is the main soluble end product in anaerobic unit and 15 to 18 per cent of the total nitrogen is converted to ammonia due to the alkaline nature of the slurry. In our country, the dung rarely contains more than one per cent of total nitrogen on dry weight basis, hence the ultimate nitrogen in slurry will not ordinarily increase 1.25 to 1.30 per cent unless other protein-rich organics are used as feed material in the process. It is directly linked to the nitrogen content initially present in such feed material. Freshly digested slurry has mineralized N to the extent of 21 per cent compared with 16 per cent of N in compost which shows the advantage of anaerobically fermented manure over aerobic decomposition.

BIOGAS SLURRY FOR AGRICULTURE

Several farmers in Gujarat having biogas plants on farm houses are incorporating the fresh slurry with irrigation water, which is to resulting in higher yields as compared to other modes of its application. This is particularly so with paddy nurseries. The application of such mixed slurry irrigation water resulted in higher yields on transplantation as compared to other methods of fertilization. But such method of disposal is possible only when the gas plant is located on a farm house. Location of the plant plays a significant role in efficient and effective utilization of the biogas slurry.

Field experiments were conducted by Kuppuswamy et al (1993) to study the effect of biogas slurry and gypsum enriched biogas slurry on rice-blackgram. Biogas slurry at 10 t/ha enriched with gypsum @ 250 kg/ha gave an additional grain yield of

1.80 t/ha compared to control. Gypsum enriched biogas slurry had an edge over slurry alone. The residual effect of FYM on the succeeding blackgram was comparatively better than that of biogas slurry. In another experiment, gypsum enriched biogas slurry in combination with 75 per cent recommended NPK resulted in higher seed yield under rice-blackgram cropping sequence.

Biogas slurry enriched with gypsum recorded maximum tiller number / hill (7.58) followed by enriched FYM and dried biogas slurry. Wet plain biogas slurry at 10 t/ha recorded increased tiller number by 0.27/hill over FYM alone. Muralikrishna Reddy (1987) had also observed an increase in tiller number through soil application of slurry enreached with gypsum. In respect of number of panicles, the enriched biogas slurry registered the maximum panicle number (412.5/m^2). These treatments resulted in an increase of panicles by 88.44 and 27.72 m^{-2} over control and FYM, respectively. FYM enriched with gypsum and dried biogas slurry at 10 t ha^{-1} and wet biogas slurry at 10 ha^{-1} gave identical panicle number. FYM alone produced more panicles than gypsum alone. Increased panicle number in rice due to application of biogas slurry was earlier reported by several researchers (Sahu and Nandu, 1988; Kuppuswamy *et al*, 1991).

TABLE 32.5: Direct and residual effect of bio-digested slurry on rice and blackgram

Treatments	Rice				Blackgram	
	Tiller number /hill	Panicle number /m2	Seed yield t/ha	Straw yield t/ha	Pod number/plant	Seed yield kg/ha
Wet bio-digested slurry @ 10 t/ha	6.83	384	7.46	13.03	9.21	422
Dried bio-digested slurry @ 10 t/ha	7.08	385	7.80	13.69	8.94	393
Wet bio-digested slurry @ 10 t/ha with gypsum 250 kg/ha (1:0.025)	7.58	413	8.41	15.25	9.12	402
Farmyard manure @ 10 t/ha	6.58	341	7.33	12.58	10.22	463
Farmyard manure @ 10 t/ha with gypsum 250 kg/ha (1:0.025)	7.26	385	8.00	14.69	10.11	431
Gypsum 250 kg/ha	6.33	330	6.78	11.54	7.83	294
Control	6.17	324	6.61	11.03	7.70	292
CD (p=0.05)	0.22	0.06	0.19	0.49	1.24	51

In respect of seed and straw yields, the trend as observed in tiller and panicle number was almost reflected. Wet biogas slurry at 10 t/ha enriched with gypsum at 250 kg/ha proved to be distinctly superior to rest of the treatments. This treatment gave an additional seed yield of 1.80 t/ha compared to control. The response was well marked with FYM enriched with gypsum and dried biogas slurry at 10 t/ha recording increased yields by 21 and 18 per cent, respectively over control. Availability of soil ammonical nitrogen and phosphorus from slurry (Zodhy *et al.*, 1984) might have been responsible for fairly higher yields in slurry treatments. Many workers have reported beneficial effect of biogas slurry on rice yields (Muralikrishna Reddy, 1987; Sahu and Nandu, 1988; Kuppuswamy *et al.*, 1991). In straw yield also, enriched biogas slurry gave the maximum straw yield (15.25 t ha^{-1}), followed by FYM enriched with gypsum (14.69 t ha^{-1}), Wet biogas slurry and FYM did not vary from each other. Increased straw yields with slurry application was also reported by Talukder *et al.*, (1988). Increased yields with gypsum enriched biogas slurry could be due to the cumulative effect of combining biogas slurry, a good source of organic matter (66.5 per cent) with NPK fertilizer and gypsum containing calcium (21.6 per cent) and sulphur (17.2 per cent).

Sufficient data is not available which compares the fertilizer effect of fermented bigas plant slurry and inorganic fertilizers on plant growth. Jewell *et. al.* (1976) carried out short green house experiments with maize for getting comparative information. He tested two soils, a mardin soil with a pH around 5.0 and honoeye with pH of 7.7 with each soil, 7 treatments were used: a control, a fermented cattle manure slurry with total nitrogen added to the pots to obtain concentration of 100, 200 and 300 ppm N and the inorganic pots with ammonium sulphate added to obtain N concentration of 100, 200 and 400 ppm N, phosphorous and potassium were supplemented to 100 ppm to avoid effects other then those caused by nitrogen. only about 50 per cent of the nitrogen in the fermented residue was in the ammonia for and the reminder was contained in the non-degraded residue as organic nitrogen. The fermented waste had a superior effect on the response of maize in the early stages. At the termination of this series of experiments of 30 days, growth difference was less obvious. However, at the higher application rates, there was more protein per plant than with higher application of ammonia via chemical fertilizers.

The contribution of nitrogen from various organic manures in crop production, FYM. compost, biogas slurry and sewage sludge performed equally well on equivalent N basis while poultry manure proved a better source. The residual effect of manure on succeeding crop also, the efficiency or FYM. as compared to that of fertilizer was noted to be 50 per cent. Due to severe loss of organic matter in sub-tropics the practice of applying heavy dose of manure only once in two years needs to be discouraged and it should be applied in small dose annually.

Rehate (1988) carried out experiments with groundnut which included absolute control with no nitrogen, and all the nitrogen of the recommended dose applied through different sources of organic manure like FYM biogas effluent sludge, PMC and urea. However, the remaining treatments were the combinations of these sources *i.e.* 50 percent of the recommended dose of nitrogen was added through urea and 50 percent through FYM, and PMC. The results showed that biogas slurry combination with urea favourably influenced the growth, nodulation, dry matter, quality over other treatment and gave significantly higher pod yields over all the treatments. The treatments including slurry plus urea or slurry alone and PMC with urea gave 59.49, 50 and 49.83 percent increase in pod yield of groundnut over absolute control, respectively. However these treatments recorded an increase in pod yield of groundnut over chemical fertilizer treatment to the extent of 37.18, 22.53 and 22.27 percent respectively.

Transfer of Biogas Technology

In India it is estimated that over 16 lakh biogas plants have been installed. Assuming 85 per cent plants in operation at a given time, 27.2 million tonnes of enriched biogas slurry is being produced every year, which is valued at over Rs. 225 crores. Thus in order to make the farmers fully aware of the benefits and utility of biogas slurry, there is a need for launching a mass awareness campaign. Ministry of Non-Conventional Energy Sources (MNES) has launched a countrywide demonstration programme in farmers field, through State Nodal Department, fertilizers, Gujarat State Fertilizer Corporation (GSFC), Indian Farmers Fertilizers Co-operative (IFFCO), Regional Biogas Development and Training Centres and Voluntary Organisations mainly FORRAD, New Delhi. Over 3000 such demonstrations have been conducted so far all over the country.

TABLE 32.6: Biogas plants installed up to March 31, 1992

Type	Number of plants installed
Family size biogas plants	15,75,000
Community biogas plants	401
Institutional biogas plants	359
Night-soil biogas plants	59

The reports received from the State Nodal Department of Haryana, Himachal Pradesh, Kerala, Karnataka, Madhya Pradesh, Gujarat, Goa, Punjab, Uttar Pradesh and Tamil Nadu have been studied and analysed for different crops for the period 1984-95 to 1990-91 and the per centage increase in crop yield in demonstration plot (slurry treated) is given at Table 32.7.

TABLE 32.7: Summary of results of demonstrations conducted by State Nodal Departments / Agencies (1984-85 to 1990-91)

Crop	No. of Demonstration	Per cent increase in crop yield in slurry treated plot over untreated plot
Wheat	93	8-38
Paddy	67	18-36
Gram	11	17-11
Peas	10	15-50
Cotton	2	21-23
Potato	16	5-19
Tomato	18	38-42
Onion	6	10-11
Mustard	10	20-23
Groundnut	24	9-25
Watermelon	5	7-25
Sunflower	13	20-21
Cabbage	7	16-17
Banana	2	7-23

TABLE 32.8: Summary of results of demonstrations conducted by FORRAD (1989-90 and 1990-91)

Crop	No. of Demonstrations	Per cent increase in crop yield in slurry treated plot over untreated plot
Wheat	103	25
Paddy	79	32
Peas	14	60
Potato	3	43
Tomato	1	71
Groundnut	7	25
Ladies Finger	1	67
Chilies	1	49
Urad	1	1
Bajra	3	37
Maize	10	49
Ragi	8	27

Crop	No. of Demonstrations	Per cent increase in crop yield in slurry treated plot over untreated plot
Banana	3	9
Turmeric	1	27
Sugarcane	2	19
Deccanhemp	1	50
Mulbery	1	25
Mustard	2	23
Total	257	35.5

Besides increase in yield of various crops, various observations were made during the field demonstrations. As reported by Tripathi (1993), these observations may be summarized as under:

1. Improvement in quality of produce. For example, the size of vegetables like cabbage, tomato, potato, brinjal, etc. were significantly increased.
2. Reduction in weed number in biogas slurry plots,
3. Biogas slurry does not attract insect breeding.
4. Reduces the usage of chemical fertilizers thus indirectly helps in reduction in unit cost of produce.
5. Improves the physical and chemical properties of soil.
6. Biogas slurry has high water holding capacity, which helps rain-fed crops.
7. Seeds treated with biogas slurry have better germination rate.
8. Contains larger amount of organic matter and free ammonia than available in composted manure.
9. Biogas slurry is ready in shortest possible time.
10. If night soil and cattle urine is added, N and P_2O_5 availability in biogas slurry is enhanced.

In the context of reduction of subsidies on chemical fertilizers, biologically supplied or recycled organic nutrients such as biogas slurry offers an alternative to complete reliance on chemical fertilizers only. The manure obtained from biogas plants has higher nitrogen compared to conventional composting. The bio gas plant will prove more economical to the farmer only when both fuel and manure are used effectively and efficiently by him. Delinking these two aspects will make it uneconomical. It is well known that addition of organic manures to the soil improves its physical, chemical and biological properties. However, more research needs to be done to clearly indicate the benefits of the fermented animal waste on crop production.

According to Santosh *et al.* (1993) for making the programme of organic farming/non-chemical farming more meangful, effective and sustainable in terms of productivity also, following should be given due attention:

1. Establishing proper demonstration site in different agroclimatic conditions.
2. Developing efficient and suitable methods of slurry management and planning for its popularisation.
3. Conservation of dung resource through the use of improved cooking devices.
4. Popularisation of improved methods of composting such as 'Nadep' technology alongwith biogas.
5. Documentation and scientific assessment of traditional farming systems, especially agricultural practices, cropping pattern, pest management, etc.
6. Maintenance unit for biogas plants in different locale.

ENERGY AND FUEL USING MICROORGANISMS

Hydrogen as Energy Source

Molecular hydrogen is an attractive *energy vector*. It is naturally occurring - it has to be manufactured, *i.e.*, it is synthetic fuel. Hydrogen is the cleanest fuel, producing only water when burnt correctly, with no carbon monooxide, carbon dioxide, hydrocarbons, or solid residues formed on combustion. Hydrogen is much used in chemicals industry. Hydrogen is readily transported and stored, is easily ignited and burns smoothly and evenly in properly designed open-flame burners, both on small domestic appliances and on large industrial units. It is also well suited for catalytic oxidation. Hydrogen is now made mainly from natural gas, but it costs approximately the same to make hydrogen from coal as to make methane from coal. Hydrogen may act as a bridge between the fossil fuel age and a nuclear or solar era. Almost all types of energy source can be used in a hydrogen-energy system.

Production of Hydrogen

Most of the hydrogen produces industrial derives from fossil fuels, although some is produced by electrolysis of water.

From Fossil Fuels: The brief outline is as follows:

1. Removal of methane and other non-hydrogen constituents from refinery tail gases or coke oven gas at low temperatures
2. Reforming of natural gas (or other hydrocarbons)

$$CH_4 + H_2O \longrightarrow CO + 3H_2$$

Followed by water-gas shift

$$CO + H_2O \longrightarrow CO_2 + H_2$$

This is followed by CO_2 removal using physical or chemical absorption techniques

3. Direct production of synthesis gas by reaction of coal with oxygen and steam

$$3C + O_2 + H_2O \longrightarrow CO + H_2$$

followed by water-gas shift and CO_2 removal

4. Partial oxidation of hydrocarbons

$$CH_4 + \tfrac{1}{2}O_2 \longrightarrow CO + H_2$$

followed by water-gas shift and CO_2 removal

Of these methods, that of (2) is the most widely used.

Desulphurized natural gas is steam reformed in the presence of a nickel catalyst. After cooling to about 375° C, the product gases undergo the water-gas shift reaction, usually with an iron/chromium catalyst.

$$CH_4 + H_2O \longrightarrow CO + 3H_2O$$

$$H_2O \downarrow$$

$$H_2 + CO_2$$

Overall:

$$CH_4 + H_2O \longrightarrow 4H_2O + CO_2$$

A second shift reaction may be carried out at about 200° C over a copper/zinc catalyst. The CO_2 is removed by physical or chemical adsorption. Overall, the thermal efficiency of the process approaches 70%.

It is clear that it is water, which represents the inexhaustible supply of hydrogen in the future; even in the steam reforming of methane, half of the product is derived from added steam.

The **electrolysis of water** can be achieved by using microorganisms. They split water during the process of photosynthesis (**photolysis of water**). The photosynthetic machinery of green plants are being used for this purpose. The chlorophyll helps in trapping solar energy in the form of photon which is converted into ATP. In this process water is subjected to photolysis, which leads to splitting of water molecule into oxygen, electrons and hydrogen ions (H^+). The hydrogen ions do not get a chance to form hydrogen gas, but is used to form energy rich compounds like glucose. However, if these hydrogen ions can be converted into hydrogen gas (H_2) the later can be collected and used as fuel. Enzyme hydrogenase and nitrogenase have been tried to convert hydrogen ions (H^+) in to hydrogen gas (H_2).

Microbial Production of Hydrogenase: Microbes like *Scenedesmus*, *Chlamydomonas*, *Dunaliella*, *Porphyridium*, *Chromatinum*, *Clostridium*, *Thiocapsa*, etc. the main sources of hydrogenase enzyme in nature. They possess the enzyme which helps the two electrons join hydrogen ions to produce one molecule hydrogen gas. These microbes have also been used to directly isolate hydrogenase enzyme from chloroplast. The liberated hydrogen gas bubble out from the solution can be easily collected. This system though presently works only for a few hours, however, it can be commercially improved.

Recently, a group of micro- organism., the purple bacteria, has been discovered which is another potential source of hydrogen. Two species of *Halobacterium*, *e.g. H. halobium* and *H. curtirubrum*, are known. Halobacteria are rod-shapeed and physiologically a unique bacteria, as they are highly halophilic (salt loving). They differ from other bacteria in respect of cell-wall and energy producing mechanisms. They require the high concentrations of salt (*e.g.* 3-4 M sodium chloride) and low amount of oxygen. Therefore, they can grow in saline water *i.e.* saline lakes and sea. In salt saturated (>3M NaCl) and oxygen poor environment they utilize sunlight to produce ATP and preserve their structure. When salt concentration reaches below 3 M the rod shaped cells become irregular or spherical Below 1 M NaCl helps in growth and intergrity of the cells. No salt, like sodium chloride has been fouond to support growth of the cells.

Microbial Production of Nitrogenase: In cyanobacteria (*Anabaena*, *Nostoc*, *Rivularia*, *etc.*), nitrogenase enzyme is the main hydrogen producing enzyme. Hydrogenase enzyme is sensitive to oxygen which is produced during photolysis of water where as nitrogenase enzyme is relatively less sensitive to oxygen. In heterocyst (nitrogen fixing organ in cyanobacteria) the concentration of oxygen is low or even nil. Therefore, the production of hydrogen becomes more efficient. The enzyme nitrogenase reduces nitrogen in to ammonia with associated release of hydrogen gas. The production of hydrogen gas depends on light, which provides electron donors and also activities nitrogenase and ATP formation in heterocyst.

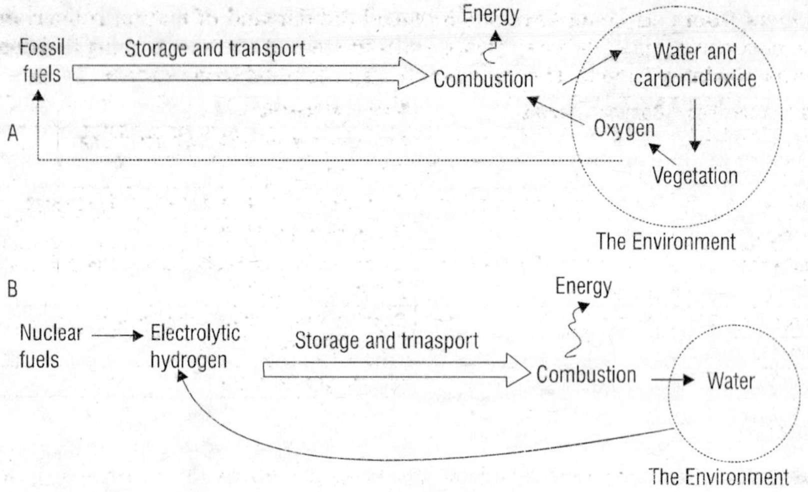

FIGURE 32.7: The environmental effects of the fossil fuel and hydrogen fuel cycles. (A) The present energy cycle. (B) The hydrogen energy cycle.

From the biological point of view, the production of fuels and chemicals from biomass is still in an early stage of development and could profit from the screening of a large number of species of plants, algae, fungi, and bacteria for their potential. Any such screening effort must be global in scope, since the organisms of potential interest are very unlikely to be encountered only in the natural ecosystems of developed countries.

PETROPLANTS

Pertroplants or petroleum plants accumulate the photosynthetic products (hydrocarbons) of high molecular weight (10,000). They were reported by Dr. M. Calvin (1979) of the University of California. He suggested that these plants may be used as substitute for conventional petroleum sources. Calvin and coworkers screened most of the plants of Family Euphorbiaceae, especially *Euphorbia* (containing 2,000 species) which reduce CO_2 beyond the carbohydrates. About 400 plant species, belonging to different families are known which grow in different part of the country. The other plant families which have been evaluated are Asclepiadaceae, Apocyanaceae, Leguminosae, Moraceae, Dipterocarpaceae, Compositate, etc. It is hoped that petroplants can yield petroleum more than 40-45 barrel/acre. Petroplants have laticiferous canals in their stem and secrete a milky latex. The latex can be either continuously tapped like *Hevea* latex and stored or extracted from the biomass by using the organic solvents.

The product rich in hydrocrackable hydrocarbon and named as **biocrude** which yields about 70.6% energy; and out of which 22% as kerosene and 44.6% as gasoline.

Hevea Rubber

Rubber plant, (*Hevea brasiliensis*) commonly known as *Hevea* rubber is the principal source of rubber which is restricted in distribution in South-East Asia. This plant meets one third of total world demand of rubber. The synthetic rubber elastomers from petroleum have not replaced the demand of natural rubber, due to its low cost aeroplanes. Rubber is trapped from stem of trees by making incision and collecting the latex from it. The latex is further processed to get rubber.

Plant group/families	Common Names	Botanical Names
Algae (Chlorophyta)		Botryococcus sp., Chlorlla pyrenoidosa
Asclepiadaceae	Aak	Calotropis procera
Compositae	Guayule Russian dandelion	Parthenium arentatum, Taraxacum koksaghyz
Dipterocarpaceae	Gurjun	Dipterocarpus turbinatus
Euphorbiaceae	Hevea rubber, Rubber plant, Sehund	Hevea brasiliensis, Euphorbia abyssinica, E. resinifera, E. lathyris, E. tirucalli
Leguminoseae	Samprani	Copaifera tangsdorfii, C. mutijuga Hardwickia pinnata
Myristicaceae		Dialynthera otoba
Pittosporaceae		Pittosporum resiniferum

Euphorbia

In Italy, Euphorbia Gasoline Refinery has been set up to tap vegetative gasoline. *Euphorbia lathyris* is an annual herb and *E. tirucalli* is a perennial one. *E. lathyris* can produce 20 tonne dry matter/ha/yr. Chemical analysis of this plant in organic solvents revealed that heptan extract and either soluble fraction constituted about 8% terperoid extract.

Guayule and Russian Dandelion

Guayule (*Partheniuum argentatum*) and *Taraxacum koksaghyz* are the members of family Compositae. These are sources of rubber. Guayule is a shrub and indigenous to North Central Mexico and South-West U.S.A. Guayule generally grows in arid, semi-arid and desert areas. The U.S. Government encouraged the cultivation of this plant after World War II to reform the economy of the country. It can tolerate temperature ranging from 32-38 °C, and can grow in Indian conditions. Like Hevea guayule contains *cis*-polyisoprene and identical physical properties.

Aak (*Calotropis procera*)

Aak belongs to family Asclepiadaceae. It is a shrub of 1-2.5 meters in hight. It occurs in hot and dry regions of India on waste dry places, river beds, roadsides and forest clearings. It secretes latex which cauces irritation to skin. Latex contains high amount of extractable hydrocarbons. The ratio of C,H,O in the hexane extract has been found as 78.03%, 11.22% and 10.71% respectively. The ratio of C and H is similar to crude oil, fuel oil and gasoline. Hydrocarbon yield and energy value of C. procera are comparable to those of *E. lathyris*. Therefore, this plant can be used as a substitute of petroleum. Researches on it are being done at the Central Arid Zone Research Institute, Jodhpur.

Jatropha curcas

The plant is also known as Purging nut or Physic nut (*Hin*: Jungli, errand, Pahari errand, Ratanjot). It is the member of family Euphorbiaceae. It is a large deciduous soft wooded shrub, 3-4 m in height with sticky juice; leaves alternate, broadly ovate, cordate, 3-5 lobed, glabrous, base seven nerved, stipules zero, flowers yellowish green in loose panicles of cymes; fruits ovoid, black, splitting into three, 2-valved cocci, seeds dull brownish black and found throughout India, in plains and in hedges. It is propogated by seeds and vegetative method. The oil is used as a source of energy. The plant contains range of acid val., sap. Val., iod. Val., hydroxyl val., R.M. val.; Polenske val., centipoises; and unsapon. Matter. The fatty acid composition of the oil is as follows; myristic, palmitic, stearic, arachidic, oleic, and linoleic acid. Recently, Ministry of Railways, Government of India initiated cultivation of this plant as a source of diesel.

Algal Hydrocarbons

Algae are used as the natural converter of solar energy in to chemical energy. They act as a possible source of energy. They have been reported to carry out photo production of hydrogen, which now a day is receiving much attention as a clean type of fuel causing no pollution. Besides, hydrogen, some algae produce hydrocarbons and methane that can be used as biofuels.

Hydrogen is a renewable source of energy and its photo production by algae involves the basic principle of photosynthesis carried out by all green plants. during photosynthesis, green pigment, chlorophyll a traps the solar energy and brings about photolysis of water into oxygen, hydrogen ions and electrons. These hydrogen ions do not get a chance to form hydrogen gas but are utilized in the production of reducing power *i.e.* $NADPH_2$.

The reducing power so produced is then used in the reduction of CO_2 to carbohydrate during the dark phase of photosynthesis. Efforts are being made to convert these hydrogen ion sand electrons in to H_2, which can serve as a source of biofuel. A lot of success has already been achieved in this direction and attempts are still on for photo production of hydrogen gas via this method on a large scale.

Two specific enzymes namely hydrogenase and nitrogenase, found in algae have been tried successfully for converting hydrogen ions in to hydrogen gas. This photo production of hydrogen by algae is being considered as eco-friendly. Hydrogen thus produced will be a non-conventional and renewable source of energy because water in the form of raw material is abundantly present and solar energy needed for photolysis of water will be available for millions of years. More over hydrogen when used, as a fuel cause no pollution and on oxidation produces water thus renewing the raw material.

Strains of *Chlorella*, *Scenedesmus*, *Synechococcus*, *Microcystis*, *Dunaliella*, *Porphyridium* and *Oscillatoria* produce hydrogen at fairly high rates though the algal cell again takes back some of the hydrogen produced. These algae posses enzyme hydrogenase that plays a key role in the photo production of hydrogen. Strains of these algae are being employed for isolation of enzyme hydrogenase. The enzyme is then used with isolated chloroplast for photolysis of water so that hydrogen protons and electrons released in the process can be made to combine to form hydrogen gas which can be collected and used as eco-friendly, non polluting biofuel. It is a clean burning fuel with potential environmental benefits and with almost zero pollution.

In oxygen evolving photosynthetic bacteria, popularly known as cyanobacteria (formerly know as BGA) besides hydrogenase, another enzyme nitrogenase is present that fixes atmospheric nitrogen ($N = N$) in to ammonia. It is the chief hydrogen-producing enzyme that reduces N_2 to NH_3 with associated release of hydrogen gas. Hydrogen evolution is controlled by solar energy that activates enzyme nitrogenase and ATP production in heterocyst of cyanobacteria. Heterocyst of Cyanobacteria contain photo system I (connected with the production of ATP) that provides energy needed for the reduction of atmospheric nitrogen to ammonia but lacks photo system II (connected with the release of oxygen) as enzyme nitrogenase gets inactivated in presence of oxygen. It can function only under anaerobic or micro aerobic condition. In strains of *Anabaena*- a heterocystous cyanobacteria, photo production of hydrogen has been reported for several days. A strain of non-heterocystous cyanobacterium, *Oscillatoria* Miami BG 7 has been reported particularly suitable for hydrogen production as it lacks uptake hydrogenase which catalyses the uptake of hydrogen by algal cells. This particular strain is reported to produce about 12 micro liter hydrogen / mg dry weight/hour and hydrogen evolution continues for several weeks. Limiting the supply of combined nitrogen to the cells can significantly enhance rate of hydrogen production in this strain. Besides this particular strain, certain marine cyanobacteria are also being used for photo production of hydrogen from saline water and there are reports that they produce hydrogen for over a month period. Arika Mitsui and his associates at Rosenstiel School of Marine and Atmospheric Sciences in Miami, Florida, U.S.A. have done a lot of work in this direction.

Another common fresh water planktonic alga, *Botryococcus braunii* of xanthophyceae, at certain stages of its development produces large amount of hydrocarbons including long chain fatty acids. Dead algal scums of the alga contain hydrocarbons as high as 70% of its dry weight which is the maximum percentage so far reported in any kind of biomass. Hydrocarbons accumulate as globules on the outer walls of the cell (97%) and in the cytoplasm (3%). This algal hydrocarbon closely resembles the crude oil and can be used as a source of biofuel. From the algal cells, hydrocarbons are recovered by centrifugation technique.

Protein rich, non-heterocystous cyanobacterium, *Spirulina* is also a good source of methane. This cyanobacterium is mixed with the sewage sludge to increase the performance of anaerobic digester used for the production of methane. *S. maxima* when mixed with sewage sludge in anaerobic digester, doubles the yield of methane. Besides this its biomass alone can be used as sole substitute for anaerobic digestion for methane production, which is not only a cheap source of energy but also abates pollution being eco-friendly.

CHAPTER 33

Biotechnology Environmental Protection

POLLUTION - A GLOBAL PROBLEM

Environmental pollution is a global problem. The decline in environmental quality as a consequence of pollution is evidenced by loss of vegetation cover and biological diversity, excessive concentration of harmful chemicals in the ambient atmosphere and in food grains, growing risks of environmental accidents and threats to **life support system**. Those substances, which cause pollution are known as pollutants. Pollutant may be defined as any chemical (redionuclide, organo-phosphorus compound or trace gases) or geo-chemical substance (dust, sediment, grit, etc), biotic component or product (pollens or products of microbial activity), or physical agent (heat, sound, etc.) that released intentionally or inadventently by man into the environment in such concentration that may have adverse, harmful or unpleasant and inconvenient effects. It is also defined as any solid, liquid or gaseous substance present in such concentration as may be or tend to be injurious to environment [Indian Environment (protection) Act, 1986]. The term pollutant is usually applied to non-living, man-made substance or other nuisances or excess in a specific location. The important pollutants are: **Gaseous pollutants** [Oxides of nitrogen, sulphur compounds (SO_2, H_2S), carbon compounds (CO_2, CO), ozone, halogens (chlorine, bromine, iodine, etc.], and chloroflurocarbons, **fluoride compounds**, **metals** (Mercury, lead, iron, zinc, nickel, tin, cadmium, etc.), **agricultural pollutants** (pesticides, herbicides, fungicides and fertilizers), **complex organic pollutants** (benzene, benzpyrens, acetic acid, ether, etc.), **biotic component** (pollens), **deposited matter** (soot, smoke, tar, dust, grit, etc.), **solid waste**, **radioactive waste**, **noise**, **heat**, etc. Soot is a black substance, essentially carbon from the incomplete combustion of wood, coal, natural gas, etc., as deposited on the inside of chimneys and other surfaces.

Detergents, pesticides and biocides, chlorofluorocarbons, plastics and plasticizers, solvents, fuel, paints, dyes, medicines, fuel and food additives, etc., are some examples of the multiplicity of chemical products made and disseminated for the benefit of man. All these have the inherent capacity to disturb the life support system.

Environmental biotechnology is the use of living organisms for a wide variety of applications in hazardous waste treatment and pollution prevention.

The vast majority of applications of environmental biotechnology use naturally occurring microorganisms (bacteria, fungi, etc.) to identify and filter manufacturing waste before it is introduced into the environment. Some more advanced systems using genetically modified microorganisms are being tested in waste treatment and pollution prevention to remove difficult-to-degrade materials.

Environmental biotechnology can more efficiently clean up many hazardous wastes than conventional methods and greatly reduce our dependence on methods for waste cleanup such as incineration or hazardous waste dump sites.

How Does It Work?

Every living organism – animals, plants, bacteria and so forth – ingests nutrients to live and produces waste byproduct as a result. Different organisms need different types of nutrients. Certain bacteria thrive on the chemical components of waste products. Some microorganisms, for example, feed on toxic materials such as methylene chloride, a variety of detergents, creosote, pentachlorophenol, sulfur and polychlorinated biphenyls (PCBs).

Environmental engineers use bioremediation, the broadest application of environmental biotechnology, in two basic ways. They introduce nutrients to stimulate the activity of bacteria already present in the soil at a hazardous waste site, or they add new bacteria to the soil. The bacteria then "eat" the hazardous waste at the site and turn it into harmless byproducts. After the bacteria consume the waste materials, they die off or return to their normal population levels in the environment.

In some cases, the byproducts of the pollution-fighting microorganisms are themselves useful. Methane, for example, can be derived from a form of bacteria that degrades sulfur liquor, a waste product of paper manufacturing.

BIOTECHNOLOGY AND POLLUTION CONTROL: SOME ASPECTS

Unfortunately, biotechnology, being still in the process of development, does not possess a sharp and easily defined form. Only in last 5 years progress has been made by microbiologists and genetic engineers, and we are hopeful to solve pollution problems. Mineral ore deposits are also becoming more scarce and expensive to recover from earth's crust. Microorganism can be used to enhance the recovery of metals from low-grade ores and effluents containing undesirable quantities of heavy meatls or other toxins. Enzyme technology is an area of considerable current interest and development. Enzymes are biological catalysts and have been used for many years as isolated agents particularly in food industry, *e.g.*, rennin, papain, and invertase. Most of the enzymes are lost in product or the effluent after process, therefore, re-usability is essential to reduce the cost of enzyme production and to improve the economics of enzyme catalysed reactions in industry. This can be possible through biotechnological applications. The conversion of cellulose to sugar is a challenge for chemists for many years. The knowledge of biotechnology has made it possible to elucidate the requirements for biological enzymatic hydrolysis of such materials as straw and wood to a carbohydrate for use as a substrate in fermentation. The important uses are in the field of: enzyme technology, fermenter technology, sewage disposal, food industry waste, heavy metal industry, pesticides and herbicides industry, uranium mining, oil recovery, biodegradation of plastics, etc.

Biotechnology deals with living processes as it is inherently less likely to give rise to major environmental problems. In fact, biotechnology may be helpful to solve existing environmental problems; the ability of microorganisms to bind heavy metals and to detoxify highly toxic substances will help us to solve the problem. The other pollutants like oil spills, pesticides, herbicides, chemical effluents and gases are some of the hazards for the society. Biotechnology can be used as a tool to solve this problem in two ways:

1. The root cause can be attacked by the introduction of biotechnological

production methods which are intrinsically less polluting.

2. Microbes can be deployed as voracious scanvengers, removing all kinds of pollutants.

One recently discovered environmental problem is a prime candidate for a biotechnology solution. The U.S. Environmental Protection Agency (EPA) recently announced it intends to ban the use of the gasoline additive methyl tertiary butyl ether (MTBE) that is required by law to be placed in gasoline. MTBE is an ether that easily migrates to public drinking water supplies and causes contamination problems. MTBE contamination has become a significant environmental problem in the northeastern states and in California.

Biotechnology offers a potential solution to this problem. Companies involved in environmental biotechnology are developing biological systems that use naturally occurring microorganisms to degrade and remove MTBE that has already polluted underground drinking water supplies.

WATER POLLUTION

Water serves as the second natural medium for the growth of microorganisms and stands next to soil. The growth of microorganisms in water mainly depends on the amount of available mineral nutrients and the dissolved oxygen present in it. It has been observed that as the amount of organic matter increases in water, the number of microorganisms also increases but upto certain limit. The number of bacteria and other microbes will always be higher in river passing by thickly populated cities then of the villages because persons living in cities, are continuously disposing sewage water and other waste products in rivers which contain a very high amount of mineral nutrients- a medium for their growth. Moreover, the pH, temperature range and inorganic phosphate content as well as the situation of the lake and river also support the growth and cause a dense population of microorganisms. These organisms (bacteria, blue green algae, etc.) form a heavy blooms under these conditions. The possible factors responsible for limiting the growth and density of microorganisms are the available amounts of zinc, copper, and the poor quantity of nitrate, nitrogen, etc. It has been noticed that the excess of calcium is harmful for the luxuriant growth of microorganisms, specially to algae in general.

Microbiology of Lake

Stored water, specially lake water are often classified into three major types on the basis of their suitability for the support of living matter.

1. **Eutrophic lake:** The lake which is well nourished, receives water from a stream draining areas, and rich in plant-vegetation is referred as eutrophic lake. This kind of lake contains a high amount of organic matter and minerals which support the luxuriant growth of micro and macroscopic aquatic organisms.
2. **Oligotrophic lake:** Such lakes are poorly nourished and is less productive. The organic and mineral contents of such lakes are very small and are not capable of supporting the growth in aquatic life.
3. **Dystrophic lake:** These lakes contain high organic matter of special type, such as the remains of incomplete digestion of matter in the area draining into the lake. Dystrophic lakes are often dark in colour, and acidic in nature. Due to the acidic nature a very few species of bacteria and other forms of aquatic life are able to grow.

System of Saprophytism in Stored Water

It is rather difficult to make a complete list of biological population of stored water because each kind of stored water differs from the other in its biological associations. Therefore, one can find a mixed microbic population of stored water. The different groups of microflora of stored water, specially of water reservoirs mainly depend on the rate of population of water and source of population that is dead or living organic and inorganic matter. The physiological properties of water reservoir may be included under the term **saprophytism**. This property depends on the amount of total organic matter present in water and the mineralization of organic matter. Mineralization helps in self-purification of water reservoirs. On the basis of this property, water reservoirs are divided broadly into three following zones:

- **Pleosaprophytic Zone:** This is the heavily polluted zone of water-reservoir and contains sufficient amount of organic residues of plants and animals. Chemically, the organic residue is rich in proteins, soluble carbohydrates, cellulose, pectin substances, glycogen, fats and other compounds. Microorganisms which are present in this zone, are of anaerobic type and grow on aforsaid organic matters after their proteolytic action. Certain species of microorganisms which are resistant to hydrogen sulphide, carbon dioxide and methane are also present in this zone. These microorganisms perform activities like putrefective deaminization of amino acids, decomposition of cellulose and pectic substances. The amount of available dissolved oxygen is insignificant or nil in this zone.
- **Mesosaprophytic Zone:** This zone is relatively less polluted due to the high rate of mineralization and oxidation of organic matter. The process such as the oxidation of ammonia into nitric acid, hydrogen sulphide into sulphuric acid and oxidation of organic substances are more common in this zone. The bacterial population is very high, sometimes it reaches upto 100,000 per ml.
- **Oligosaphrophytic Zone:** This zone contains relatively pure and clear water and is free from organic substances. It contains, therefore, a very small number of bacteria and other microorganisms. Iron bacteria constitute major part of the microbic population of this zone and oxidise ferrous oxide into ferric oxide.

Sewage

Seawage is defined as *the water supply of the used water of community*. It contains dilute water-borne wastes from residence, business houses, and industries. The chemical composition of sewage varies from day-to-day or even from hour. It also varies considerably between different cities, because they produce the wastes of different characters. Seawage water contains inorganic wastes, which create a problem of disposal, but apart from inorganic waste, undesirable organic matters, which are offensive and dangerous, are also present. Inorganic compounds of sewage water support the growth of harmful bacteria and other microorganisms which sometimes lead to the epidemics among the human beings.

Biological Oxygen Demand

The rate of removal (that is consumption) of oxygen by microorganisms in aerobic degradation of the dissolved or even particulate organic matter in water is called biochemical oxygen demand (BOD) and it is used as an index of organic pollution in water. More the oxidizable organic matter present in water, more the amount of oxygen required to degrade it biologically, hence more the BOD. It is evaluated by measuring oxygen concentration in sample before and after incubation in the dark at 20°C for 5 days.

The BOD value is useful in stream pollution control managements and in evaluating the self purification capacity of a water body. Along with the BOD, the quality of oxygen in a body of water (DO) is indicated by the kind of biotic life which lives there. When dissolved oxygen is reduced below 4 to 5 ppm of water, fishes are scare. Further reduction of the amount of oxygen results in an increase in anaerobic bacteria. However, BOD values should not be used equivalent to the organic load regardless of the presence of non-degradable organic matter, presence of toxins and local changes in populations of microorganisms. BOD test should be restricted to only suitable wastes in management of treatment plants.

BOD SENSOR

Biosensors are the combinations of biologically active material displaying characteristic specificity with chemical or electronic sensor to convert the response into electrical signal. They are, in fact, biocatalysts and are used as purified enzyme, antibody or as whole microbial cell or as an organelle. The response of biosensor is measured in terms of substrate used or product form. They are of different types like, carbon electrode, glucose electrode, ion sensitive electrode, photocell, oxygen electrode, thermister, adenosine electrode, etc.

BOD is a test for the measurement of organic pollution. Usually, BOD test requires a five-day incubation period. The results of the test are dependent on the skill of the operator. Biosensor are used for rapid test. *Trichosporon cutaneum* (a yeast) is used as biosensor. The organism is sand wiched between an oxygen permeable Teflon membrane and a porous membrane. Then the membrane is directly fixed on the surface of platinum cathode of an oxygen probe. A continuous flow system using biosensor has been developed for automatic estimation of 5-day BOD.

TABLE 33.1: BOD strengths of effluents

Effluent	BOD
Domestic sewage	350
Sulphite liquor from paper mills	20,000 -45,000
BEER	
(a) spent grains press	15,000
(b) hop press liquor	7,430
(c) mash filter cloth wash	4,930
(d) yeast wash water	7,400
(e) spoilt beer	Up to 100,000
(f) Bottle washing	550
MALTINGS	
(a) suspended solids	1,240
(b) wastes	20 - 204
(c) grain washings	1,500
Industrial alcohol stillage (molasses)	10,000 - 25,000
Distillery stillage	10,000 - 25,000
Yeast production	3,000 - 14,000
Antibiotic wastes	5,000 - 30,000

Effluent	BOD
PENICILLIN	
(a) wet mycellium from filter	40,000 - 70,000
(b) filtrate	2,150 - 10,000
(c) wash water	210 - 13,800
Streptomycin spent liquor	2,450 - 5,900
Aureomycin spent liquor	4,000 - 7,000
Solvents	Up to 2,000,000

When the sample solution containing glucose and glutemic acid is injected into the system, organic compounds permeated through the porous membrane. Then thay are assimilated by the immobilised microorganisms. Consumption of oxygen by immobilised microorganisms starts and then they cause a reduction in the dissolved oxygen around the membranes. This results into the reduction in electrode current with time until a steady state is reached within 18 min. The steady state current depends upon BOD of the sample solution.

There is a relationship between the current decrease and 5-day BOD of standard solution below 60 mg l^{-1}. The current is reproducible with ±6% of the relative error when BOD 40 mg l^{-1} of the standard solution is employed.

IMMOBILISED MICROBIAL CELLS AND WASTE WATER TREATMENT

Pollutants either of natural origin (lignified wood) or of artificial origin (organophosphates, chlorobenzenes) are not as recalcitrant as what they are thought to be. Microbes have evolved in metabolic activities either to use these chemicals as sources of nutrient or to detoxify their surrounding. These chemicals are degraded by their catabolic activity. There are certain pollutants which are tough, new strains of microbes can be developed to degrade them by mutations and genetic transfers.

Whole Cell Enzymes and Biodegradation

The enzymes are responsible for degradation of pollutants in nature. Use of complete cells as enzyme source is more effective than purified enzymes because the enzymes within the cells are better protected from denaturation by the intact cell wall and membrane. Degradation activity is usually composed of a series of reactions, therefore, it is difficult to develop different systems for different enzymes working together. Isolation and purification of the component enzymes is rather expensive and there are chances of denaturation. Sometimes, induced enzyme production occurs in cells which is required for degradation activity. The rate of degradation and microbes resistance to toxic pollutants remain better when the mixed culture cell population is used for the degradation rather than individual, independent enzyme system.

Further, it is also observed that use of immobilised cells instead of free suspended cells has additional advantages because over all capability of cells becomes more enhanced. The cells do not contaminate, the outgoing reaction mixture, and are more evenly dispersed by immobilisation (this minimise the diffusional restrictions). The immobilised cells are used with more ease to exploit the kinetic features of continuously stirred and packed bed type of reactors, minimization of product inhibition.

IMMOBILISED CELLS AND ENZYMES FOR WASTE WATER TREATMENT

Immobilised cells and enzymes system is mainly used in BOD/COD reduction, in specific pollutant detoxification, as biosensors and to get the maximum useful products from the waste.

Nitrate Reduction

Immobilised cells are used in removing the particular substances from waste water. At the East Hyde Sewage Works, waste water is forced through a sand bed on which species such as *Hypomicrobium* are grown in presence with added methanol to cause nitrate reduction.

Nitrate pollution of ground water is a health hazard. The old methods for removing nitrate are ineffective and impracticable. Use of living microorganisms for denitrify water is slow, incomplete, difficult to set up and maintain. Mobite GmbH, (Germany) and the University of Michigan have developed a new technique by a series of oxido-reductase enzyme system. The redox-process, driven by electric current results in complete conversion of nitrate into gaseous nitrogen. Such electro-bioreactors can also be used for the removal of other water contaminants like pesticides after identification of appropriate enzymes and cofactors.

In an another plant at Rye Meads, processing 81000 m^3 of water per day, uses a similar technique but without methanol addition in which nitrate reductions between 50 to 90 per cent have been obtained. *Micrococcus denitrificans* cells encapsulated in liquid membranes are also used for the reduction of nitrate to nitrite. The immobilised cells are also resistant to 10^4M $HgCl_2$ while free cells were sensitive.

Oxidation of Ammonia in Waste Water

Immobilised cells of *Nitrosomonas europaen* in alginate have been used to oxidise ammonia in waste water to NO_2 and NO_3 for reduction of BOD and prevention of algal growth. Soluble nitrates have been provided with an exogenous carbon source and reduce nitrates and nitrites completely to gaseous products.

Biological Oxygen Demand (BOD)

Immobilised cells are also used as biosensors to continuous evaluatation of BOD of waste water. These analytical procedure usually work by measuring the loss of enzyme activity caused by exposure to the pollutant. The degree of inhibition of the enzyme being proportional to the concentration of the pollutant present in the sample under test.

Wheat Strach and Paper Mill Industry

Immobilised α-amylase enzyme is used for treatment of waste waters from the wheat strach industry. This enzyme is also used for clarification of colloidal starch-clay suspensions of **white waters** from the paper mill industry.

Pulp Mill

The effluents of pulp mill are brown and contain partially chlorinated lignin derivatives known as **kraft lignins**. These are normally treated in aerated lagoons or activated sludge systems and BOD/COD is reduced. This treatment unables to reduce the colour. However, it may be decolourised by using white-rot fungus *Coriolus versicolor* entrapped in calcium alginate beads and supplemented with various carbon and energy sources. Lignolytic fungus- *Phanerochaete chrysosporium* is also used for this purpose. About 80% of the colour is removed after incubation of immobilised cells in the medium for 3 days in presence of sucrose. This method is useful because it eliminates carcinogenic chlorinated lignins.

Degradation of Phenols

Phenols degradation in waste waters of hospitals, laboratories and coal processing to coke can be achieved either by using the fungus *Aureobasidium pullulans* adsorbed by fibrous asbestos or by using cells to *Pseudomonas* spp. either adsorbed to anthacite coal or entrapped on alginate gel. This treatment is advantageous because it avoids damage to the conventional biological treatment systems.

Methane Formation

CH_4 can be continuously formed for 90 days from the waste waters by using a population of methanogenic cells entrapped in agar, collagen or polyacrylamide membranes. Methanogenic bacteria have been used to degrade waste waters from the alcohol fermentation factory to CH_4.

Glucose Production

Glucose can be produced from waste cellulose. This is also one of the means of disposing of waste material and also producing valuable products. However, no practical process using immobilisation techniques has yet to be emerged in this direction.

Lactose Hydrolysis

Immobilised enzymes are also used to hydrolyse lactose from waste water of cheese-making industry where BOD is high.

Detoxification from Cyanide

Cyanide is present in aqueous wastes and can be detoxify by using immobilised mycelia of *Stemphylium loti* which contain **cyanide hydralase**. Cyanide is converted into formamide.

SEWAGE DISPOSAL AND TREATMENT

The methods used to treat sewage before it is discharged into rivers, lakes or the ocean are not so expensive. The procedures are considered to be effective for the purpose of rendering the waste moderately safe in so far as its bacterial content is concerned. The virus load and toxic chemical content of sewage discharges have not been as thoroughly evaluated.

Sewage Disposal

Natural wastes include domestic sewage and animal slurries. Sewage may be contaminated with industrial chemicals and animals slurries with agricultural chemicals, but their polluting effect otherwise arises from organic matter, whose biological destruction consumes oxygen, and ammonia. Sewage effluent is normally discharged to a water course. Its polluting load is destroyed naturally and, if the flow of the receiving waters is sufficient in relation to the discharge, no significant effects on the river can be detected. The problems of chronic pollution of water course are less technical than economic, but research is needed on the biological effects of chronic low levels of pollution. The morden sewage plant is based on the activity of *Bacillus*, *Vorticella* and other microbes. They break down organic matter to carbon dioxide and water in `activated ludge digester' or trickling filter. In activated sludge digester air is forced through the system to encourage aerobes. In a trickling filter, liquid is run over a gravel bed.

The sewage processing plants are dependent on the action of microbes to purify waste water by consuming a wide variety of solid materials. However, how sewage is broken down is still not clear. This is because of the composition of sewage varies considerably and there are many different species of microbe at work in sewage ponds.

The waste disposal is undoubtedly the largest single application of microorganisms by man. The success of this application depends upon the enormous metabolic diversity of microbes.

There are various methods which are used to treat sewage water. The suitability of the method is mainly dependent on the area to be served and by the density of population. The sewage water may be treated by physical, chemical or biological processes to remove organic matter.

PHYSICAL TREATMENT

Using mechanical devices, various suspended and floating solids from sewage can be removed physically. Different types of screening devices are used. After screening, the sewage is passed through grit chambers to allow to the solid matter to settle. Then it is passed through sedimentation tanks. The polluted water is kept in these tanks for few hours. The supernatant liquid or effluent is drawn off. Chlorine is passed through it and finally discharged into a body of water, or into porous soil.

BIOLOGICAL TREATMENT

The method is widely used for sewage treatment. The water from toilet, bath-tubes, kitchen sinks etc. (sanitary sewage) is processed in septic tank which can handle at the most a few hundred gallons per day to municipal plants which handle of gallons.

Septic Tanks

This type of tank is commonly used in rural areas where public sewers are not available. It is constructed below the ground level near the house or within the house. It is about 3' 5' x 5' in area and about 750 gallon of sewage water may be filled in it. The domestic waste entering the tank is retained long enough to permit sufficient decomposition and sedimentation. Due to activity of anaerobic bacteria, most of the organic matter is hydrolyzed and get fermented. Sugars, alcohols, organic acids, amino acids, amines, glycerol, fatty acids and other chemicals including gases like H_2S, CH_4, CO_2, and H_2. The final products are unstable. The effluent from the tank is distributed under the soil surface through perforated pipes. This procedure, however, does not eliminate pathogenic microorganisms from the sewage. Therefore, it is essential that drinking water supply should be at the safe distance from the septic tank and disposal field. It is essential to remove undigested material which resist microbial action are termed sludge. This should be taken out periodically through pumps or by any other means. The sludge may be mixed with soil (away from houses) which can serve as a good source of humus.

Trickling filters

In this process sewage water, from city sewares is first carried to soil compartments where it undergoes physiochemical changes with the soil. It than gradually trickles down the soil to a depth of nearly 2 meters. Such filteration procedure leads to the separation of suspending particles and organic matter from it. These are then decomposed by purifying bacteria. The filtered water, then, drained out and reaches the natural pure-water-reservoirs like well. This is the most simple and cheap system of water purification where the sewage water is purified by both mechanical and biological property of soil.

Based on the above system, trickling filters have been designed. It consists of a large bed of stones 8 to 12 feet deep. The liquid sewage is sprayed over the surface of the bed either by a series of sprinklers or by a rotating sparger. The spraying of sewage water is done intermittently, so that as a layer of water goes down the filter, which draws a layer of air above it down through the filter. This helps to develop aerobic condition in the bed and the filtering medium becomes coated with a living film of aerobic microorganisms. They help in hydrolyzing and oxidizing the organic matter of sewage. This process is relatively slow. Finally clear effluent is drained off at the botton through the bed.

OIL RECOVERY

Oil is the fuel around which the world has built its major infra-structures and on which highly mobile lifestyles are based. It is almostt indispensable in today's societies and yet the impact of various predictions over the last few years that oil supplies will ultimately run out has only received serious consideration since the 1973 oil crisis.

The organic deposits of petroleum oil and natural gas were probably formed from tiny microorganisms rather than from the debris of large plants as was the case with coal. When these microscopic creatures settled on ocean floor and were later covered with mineral sediments, tiny droplets of body oil were squeezed out of them. This oil was trapped into large deposites during formation and was altered chemically by heat and pressure. Most of the oil in such reservoir is found not as vast pools of liquid, but as a coating on grains of rock. The **oil sticks** tenaciously of these grains and must be dislodged before it can be brought to the surface. Ordinary water is too thin a liquid to budge most of this oil; it simply flows past the oil-coated grains. In tertiary oil recovery (also known as **enhanced oil recovery**) materials are mixed with water to make viscous, and one such material is called **xanthan gum**.

Xanthan gum is a polysaccharide produced by the bacterium *Xanthomonas campestris*. The gum is an inert compound which thickens water and improves its ability to dive out oil trapped underground. It is, when mixed with drilling muds, it also serves as a lubricant for the giant drill as they penetrate the rock.

Under field conditions, bacteria like *Bacillus* and *Clostridium* have also been tested for oil recovery in plant of *Xanthomonas* The preliminary result are encouraging. Sugars and other nutrients are fed to these bacteria while they are deep below ground. Here they grow, produce chemicals that help wash the oil free, and yield carbon dioxide and other gases which also assist in forcing the oil to the surface.

It is interesting to note that these bacteria can tolerate high pressure and temperature, lack of water and oxygen and large quantities of salt and sulphur. The qualities of microbes will enhance the commercial use of these organisms in oil industry.

OIL POLLUTION

Various species of *Pseudomonas* have the property to consume available hydrocarbons from oil. Each species has the capacity to consume specific type of hydrocarbon, therefore, it is essential to adopt the following techniques:

1. A mixture of different strains of *Pseudomonas* can be used. This method has been successfully used to clear up oil-contaminated water in derelict ships and in cleaning up water supplies.
2. Transformation of oil consuming genes in one strain of *Pseudomonas*. Such newly developed strains have been successfully tested under field conditions. Most of the biotechnologists agree that it is unlikely that bacteria could ever cope with the large oil spills produced by tanker. But it needs careful watching.

The transformation of oil consuming genes has been done by Ananda Chakrabarty of General Electric. He created a **superbug** which would be able to mop up all types of hydrocarbon in oil spills. He introduced it in plasmids of several different strains of *Pseudomonas* into a single cell. The newly developed strain has not been used commercially. We are still hopeful to receive new stable strains of *Pseudomonas* to over come the problem of oil pollution in water and takners.

AIR POLLUTION

In this known that the major part of air pollution of artificial origin is derived from the combustion products of industry, traffic, households concentrated in urban areas. The degree of air pollution is generally proportional to the industrial development of the country. Out of many harmful gases, sulphur dioxide is an air pollutant produced by burning of coal. In air it combines with water to form sulphuric acid (**acid rain**). Its low pH causes release soluble aluminium salts into the environment and causes toxic effects. Research are on the way to develop the new strains of sulphur bacteria to clean up sulphur dioxide before it is discharged from chimneys.

PESTICIDES AND HERBICIDES POLLUTION

Pesticides are biologically active chemicals used for killing plants and animals. The first modern chemical pesticides were arsenic compounds used on potato, cotton and apples. To day, the delebrate or accidental discharge of noxious organic chemicals (pesticides and harbicides) into the environment is very common. Biotechnologists are trying to develop the strains of bacteria which can survive on these toxic chemicals! Ananda Chakrabarty and his co-workers announced that they have developed a microbe that attacked 2,4,5,-T, a very persistant herbicide and the main ingredient of the agent Orange, which was used to destryo vast areas of jungle in Vietnam. Although, the suitability of the biotechnologically developed microbes has yet to be proved.

DEGRADATION OF HERBICIDES, INSECTICIDES AND PESTICIDES

Pseudomonas putida contains dehalogenases enzyme which degrade mono -and dichloroacetates and propionates from herbicides and pesticides. Dalpon degradation activity is stable for 20,000 hrs. in chemostal. Mixed microbial population when grown on parathion was found to hydrolyse a number of organophosphate insecticides. The population contain several enzymes which could be immobilised with operational half-life of 280 days.

HEAVY METALS

Few elements are directly toxic to organisms. They are tend to be heavy and have a high atomic mass (in the form of small particles less than 5 micron or fumes). Among them are mercury, lead, cadmium, nickel, gold, platinum, silver, bismith, arsenic, selenium, vanadium, cromium and thalium. These elements have their effects on organisms and are available as the pollutants in environment. The efforts have been made to use bacteria to eliminate the toxic effects of these heavy metals.

The strains of *Pseudomonas aeruginosa* is known to accumulate great quantities of uranium (as much as half of the total weight of each cell excluding its water content). *Thiobacillus* bacteria also leach metals out of rock ores and can accumulate silver. Silver is also available in waste waters of film factories and other industrial sites. These bacteria can reduce the losses of this expensive resource.

Toxic Metal Accumulation

Zoogloea ramigera is used to accumulate copper from factory waste. Microbes also have potential to remove toxic metals in wastes including uranium.

MICROBES IN LEACHING OF METALS

It is only the last two decades that people came to know the important role of microbes in hydrometallurgical industries for the extraction of metals from their orea. They hydrometallurgical method of leaching of metals from low grade ores by passing through stacks of ores has been known from ancient times. The sulphide metals are oxidised to sulphate and sulphuric acid. The rate of this process can be increased by the activities of iron oxidising bacteria. Biological leaching is brought about by the bacteria like *Thiobacillus thiooxidants*, *T. ferroxidans*, *Ferrobacillus terrooxidans*, *F. sulfooxidans*, etc. These bacteria have been reported to be helpful in the leaching of copper, nickel, molybdenum, zinc, arsenic, antimony and germinium from their sulphates.

RECOVERY OF COPPER AND COBALT BY BIOPOLYMER GELS

Many biopolymers derived from microbes and plants are known to bind metals strongly. The use of biopolymers as absorbents for hazardous metals or strategically important metals has been a topic of intense research in recent years. Due to an excellent selectivity for certain metals by biopolymers and the low cost of producing biopolymers under mild condition, this method can offer an alternative to conventional methods of metal recovery like precipitation, electrowinning and ion exchange.

DECAY OF ORGANIC MATTER

Most of the microorganisms (bacteria, fungi) live saprophytically on dead organic matter of soil. They decompose complex organic matter into simple one and make it available for plants. In fact, they bring about decay by their various digestive and respiratory processes. Thus they form an important constituent of soil called humus. They also prevent leaching of many inorganic substances. Green manure added to the soil does not improve the physical and chemical structure of soil but various microorganisms like bacteria and fungi synthesize long chain polysacchride polymer containing uranic acid units which act as a cementing material in soil. These cementing substances are responsible for the production of soil aggregates or soil crumbs. The gum producing fungi are also important in synthesizing cementing material.

PLASTIC INDUSTRY

Plastic industry has a temptic market for biotechnological establishments. The production of acetone, glycerol and butanol are produce along with ethanol- a major product of alcohol factories. Ethanol serves as a vital starting material for the manufacture of detergents, dyes, adhesives and resins for synthetic fibres.

Reports form the University of Warwick, England in 1981 opened new direction in the field of biotechnology by using microbes in plastic industry. Microbes can able to add oxygen to alkenes. When supplied with propylene or ethylene gases, the bacterium *Methylococcus capsulatus* can insert an oxygen atom into the molecules to produce propylene oxide or ethylene oxide. This bacterium can live happily at about 45°C (113°F) and at this temperature the alkane oxides are in gaseous form. It is easier to collect a gas than that of liquid from fermentation vessel.

Biotechnological techniques have made possible the biodegradation of plastics. The disposal of waste plastic is a serious problem because it degrades very slowely. The storage compound of most of the bacterium is polydeoxybutyrate. This can be processed using bacterium like *Alcaligenes eutophus*, which degrade plastic more quickly, so making disposal easier.

CHAPTER 34

Biosensors, Biochips, Biofilms and Biosurfactents

BIOSENSORS

The natural biosensors are the *sense organs*, primarily the chemical sensors of smell and taste. Biosensors technically in their various forms share a reliance of biological materials as sensing elements. Technical biosensors have been under intense development since the middle of 1960 with the prospects of commercial potential offered by biotechnology. These are the combinations of biologically active material displaying characteristic specifically with chemical or electronic sensor to convert the response into electrical signals.

Biosensors are, in fact, biocatalysts. They are used as purified enzyme, antibody or as whole microbial cell or as an organelle. A biosensor used as an **immobolised** biological molecule (usually an enzyme or an antibody) or a whole microbial cell to detect or *sense* a particular substance. The biosensor does this by reacting specifically with the substance to be detected (hence the use of enzymes or antibodies) to give a product which is used to generate an electrical **signal** by means of a device called **transducer**.

The response of biosensor is measured in terms of substrate used or product form. They are of different types like, carbon electrode, glucose electrode, ion sensitive electrode, photocell, oxygen electrode, adenosine electrode, etc.

For example a glucose electrode is constructed by immobilising a layer of glucose oxidase in polyacrylamide gel around a platinum oxygen electrode. When a solution of glucose is brought into contact with electrode, glucose and oxygen diffuses into an enzyme layer and are converted into gluconolactone and hydrogen peroxide lowering the oxygen concentration around the electrode. O_2 concentration read by electrode is proportional to glucose concentration in the sample. The effective control of the rate of reaction is ensured by high enzyme loading and limited diffusion of substrate.

Biosensor technology couples our knowledge of biology with advances in microelectronics. A biosensor is composed of a biological component, such as a cell or antibody, linked to a tiny transducer. Biosensors are detecting devices that rely on the specificity of cells and molecules to identify and measure substances at extremely low concentrations. When the substance of interest collides with the biological component, the transducer produces a digital electronic signal proportional to the concentration of the substance. Biosensors can

- measure the nutritional value, freshness and safety of food
- provide emergency room physicians with bedside measures of vital blood components
- locate and measure environmental pollutants.

Biosensor technology is progressing very fast on the front of techniques, their applications specially in the fields of analytic medicine, industry and environment. It is sometimes also useful in monitoring the presence of specific chemicals both accurately and rapidly.

Analysis of Organic Compounds

Analysis of organic compounds in fermentation and other samples can be done with the help of biosensor. Compounds such as glucose, acetic acid, lactic acid, formic acid, alcohol, methane, glutemic acid, cephalosporin antibiotic, nystatine antibiotic, nicotinic acid, vitamin B1 etc., can be analysed.

Medical Sciences

Hepatitis antigens found in blood during infection by the virus can be detected. Abnormal amounts of urea in blood or urine in kidney diseases can be measured. Hormone gonadotropin produced during pregnancy can be tested and measured. High concentrations of creatinine produced after heart attack can be analysed.

Industrial Uses

They are used to know about the nature of industrial products of acids, alcohols, phenols, pollutants, etc. The industrial workers can know the presence and concentrations of hazardous chemicals in the environment surrounding them. Biosensors can detect various chemical warfare agents, nerve gas, etc.

Environmental Analysis (Protection)

They are used in analysis of BOD requirements, ammonia, nitrite, sulfite measurements, etc.

Biosensor technology is changing so rapidly that potentially commercializable devices quickly become obsolete as new technology emerges. Very few biosensor devices are likely to be universally applicable and thus the most appropriate sensor technology has to be linked to the market need. There has been some developments in biosensor research in the country among the institutions such as NPA, New Delhi; CECRI, Karaikud; IACS, Calcutta; TIFR, Bombay; IIT, New Delhi; CSIO, Chandigarh; CEERI, Pilani.

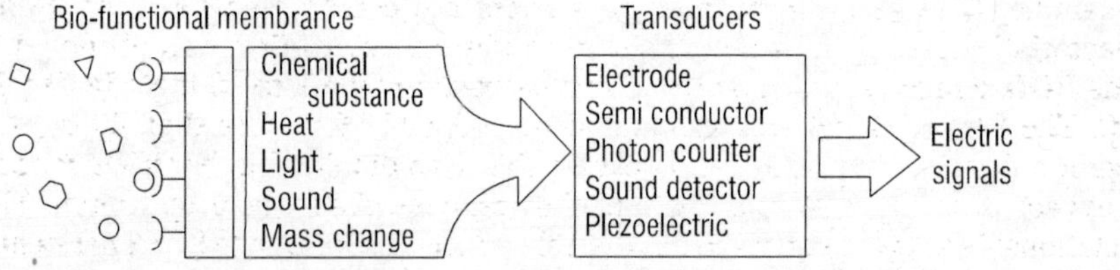

FIGURE 34.1: Biosensor Principles.

CONVENTIONAL BIOSENSOR

Biosensors are composed of a biofunctional material and a transducer and have been developed and applied to analytical fields, clinical analysis, food industry and environmental measurements. Biosensors have their roots in military research, as means of detecting nerve gases and other chemical warfare toxins. Their applications have branched out to include simple to use *alternate site* diagnostic devices for home, doctor's office, or drug use screening; medical and surgical monitors (small enough to fit inside a blood vessel) and environmental quality monitors.

Immobilized enzymes, microorganisms and antibodies are used as molecular recognition materials. Electrochemical devices have often been used for transducers. Various enzymes have been used as molecular recognition elements. An enzyme electrode is composed of an enzyme immobilized membrane and an electrode. The principle of an enzyme electrode is based on the detection of electroactive species produced or consumed by the enzyme reaction. For example, a conventional glucose sensor is composed of **glucose oxidase** (GOD) and an electrode. GOD oxidizes glucose with the consumption of oxygen and produces gluconolaction and hydrogen peroxide. Measuring the consumption of oxygen with an oxygen electrode or production of hydrogen peroxide with hydrogen peroxide electrode, the concentration of glucose can be determined. This type of glucose sensor is in commercial use for the diagnosis of diabetes. There are many kinds of biosensors using the same principle and devices, and which are developed and used in the fields of clinical analysis and measurement of foodstuffs.

MICROBIAL BIOSENSOR

Microorganisms have also been utilized as molecular recognition elements. A microbial sensor consists of a microorganism immobilized membrane and an electrode. Various kinds of microbial sensors have been developed and applied to the measurement of biological compounds. The principle of a microbial sensor is based on either the change of respiration or the amount of produced metabolites as the result of assimilation of substrates by microorganisms. Furthermore, the use of auxotrophic mutants can selectively determine many kinds of substances. For example, the vitamin B_{12} sensor was constructed by using immobilized *Esherichia coli* 215. The *E. coli* 215 strain requires vitamin B12 for its growth. The linear relationship was obtained in the range between 5 x 109 and 25 x 109 g/ml. Within 25 days, the decrease in the response was approximately only 8 per cent.

Recently, microbial sensors using thermophilic bacteria have been developed. The use of thermophilic bacteria can possibly reduce contamination of other microorganisms by the use of high temperatures to obtain long term stability. For example, BOD and carbon dioxide sensors are constructed by using thermophilic bacteria isolated from a hot spring, Good linear correlation was observed between the BOD sensor response and BOD value in the range 1 to 10 mg/1 BOD (JIS) at 50 °C. The Sensor signal was stable and reproducible for more than 40 days. For the carbon dioxide sensor, a linear relationship was obtained in $NaHCO_3$ concentration between 1 and 8 m M at 50 °C and the response time was 5 to 10 min. The linear relationship was also observed in the CO_2 concentration range 3 to 8 per cent.

Microbiosensors have many following advantages

1. Implantation in the human body and are suitable to *in vivo* measurement.
2. Can be integrated on one chip and are useful for measuring various substrates in a small amount of sample solution simultaneously.
3. Since semiconductor fabrication technology is applied to microbiosensors, it is possible to develop disposable transducers for biosensors through mass production.

Development of Microbiosensor

Microbiosensors are based on **ionsensitive field effect transistor** (ISFET) and were first reported by Bergveld (1970). Matsuo et al. (1974) improved the ISFET using silicon nitride as the gate insulator to construct micro pH sensitive devices. They show rapid response, low power consumption, low noise and no need of a high impedance amplifier. The general circuit diagram for measuring the gate output voltage is shown in below.

In this circuit, the voltage between the source and drain is controlled constantly and the current between source and drain is also held constantly. The Ag/AgC1 electrode is immersed in the same solution. The surface potential on the silicon nitride of the ISFET is affected by pH of the solution, with concomitant change in the gate voltage, which is proportional to the change in surface potential. Therefore, the surface potential change in the ISFET, caused by the change of pH, can be measured as the change in the gate output voltage.

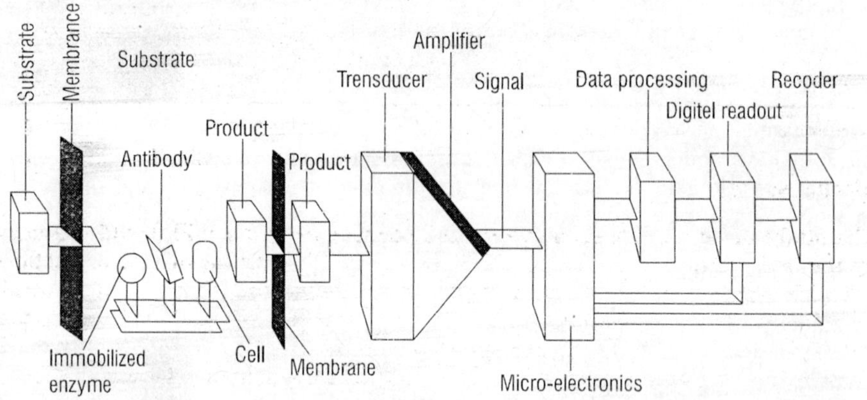

FIGURE 34.2: Schematic outline of biosensor

Fabrication

ISFETs are fabricated by using semiconductor technology. Hence, it is easy to miniaturize and integrate ISFETs on one chip. ISFET is used as a potentiometric transducer, therefore, enzymes which cause pH changes in its reaction, such as urease and oxidase, can be used.

Urea Sensor

A urea sensor consisted of a urease immobilized membrane and a pH electrode. Urease catalyzed reaction cause pH changes, so that ISFET can be used as a transducer. A micro urease sensor is fabricated as follows:

An ISFET was laid inside a vacuum chamber and 3 amino propyltriethoxysilane (3Aptes) is vaporized at 80 °C and 0.5 Torr for 30 min, followed by glutaraldehyde (GA) treatment under the same conditions. The chemically modified ISFET was covered with cellulose acetate membrane containing 1,8 diamino 4 amino methyloctane and GA. The ISFET was immersed in urease solution. The urea sensor gives the linear relationship between the initial rate of the output gate voltage and the logarithm value of urea concentration in the range 16.7 to 167 mM and can be used for 20 days with slight degradation of the enzyme activity.

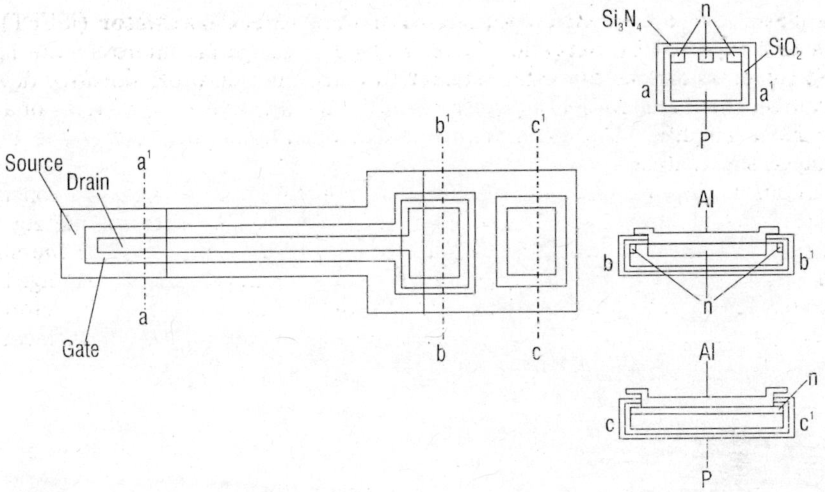

FIGURE 34.3: Structure of ISFET

Alcohol Sensor

The study of an alcohol-sensitive microbiosensor using an ISFET and the enzyme system existing in the cell membrane is reported. The cell membrane of acetic acid producing bacteria has a complex enzyme system oxidizing ethanol to acetic acid via acetaldehyde. This system consists of membrane bound alcohol dehydrogenase (ADH), aldehyde dehydrogenase (ALDH) and an electron transfer system. This complex enzyme system, therefore, can be used for application with an ISFET.

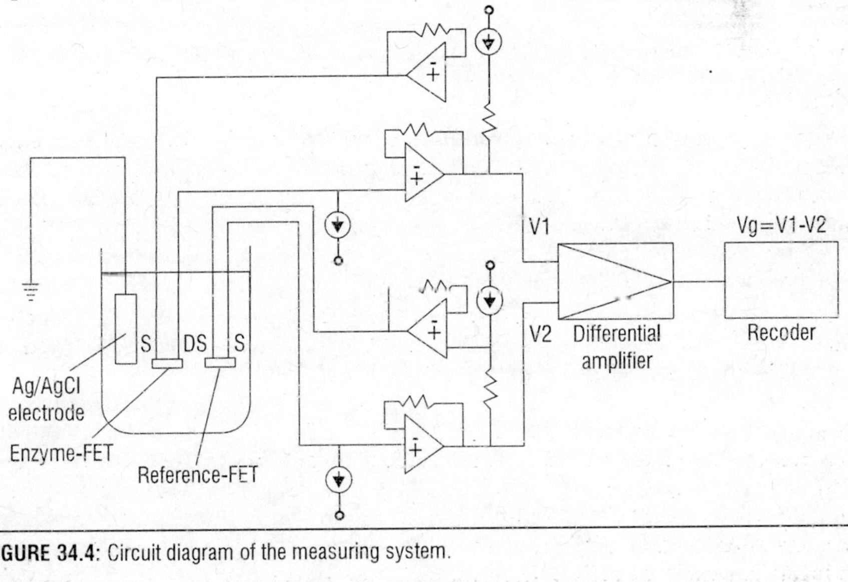

FIGURE 34.4: Circuit diagram of the measuring system.

Biosensors Using Amorphous Silicon ISFET

The ISFET device can only be manufactured by using a silicon wafer for the substrate. In recent years, devices made from amorphous silicon have received widespread attention because of their great applications potential. Various substrates such as glass and plastics can be used for preparing amorphous silicon and transistors can be fabricated with a number of different structures such as a needle of a syringe.

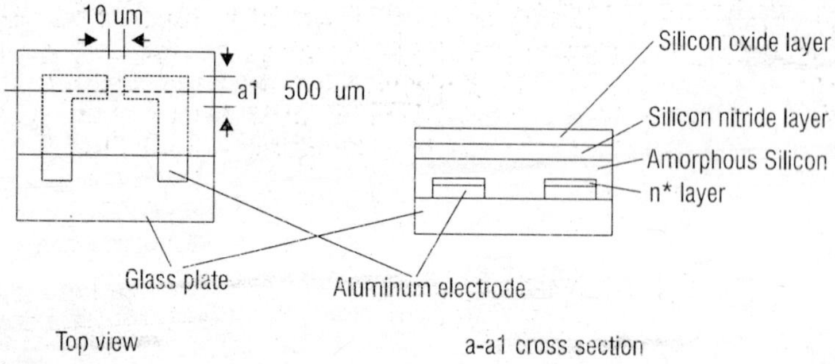

FIGURE 34.5: Structure of amorphous silicon ISFET.

Hypoxanthine and Inosine Sensor

To maintain quality, evaluation of freshness is important in the fish industry. When a fish dies, adenosine 5' triphosphate (ATP) decomposition in the fish meat occurs and adenosine 5' diphosphate (ADP) and adenosine 5' monophosphate (AMP) and related compounds are generated

$$ATP \rightarrow ADP \rightarrow AMP \rightarrow IMP \rightarrow HxR \rightarrow Hx \rightarrow X \rightarrow U$$

where IMP, HxR, Hx, X, and U stands for inosine 5' monophosphate, inosine, hypoxanthine, xanthine, and uric acid, respectively, Consequently, Hx accumulation with an increase in storage time can be used as an indicator of fish meat freshness. Therefore, simple and rapid methods for the determination of Hx and HxR are required in the seafood industry.

Hypoxanthine Sensor: Hypoxanthine is measured on the basis of the reaction catalyzed by Xanthine oxidase (XO). The pH change caused by uric acid is detected by using aSi ISFET.

Inosine Sensor: Inosine sensor is fabricated similarly to the hypoxanthine sensor by using nucleoside phosphorylase and XO co-immobilized on aSi ISFET simultaneously. After 90 seconds from injection of inosine solution, the gate voltage gradually increases and reaches a steady state in approximately 7 min. Xanthine formed by the decomposition of inosine catalyzed by nucleoside phosphorylase is subsequently oxidized to uric acid by XO. The linear relationship was obtained in the range 0.02 to 0.1 mM by plotting the initial rate of the gate voltage change with respect to the logarithm of inosine concentration. The oxidation of hypoxanthine to uric acid by xanthine oxidase is initiated immediately after injection. The response to inosine, however, has a time lag of 90 sec after injection, This phenomenon is attributed to the three step reaction. On the basis of this time lay. this sensor can determine inosine and hypoxanthine simultaneously.

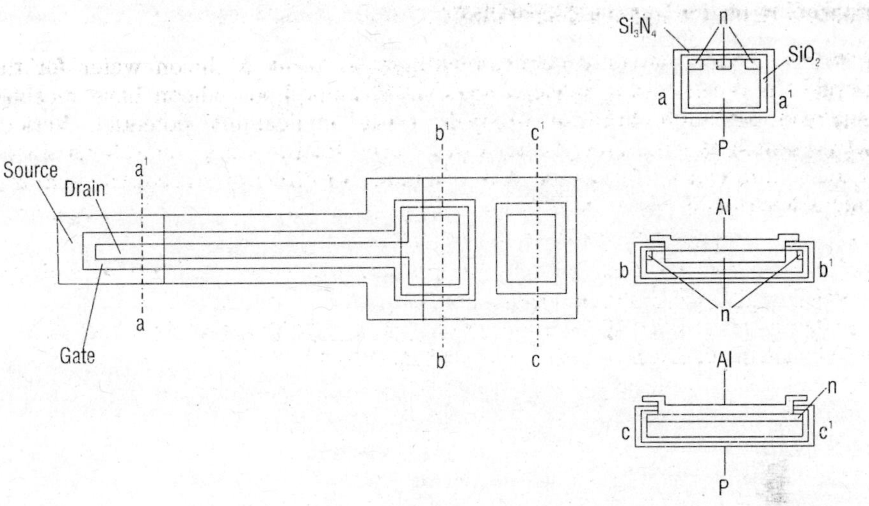

FIGURE 34.6: Fabrication process of micro-oxygen electrode.

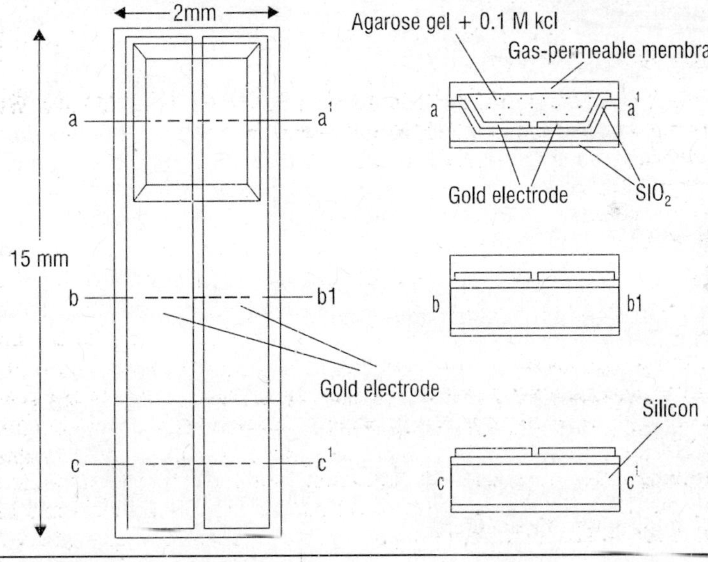

FIGURE 34.7: Structure of micro-oxygen electrode

MICRO-OXYGEN ELECTRODE

Clark-type oxygen electrodes have been applied to various biosensors, immobilizing either enzymes or microorganisms, which catalyze oxidation of biochemical organic compounds. At present. several oxygen electrodes, based on conventional semiconductor technology, have been fabricated by several groups, but they are not yet in mass production. The reason for this is that oxygen electrodes contain electrolyte solution, which results in difficult adhesion of the gas permeable membrane to the substrate, even if epoxy rexin is used. Thus, mass production of such devices is difficult. Recently, miniaturized and integrated biosensors have been required in clinical analysis.

GLUCOSE AND CARBON DIOXIDE SENSORS USING MICRO-OXYGEN ELECTRODE

The glucose sensor is fabricated by immobilizing GOD on the sensitive part of the oxygen electrode by crosslinking with bovine serum albumin (BSA) and GA. The enzyme immobilized membrane is formed by dropping the sensitive part into the mixture containing 2 mg of GOD. 20 μl of 10% BSA solution and 10 μl of 25% GA solution. The glucose sensor responds as soon as the glucose solution is injected into the buffer solution and reaches a steady state in 5 to 10 min. The sensor responded almost linearly for glucose concentrations between 0.2 and 2 mM, which is comparable to conventional glucose sensors.

A microbial CO_2 sensor using this oxygen electrode is constructed by Suzuki et al. 1988). Autotrophic bacterium named as S17, which can grow with only carbonate as the carbon source is used. (available at Fermentation Research Institute, Japan). Bacterial whole cells are immobilized on a micro-oxygen electrode. The sensitive area of the oxygen electrode is immersed in 0.2% sodium alginate solution containing S17 whole cells, then removed and immediately immersed in 5% $CaCl_2$ solution to form bacteria immobilized calcium alginate gel. The negative photo-resist as the gas permeable membrane is formed over the bacteria immobilized gel. The photo-resist in only exposed to UV light for a few minutes. The response time is 2 to 3 min. Carbon dioxide was supplied by acidification of $NaHCO_3$, the concentration of which can be related to CO_2 concentration. The linear relationship is obtained between the current decrease and $NaHCO_3$ concentration in the range 0.5 to 3.5 mM. The lowest detection limit was 0.5 mM $NaHCO_3$ within the margin of the noise amplitude. Above 3.5 mM, no significant increase in response was observed.

INTEGRATED MULTIBIOSENSOR

In clinical analysis, about 20 constituent elements are analyzed at the same time. To detect various substances in a small amount of sample solution simultaneously, it is important and necessary to develop micro multibiosensors. Recently, various kinds of integrated biosensors using ISFET and microelectrodes have been reported. These biosensors are based on the ISFETs and electrodes, which were coated with enzyme immobilized membranes. It is necessary to develop an enzyme immobilized membrane fabrication method that meets the following requirements:

1. An enzyme immobilized membrane should be precisely deposited onto a gate region or small working electrode.
2. A deposited membrane should not peel off the sensitive surface area in practical use.
3. Different enzyme membranes can be prepared without mixing.
4. Fabrication processes are applicable to a wafer and compatible with the IC process.

NOVEL BIOSENSOR BASED ON NEW TRANSDUCERS

Conventional biosensors have consisted of electrochemical devices. On the other hand, other transducers such as optical fibers, image sensors, piezoelectric devices. and SAW devices are currently used for biosensors.

Image Sensor

Most clinical analyses are based on the determination of soluble marker substances in body fluids such as blood and urine. The direct analysis in cell or tissue level is greatly important in clinical diagnosis. In the cancer detection, highly sensitive and rapid detection methods for abnormal cells are required. Cell diagnosis is carried out mainly by the visual inspection of trained experts or the use of a flow cytometer.

Recently. much attention has been focused on image analyzing systems composed of an image sensor and a microcomputer system. Image sensors are classified into XY address methods and the charge transfer method. In the XY address method, optical signals of each address are read by switching on the corresponding circuit. The charge transfer method was first demonstrated by using a bucket bridge device and presently by the more advanced charge coupled device (CCD). Most image sensors in practical use are now of the CCD type.

The CCD is an integrated semiconductor chip composed of photodiode arrays and charge transfer circuits. Electric charges accumulated at each photodiode are transferred systematically to the output terminal by controlling the electric potential in the chip. Output pulse height correlates with the brightness at the corresponding photodiode. Thus, a visual image focused on the CCD can be converted to a succession of analog pulses, Since, the photodiodes are arranged approximately by 10μm separation, the same degree of image resolution can be obtained. There are many advantages to the solid state CCD image sensor as compared with a conventional vidicon. For example, they are compact in size, have high sensitivity. are distortionless, have no afterimage, have low power consumption, and they have a long operational life.

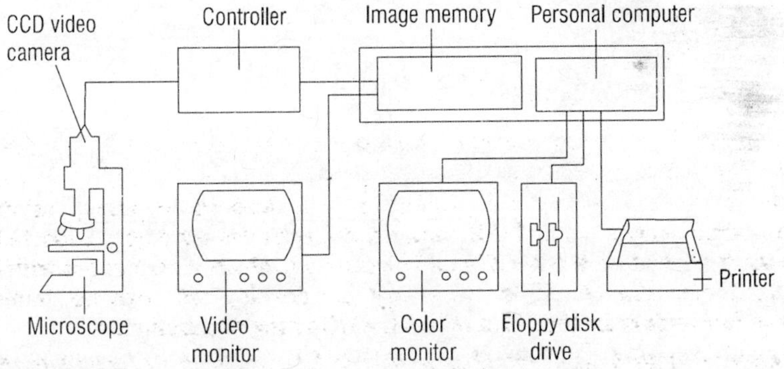

FIGURE 34.8: Schematic diagram of the imaging sensor system.

BIOCHIPS

They are made from different biological materials. Biochips can control the computer by replacing silicon chips. Biomolecular computers thus made, promise to be ten to thousand times smaller than the best super computers with much faster switching times and extremely low power dissipation.

They are made up of **semi-conducing molecules** inserted into the protein framework and fix the whole on to a protein support. The circuit is about one molecule wide. Proteins are assembled into a predetermined three-dimensional structure. The proteins molecules take the shape similar to electrical circuits. In near future biomolecular computers will become operational.

The applications of minuscule computers based on biochips are varied. They can be used in implanting of several sorts in human body, like regulation of heartbeats, responses to nerve impulses by artificial limbs (bearing such computer device), overcoming of blindness and deafness, etc. Biochips may be infected by microbes since they are made up of proteins. Biochips are also damaged if the information of protein digesting enzyme is wiped out. These are some expected dangers and problems in biochips technology.

DNA CHIP AND ITS TECHNOLOGY

The gene expression studies are useful in determining the function of a genes. However, there is a serious limitation of the current technique like monitoring gene expression, namely via Northern blots, because one can analyse expression of only *one gene at a given time*. DNA chips allows simultaneous and *en masse* analysis of hundreds and thousands of genes (DeRisi and Brown, 1997, *Science*, **278**: 68-686; Ferea and Brown, 1999, *Curr. Opin. Genei. Dev.* **9**: 715-722). In fact, it has become possible to analyse expression of all the genes of an organism such as yeast on a single chip. This technology has been given various names like, *lab-on-a-chip*, *array-of-hope*, or *revolution on a square cm*.

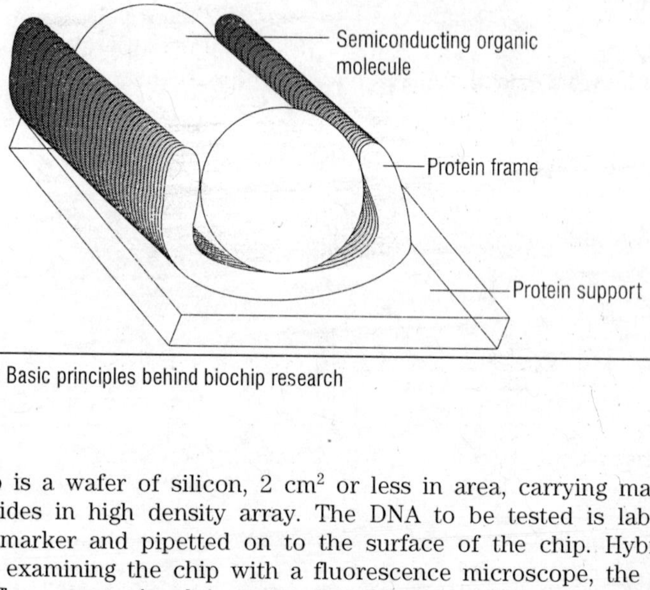

FIGURE 34.9: Basic principles behind biochip research

Structure

A DNA chip is a wafer of silicon, 2 cm^2 or less in area, carrying many different oligonucleotides in high density array. The DNA to be tested is labeled with a fluorescent marker and pipetted on to the surface of the chip. Hybridization is detected by examining the chip with a fluorescence microscope, the positions at which the fluorescent signal is emitted indicating which oligonucleotides have hybridized with the test DNA. Many SNPs can therefore be scored in a single experiment (Wang *et al.*, 1998).

A DNA chip carries a large number of DNA probes, each one with a different sequence and each at a defined position on the surface of the chip. The probes can be synthetic oligonucleotides or other short DNA molecules such as complementary DNAs. In the earliest technology, the oligonucleotides or cDNAs were spotted on to a glass microscope slide or a piece of nylon membrane to form a microarray. With this approach, only a relatively low density can be achieved, typically 6400 spots as an 80

× 80 array in an area of 18 mm by 18 mm. To prepare really high density arrays a more sophisticated technology was needed. The answer has been to synthesize oligonucleotides *in situ* on the chip surface, which in turn has required an advance in the methodology used for preparing oligonucleotides, as shown in the figure opposite. The normal method involves adding nucleotides one by one to the growing end of an oligonucleotide, the sequence determined by the order in which the dNTP substrates are added to the reaction mixture. If used for synthesis on a chip, this method would result in each oligonucleotide having the same sequence. Instead, modified dNTP substrates are used, ones that have to be light activated before they will attach to the end of a growing oligonucleotide. The dNTPs are added one after another to the chip surface, photolithography being used to direct pulses of light at individual positions in the array and hence determine which of the growing oligonucleotides will be extended by addition of the particular dNTP added at each step.

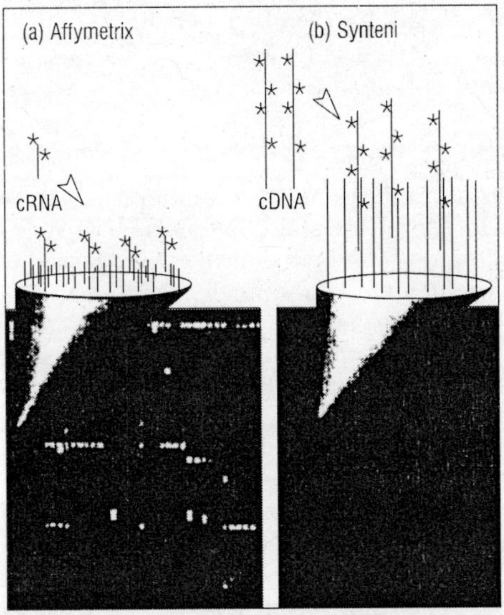

FIGURE 34.10: Diagrammatic representation of the types of DNA chips 'microarrays' that are currently available. On the left is a synthetic chip marketed by Affymetrix Company where short oligos representing unique sequences of various genes of an organism are synthesized *in situ* by a combination of photolithography and organic chemistry techniques. On the right is another kind of DNA chip for example, one pioneered by Synteny/Incyte Company where cDNAs representing various genes of an organism are spotted on glass sides or another appropriate support by a microarrayer. Both types of chips are employed to monitor gene expression by labeling the mRNAs with fluorescent tags and allowing them to hybridize to specific spots. Hybridization is monitored by a scanner attached to a computer (Gerhold, D. *et al.*, May 1999).

DNA chips are designed to allow many hybridization experiments to be performed in parallel. Their main applications have been in the screening of polymorphisms such as SNPs and comparing the RNA populations of different cells. they also have potential in novel DNA sequencing methodologies.

A density of up to one million oligonucleotides per cm^2 is possible (Ramsay, 1988), so if used for SNP screening half a million polymorphisms can be typed in a single experiment, presuming there are oligonucleotides for both alleles of each SNP. A DNA chip is not complicated to use. The chip is incubated with labeled target DNA to allow hybridization to take place. Which oligonucleotides have hybridized to the target DNA is determined by scanning the surface of the chip and recording the positions at which the signal emitted by the label is detectable. Radioactive labels can be used with a low density microarray, signals being detected electronically by phosphor-imaging. The does not provide enough resolution for a high density chip, so with these it is necessary to use a fluorescent label. The fluorescent signal is detected by laser scanning or, more routinely, by fluorescent confocal microscopy.

Under highly stringent hybridization conditions, a stable hybrid occurs only if the oligonucleotide is able to form a completely base-paired structure with the target DNA. If there is a single mismatch then the hybrid does not form. To achieve this level of stringency the incubation temperature must be just below the melting temperature or T_m of the olgonucleotide. At temperatures above the T_m, even the fully base-paired hybrid is unstable. At more than 5 °C below the T_m, mismatched hybrids might be stable. The tm for the oligonucleotide shown in the figure would be about 58 °C. this is calculated from the formula T_m = (4 × number of G and C nucleotides) + (2 × number of A and T nucleotides) °C.

BIOFILMS

Biofilms are composed of populations or communities of microorganisms adhering to environmental surfaces. These microorganisms are usually encased in an extracellular polysaccharide that they themselves synthesize. Biofilms may be found on essentially any environmental surface in which sufficient moisture is present.

Biofilms are ubiquitous. Nearly every species of microorganism, not only bacteria and archaea, have mechanisms by which they can adhere to surfaces and to each other. Biofilms can be found on rocks and pebbles at the bottom of most streams or rivers and often form on the surface of stagnant pools of water. Biofilms are important components of foodchains in rivers and streams and are grazed by the aquatic invertebrates upon which many fish feed.

In industrial environments, biofilms can develop on the interiors of pipes, which can lead to clogging and corrosion. Biofilms on floors and counters can make sanitation difficult in food preparation areas. Biofilms can also be harnessed for constructive purposes. For example, many sewage treatment plants include a treatment stage in which waste water passes over biofilms grown on filters, which extract and digest organic compounds. In such biofilms, bacteria are mainly responsible for removal of organic matter (BOD); whilst protozoa and rotifers are mainly responsible for removal of suspended solids (SS), including pathogens and other microorganisms. Slow sand filters rely on biofilm development in the same way to filter surface water from lake, spring or river sources for drinking purposes.Biofilms are also present on the teeth of most animals as dental plaque, where they may become responsible for tooth decay.

Humans have considerable use of microbial biofilms, primarily in the area of habitat remediation. Water treatment plants, waste water treatment plants and septic systems associated with private homes remove pathogens and reduce the amount of organic matter in the water or waste water through interaction with biofilms.

Their development is most rapid in flowing systems where adequate nutrients are available. Biofilm forms when bacteria adhere to surfaces in aqueous environments and begin to excrete a slimy, glue-like substance that can anchor them to all kinds of material – such as metals, plastics, soil particles, medical implant materials, and tissue. A biofilm can be formed by a single bacterial species, but more often biofilms consist of many species of bacteria, as well as fungi, algae, protozoa, debris and corrosion products.

Essentially, biofilm may form on any surface exposed to bacteria and some amount of water. Once anchored to a surface, biofilm microorganisms carry out a variety of detrimental or beneficial reactions (by human standards), depending on the surrounding environmental conditions.

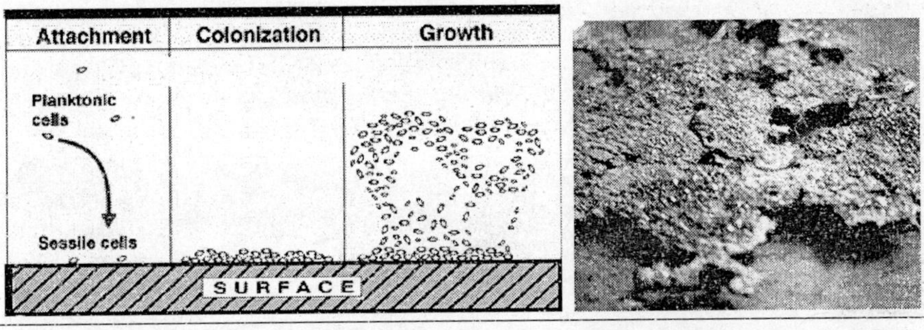

FIGURE 34.11: Formation of biofilm. Typical locations for biofilm production include rock and other substrate surfaces in marine or freshwater environments. This Microbial Mats are specialized microbial communities composed mainly of photosynthetic procaryotes. Thus the principle distinction between microbial mats and other biofilms is their dependence on photosynthetic primary productivity as their source of energy.

Formation of Biofilm on glass

Typically, within minutes, an organic monolayer adsorbs to the surface of the slide substrate. This changes the chemical and physical properties of the glass slide or other substrate. These organic compounds are found to be polysaccharides or glycoproteins. These adsorbed materials condition the surface of the slide and appear to increase the probability of the attachment of planktonic bacteria.

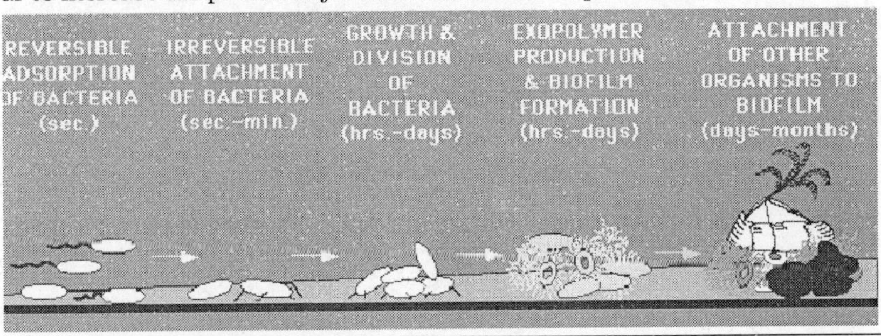

FIGURE 34.12: Steps of biofilm formation.

Free floating or planktonic bacteria encounter the conditioned surface and form a reversible, sometimes transient attachment often within minutes. This attachment called **adsorption** is influenced by electrical charges carried on the bacteria, by Van der Waals forces and by electrostatic attraction although the precise nature of the interaction is still a matter of intense debate. In some instances, as for example, in the association between a pathogen and the receptor sites of cells of its host there may be a stereospecificity which though still reversible is stronger than that achieved strictly by ionic or electrostatic forces. If the association between the bacterium and its substrate persists long enough, other types of chemical and physical structures may form which transform the reversible adsorption to a permanent and essentially **irreversible attachment**.

The final stage in the irreversible adhesion of a cell to an environmental surface is associated with the production of **extracellular polymer substances** or EPS. Most of the EPS of biofilms are polymers containing sugars such as glucose, galactose, mannose, fructose, rhamnose, N-acetylglucosamine and others. This layer of EPS and bacteria can now entrap particulate materials such as clay, organic materials, dead cells and precipitated minerals adding to the bulk and diversity of the biofilm habitat. This growing biofilm can now serve as the focus for the attachment and growth of other organisms increasing the biological diversity of the community.

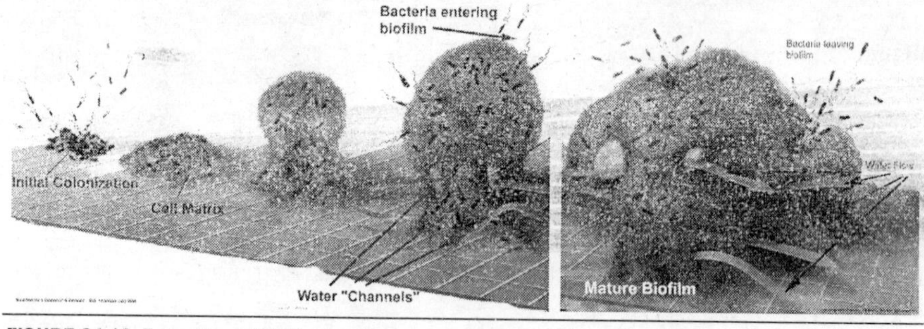

FIGURE 34.13: Formation of biofilm in soil.

Colonization and adsorption to a surface are followed by the matrix production and development of the water channels. A mature biofilm in a flowing environment may lose bacteria to the surrounding water. The biofilm may exhibit "streamers" where these cells are being lost together with some of the matrix materials

Biofilms can show surprising variation in environmental conditions within very short internal distances. Large oxygen variations occur within a few hundredths of a millimeter and significant diffusion gradients of nutrients can also be established if they are used by the bacteria in the biofilm. Another effect is that of protection of the bacteria deeper in the biofilm against toxic chemicals.

Biochemistry and Interactions in Biofilms

Bacteria such as *Pseudomonas aeruginosa* have genes that are turned on in about 15 mins after that attach to a surface. One gene is algC and is needed to make alginate - one of the components of the polysaccharide matrix material. Many biofilm bacterial cells typically make dozens or hundreds of proteins which are not found in *free-floating* cells. The cells signal to each other as the approach the "quorum" or number required to initiate biofilm formation. It seems as if a certain number of cells are needed to produce enough of the signal molecules to switch over the cells to matrix production - this is the quorum. In *Pseudomonas aeruginosa* and similar cells, the signal molecule is known - they are acylated homoserine lactones. If the genes for these compounds are missing - **no biofilms are formed**.

Some red algae produce compounds called substituted **furanones** - they have almost no biofilm on their fronds in sea water. It seems that they block the signal transmissions due to the acylated homoserine lactones since they bind to the receptor sites normally used for signaling.

BIOSURFACTENTS

There has been a great deal of interest in biosurfactents, *i.e.*, surface active compounds produced by microorganisms. Biological surfactants possess a number of potential advantages over their chemically manufactured counterparts, including lower toxicity, biodegradability, a vide variety of possible structures, and ease of synthesis from inexpensive, renewable feed stocks. Consequently, biosurfactents may have applications in numerous areas, particularly for enhance oil recovery and in foods, beverages, cosmetics, pharmaceutical preparations, etc.

Biosurfactents, however, suffer from two serious drawbacks. First, the structure of the biosurfactents produced by a given microorganism is genetically determined, thus usually not permitting any variation. Second, the very nature of biosurfactents makes their recovery from the fermentation broth and subsequent purification difficult and costly.

CHAPTER 35

Biotechnology and Biodiversity Conservation

Biological diversity means the variability among living organisms from all sources including, **inter alia**, terrestrial, marine and other aquatic ecosystems and the ecological complexes of which they are part; this includes diversity within species, between species and of ecosystems. Biodiversity, may be defined as the *sum total of species richness, i.e. the number of species of plants, animals and micro-organisms occurring in a given habitat.*

Biodiversity refers to the variety and variability among living organisms and the ecosystem complexes in which they occur. It includes diversity of forms right from the molecular unit to the individual organism, and then on to the population, community, ecosystem, landscape and biospheric levels. In the simplest sense. Biodiversity may be of following types:

- **Genetic diversity** (diversity within species). It refers to the variation of genes within species. This constitutes distinct population of the same species or genetic variation within population or varieties within a species.
- **Species diversity** (diversity between species). It refers to the variety of species within a region. Such diversity could be measured on the basis of number of species in a region.
- **Ecosystem diversity**. In a ecosystem, there may exist different landforms, each of which supports different and specific vegetation. Ecosystem diversity in contrast to genetic and specific diversity is difficult to measure since the boundaries of the communities which constitute the various sub-ecosystems are elusive. Ecosystem diversity could best be understood if one studies the communities in various ecological niches within the given ecosystem; each community is associated with definite species complexes. These complexes are related to composition and structure of the biodiversity.

Diversity is described by two parameters:

1. **Point or α-diversity:** It is represented by the number of species in a speecified areas. It increases with total number of individuals encompassed and thus with the increase with the increase in the area sampled with the productivity per unit area. It peaks along with gradient of productivity and declines in the most productive system.
2. **β-diversity:** It is represented by the turnover of species across space. It depends on how large are species ranges.

BIODIVERSITY AT GLOBAL LEVEL

At global level, it is estimated that there exists 5-30 million species of living forms on our earth. Of these, only 1.5 million have been identified. These include 3,00,000 species of green plants and fungi, 8,00,000 species of insects, 40,000 species of vertebrates, and 3,60,000 species of microorganisms.

The tropical forests are regarded as the richest in biodiversity. Scientists are of the opinion that whatever be the absolute numbers, more than half of the species on the earth live in moist tropical forests which is only 7% of the total land surface. Insects (80%) and primates (90%) make up most of the species. For instance, from a single tropical leguminous tree 43 ant species belonging to 26 genera have been retrieved. This approximately equals the ant diversity of all the British Isles. In 10 selected one hectare plots in Kalimanthan in Indonesia, Peter S. Aston of the Harvard University found more than 700 tree species, almost equal to the number of tree species native to all of North America.

The following explanations have been put forward with regard to the high species diversity in tropics:

1. In tropics, conditions for evolution were optimum and for extinction fewer;
2. In tropics, species diversity was conserved over geological time. This is because low rates of extinction prevailing there; and
3. Biological diversity is the result of interaction between climate, organisms, topography, parent soil materials, time and the heredity. The tropics is the ideal place for such an interaction.
4. However, these explanations need experimental observations and confirmation.

BIODIVERSITY AT COUNTRY LEVEL

The Indian region (8 °-30 °N and 60 °-97.5 ° E) having a geographical area of 329 million hectares is quite rich in biodiversity with a sizable percentage of endemic flora and fauna. This richness in biodiversity is due to immense variety of climatic and altitudinal conditions coupled with varied ecological habitats. These vary from the humid tropical Western Ghats to the hot desert of Rajasthan, from the cold desert of Ladakh and the icy mountain of Himalayas to the warm costs of peninsular India.

The country has over 1,15,000 species of plants and animals already identified and described. In addition, the country is very important **Vavilovian Centre** of biodiversity and origin of over 167 important cultivated plant species, and some domesticated animals. To name a few the following crops arose in the country and spread throughout the world: rice, sugarcane, Asiatic vignas, jute, mango, citrus, banana, several species of millets, several cucurbits, some ornamental orchids, several medicinal and aromatics. Infact, our country has been recognised as one of the world's top 12 megadiversity nations. This region is also a secondary centre of diversity for grain amaranthus, maize, red pepper, soyabean, potatoes and rubber plant.

There are several examples of plant germplasm from India making significant contributions to plant improvement. Two cases are well known:

1. Nearly 20 cultivar of rice contain useful genes from wild rices of Kerala, which are responsible for resistance in cultivated rices; and
2. The contribution to the cantaloup (musk melon) industry (14,000 ha) of California by powdery mildew-resistant genes from the wild musk melon of our country.

In flora, the country can boast of 45,000 species which accounts for 15 per cent of the known world plants. Of the 15,000 species of flowering plants, 35 per cent are endemic and located in 26 endemic centres. Among the monocotyledons, out of 588 genera occurring in the country, 22 are strictly endemic. The family Poaceae has the highest endemism both by genera and species.

The North Eastern region could boast of being unique treasure house of orchids in the country, the abode of about 675 species out of 1,000 available in the Indian penninsula and against 17,000 species the world over. The important Indian orchids are: *Paphiopedilum fairieyanum* (Lindl) pfitz., *Cymbidium aloiflium* Sw., *Aerides crispum* Lindl., etc.

Animal Wealth

Our country is very rich in faunal wealth also. The country has nearly 75,000 animal species, about 80 per cent of which are insects. The distribution of major animal groups are shown in Table 35.1. In animals, the rate of endemism in reptiles is 33% and in amphibians 62%. Further there is wide diversity in domestic animals, such as buffaloes, goats, sheeps, pigs, poultry, horses, camels and yalks. Domesticated animals too have come from the same cradles of civilisation as the major crops.

There are no clear estimates about the marine biota though the coastline is 7,000 km long with a shelf zone of 4,52,460 sq km and extended economic zone of 20,13,410 sq km. There is an abundance of seaweeds, fish, crustaceans, molluscs, corals, reptiles and mammals.

Information regarding other flora and fauna are patchy. Hundreds of new species may be present in our country awaiting discovery. The Western Ghats in Peninsular India, which extend in the southern states, are a treasure house of species diversity. Out of the described 15,000 species of the flowering plants in India about 5,000 species occur on the Western Ghats of Kerala; 235 are exclusive to this region. It is estimated that almost one-third of the animal varieties found in India have taken refuge in Western Ghats of Kerala alone.

TABLE 35.1: Animal species

Group	Number of Species		Percentage of Endemism	World Percentage
	World	India		
Mammals	4,231	372	8	8.79
Birds	12,450	1,200	4	9.63
Reptiles	6,300	435	33	6.90
Amphibians	4,184	181	62	4.32
Fishes	23,000	2,000	-	8.69
Insects	8,00,000	60,000	-	7.5
Molluscs	1,00,000	5,000	-	0.5

SPECIES DIVERSITY AND ECOSYSTEM STABILITY

Species diversity or diversity of genes within species increases its ability to adapt to adverse environmental conditions. When these varieties or populations of these species are destroyed, the genetic diversity within the species is diminished. In many cases, habitat destruction has narrowed the genetic variability of species lowering the ability to adapt to changed environmental conditions. Finally, this diminished genetic variability may lead to ecosystem instability. In other words, the greater the variability of the species, the more is the ecosystem stability.

Ecosystem stability has been considered to be related to the cycling and recycling of nutrients, which in turn, increases the efficiency of the resource use in the ecosystem. The high species diversity thus may be instrumental in cycling and recycling of nutrients and thereby achieving the stability of the ecosystem.

The survival and well being of the present day human population depends on several substances obtained from plants and animals. The nutritional needs of mankind are also met by wild and domesticated animal and plant species. Indeed, the biodiversity in wild and domesticated form, is the source for most of humanity's food, medicine, clothing and housing, much of the cultural diversity, and most of the intellectual and spiritual inspiration. It is, without doubt, the very basis of man's being. It is believed that ¼th of the known global diversity, which might be useful to making in one way or other, is in serious risk of extinction. This calls for an integrated approach for conserving **global biodiversity**. Establishment of nature reserves or biospheres with lot of biophysical variability, maintenance of corridors with different nature reserves for the possible migration of the species in response to climate change, etc. are the immediate steps to be taken for conserving the very precious biological diversity on the earth planet. An international consensus on establishing global network for gene banks, microbiological resource centres, and marine parks is also important. At the same time conservation must be coupled with socio-economic development, especially in countries where population pressure threatens the national biotic resources.

LOSS OF BIODIVERSITY: A GLOBAL CRISIS

The loss of biological diversity is a global crisis. There is hardly any region on the Earth that is not facing ecological catastrophes. Of the 1.5 million species known to inhabit the Earth (humans are just one of them), one fourth to one third is likely to extinct within the next few decades. Biological extinction has been a natural phenomenon in geological history. But the rate of extinction was perhaps one species every 1000 years. But man's intervention has speeded up extinction rates all the more. Between 1600 and 1950, the rate of extinction went up to one species every 10 years. Currently it is perhaps one species every year.

The destruction of the world's tropical forests, which are disappearing at an alarming rate, is one of today's most urgent global environmental issues. Rich species diversity is slowly being lost for ever. Tropical forests are estimated to contain 50 to 90 per cent of the world's biodiversity.

TABLE 35.2: Extent and loss of tropical forests in different ecosystems

Forest type	Extent 1990 ('000 ha)	Annual decline 1981-90 (Per cent)
Rain	713,790	0.6
Moist deciduous	591,779	0.9
Hill and mountain	201,417	1.1
Dry deciduous	178,579	0.9
Very dry	59,742	0.5
Desert	8,086	0.9

Rainforest, the home to half of the world's life forms, continue to be destroyed at the rate of over 100,000 Km^2 every year. This loss of biodiversity has immediate and long term effects on human survival. The majority of the world's population still depends on wild plants and animals for their daily food, medicine, housing and household material, agriculture, fodder, fuelwood, spritual sustenance, and intellectual stimulation.

The loss is even more direct in the case of domesticated biodiversity. Traditional framers of the world have developed an incredible variety of crops and livestock.

This too has been eroded over the last few decades, as lakhs of traditional crop strains and hundreds of domesticated livestock breeds being replaced by a handful of laboratory-generated hybrids or by dominant cash crops.

The traditional diversity was bred to meet diverse human needs of nutrition, test, colour, ritual, smell, and to resist drought, flood and pests. It provided several kinds of insurance against crop failure to the farmer. Modern hybrids, on the other hand, while substantially increasing the grain yield and monetary profits, have forced the farmers to look elsewhere for their other daily needs, especially fodder.

India's biodiversity is one of the most significant in the world. As many as 45,000 species of wild plants and over 77,000 of wild animals have been recorded, which comprise about 6.5 per cent of the world's known wildlife. An assessment of wildlife habitat loss in tropical Asia in 1986 showed that the country had only 6,15,095 Km^2 out of its original wildlife habitat of 30,17,009 Km^2 *i.e.* loss of about 20 per cent. In the last few decades India has lost at least half its forests, polluted over 70 per cent of its water bodies, built on or cultivated much of its grasslands, and degraded most of its coasts. Under such circumstances, none can say how many species have already lost.

The country has several problems such as overpopulation, large number of cattle heads, growing demand for land, energy, and water supply. Unplanned developmental works and overexploitation of resources have made its living resources most vulnerable. Of the world's 12 top priority biodiversity hot spots, India has two within its boundaries. Overexploitation has not only resulted in shortages of various materials but also left our biodiversity exposed to various ecological threats. Over emphasis on timber logging has affected many animal species. Faunal losses have been mainly because of over-exploitation of certain species for trading purposes; habitat alteration and destruction; and pollution of streams, lakes and coastal zones.

LISTING OF THREATENED BIODIVERSITY

Red Data Book is the name given to the books dealing with threatened plants or animals of any region. Many countries have prepared their own Red Data Books (*e.g.* Britain, New Zealand, etc.). On the global level, the IUCN published Red Data Book in two volumes. Its opposite is the **Green Book**, which lists rare plants growing in protected areas like botanic gardens. A mimeographed Green Book for India has been brought about. It deals with about a hundred rare plant species growing in garden of Botanical Survey of India (BSI). The BSI has also compiled three volumes of Red Data Book having information on endangered plant species. The UNEP has compiled endangered species of the world under the title, `**Blue Book**'. The IUCN has defined Red Data Categories which specify the state of extinction process-

- **Vulnerable**. These are the species whose population numbers are decreasing and are likely to become more severely threatened with time and in near future, they may represent the category of endangered species, if unfavourable conditions in the environment continue to operate.
- **Endangered**. The species with fewer individuals because of unfavourable environmental or human factors and that its natural regeneration is not able to keep place with exploitation or destruction by natural and unnatural means. If the same factors continue to operate, as before the species would extinct soon, *e.g.*, Indian Rhinoceros, Asiatic lion, and the great Indian Bustard.
- **Rare**. The species (or texa) with small world population that are not at present

endangered or vulnerable, but are at risk. Such species are usually localised within restricted geographical areas or habitats or are thinly scattered over a more extensive range. Rare species have a population of less than 20,000 individuals. Some species are naturally rare and have never occurred in greater numbers, yet they are able to maintain these numbers. Other species become rare through man's action or other unnatural forces.

- **Extinct**. Species that are no longer known to exist in the wild but survive in cultivation. Generally, the term Extinct is used for the species that are no longer known to exist in the wild.
- **Threatened**. It is a broader term that is used for species that fall into any of the above categories.

Threatened Animals

Though IUCN in 1988 listed 23 species of mammals as endangered or vulnerable to extinction, 75 species are totally protected as listed under schedule I of the Wildlife (Protection) Act, 1972. Forest of the Western Ghats is famous for their endemic fauna. The lion-tailed macaque, the Nilgiri Langur, the Malabar large-spotted civet, the Nilgiri tahr, etc. are some important endangered species. The Hoolock gibbon is the only ape found in the hilly forests of north-eastern India. Among the 19 primate species, 12 are endangered. The Manipur brown-antlered deer, once distributed in some parts of the northeast, is perhaps the most threatened species. There are some 50 to 100 of them in the Keibul Lamjao sanctuary of Manipur. Over exploitation is one of the major causes for the present endangered status of the Himalayan musk deer. Human population has also caused depletion in the population of the Kashmir stag or Hangul. Indian wild ass and buffalo are also among the threatened mammals.

The cheetah, lesser Indian rhinoceros have been extinct according to IUCN's Red Data Book. Other animals appear on the list are: Asiatic lion, snow leopard, swamp deer, elephant and tiger.

There are 1175 species of the birds, including 42 endemic, and 14 of these are considered threatened. N.J. Collar and P. Andrew in their book, `Birds to Watch', have identified 70 species of threatened birds, 63 on the mainland, four on the Andaman Islands and three on the Nicobar Islands. A number of threatened endemic birds are from northeast. The wood-pigeon of the Western Ghats, the white-winged wood duck of northeast India and the forest owlet of the Satpura hills are among the threatened birds.

IUCN Red data book includes Bengal florican and cheer pheasant as endangered bird species.

The reptile fauna comprises 435 species including 238 species of snakes, about 30 kinds of turtles and many crocodiles and lizards. The tropical forests of Western Ghats alone support some 20 species of snakes. In addition to their commercial exploitation for skin, the dwindling forest ecosystem also exposes these creatures to danger of extinction. The Indian python, a threatened species, is although widely distributed but its population has declined because of habitat destruction.

The four monitor lizards- the common Bengal monitor, the water monitor, the desert monitor and the yellow monitor- have been declared protected. Marine turtles, freshwater tortoises and crocodiles have also been exploited. The green turtle, the loggerhead and the Olive Ridley are the most widely consumed species. All the four species of sea turtles and five of mud turtles have been declared protected. The *gharial*, the saltwater crocodile and the marsh crocodile (mugger) are explited for their valuable skins. The three are included in IUCN list of threatened animals. But the population of crocodiles has been increased through breeding centres in Uttar Pradesh, Andhra Pradesh, Tamil Nadu, Orissa and West Bengal.

The amphibian fauna comprises 182 species, which includes salamanders, caecilians, frogs and toads. There is a high degree of endemism and out of 112 endemics, 84 occur in the Western Ghats and 20 in the northeast. Three of the Indian species, namely the Himalayan newt, *Tylatotriton verrucosus*, the Malabar tree-toad, *Pedostibes tuberculosus* and the Garo Hills tree-toad, *Pedostibes kempi*; have been identified as rare endangered by B.K. Tikader, in his **Threatened animals of India**. The first mentioned is the only species of salamander known in the country and is distributed in Sikkim, north West Bengal, Arunachal Pradesh and Manipur. The Malabar tree-toad was recently rediscovered in the Silent Valley.

TABLE 35.3: Threatened Plants of India

Plants of Ornamental Value	Aerides crispum Lindl, Cymbidium aloiflium Sw. (Orchidaceae), Diplomeris hirsuta (Orchidaceae), Paphiopedilum fairieyanum (Lindl.) Pfitz. (Orchidaceae) or `Lady's Slipper Orchid', Qaphiopedilum drurui (Orchidaceae), Rhododendron edgewortythii Hk. f. (Ericaceae), Symplocos chengapae Raiz. & Sahni (Symplocaceae).
Plants of Medicinal Value	Acorus calamus (Araceae) or `Safed Bach', Atropa acuminata Royle ex Lindl. (Solanaceae) or `Sag-angur', Dioscorea deltoidea (Dioscoreaceae), Drosera species (Droseraceae), Podophyllum hexandrum Royle (Podophyllaceae), Rauwolfia serpentina Benth. ex. Kurz (Apocyanaceae) or `Sarpagandha', Saussurea lappa Clarke (Asteraceae) or `Kuth'.
Plants of Scientific Value	Balanophora involucrata Hk. f. (Balanophoraceae), Dischidia benghalensis Coleb (Asclepiadaceae), Nepenthes Khasiana Hk. f. (Nepenthaceae), Sapria himalayana Griff. (Rafflesiaceae).
Plants of Phytogeographic Significance	Ceropegia jainii Ansari & Kulkarni (Asclepiadaceae), Frerea indica Dalz. (Asclepiadaceae), Glyphochola mysorensis (Jain & Hem.) Clayton (Poaceae/ Graminae), Helicanthes danser (Lorantahceae), Jainia nicobarica Balak (Rubiaceae), Manisuris divergens (Hack.) Ktze (Poaceae/Graminae), Willisia warm (Podostemaceae).
Trees of Forestry Importance	Dysoxylum malabaricum Hedd. (Meliaceae), Pterocarpus santalinus Linn. f. (Fabaceae/Papiolionaceae) or `Rakta chandan'.
Other Economic Plants	Decussocarpus wallichianus (Presa) de Lauben (Podocarpaceae), Phyllostachys bambusoides Sieb. & Zucc. (Poaceae/Graminae), Pinus gerardiana Wall (Pinaceae) or `Chilgoza', Santalum album Linn. (Santalaceae).

CAUSES FOR THE LOSS OF BIODIVERSITY

Proximate Causes

The important proximate causes for the loss of biodiversity are as follows:

Destruction of Habitat

The natural habitat may be destroyed by man for his settlement, grazing grounds, agriculture, mining, industries, highway construction, drainage, dam building, etc. As a consequence of this, the species must either adapt to the changes, move elsewhere or may succumb to predation, starvation or disease and eventually die. In our country, several rare butterfly species are facing extinction with the uncannity swift habitat destruction of the Western Ghats. Of the 370 butterfly species available in the Ghats, up to 70 are at the brink of extinction.

Hunting

From time immemorial, man has hunted for food. Commercially, wild animals are hunted for their products such as hides and skin, tusk, antlers, fur, meat, pharmaceuticals, perfumes, cosmetics and decoration purposes. In the country, rhino is hunted for its horns, tiger for bones and skin, musk deer for musk (have medicinal value), elephant for ivory, Gharial and crocodile for their skin, and jackal for thrivin fur trade in Kashmir. One of the most publicised commercial hunts is that of whale. The whalebone or 'baleen' is used to make combs and other products. CITES lists nine Indian animal species which have been severely depleted due to international trade. These are Fin Whale (*Balenoptera physalus*), Himalayan Musk deer (*Moschus moschiferus*), Green Turtle (*Chelonia mydas*), Hawksbill Turtle (*Eretmochelya imbricata*), Olive Ridley Turtle (*Dermochelys olivacea*), Salt-water Crocodile (*Crocodylus porosus*), Desert Monitor Lizard (*Varanus griseus*), Yellow Monitor Lizard (*V. flavescens*), and Bengal Monitor Lizard (*V. bengalensis*). Hunting for sport is also a factor for loss of animal biodiversity.

Over Exploitation

This is one of the main causes of the loss of not only economic species but also biological curiosities like the insectivorous and primitive species and other texa needed for teaching or laboratory work (like *Nepenthes*, *Gnetum*, *Psilotum*, etc.). Commercial exploitation of biodiversity has invariably meant its overuse and eventual destruction. This has been as true in the case of Indian wild mango trees which were turned into plywood as of the whales, that were hunted for tallow, in the oceans. Plants of medicinal value like Podophyllum hexandrum, *Coptis teeta*, *Aconitum*, *Discorea deltoidea*, *Rauvolfia serpentina*, *Qaphiopedilum druri*, etc., and horticultural plants like orchids and rhododendrons come under the over-exploited category. Faunal losses have been mainly because of over-exploitation. For instance, excessively harvesting of marine organisms such as fish, molluscs, sea-cows and sea-turtles has resulted in extinction of these animals.

Collection for Zoo and Research

Animals and plants are collected throughout the world for zoos and biological laboratories for study and research in science and medicine. For example, primates such as monkeys and chimpanzees are sacrificed for research as they have anatomical, genetic and physiological similarities to human beings.

Introduction of Exotic Species

Native species are subjected to competition for food and space due to introduction of exotic species. For example, introduction of goats and rabbits in the Pacific and Indian regions has resulted in destruction of habitats of several plants, birds and reptiles.

Control of pests and predators: Predator and pest control measures, generally kill predators that are a component of balanced ecosystem and may also indiscriminately poison non-target species.

Pollution

Pollutin alters the natural habitat. Water pollution especially injurious to the biotic components of estuary and coastal ecosystem. Toxic wastes entering the water bodies disturb the food chain, and so to the aquatic ecosystems. Insecticides, pesticides, sulphur and nitrogen oxides, acid rain, ozone depletion and global warming too, affect adversely the plant and animal species. The impact of coastal pollution is also very important. It is seen that coral reefs are being threatened by pollution from industrialisation along the coast, oil transport and offshore mining. Noise pollution is also the cause of wildlife extinction. This has been evidenced by the Canadian Wildlife Protection Fund. According to a study Arctic Whales are seen on the verge of extinction as a result of increasing noise of ships, particularly ice breakers and tankers.

Deforestation

One of the main causes for the loss of biodiversity is population explosion and resultant deforestation. Deforestation mainly results from population settlement, shifting cultivation, development projects, demand for fuelwood, demand of wood for industry and other commercial purposes. In India, the rate of deforestation is 13,000 sq. km. annually. If this rate of deforestation continues, one can imagine the ultimate fate of our forest and biological richness. It is presumed that in coming years, the global loss of biodiversity from deforestation alone would be 100 species everyday.

Other Factors

Other ecological factors that may also contribute to the extinction of plant and animal species are:

1. **Distribution range**: Smaller the range of distribution, the greater the threat of extinction.
2. **Degree of specialization**: The more specialized an organism is, the more vulnerable it is to extinction.
3. **Position of the organism in the food chain:** The higher the organism is in food chain, the more susceptible it becomes.
4. **Reproductive rate:** Large organisms tend to produce fewer off-springs at widely spaced intervals.

BIOTECHNOLOGY FOR BIOCONSERVATION OF DIVERSITY

In the last twenty five years, all over the world, there has been a revolution in the field of Biotechnology- new discoveries and the inventions in the area of isolation and manipulation of genes, better understanding of biological molecules and the advent of recombinant DNA technique. Biotechnologists all over the world have made efforts to create transgenic crops which will withstand the pests as also have enough resistance to withstand environmental stress. In fact, Biotechnology is inherently knowledge-intensive and having strong infrastructure would lead to value area of agriculture, animal husbandry, fisheries, forestry and medicine.

Biotechnology is not a miracle solution to the problem of biodiversity crisis. Rather, the use of biotechnology in the production of uniformity in plants and animals has threatened not only the life forms but also rendered entire community or ecosystem unstable. Further, indiscriminate and unregulated uses of genetically modified organisms pose a threat to mankind. In fact, uniformity (or homogeneity) in life forms accelerates the loss of biodiversity. The institutional structure that controls the biotechnology, therefore, should not overshadow those institutions that deal with conservation of biodiversity, and on no account ignore the rights and privileges of the local communities.

BIODIVERSITY CONSERVATION METHODS

For much of the time man lived in a hunter-gather society and thus depended entirely on biodiversity for sustenance. But, with the increased dependence on agriculture and industrialization, the emphasis on biodiversity has decreased. Indeed, the biodiversity, in wild and domesticated forms, is the source for most of humanity food, medicine, clothing and housing, much of the cultural diversity and most of the intellectual and spiritual inspiration. It is, without doubt, the very basis of life. Further that, a quarter of the earth's total biological diversity amounting to a million species, which might be useful to mankind in one way or other, is in serious risk of extinction over the next 2-3 decades. On realization that the erosion of biodiversity may threaten the very extinction of life has awakened man to take steps to conserve it.

During the last seven years, plans for biodiversity conservation have been developed by the WRI and the IUCN with support from World Bank and other institutions. Basically, the conservation plan has an holistic approach and encompasses whole spectrum of biota and activities ranging from ecosystems at the macro level (*in situ* conservation) to DNA libraries at the molecular level (*ex-situ* conservation).

To conserve the biodiversity, the immediate task will be to devise and enforce time bound programme for saving plant and animal species as well as habitats of biological resources.

CONSERVATION METHODS

In-situ Conservation

In-situ conservation refers to protection zones and areas of high biological diversity. These areas, described as natural ecosystems, will protect species with minimum human interference. The buffer zones or semi-natural ecosystems can allow for some human disturbance as long as the impact of humanity is not greater than any other factor.

For preservation of the endangered species, the only measure suggested is the strict protection against poaching of both vegetation as well as animal resources. Since most of the threatened organisms occur as components of biotic communities in open sites, restoring them in such habitats through judicious protection measures is required. For *in-situ* conservation, the biosphere reserve offers the best site of natural conservation of threatened flora. Today, India has 75 national parks and 421 wildlife sanctuaries covering an area of about 1.4 lakh km^2- constituting more than 4% of the total geographic area of the country, and one-fifth of the forest area. The protected area includes 23 tiger reserves as well as 14 biosphere reserves.

The Wildlife Institute of India has comprehensively reviewed the existing protected area network and highlighted the need to identify new protected areas in different parts of the country, in order to ensure representation of maximum wildlife habitats. It has made proposals to increase the existing network coverage in India to 147 national parks with an area of 49,435 km^2, and 519 wildlife sanctuaries with an area of 116,879 Km^2 raising the coverage upto 5.06% of the total land area. The proposed network should be accepted.

The conservation efforts towards plant species have not been given adequate attention particularly of those which are of potential economic and scientific value.

Scientific studies in regard to *in situ* conservation should focus on the following lines where very little data are available on: (1) Applied research for conservation of living resources; (2) Interlinkages between plant and animal species; (3) Quantitative assessment of the conservation status of the species; (4) Successional status of key species in different ecosystems; (5) Multiplication and restoration of endangered, rare and endemic species using biotechnology; (6) Ecological restoration of degraded micro and macro-habitats; (7) Identification of critical index species and their sensitive parameters; (8) Assessment of the impact of exotic species on the ecosystem; (9) Determination of the impact on the ecosystem of various activities in the protected areas; (10) The possible climate change and its impact on biodiversity; (11) Hydrological changes including surface run-off and percolation in the protected areas; (12) Primary production and cycling of nutrients in the soil; (13) Studies on satellite mapping of all protected areas; and (14) Development of methodologies for classification of microhabitats.

The important point in *in-situ* conservation is that the forest trees, wild plants, wild animals and micro-organisms all occur together in an ecosystem. Therefore, if an attempt is made to conserve and enrich the ecosystem, much can be achieved in a single step. This would be particularly advantageous in tropical forests where many species occur in low densities and have a high degree of endemism. Obviously there is an urgent need to coordinate efforts on the ground level. This would save not only time and effort but also the scarce fiscal resources and infrastructure.

To identify ecosystems that have been left out and are in urgent need of conservation, it is necessary to match the 12 bio-geographical provinces (*viz.* Ladakh, Himalayan highlands, Malabar rain forest, Bengal rain forest, Indus-Ganga monsoon forest, Assam-Burma monsoon forest, Mahanadian, Coromandel, Decan thorn forest, Thar desert, Lakshadweep Islands, Andaman and Nicobar Islands) with the present day protected areas network. From such a study there will emerge the additional areas which are in need of conservation. The process of identification of the additional areas must be based, among other things, on the following-

1. Vavilovian centres of diversity of crop plants in the Indian region particularly with regard to wild ancestors of the crop plant genetic resources, non-crop plant genetic resources, and forest tree genetic resources;
2. Wild relatives of livestock;
3. Fish genetic resources;
4. Fresh water systems (rivers and lakes);
5. Marine fish and other economic sea animals;
6. Mangrove and coral systems;
7. Island ecosystems;
8. Threatened/ endangered biota including materials used for teaching; and
9. Unique and fragile ecosystems, including hot spots (NE Himalayas) and endemic areas.

So far, the approach has been restricted to fauna, especially large mammals and big wats in particular, because they are at the top of the food chain. Such a restricted view must change in favour of a holistic one in order to enable the country to save as much of the biological wealth as possible.

Ex-situ Conservation

India has done commendably well as far as *ex-situ* conservation of crop genetic resources is concerned. It has also taken up such work on livestock, poultry and fish genetic resources. However, there is need to develop facilities for long and medium term conservation through:

1. Establishment of Genetic Enhancement Centres for producing good quality of seeds;
2. Enhancement in the existing zoos and botanical garden network;
3. Seed-gene banks (see chapter 32 in this book)
4. Tissue culture gene banks;
5. Pollen and spores banks;
6. Captive breeding in zoological gardens; and
7. In-vivo and in-vitro preservation

However, both *ex-situ* and *in-situ* conservation of forest trees and micro-organisms (except nitrogen-fixing blue-green algae) have not received much attention.

Ex-situ and *in-situ* conservation should be given equal importance as measures in biodiversity conservation. Release of genetically modified organisms should be regulated at national and international level, and there should be adequate dissemination of information about such release by the respective countries.

BIOTECHNOLOGY, BIODIVERSITY AND INTELLECTUAL PROPERTY RIGHTS (IPR)

In the last twenty years, all over the world, there has been a revolution in the field of Biotechnology- new discoveries and the inventions in the area of isolation and manipulation of genes, better understanding of biological molecules and the advent of recombinant DNA technique. Biotechnologists all over the world have made efforts to create transgenic crops which will withstand the pests as also have enough resistance to withstand environmental stress. In fact, Biotechnology is inherently knowledge-intensive and having strong infrastructure would lead to value area of agriculture, animal husbandry, fisheries, forestry and medicine.

Biotechnology is not a miracle solution to the problem of biodiversity crisis. Rather, the use of biotechnology in the production of uniformity in plants and animals has threatened not only the life forms but also rendered entire community or ecosystem unstable. Further, indiscriminate and unregulated uses of genetically modified organisms pose a threat to mankind. In fact, uniformity (or homogeneity) in life forms accelerates the loss of biodiversity. The institutional structure that controls the biotechnology, therefore, should not overshadow those institutions that deal with conservation of biodiversity, and on no account ignore the rights and privileges of the local communities.

POLITICS OF PATENTS AND INTELLECTUAL PROPERTY RIGHTS

Biotechnological processes use life forms or derivatives thereof, to make or modify products or processes for specific use. Under Intellectual Property Rights (IPRs), transformed microorganisms, plants and animals can be patented and become exclusive private property. The North has always used Third World Germplasm as a freely available resource and modified it. The issue of patent protection for modified life forms raises a number of unresolved political questions about the ownership and control of the genetic resource. By simply manipulating the life forms one does not acquires the patent or property right, because the modified life forms do not arise from nothing but from existing life-forms which belonging to others. Also, biotechnology does not create new genes, but merely relocates genes already existing in the organism. The advanced capitalist nations wish to retain free access to the developing world's storehouse of genetic diversity, while the South like to have the proprietory varieties of the North's industry declared a similarly public good. The North, however, resists this democracy. US has freely taken the biological diversity of Third World to earn millions of dollars of profits, none of which have been shared with Third World Countries, the original owners of the biological resource. For instance, an American Industry earned $8 million a year in 1962 simply by increasing the soluble solid contents of a wild tomato variety, *Lycopersicum chomrelewskii* taken from Peru. None of these profits or benefits were shared with Peru, the original contributor of the genetic material. The Convention on Biological Diversity is also not clear on this score. Industrialised countries, particularly the US interpreted key clauses of the treaty in a manner that would protect the interest of its own biotechnology industries. This is a clear set-back to the developing countries, who stand to lose the benefits due to them.

In absence of a proper biotech base, a developing country cannot match an industrial country although the former may be far richer in biodiversity. However, the Convention on Biodiversity, helped to place the subject matter of technology transfer and IPRs on the top of the agenda of policy and decision makers. Furthermore, access to genetic resources and transfer of technology are treated on the same plan.

On the issue of IPRs, the basic requirement of the Dunkel proposals is that inventions in all branches of technology shall be patentable, whether products or processes, if they meet the three tests of being new, involving innovative steps and being capable of industrial applications. It has also been provided that microorganisms will be patentable. In respect of plant varieties there is a separate obligation to provide them protection by patents or by an effective *sui-generis* system, or by a combination of the two. *Sui-generis* protection implies a system different from other categories of intellectual property protection (such as patents) and is a class by itself. Dunkel text, thus does not compel to patent seeds (*i.e.* plant varieties). So far we are concerned, seeds are also not patentable in India today, and we do not have any intension of changing this system. However, we will adopt our own system for the protection of plant varieties under which we may provide certificates for plant breeders right. The farmer's rights include their using the seeds for their own needs or for exchange in the village community according to their traditional custom. Since farmers right will be fully safeguarded under system of protecting the plant breeders' right, there is no truth in the allegation that the farmers will not be able to retain the seeds for their own use and that they will have to buy seeds every year from multinational companies. Furthermore, India is not in favour of the patenting naturally occurring life forms/ germplasm.

Bio-Safety Protocol

India has demanded a clear comprehensive and legally binding international protocol on bio-safety under the convention on biodiversity. Addressing the first meeting of parties to the Convention on Biodiversity, at Nassau, Bahamas, on December 8, 1994 Mr. Kamal Nath demanded immediate and adequate safeguards against hasty experimentation and use of genetically modified organisms, since these have unimaginable repercussions. He feared that the developed world could become a playground for experimentation with such genetically modified organisms and it could only be checked through a legally binding agreement.

Socio-economic and Political Causes

The socio-economic and political causes of biodiversity loss vary from region to region. In recent times, they can be linked to governmental and international support for industrial forestry, agriculture and energy programmes. The enormous fires in the Amazon have been fueled by two main sources- State subsidies for the cattle industry; and the taking over of the fertile lands in the North-East and South of Brazil by agribusiness operations to grow export crops.

CHAPTER 36

Bioinformatics

It is the combination of biology and information technology. It is the branch of science that deals with the computer-based analysis of large biological data sets. Bioinformatics incorporates the development of databases to store and search data, and of statistical tools and algorithms to analyze and determine relationships between biological data sets, such as macromolecular sequences, structures, expression profiles and biochemical pathways. It is mainly used for Map genomes and identification of genes, to determine protein structure and simulate protein interactions, to discover new therapeutic targets and design medicines aimed at the targets and to Assess the effects of virtual mutations on gene function. Computers are required in bioinformatics for their processing speed (allowing repetitive tasks to be carried out quickly and systematically) and for their problem-solving power. It requires expert human input, and the integrity and quality of the source data are also critical because bioinformatics technology uses computational tools provided by the information technology revolution, such as statistical software, graphics simulation and database management, to organize and analyze information about biological systems, which, for biotechnology, is information about cells and biological molecules. Using another product of the information revolution, the Internet, scientists broadcast this information around the world.

SEQUENCING DNA, RNA AND PROTEINS

Bioinformatics is based on the principles of **DNA sequencing**, which is performed using an automated version of the chain termination reaction, in which limiting amounts of dideoxyribonucleotides generate nested sets of DNA fragments with specific terminals bases. Four reactions are set up, one for each of the four bases in DNA, each incorporating a different fluorescent label. The DNA fragments are separated by PAGE, and the sequence is read by a scanner as each fragment moves to the bottom of the gel.

Types of DNA sequence falls under three major forms. Genomic DNA comes directly from the genome and includes extragenic material as well as genes. In eukaryotes, genomic DNA contains introns. cDNA is reverse transcribed from mRNA and corresponds only to the expressed parts of the genome. It does not contain introns. Finally, recombinant DNA comes from the laboratory and comprises artificial DNA molecules such as cloning vectors.

Genome sequencing of DNA molecules (-800 bp) can be sequences in one read. The large DNA molecules (genomes) are first broken into fragments. It is done by **Shotgun sequencing method**. It involves the generation of random DNA fragments, which are sequenced in large numbers. It provides genome of wide coverage. **Clone contigs** sequencing involves the systematic production and sequencing of subclones. High quality sequence data are generated by performing multiple reads on both DNA strands. The preliminary trace data is then base called and assessed for quality using a program such as Phred. Vector sequences and repeated DNA elements are masked off and then the sequence is assembled into contigs using a programme such as

Phrap. Remaining inconsistencies must be addressed by human curators. The sequence data of lower quality are generated by single reads (single pass sequencing). Although somewhat inaccurate, single-pass sequences such as ESTs and GSSs can be generated in large amounts very quickly and inexpensively.

Sequencing of RNA are deduced from the corresponding DNA sequences. For this purpose special methods are required for the identification of modified nucleotides. These include biochemical assays, NMR spectroscopy and MS (mass spectroscopy).

Sequencing of Protein is carried out by MS. This technique is used for accurate molecular masses and are calculated from the mass / charge ratio of ions in a vacuum. **Soft ionization methods** allow MS analysis of large macromolecules such as proteins. Sequences are deduced by comparing the masses of tryptic peptide fragments to those predicted from virtual digests of proteins in databases. *De novo* sequencing is done by generation nested sets of peptide fragments in a collision cell and calculating the difference in mass between fragments differing in length by a single amino acid residue.

TECHNIQUES FOR DETERMINATRION OF PROTEINS

Techniques for sequencing of DNA and proteins:

1. X-ray crystallography
2. NMR Spectroscopy
3. Electron microscopy
4. CD spectroscopy.

Techniques for gene and expression data:

1. DNA microarrays (Spotted DNA microarrays, Oligonucleotide GeneChips, printed onto the chips using solid-state chemical synthesis during chip manufacture).
2. 2D protein gels

Techniques for Protein-Protein interactions data:

1. **Genetic Methods:** Genetic analysis is used to know about protein interaction. Suppressor mutants may compensate for a deleterious original mutation by restoring a disrupted protein interaction. Similarly, synthetic lethal effects may reflect the inability of two mutant proteins to interact. Dominant negative mutations show that a proteins functions as a multimeric complex.
2. Physical Method (Affinity methods)
3. Molecular and atomic methods (Library-based methods)

Pattern Databases for Protein Families

Assigning sequences to protein families helps in predicting protein function these are stored in secondary protein family database. Consensun sequences provide condense the information from a multiple alignment into single sequence. Derivation of consensun sequences show that any protein family representation is subject to bias if the set of sequences from which it was derived is biased. They can not represent any probabilistic information apart from the most common residue at a particular position. The PROSITE database contains sequence patterns associated with protein family membership, specific protein functions and post-translational modifications. PRINTS and BLOCKS represent protein families by of multiply aligned ungapped segments (motifs) derived from the most highly conserved regions of the sequences. For this purpose WWW-based search engines for the databases are available.

Protein Domain families: Several proteins are built up from domains in a modular architecture. The protein families are best studied by protein **domain** families. Prodom is a database of protein domain sequence created by automatic means from the protein sequence databases. Sequence profiles represent complete domain sequences with scores for each amino acid at each position in a multiple alignment, and position specific measures of the likelihood of insertion and deletion. They are used as an alternative to sequence patterns in some PROSITE database entries. Hidden markov models are rigorous statistical models of protein domain family sequences. They can be viewed as sequences of match, insert and delete states that generate protein sequences according to probability distributions for each transition between states. Pfam and SMART can be used for protein domain family analysis. The integrated resource Interpro unites PROSITE, PRINTS, Pfam, Prodom and SMART.

PRINCIPLES OF GENOME ANNOTATION

Annotation is the method to obtain desirable information of genetic material specially structure and function of genes and other genetic elements from raw sequence data. Due to differences in gene structure and genome organization, the annotation of prokaryote and eukaryote genomes have different problems. To solve these problems, computers are being used to predict where the genes are located in genomic DNA. This is achieved by a combination of **signal sensing** (looking for regions with gene-like sequence context) and **homology searching** (looking for region that match the sequence of previously discovered genes). However, no gene finding method is 100% dependable.

The genomes of bacteria, genes are rarely interrupted by introns. For detection of such genes one has to carry out a six-frame translation of the genome sequence and to identify long ORFs (open reading frames). This method is helpful in detection of most of the genes, however, still more sophisticated approaches are needed to detect short genes, genes that use variations of the genetic code, and overlapping genes.

In higher eukaryote genomes, genes are widely dispersed and interrupted by large and numerous **introns**. **Exons** are very short and are difficult to be identified by ORF searching alone. Therefore, there is a need to combined approach involving exon detection. The preparation of whole-gene model various techniques are required like content sensing, identification of splice signals, and incorporation of auxiliary information such as cDNA sequences. Still several genes remain undetected or incorrectly delimited, and nonfunctional full or partial gene copies (pseudogenes) may be incorrectly identified as genuine genes. **RNA genes** are identified (since these do not contain a coding region) using homology searches and the prediction of secondary structure method. The annotation of human genome is very difficult. Following are the tools for gene annotation.

Gene-prediction software: Several programmes/methods have been developed for identification of genes in genomic DNA like gene prediction use ab initio methods and/or homology searches. Simple programs such as NCBI ORF finder identify ORFs by carrying out six-frame translations. For complex eukaryotic genomes, more sophisticated statistical analysis methods are required. These may incorporate simple rule-based algorithm (*e.g.* GeneFinder), neural nets (*e.g.* GRAIL) or Markov models (*e.g.* Genie, GenScan). Neural nets and Markov model algorithms must be trained on data from specific organisms.

A continuous pipeline is required to handle the large amount of data from genome projects which is to be annotate *on the fly*. Raw sequence data is fed in at one end. This is assembled and verified, annotated using one or more gene-prediction programs and the results are then fed into a database that allows sequence and annotations to be viewed using a graphical interface. Suitable formats include Artemis, Apollo, EnsEMBL, GoldenPath or AceDB.

BIOINFORMATICS: INTERNET AND WWW

The **Internet** (International computer network) is being used for a particular protocol, known as TCP/IP, to package and route data. Most academic, government and commercial institutions have access to the Internet, and individuals may also gain access by subscribing to an ISP. The Internet provides a versatile system for exchanging biological data. In case the bioinfomatic gateways do not provide the information required, general-purpose search engines can be used to locate pages containing specific key words or phrases. Otherwise, the home pages of academic institution and biotechnology companies will be useful staring points. While using a search engine it is important to refine the search and to avoid ambiguous words and phrases, as these can pull out numerous irrelevant pages. Literature databases can help by providing useful keywords and phrases to use a search terms.

The **World Wide Web** (WWW) is Internet-based system for information exchange using a protocol called **http**. Programs called browsers can access hypertext documents on the Internet. It helps in searching the relevant address, known as a URL. Hypertext documents contain text and other multimedia objects (images, audio files, etc.) but their most important property is the presence of hyperlinks that allow the browser direct access to other hypertext documents. Theses may be hosted by any computer on the Internet, and in this way, the user can rapidly jump from computer to computer around the world viewing and downloading information. Browsing, working and downloading through internet However, due to constraints in the speed of data transfer or access to the Internet, it may also be appropriate to download databases and bioinformatic software and use them on a local computer. The Internet can be daunting and intimidating. **Nine** good starting points (gateways) for bioinformatics on the Internet are listed below. Each of the sites is well maintained, simple to use and provides a wealth of resources such as links, databases and bioinormatics software.

TABLE 36.1: Important starting points for bioinformatics on the WWW

URL	Note
General Bioinfomatics 'Gatways'	
http://www.ncbi.nlm.nih.gov/	National Center for Biotechnology Infgormation homepage. It is resource for public databases, bioinformatics tools and applications. It links to various useful sites and resources for bioinformatics software.
http://www.ebi.ac.uk/	The EMBL European Bioinformatics Institute outstation. It provides resources for biological databases and software. May of them have excellent tutorial support
http://www.expasy.ch/	The ExPASy (Expert protein Analysis System) Molecular Biology Server. It is maintained by the Swiss Institute of Bioinformatics

URL	Note
	(SIB). It provides links, databases and software resources for the analysis of protein sequences, structures and expression.
http://www.embl-heideberg.de/	European Molecular Biology Laboratory homepage
http://www.grnd.de/Welcome.en.html	German National Centre for Information Technology homepage
http://links.bmn.com/	The BioMedNet is the gateway to thousands of biology websites. It includes a search facility and provides descriptions of each of the web sites listed.
Genome Projects	
http://wit.integratedgenomics.com/GOLD/	Genomes On Line Database, with links to genomic database and progress reports on genome projects. Kyoto Encyclopaedia of Genes and Genomes. A very comprehensive Japanese site including metabolic maps.
Computing Notes	
http://foldoc.doc.ic.ac.uk/foldoc/index.htm l	FOLD (Free Online Dictionary of Computing). One can look up on the meaning of computer jargon.

Primary sequence databases are used for the storage of raw experimental data while secondary databases provide information on sequence patterns and motifs. The organism-specific databases tailored for researchers working on a particular species.

DATABASE SEARCHING AND AVAILABLE DATABASE

Database searching can be carried out to search for sequences similar to the sequence that interests you. The databases can also be utilized to find out the sequence of specific genes which are utilized for vector construction. Any database sequence and its associated documentation can be retrieved and written into a personal file or a personal data library. The National Center for Biotechnology Information (NCBI) in the NIH (National Institute of Health web (www) and others can be accessed through the Genetics Computer Group (GCG). Programs like the BLAST (Basic Local Alignment Search Tool), Entrez and NLM PubMed (MEDLINE) can be used to search databases maintained at the NCBI over the internet.), Bethesda, Maryland, USA maintain several databases. There are several programs that can be used to search these databases and some of these can be searched through the world wide ograms like FastA, TFastA and several others can be used to access the GCG database.

General NCBI information can be obtained over the internet (www) at info@ncbi.nlm.nih.gov and the NCBI home page comes up. The Entrez can be clicked on if the need is to find the sequence of a particular gene. Entrez needs information about the name of the gene etc to start the search. The sequence information can then be downloaded as needed. On the other hand if a search needs to be made to find out any similar sequences to a particular protein, the BLAST program is utilized. In this program, the choice can be made to locate protein-protein similarity by specifying blastp and swissprot or Gen EMBL. The similarity sequences in nucleotide databases can also be specified by choosing the options. The information can be downloaded and utilized. The databases of fasta or tfasta can be searched for similarity sequences through the GCG programs. The GCG program is available only on the Wisconsin package. This runs on UNIX and one can logon to the system over the network by using a terminal emulation software e. g., EM340.

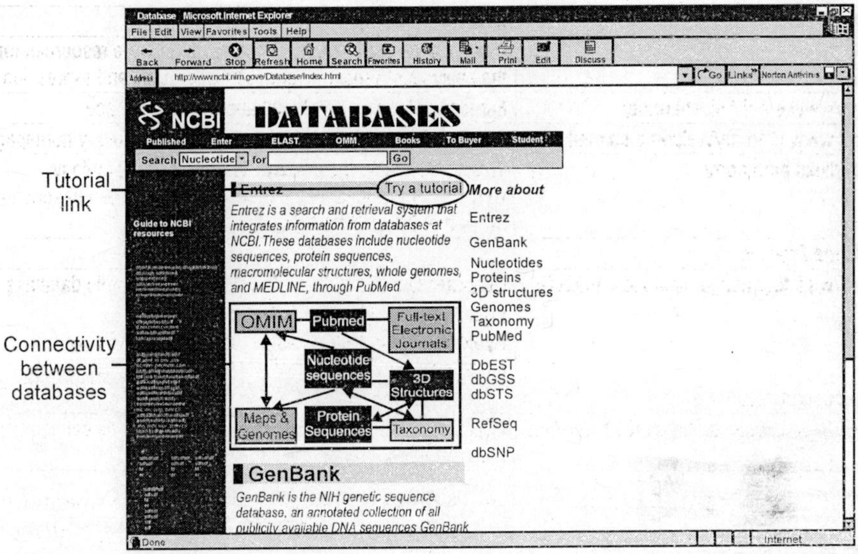

FIGURE 36.1: Entrez overview page showing the tutorial link and the relationship between eight Entrez databases.

After collection of data it is essential to format data according to International standard. The collected data of nucleic acid and protein sequences are formatted in NBRF/PIR, FASTA and GDE formats. These formats have limited facilities for comments, which must include a unique identifier code and the sequence accession number. Aligned sequences are represented in NBRF/PIR, FASTA or GDE formats but there are other formats devised especially for multiple sequence alignment, including MSF, PHYLIP and ALN. The files of structural data are recorded in flat files using the PDB format. Such files contain orthogonal atomic co-ordinates together with annotations, comments and experimental details.

Annotated Sequence Database

1. **Primary raw sequence database:** The databases recorded for primary sequence are exchanged on a daily basis. These are **GenBank** (NCBI), the **Nucleotide Sequence Database** (EMBL) and the **DNA Databank of Japan** (DDBJ). Each entry is extensively annotated and has a features table to highlight the important properties of each sequence.
2. **Subsidiary sequence databases:** Specific kinds of sequence data are stored in subsidiaries of the main sequence databases. For example, ESTs are stored in dbEST, a division of GenBnak. There are also subsidiary databases for GSSs and unfinished genomic sequence data.
3. **Swiss-Prot and TrEMBL:** It is a collection of confirmed protein sequences and shows details about structure, function and protein family assignments. The related database TrEMBL is a translation of all conding sequences in the primary nucleic acid databases. The entries in TrEMBL are less extensively annotated than those in SWISS-PROT, but are moved to SWISS-PROT when reliable annotation become available.
4. **Database interrogation** is done by using a searching tools such as **Entrez**. For

cross-reference between the primary nucleotide sequence databases and SWISS-PROT is done by search of accession number,. It provides an unambiguous identifier of genes and their products.

Genome and Organism-specific Database

1. **Organism-specific resources:** It provides information and resources for those researches working on particular species. The number or organism-specific database is growing as more genome projects are initiated, and many can be accessed from general genomics gateway sites such as **GOLD**.
2. **Database formats:** Currently no universally agreed format for genome database is available, however, several viewers and browsers have been developed with graphical displays for genomic sequence analysis and annotation. The common format is **AceDB** (originally designed for the nematode *Caenorhabditis elegans*). It is an object-oriented database architecture. It is now used in many applications outside the field of genomic bionformatics.
3. **Finding organism-specific databases:** Organism-specific data are available on the Internet. For example GOLD provides gateway and illustrated data on with Ebola virus, *Escherichia coli*, *Drosophila melanogaster* and the human genome, etc.

Miscellaneous Databases

1. **Specialized sequence database:** A number of database information have been developed for the storage and analysis of particular types of sequence, for example rRNA and tRNA sequences, introns, promoters and other regulatory elements.
2. **OMIM:** It is the online Mendelian Inheritance in Man database. It is a powerful resource for the study of human genetics and human molecular biology. Each OMIM entry provides full text summary of information known about a particular gene or trait, with links to primary sequence databases and other human genetics resources.
3. **Incyte:** It is a commercial database and belongs to the LifeSeq Foundation, It provides gene sequences and transcripts with expert annotation. It is designed specifically for drug discovery research.
4. **UniGene:** It is an Experimental facility for the clustering of GenBank sequences and related to EST data. It provides little information because currently only six vertebrate and five plant species are covered by it.
5. **Structural databases:** The primary resource for protein structural data is the PDB. It contains data derived from X-ray crystallography and NMR studies. The MMDB is another structural database. It can be accessed at the NCBI web site using Entrez.
6. **Proteins and higher-order functions:** Several databases are available which store information on particular types of proteins (*e.g.*, receptors, signal transduction components and enzymes). It is the compilation of data on different types of proteins, their functions and interaction which makes possible to deduce higher-order functional networks in the cell, such as biochemical pathways, signal transduction systems and regulatory hierarchies. The important data base is KEGG.
7. **Literature databases:** Literature databases provides information about scientific articles of various fields. One can get details about titile, authors,

keywords, and abstract. MEDLINE and PubMED are widely used literature resources on the Internet and provides information of scientific literature from the 1960s up to the present day.

Data Retrieval with ENTREZ and DBGET/ LinkDB

1. **Access to distributed data:** Entrez, DBGET and SRS (sequence retrieval system) provide biological data on WWW and are the alternative to standard search engines.
2. **Entrez:** It is a WWW-based data retrieval. It is developed by the NCBI. It is used to search for information in 11 integrated NCBI databases, including GenBank and its subsidiaries, OMIM and the literature database MEDILINE, through PubMED. Entrez is accessed via the NCBI homepae. It is a simple, user-friendly system.
3. **DBGET/LinkDB:** The Kyoto University, Japan and the University of Tokyo, Japan are maintaining this data retrieval. It covers more than 20 databases and is closely associated with KEGG. A related system, LinkDB, rinds relationships between entries in the various database covered by DBGET and others. DBGET has a simpler and more limited search format than Entrez.

Data Retrieval with Sequence similarity Searches (SRS)

It is a data retrieval tool that can be used over the WWW. However, unlike these other systems, SRS is open source software and can be installed and run on a local computer network. SRS databases are grouped but using different principle to those used by Entrez and DBGET. For example, all sequences of nucleic acid and proteins are grouped together. It is used by selecting one or more of theses groupings and, within each selected group, selecting one or more of the available database. Queries can be submitted using two styles of query form, Standard or Extended. SRS is can be installed locally.

Sequence similarity searches of databases help to extract sequences which are similar to a query sequence. Such information is used to predict the structure or function of the query sequence. Prediction using similarity is a powerful and ubiquitous idea in bioinformatics. IT also helps to know facts about molecular evolution.

1. **Sequence alignment:** Any pair of DNA sequence shows certain degree of similarity. Such alignment is the first step in quantifying this *in order* to differentiate between chance similarity and real biological relationships. Alignments show the differences between sequences as changes occur during mutations [*e.g.*, insertions or deletions (indels or gaps)]. These changes are interpreted in terms of evolution.
2. **Alignment algorithms:** Dynamic programming algorithms helps in calculating the best alignment of two sequences. There are two types of **alignment** (1) Local alignments (Smith-Waterman algorithm) and (2) Global alignments (Needleman-Wunsch algorithm). Local alignments are useful when sequences are not related over their full lengths, for example proteins sharing only certain domains, or DNA sequences related only in exons.
3. **Alignment scores and gap penalties:** A simple alignment score helps in measuring the number or proportion of indentically matching residues. **Gap penalties** are subtracted from such scores to ensure that alignment algorithms

produce biologically sensible alignments without too many gaps. The gap penalties may be constant (independent of the length of the gap) or affine (containing gap opening and gap extension contributions). Gap penalties varies according to the desired application.

4. **Measurement of sequence similarity:** It is quantified using the score from the alignment algorithm, percentage sequence identities or more complex measures.
5. **Similarity and homology:** Similarity may be observed between sequences. When sequences are evolved from a common ancestor they are called homologous and often have similar biological functions (orthologs), However, the mechanism of gene duplication allows homologous sequences to evolve different functions (paralogs).

Transcription Regulatory Regions Database (TRRD)

The Transcription Regulatory Regions Database (TRRD) is a convenient tool for studying the complex process of transcription regulation. The model of structure-function organization of transcription regulatory regions of eukaryotic genes that formed the basis of the TRRD database takes into consideration a great diversity of elements involved in transcription control, their block structure, and the hierarchy essential for their functioning. At present, the TRRD database contains five interconnections: TRRDGENES (general description of genes), TRRDEXP (description of expression patterns), TRRDSITES (description of sites), TRRDFAC (description of transcription factors), and TRRDBIB. The TRRD is installed under the SRS (http://sgi.sscc.ru/), providing easy information retrieval and integration with other databases and computer systems for data processing. The TRRD database is a part of the global system GeneExpress available at Molecular Biological Server of the Institute of Cytology and Genetics, Siberian Branch of the Russian Academy of Sciences (http://wwwmgs.bionet.nsc.ru/).

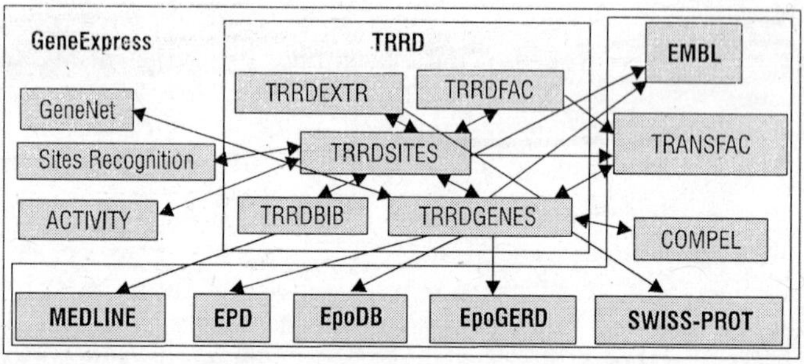

FIGURE 36.2: Structure of the TRRD database and its links to other databases and computer systems.

Glucocorticoid-Controlled Gene Regulatory Regions Database (GR-TRRD)

It is used for the elucidation of the mechanisms of chemical hepatocarcinogens action. The database GR-TRRD compiling the data on regulatory regions of 39 glucocorticoid-controlled genes. Glucocorticoids influence a vast number of complex physiological and pathological processes. They help regulate protein, fat and carbohydrate metabolism, participate in immunosupression and anti-inflammation and are important for the optimum functioning of the cardiovascular, kidney, and nervous system. Glucocorticoids bring about their multiple effects by activating the intracellular glucocorticoid receptor (GR) that binds to specific glucocorticoid responsive elements (GREs) in the vicinity of regulated genes and subsequently affect their expression. For systematization, generalization, and analysis of constantly growing amount of experimental data on the glucocorticoid-controlled genes, the GR-TRRD (Glucocorticoid Regulated genes-Transcription Regulatory Regions Database) can be used: The GR-TRRD is accessible at http://wwwicg.bionet.nsc.ru/trrd/34/gluc.htm.

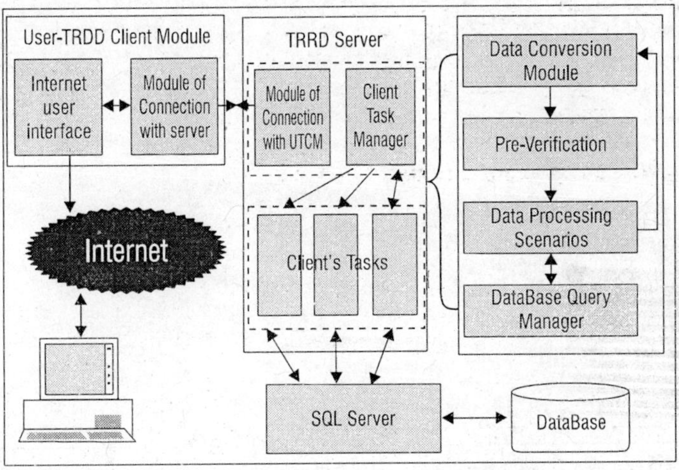

FIGURE 36.3: Basic modules of the system of data input to the TRRD database.

IIG-TRRD

The volume of experimental data on regulation of functioning of both the interferon genes proper and IFN-inducible genes is growing fast. To generalize and systematize these data for description of interferon-inducible gene transcription regulation IIG-TRRD (Interferon-Inducible Genes - Transcription Regulatory Regions Database) is available. It is a constituent of the TRRD database on transcription regulatory regions of eukaryotes and consists of two major parts: (1) A formalized description of the structure of gene regulatory regions and peculiarities of their regulation. (2) A hypertext-based description of interferon system functioning containing tables, figures, and schemes.

Interferons are cytokines with a wide range of biological action. Interferons are involved in regulation of antiviral response, cell proliferation and differentiation, modulation of immune and inflammatory responses through transcription regulation of IFN-inducible genes coding for various proteins. Investigation of the mechanisms of interferon expression regulation and their effects on the target genes is of great theoretical and applied importance, since it contributes to the understanding of the causes of organism function disorders.

Analysis of the information from the IIG-TRRD database has demonstrated that the gene sets induced by type I and II interferons are partially overlapping. IFN-inducible genes code for a variety of products: enzymes, nucleotide-binding proteins, transcription factors, major histocompatibility complex (MHC) class I and II antigens, regulatory proteins, lymphocyte antigens, certain cytokines and their receptors, Fc receptors with high affinity for IgG, and a number of proteins with yet unknown functions. As a result, a complex gene network that regulates the functioning of interferon system is formed, that is, the system regulating interferon induction and action. A fragment of this gene network involving major relevant transcription factors (STAT1a, ISGF3, IRF-1, and IRF-2).

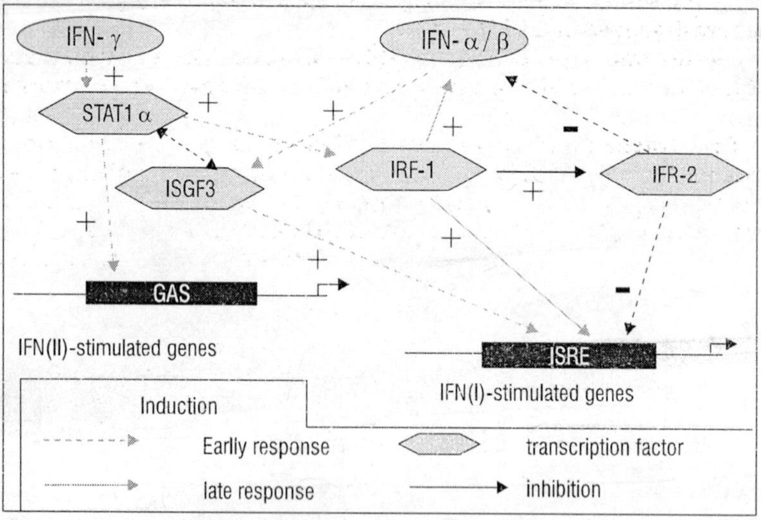

FIGURE 36.4: The main components of the IFN gene network.

ESRG-TRRD

It is a database of genes with specific transcription regulation in erythroid cells. The ESRG-TRRD (Erythroid-Specific Regulated Genes) database is a constituent of the TRRD and help to accumulate the information on the genes expressed in the erythroid cells in the course of their differentiation at different stages of vertebrate ontogenesis. This information forms two blocks:

1. The data on gene expression and structure-function organization of their regulatory regions. Peculiarities of gene expression in different cell types, organs, and tissues depending on developmental stage of the organism and effect of external factors are described in the former block along with the references to the gene regulatory regions and transcription factor binding sites involved in realization of a particular expression pattern.
2. The latter block describes the gene regulatory regions, transcription factor binding sites, and the factors binding to these sites. The database also includes a system of cross-referenced hypertexts available to the Internet users at http://www.bionet.nsc.ru/trrd/.

LM-TRRD Database

The current release of the LM-TRRD (Release 4.0) compiles the data on 48 genes of the lipid metabolism system. The database contains the description of over 60 regulatory regions (promoters, enhancers, and silencers) of lipid metabolism genes. A number of regulatory regions is distanced from the transcription start by several kbp, for example the enhancer for mouse HNF-4 gene (G001173) is located 7 kbp in the 5' direction from the transcription start; the enhancer for rat hydratase-dehydrogenase gene (G000757) is located 3 kbp upstream of the transcription initiation site. Most genes are transcribed from one promoter; however, certain genes (G000684, G001191, and G001195) have alternative promoters providing the transcription either in different tissues or under the effect of different inducers. Over 300 various transcription factor binding sites occurring in the regulatory regions of LM genes are described in the LM-TRRD.

Gene networks: Based on the LM-TRRD-contained information on transcription regulation of various vertebrate genes. The lipid metabolism gene network has two fragments:

The **first fragment** describes coordination of the genes controlling the fatty acid oxidation. Involved in this process are the following genes of enzymes of fatty acid oxidation and proteins for lipid transport: ACS (G001195), HD (G000757), ACO (G000704) and apoAI (G000203), apoCIII (G000206), respectively. The PPAR transcription factors form the key component of this gene network. Glucocorticoids are known to activate the expression of the gene encoding one of the PPAR factors in liver. In addition, the interaction with fatty acids or their derivatives increases the activity of PPAR subfamily proteins. Thus, the PPAR subfamily factors provide for the expression regulation of the above-listed genes of enzymes and transport proteins depending on the presence of fatty acids in the celi and in response to glucocorticoids.

The **second gene network fragment** unites the genes controlling the cholesterol level in the cell This fragment includes the genes of enzymes involved in mevalonate pathway of cholesterol biosynthesis and fatty acid biosynthesis: HMG-CoA-S (G001198), HMG-CoA-R (G000157), FDPS (G001191), SS (G001183) and ACC (G000684), FAS (G001196), respectively, as well as LDLR (G00190). Transcription factors of SREBP subfamily are the key elements of this gene network. It has been demonstrated that SREBP transcription factors are formed in the cell from a precursor molecule (preSREBP) by sterol-regulated protease (SRP). SRP activity is, in turn, inhibited by a high cholesterol content in the cell. Thus, SREBP proteins are involved in transcription regulation of the group of genes in question and provide for either their coordinated activation or expression inhibition depending on the cholesterol level in the cell.

PLANT-TRRD Database

A large volume of information on the structure and expression regulation of various plant genes has been accumulated. The key events of expression regulation of any genes occur at the transcription level. Interaction of protein factors with DNA regulatory regions determines the time, place, and expression level of the gene under control. Ontogenesis of each organism implies the consequent ordered switching the genes on and off and modulation. Certain complexly organized transcription systems are formed in higher plants. To generalize, analyze, and systematize these data, the PLANT-TRRD database is being used as a constituent of the TRRD (Transcription Regulatory Regions Database).

References to GenBank, EMBL, or SWISS-PROT are given. The next block describes the peculiarities of the gene expression. The fields of this block contain the data on time and place of expression. A separate block of fields, vector of gene activity, in each card is devoted to every instance of expression described. The fields of the next block describe the entire regulatory region and particular regulatory regions that constitute it, and individual transcription factor binding sites. The PLANT-TRRD database are to be further developed depending on functional grouping of the genes into gene networks. This means that each section of the database will describe the genes providing for a certain function, such as, for example, storage proteins, heat shock genes, genes of photosynthesis system, etc.

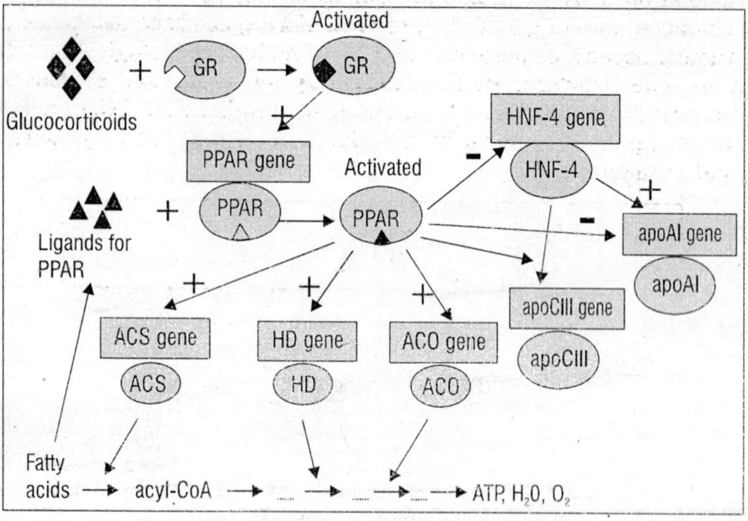

FIGURE 36.5: Gene network in the system of genes regulated by PPAR factors. The circles indicate proteins; rectangles show genes coding for these proteins. ACO, acyl-CoA oxidase; ACS, acyl-coenzyme A synthetase; poAI - apolipoprotein AI; apoCIII - apolipoprotein CIII; GR - glucocorticoid receptor; HD, Hydratase-dehydrogenase; HNF4, hepatocyte nuclear factor 4; PPAR - peroxisome proliferator activated receptor.

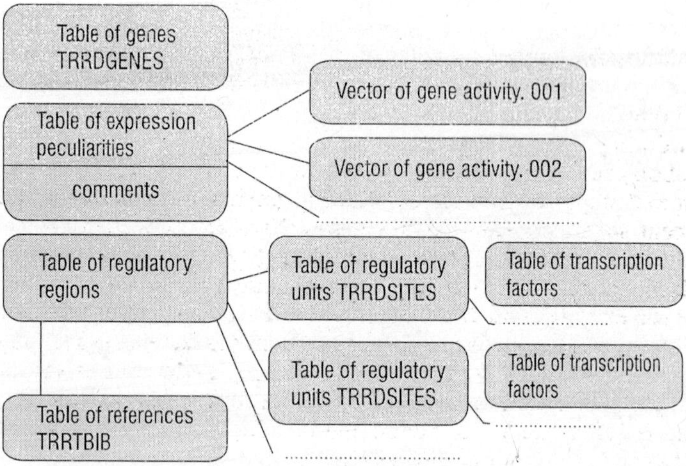

FIGURE 36.6: Structure of PLANT-TRRD database.

EPOGERD

It is a database on regulation of eukaryotic gene expression. The data on structure, function, and expression of eukaryotic genes are being accumulated rapidly. A great number of molecular biological databases have been developed aiming to systematize and accumulate these data in a user-friendly format. The largest databases of general orientation - EMBL, GenBank, PIR, and SWISS-PROT - compile the information on DNA, RNA, and protein sequences as well as certain structure-function characteristics of genes and proteins. More specialized databases deal with either particular aspects or particular objects of molecular biological investigations. The data on gene structures that are necessary for specialized databases can be partially extracted from the general databases, such as EMBL and GenBank, whereas only the original publications can be the source of information on gene expression patterns and regulation.

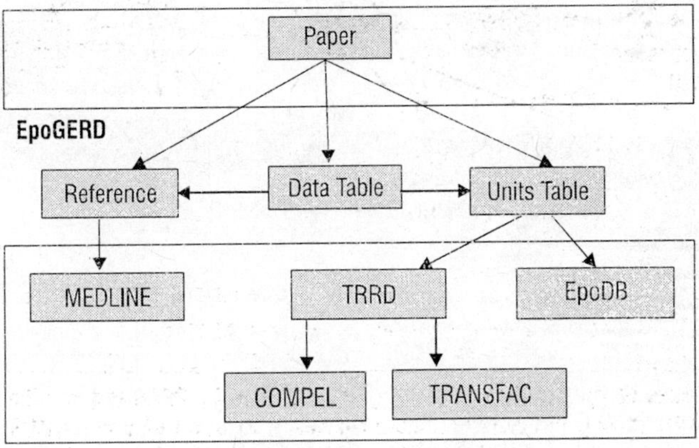

FIGURE 36.7: Distribution of input information flow from an individual publication in the EpoGERD database.

HOX-PRO DB

It is used for evolution of ensembles of homeobox genes. Nowadays homeobox genes were found for species of main invertebrate and vertebrate taxa. It is established that these genes play key role in time and space orchestration of genome expression during development. Auto- and cross regulatory functional interactions join homeobox genes into genetic networks. Mutations within homeotic hox-genes in *Drosophila melanogaster* transform defined segments of the body into the character of an adjacent segments. Homologous genes there are in vertebrates, where it has been possible to mutate them, shifts in morphological character could be produced.

The discovery of the first HOX cluster outside *Drosophila* causes great hopes. Homeobox is a *Rosetta stone* for the study of animal development. This could enable us to read the epigenetic code of other animals on the basis of our understanding of *Drosophila*. It is possible that this HOX-based epigenetic code is very ancient and was in place in the common ancestor of all modern animals. According to Slack, Holland and Graham, this character should be adopted as the defining character, or synapomorphy, of the kingdom *Animalia*.

SAMPLES and ALIGNED

These are databases for **functional site sequences**. The majority of molecular processes in the cell connected with the storage, transmission, and realization of hereditary information is controlled by relatively short regions of the DNA molecule, the so-called functional sites. A great volume of data on their location, structure, and function has been so far accumulated in such databanks as EMBL and TRANSFAC.

However, these databases contain only the data on individual sites. This is a specialized database, which provide the data for recognition methods is a timely objective. It provides database SAMPLES compiling sets of 42 transcription factor binding sites using the information contained in TRANSFAC, TRRD, and EMBL databases.

Activity

It is a database for activities of functional DNA/RNA sites. Molecular genetic processes occurring in the cell, such as replication, transcription, splicing. translation, etc., are under the control of functional sites with definite specific activities. Primary sequences, location in DNA or RNA, and the values of specific activities under various conditions have been experimentally determined for thousands of actual variants of such sites. These experimental data demonstrate that the sites of the same type located in different DNA (RNA) regions of pro- and eukaryotic genomes can differ in the values of their specific activity by several orders of magnitude. This difference was observed in naturally occurring functional sites as well as in their mutational or synthetic analogues.

B-DNA-VIDEO

It is an active database for the significant b-DNA features of transcription factor binding sites. The problem of creating methods allowing precise functional site recognition in nucleotide sequences is far from being solved. The increasing volume of experimental data demonstrating that the efficient performance of functional sites is to a large extent determined by their physical and chemical and conformational properties are being accumulated. Conformational features influence the stereochemical compatibility of the sites and the interacting proteins.

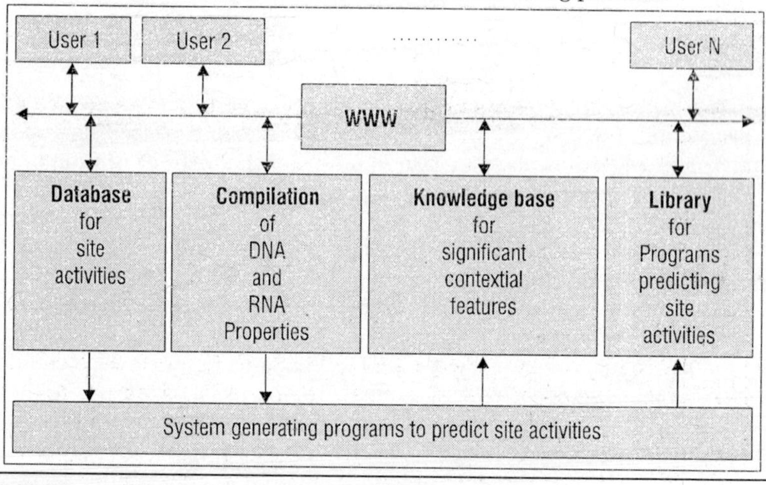

FIGURE 36.8: Schematic representation of the computer system B-DNA-VIDEO.

Numerous data obtained so far suggest the local nonuniformity of DNA conformational and physical and chemical features and their dependence on nucleotide context. Numerous experimental and theoretical studies of B-DNA helix resulted in determination of the mean values of a considerable number of conformational and physical and chemical parameters of dinucleotides

GeneExpress System

It is database for description, analysis, and recognition of regulatory sequences in eukaryotic genomes. Currently, the number of databases on gene expression and variety of software for the analysis of these data are growing fast. That is the reason why the following problems of the modern bioinformatics of gene expression regulation are challenging:

1. Creation of the unified Internet-accessible media to provide maximal integration of information-software resources on gene expression and effective navigation of users in the integrated media.
2. Development of a technique for automated discovery of knowledge on structural and functional organization of regulatory genomic sequences and on their recognition.
3. Activation of databases on regulatory genomic sequences and their conversion from passive information carriers to the active information and software modules to provide the users with various active knowledge, for example, such as the programs for analysis and recognition of regulatory genomic sequences.

The system **GeneExpress** is developing to pursue these goals. It includes following five basic units: (1) Transcription Regulation unit contains database on transcription regulatory regions of eukaryotic genes. (2) Site Recognition unit contains programs for analysis and recognition of functional sites. (3) ACTIVITY is the module designed for site activity prediction from their nucleotide sequences. (4) mRNA Translation unit is designed for analysis of translational properties of mRNAs. (5) GeneNet is the database for accumulation of the data on eukaryotic gene networks and signal transduction pathways.

All the units are integrated into the GeneExpress system on the basis of the Network Browser of Sequence Retrieval System (SRS).

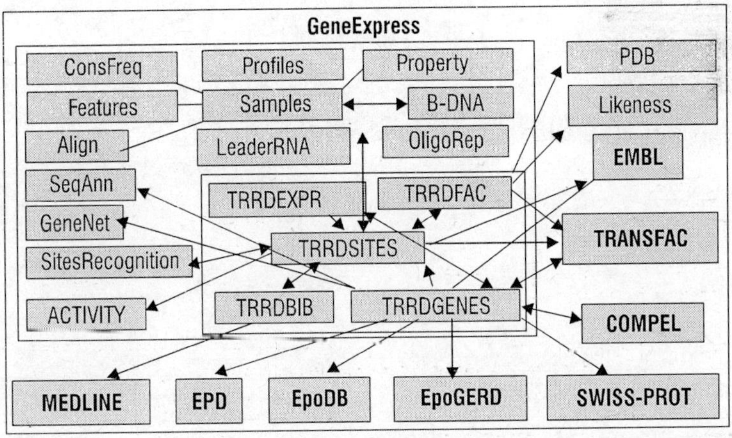

FIGURE 36.9: Principle scheme of the GeneExpress system.

There is a possibility for user to move from TRRD to a particular knowledge base of the GeneExpress system via appropriate links. Among the currently available knowledge bases of GeneExpress are the following: knowledge bases on significant conformational, physico-chemical properties of DNA sites, knowledge base on functional sites recognition, and knowledge base on functional site activities. All this knowledge is discovered automatically by the special tools of the GeneExpress system.

GeneExpress system is also supplemented with a special tool SeqAnn for activating the TRRD database while revealing putative promoters. The core idea of this approach is to use the information from the TRRD database as a ready-to-use scenarios for promoter recognition. In a simple case, it allows a user to search a target sequence for putative promoters which are similar to actual promoters described in TRRD basing on the content and approximate location of transcription factor binding sites. In the pilot release of SeqAnn, the search for sites is performed by the homology approach. At the next stage, the entire set of the site recognition methods accumulated in GeneExpress knowledge bases will be employed. And finally, as it was noted above, the simultaneous use of a large number of recognition programs for individual sites will rise the accuracy of recognition. The information on the activity of the site to be recognized will be also used for the same purpose.

The **GeneNet** database, a constituent of the GeneExpress system, describes the highest level of integration responsible for the hierarchical organization of gene expression regulation. The three following hierarchical levels are considered for using the data on transcription regulation from the TRRD database: (1) organism level, (2) the single cell level and (3) the single gene level.

GENET

It is a database of **genetic networks**. Gene networks are gene ensembles functioning in a coordinated manner to provide for the vital functions, fine regulation of physiological processes, and responses to external stimuli.

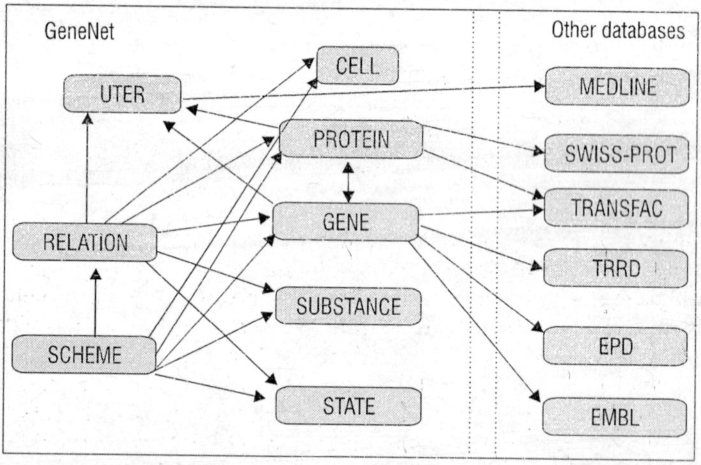

FIGURE 36.10: Structure of the GeneNet database with references to other databases.

Any gene network is composed of following functional elements: (1) a gene ensemble interacting when certain biological functions are performed; (2) proteins encoded by these genes; (3) signal transduction pathways providing the gene activation in response to an external stimulus; (4) (4) a set of positive and negative feedbacks stabilizing the parameters of the gene network (autoregulation) or providing a transition to a new functional state; and (5) external signals, hormones, and metabolites that trigger the gene network or correct its operation in response to the changes in physiological parameters. GeNet is located at www.csa.ru/Inst/gorb_dep/inbios/genet/ genet.htm and its mirror site www.mssm.edu/molbio/genet/genet.htm.

GeNet is a hypertext database designed for the World Wide Web. The database consists of text files in HTML, image files in the GIF or JPEG formats, a suite of programs for searching and generating reports, as well as user interface implemented in JAVA and as a server-side CGI-script. The database is currently running under CONVEX OS and Solaris.

ECOCYC

It is a molecular database integration used for analysis of metabolic network control. The ECOCYC system of P. Karp [P. Karp, (1992) *A knowledge base of the chemical compounds of intermediary metabolism.* CABIOS **8** (4), 347-357] was one of the first integrative molecular database systems. Today software tools are available which allow the implementation of powerful integrative analysis tools. Moreover, for the analysis of metabolic networks models and simulation environments are available. R. Hofestadt, U. Scholz (1998) presented the architecture of the *Magdeburger Molecular Information System*" (MMIS), which allows the access and analysis of metabolic networks. One important application of our MMIS is the detection of inborn errors.

MGRS

The Molecular Genetic Regulatory Systems (MGRS) aroused in the mid-60s as an application of the ideas and approaches of cybernetics to rapidly developing molecular biology and genetics. By that time, the informational cybernetic approach had yielded the first fruits. It is based on the concept that the totality of irregular cell biopolymers (DNA, RNA, proteins, and their complexes) along with the systems carrying out various processes involving these biopolymers are considered as a **MGRS** that performs various operations with **genetic information.** Sequences of monomer's symbols are considered as **genetic texts;** the rules according to which the information is written down, as the **genetic language;** and schemes of regulatory interactions between genes, enzymes, metabolites, etc., - as **genetic networks. Genetic information** is determined as an aggregate of molecular and more complex biological properties and functions encoded in the genetic texts. The genetic texts considered from the standpoint of long-term storing of genetic information form the **genetic memory.** We are applying this approach ubiquitously.

Block-modular organization of MGRS: Actual MGRS of the cell display a hierarchical block-modular organization formed in the course of evolution. The major modules of a MGRS are: (1) the archive of genetic information (hereditary memory); (2) block of self-reproduction; (3) block for control of metabolism; (4) for control of development, and (5) for control of physiological reactions; etc. The modules (1) and (2) form the **central subsystem of MGRS;** the rest, **peripheral subsystem.** The block of self-reproduction (syser) forms the core of MGRS organization. Most known dynamic modules of lower organizational levels are codons, marks of punctuation, genes, proteins, operons, replicons, mobile genetic elements (MGE), etc.

FASTA and BLAST

BLAST and FAST are two important fast searches of sequence database. Sequences similar to a query can be found in a database by aligning it to each database sequence in turn and returning the highest scoring (most similar) sequences. For this purpose dynamic programming algorithms is used. Sensitivity and specificity quantify the success of a database search strategy.

- **Sensitivity** helps in measuring the proportion of real biological sequence relationship in the database that were detected as hits in the search.
- **Specificity** is the proportion of the hits corresponding to real biological relationships.

The types of database and query sequence of protein or nucleic acid sequences required various types and combinations. The available program is BALST server it runs at the NCBI. It is used for searching various sequence database for general-purpose. FASTA is also available at the EBI. Both these servers are used on many WWW sites to search organism-specific databases like the Sanger Centre. During the course of divergent evolution sequences of protein may be changed. For presentation of these structure and function and detection of distant evolutionary relationships between sequences BLAST and FASTA methods are sometimes helpful. This kind of detection is an important part of bioinformatic researches.

PSI-BLAST is and iterative search method. This method is found more useful than BLAST and FASTA. It has improved detection rate. PSI-BLAST has some disadvantage because it has the potential for unrelated sequences to pollute the iterative search, and has difficulties associated with the domain structure of proteins.

APPLICATIONS OF BIOINFORMATICS

Bioinformatics technology uses computational tools provided by the information technology revolution, such as statistical software, graphics simulation and database management, to organize and analyze information about biological systems, which, for biotechnology, is information about cells and biological molecules. Using another product of the information revolution, the Internet, scientists broadcast this information around the world.

Biotechnological techniques like, monoclonal antibody technologies, cell culture technology, cloning technology (molecular cloning, cellular cloning, animal cloning), genetic modification technology, protein engineering technology, hybrid technologies, biosensor technology, tissue engineering technology, DNA chip technology, etc. have provided us with massive amounts of information, in addition to useful products. Without methods for organizing and analyzing the raw data, however, we will not be able to turn it into knowledge, understanding and, ultimately, products.

Bioinformatics technology provides us with tools and methods for consistently organizing, accessing, processing and integrating data from different sources. This uniformity, in conjunction with the universal language of life at the molecular level, enables international collaboration among scientists studying any plant, animal or microbe.

Bioinformatics technology provides us with tools and methods for consistently organizing, accessing, processing and integrating data from different sources. This uniformity, in conjunction with the universal language of life at the molecular level, enables international collaboration among scientists studying any plant, animal or microbe. Bioinformatics technology helps in following ways:

1. Map genomes and identify genes.
2. Determine protein structure and simulate protein interactions.
3. Discover new therapeutic targets and design medicines aimed at the targets.

4. Assess the effects of virtual mutations on gene function.
5. Study of phylogenetics

Bioinformatics in Study of Phylogenetics

Similarities and differences can be observed among species because, if two species are very similar, they are likely to have shared a recent common ancestor. Phylogenetic analysis of various kinds of character can be used for such studies *e.g.*, nucleic acid and protein sequences. These biomolecules are the most common to all life forms and allow both closely and distantly related taxa under study and they can be compared objectively. However, caution must be exercised when inferring phylogenies from sequences because the rate of mutation may not be constant and sequences may be subject to differential selection. Evolutionary relationships is generally represented by a special type of graph called a **tree**. It has n nodes and n-1 links. A phylogenetic tree is a simple way to show evolutionary relationships, with species represented by nodes and lines of descent represented by links. Such tree may be unrooted or rooted (the position of the last common ancestor of each tree member). A phylogenetic tree that shows the evolution of species as a series of bifuncations is a **cladogram** (binary tree). The links in a cladogram may vary in length and convey a sense of evolutionary period. Classification systems of biological organisms are arbitrary in nature because there is no standard measure of difference that can define a species, genus, family or order.

Bioinformatics Helps in Building Phylogenetic Trees

Percentage of matches (similarity table) or percentage of differences (distance table) are being prepared which are used for construction of a phylogenetic tree. Distance tables are used for the analysis of macromolecular sequence data. Several methods are being used for construction of a phylogenetic tree these are as follows:

- **Distance matrix methods:** These methods work by selecting the two most closely related taxa in a distance matrix and clustering them. The operation is then repeated until there is only one cluster left.
- **Maximum parsimony methods:** In these methods, sequences are compared and clustered on the basis of the minimum number of mutations required to convert one sequence into another at any given position. The final phylogenetic tree is based on the overall number of changes required throughout the whole sequence.
- **Maximum likelihood methods:** These are similar to maximum parsimony methods but include a user-defined model that allows the probability of a given substitution occurring at any given position in the sequence to be built into the algorithm. The likelihood of a given sequence change is calculated for each position in the sequence and the most reliable tree is that with the maximum overall likelihood.

Phylogenetic softwares available for phylogenetic analysis like PAUP and PHYLIP. These are suitable for distance matrix, maximum parsimony and maximum likelihood analysis.

Bioinformatics and Molecular Phylogeny

DNA accumulates mutations over evolutionary time, leading to divergence in DNA, RNA and protein sequences in different lines of descent. This principle can be used to construct phylogenetic trees. Due to differences in intrinsic mutation rate and selective constraints, different macromolecular sequences evolve at different rates, allowing the phylogenetic analysis of both closely related and distantly related organisms.

Choice of macromolecular sequences for a particular evolutionary study: The macromolecular sequence chosen for this purpose reflects the biological diversity exists in nature. Mitochondrial DNA is a rapidly evolving molecule used for such studies. For those organisms who have more diverse phylogenies, molecule of ribosomal RNA is used. Care should be taken while interpreting apparent phylogenies from poorly selected macromolecules. A few RNA viruses have rapidly evolving sequences whose repication enzymes are error-prone. Human immunodeficiency virus is an example, where up to 30 genotypes can evolve during a single infection.

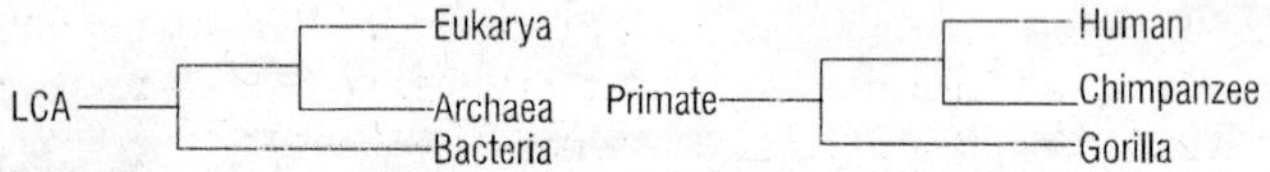

FIGURE 36.11: Presentation of rooted tree. (Left) Tree of major forms of the on this planet. (Right) Three great apes with an unspecified primate ancestor.

Bioinformatics in Discovery of Drugs

Any substance, which enters human body can change either the function or structure of the human organism. It interacts with targets, usually proteins, in the body and through such interactions cause physiological responses. The pharmaceutical industry aims to discover drugs with specific beneficial effects to treat human diseases. At **first stage**, for development of a new drug the basic requirement is the identification of a suitable target, which must contribute significantly to a human disease. Ideally, altering the activity of this target should have a beneficial effect thus showing its potential for therapeutic intervention. At **second stage** the process is lead discovery. The compounds show some of the desired activity of an ideal drug. Optimization of lead compounds results in drug candidates that may be registered and submitted for clinical trials, which establish their safety and metabolic behavior in human subjects.

Bioinformatics plays important role in drug development. Pharmaceutical industry have developed massive amount of data using various techniques of Genomics, proteomics, combinatorial chemistry and HTS The role of bioinformatics is to store, track and provide tools for the analysis of these data. The large-scale functional annotation of genes is known as **functional genomics** and incorporates areas such as homology searching, structural analysis, expression analysis, large-scale mutagenesis and the analysis of protein interactions. All of these areas are important in drug development. **Genome-scale mutagenesis** is a rich source of animal disease models for target identification and validation, and large mutant collections in simple organisms can be used for the rapid high-throughout screening of potential lead compounds.

Specific applications are modeling of protein interactions with small molecules allowing rational drug design, the association of genotype and drug response patterns (pharmacogenomics), the design and assessment of chemical diversity in combinatorial libraries, and the processing and storage of data from high-throughout screens of lead compounds.

Computational Screening

Software applications such as ·DOCK and Autodock match potential ligands to binding sites by calculating steirc constraints and bond energies. These help in searching chemical databases of potential drugs. Some applications consider the ligand and binding site as inflexible structures, rather like pieces of a jigsaw, while others can incorporate flexibility into the molecules by calculating allowable and compatible bond torsions.

Pharmainformatics

Pharmacogenomics is the study of how variation in the human population correlates with drug response patterns. It is the study of combination of biology, chemistry, mathematics and information technology that is essential for efficient data management, processing and analysis in the pharmaceutical industry.

The analysis of genomic data and its comparison with drug response data allows patients to be clustered into drug response groups, so that appropriate drugs and dose regimens can be administered. Variation is catalogued by analyzing data on mutation (particularly SNPs) and gene expression profiles.

For advancement of pharmainformatics diverse chemical libraries are needed. Such libraries will provide insight in binding properties of the drug target. Conversely, focused libraries are required if the structure of the target is known, since this defines a particular set of ligands. Chemical diversity can be defined by comparing molecules on the basis of descriptors (functional groups) and how these fill chemical space. A number of software tools are available for the design and assessment of diverse of focused chemical libraries, and virtual screening against drug targets.

Cheminformatics

The study of cheminformatics is a combination of chemistry and information technology, is required for the processing and analysis of chemical data. Cheminformatics is relevant to biologists because chemistry data are important in many areas of molecular biology, for example in the study of protein interactions and metabolism.

Molecular Formulae

Molecules can be represented in the form of simple formulae. They represent the number and type of atoms. However, this does not show how they are connected. Structural formulae provide some information about the arrangement of atoms in a molecule and thus allow isomers to be distinguished. Molecules are represented by using simple **graphs**. They show atoms as nodes and bonds as links. For organic molecules, further simplification is achieved by assuming that carbon atoms make up the molecular backbone and that the valency of four is satisfied by hydrogen atoms unless otherwise shown. Such diagrams present all molecules as planar shapes and do not indicate the spatial distribution of atoms in three dimensions.

If four different groups are coordinated around a central carbon atom, the molecule is described as **chiral** and the concept is known as **Chirality**. Chiral molecules exist in two conformations:

1. **Enantiomers** (mirror-images of each other). Although enantiomers have the same chemical properties, many enzymes and other proteins show chiral

selectivity, which is important in drug development and related fields.

2. **Diastereoisomers** (molecules may contain any number of chiral centers and a series of forms). These may have different chemical properties because of the way different groups interact within the molecule. The absolute configuration of groups around a chiral carbon atom is described by using a number of conventions. In the **DL system**, molecules are named **D** or **L** according to whether the coordinated groups are arranged in a similar fashion to those in D-glyceraldehyde or L-alanine. In the **RS system**, molecules are named **R** (*rectus*) or **S** (*sinister*) according to the size of the chemical groups surrounding the carbon atom.

Resources

- **SMILES:** This system represents chemical formulae as strings, based on a valence model in which all valencies are considered to be satisfied by hydrogen atoms unless otherwise shown. The system has conventions for representing different bond types, cyclic molecules, branches, *cis/trans* isomers and chirality.
- **RasMol and Chime:** There are several specialized data formats for chemical structures based on the principle of a molecular formula and associated table of connections. Viewing utilities such as RaasMol and Chime can interpret these file formats and display interactive molecular structures in a variety of user-defined schemes and colors.
- **Chemical Structure Databases:** A number of comprehensive WWW resources, including Chemical Abstracts On-Line, Chemfinder and MedChem are avilable. Each resource provides a chemical database that can be searched using a variety of query formats, for example systematic name, nonsystematic name, formula, molecular weight or CAS registry number. Search results provide physical, chemical and biomedical information with links to other databases and resources. MedChem also provides the SMILES string.
- **QSAR:** It is a statistical method used to determine how the structural features of a molecule are related to biological activity. The QSAR approach is particularly useful for categorizing the activities of related molecules with multiple functional groups. Each molecule is broken down into a series of descriptors (molecular properties) and the QSAR determines which descriptors are most likely to promote biological activity. This gives rise to a set of rules that can be used to evaluate the potential activity of new molecules.

Protein Interaction Informatics

Proteins that physically interact with each other may be involved in the same molecular pathway or network, or may form part of a multisubunit complex. Using this principle, pathways can be reconstructed based on evidence of protein interactions. However, information from other sources for example gene expression patterns and mutant phenotypes may also be useful.

Handling Y2h Data

Yeast two-hybrid (Y2H) screens produce large amounts of protein interaction data, but there is a relatively high level of spurious results (false positives and false negatives). This problem can be addressed by scoring interactions for reliability, based either on the repeatability of interactions over multiple experiments, or by the number of times a given bait will trap independent clones representing the same prey. Even so, similar large-scale screen tend to identify different (although overlapping) sets of interactions.

Protein Interaction Databases

Several databases have been set up to store the interaction data arising from large-scale Y2H screens. However, much more information on protein interactions is available in the scientific literature and a current challenge in bioinformatics is the assimilation of these interaction data from diverse sources.

The Interactome

The interactome is the sum of all protein interactions in the cell. The simplest way to represent protein interactions is a graph with proteins as nodes and interactions as links. However, when large numbers of proteins are considered, the graphs become too complex. They can be simplified by clustering functionally similar proteins, resulting in a functional interaction map that links fundamental cellular processes.

CHAPTER 37

Nanotechnology

Nanotechnology is an anticipated manufacturing technology that allows through, inexpensive control of the structure of matter by working them with atom. It will allow many things to be manufactured at low cost and with no pollution. It will lead to the production of nanomachines, which are sometimes also called nanodivices.

Wilson et. al., 2004

Nanotechnology is crucial physical and informational technologies. The term nanotechnology was introduced to describe physicist Richard Feynman's vision of factories using nanomachines to build complex products, including additional nanomachines. Engineering analysis indicates that this will be an extremely powerful capability, able to make large products with atomic precision, building them with superior materials, cleanly, and at low cost. This original vision for nanotechnology is sometimes termed **molecular manufacturing** or "MNT" (for molecular or molecular-manufacturing-based nanotechnology).

In recent years, a group of scientists, technologists, business leaders, and bureaucrats have exploited the excitement around nanotechnology by using the term to label existing and near-term products, which have significant features less than 100 nanometers in size. By this new, loose definition, nanotechnology is not about making nanoscale productive systems, but about making nanoscale products. It can describe anything with small features, ranging from fine particles to thin coatings to large molecules- even big things with tiny holes. Many parts of chemistry, materials science, microelectronics, and biotechnology are now marketed as nanotechnology. This redefinition has created confusion, raised false expectations, and hampered progress toward the original, more powerful goal.

Similar to genetic engineering, nanotechnology is a new science emerging with a big growth area of this century. The understanding in this science for students is not much. Nanotechnology is as big as biotechnology– or it soon will be. Using nanosystems, better and cheaper products can be obtained by using conventional materials. In the future we can expect computer controlled molecular machines much smaller than a speck of dust that have the accuracy and precision of today's target drug molecules. In nanomedicine, these will perform controlled surgery at the cellular and molecular level.

Nanotechnology is the molecular manufacturing and will revolutionize physical technology. Current research in nanotechnology is laying the foundation for a breakthrough development: manufacturing systems based on extremely productive nanoscale devices. These molecular manufacturing systems can be used to build large, complex products cleanly, efficiently, and at low cost. Building with atomic precision, desktop-scale (and larger) molecular manufacturing systems can be used to produce:

Scientific research related to nanotechnology, however, is not enough-successful development of molecular manufacturing systems will require a focused effort guided by systems engineering.

BASIC PRINCIPLES

The basic principles of nanomachines and molecular manufacturing have been subjected to extensive technical analysis, based on established knowledge in chemistry, applied physics, and mechanical engineering.

The basic idea is simple, where chemists mix molecules in solution, allowing them to wander and bump together at random, nanomachines with instead position molecules, placing them in specific locations in a carefully chosen sequence. Letting molecules bump at random lead to unwanted reactions- a problem that grows worse as products get larger. By holding and positioning molecules, nanomachines will control how the molecules react, building up complex structures with atomically precise control. Complete molecular manufacturing systems will have many subsystems, designed to meet many constraints.

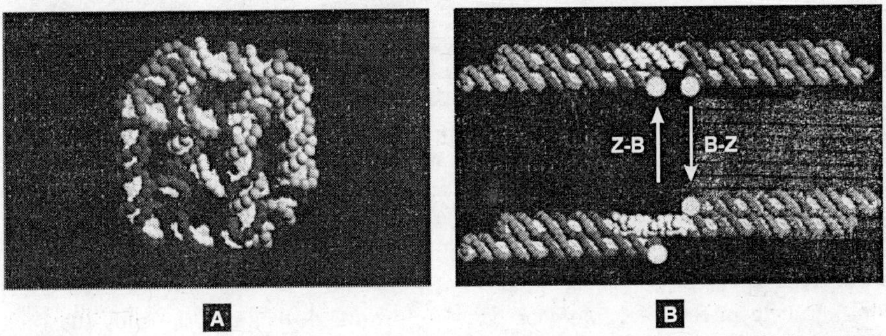

FIGURE 37.1: Molecular models of DNA. (A) A DNA Cube, (B) A chemically driven molecular hinge (After Wilson, 2004).

Structural DNA Nanotechnology

Structural DNA nanotechnology is for nanoelectronics, nanorobotics, and smart materials. The Structural DNA nanotechnology consists of combining unusual DNA motifs by specific structurally well-defined cohesive interactions (primarily sticky ends) to produce target materials with predictable 3D structures. This effort has generated DNA polyhedral catenanes, robust nanomechanical devices, and a variety of periodic arrays in two dimensions. The system has been used to produce specific patterns on the mesoscale through designing and combining specific DNA strands, which are then examined by atomic force microscopy. The combination of these constructions with other chemical components is expected to contribute to the development of nanoelectronics, nanorobotics, and smart materials. The organizational capabilities of structural DNA nanotechnology are just beginning to be explored, and the field is expected ultimately to be able to organize a variety of species that will lead to exciting and possibly revolutionary materials (Seeman, 2003).

Convergent assembly

Convergent assembly is based on the idea that smaller parts can be successively assembled into ever larger parts. The particular architecture proposed should be able to produce meter-sized products in a few minutes from nanometer-sized parts while going through about 30 stages. At each stage the parts are approximately double the size of the parts from the previous stage and half the size of the parts in the succeeding stage. These conclusions are based primarily on simple scaling laws. Deviations from simple scaling laws that might occur when dealing with smaller parts should not substantially change these conclusions.

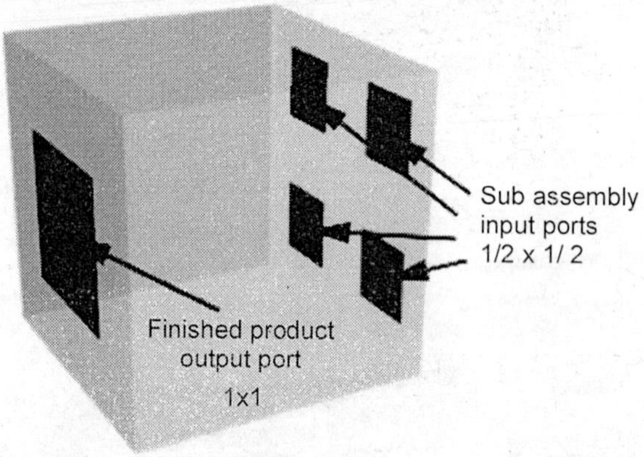

FIGURE 37.2: A single assembly module able to accept subassemblies from the four input ports to the right, and which produces a finished assembly to the left through the single output port. If the output port has a size of one meter by one meter, each input port would have a size of 0.5 meters by 0.5 meters.

Convergent assembly has many clear advantages but seems ill-suited for manufacturing of flexible, liquid or gaseous products. It is not the only method of making large products from small parts. Further research into both convergent assembly and other approaches appears worthwhile.

Convergent assembly is likely to prove most useful in the manufacture of relatively rigid structures made from rigid components. This should include computers with a large number of molecular logic gates densely packed into a three dimensional volume; structural elements useful in load bearing applications in cars, airplanes, bicycles, buildings, furniture, etc.; high density memories; and many more. In aerospace applications the great strength-to-weight ratio of diamond (over 50 times that of steel) should prove particularly useful.

Convergent assembly is only one approach to making large objects from small objects. An oak tree does not use convergent assembly, but quite effectively makes something large starting with only a small seed. Approach has been considered in which relatively rigid parts have approximately similar X, Y and Z sizes. It would be possible to consider parts which are basically one dimensional. This might be useful in the manufacture of products similar to cables, in which long thin strands are woven together into a final product. Two dimensional parts, *e.g.*, sheets, could also be produced and then pressed together into a final product.

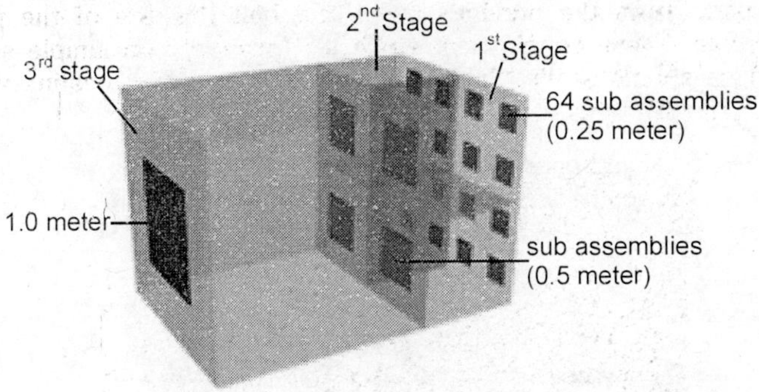

FIGURE 37.3: Two stages of assembly starting with 64 sub-subassemblies with a size of about 0.25 meters, producing 8 subassemblies with a size of about 0.5 meters, and producing a finished product with a size of about 1.0 meters.

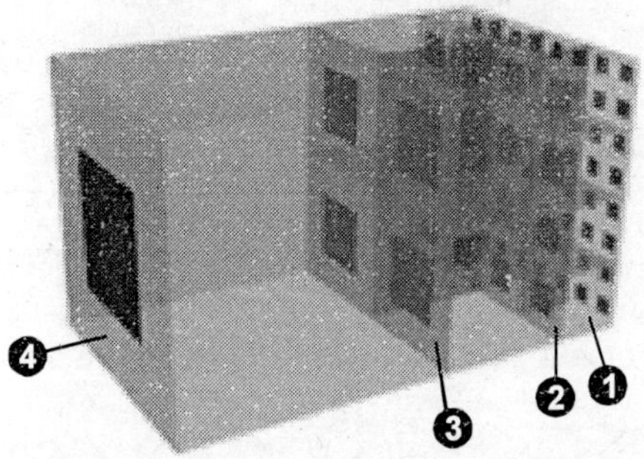

FIGURE 37.4: Three stages of convergent assembly produce a final product of ~1.0 meters in size from 512 sub-sub-subassemblies each of which is ~0.125 meters in size.

FIGURE 37.5: Nanomachine (Convergent assembly) showing reagent preparation and molecular assembly.

Important Characteristics

The following rules hold approximately for a convergent assembly system which doubles the size of product produced at each stage, which starts with building blocks with a characteristic length of *lambda* meters, and which has a characteristic assembly time to manipulate those building blocks of *tau* seconds. Values for *lambda* and *tau* might be 10^-9 meters (one nanometer) and 10^-7 seconds (100 nanoseconds).

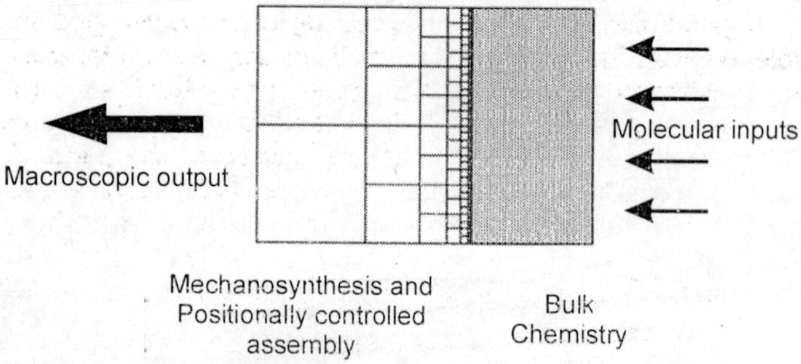

FIGURE 37.6: Convergent assembly: schematic side view.

1. The size of product that can be made at stage N is 2^N x *lambda* meters.
2. The time required for an assembly module in the Nth stage to produce an assembly of size 2^N × *lambda* meters given that eight subassemblies of size 2^(N-1) × *lambda* meters are already available is 2^N × *tau* (τ) seconds. We will further assume that the assembly process can be started when only four subassemblies are available, effectively allowing stage N to begin operation after stage N-1 has produced only half the required subassemblies.
3. The time required to produce a product of size 2^N × *lambda* meters, including the time taken by all preceding stages (*i.e.*, assuming all stages start empty, with no assemblies or subassemblies in them, but that they have been provided with appropriate instructions for the manufacture of the desired product) is 2^(N+1) × *tau* seconds.
4. Such a system can be pipelined, in which case a steady stream of finished products of size 2^N × *lambda* meters can be produced at a rate of one new product every 2^N × *tau* seconds.
5. The area of the output port of an assembly module equals the sum of the areas of its input ports. The total area of all output ports at stage N is equal to the total area of all output ports at stage N-1.
6. The average speed with which material flows through the system is approximately equal at all stages, and is approximately *lambda* / *tau* meters per second. For the example values of *lambda* and *tau* chosen here, this speed is roughly 0.01 meters/second.

Brownian assembly

Brownian assembly is a powerful technique with substantial difficulties and limitations. Brownian motion (the motion of small particles in a fluid, resulting from thermal agitation) can be used to put parts in place. The fundamental advantage of Brownian assembly is that motion comes for free. No motors or conveyance machines are needed to move parts, because thermal agitation moves them spontaneously. The fundamental disadvantage of Brownian assembly is that motion is uncontrolled. Every part moves at random, twisting, shifting, and bumping in all possible positions and orientations. Only the properties of the parts themselves can guide the process, biasing motion through electrostatic fields and selecting favorable positions through the selective fit and stickiness of interfaces (bumps matching hollows, positive charges opposite negative charges, and so forth).

This presents substantial difficulties and limitations. In ordinary engineering, parts must fit together and perform a function; they can be assembled under flexible, programmable control. In engineering for Brownian assembly, parts must do likewise, and in addition must suspend themselves in a fluid, stick to the proper place in the pre-existing structure, and fail to stick to any other surface. Assembly behavior is thus largely *hard wired* into the structure of the parts. These added requirements add to the difficulty of designing parts and of redesigning systems based on those parts. Moreover, the resulting structures have within them many weak, intricate interfaces that are a residue of the assembly process, serving no function in the product. Stronger, more compact systems must be built by other means.

Despite these difficulties and limitations, Brownian assembly is a powerful technique. It is the basis for most molecular assembly in biology and for an increasing range of artificial nanostructures. Brownian assembly of artificial molecular parts is a leading candidate among techniques for implementing first-generation molecular machine systems, including machines that can perform assembly under flexible, programmable control.

Brownian assembly is commonly called "self assembly", but this term has a range of other meanings and tends to create confusion. In manual or robotic assembly, manual or robotic motions put parts in place; in Brownian assembly, Brownian motion puts parts in place. The term "self assembly" suggests that a product somehow acts to build itself before it itself exists, a concept as mysterious as it is inaccurate.

MOLECULAR MANUFACTURING

Molecular manufacturing will be used to prepare nanomachines for large scale production with atomic precision. Molecular manufacturing is an anticipated future technology based on Feynman's vision of factories using nanomachines to build complex products, including additional nanomachines. It promises to bring great improvements in the cost and performance of manufactured goods, while making possible a range of products impossible today. Molecular manufacturing will be use nanomachines to build large products with atomic precision.

Every manufacturing method is a method for arranging atoms. Most methods arrange atoms crudely; even the finest commercial microchips are grossly irregular at the atomic scale. Many of today's nanotechnologies face the same limit. Chemistry and biology, however, make molecules defined by particular arrangements of atoms-always the same numbers, kinds, and bonds. **Chemists** do this by using clever tricks that do not scale up well to building large, complex structures. **Biologists**, however, uses a more powerful method: cells contain molecular machines that read digital genetic data to guide the assembly of large molecules (proteins) that serve as parts of molecular machines. Molecular manufacturing will likewise use stored data to guide construction by molecular machines, greatly extending abilities in nanotechnology.

Molecular manufacturing will be able to make a wide range of superior products, many with unprecedented abilities.

With its ability to make a wide range of structures with atomic precision, molecular manufacturing will greatly expand the limits of technological possibility. It will make possible micron-scale computer CPUs efficient enough (operating power ~100 nanowatts) to let air-cooled desktop systems contain a billion processors. It will make possible materials about 100 times stronger than those in common use today, enabling large reductions in the mass of products (particularly aerospace products) and in raw materials consumption. Mechanical systems using efficient, nanoscale, DC electric motor-generators will be able to interconvert electrical and mechanical power with high power density (>1 GW/cm^3). Systems combining nanoscale sensors, computers, and tools will bring surgical control to the molecular level, enabling the precise destruction of cancer cells and AIDS viruses. Molecular manufacturing systems can even be used to build more molecular manufacturing systems.

An advance of this scale will bring both enormous opportunities and the potential for enormous abuse and disruption. In the military sphere, the resulting capabilities are likely to prove decisive. Much of the reason for examining molecular manufacturing today is to enable better decisions about the future.

Research worldwide is advancing along multiple paths toward molecular manufacturing. Advanced molecular manufacturing systems will be constructed from parts and materials that cannot be made in the laboratory today. It would be futile to try to build them directly, yet many areas of research are helping to develop tools that will eventually make molecular manufacturing a reality.

On the process side, the key to molecular manufacturing will be using control of molecular positioning to build molecular structures. Scanning probe instruments (STM, AFM) have been used to move individual molecules, and to split and combine them. Catalysts in organic chemistry and enzymes in biochemistry guide molecular motions in a limited way, and both are today active targets for further development.

On the product side, the key to molecular manufacturing will be improving abilities to build atomically precise building blocks, then building nanomechanical systems by assembling them using scanning probes or Brownian motion. Numerous research groups around the world are working to extend this ability by designing and synthesizing new structures built from organic molecules, proteins, and nucleic acids. Reports of new, artificial molecular machines have in recent years become routine.

Most of these laboratory researchers are pursuing shorter-term goal than molecular manufacturing- goals such as catalysts for cleaner, more efficient chemical process, molecular frameworks that could support molecular electronic devices, or molecules useful in medical therapies. History, however, shows that research often has unintended consequences, and a natural consequence of improved abilities in chemical and nanoscale technologies will be the emergence of a technology base that can be used to implement the machines needed for ever more advanced molecular manufacturing systems. Following are the fields where molecular manufacturing systems can be used:

Computers

Recall that powerful processors can be built with fewer than 10^7 transistors, while a cubic micron contains 10^9 cubic nanometers, and can contain $>10^{11}$ atoms. Analysis of a specific implementation technology yields volume and power consumption number consistent with the statement above.

Strong materials

The statement above is equivalent to saying that molecular manufacturing will be able to build structures with the strength of high-quality graphite, diamond, or carbon nanotubes. These materials form under laboratory conditions when reactive carbon-containing species bond to (and transfer hydrogen to and from) surfaces. Molecular manufacturing systems can use analogous reactions, but using mechanical control to guide the carbon deposition process with atomic precision.

High power-density motor-generators

Recall that small mechanical devices can operate at high frequencies, resulting in high throughputs of (for example) charge on a per unit volume basis.

Destruction of pathogens and cancer cells

Molecular machine systems in nature demonstrate that devices capable of the required sorts of molecular-scale sensing and action are feasible. Molecular manufacturing will enable the construction of a wider range of devices, both imitating and extending natural systems. In particular, it will enable the use of programmable computers of sub-cellular size to evaluate sensor data and select targets.

Building more molecular manufacturing systems

The range of structures that can be built by mechanically guiding molecular assembly is extremely large, and includes structures that can mechanically guide molecular assembly. Molecular manufacturing systems need contain no parts of sorts that cannot be made and combined using molecular manufacturing.

Decisive military capabilities

Expected advances in computation, materials, and production cost seem large enough to enable developments that can overwhelm forces based on previous technologies.

Further, all these components must include adequate redundancy to enable operation the presence of a significant fraction of failed nanoscale components (chiefly due to damage from background radiation). Individual operations must either be subject to testing and correction, or must be extremely reliable. Moving parts must be supported by bearings. Building blocks must be relatively rigid, and must be designed to fit and join when brought together with correct alignment. The analysis of molecular operations must take account of quantum phenomena and thermal vibration. The overall analysis must take account of entropy and thermodynamic issues. Finally, one must consider how such technologies can be implemented in the first place.

Note that this rate is far less than what a simple scaling analysis of submicron assembly might suggest- as it should be, because larger, lower-frequency parts form much of the system. It is also substantially slower than the rates enabled by more recent convergent assembly concepts. A reanalysis based on these more recent concepts would describe substantially faster systems with limits set chiefly by cooling constraints.

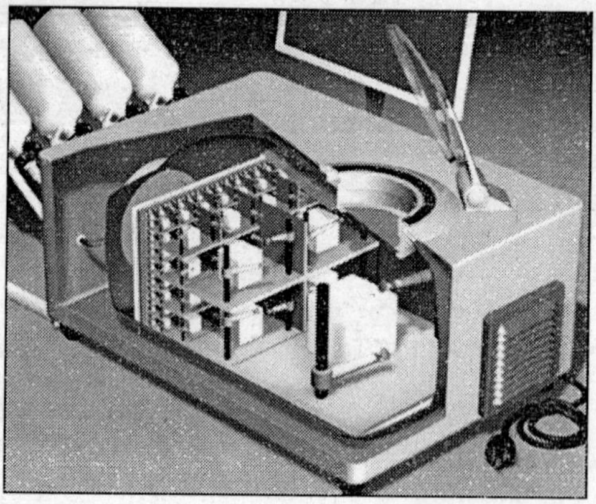

FIGURE 37.7: A Nanomachine: A complete molecular manufacturing system (like a complete conventional manufacturing system) will be complex. It must have, for example: (1) a casing to protect its interior from air, moisture, and dirt, (2) inlets for liquid feedstocks to supply molecules for processing, (3) molecular sorting mechanisms to purify inputs, (4) alignment and binding mechanisms to organize streams of molecules, (5) mechanosynthetic devices to process inputs into reactive tools, (6) mechanosynthetic devices to apply tools to workpieces, (7) mill-style mechanisms to join workpieces into larger blocks, (8) programmable mechanisms to join blocks into complex products, (9) a port to deliver finished products while protecting the interior space, (10) motors to drive moving parts, (11) computers to control material flows and assembly mechanisms, (12) stored data and programs to direct the computers, (13) data communication channels to coordination actions, (14) electrical systems to distribute power, (15) a cooling system to dissipate waste heat, and (16) a structural framework to support the casing and internal components. (Image by John Burch, Lizard Fire Studio).

MOLECULAR MILLS

Manufacturing of Molecular Mills is also based on Nanotechnology, which can perform repetitive assembly steps using simple, efficient mechanisms. The convergent assembly can quickly build large products from nanoscale parts. At the smallest scales, mill-style machines can be used to prepare molecular building blocks in the nanometer size range. Molecular mills can perform repetitive assembly steps using simple, efficient mechanisms.

Molecular mill can perform a series of hydrogen deposition operations. A belt carrying molecular workpieces travels from left to right across the bottom. A second belt carrying molecular tools enters at the top left, circles around a bearing-mounted wheel, and exits at the top right. (Atomic detail in the mechanical parts is suppressed for simplicity and clarity). Each tool enters carrying a hydrogen atom (white) bound to germanium (purple); each workpiece enters with an upward-facing carbon radical (green).

At the contact point, aided by pressure and thermal vibration, the hydrogen transfers from the germanium to the carbon, forming a stronger bond. In chemical terms, the carbon radical *abstracts* the weakly bound hydrogen from the tool; in operational terms, the tool *deposits* the hydrogen on the workpiece. Hydrogen abstraction is a simple, well-understood reaction.

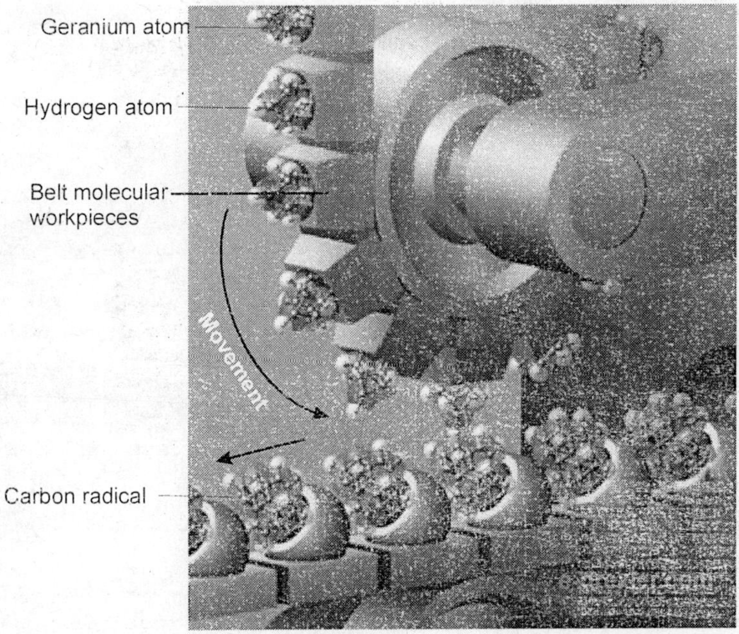

FIGURE 37.8: Schematic illustration of a molecular mill.

Molecular mills based on more elaborate mechanical systems can hold tools and workpieces together for longer times and move them in more complex patterns. Systems of molecular mills can regenerate tools using molecular fragments derived from simple feedstock molecules (*e.g.*, recharging a tool with hydrogen). On a larger scale, molecular mills can bring together and join nanoscale molecular building blocks (as large or larger than the workpiece shown here) to form still larger building blocks- mills can serve as the smallest-scale assembly mechanisms in a convergent assembly system.

Molecular mills can be extremely productive. A mechanochemical system using belts moving at 1 m/s with tools spaced 10 nm apart will perform 10^8 operations per second. A 10^4 atom mechanism (about 100 nm^3 of solid structure) that transfers ~ 1 atom per operation will process its own mass in ~ 10^{-4} s. A system based on such mechanisms that performs 10 operations per net transfer of one atom (to allow for regeneration of tools) will process its own mass in ~ 10^{-3} s.

APPLICATIONS OF NANOTECHNOLOGY

Nanotechnology will have an impact on war, crime, terrorism and the massive industries that go with them, namely security and law enforcement. The military has a great interest in nanotechnology, especially optical systems, but also in nanorobotics, nanomachines, smart weapons, nanoelectronics, virtual reality, massive memory, new ultra hard materials for armour, new energy-absorbing nanobased materials for stopping bullets dead, and bio-nanodevices to detect and destroy chemical and biological agents. Much of this is about protection against attack and minimizing risk to military personnel. In the future, nanorobots may be able to repair defective airframes or the hulls of ships before any damage develops.

Such a scenario is not yet possible, but it is feasible (Wilson et. al., 2002). As for crime, the techniques of nanoscience will have a lot to offer forensic investigations, both for biological analysis, and materials and chemical studies. Portable instruments with sophisticated nanosensors will be able to perform accurate high level analysis at the crime site.

Nanoscience may open up new ways of making computer systems and message transfer secure using special hardware keys that are immune to any form of hacking. Very few current computer firewalls are able to keep out really determined hackers. Nanoimprinting, which already exists, could be used to make 'keys', or even special nano-based biosensors coded with a dynamic DNA sequence.

Nanoimprinting is in use to make banknotes virtually impossible to forge by creating special holograms in the clear plastic. Only if the master stamps were actually stolen would forgery be possible, and then a new hologram could be made.

In near future new chemical industry, based on particles with internal open nanostructures will lead to a world-wide market of around $200 billion per year. Totally new types of paints are starting to emerge as we learn to control the optical and thermal properties of the pigments using better nanoscience.

The first large growth areas are occurring right now, where existing large scale industrial production equipment can be adapted to use nanotechnology. Examples are nanoparticle-doped plastics, sunscreens, bathroom and window cleaners, car duco protection products, extremely hard new types of metals containing separate nanoparticles, and special industrial polishing powders. Of course there is also the microelectronics industry, which will become nanoelectronics industry, with the next generation of chips having device features near and below 100 nanometres. In 20 years or so all devices and computer chips will be nanodevices! Nanoscale magnetic or optical memories are also coming soon. They will be extremely dense and cheap: many full stereo movies could be stored on one small disk.

Nanotechnology will help to develop new home and health products, new industrial and manufacturing processes, and new ways to keep our environment clean and sustainable. This leads us into the world of nano-optics and nano-photonics where much current research is happening.

The problems of making the most of solar energy and natural light, and of cleaning up and in future controlling the quality and availability of our land, water and air have something in common. They all involve very largescale activities in terms of areas and volumes.

What solutions can nanotechnology offer on such a large scale? The answer is the solutions we have been seeking for many years. The grand scale technologies not only have to be clever but they must also be very cheap to have any real impact.

Nanotechnologists are struggling to develop solar technologies for widespread use because the options are too expensive to make on the vast scale needed to achieve an economically significant uptake. Nanotechnology may overcome this hurdle and enable us to make the most of our great environmental resources at much lower cost and with minimal environmental effects. The costs of one kilowatt hour of solar electricity; of replacing 15 Wm^{-2} of lamp lighting in a building with visually comfortable daylight; and of a megalitre of pure water obtained from salty ground, river or sea water, are what ultimately counts, especially for the developing world.

Nanotechnology may turn out to be a force for greater economic equality. Therefore, the public needs to be informed about many scientific issues, such as information technology, genetic engineering and genetic code.

Glossary

β-replicase: It helps in replication of viral RNA.

Aberrant: A growth that deviates from the normal or usual type; as exceptional growths **(aberrations)** which occur in some tissue cultures.

Abort: To stop or fail to reach full development (maturity) or to develop imperfectly; as some hybrids are prone to embryo **abortion** or as some attempts to culture a plant may fail (**abortive** attempt).

Accession: Plant or seed sample, strain or population held in a genebank or breeding programme for conservation and use.

Acetosyringone: One of the phenolic compounds released by wounded plant cells which can stimulate the transcription of the *vir* region of the *Ti* plasmid in the initial stages of transfer of DNA from *Agrobacterium* to the plant cell.

Acoustic coupler: An attachment for a Modem that allows data to be transmitted and received *via* a telephone handset rather than making direct electrical connections to the telephone network.

Activator: A substance or physical agent that stimulates transcription of a specific gene or operon.

Active Genepool Collection: A collection of germplasm used for regereration, multiplication, distribution, chracterization and evaluation. Ideally, germplasm in the active collection should be maintained in sufficient quantity to be available on request. Active collection germplasm is commonly duplicated in a base collection and is often stored under medium to long-term storage.

Adenosine Triphosphate (ATP): The general energy donor molecule in all organisms.

Adsorb: the adhesion of a liquid, gas or dissolved material to a solid surface, resulting in concentration of the **adsorbate** (the **adsorbed** material) to the **adsorbent** (the **adsorbing** agent, such as activated charcoal). The process is **adsorption**.

Adventitious: 1. Produced in an abnormal or unusual position, or at an unusual time of development or away from the natural habitat; as when plant organs (buds, shoots, roots, others) develop on callus or nonzyotic embryos (embryoids) develop without an ovary or fertilization on callus (**adventive** embryony). **2.** A manner of growth relying on adventive processes.

Aerate: To supply with or mix with air or gas. The process is **aeration**.

Aerobic or aerobiotic: Refers to an organism that lives in or a process occurring in the presence of molecular oxygen.

Agar or agar-agar: A gelatinous polysaccharide obtained from the red alga Gelidium corneum and from several other red algae. It is a solidifying agent that mixed with nutrient media (0.6-1%), forms a gel for growing tissue cultured plants and for other purposes. Its firmness as a gelling agent is affected by medium pH (it is softer when the medium is more dilute). Agar gels melt at about 100°C but solidify at about 44° C.

Age: 1. The period in the life cycle of an organism; the process of growing older, mature. **2.** The state of being old or senescent. **3.** Culture age is a function of the number of subcultures and the time after subculture.

Agenesis: The absence of development.

Agglutinate: 1. To cause to unite. adhere; as if glued. **2.** To gather into a clump or mass; as protoplasts and bacteria, in the presence of specific antibodies, tend to stick to one another. The process is **agglutination.**

Agglutinin: An antibody capable of clumping bacteria or other cells.

Agrenet: The computer communications network established by the Agriculture and Food Research Council (AFRC) for the agriculture and botanical research community in the

United Kingdom.

Agrobacterium tumefaciens: The bacterium causing crown gall disease of plants, inducing tumors to form. Tumors may be cultured *in vitro* and are useful in the study of this disease. The Ti plasmid of *A. tumefaciens*is known to cause the disease and a small portion of it is used as a vector inthe genetic modification of higher plant cells. Novel DNA sequences are spliced into the plasmid DNA segment, the DNA is circularized and introduced into the cultured plant cells.

Agroinfection: A method for initiating viral infection by inoculating host plants with *Agrobacterium* containing viral-specific DNA within the T-DNA.

Airlift fermenter: A cylindrical fermentation vessel in which the cells are mixed by air, which is introduced at the base of the vessel and rises through the column of culture medium. The cell suspension circulates around of the column as a consequence of the gradient of air bubbles in different parts of the reactor.

Aliquot or aliquot part: An evenly divided unit, portion or sample (fraction) of the whole.

Allopolyploid: hybrids between two (or more) species or genera containing the sum of the complete chromosome set of the different parental species, which can be a different ploidy (chromosome multiplicity) levels.

Allotetraploid: hybrids between two species or genera containing the sum of the complete diploid chromosome complements of each parent.

Alphanumeric: The set of symbols used to represent letters of the alphabet and the integers 0-9.

Ambiguity code: A character other than the standard codes for representing the DNA and RNA bases (ACGT and U) used to indicate a base with an ambiguous identity.

Amphidiploid: hybrids between two species or genera containing the sum of the complete chromosome complements, which can be of different ploidy levels, of each parent.

Amplification Fragment Length Polymorphism (AFLP): A variant DNA amplification product produced by DAF, PCR, or RAPD of different size.

Anther culture: Refers to culture of single pollen grains or of the anther, containing the male gametophytes or microspores, with the objective of producing monoploid plants.

Antibiosis: The prevention of growth or development of an organism by a substance or another organism.

Antigen: A compound that induces the production of antibodies.

Anti-idiotype antibody: An antibody that has the properties of an antigen.

Antisense construct: A plasmid that contains the coding regions of a gene placed adjacent to a promotor in such an orientation as to cause the gene to be transcribed from the DNA strand complementary to that from which RNA is normally transcribed.

Antisense DNA: (1) The sequence of chromosomal DNA that is transcribed. (2) A DNA sequence that is complementary to all or part of a functional RNA (mRNA).

Antisense RNA: A RNA sequence that is complementary to all or part functional RNA (mRNA).

Artificial seed: Encapsulated or coated somatic embryos (embryoids) that are planted and treated like seed.

Asepsis: Without infection or contaminating microorganisms.

Aseptic technique: Procedures used to prevent the introduction of fungi, bacteria, viruses, mycoplasma or other microorganisms into cell, tissue and organ cultures.

Aseptic: Free of pathogens, contaminants, algae, bacteria, fungi, viruses, etc; absence of all microorganisms. **asepsis** is a fundamental requirement for plant tissue culture (aseptic culture).

Asparagine (Asp, $C_4H_8N_2O_3$ mw 132.12): An amino acid occasionally included in plant tissue culture media, as a source of reduced nitrogen.

Aspirate: To draw something in or out, up or through using suction or a vacuum; as **aspiration** (vacuum) may be used in the disinfection process to draw disinfectant into the surface layers of plant tissue.

Assay: 1. To test or evaluate. **2.** The substance to be analyzed or the process of examining or testing it (chemically or by other means).

Assembler: The lowest level of computer programming language that can be read by humans. The operations are close to machine code and are programmed using memonics for the processor instruction set.

Asymmetric Somatic hybridization/partial genome transfer: The production of viable and fertile hybrid plant by irradiating protoplasts from one parental line (the donor) in order to pulverize the chromosomes and facilitate the elimination of substantial amount of the donor genome. Thereafter, the irradiated donor genome may be transferred into the genome of the recipient by protoplast fusion which can be carried out using three different methods: chemicals, an electrical field or a UV laser microbeam. Partial genome transfer system has potential use for the transfer of molecularly uncharacterized traits and multigenetic characters.

Attachment efficiency: The percentage of cell plated (seeded, inoculated) which attach to the surface of the culture vessel within a specified period of time. The conditions under which such a determination is made, should always be stated.

Autoclave: 1. An closed chamber in which to heat substances under pressure to above their boiling points, to sterilize utensils, liquids, glassware, etc., using steam. The routine method uses steam pressure of 103.4 X 10_3 Pa at 121° C for 15 minutes, or longer for large volumes to reach temperature. **2.** A pressure cooker. These employed in medium and instrument sterilization for plant tissue culture work. Over-sterilization degrades culture media constituents and caramelizes sugars, so is to be avoided. Under-sterilization results in culture media or equipment contamination. Heat labile components of tissue culture media cannot be **autoclaved**. These are commonly filter-sterilized. **3.** To carry out the process of **autoclaving.**

Autonomous replicating sequence (ARS): Any cloned DNA sequences that initiates and supports extrachromosomal replication of a DNA molecule in a host cell; often used in yeast cells. Also called autonomous(ly) replicating segment, autonomously replicating sequence.

Autoradiography: A technique that captures the image formed in a photographic emulsion as a result of the emission of either light or radioactivity from a labeled component that is placed next to unexposed film.

Auxin: One of a large class of plant hormones (phytohormones) allegedly produced in the growing tips of stems and roots. It causes cell enlargement and elongation but in excised, cultured systems they may promote cell division.

Auxotroph: A microorganism or plant cell line possessing atypical nutritional requirements for some item(s) (growth factors) in addition to those required by the control or wild type which can synthesize them; as **auxotrophic** cells requiring certain amino acids.

Axenic culture: A culture without foreign or undesired life forms. An axenic culture may include the purposeful co-cultivation of different types of cells, tissues or organisms.

Axenic: A pure culture of one species. This implies that cultures are free of microorganisms (aseptic or germ free).

Axis: The main plant stem.

B vitamin: One of a complex of vitamins made in plants and though to be essential for healthy growth. Some are routinely added to plant tissue culture media to promote growth. The latter include thiamine **(B_1)**, niacin **(B_3)**, adenine **(B_4)** and pyridoxine **(B_6).**

BA or BAP: See N-(phenylmethyl)-1H-purin-6-amine or **6-benzylaminopurine.**

Bactericide: A substance or agent that kills **bacteria** (usually rapidly); is **bactericidal**.

Batch culture : A cell suspension grown in liquid medium of a set volume. Inocula of successive subcultures are of similar size and cultures contain about the same cell mass at the end of each passage. Cultures commonly exhibit five distinct phases per passage; a lag phase follow inoculation, then an exponential growth phase, a linear growth phase, next a deceleration phase and finally a stationary phase.

Bcteriostat: A chemical or other agent that does not kill but prevents bacterial growth and multiplication; is **bacteriostatic**.

Bergmann, L. (1960): He was first to obtain callus by plating cells from suspension cultures onto solid medium.

Bioassay: A biological assay performed on living cells or on a living organism; sometimes used to detect minute amounts of substances which influence or are essential to growth.

Biotechnology: The industrial use of biological processes; as yeast fermentation for alcohol production or plant cell culture for extraction of secondary products. The scope of biotechnology has been dramatically increased through genetic engineering.

Biotin ($C_{10}H_{16}O_3N_2S$ mw 244.31): Part of the vitamin B complex. It is also called vitamin H. It is present in all living cells, bound to polypeptides or proteins, and is of import in fat, protein and carbohydrate metabolism. It is a common addition to plant tissue culture media.

Bleach: A fluid, powder or other whitening **(bleaching)** or cleaning agent. Bleach contains calcium hypochlorite or sodium hypchlorite and is a common disinfectant used for cleaning working surfaces, tools and plant materials in plant tissue culture.

Bud-sport or bud mutation: A somatic mutation in a bud giving rise to a branch, fruit or flower that is a typical of the plant on which they occur. These characters (if beneficial) may be retained through vegetatrive propagation from the affected area.

Buffer: A substance in solution, or system that resists pH change, (despite addition of some small amount of acid or base) and withstands shock; as **buffered** media can resist pH drift. The degree to which pH change is resisted is a measure of the solution's **buffering capacity.**

Bung: A stopper or closure.

Burgeon: To flourish, bud, sprout or grow.

Calcium hypochlorite ($Ca(OCl)_2.4H_2O$ mw 215): An algicide, bactericide and fungicide capable of disinfecting and bleaching. It is used in dilute solution (5-10% w/v) as a plant tissue disinfectant often when agitating or using a vacuum. Tissue damage occurs if contact is prolonged. Thorough washing with sterile water generally follows treatment.

Callus, pl. *calli* or calluses: 1. Wound tissue, tissue formed on or below a wounded surface. **2.** Disorganized tumor-like masses of plant cells that form in culture. These proliferate in an irregular tissue mass, and vary widely in texture, appearance and rate of growth; a function of the tissue type (species and explant) and the composition of the medium. The process of callus formation is **callogenesis.**

Cannula: A small tube for insertion into tissue; as a cork borer.

Carbon source: A source of the non-metallic element carbon (C); as organic substances like sugars taken up and metabolized by plant tissue cultures.

Casamino acid: An amino acid obtained through the digestion (acid hydrolysis) of the milk protein **casein**. Protein digest yields **casamino acids** and other substances. These are undefined constituents of some plant tissue culture media.

Casein hydrolysate (edamin): A milk protein digest product composed of amino acids (casamino acids) and other substances. This complex (undefined) product is sometimes used as an addition (0.02-2.10%) in nutrient solutions used in plant tissue culture as a non-specific source of organic nitrogen.

Casein: the principal protein of milk, a phosphoprotein.

Caulogenesis: Shoot formation; as de novo shoot development from callus.

Cell count: The number of cells per unit suspension volume or callus weight. Tissue is treated with chromic acid (5-8%) or pectinase (0.25%) for up to 15 minutes followed by mechanical dispersion, then cell numbers are estimated with a hemocytometer (haemocytometer).

Cell culture: The culture of single or groups of cells on solid or dispersed in liquid nutrient media (cell suspension cultures) usually following a set of defined growing conditions (protocols).

Cell hybridization: Formation of synkaryons, viable cell **hybrids** produced through cell fusion. they are identifiable by their increased chromosome number compared to the parent cells and the possession of characters found in one or another of the parental cells.

Cell line: Developmental history or descent, through cell division from a single original cell; as callus may constitute a group of cell, all descendants from a single cell plating. Numerous **cell lines** may be present in a culture. Any deviation in culture technique may favor one cell line over another.

Cell number: The absolute number or approximation of the number of cells per unit area of a culture or medium volume.

Cell selection: Selection within a group of genetically different cells; involves competition between cells often under some stress. Selection criteria may involve cell viability l a unique phenotype or biochemical activity; or another basis for choice. Select cells or cell lines are generally relocated to fresh medium for continued selection and often are exposed to an increased level of the stress agent. The final objective is usually to regenerate plants from those select cells, in hope that the plants will exhibit the traits selected for at the cellular level.

Cell suspension: Cells and small aggregates of cells suspended in a liquid medium; as in cell suspension cultures. Explants, or callus derived from them are transferred to liquid medium and the cultures are then agitated on a mechanical shaker. The ensuing single cells and small cell clusters are used for a number of purposes in plant tissue culture; as in single cell cloning.

Centrifuge: An apparatus used for separating particles from suspension using centrifugal force. Balanced tubes containing the suspension are rapidly rotated causing sedimentation of particles to the bottom of the tubes (pelleting) based on their weight and the density of the suspending medium.

Chelate: A chemical compound with which metal atoms may be combined in order to prevent them from precipitating out of solution and so being unavailable to plants; as ethylenediamine tetra-acetic acid, disodium salt (Na_2EDTA) is complexed to iron (and other metal ions) in nutrient solutions used for plant tissue culture. The process is **chelation.**

Chemically defined medium: A nutrient medium for plant tissue culture in which all of the chemical components are fully known and stated. Quality (high purity) chemicals are utilized, and no undefined constituents are included.

Chemotherapeutant: A chemical used to pretreat diseased source plants prior to excision or incorporated into media to support some therapeutic objective; as malachite green or virazole (ribavirin) are used to eliminate virus in meristem tip culture. The process is **chemotherapy.**

Chimera or chimaera: A plant or tissue composed of more than one kind of genetic tissue. In a periclinal chimera one genotype occurs in a superficial layer, covering a genetically different core. In a mericlinal chimera one genotype occurs in a localized part of the plant and the rest is occupied by another genotype. In a sectorial chimera two genotypes share distinct sectors of the plant. Chimeras can occur naturally; be established artificially by grafting; or developed through somatic mutation by chemicals such as colchicine, or by other means in plant tissue cultures.

Choline chloride ($C_5H_{14}ClNO$, mw 139.63): An alkaloid, (B complex vitamin), occasionally added to plant tissue culture media. **Choline,** found in many plant organs, is the basic constituent of lecithin.

Chromic acid or chromium trioxide (CrO_3 mw 100.01): This compound exists only in solution and is made by mixing potassium dichromate and concentrated sulphuric acid. A dilute solution may be used to prepare tissues for hemocytometer (haemocytometer) counts to determine cell numbers in cell suspension cultures. Concentrated solutions were once used for cleaning new or dirty glassware but have now been supplanted by detergents.

Clonal multilication or clonal propagation: Vegetative (asexual) propagation from a single cell or plant. See **clone.**

Clone: 1. A basic category of cultivar. The original cultivar or variety. Not to be confused with source clone, indicating different originals within the clone. Members have a common origin, are the extension of a single cell (via mitosis) or plant and have been produced by vegetative means only. Genetic uniformity is accepted. A clone may have one or more sources. **2.** While the expectation is that members of a clone are both phenotypically and genotypically identical, this assumption is not always true and members may not be genetically or phenotypically equivalent (varients). the objective of much tissue culture propagation is to propagate very large numbers of selected plants with the same genotype. The process is **cloning.** The prefix meri reflects the explant used to initiate the clone (meristem tip source clone). In a **calliclone** cloning involves the callus stage. **3.** Specific DNA sequences are said to be **cloned** when isolated and propagated.

Closed continuous culture: A cell suspension culture with a continuous influx of fresh medium, maintained at constant volume by the efflux of spent medium. All cells are retained within the unit. See **continuous culture.**

Cocking, E. C. (1960): Obtained the first higher plant protoplasts using root cells subjected to fungal cellulase and demonstrated new cell wall regeneration on protoplasts from tomato fruit locule tissue.

Coconut milk or coconut water: Liquid endosperm from the center of the coconut seed. A complex, undefined addendum of variable quality and effects in some nutrient solutions (2-15%, v/v) for plant tissue culture. It has growth promoting effects and cell division factors. It is replaceable in some cases by cytokinins and/or sugar. It was first used by van Overbeek et al. (1941) to stimulate *Datura* embryo cultures.

Co-culture: The joint culture of two or more types of cells; as a plant cell and a microorganism or two types of plant cells; as is done in various dual culture systems or the nurse culture technique.

Complex substance: A complicated and undefined substance; as in some addenda to nutrient solutions used in plant tissue culture. Examples include protein hydrolysate, yeast or malt extracts, endosperm from corn or coconuts, juices like oranges or tomato juice and others.

Contaminant: An undesirable bacterial, fungal or algal microorganism accidentally introduced to a culture or culture medium. It may overgrow the plant cells or inhibit their growth through release of toxic metabolities. Rigorous exclusion of potential **contaminants** must be practiced in plant tissue culture.

Contaminate: To accidentally introduce a substance or organism **(contaminant)** into a medium or culture. The process is **contamination**.

Continuous culture: A cell suspension culture with a continuous influx of fresh medium, maintained at constant volume by the efflux of spent medium (closed continuous) or with the efflux of cells and spent medium (open continuous).

Control: **1.** The untreated plant or unchanged (standard) protocol or treatment for comparison with the experimental treatment. **2.** To direct or regulate; as in induction of organogenesis in cultures through hormone regulation.

Controlled environment: A chamber, room or situation in which the environmental parameters of light, temperature, and relative humidity are controlled. The partial pressure of gases may also be controlled.

Corn milk: Corn endosperm tissue. An undefined complex addendum to some plant tissue culture media.

Criticl concentration: The chemical concentration above or below which reaction or developmental process will not proceed.

Crown gall: A disease of plants in which tumors form. The causal agent is the bacterium, *Agrobacterium tumefaciens*. Gall tissue has been grown *in vitro*. A tumor inducing portion of the bacterial genome (the Ti plasmid) my be used experimentally as a genetic tool to incorporate (vector) genetic information into plant cells.

Cryoprotectant: An agent able to prevent freezing and thawing damage to cells as they are frozen or defrosted. These substances have high water solubility and low toxicity. They are classified either as permeating (glycerol and dimethyl sulfoxide) or non-permeating (sugars, dextran, ethylene glycol, polyvinyl pyrolidone and hydroxyethyl starch) agents.

Culture alteration: A persistent change in a cultured cell or tissue anatomy or physiology, including a change in one or more nutritional requirements or a change in its proliferative capacity.

Culture medium: A prepared nutrient solution (substrate) that may be chemically defined for growing plant tissues or other organisms *in vitro*.

Culture room: A controlled-environment room (light, temperature, relative humidity, often air conditioned, etc.) for incubation of plant cultures.

Culture tube: A test tube used to contain medium and an explant or culture derived from it, usually incubated in a controlled environment.

Culture vessel: A container used to hold medium and an explant or culture derived from it, usually incubated in a controlled environment.

Culture: **1.** A general term for the **cultivation** of microorganisms, animals, plants or their cells *in vivo* or *in vitro* especially in order to improve the breed. **2.** *In vitro* aseptic cultivation of microorganisms or of cells, tissues, or organs of plants, animals in or on prepared nutrient media under controlled, aseptic conditions.

Cybrid: A cell or plant cytoplasmic hybrid (heteroplast) with the nucleus of one and chtoplasmic organelles of another, or of both cells or plants.

Cysteine hydrochloride ($C_3H_7NO_2S.$ HCl mw 157.63): An occasionl, amino acid (cysteine) salt additive in plant tissue culture media. It is included primarily for its antioxidant properties.
Cytochimera or chromosomal chimera: Cells within a tissue possessing different chromosomal numbers, as when a callus consists of diploid and polyploid regions of cells.
Cytodifferentiation: A functional and/or morphological differentiation occurring in cells during ontogenesis, affecting their phenotype.
Cytolysis: Cell dissolution or disintegration.
Cytoplasmic hybrid or cybrid: A cell or plant hybrid (heteroplast) with the nucleus of one and the cytoplasmic organells of another or of both cells or plants.
Cytoplasmic variant: A maternally inherited change in a cellular trait.
Cytotoxic: A chemical or other agent toxic to cells.
De novo: (Latin: *fromthe beginning, anew*). Arising, sometimes spontaneously, from unknown or very simple precursors.
Decereration phase: the declining growth rate phase following the linear phase and preceeding the stationary phase in most batch suspention cultures.
Decontaminate: To free from **contamination** or surface sterilize.
Dedifferentiation: The resumption of meristematic activity by more or less mature cells through a reversal of the process of cell or tissue **differentiation**. Cell division leading to the formation of small, microvacuolate, isodiametric cells with prominent nuclei, that are capable of organized development; as when adventitious buds or roots develop on mature tissue.
Dehumidifier: An apparatus that removes moisture from the air.
Deionized water: Water that has been passed through an ion exchange device to remove soluble minerals and some organic salts. The process is **deionization.**
Deletion: 1. Omission, removal or cancellation of some factor. **2.** The lost portion of a chromosome or a nucleotide sequence in nucleic acid.
Derepression: The mechanism by which repression is alleviated; as when a **repressing** metabolite is removed, resulting in the increased level of a protein or enzyme.
Detergent: A cleaning agent; one of numerous synthetic cleaning preparations chemically different from soap. **Detergents** are commonly used to prepare work areas for aseptic plant tissue culture manipulations and to remove dirt and microorganisms from plant material prior to explantation.
Dewar flask: A double-walled glass flask used to keep liquids at other than ambient temperatures; as a thermos does.
Direct embryogenesis: Embryoid formation directly on the surface of zygotic or somatic embryos or on seedlng plant tissues in culture, without an intervening callus phase.
Direct organogenesis: Organ formation directly on the surface of relatively large intact explants, without an intervening callus phase.
Dispense: To give, deal or porton out; as nutrient medium is portioned into glassware for plant tissue culture.
Distilled water: Water that has been converted to steam and the vapour recondensed. This process removes dissolved materials, particulates and microorganisms. The process may be repeated (double distilled) for added purity, often in a glass apparatus (glass distilled) to minimize metal recontamination. Water of this purity is commonly used to make nutrient media for plant tissue culture.
DNA ligases: Enzymes which bind DNA fragments together
Donor plant (mother plant): The source that plant used for propagation, whether an explant, graft or cutting. Source plants used for micropropagation are usually poathogen-tested (disease-free).
Dry ice: Frozen (solid) carbon dioxide (CO_2). It is commonly used as a refrigerant.
Dual culture: A culture system that includes plant tissue and one organism (such as a nematode species) or microorrganism (such as a fungus). Dual cultures are used to study host-parasite interactions or in the production of axenic cultures for a variety of purposes. Usually the microorganism selected is an obligate parasite.
Embryo culture : 1. Denotes a culture in which the explant was n embryo. **Embryo cultures** have been used to obtain viable offspring from seeds with a tendency for embryo abortion

or when viable seed are limited in number. **2.** Cultures in which embryos are induced to form (embryogenesis) whether in suspension or on a variety of explants or cultures on solidified media. More correctly, these nonzygotic or somatic embryos are termed embryoids.

Enation: Outgrowth on a plant surface.

Enhancer element: These are short regions of DNA which have the effect of increasing the levels of transcription, but unlike promotors, they affect genes from chromosomal loci at a long distance.

Environmental chamber: A controlled environment cabinet (incubator) in which temperature, light quality, intensity and duration; and preferably also the relative humidity and airflow are controlled.

Enzyme: Any one of a number of specialized proteins produced in living cells, that speed the rate of specific chemical reactions, even at very low concentrations (organic catalyst), but is not used up in the reaction.

Epigenetic gene control: This is the new concept. It describes that the control of gene expression in higher eukaryotic organisms is related to the methylation of cytosine residues in gene coding sequence.

Epigenetic gene control: This is the new concept. It describes that the control of gene expression in higher eukaryotic organisms is related to the methylation of cytosine residues in gene coding sequence.

Equimolar: The same amount of solute per litre of solution, the same **molar** concentration.

Established culture : 1. Achievement of an aseptic viable explant, synonymous with Stage I culture (culture establishment) or transplant, synonymous with Stage IV culture (establishment in soil). **2.** A suspension culture subjected to several passages, adjusted so that cell number per unit time is consstant from subculture to subculture.

Ethylenediaminetetraacetic acid, disodium salt (Na_2EDTA, $C_{10}H_{14}N_2O_8Na_2.2H_2O$ mw 372.25): A chelating agent which reversibly binds positive ions such as iron, magnesium, etc. It is commonly added to plant tissue culture media to keep iron and other salts available by releasing them slowly into the medium as required.

Ex vitro: (Latin; *from glass*). Organisms removed from culture and transplanted, generally to soil or potting mixture.

Excise: To cut, sever or otherwise remove or extract an organ or a segment of tissue from a plant or plant part; as the surgical removal of shoot tips. The process is **excision.**

Explant donor: The source plant or mother plant from which the explant used to initiate a culture is taken.

Explant: The excised plant portion used to initiate a tissue culture.

Factor: 1. A condition, influence or constituent to be taken into account. **2.** A genetic character determinant (gene).

Field test: An evaluative test whereby the field performance of experimental plants is assessed in comparison to controls.

Filter sterilize: to sterilize by passing a solution through a porous material capable of separating out suspended microbes or their spores; as heat-labile components of nutrient media are sterilized.

Fixative: A compound that stabilizes, sets or **fixes** other compounds or structures securely so that their structural integrity is retained; as the process of **fixation** utilizes chemical agents to permanently prepare cells or tissues for microscopy.

Floccule: An aggregation (coalescence) of microorganisms or colloidal particles floating in or on a liquid. **Flocculation** is seen in some contaminated liquid media appearing as a cloud.

Folic acid ($C_{19}H_{19}N_7O_6$ mw 441.40): A member of the vitamin B group (Bc). It is also known as vitamin M. It is present in green leaves and has some coenzyme activities. It is occasionally added to plant tissue culture media.

Freeze-dry or lyophilize: To dry in a frozen state under vacuum; as tissues are **freeze-dried** to obtain a dry weight or to preserve them for analysis.

Fresh weight or wet weight: The weight of a plant or plant part including the water content.

Fusogen: A fusion-inducing agent used for protoplast agglutination in somatic hybridization studies; as is polyethylene glycol.

Gametoclone: A plant regenerated from a tissue culture originating from gametic tissue.

Gelatin: A glutinous, proteinaceous material produced by boiling, which partially hydrolyzes the collagen, of animal connective tissues. It is sometimes used to **gel** or solidify nutrient solutions for plant tissue culture. Other **gelling** agents, specifically agars, are usually preferred.

Gelrite: The brand name of a synthetic (*Pseudomonas*-derived) refined polysaccharide used as a gelling agent and agar substitute.

Generation time: The time between successive generations of cells or organisms within a population.

Genetic engineering or recombinant DNA technology: Technology involving man-made changes in the genetic constitution of cells (apart from selective breeding). This technology usually employs a vector (such as the Ti plasmid of *Agrobacterium tumefaciens*) for transferring useful genetic information from a donor organism into a cell or organism that does not possess it. Genetic engineering has mny potential uses.

Genetic selection: Selection of genes, cells (cell selection), clones, etc., by man within populations or between populations or species. The usual purpose is to alter a specific phenotypic character. Such selection usually results in differential success rates of the various genotypes, reflecting many variables including selection pressure and genetic variability in populations.

Genetic transformation: The transfer of extracellular DNA (genetic information) among and between species; as, for example, with the use of bacterial or viral vectors.

Genetic variation: Differences in individuals derived from the same genotype in distincton to differences caused by the environment. **Genetic variance** denotes the proportion of pohenotypic variance caused by differences in the genetic make-up of an individual.

Genome: The basic haploid chromosome set of an individual; the sum of its **genes.**

Genotoxic: Carcinogenic; toxic to the chromosomes.

Geotaxis: Plant orientation with respect to gravity.

Germplasm or germ plasm: 1. The reproductive body tissues distinct from somatic (nonreproductive tissues). The genetic material, basis of heredity of an organism, passed on through previous generations. **2.** An individual representing a type of species or culture that may bve held in a repository for agronomic, historic (or other) reasons.

Gibberellic acid (gibberellin A_3 or GA_3, $C_{19}H_{22}O_6$ mw 346.37): One of the **gibberellins,** a group of growth hormones promoting cell division and elongation. The first of the group to be isolated and the most widely used gibberellin in plant tissue culture. Isolated from the fungal pathogen *gibberella fujikuroi.* It dissolves in base (ca. 1M KOH or NaOH).

Guha, S. and S. C. Maheshwari (1966): Were among the first to obtrain haploid (n) plantlets from another culture.

Gyrase: It is Type-II topoisomerase that catalyzes conversion of relaxed DNA to a superhelical form and requires ATP.

Haberlandt, G.: An inspirational pioneer botanist who was the first to attempt to culture plant cells at the turn of the 20th century. He predicted the existence of hormones that would stimulate cell division (auxins) and suggested the possibility of exploiting the totipotentiality of plant cells.

Hemicellulase: An enzyme from *Aspergillus niger*, available as a commercial preparation, that degrades hemicellulose to galactose.

HEPA filter: An acronym for **high efficiency particulate air filter.** A filter capable of screening out particles larger than 0.3 m. They are used in laminar air flow cabinets (hoods) for sterile transferr work.

Heterograft or xerograft: An interspecific graft. The likelihood of success of this graft is proportional to the degree of relatedness between the donor and recipient.

Heteroplasmon or heteroplast: A cell with a mixture of two types of cytoplasm (cytoplasmic hybrid); cell with foreign organelles.

Hexitol: A sic carbon sugar alcohol, such as (meso-, myo-, or i-) inositol.

Hood: Laminar air flow cabinet.

Hydrate: To add or incorporate water. The process is **hydration.**

Hypertrophy: An abnormal increase in cell size causing irregular swelling oir growth. Hypertrophy is usually a disease or other stress-induced response.

Hypochlorite: A salt of hypochlorous acid **(sodium hypochlorite, potassium hypochlorite**

or **calcium hypochlorite).** All are oxidizing agents used for disinfecting and for bleaching.

In situ: In the natural, original place or position; as in the location of the explant on the mother plant prior to excision.

In vitro: (Latin = *in glass*). Experimentation on organisms or portions thereof in glassware or culture; growing under artificial conditions as in tissue culture. The antonym of *in vivo*.

In vivo: (Latin = *in life*) Experimentation on organisms under natural conditions within intact living organisms. the antonym of *in vitro*.

Incubate: To maintain under conditions favorable for development, often in an **incubator**. The process is **incubation.**

Incubator: An apparatus providing controlled environmental conditions, (light, photoperiod, temperature, humidity, etc.) suitable for **(incubating)** plants or plant cultures. This term is sometimes used as synonym for cabinet (growth cabinet) but usually implies a greater degree of environmental control.

Indirect embryogenesis: Embryoid formation on callus tissues derived from zygotic or somatic emtryos, seedling plant or other tissues in culture. The antonym is direct embryogenesis.

Indirect organogenesis: Organ formation on callus tissues derived from explants. the antonym is direct organogenesis.

Induction media: 1. Media that can induce organs or other structures to form. **2.** Media that will cause variation or mutation in the tissues exposed to it.

Infestation: Occupation by threatening numbers of insects, mites or potential disease agents; as mite **infestations** in incubators. An **infesting** organism can cause contamination of tissue cultures. This should not be confused with infected, as infection is not necessarily implied.

Infrared gas analyzer (IRGA): An instrument for measuring the proportion of a particular gas in a mixture; as changes in CO_2 concentration can be monitored to evaluate a plant's photosynthetic or respiratory activity.

Innoculum: 1. Material introduced **(inoculated)** onto or into a host or medium. **2.** Potential inculum implies that it is infective and may by chance result in natural **inoculation** of a host.

Inoculate: 1. To deliberately introduce something into; as **inoculum** is placed into (or onto) medium to initiate a culture. This process is **inoculation,** but should not be confused with contaminate. **2.** Vaccinate.

Inositol; myo, meso, or i-inositol or hexahydroxycyclohexane ($C_6H_{12}O_6$ mw 180.16): A widely distributed sterioisomeric sugar alcohol in plants and essential in animals. Inositol is included by many in the B complex vitamin group. It is involved in the synthesis of phospholipids, cell wall pectins and membrane systems in cell cytoplasm. It is commonly added to the nutrient medium used for plant tissue culture (ca. 100 mg/1) for its growth promoting effects.

Introns: Sequences in DNAs which are in fact transcribed into mRNAs but are subsequently split out and there fore form no permanent constituents of the mRNAs (only in eucaryotes)

Irradiance: The total radiation on an exposed surface.

Irradiate: 1. To illuminate. **2.** To emit or expose to waves of light, heat or nuclear emissions. **3.** To treat by exposure to radiation. The process is **irradiation.**

Isograft or syngraft: A graft or transplant among isogenic (genetically identical) individuals; as on the same organism.

Isolation medium: A medium suitable for explant survival and development. It may be synonymous with Stage I medium, or contain antioxidant(s), reduced hormone concentration, bacterial indicators or other addenda, and precedes Stage I culture.

Jiffy pots: A brand name for peat pots that are sometimes used for ex vitro transplantation.

Kinases: They catalyze the transfer of the α-phosphate of a nucleoside 5'-triphosphate to the 5'-OH terminus of a DNA or RNA molecule.

Kinin: The original class name for substances promoting cell-division to which the prefix *cyto* has been added **(cytokinins)** to distinguish them from **kinins** in animals systems.

Laminar air flow cabinet or hood: A structure in which a uniform flow of filtered air prevents settling of particles in the work area. The air is filtered through prefilter (furnace-filter quality), then a high efficiency particulate air (HEPA) filter that strains out particles greater than 0.3 m. These hoods are commonly employed for aseptic plant tissue culture manipulations and are designed to accommodate one to the several persons, depending on the model.

Layering: 1. Covering stems, runners or stolons with soil causing adventitious roots to form at the nodes enabling propagation by rooted cuttings. This procedure is used commercially to propagate many plants, such as the brambls. **2.** *In vitro* layering involves the horizontal placement on agar of cultured shoots (with or without leaves) or nodal segments to promote axillary bud proliferation.

Lecithin: A naturally occurring, choline-containing phospholipid present in animal and plant tissue. Chemically **lecithins** are similar to fat, but they also contain phosphorus and nitrogen.

Ligases: They catalyze formation of phosphodiester linkages between DNA chain segments.

Ligation: Direct linkage of nucleic acid fragments

Limiting requirement or factor: An environmental variable whose absolute levels at given time limits the growth or other activity of an organism.

Linear phase: The constant increase in cell number following the exponential growth phase and proceeding the deceleration phases in most batch suspension cultures.

Liquid culture: The culture of plant cells on liquid medium, in suspension or on supports. Cultures are either held steady (stationary culture) or are shaken (agitated culture or shake culture).

Liquid medium: Medium not solidified with a gelling agent. **Liquid media** are used for suspension cultures and for a wide range of research purposes. They are also useful for Stage I culture in some micropropagation protocols. Usually a support structure or wick is used to hold the tissue above the nutrient medium.

Lysis: Cell rupture or destruction, as through enzymatic action.

Macerase: A brand name for pectinase. Pectinase is useful in the isolation of intact cells and protoplasts of higher plants.

Macerate: To disintegrate or separate tissues through cutting, soaking, enzymatic or other action, resulting in cell dissociation.

Magnetic stirrer: An apparatus used for stirring solutions. A magnetic stir bar is placed at the bottom of the container and is twirled in the solution that requires mixing by an electrically driven, rotating magnet below the platform of the apparatus.

Malachite green ($C_{22}H_{25}N_2Cl$ mw 364.66): A chemical used as a seed disinfectant in

Mannose ($C_6H_{12}O_6$ mw 180.16): A hexose component of many polysaccharides and mannitol. It is occasionally employed as a carbohydrate source in plant tissue culture media.

Maternal inheritance: Inheritance controlled by extrachromosoml (cytoplasmic) hereditary determinants.

MDA: microdroplet array technique.

Medium formulation: One of many available, usually derived formulas that are used in plant tissue culture. The formulas commonly contain the microelements and microelements (high and low salt formulas are available), some vitamins (B vitamins, inositol), hormones (auxin, cytokinin and sometimes gibberellin), a carbohydrate source (usually sucrose or glucose) and often other substances such as amino acids (the most common addition is glycine) or complex growth factors. Media may be liquid or solidified with agar, the pH is adjusted (ca. 5-6) and the solution is sterilized (usually by filtration or autoclaving). Some formulations are very specific in the kind of explant or plant species that can be maintained some are very general.

Medium: The substrate for plant growth; as nutrient solution, soil, sand, etc. This is a general term for the liquid or solidified formulation upon which plant cells tissues or organs develop in plant tissue culture.

Mercuric chloride or mercury bichloride ($HgCl_2$ mw 271.52): This compound was once commonly used as an antiseptic and fixing agent (0.05-0.10percentage) for plant material. However, it is highly toxic and is now little used for this purpose.

Mericlinal: A meristem tip source clone. This term can be synonymous with calli clone or may not involve callus.

Meristem culture: The culture of meristems; meristematic dome tissue without adjacent leaf primordia or stem tissue. In practice this usually means meristem tip culture. This may more generally imply the culture of meristemoidal regions of plants or of meristematic growth (associated with or sharing the characteristics of the meristem) in culture.

Meristem tip culture: Cultures derived from meristem tip explants. They are excised for virus elimination or axillary shoot proliferation purposes, less commonly for callus production.

Meristem tip: A common explant comprised of the meristem (meristematic dome) and usually one pair of leaf primordia. Also refers to apical (apical meristem tip) or lateral (lateral or axillary meristem tip) origin. The term meristem tip is often confused with the term shoot tip, which is much larger and usually has more immature leaves and some stem tissue.

Meristemming: the utilization of or process of utilizing meristem tips for explants. This term is often used to refer to micropropagation via axillary shoot proliferation.

Meristemoid: A cluster of small, isodiametric **meristematic** cells with a **meristem**, or cultured tissue, with the potentialk for developmental (totipotential) growth. These cells have a dense microvacuolated cytoplasm and a high nucleo-cytoplasmic ratio. They may give rise to plant organs (shoots, roots) or entire plantlets in culture.

Methionine (Met, $C_5H_{11}NO_2S$ mw 149.21): An amino acid precursor in ethylene synthesis and occasionally added to plant tissue culture media.

Methyl methanesulfonate (MMS, $C_2H_6SO_3$ mw 110.13): A frequently used, very potent chamical mutagen which acts by adding methyl groups to guanine and subsequently causes base pairing errors as it binds to adenine.

Methylases: They catalyze transfer of methyl groups from donar *S*-adenosyl-L-methionine (AdoMet) to specific bases of acceptor DNA molecules.

Microclimate or microhabitat: The climate in the immediate vicinity or surrounding an organism or its parts.

Microcutting: A tiny cutting; as an explant such as a meristem tip removed for culture with the use of a dissecting microscope.

Microdroplet array or multiple drop array (MDA) or hanging droplet technique: Introduced by Potrykus, Harms and Lorz (1979), this technique is used to evaluate large numbers of media modifications, employing small quantities of medium into which are placed small numbers of cells. Droplets of liquid culture (medium and suspended cells or protoplasts) are arranged on the lid of a petri dish, inverted over the bottom half of the dish containing a solution with a lower osmotic pressure, and the dish is sealed. The cells or protoplasts form a monolayer at the droplet meniscus and can easily be examined.

Micrograft: An *in vitro* graft. This procedure involves placing a meristem tip or shoot tip explant onto a decapitated rootstock, that has been grown aseptically from seed or micropropaged. The purpose may vary, from virus elimination, using meristem tips and virus-free rootstocks, to viral assays or to erxpedite grafting that is usually done in the greenhouse. The explanted scion is placed directly on the cambium of the severed stock or inserted into a T or inverted T-shaped epidermal incision onthe stock. This technique has been used to eliminate viruses, viroids and mycoplasmas from Citrus species.

Micromole (M): One millionth (0,000001) of mole (10^{-6} M). The unit of concentration used for microelements, vitamins, hormones and some other organic addenda used in plant tissue culture media.

Micropropagation: Refers to propagation in culture by axillary or adventitious means. It is a general term for vegetative (asexual) *in vitro* propagation. It sometimes refers specifically to axillary bud proliferation.

Minimum inoculum size: The smallest inoculum that can be successfully used for subculture.

Mitotic index (MI): The ratio of nuclei undergoing mitosis (including prophase) to total nuclei. MI = (Number of nuclei in mitosis/Total number of nuclei examined in the sample) X 100. A MI of 0.3 means that 30% of cells in the population are observed in mitosis.

Mitotic index (MI): The ratio of nuclei undergoing mitosis (including prophase) to total nuclei. MI = (Number of nuclei in mitosis/Total number of nuclei examined in the sample) X 100. A MI of 0.3 means that 30% of cells in the population are observed in mitosis.

Mitotic nondisjunction: Occurs when sister chromatids fail to migrate to opposite poles of the cell during mitotic anaphase. The result is daughter cells with hyperploid and hypoploid chromosome counts.

Monoculture: A one-crop agriculture system. An intensified monoculture could refer to a clonal (one genotype) agricultural system.

Mononucleotide: A nucleic acid basic-building-block. Composed of a pentose, a phosphoric acid plus a purine or pyrimidine base.

MS: An abbreviation for the **Murashige, T. and F. Skoog (1962)** medium formulation.

Mutability: the propensity of an individual's genes or genotype to undergo heritable mutation.

Mutagen: A chemical or physical treatment or agent capable of producing genetic mutation. Causes insertion, deletion or alteration of a base or part of the nucleic acid chain (DNA). Artificial mutations can be induced in cells using chemicals or ionizing radiation. The process is **mutagenesis**. Electromagnetic and particle radiation, such as UV, X-rays and b particles all increase mutation frequency. So do chemical mutagens such as ethylmethanesulphonate, acridine, nitrous oxide and many others

Naphthaleneacetic acid: 1-naphthaleneacetic acid.

Natural complex: A complicated, non-synthetic, often undefined addendum in plant tissue culture media, such as orange or tomato juice or coconut milk.

Neoplasm: Localized cell multiplication or tumor; a collection of cells which have undergone genetic transformation. These cells differ in structure and function from the original cell type.

Neoteny: The occurrence (retention) of juvenile characters in the adult state or vice versa.

Newcommer's fluid: A fixative used in chromosome analysis composed of 6 parts isopropyl: 3 parts propionic acid: 1 part petroleum ether:1 part acetone: 1 part dioxane (with or without ferric acetate).

Niacin or nicotinic aid ($C_6H_5NO_2$ mw 123.11): Vitamin B_3 forming part of a respiratory coenzyme. It is a common micronutrient addition to plant tissue culture media. It is sometimes also known as vitamin PP.

Niacinamide or nicotinamide ($C_6H_6N_2O$ mw 122.12): An amide of niacin occasionally added to plant tissue culture media.

Nitsch, J. P. and C. Nitsch (1969): Developed a now widely used plant tissue culture medium formulation **NN**, for use in anther culture.

NN: An abbreviation for the **Nitsch, J. P. and C. Nitsch (1969)** medium formulation.

NOA: (2-naphthalenyloxy) acetic acid.

Nobecourt, J. R. (1937): was among the first to describe the prolonged culture of carrot callus.

Nucellar embryony: The process by which individual cells of the nucellus give rise to somatic embryos (embryoids). Plants on which this occurs naturally are considered good candidates for tissue culture of somatic embryoids.

Nucleases: They catalyze hydrolysis of the phospho-diester bonds of polynucleotides.

Nucleo-cytoplasmic ratio: The ratio of cell nuclear to cytoplasmic volume. This ratio is elevated in meristematic cells and low in differentiated cells.

Nutrient film technique (NFT): Hydroponic plant growth whereby plant roots are suspended in shallow, slowly circulating nutrient solutions delivered as a continuous film of liquid rather than in bursts of liquid.

Nutrient gradient: A diffusion gradient of nutrients and gases is set up in tissues where only a portion of the tissue is in contact with the medium. This is common in callus culture and causes differential growth rates and senescent regions of callus. Similarly, diffusion gradients of nutrients are set up in the medium adjacent to the tissue. Gradients are less likely to form in liquid media.

Ontogeny: The developmental (**ontogenetic**) life history of an organism, its development from fertilized egg (zygote) to seed-forming adult (reproductive phase), with emphasis on embryonic development.

Open continuous culture: A cell suspension culture with a continuous influx of fresh medium, maintained at constant volume by the efflux of cells and spent medium.

Operator: Regulatory section in a nucleic acid with binding capacity for a repressor protein for blocking the synthesis of mRNAs.

Organ culture: The growth in aseptic culture of plant organs such as roots or shoots, beginning with organ primordi or segments and maintaining the characteristics of the organ.

Organized growth: The *in vitro* development of organized explants such as meristem tips or shoot tips, floral buds or organ primordia, or their de novo formation from **unorganized** tissues.

Organogenesis: The initiation (de novo) and growth of organs (roots and shoots, usually) from cells or tissues; as in organ culture. Organs may form on the surface of explants (direct organogenesis) or upon an intervening callus phase (indirect organogenesis).

Organoid: An anomalous organ-like structure formed in culture; as on leaves, roots or callus.

Ortet: The original mother plant or donor plant from which vegetatively propagated plants are derived.

Osmium tetroxide or osmic acid (OsO_4 mw 254.20): A fixing agent used to prepare tissues for electron microscopy.

Osmolarity: The total molar concentration of the solutes affecting the **osmotic** potential of a solution or nutrient medium.

Ovule culture: A culture derived from an explanted ovule; which may be fertilized in culture (*in vitro* fertilization). This technique is used to study development of zygotes and young embryos and is sometimes used to rescue embryos susceptible to abortion when embryo culture is not possible.

Oxygenase: An enzyme enabling an organism or system to utilize atmospheric oxygen.

Packed cell volume (PCV): A quantitative method of estimating cell growth. It is based on the total cell volume in an aliquot of suspension culture. The aliquot is centrifuged for 5 minutes at 200 g after which the packed cell volume is expressed as a percentage of the aliquot volume.

Panicle culture: Aseptic culture of grain panicle segments, usually in an effort to induce microspore development.

Pantothenic acid ($C_9H_{17}NO_5$ mw 219.23): Also known as vitamin B_5 it is of wide occurrence in most plant and animal tissue, is essential for cell growth and is an important coenzyme in fat metabolism. It is added to some plant tissue culture media as the calcium salt.

Papain: A water soluble proteolytic enzyme (protease) extracted from papaya fruit and used especially as a meat tenderizer.

Paper raft technique: A technique developed by W. H. Muir (1953) to promote development of single cells taken from suspension cultures in which cells are placed onto filter paper squares set on actively growing callus (nurse tissue). Growth factors and nutrients from the callus tissue diffuse through the filter paper, promoting cell growth and development.

Para-amino-benzoic acid (PABA, $C_7H_7NO_2$ mw 137.12): An occasional addition (vitamin Bx) to plant tissue culture media.

Parahormone: A substance with hormone-like properties that is not a secretory product; such as ethylene or carbon dioxide.

Parasexual hybridization: Refers to genetic recombination by means other than through fertilization of germ cells (parasexual) leading to hybrid cells or individuals; as in hybrid cells or plants derived from somatic cell fusion.

Particle radiation: Refers to - particles (positively charged) and B-particles (negatively charged), electrons, protons and neutrons. These particles are used to produce mutant cells or organisms in plant tissue culture.

Parts per million(ppm): This term has largely been replaced by the equivalent mg/l of solution or mu1/1 for liquids or gasses.

Passage number: The number of subculture intervals. Culture age is a function of passage number and the culture dilution ratio.

Passage time; The interval between subcultures or the culture period.

Pasteur pipette: A causal agent of a disease; as a **pathogenic** fungus, bacterium or virus.

PCV: packed cell volume.

Pectinase: An enzyme that degrades **pectin,** the adhesive material that cement cells together. It is used alone or with other enzymes to digest the polygalacturonic acid of plant cell walls (to sugar and galacturonic acid) in protoplast production.

Peptide: A compound consisting of two or more amino acids covalently linked. **Peptides** with three or more amino acids are **polypeptides.**

Periclinal chimera: Refers to a condition in which geno-typically or cytoplasmically different tissues are arranged in concentric layers.

Periclinal chimera: Refers to a condition in which geno-typically or cytoplasmically different tissues are arranged in concentric layers.

pH: A measurement of the degree of acidity or alkalinity of a solution. The negative log of the hydrogen ion concentration, in moles perr litre (M/1). On the pH scale from 0-14, there is a 10 fold difference for each unit of change of pH. The lower the value, the more alkaline (more hydroxyl ions it contains). Most culture media are adjusted in the range pH 4-6 using 1M NaOH or HCl.

Phenocopy: A non-hereditary phenotypic change that is environmentally induced, during a limited developmental phase of an organism, that mimics the effect of a known genetic mutation.

Phenolic oxidation: The process by which many plant species which contain phenolics blacken through oxidatin when they are wounded; as *in vitro*, soon after subculture. This may lead to growth inhibition or, in severe cases, to tissue necrosis and death. Antioxidants are incorporated into the sterilizing solution or isolation medium to prevent or reduce oxidative browning.

Phenols or phenolics: A class of organic compounds with hydroxyl group(s) attached to the benzene ring forming esters, ethers and salts. **Phenolic** substances may bleed from newly explanted tissues, oxidizing to form colored compounds visible in nutrient media or on the filter wicks supporting the tissue.

Phloretic acid: A phenolic acid formed by the oxidation of a hydroxyl (OH) of 1,3,5-trihydroxybenzene. An occasional constituent of some plant tissue culture media.

Photoheterotroph: A photosynthetic organism that requires an organic hydrogen source. The condition is **photoheterotrophy.**

Photometer: An instrument for measuring the luminous intensity of light sources.

Phytokinin: An absolute term for cytokinin.

Phytotron: A controlled environment building or chamber for studying plant growth under defined conditions.

Plant tissue culture: A general term encompassing the *in vitro* culture of plant cells, tissues, organs and whole plantlets.

Plantlet: A shoot, sometimes exclusively a rooted shoot, growing in culture or derived from culture.

Plasmid: Annular nucleic acid in cells outside the central chromosome with a lower molecular weight than the central chromosome; bearer of nonessential additional information, *e.g.*, sex factors (F factors) and resistance factors (R ractors), plasmids and viral nucleic acids with known functions such aş resistance or sequences are denoted by trivial abbreviation derived from their function or origin, *e.g.*, SV 40 for simian virus, p^{BR322} for a plasmid imparting resistance to antibiotics.

Plasmotype: A cell type displaying features which are expressions of cytoplasmic, rather than nuclear inheritance.

Pleiotropy: The condition in which several characteristics are effected by a single gene.

Pollen culture: The culture of pollen grains, which germinate *in vitro*. Such cultures may eventually form monoploid callus, from which shoots or embryoids develop into monoploid plants.

Poly(A) adding enzymes: They attach AMP residues, from ATP, to the 3', 5' phosphodiester bond.

Polyethylene glycol (PEG) or carbowax: A fusion-inducing agent (fusogen) for agglutinating protoplasts, which is used in somatic hybridization studies. This compound is also sometimes used in media as a non-metabolite osmoticum and is available in various molecular weights, ranging from ca. 200 to 6,000.

Polygalacturonic acid: A long chain sugar acid polymer composed of galacturonic acid and hexose subunits.

Polygenes: Systems of genes associated with quantitative character variation in which each gene individually effects the phenotype in a minor way.

Polymerases: They catalyze addition of nucleoside triphosphates to 3'-OH terminals of single strands of preexiting polynucleotides (primers) with release of pyrophosphate.

Polypropylene: A strong, flexible, transparent thermoplastic formed by the polymerization of propylene. It is used in many labware products.

Population density: Cell number per unit medium area or medium volume.

Potassium hypochlorite (KClO mw 90.6): A water-soluble bleaching or disinfecting agent used in plant tissue culture practices.

Potato extract: A common (undefined) organic addendum to plant tissue culture media in monocot and another culture systems.

Preadaptation: In possession of advanageous characters enabling an organism to be well suited **(adapted)** to environmental conditions previously unknown to it.

Precipitin test or microprecipitin test: A serological assay in which visible particulates **(precipitates)** form when soluble antigen and antibody react. This precipitin reaction detects and identifies antigens.

Prefilter: A coarse filter (furnace filter) such as those used in a laminar air flow cabinet to screen out large particles before air is forced through a much finer filter (HEPA filter).

Premix: To mix before use; as nutrient mixtures are commercially available as dry powders of pre-weighed ingredients, which are put into solution when required.

Primary culture: 1. May be synonymous with Stage I culture. **2.** A recent culture not yet subcultured for the first time.

Probe DNA: A radioactively labelled (usually ^{32}P) DNA molecule used to detect complementary-sequence nucleic acid molecules by molecular hybridization. To localize the probe DNA sequence and reveal the complementary hybridization sequence auto-radiography is often used.

Promeristem or protomeristem: The embryonic meristem-containing organ initials or foundation cells.

Propagule: The form or portion of an organism used for reproduction or propagation; as new shoots or callus derived from explants are subdivided into **propagules** and re-culturd for further multiplication.

Protein digest: The enzymatic hydrolysis of proteins to yield their building block components, amino acids and short chain peptides (chains consisting of two to several amino acids normally without enzymatic function).

Protein stability: Protein, in eukaryotic cells have very diverse half-lives ranging from a few minutes to several hours. The degradation of unnecessary proteins is dependent upon the small protein ubiquitin, which when conjugated to proteins leads to their rapid degradation.

Protoclone: Distinct phenotypic regenerates from a plant protoplast. A clone initiated from a protoplast or protoplast-fusion product.

Protocol: A sequence of activities, techniques or procedures linked to achieve a specific goal; as a schedule for protoplast preparation.

Protoplast culture: The isolation and culture of plant protoplasts by mechanical means or by enzymatic digestion of plant tissues or organs, or cultures derived from these. Protoplasts are utilized for selectio or hybridization at the cellular level and for a variety of other purposes.

Protoplast fusion: The coalescence of the plasmalemma and cytoplasm of two or more **protoplasts** in contact with one another. Initial adhesion is a random process but coalescence may be promoted in various ways (induced fusion). When adhesion occurs between adjacent protoplasts during enzymatic wall degradation or between freshly isolated protoplasts in the absence of a fusion agent, it is termed spontaneous fusion.

Pure culture: Axenic culture.

Pure line: All cell or individual members are homozygous for one or more characters or genes and will give rise to more cells or organisms with the character(s) under consideration.

Quiescent: Quiet, at rest, not necessarily dormant and having the potential for resumed activity; can apply to cells unlikely to divide, the non-meristematic cells.

Radiation: Rays of heat, light or particles in wave form.

Ramet: The vegetatively propagated offspring of an ortet. An individual of a clone.

Reaction norm: The range of phenotypic responses of a particular genotype in response to the environmental influences.

Reciprocating shaker: A plateform shaker with a back and forth action used for agitating culture flasks at variable speeds.

Recombinant DNA technology: genetic engineering.

Recombinant DNA: Genetic material with novel gene sequences produced by cross-overs, chromosome reassortment, by other natural means or through genetic engineering.

Reconstructed cell or recon: A viable cell hybrid, cybrid or a transformed cell resulting from genetic engineering.

Reculture or subculture: The aseptic transfer of a culture or a portion (division when necessary) of that culture (inoculum) to fresh nutrient medium.

Redifferentiation:L Cell or tissue reversal in differentiation from one type to another type of cell or tissue.

Reinert, J. (1958): Among the first to observe adventative embryogenesis in cell cultures of carrot.

Rejuvenation: 1. Synonymous with dedifferentiation. **2.** Treatment that leads to culture invogoration (such as subculture) or revival (dormancy breaking).

Repelcote: The brand name of a material (dimethyl dichloro-silane) used to coat glassware (soda glass); for tissue culture containers and for other purposes.

Repression: Altered gene expression resulting in the failure of a specific protein synthesis.

Repressor: Regulatory protein with binding capacity for operators.

Resistance transfer factor: A plasmid, present in certain types of bacteria such as E. coli, that can impart resistance to antibiotics in animals exposed to them.

Resistivity: The degree of resistance (in ohm-cm or ohm-m) or interference to the flow of an electrical current or the movement of particles from place to place. A measure of water purity; the purer the water, the greater its **resistivity.** The reciprocal of conductivity.

Restriction endonucleases: Enzymes which specifically cleave DNAs at a definite information-bearing sequence of nucleotides and thereby permit an insertion of foreign sequences. Restriction endonucleases are named in genetic engineering by trivial cell, *e.g.*, EcoRI from *Escherichia coli* R Y 13, HindII from *Haemophilus influenza* Hpall from *Haemophilus parainfluenzq* or psti from *providencia stuartii*

Reverse transcriptase: It catalyze transcription of RNA nucleotide sequence into complementary DNA (cDNA).

Reverse transcriptase: It catalyze transcription of RNA nucleotide sequence into complementary DNA (cDNA).

Rhizogenesis: Root formation and growth; as in root development de novo from callus.

Rhodamine isothiocyanate or tetramethylrhodamine isothiocyanate ($C_{25}N_3SO_3H_{21}$ mw 536.10): A dye used to stain plant protoplasts in the identification of fusion products.

Root culture: Isolated root tips of apical produce *in vitro* root systems with indeterminate growth habits. These were among the first kinds of plant tissue cultures (White, 1934) and remain important research tools in the study of developmental phenomena; mycorrhizal; symbiotic and plant-parasitic relationships.

Rotary shaker: A platform shaker with a circular motion used for agitating culture flasks at vaariable speeds.

Rotating culture or rotator: A wheel-like device for slowly (ca. 1 rpm) rotating and gently agitating cultures, usually in a vertical plane.

S phase: The cell cycle phase during which DNA synthesis occurs.

Schiff's reagent: A mixture of pararosaniline. HCl (an analine dye) and sodium bisulfite ($NaHSO_3$), used in staining chromosomes and nuclear material. See **Feulgen's test.**

Scion or cion: The portion of a bud or shoot used for grafting onto another plant (the stock).

Screen house: A metal or plastic mesh enclosure similar in function to a greenhouse but with more exposure to the elements.

Scutellum: That part of the cotyledon in Gramineae (grasses) that absorbs food from the endosperm at germination. An explant source for plant tissue culture.

Selection culture: Utilizes difference(s) in environmental conditions or more usually in culture medium composition, such that preferred variant cells or cell lines (presumptive or putative mutants) are favored over other variants or the wild-type.

Selection pressure: The measure of the effectiveness of natural or experimental selection in altering the genetic composition of a population.

Selection unit: Single cells or small clusters, units of optimum size for isolating and regenerating variants or mutants;l the minimum number of cells effective in the screening process.

Semicontinuous culture: The maintenance of cells in a culture vessel in an actively dividing state by periodically draining the medium and adding fresh medium.

Serial float culture: Sunderland's (1977-1979) technique of floating anthers on liquid mediumand subculturing them to new medium at several day intervals and anther dehiscence, pollen release and development occur, increasing anther productivity.

Shake culture: An agitated suspension culture. Usually a flask (commonly an Erlenmeyer flask) containing the culture is attached to a horizontal or platform shaker, or agitated with a magnetic stirrer, to provide adequate aeration for cells in the liquid medium.

Shakeror platform shaker: A platform fitted with clips for grasping flasks (usually Erlenmeyer flasks), or with surfaces suitable for attaching flasks, with set or variable speed control. It is desirable to adjust the **shaking** speed for gentle, even agitation of suspension cultures.

Shoot tip graft or micrograft: The grafting of a very small shoot tip or meristem tip onto a prepared seedling or mcropropagated rootstock in culture. Meristem tip grafting is used for *in vitro* virus elimination with Citrus and for other plants as an alternative to grafting in the greenhouse.

Sodium hypochlorite (NaOH mw 74.44): A frequently used plant tissue sterilant at 0.5-2% w/v. The usual source is dilute (10-21% v/v) commercial laundry bleach, sometimes with surfactant is common. Tissue damage may occur if contact with tissue is prolonged. Thorough washing with sterile water generally follows treatment.

Somaclone: A plant regenerated from a tissue culture originating from somatic tissue.

Somatic cell embryogenesis: The production of embryos from somatic cells of explants (direct embryogenisis) or by induction on callus formed by explants (indirect embrygenesis). These two processes may not be materially different in results.

Somatic cell variant or embryoid: An organized embryonic structure morphologically similar to a zygotic embryo but initiated from somatic (non-zygotic) cells. These develop into plantlets *in vitro* through developmental processes that are similar to those of zygotic embryos.

Somatic hybrid: A cell or plant product of somatic cell fusion; as the result of cell or protoplast fusion and implying genomic integration. The process is **somatic hybridization.**

Somatic mutation: Mutation occurring in vegetative cells or tissues.

Somatic organogenesis: The production of shoots, roots or other organs on somatic tissues of explants (direct organogenesis) or by induction on callus formed by explant (indirect organogenesis).

Spontaneous fusion: Uninduced protoplast fusion which may occur between freshly isolated protoplasts or following adhesion of adjacent cells during enzymatic cell wall degradation.

Spontaneous variation: The variation in plant populations derived fromtissue cultures not exposed to mutagens but occurring as a result of the culture conditions.

Stages of culture (I-IV): Stage I: Aseptic explantation or establishment of the explant in culture. **Stage II:** Multiplication of the propagules. **Stage III:** Rooting of the progagules and preparation for transplant to soil. **Soil IV:** Establishment of Stage II or III propagules ex vitro in soil or potting mix.

Stationary culture: A non-agitated culture. the antonym is shake culture.

Stock plant: The source plant from which cuttings or explants are made. These are usually maintained carefully in an optimum state for (sometimes prolonged) explant use. Preferably they are certified, pathogen-free plants.

Stock solution: A solution, usually concentrated (10 to 100 times the final medium concentration), of select medium constituents that re grouped for compatability to avoid precipitation and prepared before hand to save time during medium preparation. Usually they are frozen or stored in the refrigerator and portions are utilized as media are prepared.

Stock: 1. The root and a portion of the stem (rootstock) of a plant to which is grafted a part of the same or another plant (scion). **2.** A group of closely related plants.

Subculture or passage: A culture derived from another culture or the aseptic division and transfer of a culture or a portion of that culture (inoculum) to fresh nutrient medium. Subculturing is usually done at set time intervals, the length of which is called the subculture interval or passage time.

Subline: A cell line regenerated from a unique cell line of a hybrid callus colony.

Supraoptimum: An amount (level) greater than required; as an inhibitory concentration of an exogeneous growth factor.

Surface sterilization: The removal of plant surface microflora prior to aseptic excision of explants. Surface sterilization is accomplished by immersion of tissue in one of many sterilants, such as calcium hypochlorite or sodium hypochlorite, hydrogen peroxide, mercuric chloride, silver nitrate or bromine water for an empirically determined period of time.

Suspension culture: Cells and group of cells (aggregates) dispersed in an aerated, usually agitated, liquid culture medium. These are obtained by adding friable callus to the medium. The plant species, explant type and treatment; the composition of the nutrient medium; and many other features determine the size and nature of the cell aggregates, which may appear different during each culture growth phase. These cultures are used to study cell division, differentiation and metabolism, in secondary product synthesis or form the basis for single cell lines, callus cultures, somatic cell embryogenesis and many other culture purposes.

Synchronized cells: Synchronized mitosis in a group of cells in culture by natural or artificial means.

Synchronous culture: A plant cell or microbial culture treated in such a way as to have all (or most) cells or individuals in the same stage of development or mitosis. This can be achieved in various ways including via temperature variation and nutrient limitation.

Ti plasmid: A portion of the genome of the bacterium *Agrobacterium tumefaciens*, the agent involved in crown gall disease. This plasmid is a useful (experimental) vector for the transfer of genetic information into plant cells.

Tissue explant: An excised plant portion of tissue used to initiate a culture.

Totipotency: the potential **(totipotential)** or inherent capacity of a plant cell or tissue to develop into (recreate) an entire plant if suitably stimulated. Totipotency implies that all the information necessary for growth and reproduction of the organism is contained in the cell. Although theoretically all plant cells are **totipotent** the meristematic cells are best able to express it.

Toxic: Poisonous; as are some chemicals **(toxicants)** or any substances present to excess and detrimental to normal plant function or growth.

Trace element: Miroelement.

Tracer: A substance that can be followed within a reaction or an organism; as radioactive isotopes and certain dyes.

Transcription: Conversion of a DNA (gene) information sequence into a mRNA sequence

Transduction: Introduction of foreign genetic material into a cell by means of a virus or, in the case of bacteria, by means of phages

Transfer room: A small room, sometimes sterilized internally by a bactericidal lamp (u.v. irradiation) and provided with clean (filtered) air; employed for sterile transfer work.

Translation control: In certain cases, after a gene has been transcribed, the mRNA can fold back upon itself to prevent its translation. This process is known as attenuation.

Tumor inducing principle (TIP): The plasmid carried by *Agrobacterium tumefaciens*, the crown gall organism. Through incorporation into the host genome the host tissue is transformed into tumor tissue.

Tyrosine (Tr, $C_9H_{11}NO_3$ mw 181.19): An amino acid, sometimes used in plant tissue culture media as a source of nitrogen.

Ultrasonic cleaner: A device to include high frequency vibration of materials, removing adhering substances from surfaces by mechanical action. This device is useful for cleaning glassware and for disinfecting plant material.

Ultraviolet light (UV): Radiation with wavelength (100-400 nm) at the violet end of the visible spectrum.

Unorganized growth: *In vitro* formation of tissues with few differentiated cell types and lacking recognizable structure; as with many calli.

Unwinding enzymes: They catalyze separation of complementary strands of DNA; require ATP.

Valine (Val, $C_5H_{11}NO_2$ mw 117.1: An amino acid found in seeds and proteins. Occasionally added to plant tissue culture media.

Vector: Plasmid or virus that after ligation with a foreign DNA is used to introduce new information into the cell.

Virus elimination: Thermotherapy, chemotherapy and meristem or meristem tip culture, used alone or in combination have been employed for the elimination of systemic viruses from plants.

Virus-tested or virus-free: A plant that appears healthy and repeatedly tests negatively for the presence of one or more identifiable viruses. Such a plant may then be used as a stock or donor plant (explant source) for propagation purposes, and may be certified as virus tested (certified virus tested). The term virus-free is incorrect in most cases, as such a plant may contain one or more viruses which have not been assayed.

Vitamin B complex: Includes a large group of water soluble vitamins that function as coenzymes; thiamine (**B_1**), riboflavin or vitamin G (**B_2**), niacin or nicotinic acid (**B_3**), pantothenic acid (**B_5**), pyridoxine (**B_{12}**), biotin or vitamin H, folic acid or vitamin M (**BC**), inositl, choline and others.

Vitamin B_x: para-amino-benzoic acid.

Vitamin C: ascorbic acid.

Vitamin D: A fat-soluble vitamin composed of a group of related steroids. Present in all plants.

Vitamin E: See **tocopherol.**

Vitamin K: A fat-soluble quione involved in photosynthetic electron transfer in plants and blood clotting in animals.

w/m^2 or watt per square metre: A common unit of light measurement.

W/v: Weight in volume; as the number of grams of constituent in 100 cm^3 (mls) solution.

Water of hydration: The amount of water chemically bound to a substance. This amount may be variable and must be taken into account when solutions of salts are prepared; as in medium preparation.

Woody plant medium (WPM): A modified MS (1962) medium developed for woody plant species by G. Lloyd and B. McCown (1980). It has less nitrogen (both ammonium and nitrate), sodium, potassium and chloride than does MS (1962) medium. It has been increasingly used for the commercial propagation of ornamental trees and shrubs.

Wound tissue: See callus.

Xerograft: See **heterograft.**

X-ray or Roentgen ray (r): Electromagnetic radiation of short wave length produced by high speed electrons impacting on a metal object under vacuum.

Yeast extract: A complex, undefined, B vitamin-containing addendum to some plant tissue culture media.

Yield test: Productivity assessment.

Zeatin or 2-methyl-4-(1H-purin-6-ylamino)-2-buten 1-ol (Z, $C_{10}H_{13}N_5O$ mw 215.21): A natural cytokinin first isolated from corn. It is sometimes included in plant tissue culture media. It dissolves in acid (HCl ca. 1 M